W9-BRZ-137

FUNDAMENTALS
of
ENGINEERING DRAWING

Other Books by the Author

TECHNICAL DRAFTING ESSENTIALS, 1st. Ed. Prentice-Hall, Inc., 1950.

PROBLEMS IN ENGINEERING DRAWING, 3rd. Ed. Prentice-Hall, Inc., 1950.

PURDUE UNIVERSITY ENGINEERING DRAWING FILMS, with J. Rising, et al.

FUNDAMENTALS *of* ENGINEERING DRAWING

For Technical Students and Professional Draftsmen

by

WARREN J. LUZADDER PURDUE UNIVERSITY · REGISTERED PROFESSIONAL ENGINEER · MEMBER OF NATIONAL SOCIETY OF PROFESSIONAL ENGINEERS AND AMERICAN SOCIETY FOR ENGINEERING EDUCATION

Third Edition

PRENTICE-HALL, INC.
Englewood Cliffs

L.C. CAT. CARD NO.: 52-11999

First printing.............October, 1952
Second printing.........December, 1952
Third printing................June, 1953
Fourth printing..............June, 1953
Fifth printing...............June, 1954
Sixth printing.............August, 1955
Seventh printing...........March, 1956

PRINTED IN THE UNITED STATES OF AMERICA

33843

PREFACE TO THE THIRD EDITION

The necessity for making a complete revision of *Fundamentals of Engineering Drawing* was recognized by the author immediately after World War II because of rapidly changing industrial drafting room practices brought about by improved production processes. Furthermore there appeared a growing interest in the standardization of drafting room practices for drawing and design in various sections of American industry. The automotive and aircraft industries took action toward the creation of drafting standards under the sponsorship of the Society of Automotive Engineers. Others became interested, and finally the American Standards Association Committee Z14 was reactivated in 1948. A new standard ASA Z14.1 is now being prepared with full recognition being given to the practices recommended in other standards.

In preparing this revision the original aim of the first edition, which was to create almost a self-teaching book, was kept constantly in mind. Improvements were made with the intent of having a more understandable text. New material on graphical calculus has been added to the chapter on Engineering Graphs and Charts so that the student may become acquainted with the use of graphics to solve problems involving technical data. Many teachers, who have used the two previous editions of this text, have expressed a desire for a chapter on Architectural Drawing. It is believed that the new chapter on this phase of drawing will fulfill their needs.

The text material and problems have been made to conform to the latest edition of American Standard Drawing and Drafting Room Practice, ASA Z14.1-1946, and the newly published SAE Automotive Drafting Standards, 1950. Whenever these two standards differ, alternate practices have been shown. The General Motors Drafting Standards, which are now under revision and are being expanded, were consulted constantly along with other standards so that the practices presented to the teacher and student will be in agreement with the up-to-date practices of a large segment of American industry.

The new British-Canadian-American Unified thread form is presented in the chapter covering screw threads and fasteners; and related Unified and American Screw Thread Series Tables, prepared from the publication ASA B1.1- 1949, appear in the Appendix. Problems which require the drawing and specification of screw threads have been made to agree with the new unified screw thread series so that the student may become thoroughly familiar with the new thread standard which is being so rapidly adopted by industry.

An improved illustration replaces an old illustration in almost every case where improvement could be made in presentation and appearance. Many new illustrations also have been added to clarify and emphasize text material.

The chapter on Dimensioning has been almost completely re-written and expanded to bring the material more nearly into agreement with the new standards and rapidly changing industrial practices. The author is deeply indebted to Dean Jasper Gerardi of the University of Detroit and Mr. William A. Siler of the Delco-Remy Corporation for their valued suggestions on content and presentation.

Grateful acknowledgment must be made for the text material prepared by Mr. William J. Hornung, Director of Training, National Technical Institute. Mr. Hornung prepared the entire chapter on Architectural Drawing.

Mr. M. T. Ward of the American Bridge Company revised and expanded the chapter on Structural Drawing in order to make the text material conform to the latest practices in the steel fabrication industry. For his work the author wishes to express his appreciation.

An acknowledgment of indebtedness must be made for the helpful criticism and sound suggestions made so unselfishly by the many drawing teachers from institutions in all sections of the country. In particular, however, special mention must be made for the interest shown and advice given by the staff at Purdue University—to M. H. Bolds, Mr. K. E. Botkins, Mr. W. E. Thomas, and Professor H. C. Thompson. Professor J. N. Arnold read the section on graphical calculus and offered valuable ideas for worthwhile improvements. Professor J. H. Porsch, Chairman of the Department of Engineering Drawing, gave numerous suggestions and served as the author's constant adviser during the preparation of the manuscript for the revision.

Finally, special appreciation must be expressed here for the kindness of Professors L. O. Johnson and Irwin Wladaver of New York University who carefully read the entire manuscript and offered many helpful comments. The author's close friend, Captain R. H. Hammond of the United States Military Academy, read all of the new manuscript material and checked all of the new problems.

W. J. LUZADDER

Purdue University
West Lafayette, Indiana

PREFACE TO THE FIRST EDITION

In teaching the present-day large classes, a teacher finds that it is almost impossible to give a student a sufficient amount of individual instruction. Even if he is able to spend as much as five minutes of a period with each student, he finds that the time is taken up explaining some small item that could be just as well presented in some other way. Needless repetition is a waste of the students' time and tends to make the instructor's work monotonous. With this thought in mind, an attempt has been made to create a nearly self-teaching book with simple explanations of all the more common difficulties. An equal effort has been put forth to make each illustration repeat fully in graphical language the ideas presented by the accompanying printed words.

The material for this text has been selected and organized with a full realization of the fact that engineering drawing courses vary somewhat in our many technical schools. The methods of presentation are different because of divergence of opinion among teachers concerning the best scheme for teaching the subject. Course content varies because courses are designed for different purposes. The author does not feel qualified to criticize any method of presentation because of his deep respect for the intelligence and sincerity of every teacher of the subject, many of whom are more than chance acquaintances.

A majority of teachers seem to agree, however, that engineering drawing, in reality a graphic language, should be taught as any other language. That is, they feel that the elementary principles and rules of composition should be studied and learned step by step before an attempt is made to compose working drawings. The idioms of the language should be taught after the basic principles have been thoroughly mastered. The same teachers frown upon the practice of copying drawings because they realize that engineering drawing requires more than manual skill and that the technical draftsman must possess constructive imagination and a knowledge of industrial practices.

Models of mutilated blocks may be used at the very beginning of the elementary course to help a student to visualize, if they are used judiciously. Machine parts furnish excellent sketching and working-drawing problems. In the case of large classes, however, it is almost impossible to handle the great number of models and parts that would be required. The dimensioned pictorials of machine parts given at the end of many of the chapters furnish an answer to this problem and should prove to be excellent substitutes.

Laboratory drawing periods should be supplemented by lectures, recitations, and quizzes. The instructors at many institutions have found that basic material can be best presented through the use of motion pictures. More subject matter can be covered in a given amount of time, and each student observes a demonstration equally well. For a further discussion of the use of motion pictures prepared by Professor Justus Rising and the author, see the Appendix.

The drawing plates used in a beginning course should be small (8½″ × 11″ to 11″ × 17″) so that no student will become completely discouraged by being forced to work many hours upon a drawing that he feels is not of a quality he desires. A new start always brings new hope, which in turn leads to better work. If partial layouts are used, more subject matter can be presented, and many additional experiences may be offered. By their use, unnecessary work that the student is fully capable of doing can be avoided.

The publication *American Standard Drawings and Drafting Room Practice* (ASA Z14.1-1935) has been used as a guide in the preparation of much of the material presented in this text. All related standards have also been consulted. The Appendix contains a considerable amount of handbook material, mostly in the form of tables, many of which were prepared from these standards. The author highly endorses the valuable work of this association and its allied organizations. Every effort has been made by the author to keep in step with modern engineering practice.

In the chapters covering the specialized divisions of engineering drawing, sufficient material has been presented to permit the assignment of practical problems. It has been the intent, however, to avoid the field of design. The chapters on shop processes should help the student to understand more fully the practices of dimensioning.

Because of the interest and co-operation of many manufacturers, it has been possible to present a number of commercial drawings as illustrations and as problems. Special acknowledgment of their courtesy has been made throughout the text.

The author wishes to express his appreciation for the ideas of known and unknown persons. They are so many that their names cannot be given here, but each at some time presented some drawing practice that appears somewhere on these pages. Grateful acknowledgment is made here for the aid of M. T. Ward and R. S. Green in the preparation of the chapter on structural drawing. Also to Professors J. N. Arnold and M. R. Graney, who, along with Messrs. C. E. Mayfield and M. H. Bolds, gave constructive criticisms of the manuscript. Acknowledgment is due to Mr. E. W. Azpell for material on gears and cams and to Professor Justus Rising for his contribution to the chapter on lettering and constant help throughout the entire time that this book was in preparation. For the aid of G. S. Palmer and others in the preparation of some of the drawings no more need be said than that their work was well done.

Special appreciation must be expressed here for the aid and encouragement given by Dean A. A. Potter, Professor C. W. Beese, and Professor H. F. Owen, all of Purdue University.

Finally, the author wishes to acknowledge with thanks his appreciation for the kindness of Professors E. F. Watts, of Massachusetts Institute of Technology, and Horace P. Fry, of the University of Pennsylvania, who took time during these busy days to review the manuscript and offer many helpful suggestions.

W. J. Luzadder

Purdue University
West Lafayette, Indiana

CONTENTS

FUNDAMENTALS *of* ENGINEERING DRAWING

1 INTRODUCTION

1.1. Engineering drawing is a graphic language that is used universally by engineers to describe the shape and size of structures and mechanisms. It has developed through the centuries, much as have various spoken and written languages, until at the present time its fundamental principles are understood by trained persons in all civilized nations. If an engineer is not to be an illiterate member of his profession, he must understand not only the theory of projection and dimensioning as related to working drawings, but he must be familiar with the idioms and conventions as well. It can be truthfully said that any supposedly trained engineer who cannot read a drawing will be of very little value to the firm that employs him. In fact, he can be compared to an unskilled laborer, employed at ordinary work, who cannot read or write.

Engineering drawing is not, as many students are prone to believe, something a draftsman alone need understand. The language belongs to the engineer. It is his means for recording his ideas and conveying his instructions to others. Although many graduates of technical colleges serve an apprenticeship at the drawing board, few remain at it long enough to develop the degree of skill possessed by a good draftsman. The lack of such skill often proves a real handicap, for the ability to execute a neat and accurate drawing can be the one thing that will attract attention and lead to the quick promotion of a young graduate into responsible engineering work.

The usual work of an engineer is to direct the preparation of drawings. To do this he must prepare preliminary design drawings and instructive sketches made in accordance with the basic principles underlying the preparation of working drawings. From time to time he must inspect the draftsmen's work to see that the drawings will convey his ideas as he wishes them to be conveyed.

1.2. The purpose of this text is to present the grammar and composition of drawing so that those who conscientiously study the basic principles will be able to execute satisfactory drawings and, after some practical experience, be capable of directing the work of others. To facilitate study, the subject matter has been separated into its various component parts: lettering, geometry, multiview drawing, dimensioning, pictorial drawing, sketching, and so forth. Later chapters discuss the preparation of working drawings, both detail and assembly, the preparation of topographic drawings, and the construction of charts and graphs. The major portion of the material presented leads up to the preparation of machine drawings, which the prospective members of some branches of the engineering profession think is not of interest to them. Since the methods used in the preparation of machine drawings, however, are the same methods used in the preparation of drawings in other fields of engineering, a thorough understanding of machine drawing assures a good foundation for later study in some specialized field, such as structural drawing. For those interested in specific types of drawing, some material has been presented with the assumption that the student already possesses a working knowledge of projection and dimensioning.

1.3. Engineering drawing offers students an insight into the engineer's methods of attacking engineering problems. Its lessons teach the principles of accuracy, exactness, and positiveness with regard to the information necessary for the production of a nonexisting structure. Finally, it develops the engineering imagination that is so essential to the creation of successful design.

2 DRAWING MATERIALS AND EQUIPMENT

2.1. The necessary instruments and materials needed for making ordinary engineering drawings are shown in Fig. 2.1. The instruments in the plush-lined case should be particularly well made and easy to service, for with cheap, inferior ones, it is often difficult to produce accurate drawings of professional quality. Since good equipment will last many years if treated with reasonable care, it is poor economy for the beginner to pur-

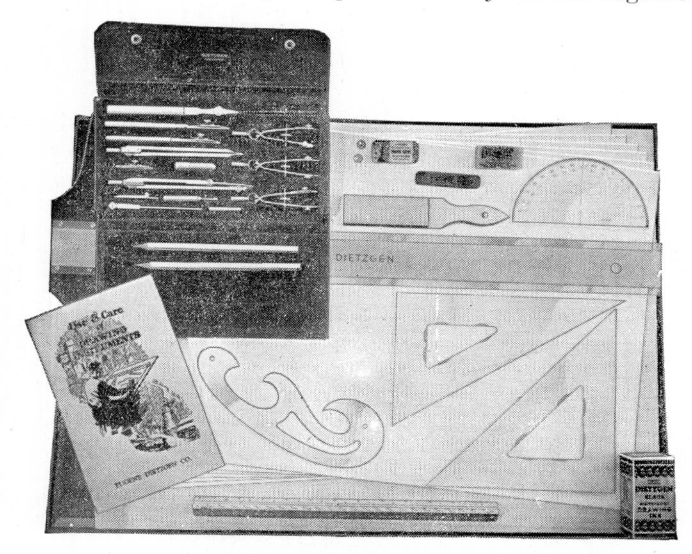

Fig. 2.1. Essential drafting equipment.

chase an inferior set, simply because it is cheap, with the intention of later obtaining a better one. It is not easy to distinguish good instruments from poor ones merely by observing their general appearance or by studying the figures on price tags. The student, before purchasing his equipment, should seek the advice of an expert or consult the catalogs of dealers whom he knows to be reliable. He should then procure the very best he can afford.

2.2. List of equipment and materials. The following list is a practical selection of equipment and materials necessary for making pencil drawings and ink tracings.

(1) Case of drawing instruments containing the following: 6″ compass with lengthening bar, pencil leg, and pen leg; 6″ dividers (with hair-spring adjustment); ruling pens; bow pencil; bow pen; bow dividers.
(2) Drawing board.
(3) T-square.
*(4) 45° triangle.
(5) 10″ 30°–60° triangle.
(6) French curve.
(7) Scale (either one triangular or three flat scales).
(8) Drawing pencils (6*H*, 4*H*, 2*H*, and *F* or *H*).
(9) Pencil pointer (file or sandpaper pad).
(10) Thumb tacks, brad machine, or Scotch tape.
(11) Pencil eraser.
(12) Cleaning eraser.
(13) Erasing shield.
(14) Dusting brush.
(15) Bottle of black waterproof drawing ink.
(16) Pen wiper.
(17) Penholder.
(18) Lettering pens.
(19) Protractor.
(20) Pad of sketching paper (plain or ruled).
(21) Drawing paper.
(22) Tracing paper.
(23) Tracing cloth.

To these may be added the following useful items:

(24) Hard Arkansas oilstone.
(25) Piece of soapstone.
(26) Ink-bottle holder.
(27) Lettering instrument.
(28) Steel eraser.
(29) Tack lifter.
(30) Slide rule.

2.3. The set of instruments. A standard set of drawing instruments in a velvet-lined case and an alternative set, which is capable of fulfilling the needs of most draftsmen, are shown in Figs. 2.2 and 2.3 respectively.

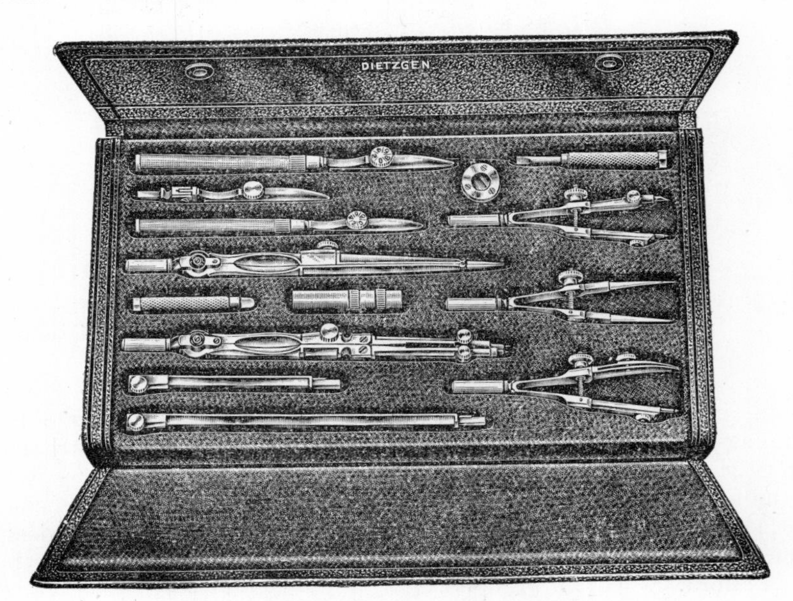

Fig. 2.2. A standard set of drawing instruments.

* A 6″ 45° Braddock Lettering Triangle, which may be used as either a triangle or a lettering instrument, may be substituted for this item.

It should be remembered that while good instruments may seem costly, they are carefully and accurately made from select materials by master craftsmen, and are of simple, sturdy construction. The cheap ones are usually poorly made imitations, a fact that becomes evident after a short period of use.

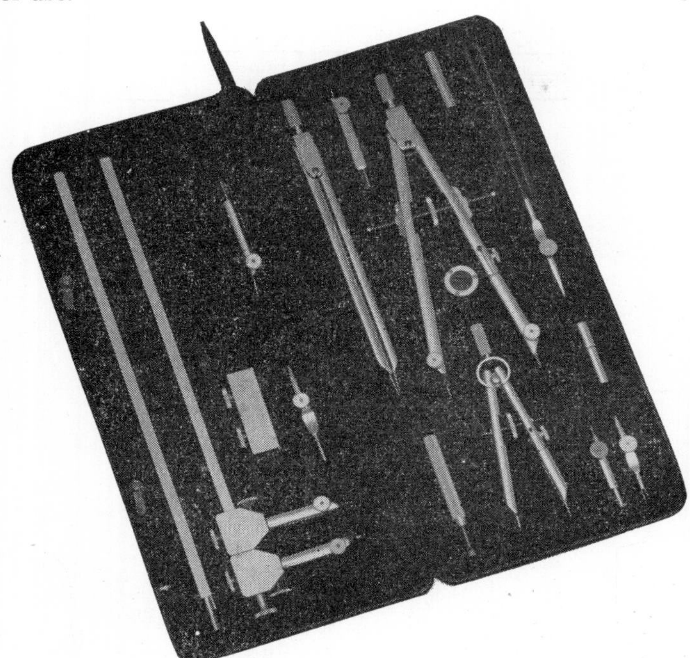

Fig. 2.3. The Purdue Riefler set.

A purchaser should not be misled by a large set containing many pieces that is offered at the same price as a small set containing only a few. The instruments in the smaller set are better, and will prove more satisfactory and economical over a period of years. If an additional instrument is required for a special type of drawing, it is advisable to purchase it as a separate piece.

2.4. Compasses and dividers. The three common patterns (square, flat, and round) are shown in Fig. 2.4. Although good instruments may be obtained in all three patterns, the best ones offered by leading manufacturers are of the square form, the type favored by draftsmen in the United States.

The legs of a modern high-grade compass are fastened by a pivot joint. Usually the joint consists of two discs held in a yoke between adjustable cone-shaped or ball-shaped pivots. The screws in the yoke regulate the pressure between the discs so that the friction will be sufficient to allow the legs of the compass to be adjusted easily and yet maintain settings.

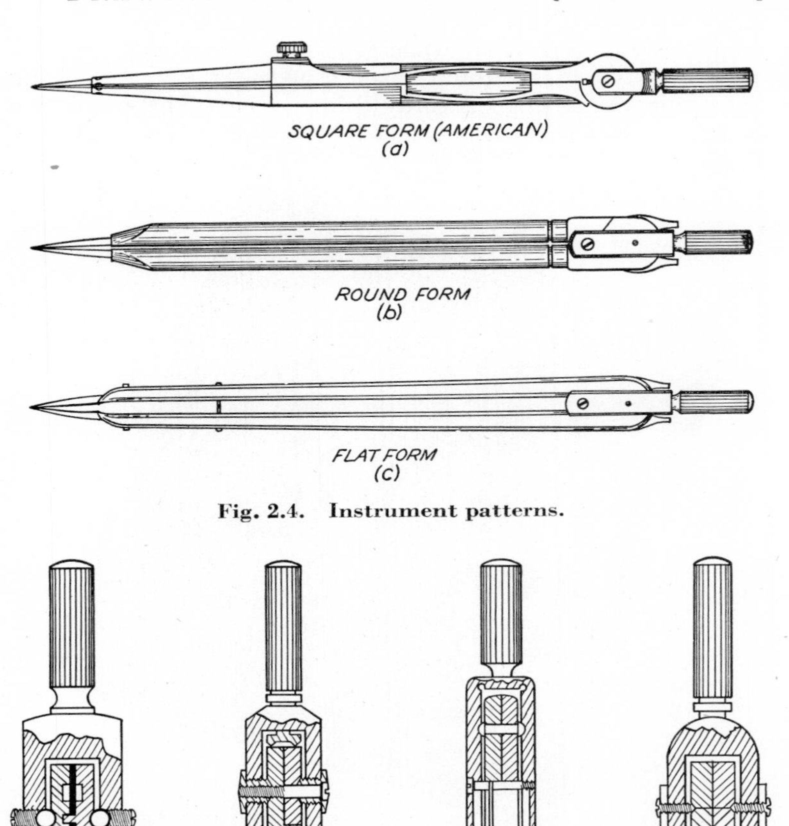

Fig. 2.4. Instrument patterns.

(a) (b) (c) (d)

Fig. 2.5. Compass joints.

Most instruments of recent manufacture have a convenient handle that improves manipulation attached to the yoke. A few are made with straightening devices for keeping the handle centered in a vertical position when the instrument is in use. Centering devices are highly regarded by many draftsmen.

One leg of nearly all compasses is manufactured with a socket joint, which allows the insertion of either the pen leg for ink work or the lengthening bar for a longer working radius. It is essential for the shank of an attachment to be well fitted in the socket so that when it is clamped in place it will be in perfect alignment and fixed firmly with the leg to which it is attached. Both legs of a compass are provided with knee joints. These allow the legs to be adjusted perpendicular to the paper when a large circle is being drawn. Fig. 2.7 shows the method for testing a compass for alignment. It should be observed that the alignment of

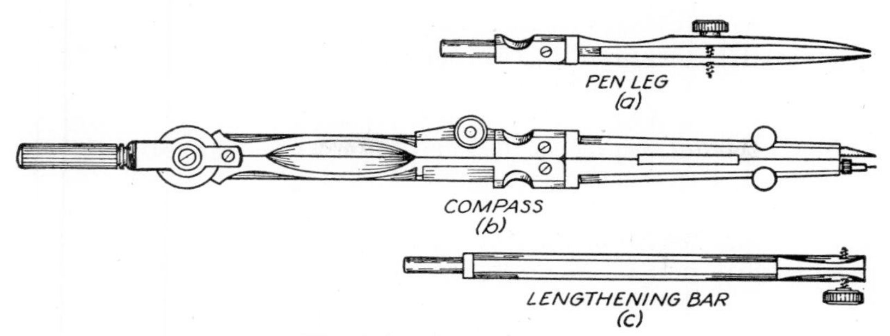

Fig. 2.6. The compass.

the compass is perfect only if the point of the needle touches the end of the closed nibs exactly at the center of the point. A few compasses are equipped with a hairspring on the pivot leg for making minute adjustments in the distance between the points.

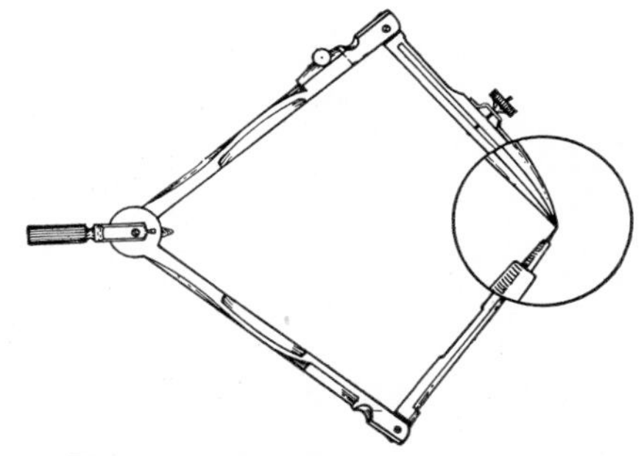

Fig. 2.7. Testing a compass for alignment.

Since dividers are used to transfer measurements or to divide lines into any number of equal parts, they differ from the compass in that both legs terminate in sharp steel points. The legs may be alike, as shown in Fig. 2.8(*a*) or one leg may be provided with a hairspring adjustment, as in Fig. 2.8(*b*). The hairspring is convenient for making minute variations between the points, and is therefore to be preferred.

2.5. Bow instruments. The bow instruments include the bow dividers, bow pencil, and bow pen. These instruments are of two general designs: (1) the continuous or single type (Fig. 2.9*a*, *b*), and (2) the hook or loop-spring type (Fig. 2.9*c*, *d*). Either pattern may be purchased with side-screw (see *a*) or center-screw (see *b*, *c*, *d*) adjustment.

The spring in either type should be strong enough to keep the legs apart and insure a steady setting throughout the range of the instrument,

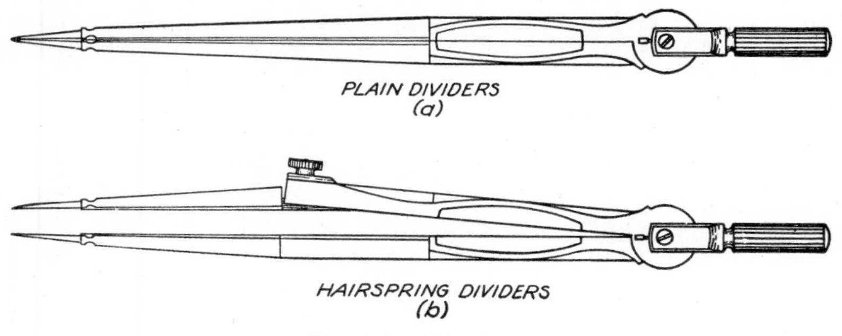

Fig. 2.8. Dividers.

particularly when it is open to the extreme working limit. Loop-spring instruments have a more uniform spring pressure than the single-piece spring type, and are usually much larger and heavier.

The side-screw type is the choice of some draftsmen, because the pressure on the nut can be relieved and the wear on the thread minimized by holding the legs together and spinning the nut to the required position. The center-screw type is preferred by its advocates because the double-action screw makes for faster adjustment.

2.6. Ruling pens. The most satisfactory type of ruling pen consists of two steel blades formed from one solid piece of high-grade steel, a thumb screw for regulating the distance between the ends (nibs) of the blades, and a handle made of wood (sometimes ebony), or metal. The best drawing pens have blades of high-speed steel or noncorrosive stainless steel with butt-welded, high-speed steel points. Pens of this type cost more than ordinary pens, but the points retain their shape and edge four

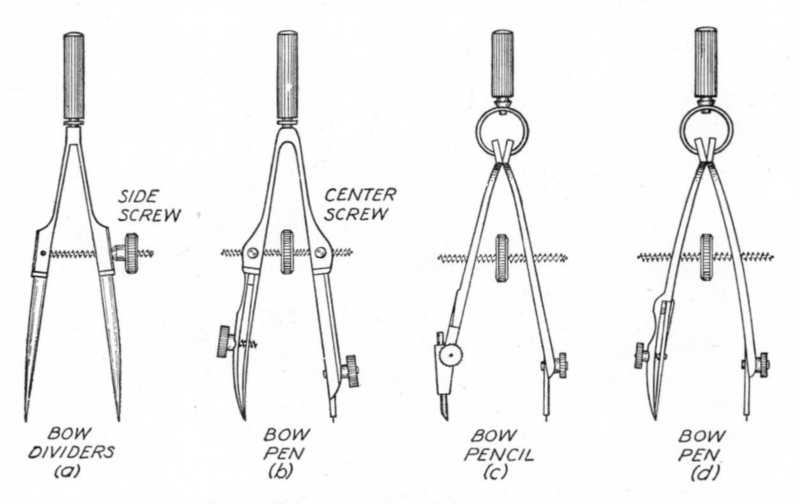

Fig. 2.9. The bow instruments.

or five times as long as ordinary points, even when the ordinary points are made of the finest carbon steel. Good pens, coming from the factory correctly shaped and sharpened as they do, rarely require touching up, and the excellent quality of line work that can be achieved with them justifies the higher price they command. Cheap pens usually require frequent sharpening and are an annoyance from the start.

Many devices have been invented for opening the blades for cleaning without changing the setting of the adjusting screw (Fig. 2.10*b*, *c*, *d*), but most of these are troublesome and are not as satisfactory as the plain spring-blade type. The slide-catch design (Fig. 2.10*b*) is the type usually found in medium-priced drawing sets.

The detail or Swede (Fig. 2.10*e*) wide-blade pen holds more ink than an ordinary ruling pen, and consequently is well suited for drawing very long or very wide lines.

2.7. The drawing board. Drawing boards should be made of selected straight-grained, soft wood strips that have been thoroughly seasoned. The most popular type is constructed of $\frac{3}{4}''$ to $1''$ soft white pine or basswood reinforced by end strips (cleats), which are attached to the main body with tongue-and-groove or dovetailed and glued joints. The cleats provide for expansion, prevent splitting and warping, and furnish a smooth guiding edge for the T-square head. The working surface

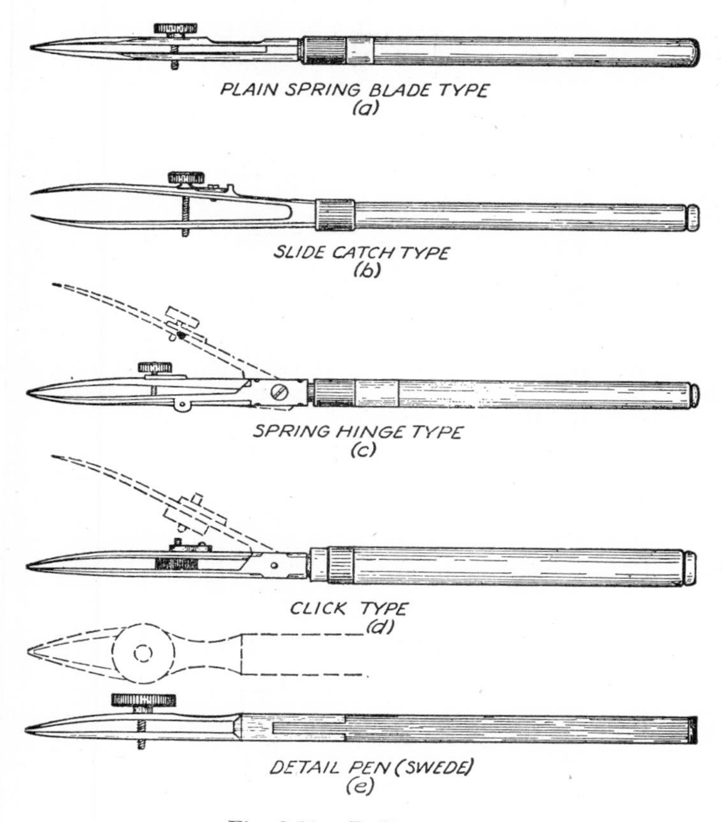

Fig. 2.10. Ruling pens.

(top) must be smooth as well as a true plane, and both edges should be perfectly straight so that either may be used as a working edge. The board shown in Fig. 2.11 has two working surfaces.

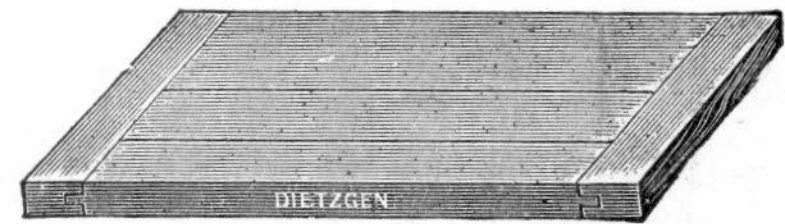

Fig. 2.11. Drawing board.

Large-size boards are reinforced by hardwood ledges on the underside, and strips are set on the ends to provide a smooth working edge for the T-square head. The screws through the ledges are set in slots with metal washers to provide for expansion and contraction.

Drawing boards range in size from 12″ × 17″ to 60″ × 120″. A 20″ × 26″ board is sufficiently large to accommodate drawings up to 18″ × 24″.

2.8. The T-square. The most popular T-square for ordinary work (Fig. 2.13*a*) is made with a head of hardwood to which is fastened rigidly a blade lined with transparent material to resist warping and to permit lines

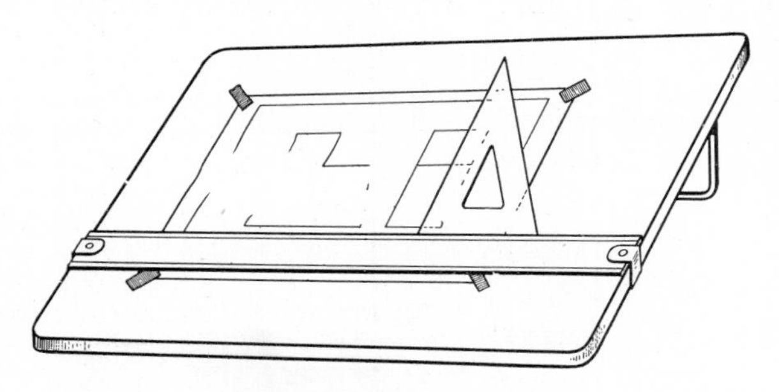

Fig. 2.12. Esco board.

of the drawing to be seen beneath the edge. The working edges, which are the upper edge of the blade and the inside edge of the head, should be perfectly straight. Although it is not necessary, it is desirable that these edges be at right angles to each other.

T-squares usually have ebonized hardwood heads and straight-grained maple blades, although such woods as ash, boxwood, mahogany, and

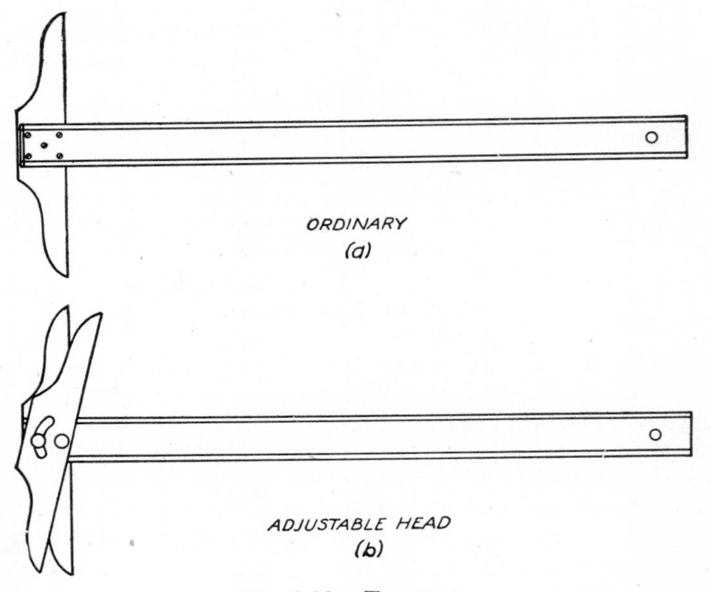

Fig. 2.13. T-square.

pearwood are often used. Occasionally T-squares with steel blades and metal heads are desirable for very accurate work.

Some draftsmen prefer a T-square with an adjustable double head. The type of head shown in Fig. 2.13(*b*) is designed for drawing parallel inclined lines.

In commercial drafting rooms, the Universal Drafting Machine, Fig. 2.41 and the parallel-rule attachment are often used in preference to a T-square.

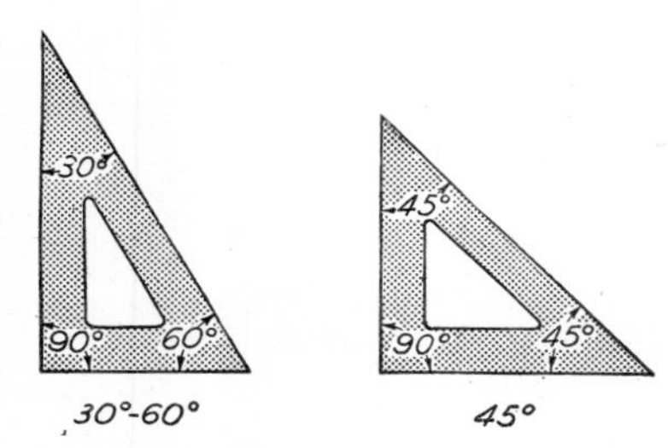

Fig. 2.14. Triangles.

Fig. 2.15. Testing a triangle for nicks.

The parallel rule is chosen by many draftsmen because the straightedge, when properly handled, usually remains in perfect alignment.

2.9. The triangles. Triangles are made of various materials, but the transparent amber-colored celluloid ones are to be preferred, for they not only permit the drawing to be seen beneath them, but also are less likely to warp or nick than are those made of wood. The working edges of a triangle should be perfectly straight and all the angles between them should be true.

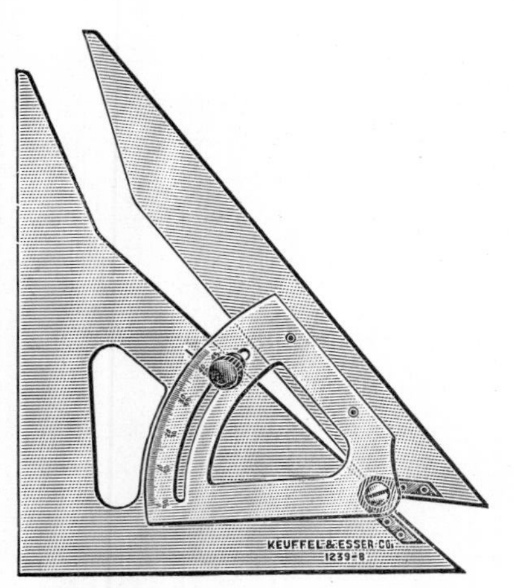

Fig. 2.16. Protractor angle.

The 45° and the 30° × 60° triangles are the ones commonly used for ordinary work. Special triangles, such as the 15° × 75°, and the $22\frac{1}{2}$° × $67\frac{1}{2}$°, are convenient but not essential.

A popular combination consists of a 10″ or 12″ 30° × 60° triangle and an 8″ or 10″ 45° triangle. These should be at least 0.06″ in thickness and have finger lifts.

Although it is not widely used, the protractor angle (Fig. 2.16) is a useful device. It is hinged in such a manner that it may be substituted for a protractor and a set of triangles.

The Line-o-graph triangle shown in Fig. 2.17 combines the functions of the triangles, scale, protractor, and lettering instrument.

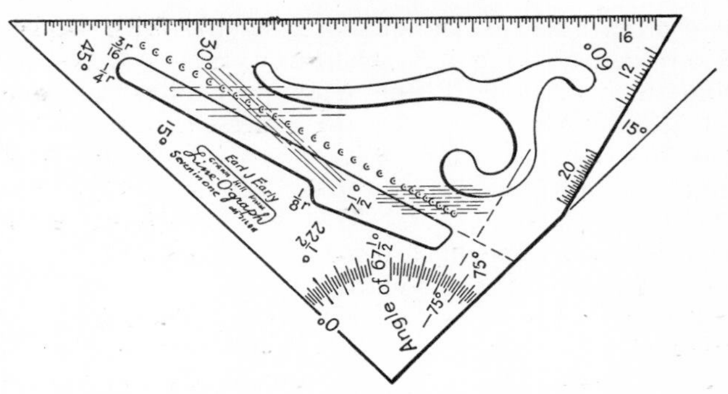

Fig. 2.17. **Combination triangle.**

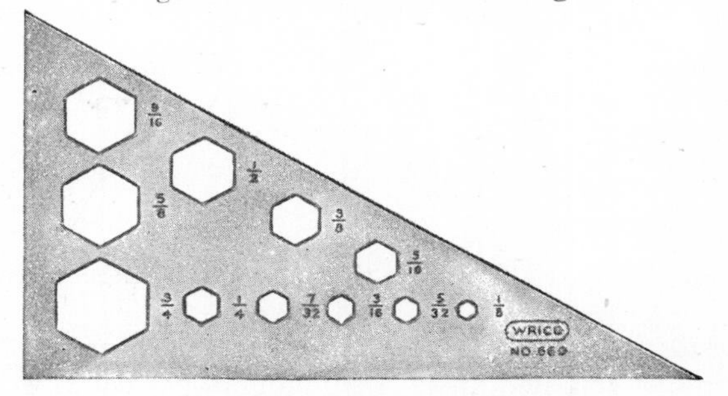

Fig. 2.18. **Wrico triangle.**

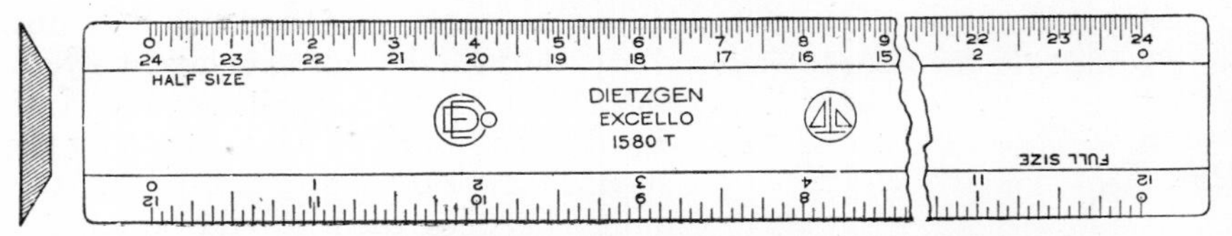

Fig. 2.19. **Mechanical engineers' scale. Full divided.**

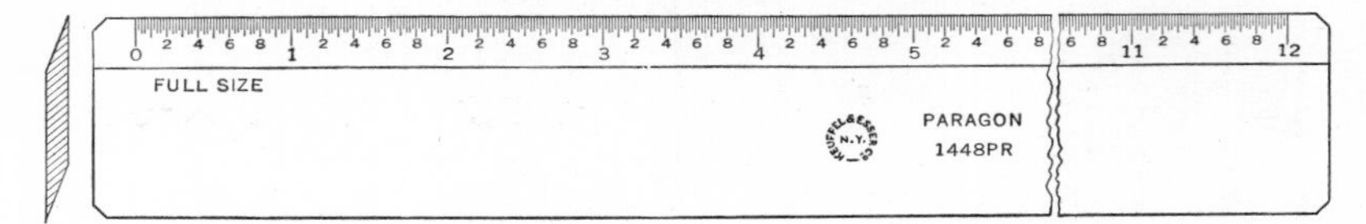

Fig. 2.20. **Aircraft engineers' decimal scale.**

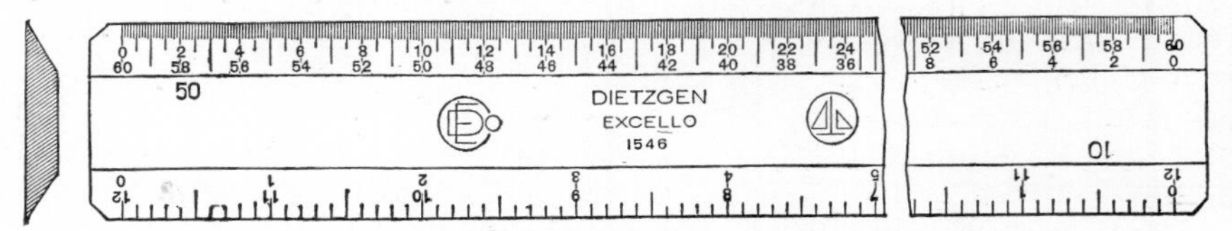

Fig. 2.21. **Civil engineers' scale.**

2.10. Scales. There are four kinds of scales available for particular types of engineering design. They are classified as mechanical engineers' scales, civil engineers' scales, architects' scales, and metric scales. The mechanical engineers' scales are generally of the full-divided type that are graduated proportionally to give reductions based on inches. The principal units are divided into the common fractions of an inch (4, 8, 16, 32 parts) (Fig. 2.19). The scales are indicated on the stick as eighth-size ($1\frac{1}{2}$ in. = 1 ft.), quarter-size (3 in. = 1 ft.), half-size (6 in. = 1 ft.), and full-size. On some special triangular sticks these same scales are given as $\frac{1}{8}'' = 1''$, $\frac{1}{4}'' = 1''$, $\frac{1}{2}'' = 1''$, $\frac{3}{4}'' = 1''$. Open-divided scales, having only the end divisions subdivided, are used by many industrial draftsmen.

The new aircraft engineering scale with instant-reading decimal graduations is recommended by the Society of Automotive Engineers for use with a complete decimal system (Fig. 2.20). This scale, which has the principal units divided into fiftieths, is particularly suited for the use of a two-place decimal system.

The civil engineers' (chain) scales are full-divided, and are graduated in decimal parts, usually 10, 20, 30, 40, 50, 60, 80, and 100 divisions to the inch (Fig. 2.21).

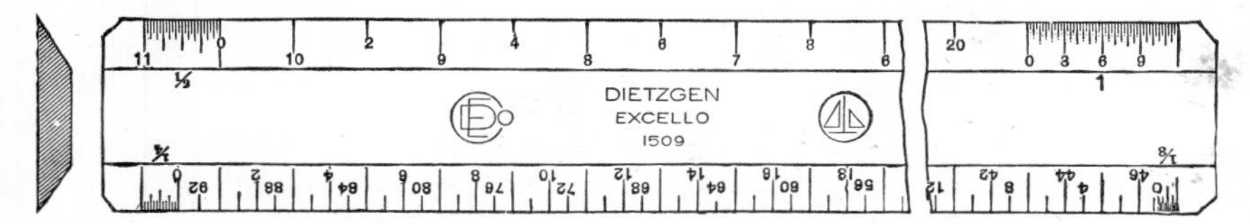

Fig. 2.22. Architects' scale. Open-divided.

Architects' scales differ from mechanical engineers' scales in that the divisions represent a foot, and the end units are divided into inches, half inches, quarter inches, and so forth (6, 12, 24, 48, or 96 parts). The usual scales are $\frac{1}{8}'' = 1'$, $\frac{1}{4}'' = 1'$, $\frac{3}{8}'' = 1'$, $\frac{1}{2}'' = 1'$, $1'' = 1'$, and $3'' = 1'$ (Fig. 2.22).

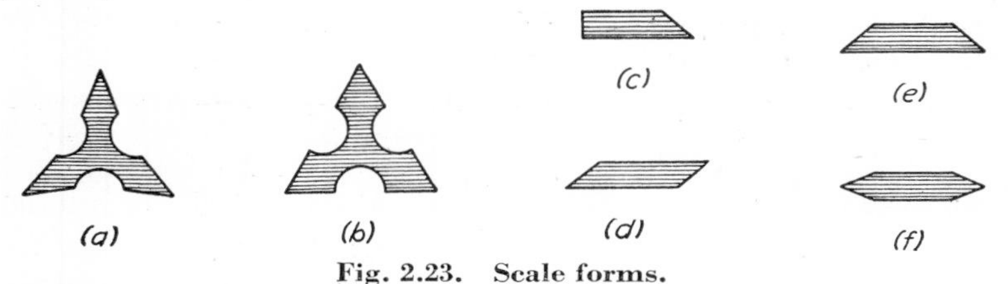

Fig. 2.23. Scale forms.

Practically all scales are made of thoroughly seasoned boxwood, with the divisions indicated along the edges. The cheaper ones are of natural wood finish, while the better ones are coated with white celluloid. Scales are available in either the triangular form (Fig. 2.23*a* and *b*) or one of the flat forms shown in Fig. 2.23(*c*), (*d*), (*e*), and (*f*). Triangular scales are used principally in technical schools because these scales combine eleven scales on one stick. The professional draftsman, however, feels less time is wasted finding the scale he wants when he uses the flat scale, and for this reason flat scales are

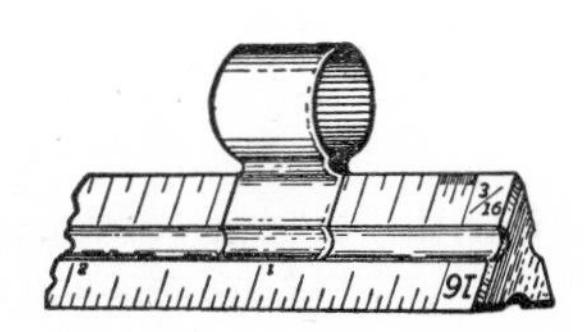

Fig. 2.24. Scale guard.

generally used in commercial drawing rooms. The disadvantage of the triangular scale can be eliminated by the use of a scale guard (Fig. 2.24).

2.11. Curves. Irregular or French curves are used for drawing curves other than circular arcs. Their ruling edges are composed of combinations of spirals, ellipses, and parabolas. Although many commercial draftsmen own a variety of curves or have access to specialized sets of curves that are suitable for their particular type of work, students in technical schools usually find that a curve similar to any of those shown in Fig. 2.25 is adequate.

Courtesy Keuffel & Esser Co.

Fig. 2.25. Irregular curves.

Probably the most satisfactory curves are those made of transparent amber celluloid through which the lines of the drawing may be seen.

The flexible curves shown in Fig. 2.26, however, because of their limitless variations, are extremely convenient. The type shown in (*a*) consists of a lead bar enclosed in rubber. Unfortunately, rubber becomes brittle with age and cracks off. The more desirable one shown in (*b*) has a steel ruling edge attached to a spring enclosing a lead core.

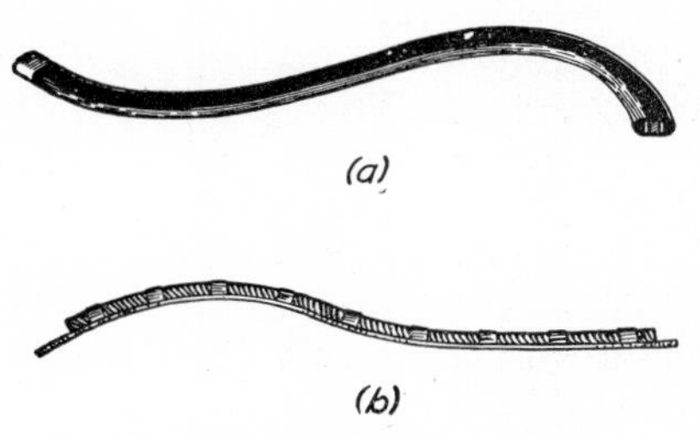

Fig. 2.26. Flexible curves.

2.12. Pencils. Good quality drawing pencils, having uniform leads enclosed in straight-grained wood that will sharpen well, are essential to good technical drawing. Cheap pencils should be avoided.

Pencil manufacturers grade drawing pencils from 9H (hard) to 6B (very soft). Ordinarily, the professional draftsman has available a selection of good, well sharpened pencils graded from hard to medium soft. Pencil leads are graded as follows: 9H, 8H, 7H, and 6H, very hard; 5H and 4H, medium hard; 3H and 2H, medium;

H and F, medium soft; HB and B, soft; 2B, 3B, 4B, 5B, and 6B, very soft. The grades from 2B to 6B are suited for sketching and rendering. A few manufacturers offer additional grades, indicated as tracing pencils, which produce very opaque lines on tracing paper and pencil cloth. In selecting the grade of pencil to be used, consideration always must be given to the type of surface and the hardness of the paper to be employed.

Drawing pencils are made with either round or rectangular leads, the latter being for draftsmen who prefer the wedge point.

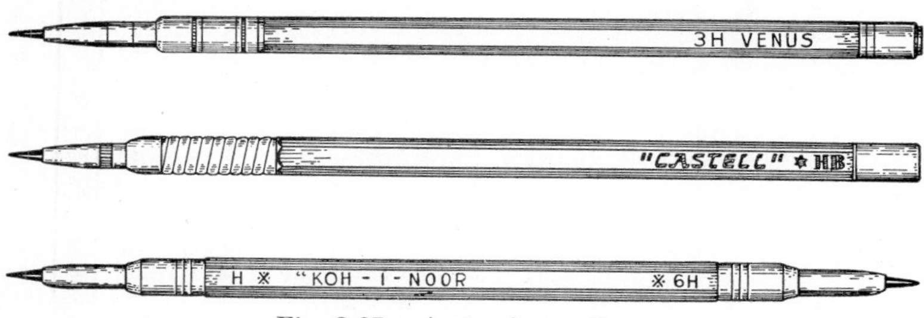

Fig. 2.27. Artists' pencils.

Because of the time consumed in cutting back the wood to repoint an ordinary drawing pencil, some draftsmen favor the use of artists' automatic pencils. Separate leads for these pencils may be purchased in any of the seventeen degrees of hardness obtainable in regular drawing pencils.

2.13. Pencil pointers. Either a sandpaper pad or an ordinary flat file is satisfactory for sharpening pencil and compass leads.

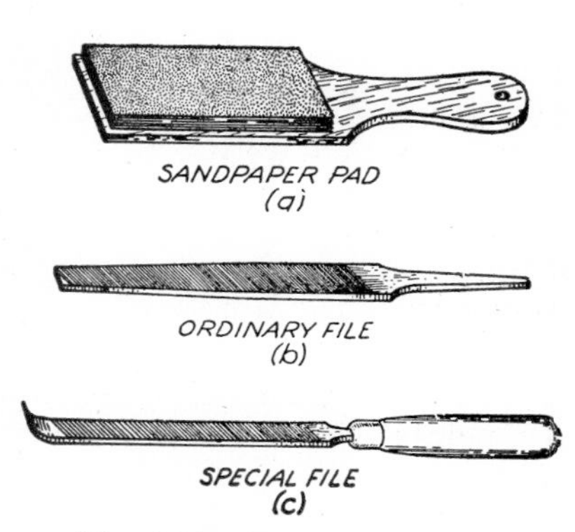

Fig. 2.28. Pencil pointers.

2.14. Thumb tacks. The thumb tacks best suited for use on drawing boards have thin-edge nickel-silver heads into which short tapering steel pins are screwed and riveted. These offer no obstruction to the T-square. They are easy to insert and remove, and at the same time grip firmly. The stamped steel tacks are a poor investment. Their points frequently break off and their thick flat heads obstruct the movement of the T-square.

Some draftsmen use regular Scotch drafting tape instead of thumb tacks, because its smooth surface allows the T-square and triangles to slide easily, and it eliminates punching holes in the drawing board. Scotch tape, however, frequently rolls up under the T-square or straightedge.

Fig. 2.29. Thumb tacks.

A stapling machine, which fastens a sheet of paper to a drawing board with wire brads, may also be used.

2.15. Erasers. A *hard pencil eraser*, only moderately gritty, is the only eraser that should ever be used for erasing pencil and ink lines on drawing paper, tracing paper, or tracing cloth. A large-size pencil eraser with beveled ends, or its equivalent, is favored by many commercial draftsmen. Although ink erasers are highly abrasive and remove ink lines more quickly, they damage the paper to such an extent that it is difficult to redraw or draw other ink lines over surfaces where they have been used. A *soft cleaning eraser* is needed for erasing light pencil lines and cleaning soiled spots on drawings. This eraser (about $2'' \times 1'' \times \frac{3}{4}''$ in size) should be self cleaning, should not crumble, and should not weaken ink lines.

Fig. 2.30. Steel eraser.

A steel eraser, razor blade, or pocketknife is useful to a draftsman for clipping off small projections, but should *never* be used for scratching or removing inked lines or even small segments of inked lines. Its use seriously damages the surface of the paper.

2.16. The erasing shield. An erasing shield is a thin sheet of celluloid or metal used to prevent any wrinkling of the paper and to protect other lines near a line that is being erased. A shield made of tempered spring steel, which will resist wear and will spring back flat after being bent, is to be preferred. Celluloid shields and those made of soft steel soon wear or kink.

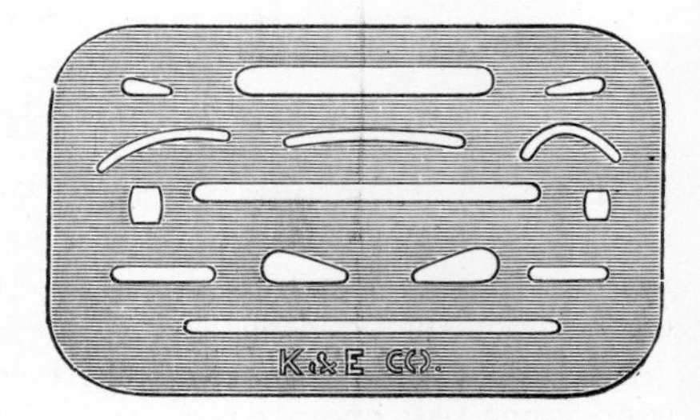

Fig. 2.31. Erasing shield.

2.17. Drawing ink. A good waterproof black drawing ink (India ink) is absolutely essential to successful drafting. It must be free-flowing and quick-drying and should make very black opaque lines that will not smudge. It should not contain chemicals that will injure instruments, or ingredients that will separate out of solution or evaporate quickly and cause the ink to become thick and gummy.

2.18. Pen points and penholders. The selection of penholders and pen points depends so much upon personal preference that individual experience is probably the best guide. It is recommended, however, that the selection of pen points be made from the assortment illustrated in Fig. 5.2.

2.19. The protractor. The protractor, which is used for measuring and laying off angles, is usually semicircular in form. Although the best protractors are made of nickel silver, those made of celluloid or sheet metal are suitable for ordinary work.

2.20. Drawing paper. Drawing papers are available in a variety of types, weights, and colors. For ordinary engineering drawings in pencil (working drawings, design drawings, and so forth), a heavy buff-color detail paper is preferred. It should have a slightly grained surface in order to take pencil marks readily, and should be able to withstand repeated erasing without serious damage. Paper of this type may be purchased in sheets or rolls.

White papers are preferred in commercial practice for display drawings of mechanisms, architectural drawings, sketches, and water-color paintings. For these, Whatman's handmade papers in the three finishes,

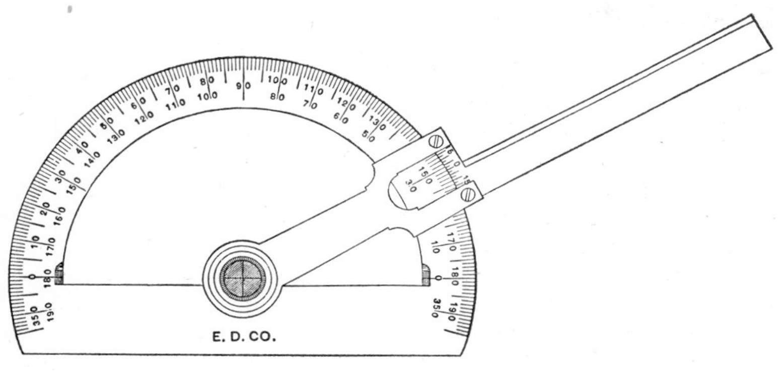

Fig. 2.32. Protractor.

HP (hot-pressed) suitable for fine-line ink work, *CP* (cold-pressed) suitable for pencil drawing and water-color sketches, and *R* (rough) suitable for charcoal work and water sketches, are quite generally used. Bristol (ply) board is also excellent because it is suitable for fine line work and has the added advantage of being stiff.

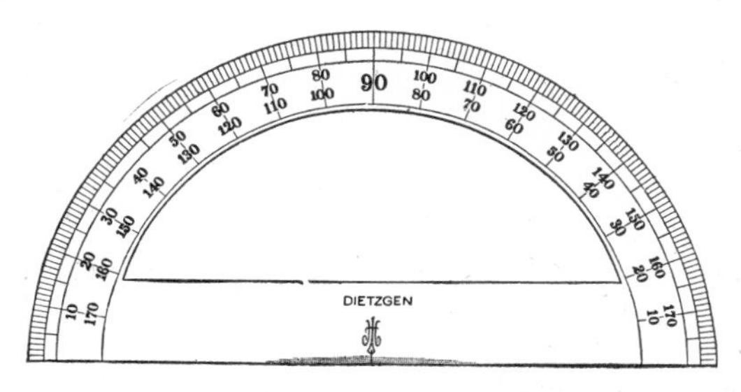

Fig. 2.33. Inexpensive protractor.

White light-weight bond paper, on which pencil drawings can be made and from which blueprints can be produced without making tracings, is used in many commercial drafting rooms in order to keep labor costs at a minimum.

2.21. Tracing papers and cloth. A large variety of natural and specially prepared tracing papers are available for making ink tracings and pencil drawings from which blueprints, ozalid prints, and so forth, are made for the shop. It is important that the paper selected be highly translucent and able to hold a workable surface under repeated erasing.

Fig. 2.34. Erasing machine.

Fig. 2.35. Draftsman's pencil sharpener.

The types that are treated with undesirable oils should be avoided, because they become brittle and discolor with age.

The two general types of cloth available are ink cloth and pencil cloth. The cloth used for ink is clear and transparent, dull on one side, and glossy

Fig. 2.36. Drafting brush.

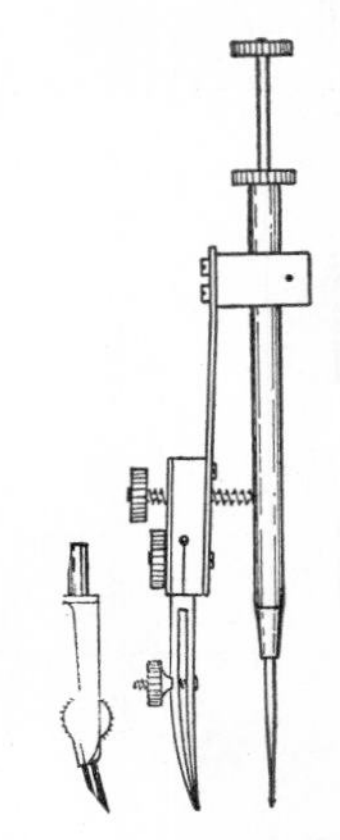

Fig. 2.37. Drop pen (pencil).

on the other. Pencil cloth is a white cloth with a surface specially prepared to take pencil marks readily. It may be dull on one side only or on both sides.

2.22. A few of the many other special instruments that are convenient for drawing but are not necessary for ordinary work are shown in Figs. 2.34 to 2.40.

The drafting machine (Fig. 2.41) is a device that is designed to combine the functions of the T-square, triangles, scale, and protractor. Drafting

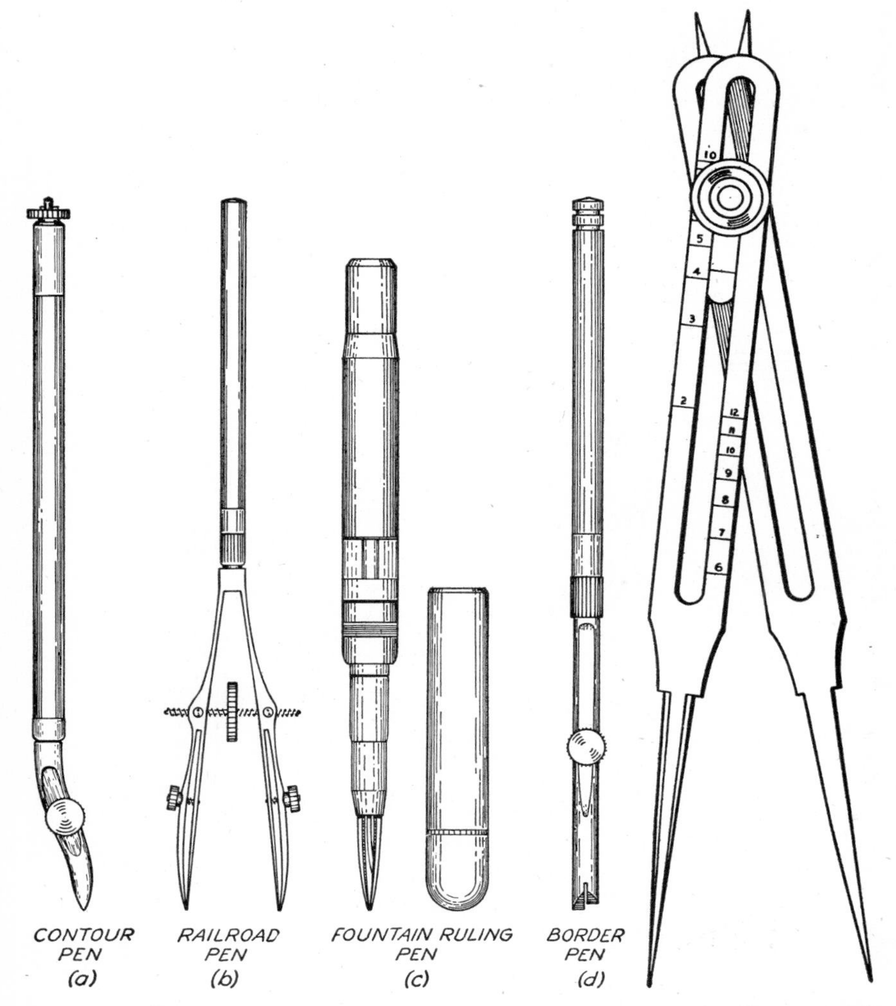

Fig. 2.38. Special ruling pens.

Fig. 2.39. Proportional dividers.

machines are used extensively in commercial drafting rooms because it has been estimated that their use leads to a 25 to 50 per cent saving in time.

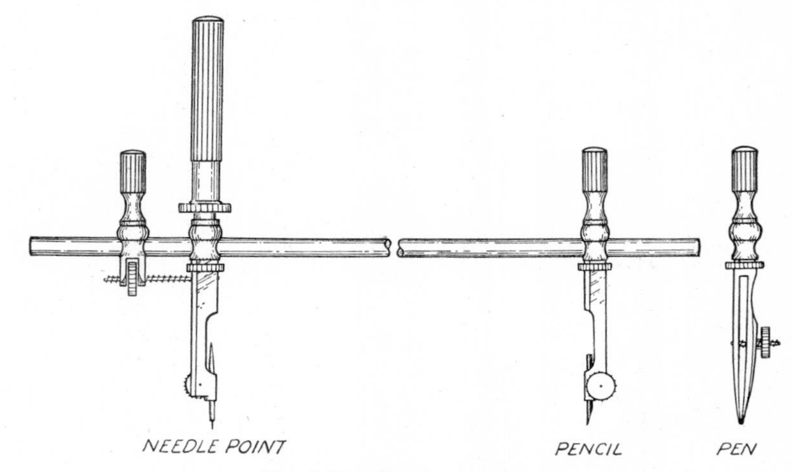

Fig. 2.40. Beam compass.

Courtesy Keuffel & Esser Co.

Fig. 2.41. Drafting machine.

3 USE OF INSTRUMENTS AND EQUIPMENT

3.1. It is essential that a beginner acquire a knowledge of the proper manipulation and adjustment of drawing instruments and practice the correct technique before attempting even simple engineering drawings. If he concentrates on the right methods of handling at the very start, he will be rewarded later by neat and accurate work of professional quality. Speed will develop naturally, and he will acquire a snap and swing that is free of unnecessary motions and awkward handling.

3.2. Pencils. As stated in the preceding chapter, the grade of pencil to be used for various purposes depends upon the type of line desired,

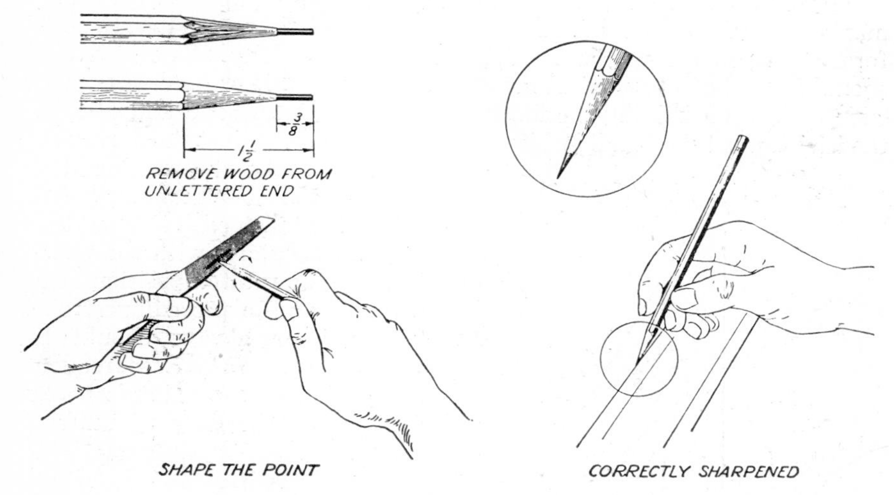

Fig. 3.1. Conical point.

the kind of paper employed, and the humidity, which affects the surface of the paper. On a humid day the paper surface is less resistant to the pencil and will therefore require a softer grade than when the air has much less moisture. There is a considerable difference of opinion among teachers and draftsmen on pencil grades because of the variation among different brands of pencils of the same grade. Drafting-room standards for line quality usually will govern. Ordinarily, however, a draftsman should have available at least one hard pencil (6H) for the light construction lines in layout work where accuracy is required, some softer pencils (2H-4H) for repenciling finished lines, and two medium-soft ones (F-H) for freehand work.

Many draftsmen prefer the conical point for general use (Fig. 3.1), while others find the wedge point more suitable for straight-line work, because it requires less sharpening and makes a denser line (Fig. 3.2).

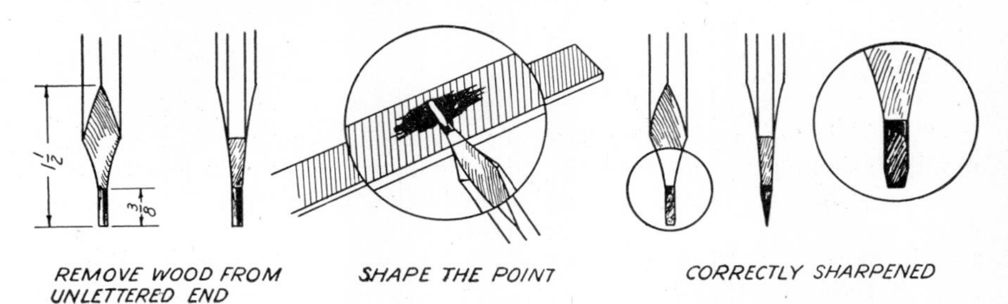

Fig. 3.2. Wedge point.

When sharpening a pencil, the wood should be cut away (on the unlettered end) with a knife or a pencil sharpener equipped with draftsman's cutters. About $\frac{3}{8}$ inch of the lead should be exposed and should form a cut, including the wood, about $1\frac{1}{2}$ inches long. The lead then should be shaped to a conical point on the pointer (file or sandpaper pad). This is done by holding the file stationary in the left hand and drawing the lead toward the handle while rotating the pencil against the movement (Fig. 3.1). All strokes should be made in the same manner, a new grip being taken each time so that each stroke starts with the pencil in the same rotated position as at the end of the preceding stroke. The pointer always should be within easy reach because frequent sharpening of the point is necessary to obtain lines of uniform width.

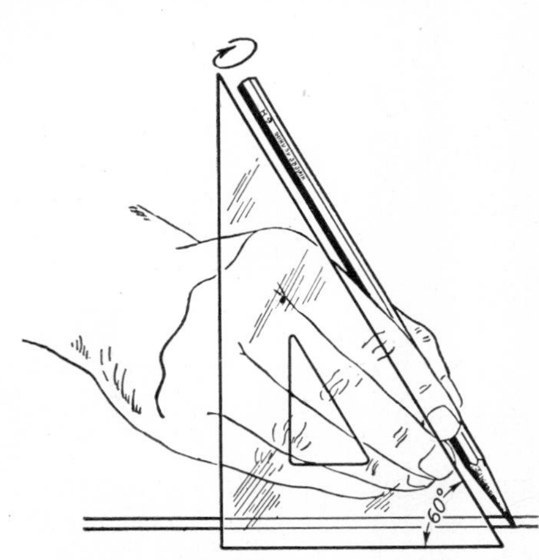

Fig. 3.3. Using the pencil.

3.3. Drawing pencil lines. Pencil lines should be sharp and uniform along their entire length, and sufficiently distinct to fulfill their ultimate purposes. Construction lines (preliminary lines) should be drawn *very* lightly so that they may be easily erased. Finished lines should be made boldly and distinctly, with definite contrast between object lines and auxiliary lines, such as dimension lines, center lines, and section lines. To give this contrast, which is necessary for clearness and ease in reading, object lines should be of medium width and very black. Auxiliary lines should be dark and not so wide as object lines.

When drawing a line, the pencil should be inclined slightly (about 60°) in the direction in which the line is being drawn. The pencil should be "pulled" (never pushed) at the same inclination for the full length of the line. If it is rotated (twirled) slowly between the fingers as the line is drawn, a symmetrical point will be maintained and a straight uniform line will be insured. This procedure helps keep the line straight and parallel to the ruling edge.

3.4. Placing and fastening the paper. For accuracy and ease in manipulating the T-square, the drawing paper should be located well

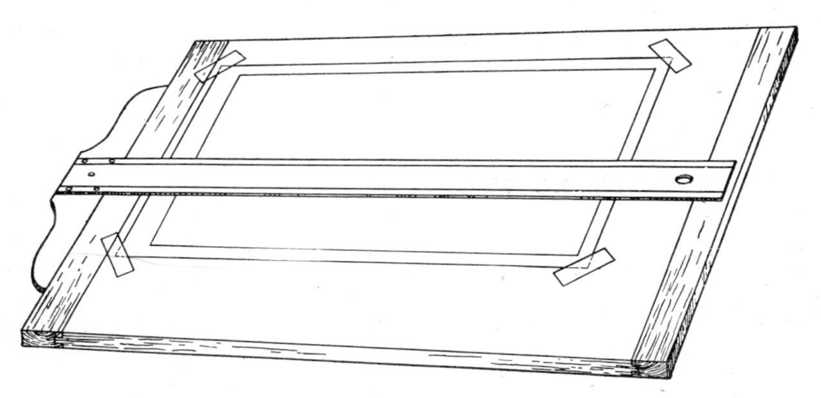

Fig. 3.4. A sheet of drawing paper fastened down.

up on the board and near the left-hand edge. The lower edge of the sheet (if plain) or the lower border line (if printed) should be aligned along the working edge of the T-square before the sheet is fastened down at all four corners with thumb tacks, Scotch tape, or staples. The T-square should be in complete contact with the working edge of the board while squaring the paper.

3.5. The T-square. The T-square is used primarily for drawing horizontal lines and for guiding the triangles when drawing vertical and inclined lines. It is manipulated by sliding the working edge (inner face) of the head along the left edge of the board until the blade is in the required position. The left hand then should be shifted to a position near the center of the blade to hold it in place and to prevent its deflection while drawing the line. Experienced draftsmen hold the T-square, as shown in Fig. 3.5(*b*), with the fingers pressing on the blade and the thumb on the paper. Small adjustments may be made with the hand in this position by sliding the blade with the fingers.

If a horizontal line is to be drawn through a given point, the T-square is moved into position by placing the pencil on the point at the ruling angle and sliding the T-square into contact with the pencil point.

Horizontal lines are drawn from left to right along the upper edge of the T-square. (*Exception*: left-handed persons should use the T-square

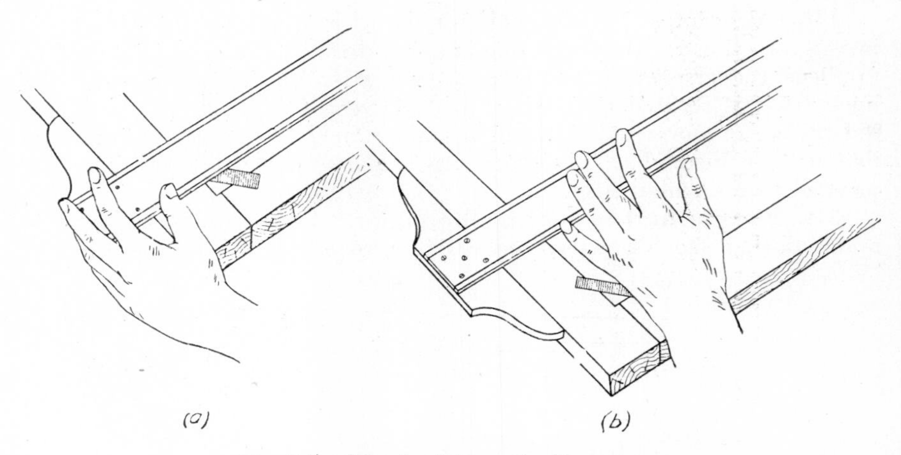

Fig. 3.5. Manipulating the T-square.

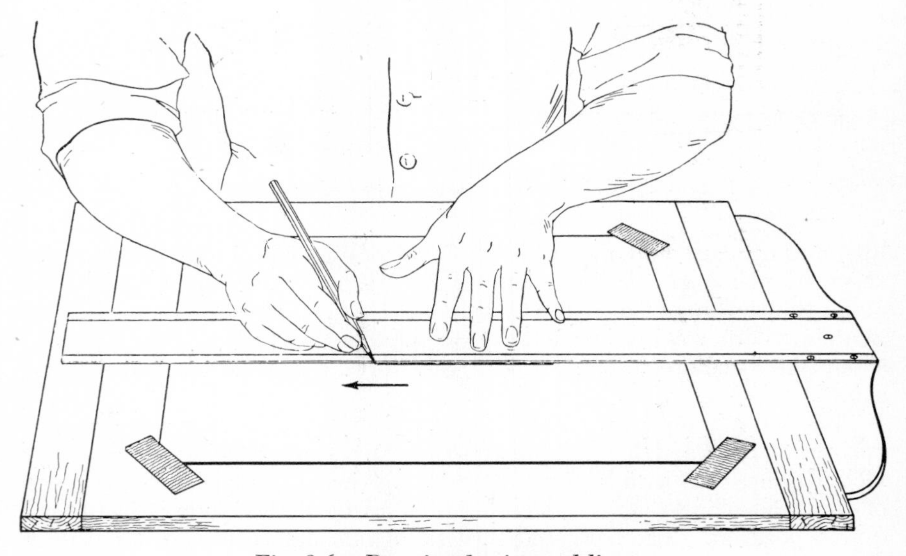

Fig. 3.6. Drawing horizontal lines.

head at the right side of the board and draw from right to left.) While drawing the line, the ruling hand should slide along the blade on the little finger. The beginner should cultivate the habit of making certain the T-square head has made perfect contact with the board before he begins drawing a line.

The T-square should never be used with the head against the top or bottom edges of the board because manufacturers do not true-up these edges to make 90° with the end strips.

3.6. Vertical lines. Vertical lines are drawn upward along the vertical leg of a triangle whose other (horizontal) leg is supported and guided by the T-square blade. The blade is held in position with the palm and thumb of the left hand, and the triangle is adjusted and held by the fingers as shown in Fig. 3.7. In the case of a right-handed person, the triangle should be to the right of the line to be drawn.

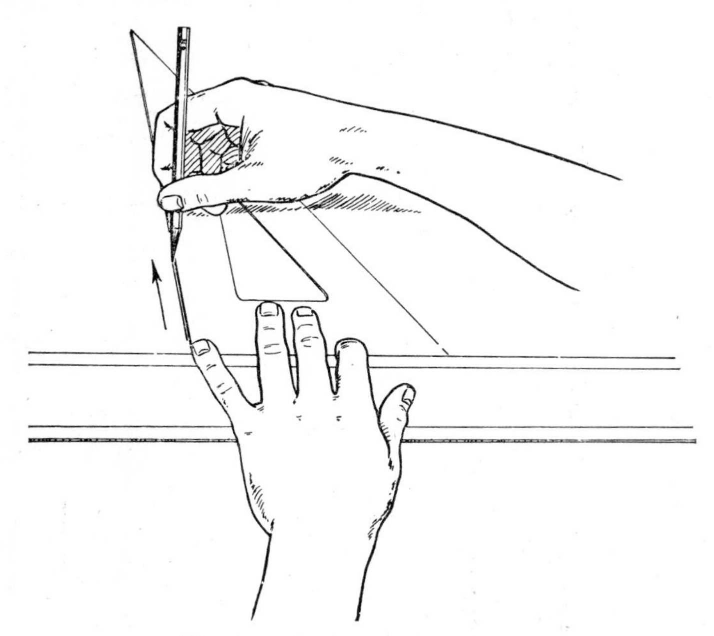

Fig. 3.7. Drawing vertical lines.

If the vertical line is to be drawn through a given point, the triangle is moved into position by placing the pencil on the point at the ruling angle, and sliding the triangle along the guiding edge of the T-square until the vertical leg is in contact with the pencil point. To insure that the line will pass accurately through the point, always place the T-square well below the starting point. Never draw to or from an extreme corner of a triangle.

Either the 30° × 60° or the 45° triangle may be used since both triangles have a right angle. However, the 30° × 60° is generally preferred because it usually has a longer perpendicular leg.

3.7. Inclined lines. Triangles also are used for drawing inclined lines. Lines that make angles of 30°, 45°, or 60° with the horizontal may be drawn with the 30° × 60° or the 45° triangle in combination with the

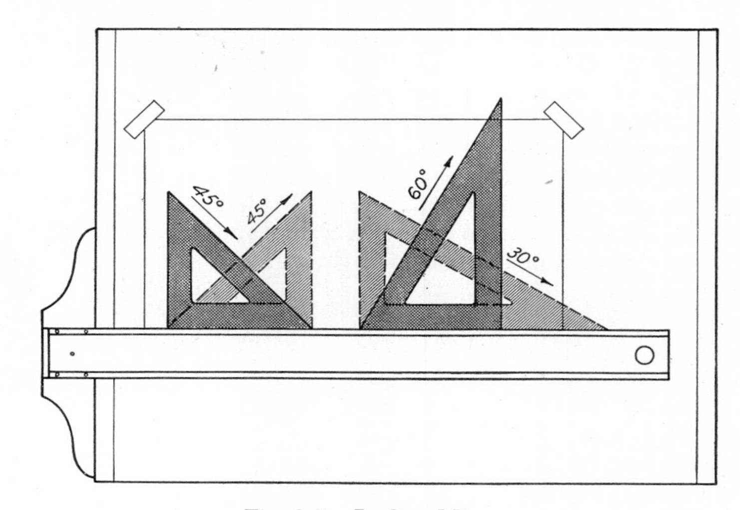

Fig. 3.8. Inclined lines.

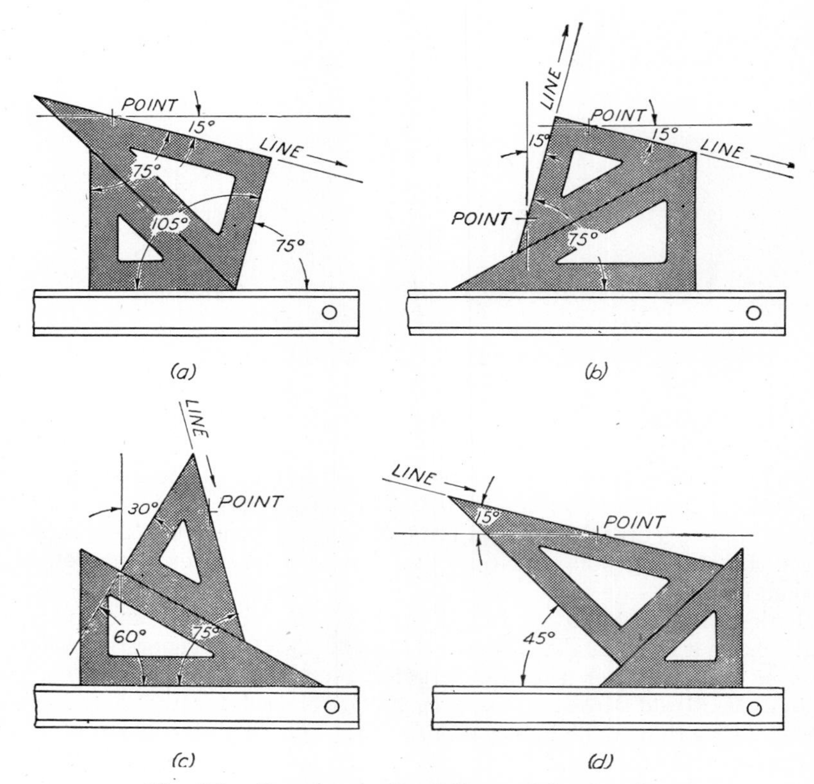

Fig. 3.9. Drawing inclined lines with triangles.

T-square, as shown in Fig. 3.8. If the two triangles are combined, lines that make 15° or a multiple of 15° may be drawn with the horizontal. Several possible arrangements and the angles that result are shown in Fig. 3.9. It is interesting to note that whenever the hypotenuse of one triangle is placed against the hypotenuse of the other, a 15° and a 75° angle are both available from the single setting; whereas, if the leg of one rests against the hypotenuse of the other, either a 15° or a 75° angle and another, such as a 30°, 45°, or 60° angle, results. The length of a line drawn along the hypotenuse may be extended by shifting the T-square and triangles, as shown in Fig. 3.10.

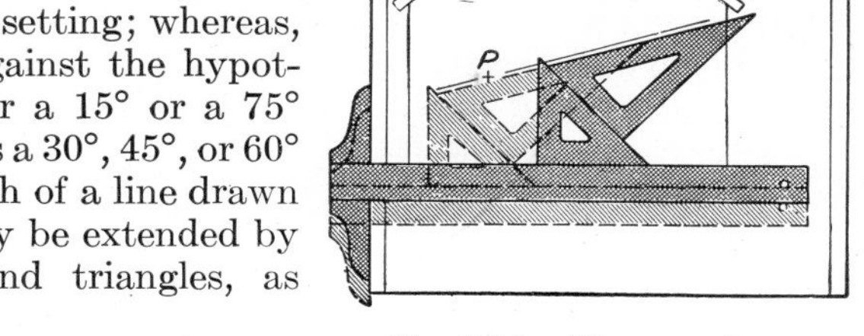

Fig. 3.10. To extend an inclined line.

The triangles used singly or in combination offer a useful method for dividing a circle into four, six, eight, twelve, or twenty-four equal parts. For angles other than those divisible by 15, a protractor must be used.

3.8. Parallel lines. The triangles are used in combination to draw a line parallel to a given line. To draw such a line, place a ruling edge of a triangle, supported by a T-square or another triangle, along the given line; then slip the triangle, as shown in Fig. 3.11(a), to the required

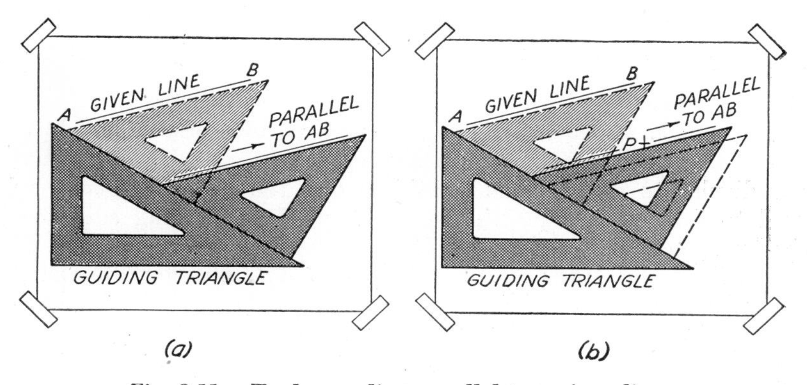

Fig. 3.11. To draw a line parallel to a given line.

position and draw the parallel line along the same ruling edge that previously coincided with the given line. If the line is to be drawn through a given point, the ruling edge should be moved beyond the point so that the pencil may be placed on the point at the ruling angle, and the ruling edge moved into contact with the pencil point, as in Fig. 3.11(b).

3.9. Perpendicular lines. Either the sliding triangle method (Fig. 3.12a) or the revolved triangle method (Fig. 3.12b) may be used to draw a line perpendicular to a given line. When using the sliding triangle method, adjust to the given line a side of a triangle that is adjacent to the right angle. Guide the side opposite the right angle with a second triangle as shown in Fig. 3.12(*a*); then slide the first triangle along the guiding triangle until it is in the required position for drawing the perpendicular along the other edge adjacent to the right angle.

Although the revolved triangle method is not so quickly done, it is widely used. To draw a perpendicular using this method, align along the given line the hypotenuse of a triangle, one leg of which is guided by the T-square or another triangle, then hold the guiding member in position and revolve the triangle about the right angle until the other leg is against the guiding edge. The new position of the hypotenuse will be

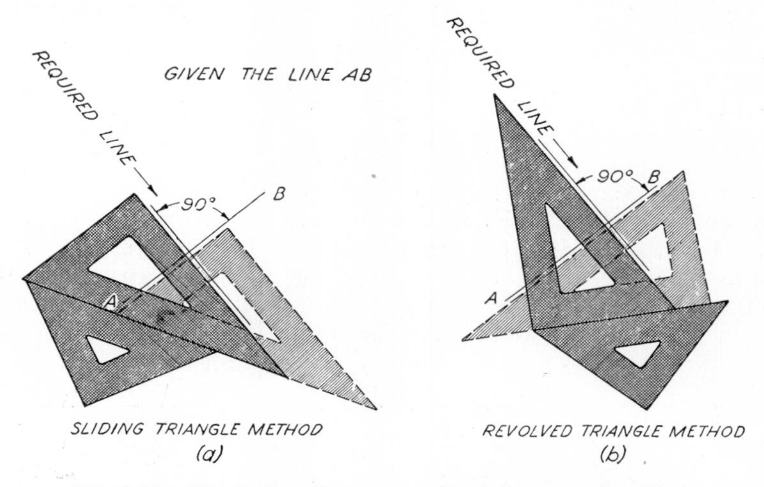

Fig. 3.12. To draw a line perpendicular to another line.

perpendicular to its previous location along the given line and, when moved to the required position, may be used as a ruling edge for the desired perpendicular.

3.10. Inclined lines making 15°, 30°, 45°, 60°, or 75° with an oblique line. A line making with an oblique line an angle equal to any angle of a triangle may be drawn with the triangles. The two methods previously discussed for drawing perpendicular lines are applicable with slight modifications. To draw an oblique line using the revolved triangle method (Fig. 3.13*a*), adjust along the given line the edge that is opposite the required angle, then revolve the triangle about the required angle, slide it into position, and draw the required line along the side opposite the required angle.

To use the sliding triangle method, illustrated in Fig. 3.13(*b*), adjust to the given line one of the edges adjacent to the required angle, and guide the side opposite the required angle with a straight edge; then slide the triangle into position and draw the required line along the other adjacent side.

To draw a line making 75° with a given line, place the triangles together so that the sum of a pair of adjacent angles equals 75°, and adjust one side of the angle thus formed to the given line; then slide the triangle,

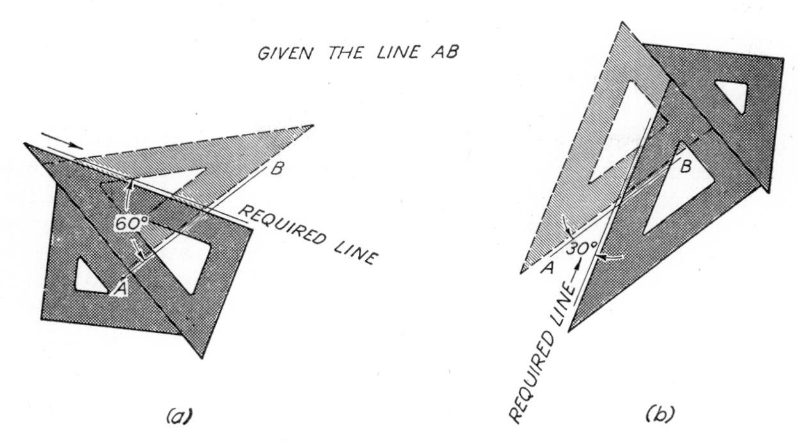

Fig. 3.13. To draw lines making 30°, 45°, or 60° with a given line.

whose leg forms the other side of the angle, across the given line into position, and draw the required line, as shown in Fig. 3.14(*a*).

To draw a line making 15° with a given line, select any two angles whose difference is 15°. Adjust to the given line a side adjacent to one

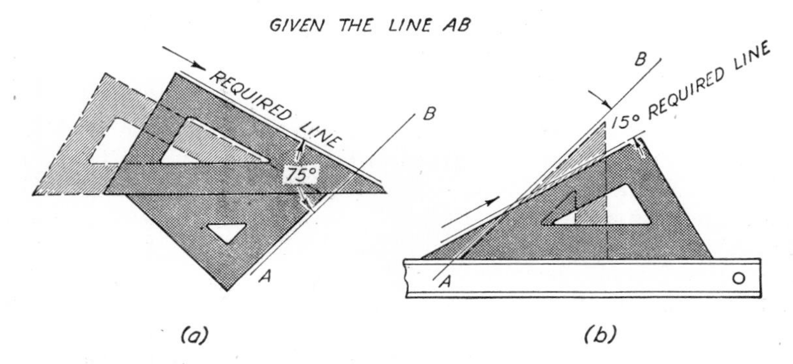

Fig. 3.14. To draw lines making 15° or 75° with a given line.

of these angles, and guide the side adjacent with a straight edge. Remove the first triangle and substitute the other so that one adjacent side of the angle to be subtracted is along the guiding edge, as shown in Fig. 3.14(*b*); then slide it into position and draw along the other adjacent side.

3.11. The scale. The sole purpose of the scale is to reproduce the dimensions of an object full size on a drawing or to reduce or enlarge them to some regular proportion such as eighth size, quarter size, half size, or double size. The scales of reduction most frequently used are as follows:

Full Size	(12″ = 1′ or 1″ = 1″)
Half Size	(6″ = 1′ or $\frac{1}{2}$″ = 1″)
Quarter Size	(3″ = 1′ or $\frac{1}{4}$″ = 1″)
Eighth Size	($1\frac{1}{2}$″ = 1′ or $\frac{1}{8}$″ = 1″)

$1'' = 1'$	$\frac{1}{4}'' = 1'$
$\frac{3}{4}'' = 1'$	$\frac{3}{16}'' = 1'$
$\frac{1}{2}'' = 1'$	$\frac{1}{8}'' = 1'$
$\frac{3}{8}'' = 1'$	$\frac{3}{32}'' = 1'$

The first four scales, full size, half size, quarter size, and eighth size, are the ones most frequently selected for drawing machine parts although other scales can be used. Since objects drawn by structural draftsmen and architects vary from small to very large, scales from full size to $\frac{3}{32}'' = 1'$ ($\frac{1}{128}$ size) are commonly encountered. For maps the civil engineers' decimal scale having 10, 20, 30, 40, 50, 60 and 80 divisions to the inch is used for representing 10′, 20′, 30′, and so forth to the inch. The "50 scale" is convenient for making machine drawings when the decimal system is used. The decimal system has been widely adopted by the aircraft and automotive industries.

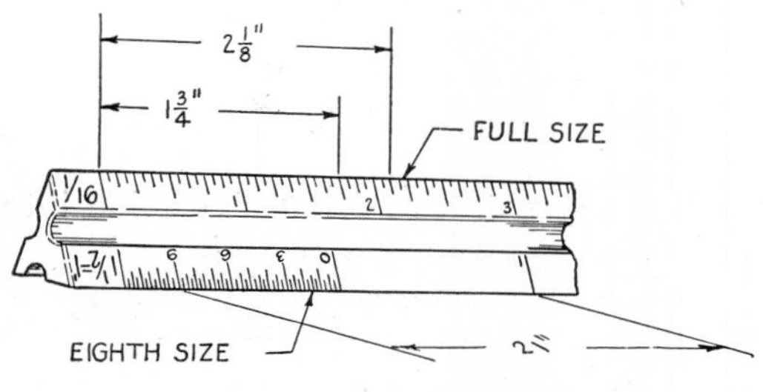

Fig. 3.15. Reading a scale.

It is essential that a draftsman always think and speak of each dimension as full size when scaling measurements, because the dimension figures given on the finished drawing indicate full-size measurements of the finished piece, regardless of the scale used.

The reading of an open-divided scale is illustrated in Fig. 3.15 with the eighth-size ($1\frac{1}{2}'' = 1'$) scale shown. The dimension can be read directly as 21 inches, the 9 inches being read in the divided division to the left of the cipher. Each long open division represents twelve inches (one foot).

To lay off a measurement, using a scale starting at the left of the stick, align the scale in the direction of the measurement with the zero of the scale being used toward the left. After it has been adjusted to the correct location, make short marks opposite the divisions on the scale that establish the desired distance. For ordinary work most draftsmen use the same pencil employed for the layout work. When extreme accuracy is necessary, however, it is better practice to use a pricker and make slight indentations (not holes) at the required points. If a regular pricker is

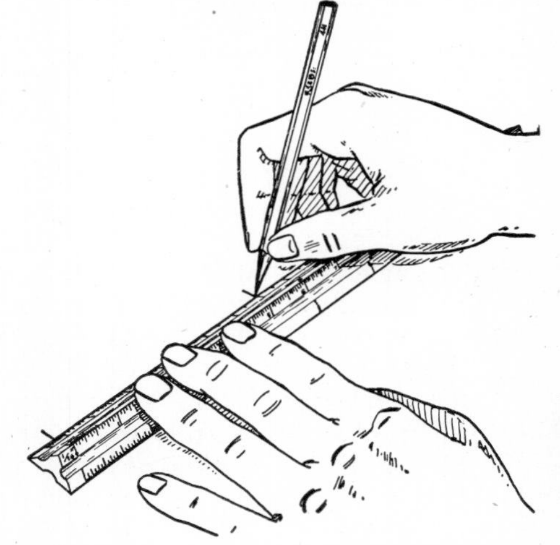

Fig. 3.16. To lay off a measurement.

not available, the dividers may be opened to approximately 60° and the point of one leg used as a substitute.

To insure accuracy, place the eye directly over the division to be marked, hold the marking instrument perpendicularly to the paper directly in front of the scale division, and mark the point. Always check the location of the point before removing the scale. If a slight indentation is made, it will be covered by the finished line; if a short mark is made, and it is *very* light, it will be unnoticeable on the finished drawing.

To set off a measurement (say 2′-9″) to half scale, the scale indicated either as $\frac{1}{2}$ (Fig. 3.17) or $\frac{1}{2}''$ = 1′ should be used. If the measurement is to be made from left to right, place the 9-inch fractional division mark (counted toward the left from the cipher) on the given line, and make an indentation (or mark) opposite the 2-foot division point. (See Fig. 3.17*a*.)

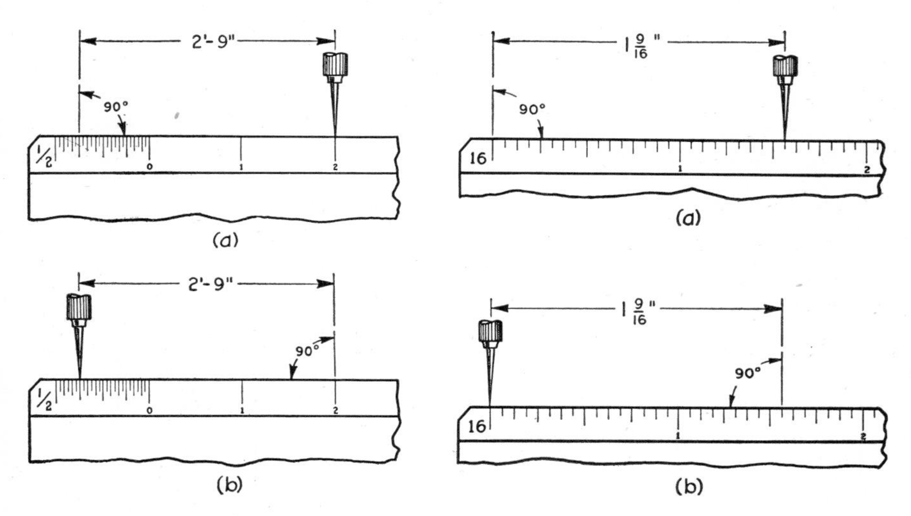

Fig. 3.17. To lay off a measurement. **Fig. 3.18. To lay off a measurement (full size).**

The distance from the line to the point represents 2′-9″, although it is actually $1\frac{3}{8}$ inches. To set off the same measurement from right to left, place the 2-foot mark on the given line, and make an indentation opposite the 9-inch fractional division mark. (See Fig. 3.17*b*.)

The procedure for setting off a distance to full size is illustrated in Fig. 3.18. The scale that is full divided into inches and sixteenths is best suited for this purpose.

To set off a measurement (say $1\frac{9}{16}$ inches) from left to right, place the initial mark at the start of the scale on the given line, and make an indentation opposite the $1\frac{9}{16}$-inch mark (Fig. 3.18*a*). To set off the same measurement from right to left, place the $1\frac{9}{16}$-inch mark on the given line, and make an indentation opposite the initial division mark at the start of the scale.

When scaling, there are certain practices that, if observed, will insure great accuracy and speed up the layout work. Although the practices recommended in the following paragraphs refer principally to the full-size scale, any scale that is full divided may be used similarly.

Whenever it is necessary to divide a dimension by two, divide the whole number and fraction separately and add them on the scale. The fraction is divided by multiplying its denominator by the divisor. For example, it is necessary to draw a circle $3\frac{7}{8}$ inches in diameter. One half of the whole number, 3 inches, equals $1\frac{1}{2}$ inches, and one half of $\frac{7}{8}$ of an inch equals $\frac{7}{8} \times \frac{1}{2}$ or $\frac{7}{16}$ of an inch. To lay off the measurement, set the $1\frac{1}{2}$-inch mark at the center, move the scale $\frac{7}{16}$ of an inch to the left, and mark (or indent) opposite the 0-inch and $3\frac{7}{8}$-inch division marks.

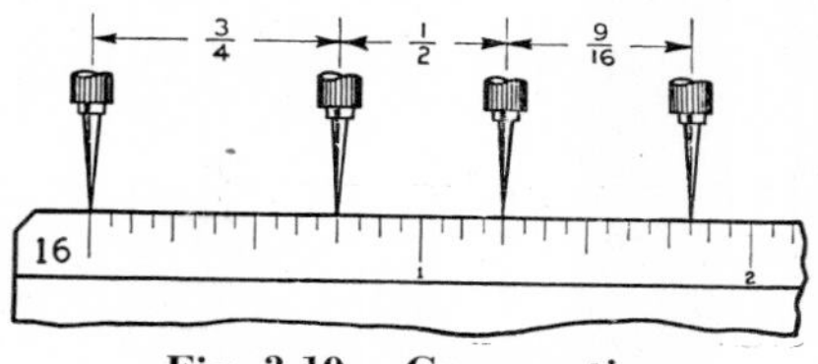

Fig. 3.19. Consecutive measurements.

In order to avoid cumulative errors and to provide a check on the work, consecutive measurements along a line should be set off by keeping the stick stationary and marking off the distances (from the 0 division mark) one after another, by adding each distance to the preceding ones. The last scale reading should equal the over-all dimension. (See Fig. 3.19.)

The full-size scale provides expert draftsmen with a quick and accurate method for bisecting a line. (See Fig. 3.20.) Since the distance between X and Y in the example is slightly less than $2\frac{1}{4}$ inches by actual measurement, the 6-inch mark, or some other major scale division placed approximately $1\frac{1}{8}$ inches to the right of point X, will be near the required mid-point. If the scale is shifted slightly until the distance from the 6-inch mark to point X equals the distance from the 6-inch mark to point Y, the 6-inch division will be exactly centered, and may be used to mark the required mid-point.

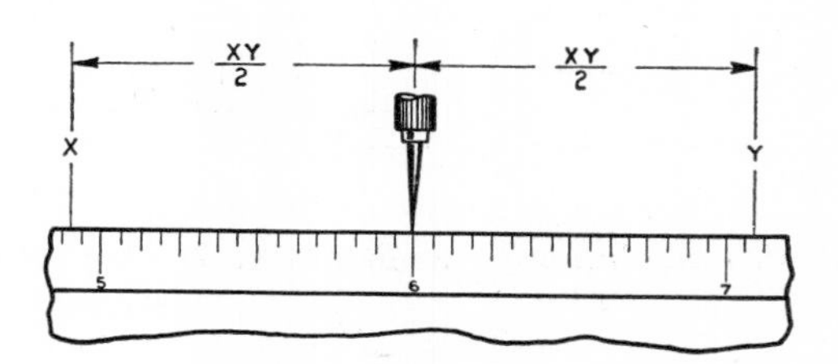

Fig. 3.20. To bisect a line.

3.12. The compass. The compass is used principally for drawing circles and circle arcs having radii beyond the working range of the bow pencil and bow pen. For drawing pencil circles, the style of point illustrated in Fig. 3.22(c) should be used because it gives more accurate results and is easier to maintain than most other styles. This style of point is formed by first sharpening the outside of the lead to a long flat bevel

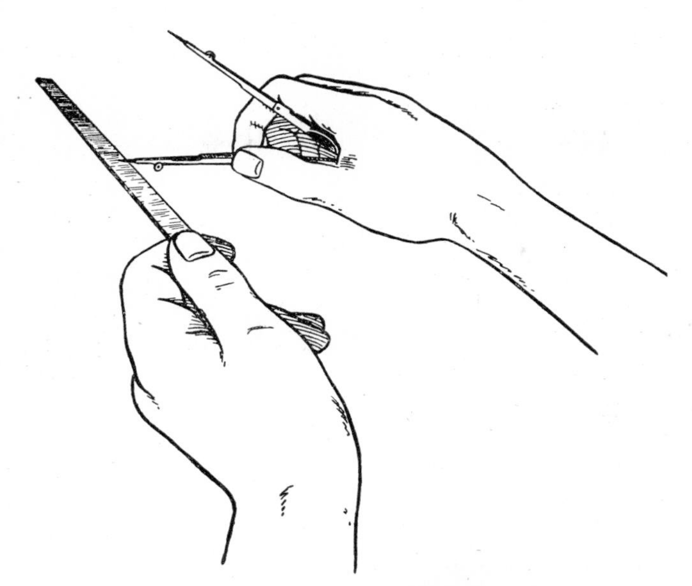

Fig. 3.21. Sharpening the compass lead.

approximately $\frac{1}{4}$ of an inch long (see Fig. 3.22*a*), and then finishing it (see Fig. 3.22*b*) with a slight rocking motion to reduce the width of the point. Although a hard lead (4*H* to 6*H*) will maintain a point longer without resharpening, it gives a finished object line that is too light in

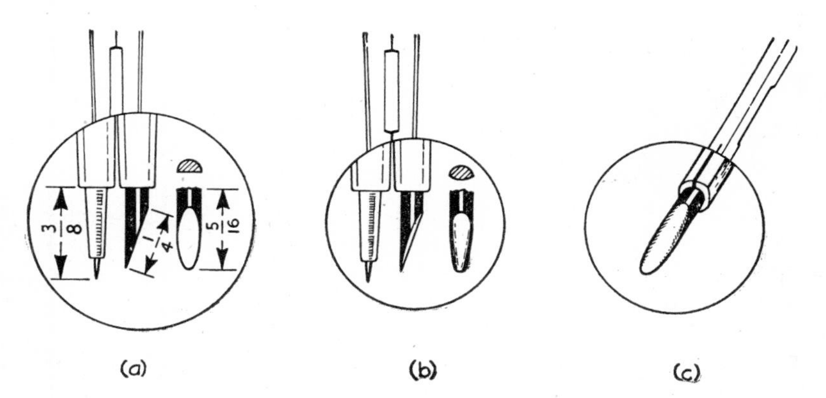

Fig. 3.22. Shaping the compass lead.

color. Soft lead (*F* or *H*) gives a darker line but quickly loses its edge and, on larger circles, gives a thicker line at the end than at the beginning. Some draftsmen have found that a medium grade (2H-3H) lead is a satisfactory compromise for ordinary working drawings. For design drawings, layout work, and graphical solutions, however, a harder lead will give better results.

The needle point should have the shouldered end out, and should be adjusted (approximately $\frac{3}{8}$ of an inch beyond the end of the split sleeve) so that it is slightly longer than the pen point. When the pencil leg is used, the lead should be adjusted slightly shorter and, as it is resharpened, should be readjusted (Fig. 3.23). The length of the needle point must never be changed after it once has been set for the pen.

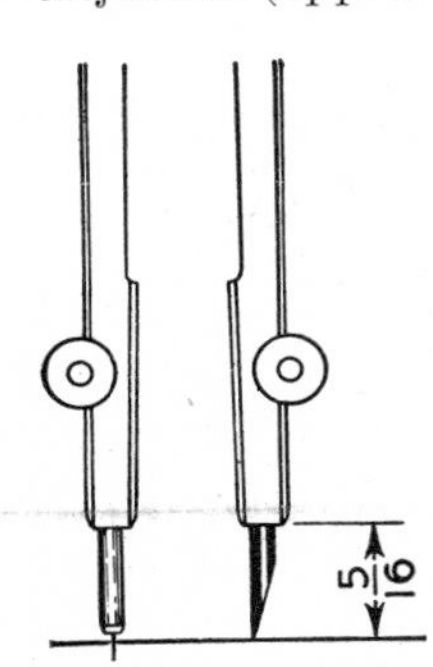

Fig. 3.23. The adjustment of the needle point.

3.13. Using the compass. To draw a circle, it is first necessary to draw two intersecting center lines at right angles and mark off the radius as previously explained. The pivot point may be guided accurately into position at the center with the little finger of the left hand. After the pencil point has been adjusted to the radius mark, the circle is drawn in a clockwise direction by holding the compass as shown in Fig. 3.24, and rotating the handle between the thumb and forefinger. While drawing the circle, the compass should be inclined slightly forward. If the pencil line is not dark enough, it may be brightened by drawing around it again.

For a radius larger than 2 inches, the legs should be bent at the knee

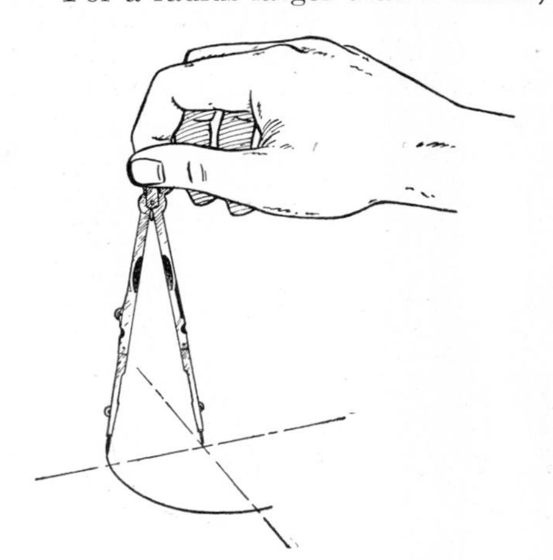

Fig. 3.24. Using the compass.

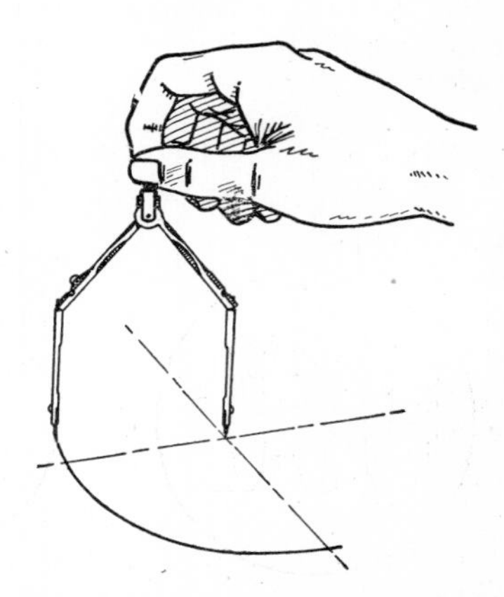

Fig. 3.25. Using the compass (leg bent).

joints to stand approximately perpendicular to the paper (Fig. 3.25). It is particularly important that this adjustment be made when drawing ink circles, otherwise both nibs will not touch the paper. For circles whose radii exceed 5 inches, the lengthening bar should be used to increase the capacity. In this case the instrument is manipulated by steadying the pivot leg with one hand, and rotating the marking leg with the other (Fig. 3.26). Care must be taken to avoid changing the adjustment while drawing the circle.

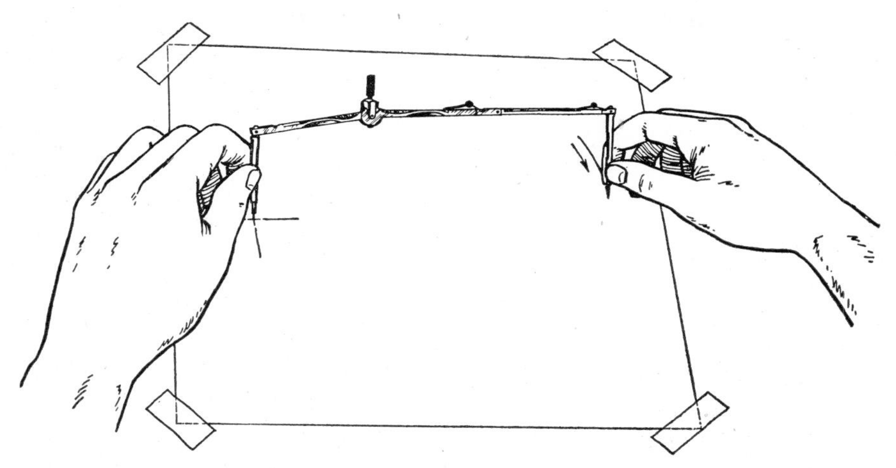

Fig. 3.26. Drawing large circles.

3.14. The dividers. The dividers are used principally for dividing curved and straight lines into any number of equal parts, and for transferring measurements. If the instrument is held with one leg between the forefinger and second finger, and the other leg between the thumb and third finger, as illustrated in Fig. 3.27, an adjustment may be quickly and easily made with one hand. The second and third fingers are used to "open out" the legs, and the thumb and forefinger to close them. This method of adjusting may seem awkward to the beginner at first, but with practice absolute control can be developed. Close variations to the smallest fraction of an inch are possible with the hairspring. When its use is necessary, the grip on the instrument must be changed so that the forefinger and thumb may be used to turn the adjusting screw.

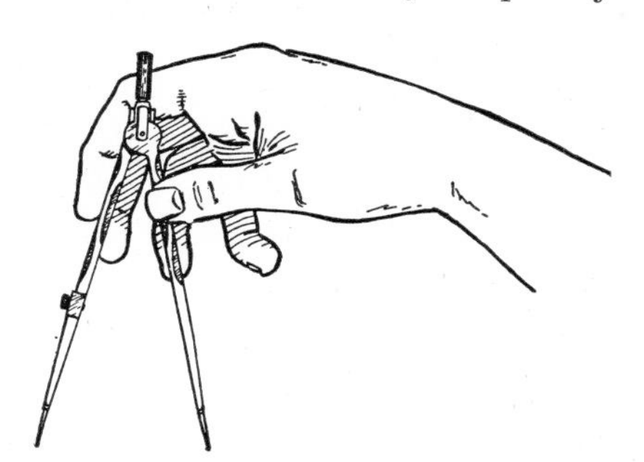

Fig. 3.27. To adjust the large dividers.

3.15. Use of the dividers. The trial method is used to divide a line into a given number of equal parts. (See Fig. 3.28.) To divide a line into a desired number of equal parts, open the dividers until the distance between the points is estimated to be equal to the length of a division, and step off the line *lightly*. If the last prick mark misses the end point, increase or decrease the setting by an amount estimated to be equal to

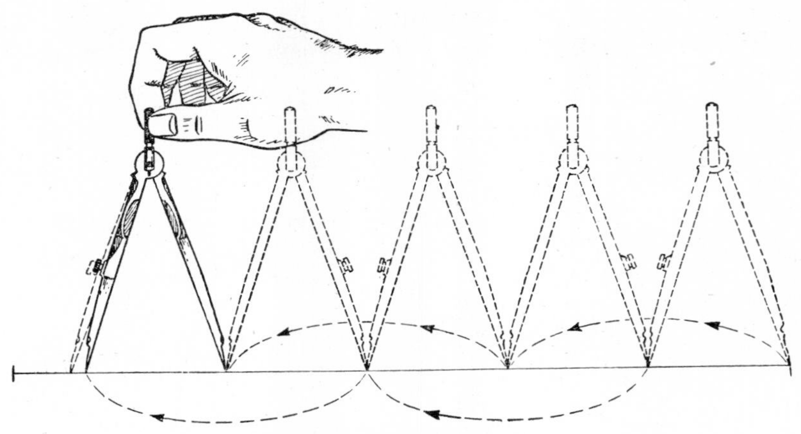

Fig. 3.28. Use of the dividers.

the error divided by the number of divisions, before lifting the dividers from the paper. Step off the line again. Repeat this procedure until the dividers are correctly set, then space the line again and indent the division points. When stepping off a line, the dividers are rotated alternately

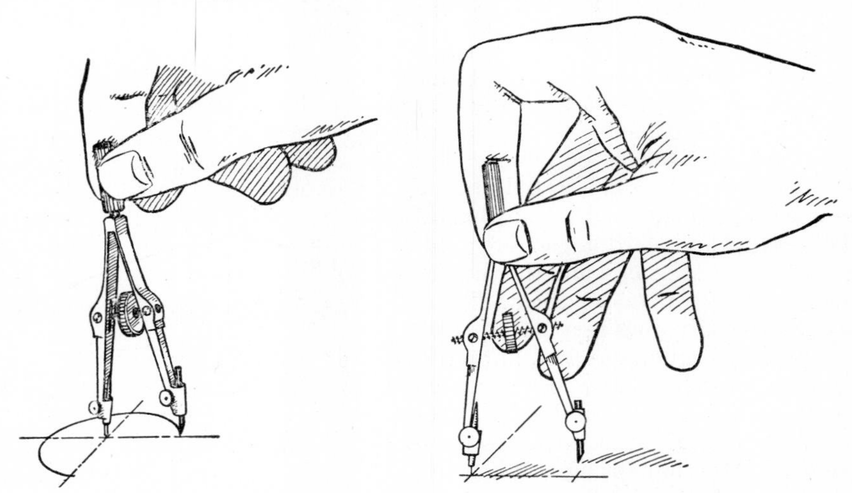

Fig. 3.29. Use of the bow pencil. **Fig. 3.30. Small adjustments.**

in an opposite direction on either side of the line, each half revolution, as shown in Fig. 3.28.

Although the dividers are used to transfer a distance on a drawing, they should never be used to transfer a measurement from the scale, as the method is slow and inaccurate and results in serious damage to the graduation marks. Care should be taken to avoid pricking large unsightly holes with the divider points. It is the common practice of many expert draftsmen to draw a small free-hand circle around a very light indentation to establish its location.

3.16. Use of the bow instruments. The bow pen and bow pencil are convenient for drawing small circles having a radius of 1 inch or less (Fig. 3.29). The needle points should be adjusted slightly longer than the marking points, as in the case of the compass.

Small adjustments are made by the fingers of the hand holding the instrument, with the pivot point in position at the center of the required

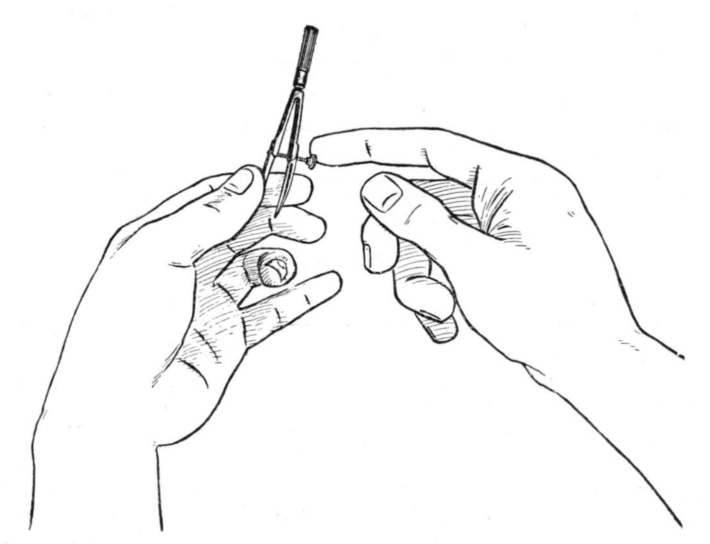

Fig. 3.31. Large adjustments (side-screw instruments).

circle or arc (Fig. 3.30). When a side-screw type of instrument is being used, and it is necessary to make a large change, damaging wear on the thread can be minimized by closing the legs with the fingers of the left hand to relieve the pressure while setting the adjustment nut in the required position (Fig. 3.31).

The bow dividers are used for the same purposes and in the same manner as the large dividers. Since they hold a setting better, however, they are more suited for very accurate or small work.

3.17. Conventional line symbols. Symbolic lines of various weights are used in making technical drawings. The American Standards Association suggests:

> Three weights of lines, heavy, medium, and light are considered desirable on finished drawings in ink, both for legibility and appearance, although in rapid practice and in particular on penciled drawings from which blue prints are to be made this may be simplified to two weights, medium and light. For pencil drawings the lines should be in proportion to the ink lines, *medium* for outlines, hidden, cutting plane, short breaks, adjacent part and alternate position lines and *light* for section, center, dimension, long break, and ditto lines.

The lines illustrated in Fig. 3.32 are shown full size. When symbolic lines are used on a pencil drawing they should not vary in color. For example, center lines, extension lines, dimension lines, and section lines should differ from object lines only in width. The resulting contrast makes a drawing easier to read. All lines, except construction lines, should be very dark and bright to give the drawing the "snap" that is needed for good appearance. If the drawing is on tracing paper the lead must be "packed on" so that a satisfactory print can be obtained. Construction lines should be drawn *very* fine so as to be unnoticeable on the

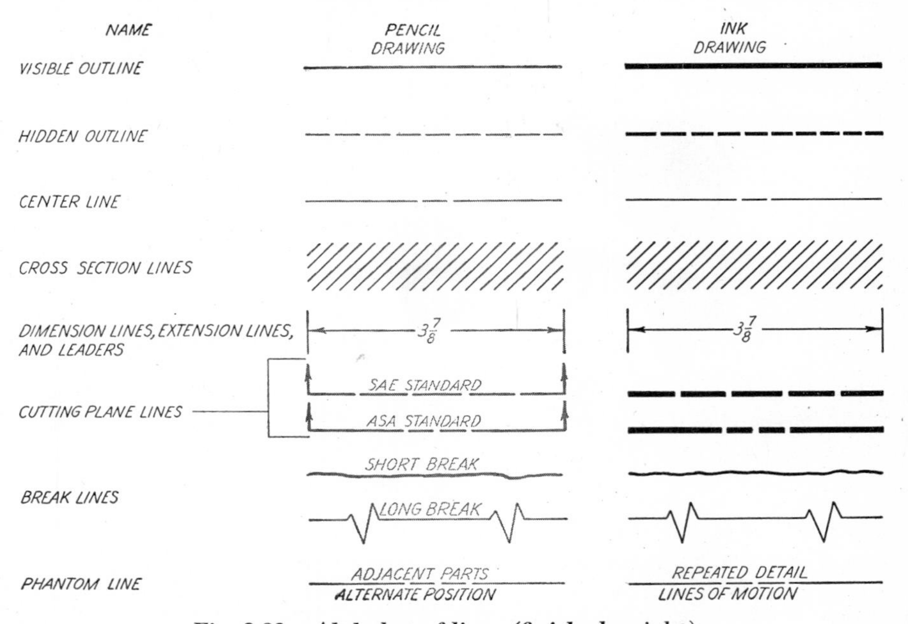

Fig. 3.32. Alphabet of lines (finished weight).

finished drawing. The lengths of the dashes and spaces, shown in Figs. 7.28 and 10.22, are recommended for the hidden lines, center lines, and cutting plane lines on average-size drawings.

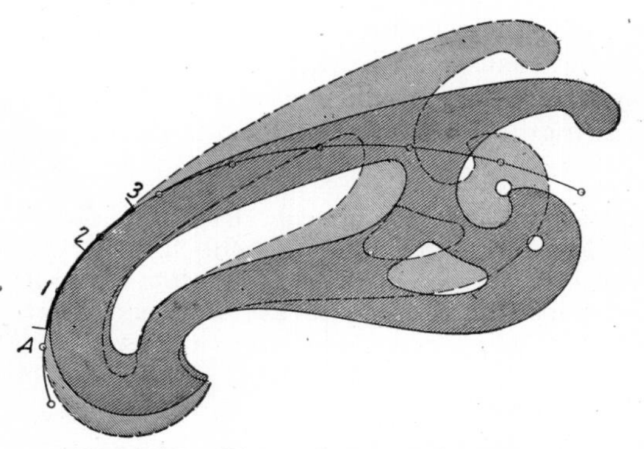

Fig. 3.33. Using the irregular curve.

3.18. Use of the French curve. A French curve is used for drawing irregular curves that are not circle arcs. After sufficient points have been located, the French curve is applied so that a portion of its ruling edge passes through at least three points, as shown in Fig. 3.33. It should be so placed that the increasing curvature of the section of the ruling edge being used follows the direction of that part of the curve that is changing most rapidly. To insure that the finished curve will be free of humps and sharp breaks, the first line drawn should start and stop short of the first and last points to which the French curve has been fitted. Then the curve is adjusted in a new position with the ruling edge coinciding with a section of the line previously drawn. Each successive segment should stop short of the last point matched by the curve. When inking a curve, overlapping should be avoided because sharp changes in the thickness or the color of the line may result. In Fig. 3.33, the curve fits the three points, A, 1, and 2. A line is drawn from between point A and point 1 to between point 1 and point 2. Then, the curve is shifted, as shown, to again fit points 1 and 2 with an additional point 3, and the line is extended to between point 2 and point 3.

Draftsmen sketch a smooth continuous curve through the points in pencil before drawing the mechanical line. This procedure makes the task of drawing the curve less difficult, since it is easier to adjust the ruling edge to segments of the free-hand curve than to the points. When tracing a curve in ink the pen must be held perpendicular to the paper and the blades kept parallel to the ruling edge. A beginner's inability to control a pen is usually due to the instrument being held incorrectly.

A curve that cannot be fitted accurately may sometimes be drawn by varying the distance of the marking point from the guiding edge. This should be done only as a last resort, however, and should not be practiced to avoid the sometimes tedious task of finding a portion of the curve that will match at least three points.

3.19. Use of the erasing shield and eraser. An erasure is made on a drawing by placing an opening in the erasing shield over the work to be erased and rubbing with a pencil eraser (never an ink eraser) until it is removed (Fig. 3.34). Excessive pressure should not be applied to the eraser, because, although the lines will disappear more quickly, the surface of the paper is likely to be permanently damaged. The fingers holding the erasing shield should rest partly on the drawing paper to prevent the shield from slipping.

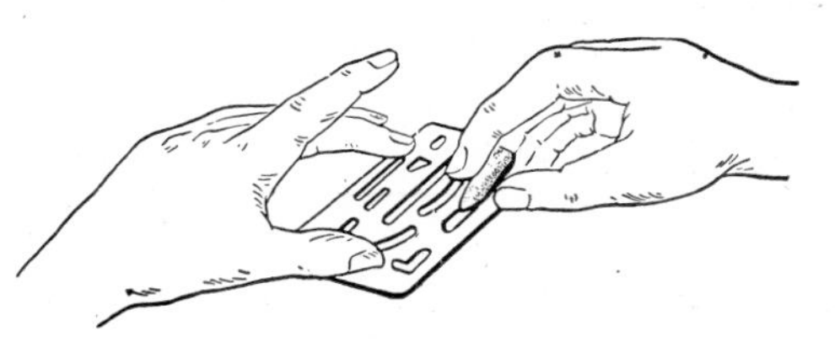

Fig. 3.34. Using the erasing shield.

3.20. Exercises in instrumental drawing. The following elementary exercises have been designed to offer experience in the use of the drafting instruments. The designs should be drawn *lightly* with a hard pencil. After making certain that all constructions shown on a drawing are correct, the lines forming the designs should be heavied with a medium hard pencil. The light construction lines need not be erased if the drawing has been kept relatively clean. All dimensions and letters should be omitted except in problem 11.

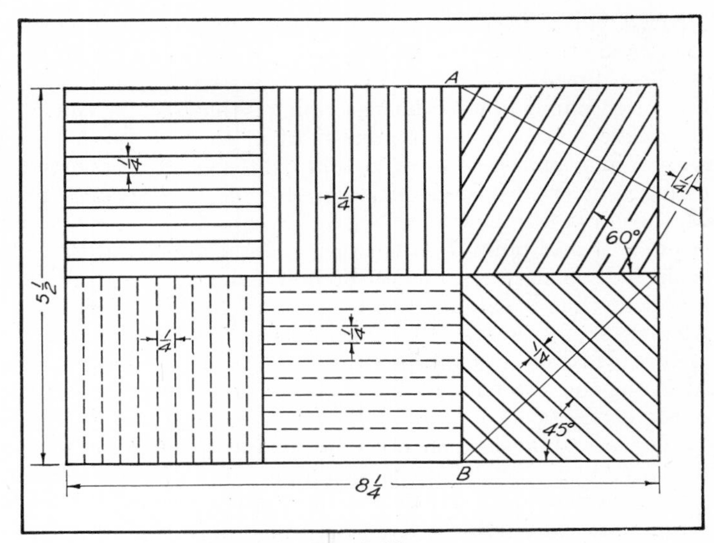

Fig. 3.35.

1. (Fig. 3.35). On a sheet of drawing paper reproduce the line formations shown. If the principal border lines have not been printed on the sheet, they may be drawn first so that the large $5\frac{1}{2}'' \times 8\frac{1}{4}''$ rectangle can be balanced horizontally and vertically within the border. To draw the inclined lines, first draw the indicated measuring lines through the lettered points at the correct angle, and mark off $\frac{1}{4}''$ distances. These division points establish the locations of the required lines of the formation. The six squares of the formation are equal in size.

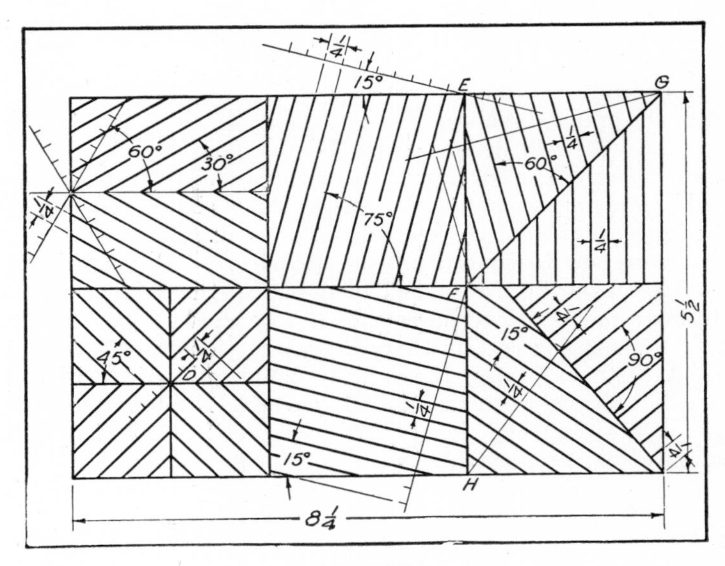

Fig. 3.36.

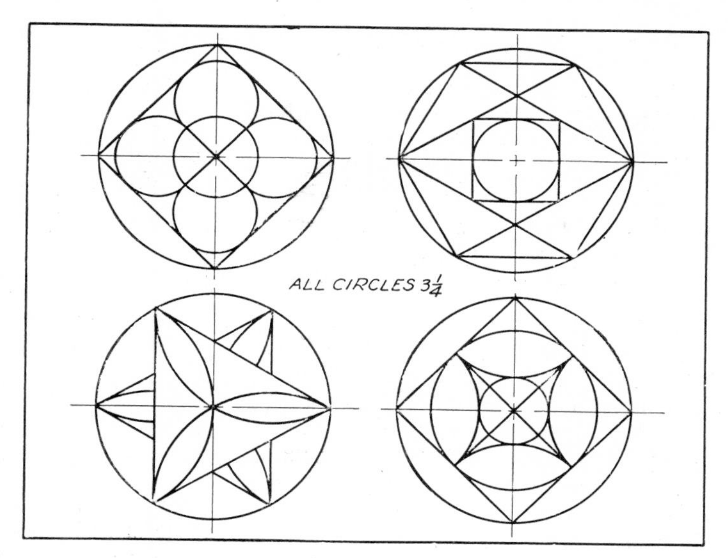

Fig. 3.37.

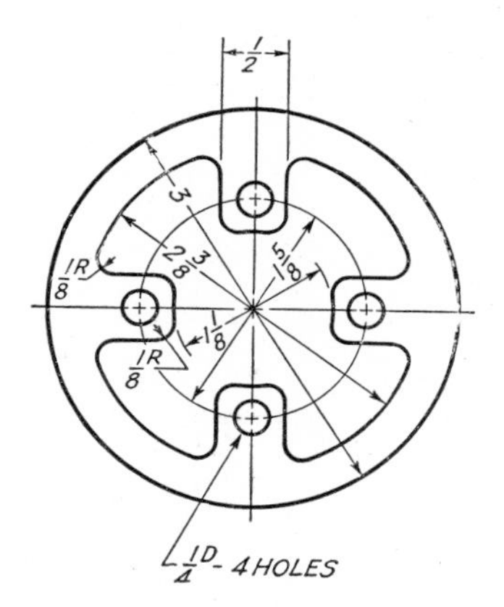

Fig. 3.38.

2. (Fig. 3.36.) Reproduce the line formations shown, following the instructions given for problem 1.

3. (Fig. 3.37.) This exercise is designed to give the student practice with the bow pencil and compass by drawing some simple geometrical figures. The line work within each large circle may be reproduced with the knowledge only that the diameter is $3\frac{1}{4}''$. All circles and circle arcs are to be made finished weight when they are first drawn, since retracing often produces a double line. Do not "overrun" the straight lines or stop them too short.

4. (Fig. 3.38.) Reproduce the contour view of the stamping.

5–7. (Figs. 3.39, 3.40, 3.41.) Reproduce the designs following the instructions given for problem 3, making the dashes of the arcs approximately $\frac{1}{8}''$ long.

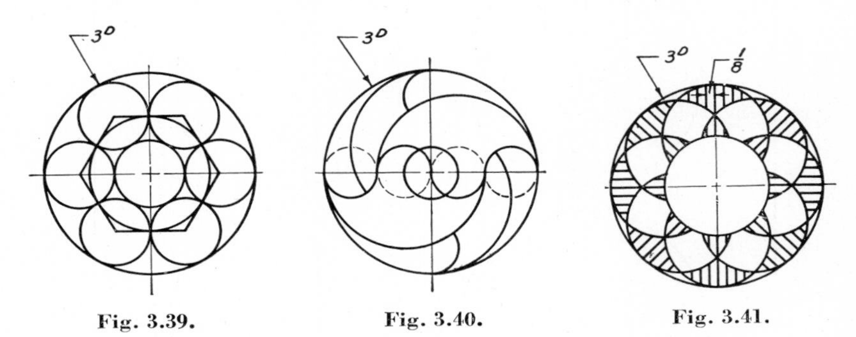

Fig. 3.39. Fig. 3.40. Fig. 3.41.

8–10. (Figs. 3.42, 3.43, 3.44.) Reproduce the line work within each square using the dimensions given. The dimensions shown, however, are for the student's use only and should not appear on the finished drawing. Arcs should be made finished weight when first drawn. The straight lines of each design may be drawn with a hard pencil and later heavied with a softer pencil. Do not erase the construction lines.

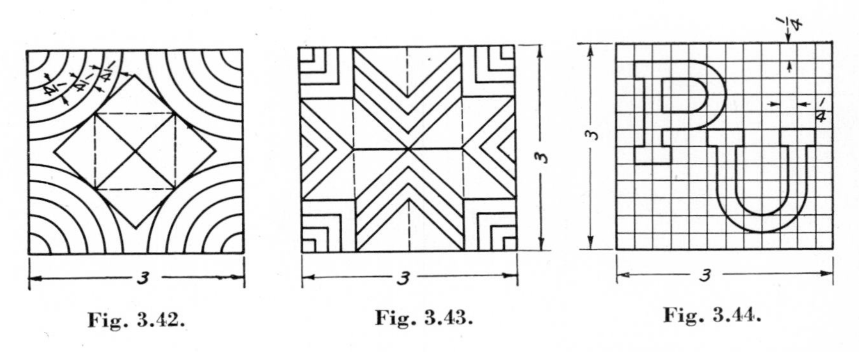

Fig. 3.42. Fig. 3.43. Fig. 3.44.

11. (Fig. 3.45.) Select a suitable scale and reproduce the design of the highway intersection shown. Using $\frac{3}{16}''$ capital letters, letter the words HIGHWAY INTERSECTION. Using $\frac{1}{8}''$ letters and numerals, letter the dimensions. Draw the arrows indicating the direction of traffic flow.

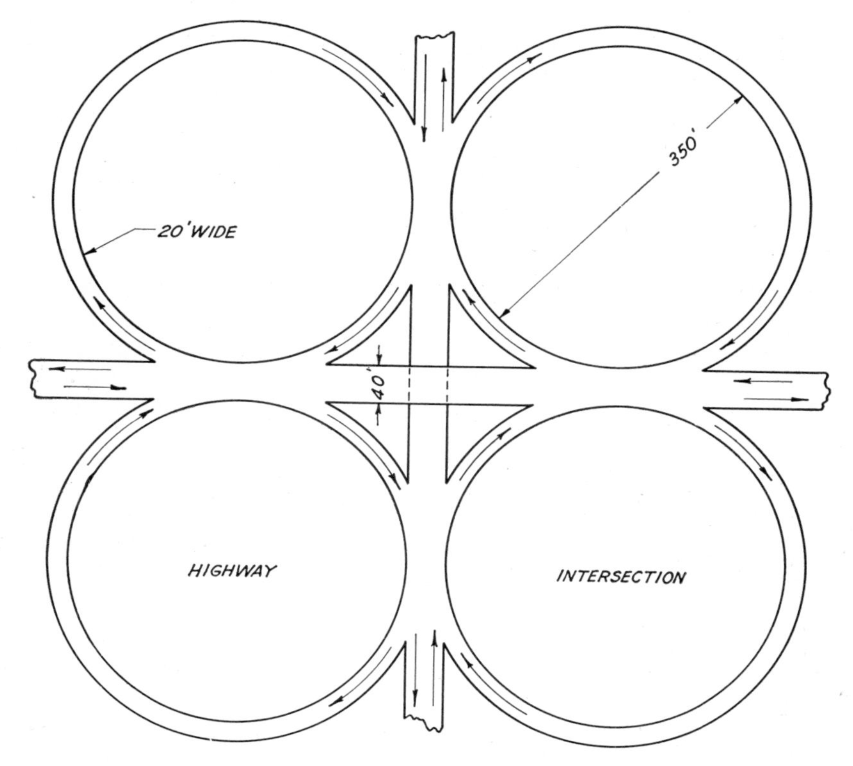

Fig. 3.45.

12–15. (Figs. 3.46, 3.47, 3.48, 3.49.) Reproduce the geometrical shapes.

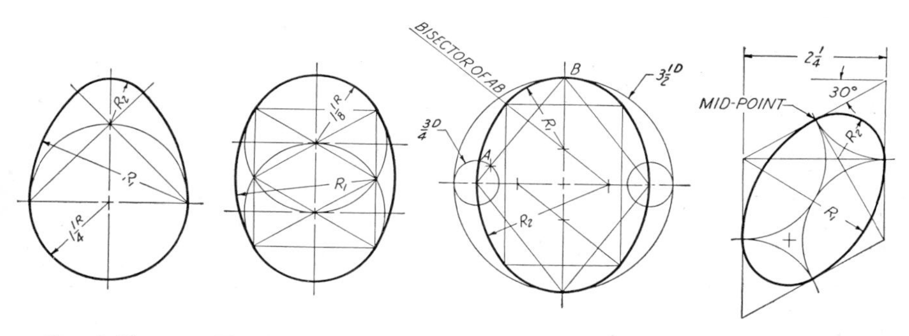

Fig. 3.46. Oval.

Fig. 3.47. Ellipse (approximate).

Fig. 3.48. Ellipse (approximate).

Fig. 3.49. Ellipse (pictorial).

4 ENGINEERING GEOMETRY

4.1. Introduction. The simplified geometrical constructions presented in this chapter are those with which a draftsman should be familiar, for they frequently occur in engineering drawing. The methods are applications of the principles found in textbooks on plane geometry. The constructions have been modified to take advantage of time-saving methods made possible by the use of drawing instruments.

Since a study of the subject of plane geometry should be a prerequisite for a course in engineering drawing, the mathematical proofs have been omitted intentionally. Geometrical terms applying to lines, surfaces, and solids, however, are given in Figs. 4.53 and 4.54 for the purpose of review.

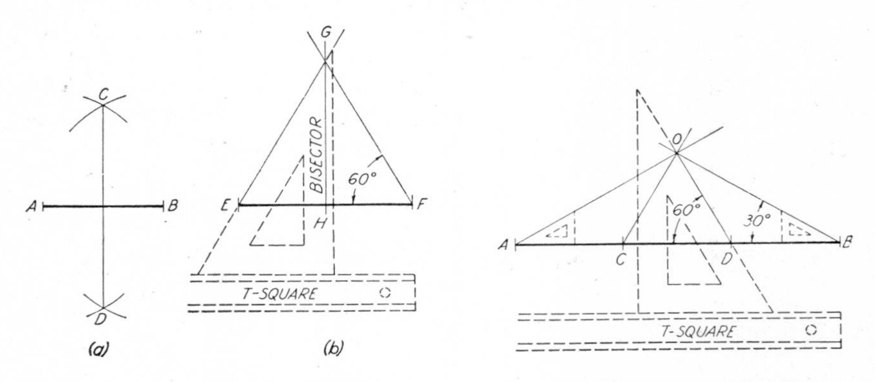

Fig. 4.1. To bisect a straight line. **Fig. 4.2. To trisect a straight line.**

4.2. To bisect a straight line (Fig. 4.1).

(*a*) With A and B as centers, strike the interesecting arcs as shown using any radius greater than one-half of AB. A straight line through points C and D bisects AB.

(*b*) Draw either 60° or 45° lines through E and F. Through their intersection draw the perpendicular GH that will bisect EF.

The use of the dividers to divide or bisect a line by the trial method is explained in Sec. 3.15.

4.3. To trisect a straight line (Fig. 4.2). Given the line AB. Draw the lines AO and OB making 30° with AB. Similarly, draw CO and OD making 60° with AB. AC equals CD equals DB.

4.4. To bisect an angle (Fig. 4.3).

(*a*) Given the angle *BAC*. Use any radius with the vertex *A* as a center, and strike an arc that interesects the sides of the angle at *D* and *E*.

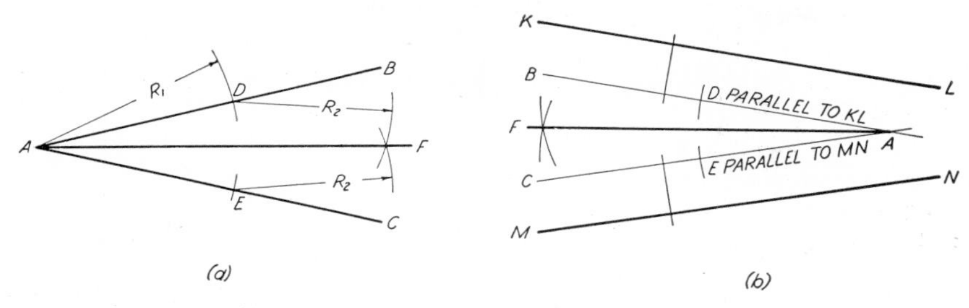

Fig. 4.3. To bisect an angle.

With *D* and *E* as centers and a radius larger than one-half of *DE*, draw intersecting arcs. Draw *AF*. Angle *BAF* equals angle *FAC*.

(*b*) Given an angle formed by the lines *KL* and *MN* having an inaccessible point of intersection. Draw *BA* parallel to *KL* and *CA* parallel to *MN* at the same distance from *MN* as *BA* is from *KL*. Bisect angle *BAC* using the method explained in (*a*). The bisector *FA* of angle *BAC* bisects the angle between the lines *KL* and *MN*.

4.5. To draw parallel curved lines about a curved center line (Fig. 4.4). Draw a series of arcs having centers located at random along the given center line *AB*. Using the French curve, draw the required curved lines tangent to these arcs.

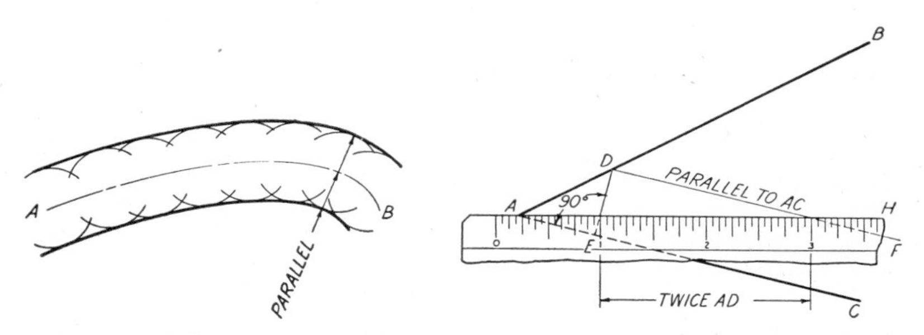

Fig. 4.4. To draw parallel curved lines.

Fig. 4.5. To trisect an angle.

4.6. To trisect an angle (Fig. 4.5). Given the angle *BAC*. Lay off along *AB* any convenient distance *AD*. Draw *DE* perpendicular to *AC* and *DF* parallel to *AC*. Place the scale so that it passes through *A* with a distance equal to twice *AD* intercepted between the lines *DE* with *DF*. Angle *HAC* equals one-third of the angle *BAC*.

4.7. To divide a straight line into a given number of equal parts (Fig. 4.6). Given the line *LM* which is to be divided into five equal parts.

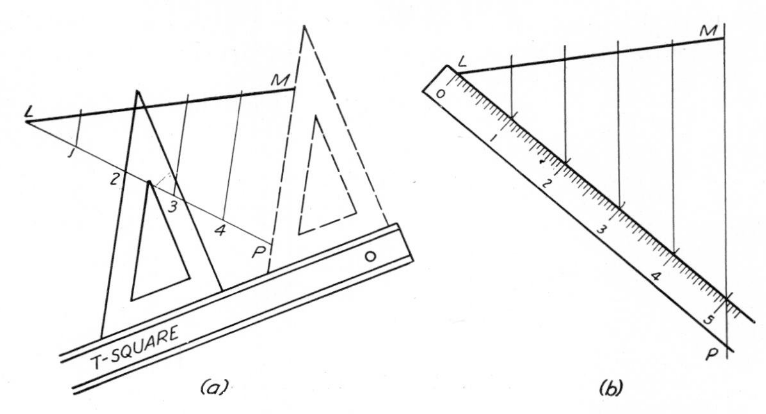

Fig. 4.6. To divide a straight line into a number of equal parts.

(*a*) Step off, with the dividers, five equal divisions along a line making any convenient angle with *LM*. Connect the last point *P* with *M*, and through the remaining points draw lines parallel to *MP* intersecting the given line. These lines divide *LM* into five equal parts.

(*b*) Some commercial draftsmen prefer a modification of this construction known as the scale method. For the first step, draw a vertical *PM* through point *M*. Place the scale so that the first mark of five equal divisions is at *L* and the last mark falls on *PM*. Locate the four intervening division points, and through these draw verticals intersecting the given line. The verticals will divide *LM* into five equal parts.

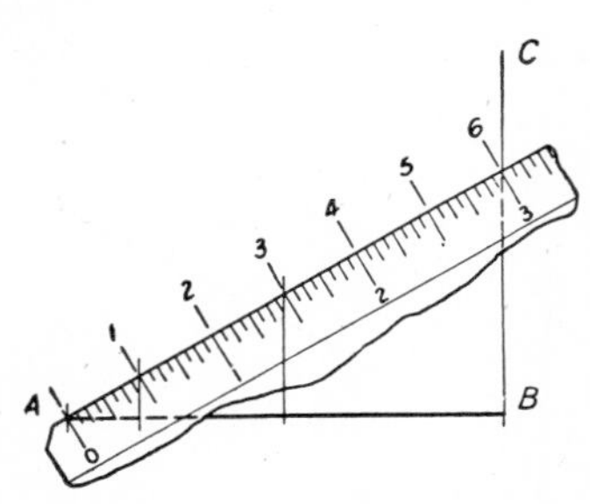

Fig. 4.7. To divide a line proportionally.

4.8. To divide a line proportionally (Fig. 4.7). Given the line *AB*. Draw *BC* perpendicular to *AB*. Place the scale across *A* and *BC* so that the number of divisions intercepted is equal to the sum of the numbers representing the proportions. Mark off these proportions and draw lines parallel to *BC* to divide *AB* as required. The proportions in Fig. 4.7 are 1:2:3.

4.9. To construct an angle equal to a given angle (Fig. 4.8). Given the angle *BAC* and the line *A′C′* that forms one side of the trans-

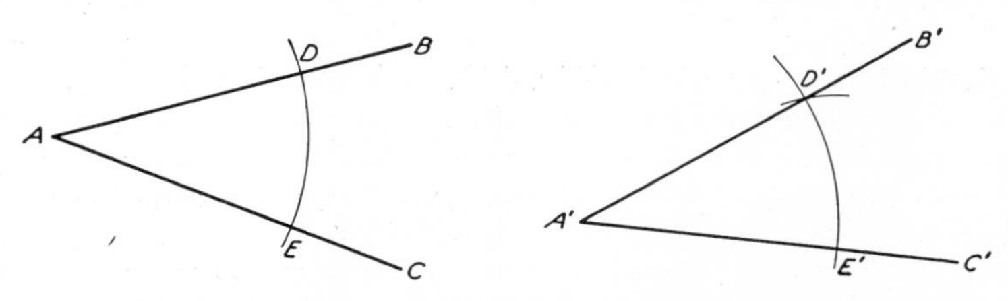

Fig. 4.8. To construct an angle equal to a given angle.

ferred angle. Use any convenient radius with the vertex A as a center, and strike the arc that intersects the sides of the angle at D and E. With A' as a center, strike the arc intersecting $A'C'$ at E'. With E' as a center and the chord distance DE as a radius, strike a short intersecting arc to locate D'. $A'B'$ drawn through D' makes angle $B'A'C'$ equal angle BAC.

4.10. To draw a line through a given point and the inaccessible intersection of two given lines (Fig. 4.9). Given the lines KL and MN, and the point P. Construct any triangle such as PQR having its vertices falling on the given lines and the given point. At some convenient location construct triangle STU similar to PQR, by drawing SU parallel to PR, TU parallel to QR, and ST parallel to PQ. PS is the required line.

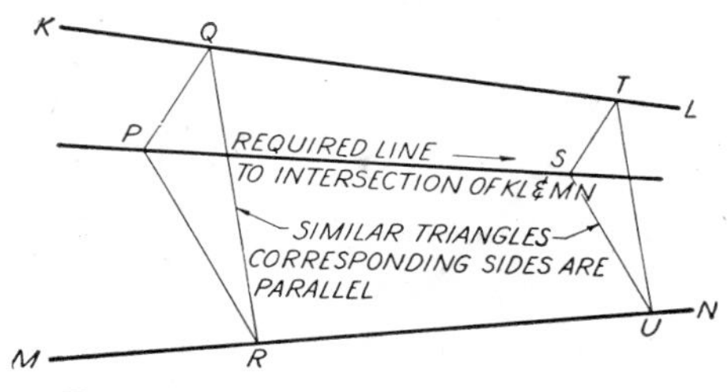

Fig. 4.9. To draw a line through a given point and the inaccessible intersection of two given lines.

4.11. To construct an angle, tangent method (Fig. 4.10). Draftsmen often find it necessary to draw long lines having an angle between them that is not equal to an angle of a triangle. Such an angle may be laid off with a protractor, but it should be remembered that as the lines are extended any error is multiplied. To avoid this situation, the tangent method may be used. The tangent method involves trigonometry but, since it is frequently used, a discussion of it here is pertinent. (See Table XXXVI of the Appendix.)

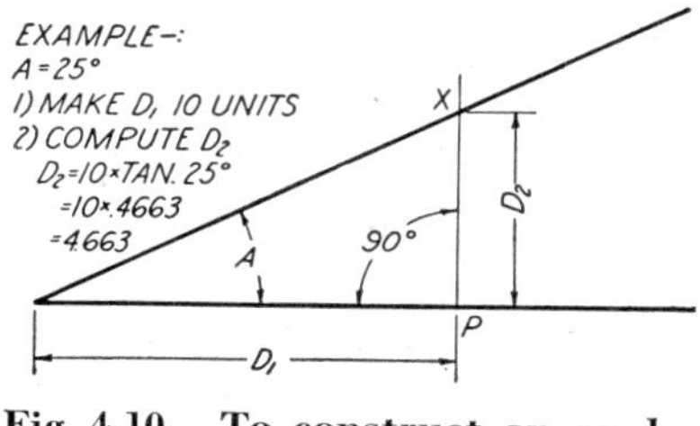

In this method, a distance D_1 is laid off along a line that is to form one side of the angle, and a distance D_2, equal to D_1 times the natural tangent of the angle, is marked off along a perpendicular through point P. A line through point X is the required line, and angle A is the required angle. In laying off the distance D_1, unnecessary multiplication will be eliminated if the distance is arbitrarily made 10″. When the use of 10″ for D' makes P fall off the drawing, a temporary auxiliary sheet will furnish space needed to carry out the construction.

EXAMPLE–:
A = 25°
1) MAKE D_1 10 UNITS
2) COMPUTE D_2
D_2 = 10 × TAN. 25°
= 10 × .4663
= 4.663

Fig. 4.10. To construct an angle, tangent method.

This method is also used for angles formed by short lines whenever a protractor is not available.

4.12. To construct a triangle having its three sides given (Fig. 4.11). Given the three sides AB, AC, and BC. Draw the side AB in its correct location. Using its end points A and B as centers and radii equal to AC and BC, respectively, strike the two intersecting arcs locating point C. ABC is the required triangle. This construction is particularly useful for developing the surface of a transition piece by triangulation.

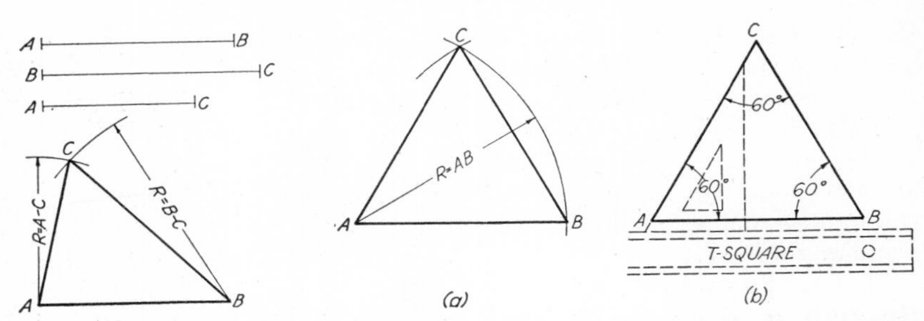

Fig. 4.11. To construct a triangle with three sides given.

Fig. 4.12. To construct an equilateral triangle.

4.13. To construct an equilateral triangle (Fig. 4.12). Given the side AB.

(a) Using the end points A and B as centers and a radius equal to the length of AB, strike two intersecting arcs to locate C. Draw lines from A to C and C to B to complete the required equilateral triangle.

(b) Using a 30–60° triangle, draw through A and B lines that make 60° with the given line. If the line AB is inclined, the 60° lines should be drawn as shown in Fig. 3.13.

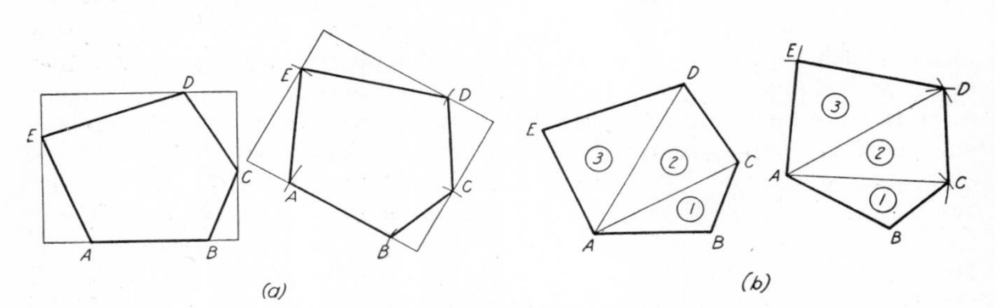

Fig. 4.13. To transfer a polygon.

4.14. To transfer a polygon (Fig. 4.13). Given the polygon $ABCDE$.

(a) Enclose the polygon in a rectangle. Draw the "enclosing rectangle" in the new position and locate points A, B, C, D, and E along the sides by measuring from the corners of the rectangle. A compass may be used for transferring the necessary measurements.

(b) To transfer a polygon by the triangle method, divide the polygon into triangles and, using the construction explained in Sec. 4.12, reconstruct each triangle in its transferred position.

4.15. To construct a square (Fig. 4.14).

(a) Given the side AB. Using a T-square and a 45° triangle, draw perpendiculars to line AB through points A and B. Locate point D at the intersection of a 45° construction line through A and the perpendicular from B. Draw CD parallel to AB through D to complete the square. To eliminate unnecessary movements the lines should be drawn in the order indicated.

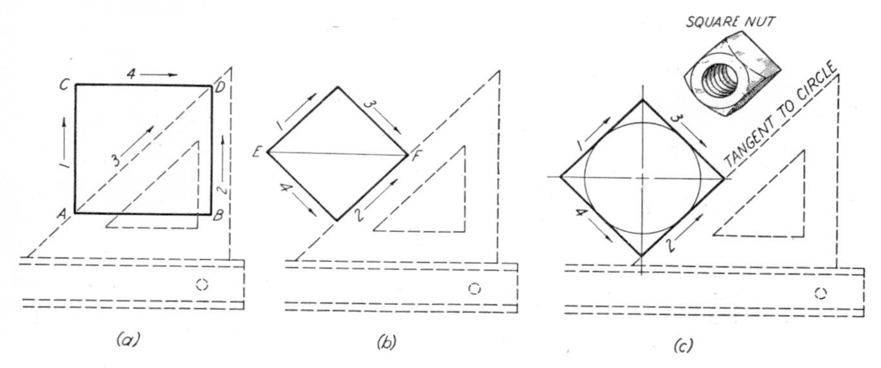

Fig. 4.14. To construct a square.

(*b*) Given the diagonal length *EF*. Using a T-square and a 45° triangle, construct the square by drawing lines through *E* and *F* at an angle of 45° with *EF* in the order indicated.

(*c*) The construction of an inscribed circle is the first step in one method for drawing a square when the location of the center and the length of one side are given.

Using a T-square and a 45° triangle, draw the sides of the square tangent to the circle. This construction is used in drawing square bolt heads and nuts.

4.16. To construct a regular pentagon (Fig. 4.15). Given the circumscribing circle. Draw the perpendicular diameters *AB* and *CD*. Bisect *OB* and, with its mid-point *E* as a center and *EC* as a radius, draw the arc *CF*. Using *C* as a center and *CF* as a radius, draw the arc *FG*. The line *CG* is one of the equal sides of the required pentagon. Locate the remaining vertices by striking off this distance around the circumference.

If the length of one side of a pentagon is given, the construction shown in Fig. 4.18 should be used.

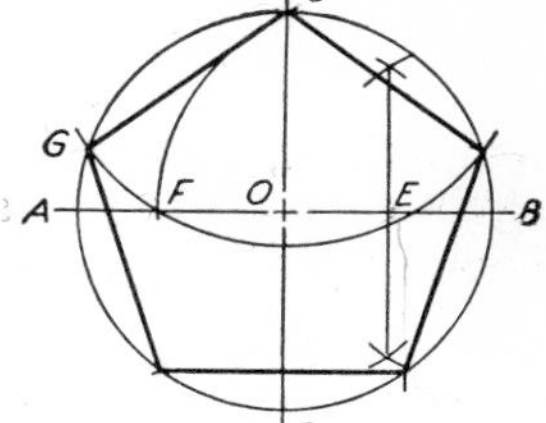

Fig. 4.15. To construct a regular pentagon.

4.17. To construct a regular hexagon (Fig. 4.16).

(*a*) Given the distance *AB* across corners. Draw a circle having *AB* as a diameter. Using the same radius and with points *A* and *B* as centers, strike arcs intersecting the circumference. Join these points to complete the construction.

(*b*) Given the distance *AB* across corners. Using a 30–60° triangle and a T-square, draw the lines in the order indicated by the numbers on the figure.

(*c*) Given the distance across flats. Draw a circle whose diameter equals the distance across flats. Using a 30–60° triangle and a T-square, as shown, draw the tangents that establish the sides and vertices of the required hexagon.

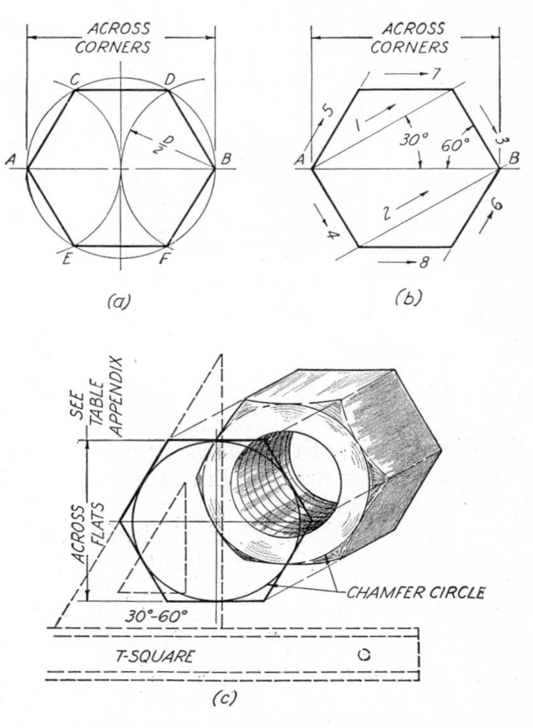

Fig. 4.16. To construct a regular hexagon.

This construction is used in drawing hexagonal bolt heads and nuts.

4.18. To construct a regular octagon (Fig. 4.17).

(*a*) Given the distance across flats. Draw the circumscribed square and its diagonals. Using the corners as centers and one-half the diagonal as a radius, strike arcs across the sides of the square. Join these points to complete the required octagon.

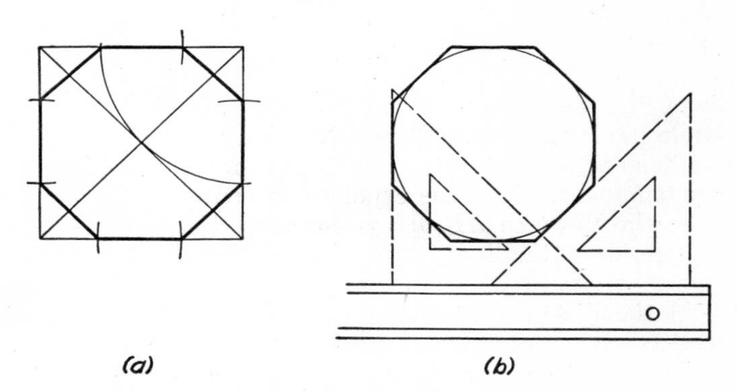

Fig. 4.17. To construct a regular octagon.

(*b*) Given the distance across flats. Draw the inscribed circle; then, using a 45° triangle and T-square, draw the tangents that establish the sides and vertices of the required octagon.

4.19. To construct any regular polygon having one side given (Fig. 4.18). Given the side *LM*. With *LM* as a radius, draw a semicircle and divide it into the same number of equal parts as the number of sides needed for the polygon. Suppose the polygon is to be seven-sided. Draw radial lines through points 2, 3, and so forth. Point 2 (the second division point) is always one of the vertices of the polygon, and line *L*2 is a side. Using point *M* as a center and *LM* as a radius, strike an arc across the radial line *L*6 to locate point *N*. Using the same radius with *N* as a center, strike another arc across *L*5 to establish *O* on *L*5. Although this procedure may be continued with point *O* as the next center, more accurate results will be obtained if point *R* is used as a center for the arc to locate *Q*, and *Q* as a center for *P*.

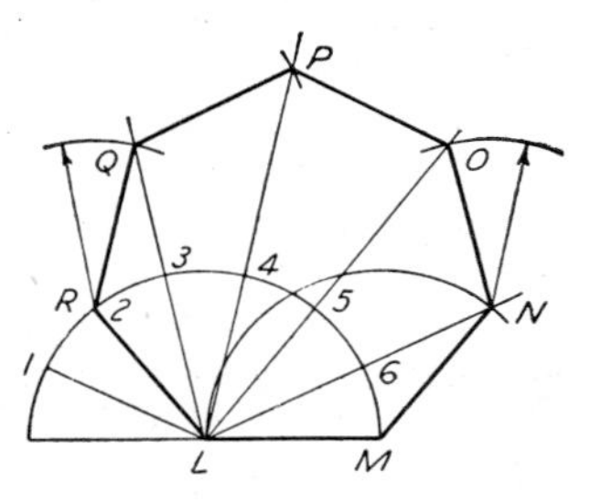

Fig. 4.18. To construct any regular polygon, having one side given.

4.20. To divide the area of a triangle or trapezoid into a given number of equal parts (Fig. 4.19).

(*a*) Given the triangle *ABC*. Divide the side *AC* into (say five) equal parts, and draw a semicircle having *AC* the diameter. Through the division points (1, 2, 3, and 4) draw perpendicular lines to points of intersection with the semicircle (5, 6, 7, and 8). Using *C* as a center, strike arcs through these points (5, 6, 7, and 8) that will cut *AC*. To complete the construction, draw lines parallel to *AB* through the points (9, 10, 11, and 12) at which the arcs intersect the side *AC*.

(*b*) Given the trapezoid *DEBA*. Extend the sides of the trapezoid to form the triangle *ABC* and draw a semicircle on *AC* with *AC* as a diameter. Using *C* as a center and *CD* as a radius, strike an arc cutting the semicircle at point *P*. Through *P* draw a perpendicular to *AC* to locate

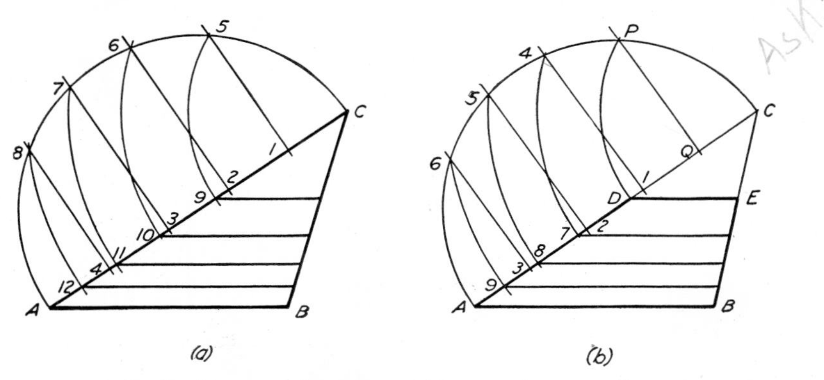

Fig. 4.19. To divide the area of a trapezoid into a given number of equal parts.

point Q. Divide QA into the same number of equal parts as the number of equal areas required (in this case four), and proceed using the construction explained in (a) for dividing the area of a triangle into a given number of equal parts.

4.21. To find the center for a circle through three given points not in a straight line (Fig. 4.20). Given the three points A, B, and C. Join the points with straight lines (which will be chords of the required circle), and draw the perpendicular bisectors. The point of intersection O of the bisectors is the center of the required circle, and OA, OB, or OC is its radius.

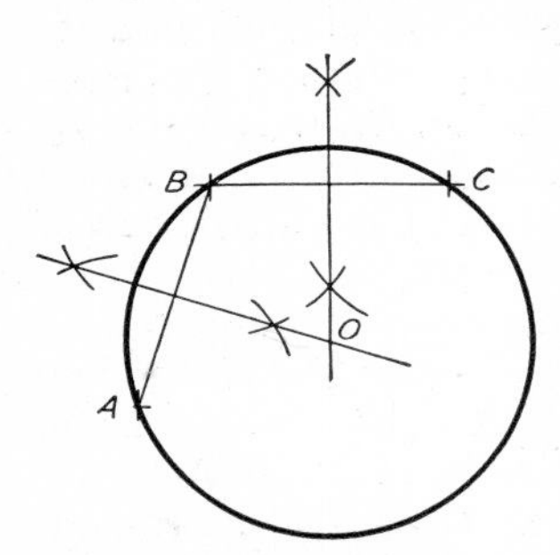

Fig. 4.20. To find the center of a circle through three points.

4.22. Tangent circles and arcs. Fig. 4.21 illustrates the geometry of tangent circles. In (a) it can be noted that the locus of centers for circles of radius R tangent to AB is a line that is parallel to AB at a distance R from AB. The locus of centers for circles of the same radius tangent to CD is a line that is parallel to CD at R (radius) distance from CD. Since point O at which these lines intersect is R distance from both AB and CD, a circle of radius R with center at O must be tangent to both AB and CD.

In (b) the locus of centers for circles of radius R_3 that will be tangent to the circle with a center at O and having a radius R_1 is a circle that is concentric with the given circle at R_3 distance. The radius of the locus of centers will be $R_1 + R_3$. In the case of the circle with center at point P, the radius of the locus of centers will be $R_2 + R_3$. Points Q and Q_1 where these arcs intersect are points that are R_3 distance from both circles. Therefore, circles of R_3 radius that are centered at Q and Q_1 will be tangent to both circles with centers at O and P.

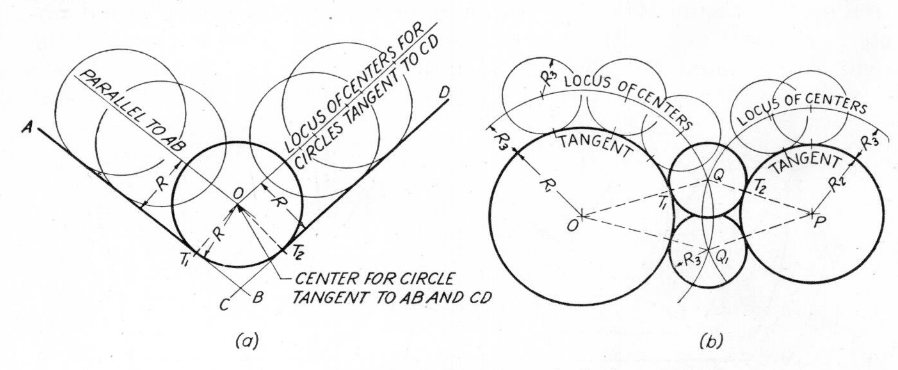

Fig. 4.21. Tangent circles.

4.23. To draw a circular arc of radius R tangent to two lines (Fig. 4.22).

(a) Given the two lines AB and CD at right angles to each other, and the radius of the required arc R. Using their point of intersection X as a center and R as a radius, strike an arc cutting the given lines at T_1 and T_2 (tangent points). With T_1 and T_2 as centers and the same radius, strike the intersecting arcs locating the center O of the required arc.

(*b*) and (*c*) Given the two lines AB and CD, not at right angles, and the radius R. Draw lines EF and GH parallel to the given lines at a distance R. Since the point of intersection of these lines is distance R from both given lines, it will be the center O of the required arc. Mark the tangent points T_1 and T_2 that lie along perpendiculars to the given lines through O.

These constructions are useful for drawing fillets and rounds on views of machine parts.

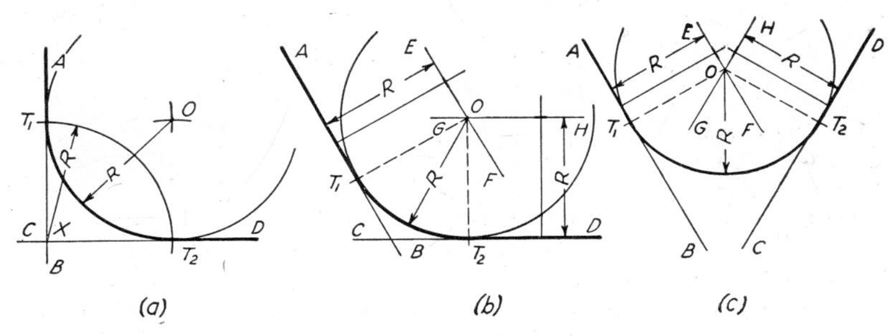

Fig. 4.22. To draw a circular arc tangent to two lines.

4.24. To draw a circular arc of radius R_1 tangent to a given circular arc and a given straight line (Fig. 4.23). Given the line AB and the circular arc with center O.

(*a*) and (*b*) Let R_1 be the radius of the required arc. Draw line CD parallel to AB at a distance R_1. Using the center O of the given arc and a radius equal to its radius plus or minus the radius of the required arc (R_2 plus or minus R_1), swing a parallel arc intersecting CD. Since the

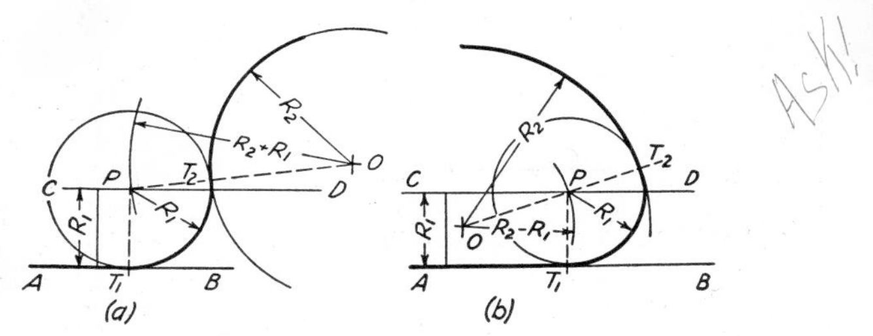

Fig. 4.23. To draw a circular arc tangent to a given circular arc and a line.

line CD and the intersecting arc will be the loci of centers for all circles of radius R_1, tangent respectively to the given line AB and the given arc, their point of intersection P will be the center of the required arc. Mark the points of tangency T_1 and T_2. T_1 lies along a perpendicular to AB through the center P, and T_2 along a line joining the centers of the two arcs.

This construction is useful for drawing fillets and rounds on views of machine parts.

4.25. To draw a circular arc of a given radius R_1 tangent to two given circular arcs (Fig. 4.24). Given the circular arcs AB and CD with centers O and P, and radii R_2 and R_3, respectively. Let R_1 be the radius of the required arc.

(*a*) and (*b*) Using O as a center and R_2 plus R_1 as a radius, strike an arc parallel to AB. Using P as a center and R_3 plus R_1 as a radius, strike an intersecting arc parallel to CD. Since each of these intersecting arcs is

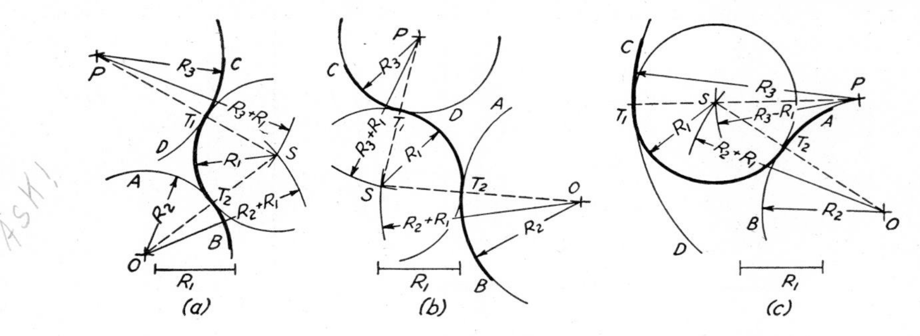

Fig. 4.24. To draw a circular arc tangent to two given arcs.

the locus of centers for all circular arcs of radius R_1 tangent to the given arc to which it is parallel, their point of intersection S will be the center for the required arc that is tangent to both. Mark the points of tangency T_1 and T_2 that lie on the lines of centers PS and OS.

(*c*) Using O as a center and R_2 plus R_1 as a radius, strike an arc parallel to AB. Using P as a center and R_3 minus R_1 as a radius, strike an intersecting arc parallel to CD. The point of intersection of these arcs is the center for the required arc.

4.26. To draw a reverse (ogee) curve (Fig. 4.25). Given the two parallel lines AB and CD. At points B and C, the termini and tangent points of the reverse curve, erect perpendiculars. Join BC with a straight line and assume a point E that will be the point at which the curves will be tangent to each other. Draw the perpendicular bisectors of BE and EC. Since an arc tangent to AB at B must have its center on the perpendicular BP, point of intersection P of the bisector and the perpendicular is the center for the required arc that is to be tangent to the line at B and the other required arc at point E. For the same reason, point Q is the center for the other required arc.

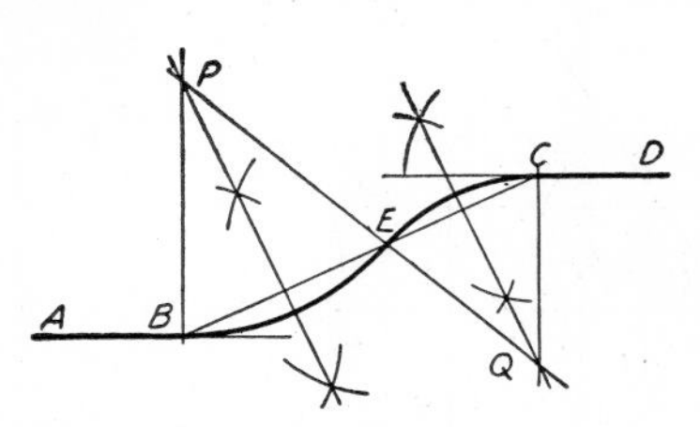

Fig. 4.25. To draw a reverse curve.

This construction is useful to architects in drawing mouldings, and to engineers in laying out center lines for railroad tracks, pipe lines, and so forth.

4.27. To draw a line tangent to a circle at a given point on the circumference (Fig. 4.26). Given a circle with center O and point P on its circumference. Place a triangle supported by a T-square or another triangle in such a position that one side passes through the center O and point P. When using the method illustrated in (*a*), align the hypotenuse of one triangle to the center of the circle and the point of tangency; then, with a guiding triangle held in position, revolve the triangle about the 90° angle and slide into position for drawing the required tangent line.

Another procedure is shown in (*b*). To draw the tangent by this method, align one leg of a triangle, which is adjacent to the 90° angle, through the center of the circle and the point of tangency; then, slide it along the edge of a guiding triangle into position.

This construction satisfies the geometrical requirement that a tangent must be perpendicular to a radial line drawn to the point of tangency.

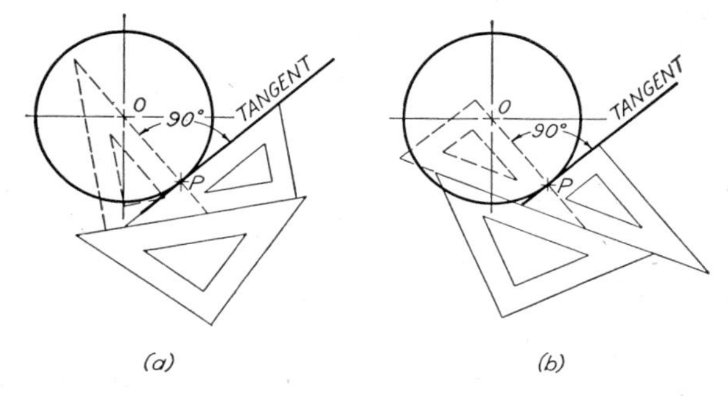

Fig. 4.26. To draw a line tangent to a circle at a point on the circumference.

4.28. To draw a line tangent to a circle through a given point outside the circle (Fig. 4.27). Given a circle with center O, and an external point P.

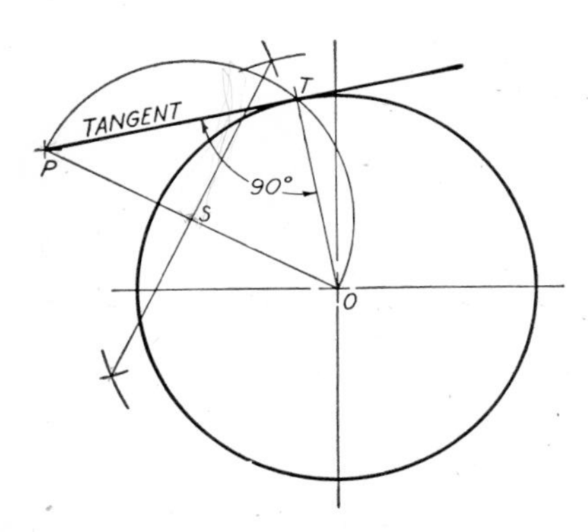

Fig. 4.27. To draw a line tangent to a circle through a given point outside.

Join the point P and the center O with a straight line, and bisect it to locate point S. Using S as a center and SO (one-half PO) as a radius, strike an arc intersecting the circle at point T (point of tangency). Line PT is the required tangent.

4.29. To draw a tangent through a point *P* on a circular arc having an inaccessible center (Fig. 4.28). Draw the chord PB; then, erect a perpendicular bisector. With point P as a center swing an arc through point C where the perpendicular bisector cuts the given arc. With C as a center and a radius equal to the chord distance CE, draw an arc to establish the location of point F. A line drawn through points P and F is the required tangent.

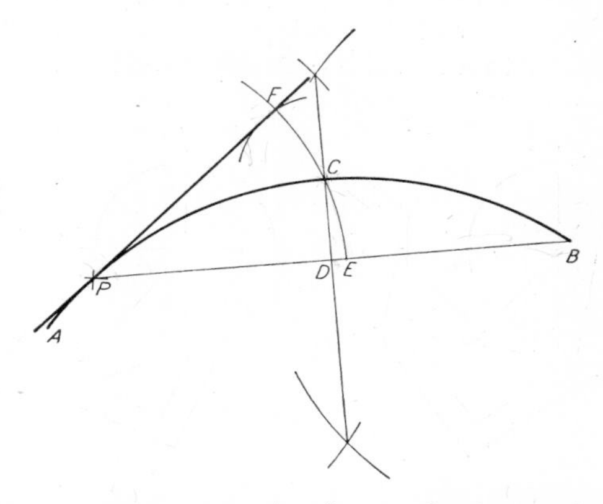

Fig. 4.28. To draw a tangent to a circular arc having an inaccessible center.

4.30. To draw a line tangent to a circle through a given point outside the circle (Fig. 4.29). Place a triangle supported by a T-square or another triangle in such a position that one leg passes through point P tangent to the circle, and draw the tangent. Slide the triangle along the guiding edge until the other leg coincides with the center O, and mark the point of tangency. Although this method is not as accurate as the geometrical one explained in Sec. 4.28, it is frequently employed by commercial draftsmen.

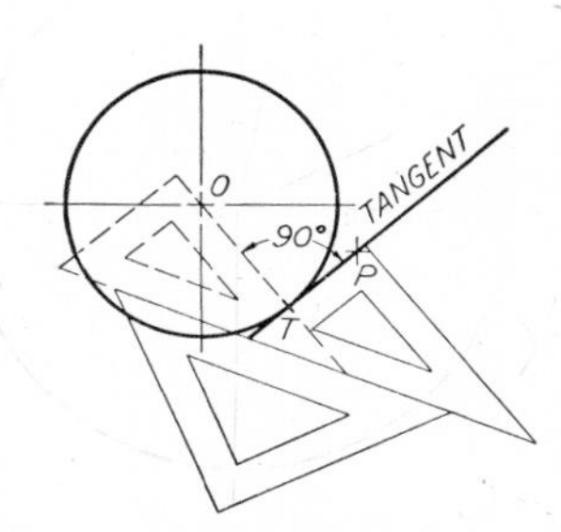

Fig. 4.29. To draw a line tangent to a circle through a given point outside.

4.31. To draw a line tangent to two given circle arcs (circles) (Fig. 4.30). Given two circle arcs with centers O and Q, respectively.

Let R and R_1 be the radii of the circle arcs. Using O as a center and a radius equal to R minus R_1, draw an arc. Through Q draw a tangent to this arc and mark the point of tangency T. Project the radius OT to locate T', and draw QT_1 parallel to OT'. The line from T_1 to T' is the required tangent to the given circle arcs (circles).

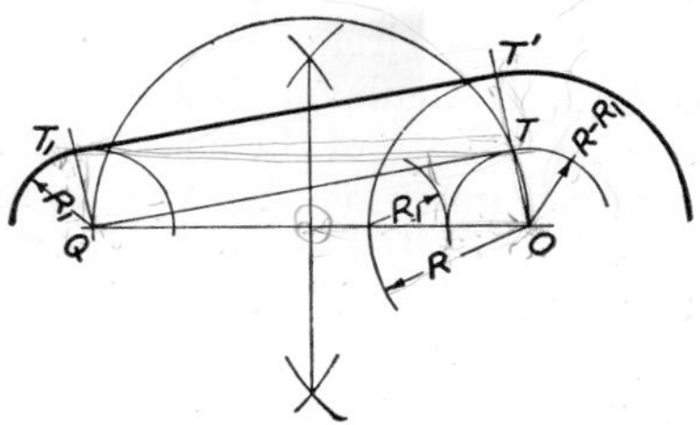

Fig. 4.30. To draw a line tangent to two given circles.

4.32. To approximate a curve with tangent circular arcs (Fig. 4.31). Draftsmen often find it desirable to approximate a noncircular curve with a series of tangent arcs. If the curve consists of a number of points a pleasing curve should be sketched lightly through points before starting to draw the arcs. The centers and radii are selected by trial but it must be remembered after the first arc has been drawn as far as it coincides with the sketched curve that when arcs are tangent the centers are on a common normal through their point of tangency. Sometimes draftsmen use this method to draw curves in ink instead of using a French curve.

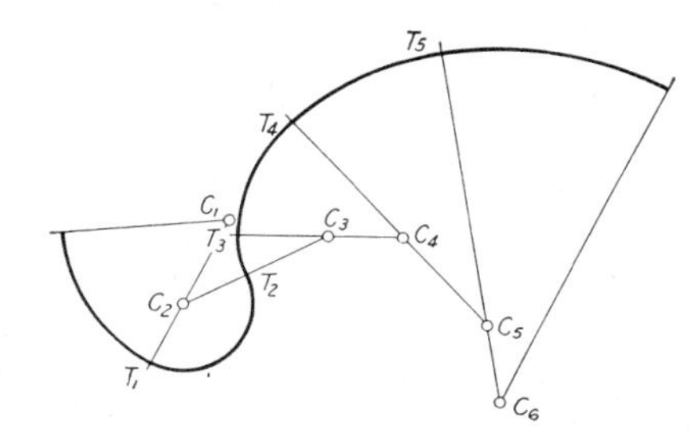

Fig. 4.31. To approximate a curve with tangent circular arcs.

4.33. To lay off the approximate length of the circumference of a circle (Fig. 4.32). Draw a line through point A tangent to the circle

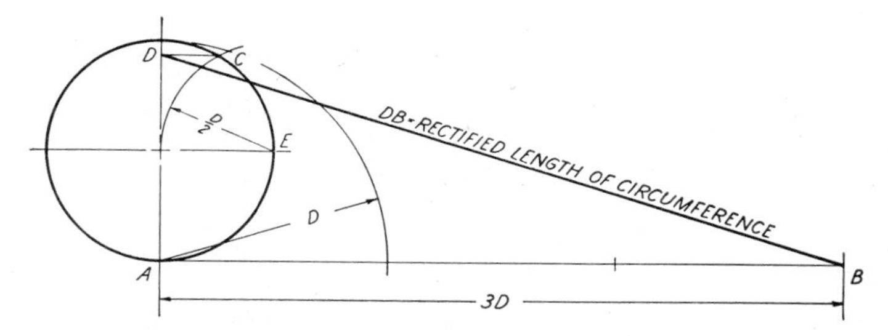

Fig. 4.32. To lay off the approximate length of the circumference of a circle.

and lay off along it a distance AB equal to three times the diameter ($3D$). Using point E on the circumference as a center and a radius equal to the radius of the circle strike an arc to establish the location of point C. Draw CD perpendicular to the vertical center line through point A. DB is the rectified length of the circumference; however, it is slightly longer than the true circumference by a negligible amount (approximate error 1/21,800).

4.34. To lay off the approximate length of a circular arc on its tangent (Fig. 4.33). Given the arc AB.

(*a*) Draw the tangent through A, and extend the chord BA. Locate point C by laying off AC equal to one-half the length of the chord AB. With C as a center and a radius equal to CB, strike an arc intersecting the tangent at D. The length AD along the tangent is slightly shorter than the true length of the arc AB by an amount that may be disregarded, for, when the angle between the chord and the tangent is less than 60°, the

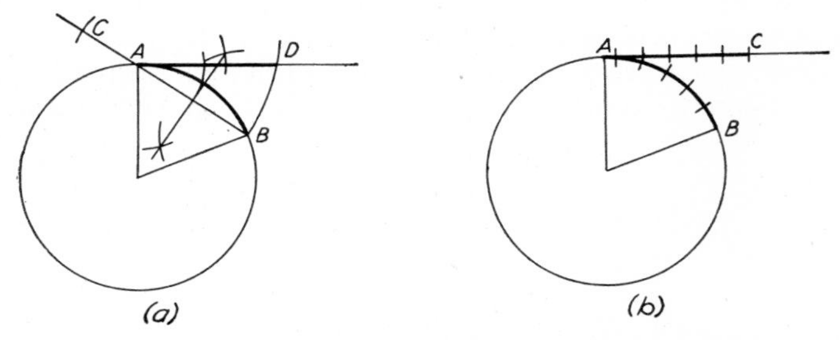

Fig. 4.33. To lay off the approximate length of a circular arc on its tangent.

length of AD differs from the true length of the arc AB by less than 6′ in one mile; when 30°, the error is $4\frac{1}{2}''$ in one mile.

(*b*) Draw the tangent through A. Using the small dividers, start at B and step off equal chord distances around the arc until the point nearest A is reached. From this point (without raising the dividers) step off along the tangent an equal number of distances to locate point C. If the point nearest A is indented into the tangent instead of the arc, the almost negligible error in the length of AC will be still less.

Since the small distances stepped off are in reality the chords of small arcs, the length AC will be slightly less than the true length of the arc. For most practical purposes the difference may be disregarded.

4.35. Conic Sections (Fig. 4.34). When a right circular cone of revolution is cut by planes at different angles four curves of intersection are obtained that are called conic sections.

When the intersecting plane is perpendicular to the axis the resulting curve of intersection is a circle.

If the plane makes a greater angle with the axis than do the elements the intersection is an ellipse.

If the plane makes the same angle with the axis as the elements the resulting curve is a parabola.

Finally, if the plane makes a smaller angle with the axis than do the elements or is parallel to the axis the curve of intersection is a hyperbola.

The geometric methods for constructing the ellipse, parabola, and hyperbola are discussed in succeeding sections.

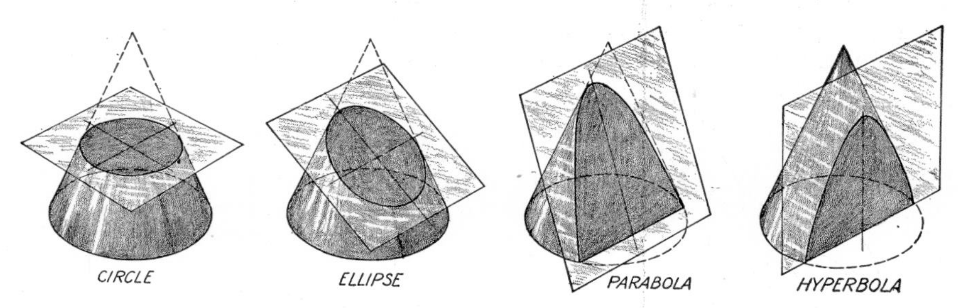

Fig. 4.34. Conic Sections.

4.36. The ellipse. Mathematically the ellipse is a curve generated by a point moving so that at any position the sum of its distances from two fixed points (foci) is a constant (equal to the major diameter). It is encountered very frequently in orthographic drawing when holes and circular forms are viewed obliquely. Ordinarily, the major and minor diameters are known.

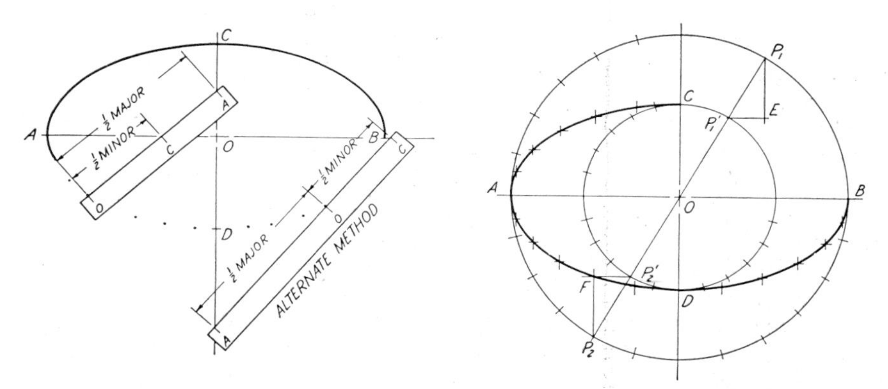

Fig. 4.35. To construct an ellipse, trammel method.

Fig. 4.36. To construct an ellipse, concentric circle method.

4.37. To construct an ellipse, trammel method (Fig. 4.35). Given the major axis AB and the minor axis CD. Along the straight edge of a strip of paper or cardboard, locate the points O, C, and A, so that the distance OA is equal to one-half the length of the major axis and the distance OC is equal to one-half the length of the minor axis. Place the marked edge across the axes so that point A is on the minor axis and point C is on the major axis. *Point O will fall on the circumference of the ellipse.* Move the strip, keeping A on the minor axis and C on the major axis, and mark at least five other positions of O on the ellipse in each quadrant. Using a French curve, complete the ellipse by drawing a smooth curve through the points. The ellipsograph, which draws ellipses mechanically, is based on this same principle. The trammel method is an accurate method.

An alternate method for marking off the location of points A, O, and C is given in Fig. 4.35.

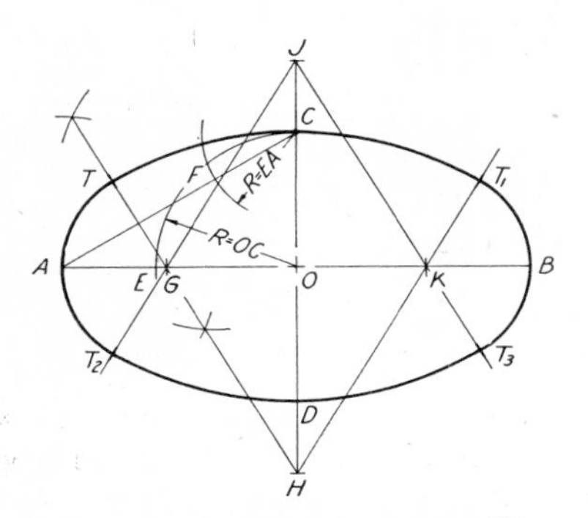

Fig. 4.37. To construct an ellipse, center method.

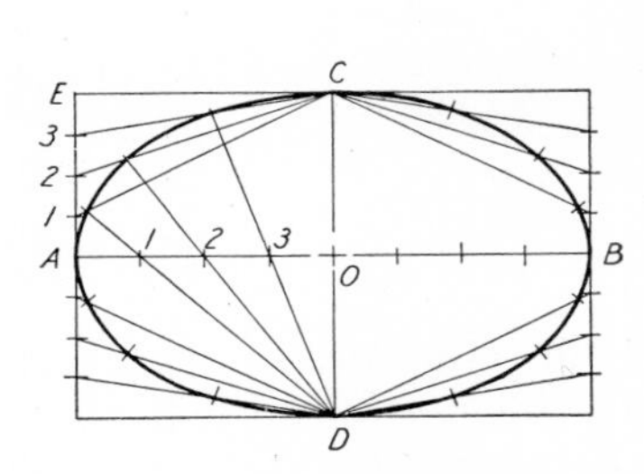

Fig. 4.38. To construct an ellipse, parallelogram method.

4.38. To construct an ellipse, concentric circle method (Fig. 4.36). Given the major axis AB and the minor axis CD. Using the center of the ellipse (point O) as a center, describe circles having the major and minor axes as diameters. Divide the circles into equal central angles and draw diametrical lines such as P_1P_2. From point P_1 on the circumference of the larger circle, draw a line parallel to CD, the minor axis, and from point P_1' at which the diameter P_1P_2 intersects the nner circle, draw a line parallel to AB, the major axis. The point of intersection of these lines, point E, is on the required ellipse. At points P_2 and P_2' repeat the same procedure and locate point F. Thus, two points arc established by the line P_1P_2. Locate at least five points in each of thc four quadrants. The ellipse is completed by drawing a smooth curve through the points.

This is one of the most accurate methods used to form ellipses.

4.39. To construct an ellipse, four-center method (Fig. 4.37). Given the major axis AB and the minor axis CD. Draw the line AC. Using the center of the ellipse O as a center and OC as a radius, strike an arc intersecting OA at point E. Using C as a center and EA as a radius, strike an arc intersecting the line AC at F. Draw the perpendicular bisector of the line AF. The points G and H, at which the perpendicular bisector intersects the axes AB and CD (extended) are the centers of two of the arcs forming the ellipse. Locate the other two centers, J and K, by laying off OJ equal to OH and OK equal to OG. To determine the junction points (tangent points), T, T_1, T_2, and T_3, for the arcs, draw lines through the centers of the tangent arcs. The figure thus formed by the four circle arcs approximates a true ellipse.

4.40. To construct an ellipse, parallelogram method (Fig. 4.38). Given the major axis AB and the minor axis CD. Construct the circumscribing parallelogram. Divide AO and AE into the same number of equal parts (say four) and number the division points from A. From C draw a line through point 3 on line AE, and from D draw a line through point 3 on line AO. The point of intersection of these lines is on the required ellipse. Similarly, the intersections of lines from C and D through points numbered 1 and 2 are on the ellipse. A similar construction will locate points in the other three quadrants of the ellipse. Use of a French curve will permit a smooth curve to be drawn through the points.

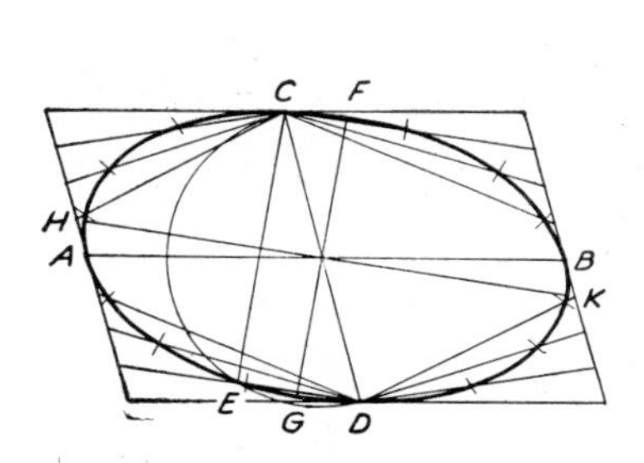

Fig. 4.39. To draw the major and minor axes of an ellipse, given the conjugate diameters.

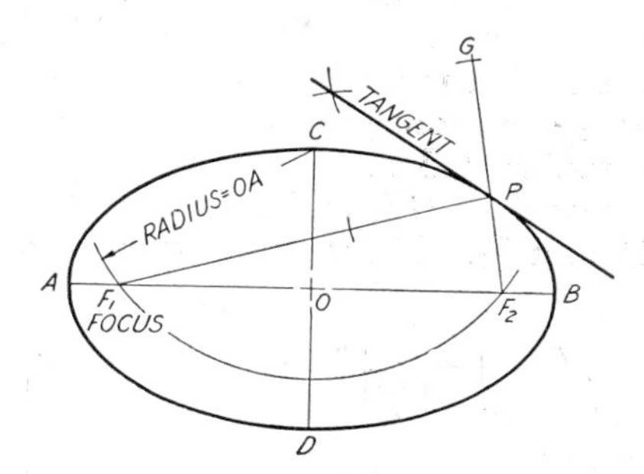

Fig. 4.40. To draw a tangent to an ellipse.

Had the circumscribing parallelogram not been a rectangle as in Fig. 4.38, the completed construction would appear as in Fig. 4.39, and AB and CD would be conjugate axes. To establish the major and minor axes, draw a semicircle on CD as a diameter, intersecting the ellipse at E. FG, running parallel to CE through the center of the ellipse, will be the required minor axis. HK, running through the center of the ellipse parallel to DE and perpendicular to FG, will be the major axis.

4.41. To draw a tangent to an ellipse at any given point (Fig. 4.40). Given any point, such as P, on the perimeter of the ellipse $ABCD$. Using C as a center and a radius equal to OA (one-half the major diameter),

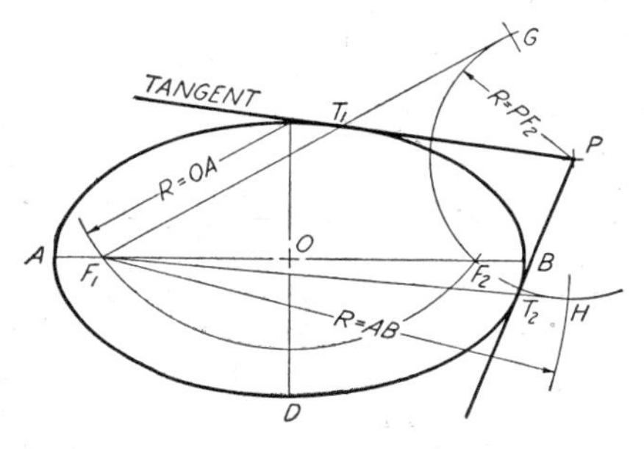

Fig. 4.41. To draw a tangent to an ellipse through a point outside of the ellipse.

strike arcs across the major axis at F_1 and F_2. From these points, which are foci of the ellipse, draw F_1P and F_2G. The bisector of the angle GPF_1 is the required tangent to the ellipse.

In practice it will often be convenient to use the chord method explained in Sec. 29.24 for constructing tangents. See Fig. 29.30.

4.42. To draw a tangent to an ellipse from a given point *P* outside of the ellipse (Fig. 4.41). With the end of the minor axis as a center and a radius R equal to one-half of the length of the major axis, strike an arc to find the foci F_1 and F_2. With point P as a center and the distance PF_2 as a radius, draw an arc. Using F_1 as a center and the length AB as a radius strike arcs cutting the arc with center of P at points G and H. Draw lines GF_1 and HF_1 to establish the location of the tangent points T_1 and T_2. Draw the required tangent.

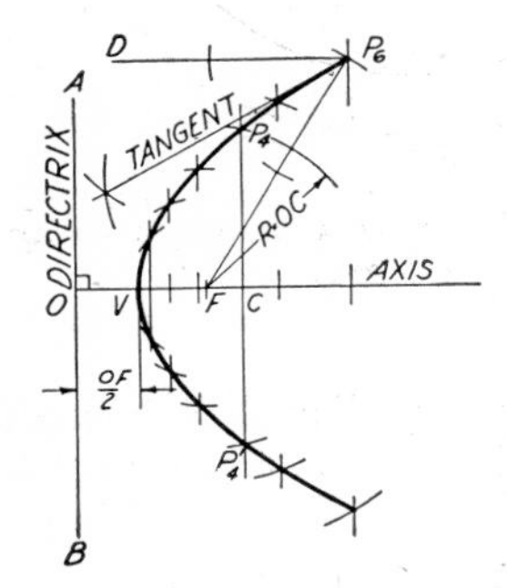

Fig. 4.42. To construct a parabola.

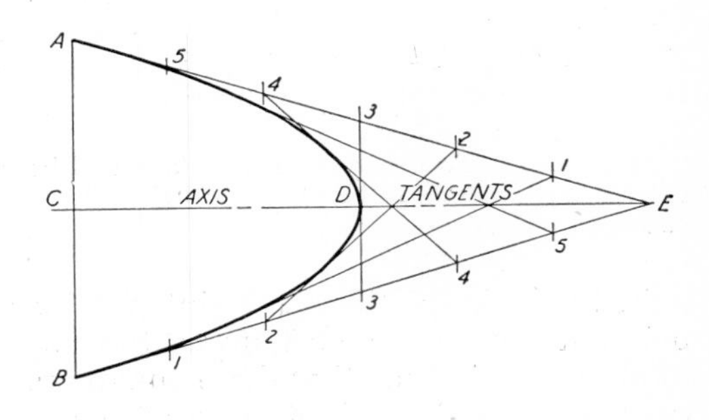

Fig. 4.43. To construct a parabola, tangent method.

4.43. The parabola. Mathematically the parabola is a curve generated by a point moving so that at any position its distance from a fixed point (the focus) is always exactly equal to its distance to a fixed line (the directrix). The construction shown in Fig. 4.42 is based on this definition.

In engineering design, the parabola is used for parabolic sound and light reflectors, for vertical curves on highways, and for bridge arches.

4.44. To construct a parabola (Fig. 4.42). Given the focus F and the directrix AB. Draw the axis of the parabola perpendicular to the directrix. Through any point on the axis, for example point C, draw a line parallel to the directrix AB. Using F as a center and the distance OC as a radius, strike arcs intersecting the line at points P_4 and P_4'. Repeat this procedure until a sufficient number of additional points have been located to determine a smooth curve. The vertex V is located at a point midway between O and F.

To construct a tangent to a parabola, say at point P_6, draw the line P_6D parallel to the axis; then, bisect the angle DP_6F. The bisector of the angle is the required tangent. Read Sec. 29.24 and study Fig. 29.30.

4.45. To construct a parabola, tangent method (Fig. 4.43). Given the points A and B and the distance CD from AB to the vertex. Extend the axis CD, and set off DE equal to CD. EA and EB are tangents to the parabola at A and B respectively.

Divide EA and EB into the same number of equal parts (say six), and number the division points as shown. Connect the corresponding points 1 and 1, 2 and 2, 3 and 3, and so forth. These lines, as tangents of the required parabola, form its envelope. Draw the tangent curve.

4.46. To construct a parabola, offset method (Fig. 4.44). Given the enclosing rectangle $A'ABB'$. Divide DA' into any number of equal parts (say four), and draw from the division points the perpendiculars parallel to DC, along which the offset distances are to be measured off. The offsets vary as the square of their distances from D. For example, since $D1$ is one-fourth of the distance from A' to D, 1–1′ will be $(\frac{1}{4})^2$, or one-sixteenth of $A'A$. Similarly, 2–2′ will be $(\frac{1}{2})^2$, or $\frac{1}{4}$ of $A'A$; and 3–3′ will be $\frac{9}{16}$ of $A'A$. To complete the parabola, lay off the computed offset values along the perpendiculars and form the figure with a French curve.

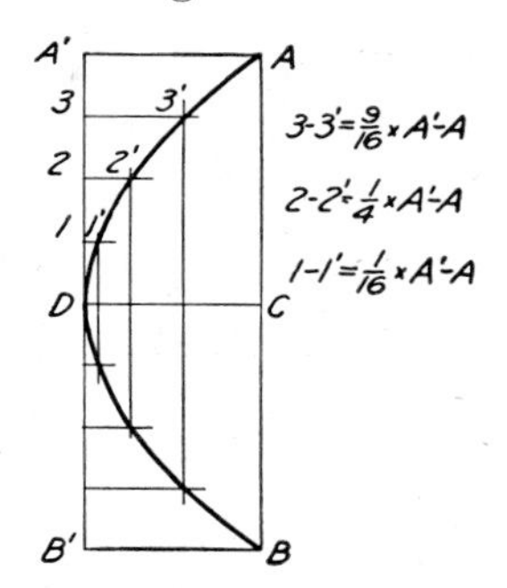

Fig. 4.44. To construct a parabola, offset method.

This method is preferred by civil engineers for laying out parabolic arches and computing vertical curves for highways.

4.47. To construct a curve of parabolic form through two given points (Fig. 4.45). Given the points A and B. Assume a point C. Draw the tangents CA and CB, and construct the parabolic curve using the tangent method shown in Fig. 4.43. This method is frequently used in machine design to draw curves that are more pleasing than circular arcs.

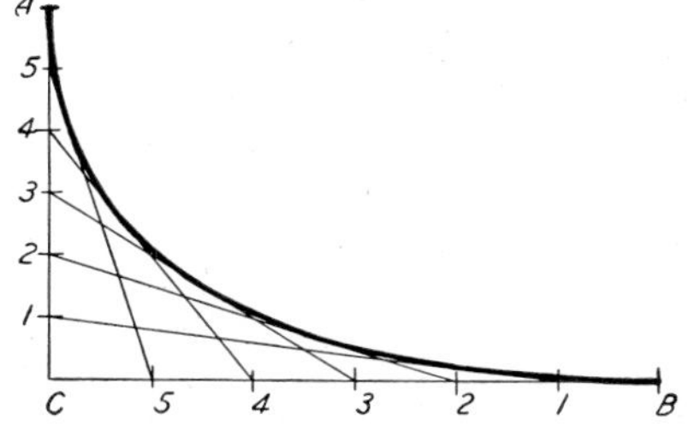

Fig. 4.45. To construct a curve of parabolic form.

4.48. The hyperbola. Mathematically, the hyperbola can be described as a curve generated by a point moving so that at any position the difference of its distances from two fixed points (foci) is a constant (equal to the transverse axis of the hyperbola). This definition is the basis for the construction shown in Fig. 4.46.

4.49. To construct a hyperbola (Fig. 4.46). Given the foci F_1 and F_2, and the transverse axis AB. Using F_1 and F_2 as centers and any radius R_1 greater than F_1B, strike arcs. With these same centers and a radius equal to R_1–AB, strike arcs intersecting the first arcs at point P. Point P is on the required hyperbola. Repeat this procedure and locate as many additional points, such as P_1, P_2, and so forth, as are required to form the hyperbola accurately with a French curve.

The tangent to the hyperbola at any point, such as P, is the bisector of the angle between the focal radii F_1P and F_2P. Read Sec. 29.24 and study Fig. 29.30.

4.50. An involute. The spiral curve traced by a point on a chord as it unwinds from around a circle or a polygon is an involute curve. Fig. 4.47(*a*) shows an involute of a circle, while (*b*) shows that of a square. The involute of a polygon is obtained by extending the sides and drawing arcs using the corners, in order, as centers. The circle in (*a*) may be considered to be a polygon having an infinite number of sides.

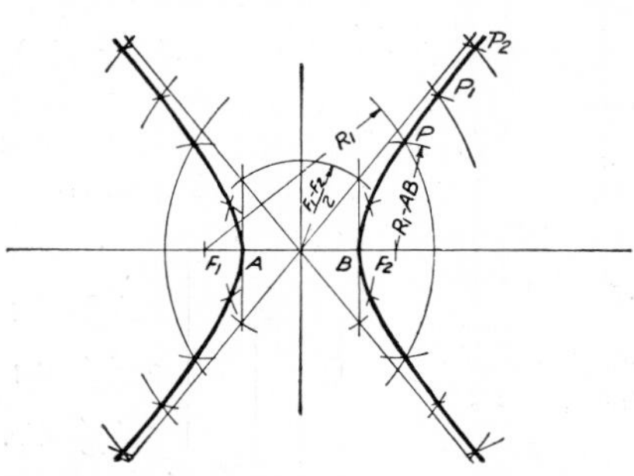

Fig. 4.46. To construct a hyperbola.

4.51. To draw an involute of a circle (Fig. 4.47*a*). Divide the circumference into a number of equal parts. Draw tangents through the division points. Then, along each tangent, lay off the rectified length of the corresponding circular arc, from the starting point to the point of tangency. The involute curve is a smooth curve through these points. The involute of a circle is used in the development of tooth profiles in gearing.

4.52. To draw the involute of a polygon (Fig. 4.47*b*). Extend the sides of the polygon as shown in (*b*). With the corners as centers, in order around the polygon, draw arcs terminating on the extended sides. The first radius is equal to the length of one side of the polygon. The radius of each successive arc is the distance from the center to the terminating point of the previous arc.

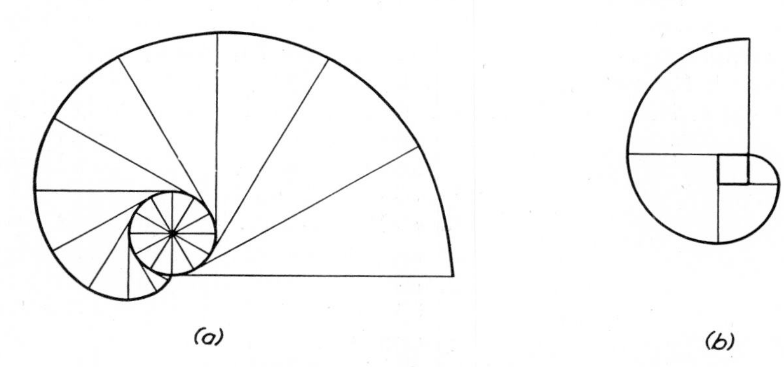

Fig. 4.47. The involute.

4.53. A cycloid. A cycloid is the curve generated by a point on the circumference of a moving circle when the circle rolls in a plane along a straight line, as shown in Fig. 4.48.

4.54. To draw a cycloid (Fig. 4.48). Draw the generating circle and the line AB tangent to it. The length AB should be made equal to the circumference of the circle. Divide the circle and the line AB into the same number of equal parts. With this much of the construction completed, the next step is to draw the line of centers CD through point O and project the division points along AB to CD by drawing perpendiculars.

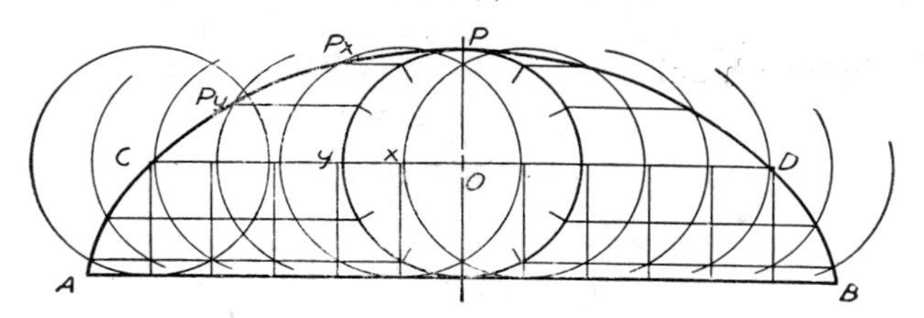

Fig. 4.48. A cycloid.

Using these points as centers for the various positions of the moving circle, draw circle arcs. For the purpose of illustration, assume the circle is moving to the left. When the circle has moved along CD to x, point P will have moved to point P_x. Similarly, when the center is at y, P will be at P_y. To locate positions of P along the cycloidal curve, project the division points of the divided circle in their proper order, across to the position circles. A smooth curve through these points will be the required cycloid.

4.55. An epicycloid (Fig. 4.49). An epicycloid is the curve generated by a point on the circumference of a circle that rolls in a plane on the outside of another circle. The method used in drawing an epicycloid is similar to the one used in drawing the cycloid.

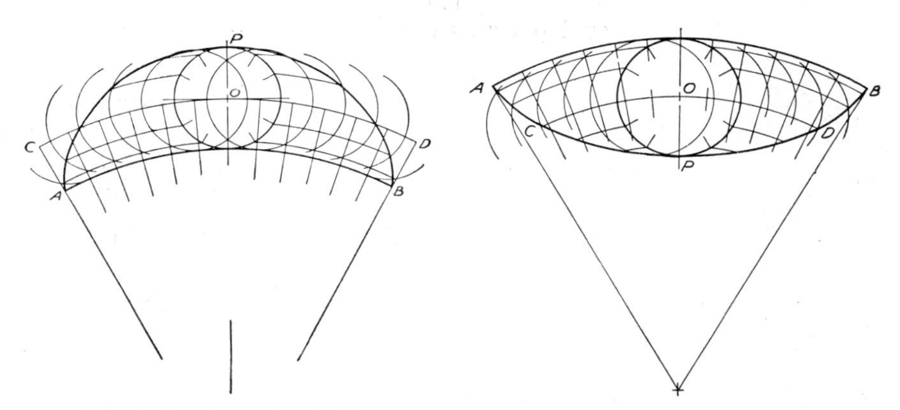

Fig. 4.49. An epicycloid. **Fig. 4.50. A hypocycloid.**

4.56. A hypocycloid (Fig. 4.50). A hypocycloid is the curve generated by a point on the circumference of a circle that rolls in a plane on the inside of another circle. The method used to draw a hypocycloid is similar to the method used to draw the cycloid.

Practical examples of the use of cycloidal curves to form the outlines of cycloidal gear teeth are shown in the chapter on gears in this text.

4.57. Spiral of Archimedes. Archimedes spiral is a plane curve generated by a point moving uniformly around and away from a fixed point. In order to define this curve more specifically, it can be said that it is generated by a point moving uniformly along a straight line while the line revolves with uniform angular velocity about a fixed point.

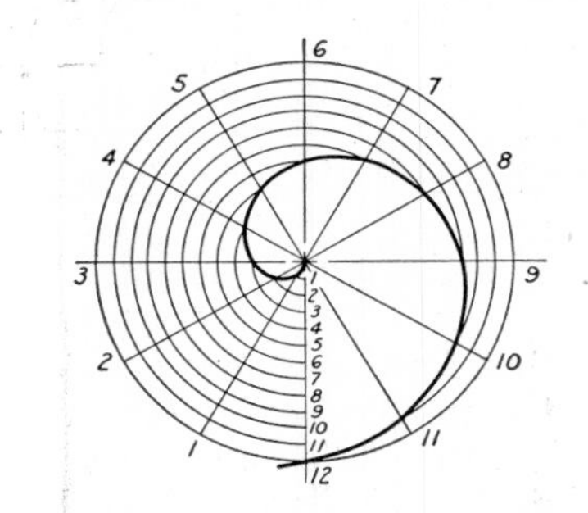

Fig. 4.51. Spiral of Archimedes.

The definition of the Spiral of Archimedes is applied in drawing this curve as illustrated in Fig. 4.51. To find a sufficient number of points to allow the use of an irregular curve for drawing the spiral it is the practice to divide the given circle into a number of equal parts (say twelve) and draw radial lines to the division points. Next, divide a radial line into the same number of equal parts as the circle and number the division

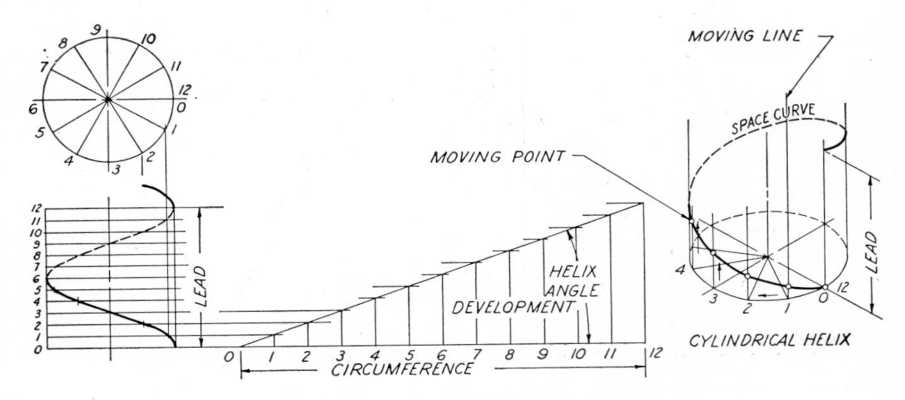

Fig. 4.52. The helix.

points on the circumference of the circle beginning with the radial line adjacent to the divided one. With the center of the circle as a center draw concentric arcs that in each case will start at a numbered division point on the divided radial line and will end at an intersection with the radial line that is numbered correspondingly. The arc starting at point *1* gives a point on the curve at its intersection with radial line *1*; the arc starting at *2* gives an intersection point on radial line *2*; etc. The spiral is a smooth curve drawn through these intersection points.

4.58. The helix (Fig. 4.52). The cylindrical helix is a space curve that is generated by a point moving uniformly on the surface of a cylinder. The point must travel parallel to the axis with uniform linear velocity while at the same time it is moving with uniform angular velocity around the axis. The curve can be thought of as being generated by a point moving uniformly along a straight line while the line is revolving with uniform angular velocity around the axis of the given cylinder. Study the pictorial drawing.

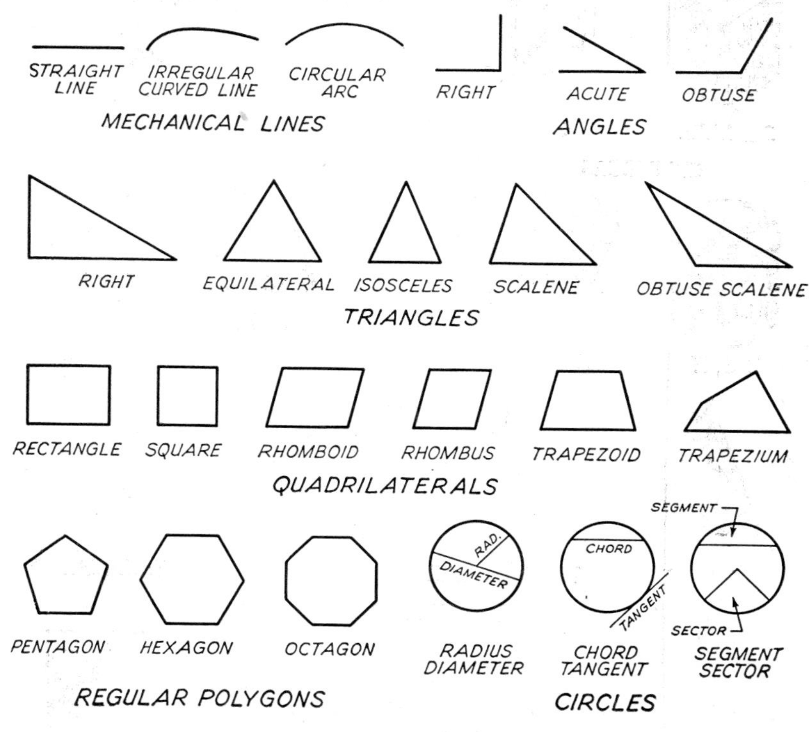

Fig. 4.53. Geometric shapes.

The first step in drawing a cylindrical helix is to lay out the two views of the cylinder. Next, the lead should be measured along a contour element and divided into a number of equal parts (say twelve). Divide the circular view of the cylinder into the same number of parts and number the division points.

The division lines of the lead represent the various positions of the moving point as it travels in a direction parallel to the axis of the cylinder along the moving line. The division points on the circular view are the related positions of the moving line. For example, when the line has moved from the *0* to the *1* position, the point has traveled along the line a distance equal to one-twelfth of the lead; when the line is in the *2* position the point has traveled one-sixth of the lead. (See pictorial drawing.) In constructing the curve the necessary points are found by projecting from a numbered point on the circular view to the division line of the lead that is numbered similarly.

A helix may be either right-hand or left-hand. The one shown in Fig. 4.52 is a left-hand helix.

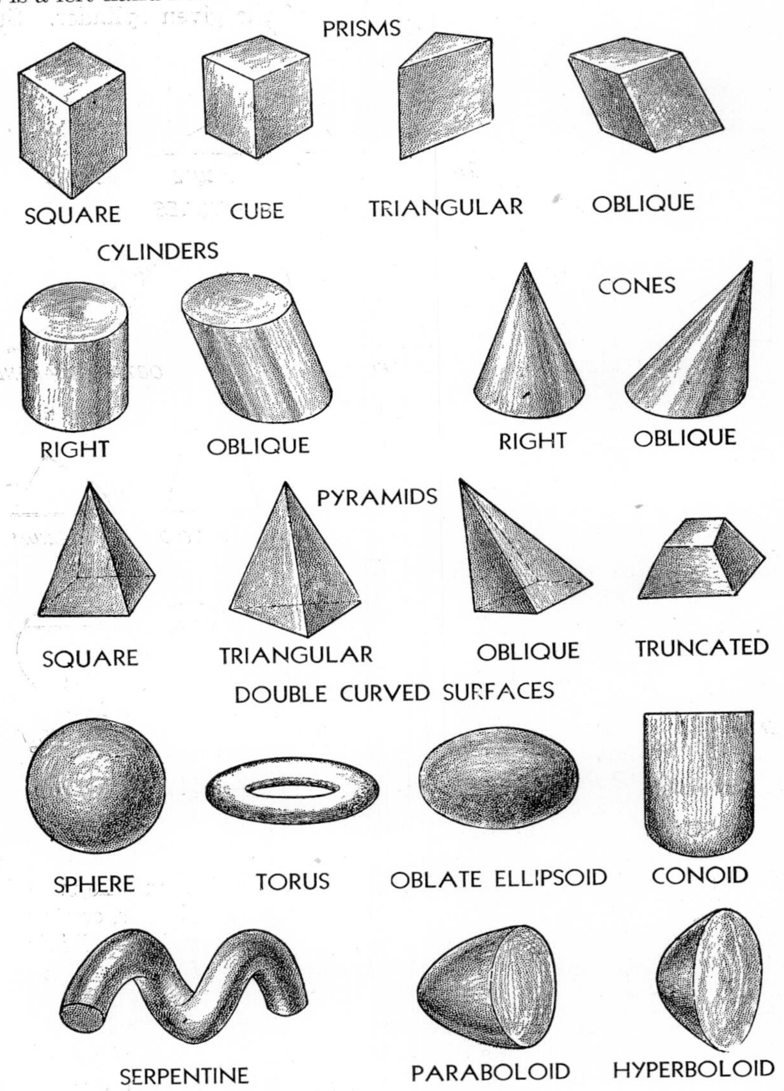

Fig. 4.54. Geometric shapes.

When the cylinder is developed, the helix becomes a straight line on the development as shown. It is inclined to the base line at an angle known as the "helix angle."

A screw thread is an example of a practical application of the cylindrical helix.

4.59. Problems. The following exercises not only require the student to study and use certain common geometrical constructions, but also furnish additional practice in applying good line technique to the drawing of instrumental figures and practical designs. All work should be very accurately done. Tangent points should be indicated by a light short dash across the line.

1. Draw a horizontal line $4\frac{3}{8}''$ long. Bisect it by the method shown in Fig. 4.1(*b*).

2. Draw a line $3\frac{3}{4}''$ long, inclined at 30° to the horizontal. Divide it into five equal parts. Use the method illustrated in Fig. 4.6(*a*).

3. Draw a line $3\frac{1}{4}''$ long. Divide it into three equal parts. Use the method shown in Fig. 4.2.

4. Draw a line $3\frac{1}{8}''$ long. Divide it proportionally in the ratio 1:2:3. Use the method shown in Fig. 4.7.

5. Using a line $3\frac{1}{4}''$ long as the base line, construct a triangle having sides $2\frac{1}{2}''$, $3\frac{1}{4}''$, and $3\frac{3}{4}''$ long, respectively. Study the method that is illustrated in Fig. 4.11.

6. Construct a regular hexagon having a $2\frac{1}{2}''$ distance across flats. Select the most practical procedure.

7. Construct a regular hexagon having a $3\frac{1}{4}''$ distance across corners. Select the most practical method.

8. Construct a regular pentagon having $1\frac{1}{4}''$ sides. Use the method illustrated in Fig. 4.18.

9. Divide the area of the triangle in problem 5 into four equal parts. Use the method shown in Fig. 4.19(*a*).

10. Trisect the angle between the $3\frac{1}{4}''$ and $3\frac{3}{4}''$ sides of the triangle in problem 5. Use the method illustrated in Fig. 4.5.

11. Draw two horizontal lines 2″ apart. Locate two points 3″ apart horizontally, one on each line. Draw an ogee curve tangent to these lines. Study the procedure illustrated in Fig. 4.25.

12. Draw a $2\frac{1}{2}''$ circle. Select a point 2″ from the center and draw a line tangent to it, using the method illustrated in Fig. 4.27(*a*).

13. Draw a $2\frac{3}{4}''$ circle, and draw tangent to it a line that makes 15° with the horizontal. Draw a $1\frac{1}{2}''$ circle tangent to the line and the $2\frac{3}{4}''$ circle. Use the method illustrated in Fig. 4.23.

14. Draw a 3″ circle. Inside this circle, and tangent to it, draw a $1\frac{3}{4}''$ circle. See that the centers of both circles are on the same vertical center line. Draw two 1″ circles tangent to the 3″ and the $1\frac{3}{4}''$ circles. Use the method illustrated in Fig. 4.24.

15. Construct an ellipse having a major diameter of $4\frac{1}{4}''$ and a minor diameter of $2\frac{3}{4}''$. Use the trammel method illustrated in Fig. 4.35.

16. Construct an ellipse having a major diameter of $4''$ and a minor diameter of $2\frac{3}{4}''$. Use the concentric circle method illustrated in Fig. 4.36. Find a sufficient number of points to obtain a smooth curve.

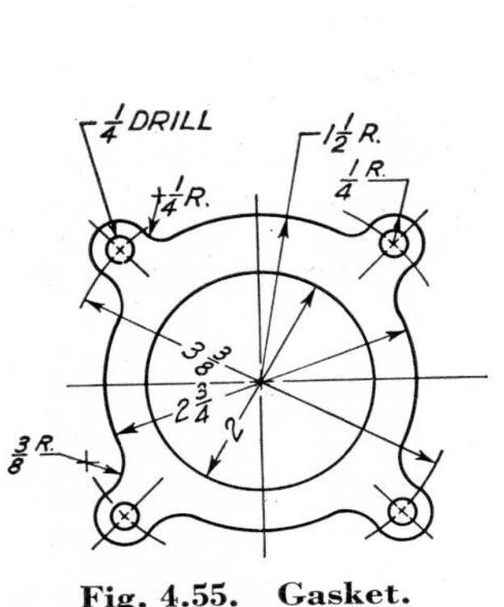

Fig. 4.55. Gasket.

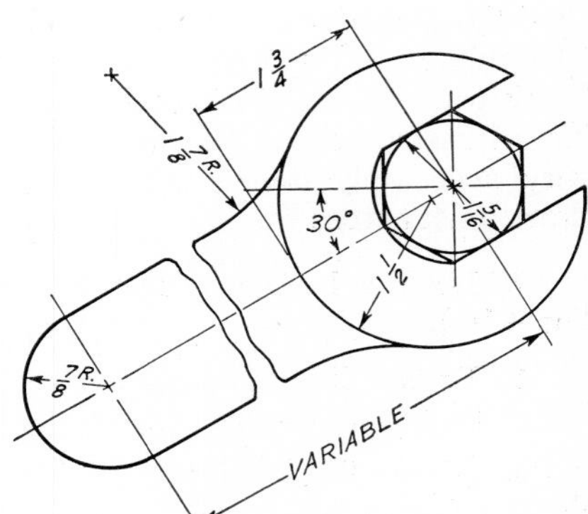

Fig. 4.56. Wrench.

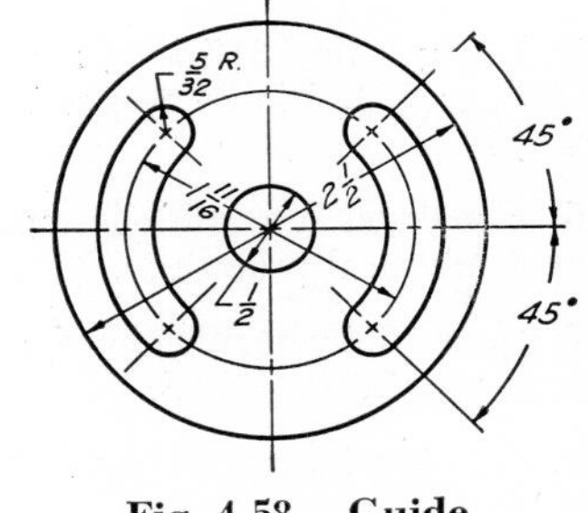

Fig. 4.58. Guide.

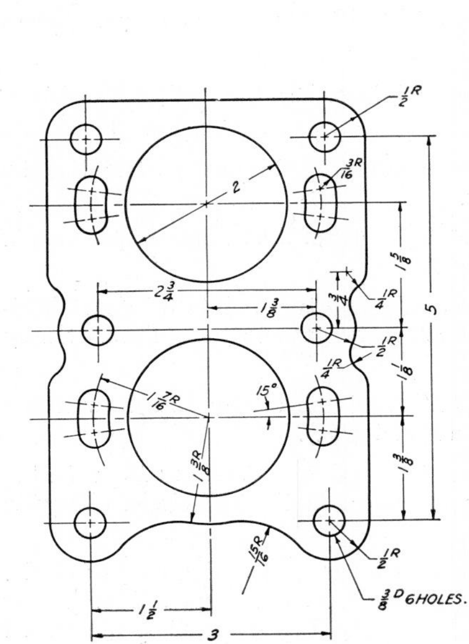

Fig. 4.57. Gasket.

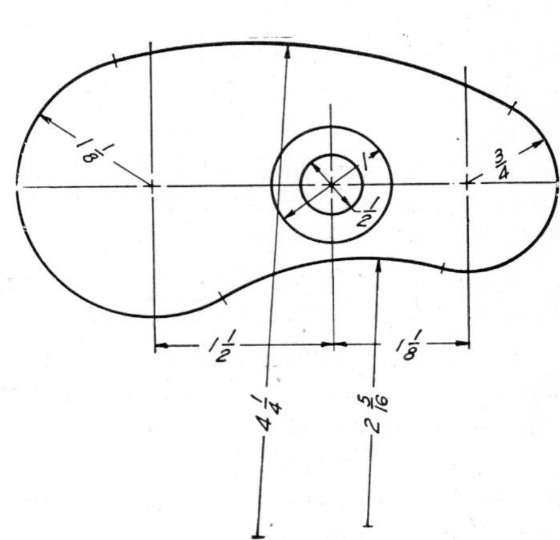

Fig. 4.59. Cam.

17. Construct the ellipse required in problem 16, using the four-center method. Study Sec. 4.39 and Fig. 4.37.

18. Construct an ellipse having conjugate axes $3\frac{3}{4}''$ and $2\frac{1}{2}''$ long inclined one to the other at 75°. Determine the major and minor axes (Fig. 4.39).

19. Construct a parabola with axis vertical. Make the focus $\frac{3}{4}''$ from the directrix. Select a point on the curve and draw a line tangent to the parabola. Study Sec. 4.44 and Fig. 4.42.

20. Construct a hyperbola having a transverse axis of 1″ and foci $1\frac{5}{8}''$ apart. Study Sec. 4.49 and Fig. 4.46.

21. Construct the involute of an equilateral triangle with 1″ sides. Study Sec. 4.52.

22. Construct the involute of a circle $\frac{7}{8}''$ in diameter. Study Sec. 4.51 and Fig. 4.47(*a*).

23. Construct the cycloid generated by a $1\frac{1}{2}''$ circle. Study Sec. 4.54 and Fig. 4.48.

24. Construct the epicycloid generated by a $1\frac{1}{2}''$ circle rolling on a 5″ circle. Study Sec. 4.55 and Fig. 4.49.

25. Construct the hypocycloid generated by a $1\frac{1}{2}''$ circle rolling on a $4\frac{1}{2}''$ circle. Study Sec. 4.56 and Fig. 4.50.

26. Reconstruct the view of the gasket shown in Fig. 4.55 to full scale. Mark all of the tangent points with short lines. Study Fig. 4.24. Do not place dimensions on the finished drawing.

27. Reconstruct the view of the wrench shown in Fig. 4.56. Mark all tangent points with short lines.

28. Reconstruct the view of the gasket shown in Fig. 4.57. Mark all tangent points with short marks across tangent lines.

29. Reconstruct the view of the guide shown in Fig. 4.58.

30. Reconstruct the view of the cam shown in Fig. 4.59. Mark all tangent points.

31. Construct the shape of the slotted guide shown in Fig. 4.60. Show all construction for locating centers and mark points of tangency.

32. Construct the adjustable Y-clamp shown in Fig. 4.61. Show all construction for locating centers and mark points of tangency.

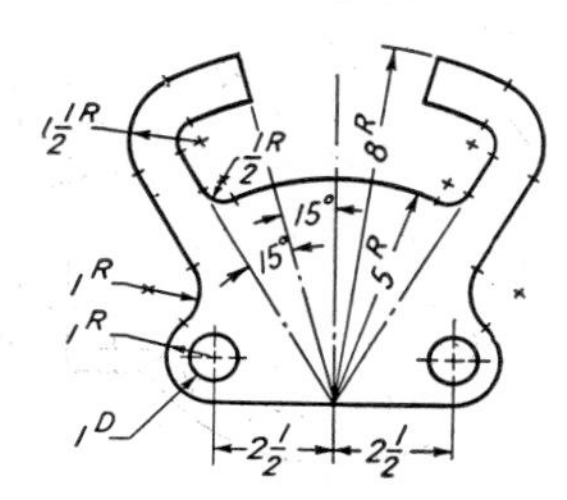

Fig. 4.60. **Slotted guide.**

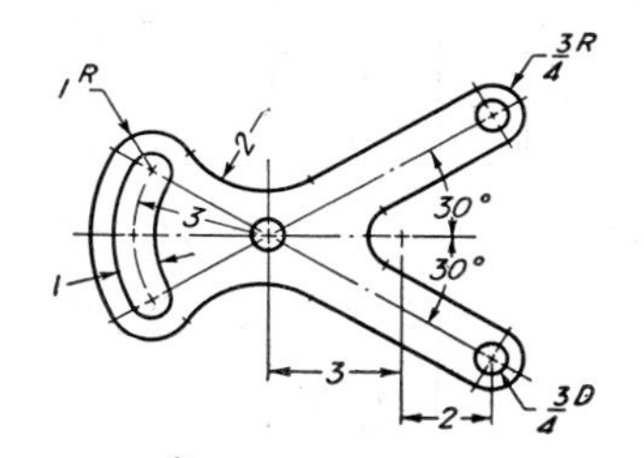

Fig. 4.61. **Adjustable Y-clamp.**

33. Reconstruct the geometrical design shown in Fig. 4.62. Mark all tangent points with short marks across tangent lines, as shown in the given view.

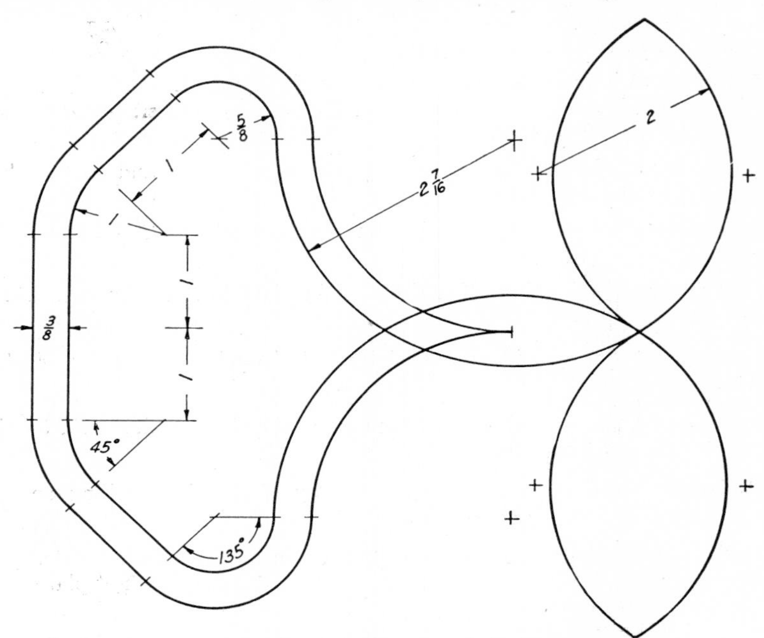

Fig. 4.62. Geometrical design.

34. Reconstruct the view of the cover gasket shown in Fig. 4.63.

35. Reconstruct the view of the C-ring shown in Fig. 4.64.

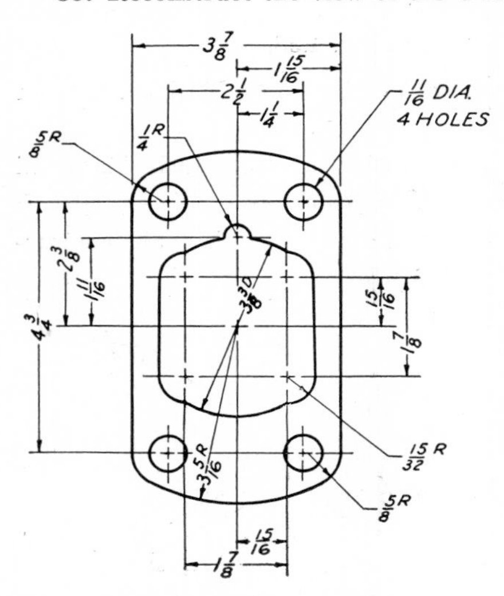

Fig. 4.63. Cover gasket.

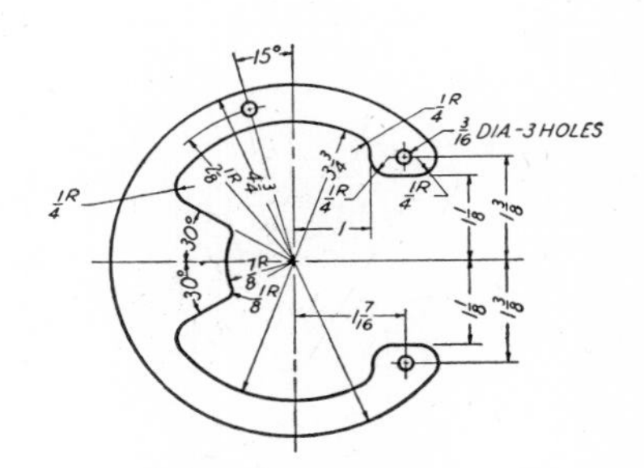

Fig. 4.64. C-ring.

36. (Fig. 4.65.) Using an eighth size scale, make a one-view drawing of the housing gasket. Use approved geometrical constructions and mark all tangent points with $\frac{1}{8}''$ dash across the line. Be prepared to explain to your instructor the procedure for determining the locations for centers and tangent points and demonstrate the manipulation of the triangles for the 15° angles. Study Sec. 4.11. *Supplementary information:* (1) the three small circular holes are to be 6″ in diameter, (2) the large hole in the center of the gasket must have a $10\frac{1}{2}''$ diameter, (3) all small radii are 2″, (4) the gasket is to be cut from $\frac{1}{16}''$ fiber stock.

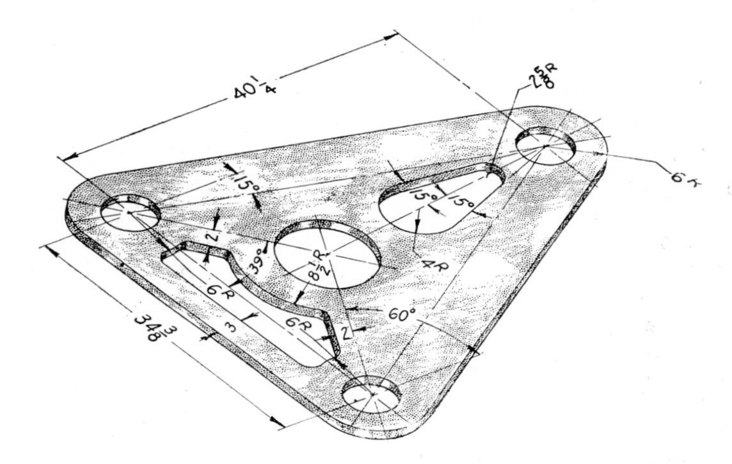

Fig. 4.65. Housing gasket.

5 TECHNICAL LETTERING

5.1. To impart to the men in the shops all the necessary information for the complete construction of a machine or structure, the shape description, which is conveyed graphically by the views, must be accompanied by size descriptions and instructive specifications in the form of figured dimensions and notes.

All dimensions and notes should be lettered freehand in a plain legible style that can be rapidly executed. Poor lettering detracts from the appearance of a drawing, and often impairs its usefulness, regardless of the quality of the line work.

5.2. Lettering.* "To acquire proficiency in any art one must know what to do, how to do it, and then practice.

"Learning to letter requires:

"(*a*) A knowledge of the shapes and proportions of the individual characters.

"(*b*) A knowledge of the order of stroke and direction of stroke used in making them.

"(*c*) A knowledge of the rules for combining letters into words and words into sentences.

"(*d*) Practice."

5.3. Single-stroke Gothic letters (Reinhardt). The simplified single-stroke Gothic letters developed by Charles W. Reinhardt are now used universally for working drawings. This style is particularly suitable for most technical purposes because it possesses the qualifications necessary for legibility and speed. On commercial drawings it appears in slightly modified forms, however, as each draftsman finally develops a style that reflects his own individuality.

The expression "single-stroke" means that the width of the straight and curved lines that form the letters are the same width as the stroke of the pen or pencil. The term should not be understood to imply that the entire letter is made with one continuous movement.

5.4. The recommendations of the American Standards Association. After a thorough study of the practices of the leading industrial manufacturing companies and technical schools, the American Standards Association made the following recommendations.

---

* By Justus Rising from the *Purdue University Problem Book.*

"(*a*) That single-stroke commercial gothic lettering, either vertical or inclined at a slope of 2 in 5, be used on all working drawings for titles, notes, and so forth.

"(*b*) That only capitals be used in the title box.

"(*c*) That for notes, bills of material, and so forth, if the vertical style is chosen the letters should be all caps. If the inclined style is chosen the letters may be all caps or caps and lower-case."

5.5. The general proportions of letters. Although there is no fixed standard for the proportions of the letters, certain definite rules in their design must be observed by a draftsman if he wishes to have his lettering appear neat and pleasing to the eye. The recognized characteristics of each letter should be carefully studied, and then thoroughly learned through practice, before any attempt is made to letter complete notes and sentences.

It is advisable for the beginner, instead of relying on his untrained eye for proportions, to follow the fixed proportions given in this chapter. Otherwise, his lettering most likely will be displeasing to the trained eye of a professional engineer or draftsman. Later, after he has thoroughly mastered the art of lettering, his individuality will be revealed naturally by slight variations in the shapes and proportions of some of the letters.

NORMAL LETTERS

COMPRESSED LETTERS

EXTENDED LETTERS

Fig. 5.1. Compressed and extended letters.

It is often desirable to increase or decrease the width of letters in order to make a word or group of words fill a certain space. Letters narrower than normal letters of the same height are called *compressed letters;* those that are wider are called *extended letters.* (See Fig. 5.1.)

5.6. Lettering pencils, pens, and equipment. Pencil lettering is usually done with a medium-soft pencil. Since the degree of hardness of the lead required to produce a dark opaque line will vary with the type of paper used, a pencil should be selected only after drawing a few trial lines. In order to obtain satisfactory lines, the pencil should be sharpened to a long conical point and then rounded slightly on a piece of scratch paper. To keep the point symmetrical while lettering, the pencil should be rotated a partial revolution before each new letter is started.

The choice of a type of pen point for lettering on ordinary working drawings depends largely upon the personal preference and characteristics of the individual. The beginner can learn only from experience which of the many types available are best suited to him. A few of the more popular points and their strokes are illustrated in Fig. 5.2. Every draftsman should have an assortment of points varied enough in type to suit whatever size of letters and kind of paper he may be called upon to use.

A pen that makes a heavy stroke should be used for bold letters in titles and so forth, while a light-stroke pen is required for the lighter letters in figures and notes.

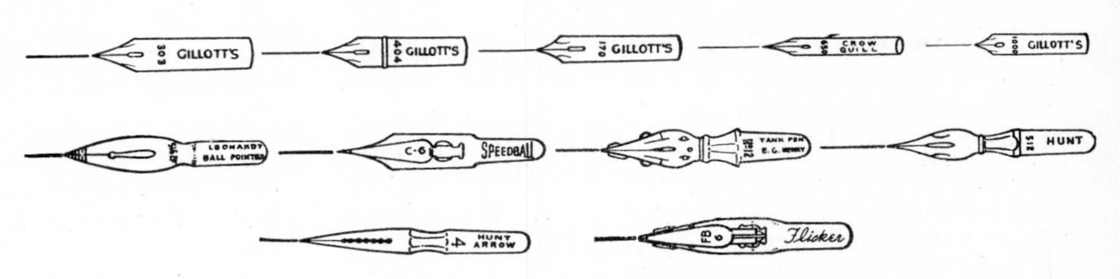

Fig. 5.2. Pen points.

A very flexible point never should be used for lettering. Such a point is apt to shade the downward stem strokes as well as the downward portions of curved strokes. A good point is one that has enough resistance to normal pressure to permit the drawing of curved and stem strokes of uniform width.

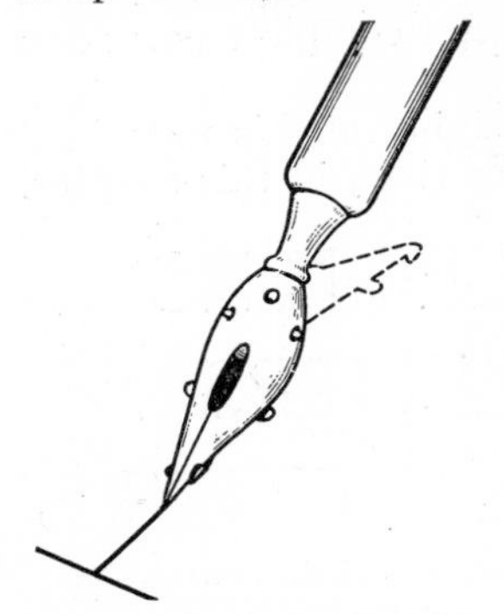

Fig. 5.3. Henry tank pen.

There are ordinary steel pen points with special ink-holding devices that make them especially adapted for lettering. The *Henry tank* pen, for example, shown in Fig. 5.3, has an ink reservoir that holds the ink above the point so that it feeds down the slit in an even flow. The device further assists in maintaining a uniform line by preventing the point from spreading.

Four of the many special pens designed for single-stroke letters are illustrated in Fig. 5.4. The *Barch-Payzant* pen (*a*) is available in graded sizes from No. 000 (very coarse) to No. 8 (very fine). The very fine size is suitable for lettering $\frac{1}{8}$ inch to $\frac{3}{16}$ inch high on technical drawings. The *Edco* (*b*) has a patented holder into which any one of a graded set of lettering nibs (ranging in sizes from No. 0 to No. 6) may be screwed. The tubular construction of the point makes it possible to draw uniform lines regardless of the direction of the stroke. Also of tubular construction is the *Leroy* (*c*). The *Speedball* (*d*) may be obtained in many graded sizes.

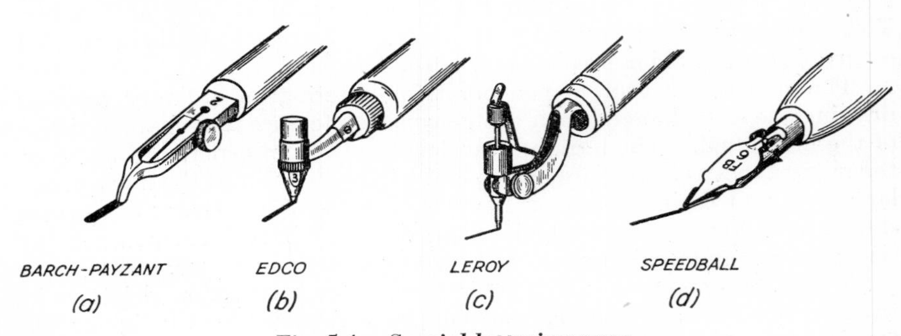

Fig. 5.4. Special lettering pens.

5.7. Devices for drawing guide lines and slope lines. Devices for drawing guide lines are available in a variety of forms. The two most popular are the *Braddock Lettering Triangle* (Fig. 5.5), and the *Ames Lettering Instrument* (Fig. 5.6).

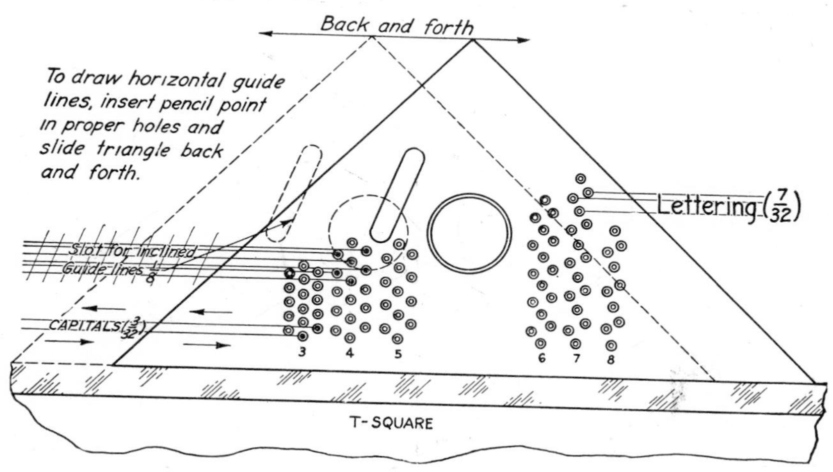

Fig. 5.5. Braddock lettering triangle.

The Braddock Lettering Triangle is provided with sets of grouped countersunk holes that may be used to draw guide lines by inserting a sharp-pointed pencil (4*H* or 6*H*) into the holes and sliding the triangle back and forth along the guiding edge of a T-square or a triangle supported by a T-square. The holes are grouped to give guide lines for capitals and lower-case letters. The numbers below each set indicate the height of the capitals in thirty-seconds of an inch. For example, the No. 3 set is for capitals $\frac{3}{32}''$ high, the No. 4 set is for capitals $\frac{1}{8}''$ high, the No. 5 is for capitals $\frac{5}{32}''$ high, and so on.

The following practice is recommended for drawing guide lines on

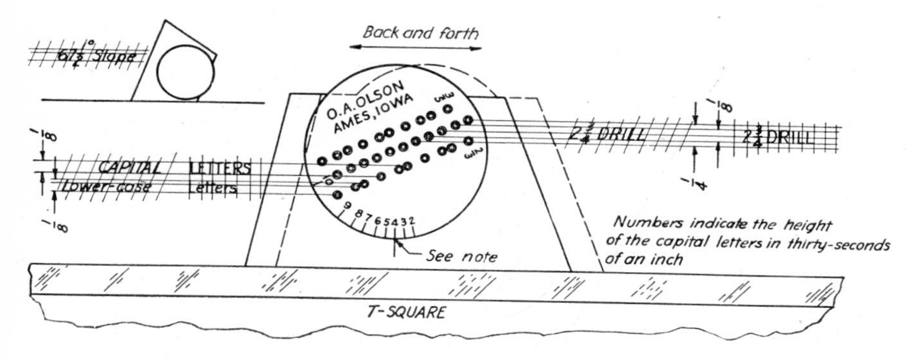

Fig. 5.6. Ames lettering instrument.

drawings of ordinary size ($8\frac{1}{2}'' \times 11''$, $9'' \times 12''$, $11'' \times 17''$, and $12'' \times 18''$):

Notes and detail titles. To draw guide lines for notes and detail titles, use the top and bottom holes of the lower group in size No. 4.

Sheet titles. To draw guide lines for single-line sheet titles, use the top

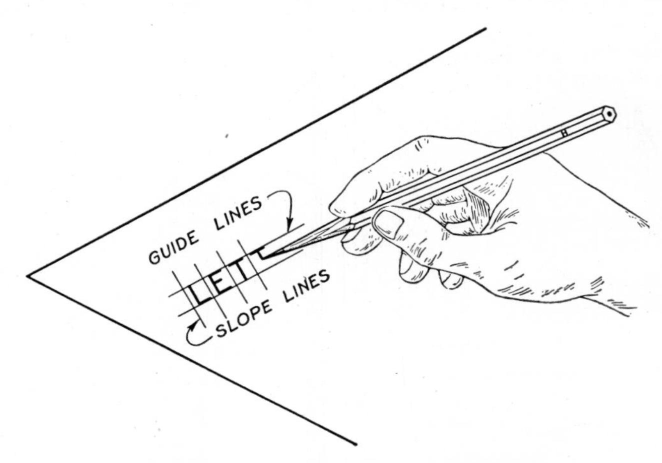

Fig. 5.7. Guide lines and slope lines.

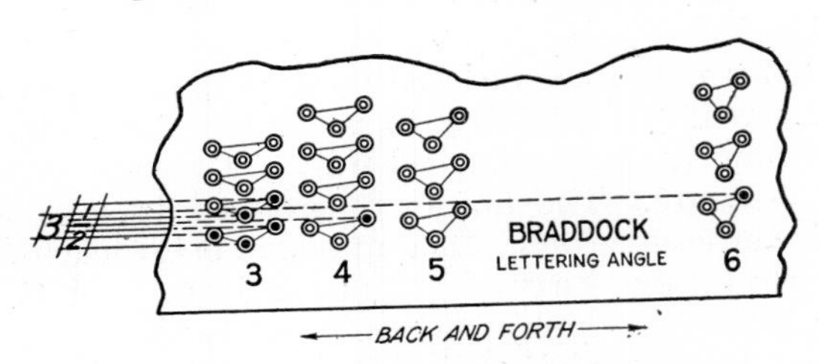

Fig. 5.8. Guide lines for fractions.

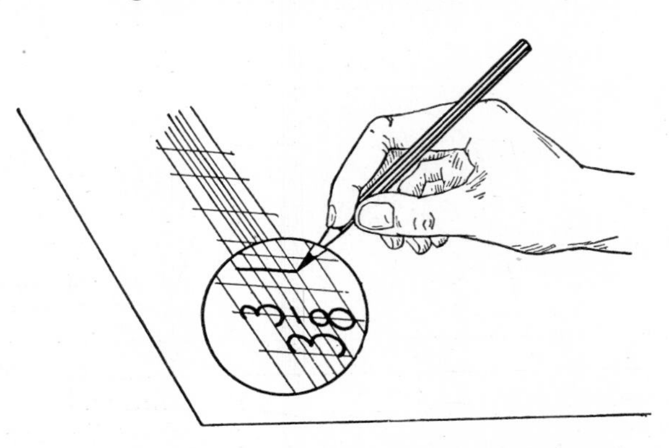

Fig. 5.9. Lettering numerals and fractions.

and bottom holes of the lower group in size No. 6. For two-line titles use the top and bottom holes of the two lower groups in size No. 4.

Combined whole numbers and fractions. To draw the seven guide lines required for a whole number and a fraction, use the countersunk holes indicated with black centers in Fig. 5.8.

These lines are made by inserting a sharp pencil in the indicated holes and moving the triangle, guided by a T-square held in a fixed position, back and forth with the pencil point. The height of a fraction numeral will be three-fourths the height of the whole number, and the total height of the fraction will be twice that of the whole number. If this useful

UNIFORMITY IN HEIGHT, INCLINATION,
AND STRENGTH OF LINE IS ESSENTIAL
FOR GOOD LETTERING.

Fig. 5.10. Uniformity in lettering.

combination is analyzed, it can be observed that the middle hole of the lower group in No. 3 and the top hole of the lower group in No. 6 give the guide lines for the whole number. The upper hole of the lower group in No. 4 gives the fraction bar, while the top and bottom holes in the two lower groups in No. 3 give the guide lines for the numerator and denominator.

5.8. Uniformity in lettering. Uniformity in height, inclination, spacing, and strength of line is essential for good lettering. Professional

Fig. 5.11. Letter areas.

appearance depends as much upon uniformity as upon the correctness of the proportion and shape of the individual letters. Uniformity in height and inclination is assured by the use of guide lines and slope lines; uniformity in weight and color, by the skillful use of the pencil and proper control of the pressure of its point on the paper. The ability to space letters correctly becomes easy after continued thoughtful practice.

5.9. Composition. In combining letters into words, the spaces for the various combinations of letters are arranged so that the areas appear to be equal. For standard lettering, this area should be about equal to one-half the area of the letter *M*. If the adjacent sides be stems, this area is obtained by making the distance between the letters slightly greater than one-half the height of a letter, and a smaller amount depending on the contours, for other combinations. Examples of good and poor composition are shown in Fig. 5.11.

The space between words should be equal to or greater than the height of a letter, but not more than twice the height. The space between sentences should be somewhat greater. The distance between lines of lettering may vary from one-half the height of the capitals to one and one-half times their height.

5.10. Stability. If the areas of the upper and lower portions of certain letters are made equal, an optical illusion will cause them to appear to be unstable and top heavy. To overcome this effect, the upper portions of the letters *B, E, F, H, K, S, X,* and *Z* and the figures *2, 3,* and *8* must be reduced slightly in size.

An associated form of illusion is the phenomenon that a horizontal line drawn across a rectangle at the vertical center will appear to be below the center. Since the letters *B, E, F,* and *H* are particularly subject to this illusion, their central horizontal strokes must be drawn slightly above the vertical center in order to give them a more balanced and pleasing appearance.

The letters *K, X, S, Z* and the figures *2, 3,* and *8* are stabilized by making the width of the upper portion less than the width of the lower portion.

5.11. The technique of freehand lettering. Any prospective draftsman or engineer can learn to letter if he practices intelligently and is persistent in his desire to improve. Unguided practice, however, is little better than no practice at all if mistakes are ignorantly repeated. The necessary muscular control, which must accompany the knowledge of lettering, can be developed only through constant repetition.

Fig. 5.12. "Inking" the pen.

Pencil letters should be formed with strokes that are dark and sharp; never with strokes that are gray and indistinct. Beginners should avoid the tendency to form letters by sketching, as strokes made in this manner vary in color and width.

When lettering with ink, the results obtained depend largely upon the manner in which the pen is used. Many draftsmen blunder along with incorrect habits, then complain that the execution of good freehand lettering is impossible with an ordinary pen point. The most common result of these habits is an inability to make strokes of uniform width. This may be due to one of four causes: (1) excessive pressure on the pen point; (2) an accumulation of lint, dirt, or dried ink on the point; (3) tilting the point while forming a stroke; or (4) fresh ink on the point. The latter cause requires some explanation, since very few draftsmen know the proper method of "inking" the pen. The pen should be wiped thoroughly clean, and the ink should be deposited on the under side over the slot, as shown in Fig. 5.12. When the pen is filled in this manner, the ink feeds down the slit in an even flow, making possible the drawing of uniform curved and straight lines. If ink is placed on the point or allowed to run to the point, an excessive amount of ink will be deposited on the first letters made, and the width of the strokes will be somewhat wider than the strokes of, say, the sixth or seventh letter. (See Fig. 5.13.)

When lettering, the pen is held as shown in Fig. 5.14. It should rest so loosely between the fingers that it can be slid up and down with the other hand.

Fig. 5.13.

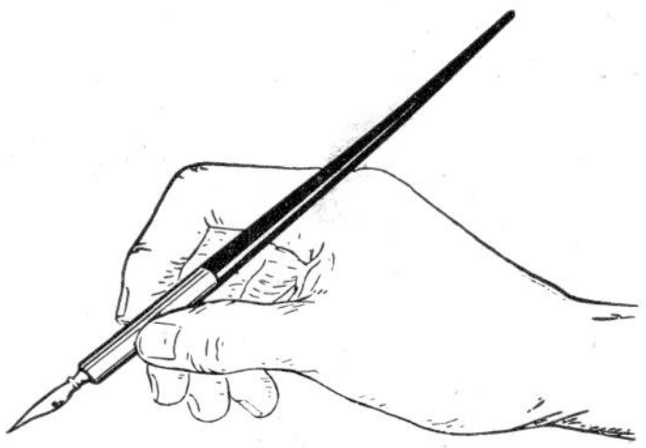

Fig. 5.14. Holding the pen.

The thin film of oil on a new point must be removed by wiping before it is used. However, never "break in" a new point unless absolutely necessary, for an old one that is clean and in good condition will give the most satisfactory results. A lettering pen point is a valuable instrument and must be treated as such. When not in use, it should be removed from the holder and placed in the instrument case. To protect a point from abuse, it should never be loaned.

5.12. Letter groups. The inclined letters shown in the following figures have been arranged in related groups. In laying out the characters, the number of widths has been reduced to the smallest number consistent with good appearance; similarities of shape have been emphasized and minute differences have been eliminated. Each letter is drawn to a large size on a cross-section grid that is two units wider, to facilitate the study of its characteristic shape and proportions. Arrows with numbers indicate the order and direction of the strokes.

INCLINED STRAIGHT-LINE LETTERS

5.13. The I, T, L, E, and F (Fig. 5.15). The letter *I* is the basic or stem stroke. The horizontal stroke of the *T* is drawn first, and the stem starts at the exact center of the bar. The *L* is 5 units wide, but it is often desirable to reduce this width when an *L* is used in combination with such letters as *A* and *T*. It should be observed that the letter *L* consists of the first two strokes of the *E*. The middle bar of the *E* is $3\frac{1}{2}$ units long and is placed slightly above the center for stability. The top bar is one-half unit shorter than the bottom bar. The letter *F* is the *E* with the bottom bar omitted.

5.14. The H and N (Fig. 5.16). Stroke 3 of the *H* should be slightly above the center, for stability. The outside parallel strokes of the *N* are drawn first to permit an accurate estimate of its width. The inclined stroke should intersect these accurately at their extremities.

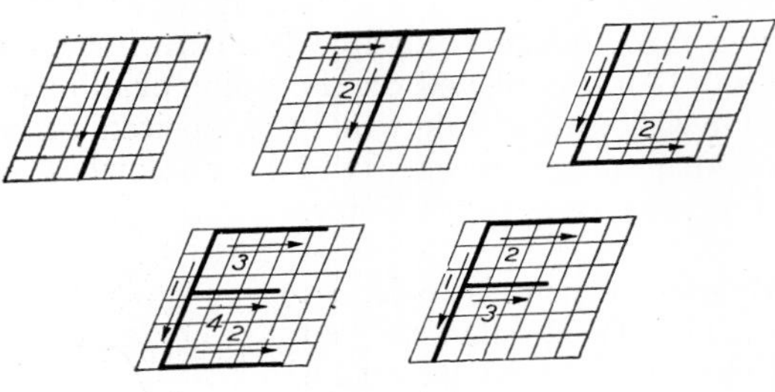

Fig. 5.15.

5.15. The Z and X (Fig. 5.17). The top of the *Z* should be one unit narrower than the bottom, for stability. In the smaller sizes, this letter may be formed without lifting the pen. The *X* is similar to the *Z* in that the top is made one unit narrower than the bottom. The inclined strokes cross slightly above center.

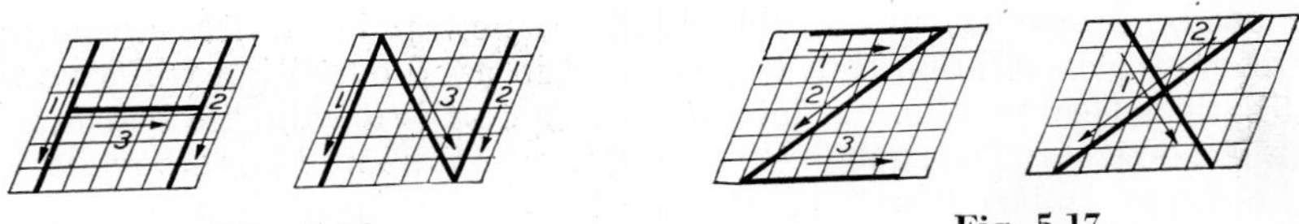

Fig. 5.16. **Fig. 5.17.**

5.16. The A, V, M, and W (Fig. 5.18). The horizontal bar of the *A* is located up from the bottom a distance equal to one-third of the height of the letter. It should be noted that the bisector of the enclosing parallelogram passes though the vertex, and that the inclined strokes are not parallel to the slope lines. The *V* is the letter *A* inverted without the

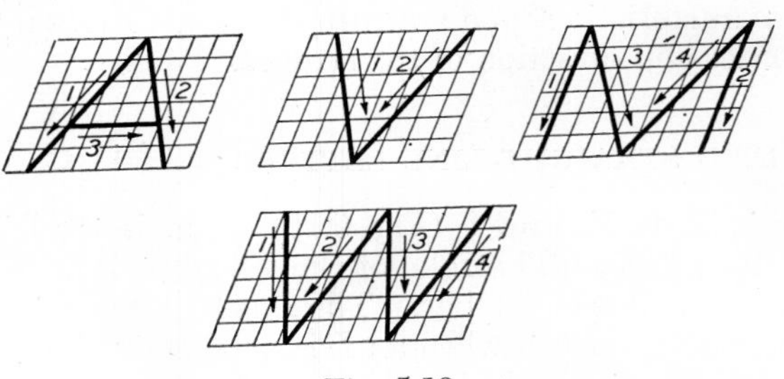

Fig. 5.18.

crossbar, and is the same width. The letters *M* and *W* are the widest letters of the alphabet. The outside strokes of the *M* are drawn first, so that its width may be judged accurately. The outside strokes of this letter are parallel, and the inside strokes meet at the center of the base.

The *W* is formed by two modified *V*'s. Strokes 1 and 3 are practically vertical. Alternate strokes are parallel.

5.17. The K and Y (Fig. 5.19). The top of the letter *K* should be one unit narrower than the bottom, for stability. Stroke 2 intersects the stem one-third up from the bottom. Stroke 3 is approximately perpendicular to stroke 2, and, if extended, would touch the stem at the top. The strokes of the *Y* meet at the center of the enclosing parallelogram.

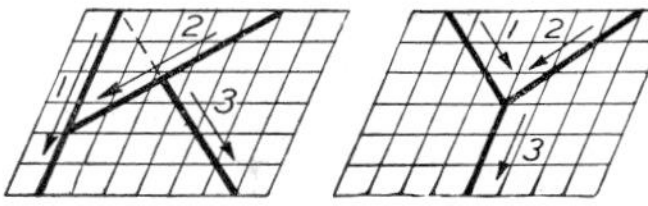

Fig. 5.19.

INCLINED CURVED-LINE LETTERS

5.18. The O, Q, C, and G (Fig. 5.20). The letters *O*, *Q*, *C*, and *G* are formed by ellipses. Stroke 1 of the letter *O* starts just to the right of the top and continues to the left around the side to a point beyond the bottom. Thus stroke 1 forms more than half of the ellipse. The *Q* is the

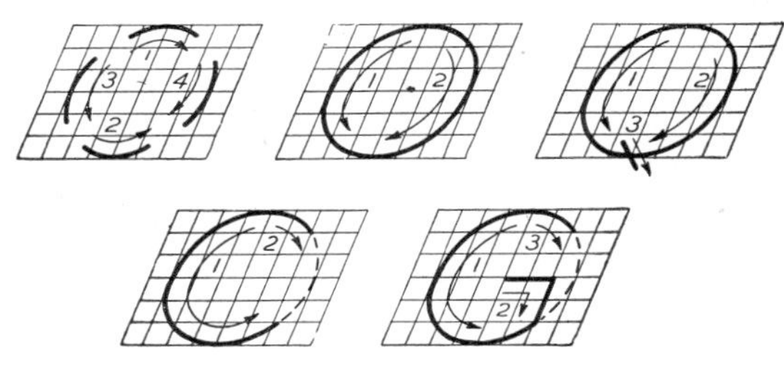

Fig. 5.20.

letter *O* with the added kern, which is a straight line located slightly to the right of the bottom tangent point. The *C* is based on the *O*, but since it is not a complete ellipse, it is narrower than either the *O* or *Q*. The top extends one unit down and the bottom one unit up on the right side. *G* is similar to *C*. The horizontal portion of stroke 2 starts at the center, and the inclined portion is parallel to the side of the parallelogram.

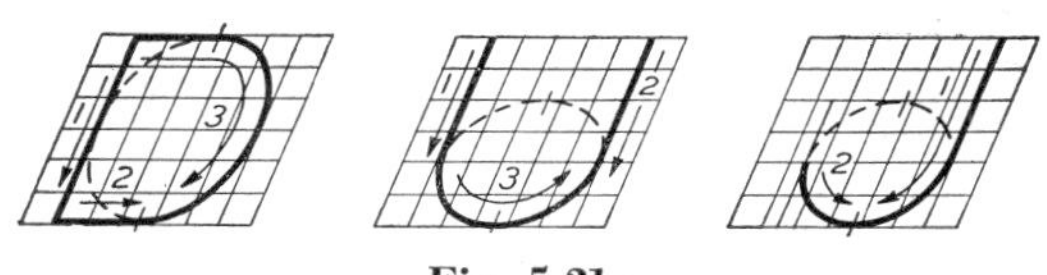

Fig. 5.21.

5.19. The D, U, and J (Fig. 5.21). The first two strokes of the *D* form an incomplete letter *L*. Stroke 3 starts as a horizontal line, and then forms one-half of a perfect ellipse. The bottom third of the *U* is one-half of an ellipse, and the stroke making it starts one-third up from the base line. *J* is similar to the letter *U*. The bottom third is one-half of a perfect ellipse.

5.20. The P, R, and B (Fig. 5.22). The middle horizontal bar of the *P* is located at the center of stroke 1. The curved portion of stroke 3 is one-half of a perfect ellipse. The *R* is constructed similarly to the *P*. The tail joins at the point of tangency of the ellipse and middle bar. To

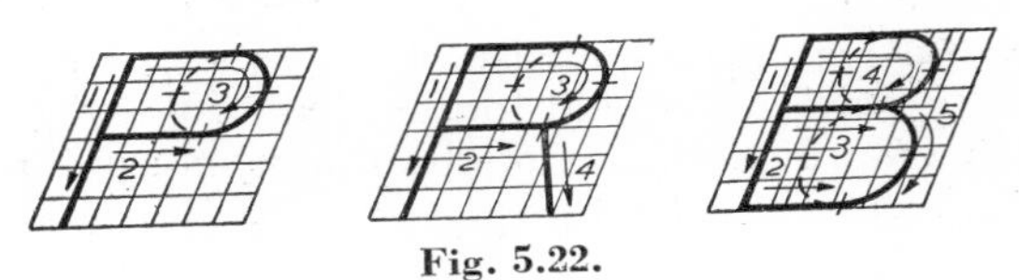

Fig. 5.22.

stabilize the letter *B*, the top is made one-half unit narrower than the bottom and the middle bar is placed slightly above the center. The curves are halves of ellipses.

5.21. The S and & (Fig. 5.23). The upper and lower portions of the *S* are perfect ellipses with one-quarter removed. The top ellipse should be made one-half unit narrower than the lower one, for stability. In the smaller sizes this letter may be made with one or two strokes, depending upon its size. The true ampersand is made with three strokes.

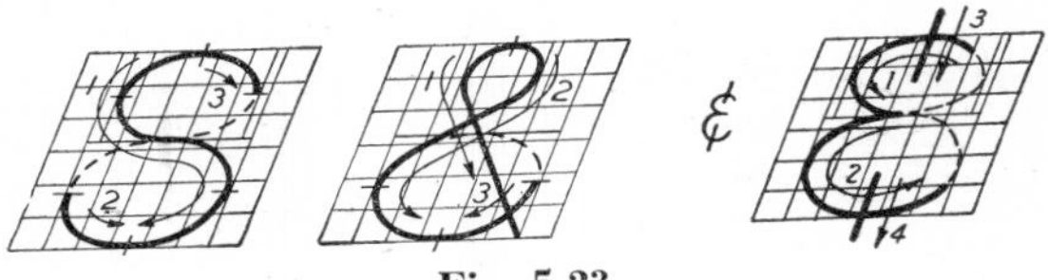

Fig. 5.23.

Professional draftsmen, however, usually represent an ampersand with a character formed by using portions of the upper and lower ellipses of the numeral 8 with the addition of two short bars.

INCLINED NUMERALS

5.22. The 1, 7, and 4 (Fig. 5.24). The stem stroke of the *4* is located one unit in from the right side. The bar is one and one-half units above the base. The stem of the *7* terminates at the center of the base of the parallelogram directly below the left end of the bar.

5.23. The 0, 6, and 9 (Fig. 5.25). The cipher, which is one unit narrower than the letter *O*, is the basic form for this group. In the figure *6*, the right side of the large ellipse ends one unit down from the top, and

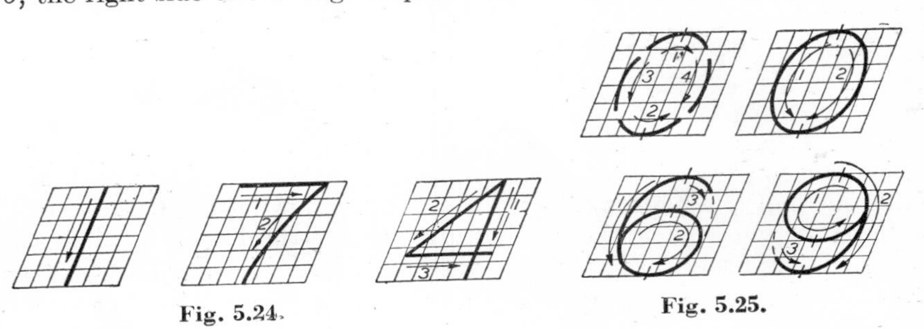

Fig. 5.24. Fig. 5.25.

the left side ends at the center of the base. The small loop is slightly more than three-fourths of a perfect ellipse. The *9* is the *6* inverted.

5.24. The 8, 3, and 2 (Fig. 5.26). Each of these figures is related to the letter *S*, and the same rule of stability should be observed in their construction. The top portion of the figure *8* is shorter and one-half unit narrower than the lower portion. Each loop is a perfect ellipse tangent to the sides of its enclosing parallelogram. The figure *3* is the *8* with the lower left quarter of the upper loop and the upper left quarter of the lower loop omitted. The *2* is simply three-quarters of the upper loop of the *8*

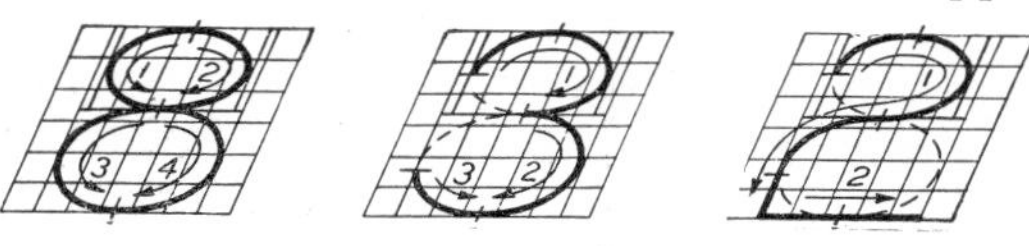

Fig. 5.26.

and the upper left quarter of the lower loop of the *8* with straight lines added.

5.25. The 5 (Fig. 5.27). This figure is a modification of the related groups previously described. The top is one-half unit narrower than the bottom, for stability. The curve is a segment of a perfect ellipse, ending one unit up from the bottom.

Fig. 5.27. **Fig. 5.28.**

5.26. Single-stroke lower-case letters. Single-stroke lower-case letters, either vertical or inclined, are commonly used on map drawings, topographic drawings, structural drawings, and in survey field books. They are particularly suitable for long notes and statements because, first, they can be executed much faster than capitals and, second, words and statements formed with them can be read more easily.

5.27. Inclined lower-case letters. The construction of inclined lower-case letters is based upon the straight line and the ellipse. This basic principle of forming letters is followed more closely for lower-case letters than for capitals. The body portions are two-thirds the height of the related capitals. As shown in Fig. 5.28, ascenders extend to the cap line, and descenders descend to the drop line. For lower-case letters based on a capital letter six units high, the waistline is two units down from the top and the drop line two units below the base line.

The order of stroke, direction of stroke, and formation of the letters follow the same principles as for the capitals. The letters are presented in family groups having related characteristics, to enable the beginner to understand their construction.

5.28. The i, l, k, and t (Fig. 5.29). All letters of this group are formed by straight lines of standard slope. The *i* is drawn four units high, and the dot is placed halfway between the waistline and cap line. Stroke 2 of the *k* starts at the waistline and intersects stroke 1 two units above the base. Stroke 3, extended, should intersect stroke 1 at the top. The *t* is five units high, and the crossbar is on the waistline.

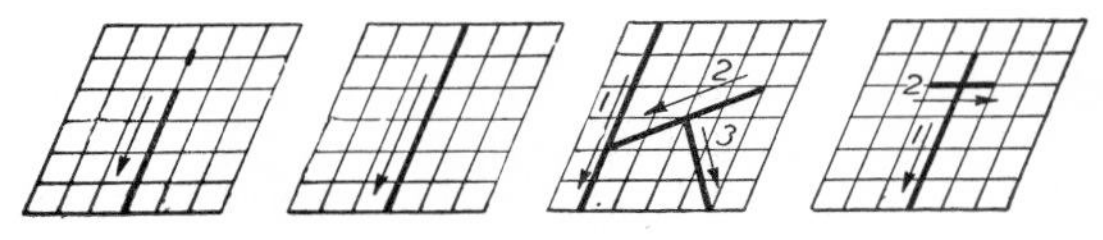

Fig. 5.29.

5.29. The v, w, x, and z (Fig. 5.30). All of these letters are similar to the capitals. Stroke 1 of the *w* is practically vertical, and the alternate strokes are parallel. The width of the top of both the *x* and the *z* is made one-half unit less than the width across the bottom, for stability.

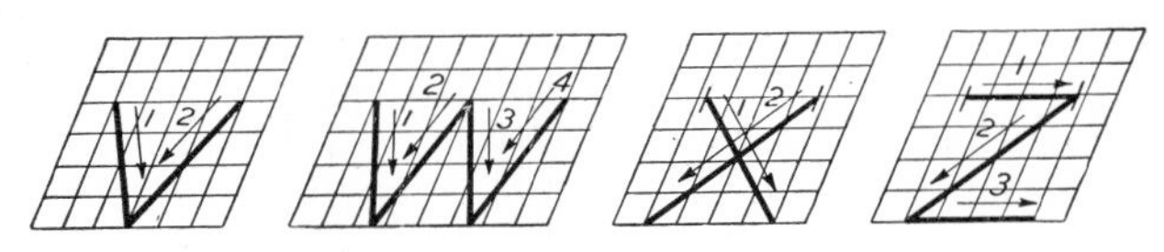

Fig. 5.30.

5.30. The o, a, b, d, p, and q (Fig. 5.31). The bodies of the letters in this group are formed by the letter *o*, and they differ only in the position and length of the stem stroke. The *o* is made with two strokes, and the first stroke should form more than half of the ellipse.

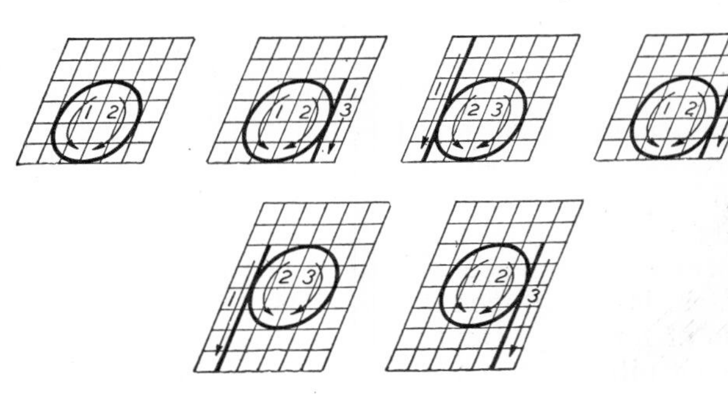

Fig. 5.31.

5.31. The g and s (Fig. 5.32). The *g* is related to the letters *o* and *y*. Stroke 3 starts at the waistline and ends slightly beyond the point of tangency of the curve with the drop line. The lower-case *s* is almost identical to the capital *S*.

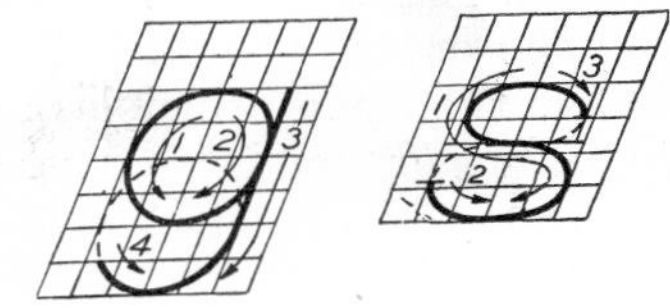

Fig. 5.32.

5.32. The j and f (Fig. 5.33). The portion of the *j* above the base line is the letter *i*. The elliptical curve is the same as that which forms the tail of the *g*. The *f* is two and one-half units wide, stroke 1 starting slightly to the right of the point of tangency with the cap line.

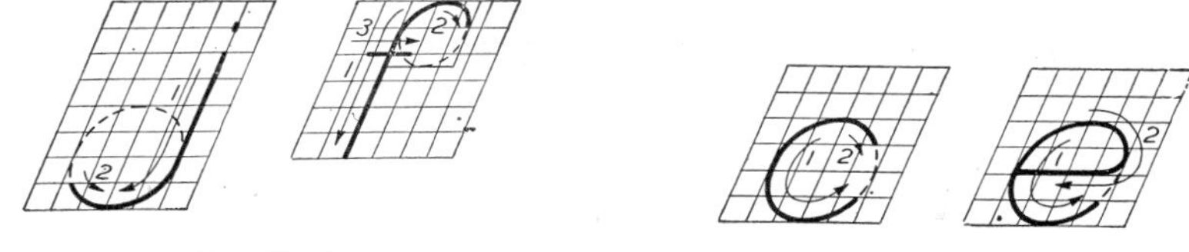

Fig. 5.33. Fig. 5.34.

5.33. The c and e (Fig. 5.34). The *c* is a modified letter *o*. It is not a complete ellipse. Therefore, its width is less than its height. Stroke 1 ends one unit up on the right side, stroke 2 one unit down. The *e* is similarly constructed, except for the fact that stroke 2 continues as a curve and finishes as a horizontal line that terminates at the middle of the back.

5.34. The h, n, r, and m (Fig. 5.35). The curve of the *h* is the upper portion of the letter *o*. Stroke 2 starts 2 units above the bottom of the stem and finishes parallel to stroke 1. The *n* differs from the *h* in that the

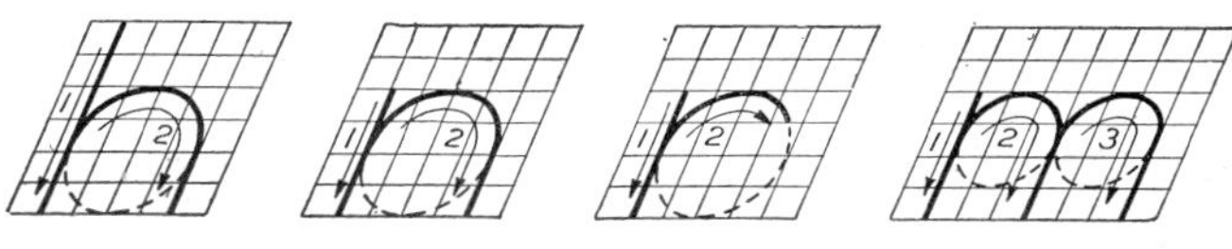

Fig. 5.35.

stem stroke extends only from the waistline to the base line. The *r* is a portion of the letter *n*, stroke 2 ending one unit down from the top. The *m* consists of two modified letter *n*'s. The straight portions of strokes 2 and 3 are parallel to stroke 1.

5.35. The u and y (Fig. 5.36). The letter *u* is an inverted *n*, and the curve is a portion of the letter *o*. It should be noted that stroke 2 extends to the base line. The *y* is a partial combination of the letters *u* and *g*.

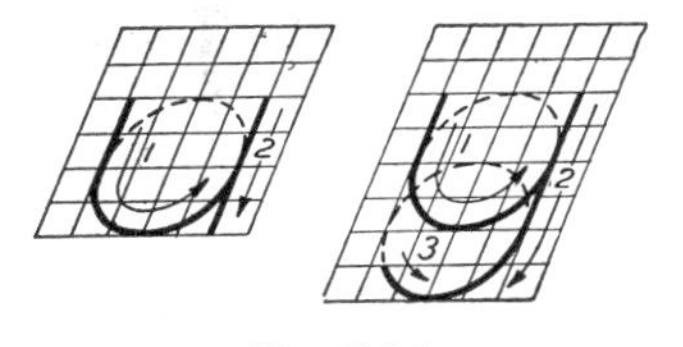

Fig. 5.36.

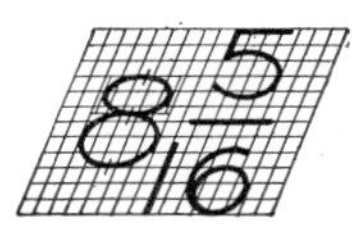

Fig. 5.37.

5.36. Fractions. The height of the figures in the numerator and denominator is equal to three-fourths the height of the whole number, and the total height of the fraction is twice the height of the whole number. The division bar should be horizontal and centered between the fraction numerals as shown in Fig. 5.37. It should be noted that the sloping center line of the fraction bisects both the numerator and denominator and is parallel to the sloping center line of the whole number.

To assure the best possible appearance, it is advisable to use seven horizontal guide lines for a combined whole number and a fraction (Figs. 5.8 and 5.9).

5.37. Vertical capitals. Although many commercial draftsmen favor the inclined letters, recent surveys indicate that vertical letters are being more generally used. Since the order and direction of the strokes as well

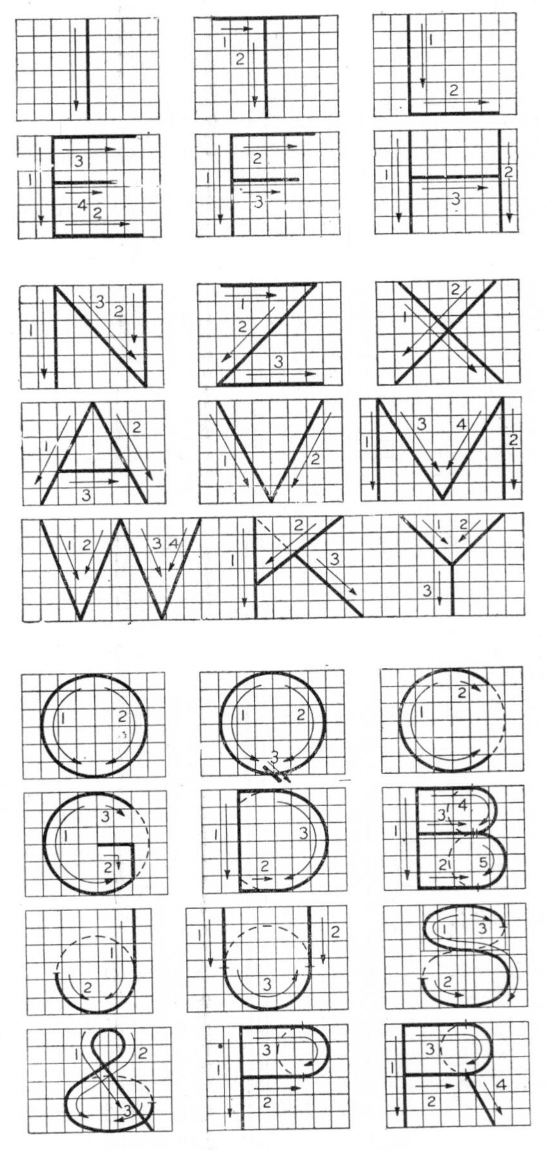

Fig. 5.38. Vertical capitals.

as the general proportions of the vertical letters are the same as previously explained for the inclined form, there is no need for further description. Their general formation is illustrated in Fig. 5.38.

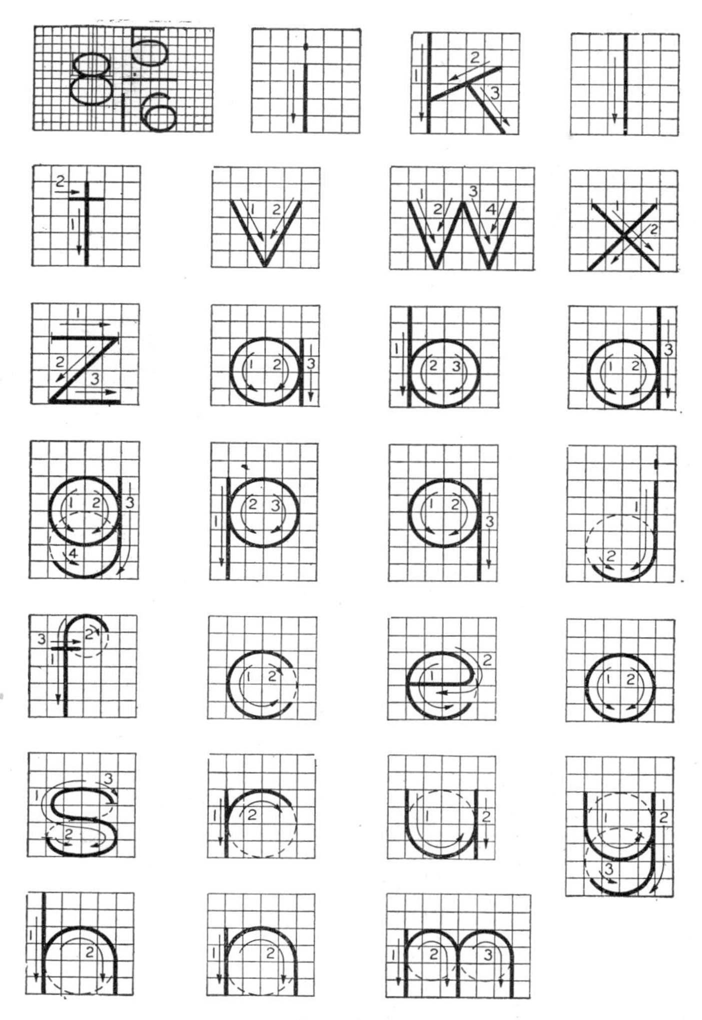

Fig. 5.39.

5.38. Vertical lower-case. The vertical lower-case letters, illustrated in Fig. 5.39, are constructed in the same manner as inclined letters. The order and direction of strokes, as well as the proportions, are essentially the same.

5.39. Vertical numerals. Vertical numerals are made with the same order and direction of stroke and have the same proportions as the inclined numerals (Fig. 5.40).

5.40. Large caps and small caps in combination. Many commercial draftsmen use a combination of large caps and small caps in forming words, as illustrated in Fig. 5.41. When this style is used, the height of the small caps should be approximately four-fifths the height of the first capital letter of the word.

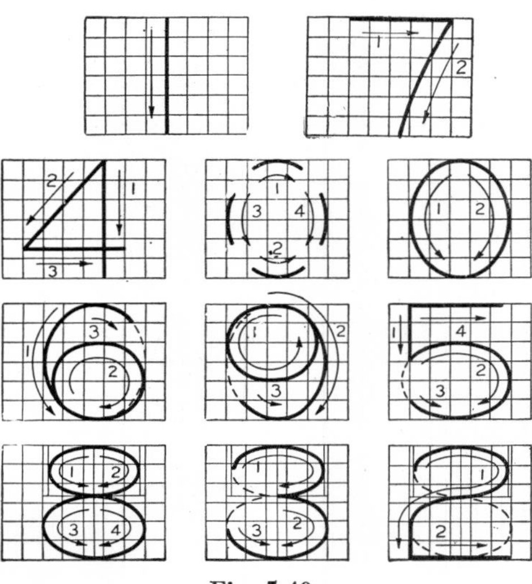

Fig. 5.40.

5.41. Titles. Every drawing, sketch, graph, chart, or diagram has some form of descriptive title to impart certain necessary information and to identify it. On machine drawings, where speed and legibility are prime requirements, titles are usually single-stroke Gothic. On display drawings, maps, architectural designs, and so on, which call for an artistic effect, the titles are usually composed of "built-up" ornate letters.

Fig. 5.42 illustrates a title that might be used on a machine drawing. It should be noted that the important items in the title are made more prominent by the use of larger letters formed with heavier

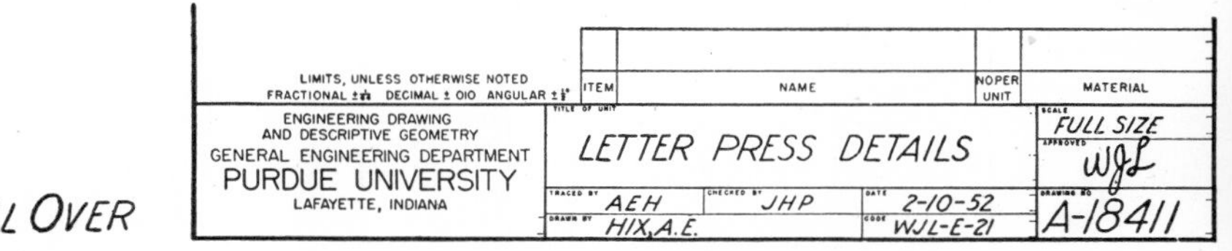

FINISH ALL OVER
LIMITS, UNLESS OTHERWISE NOTED
ITEM
NAME
MATERIAL
ENGINEERING DRAWING
AND DESCRIPTIVE GEOMETRY
GENERAL ENGINEERING DEPARTMENT
PURDUE UNIVERSITY
LAFAYETTE, INDIANA
LETTER PRESS DETAILS
FULL SIZE
AEH
JHP
2-10-52
HIX, A.E.
WJL-E-21
A-18411

Fig. 5.41. Fig. 5.42.

lines. Less important data, such as the scale, date, drafting information, and so on, are given less prominence.

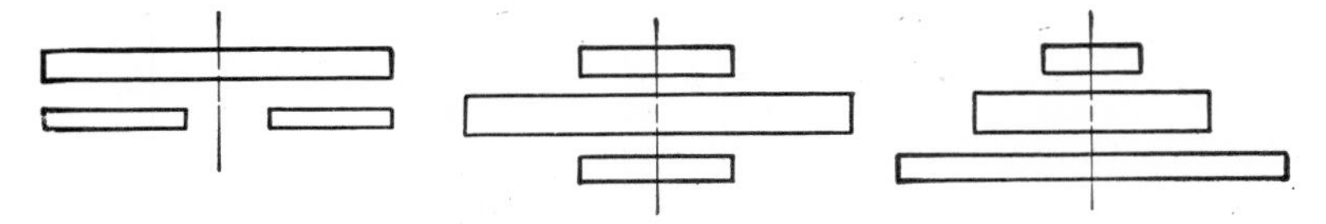

Fig. 5.43. Symmetrical titles.

To be pleasing in appearance, a title should be symmetrical about a vertical center line and should have some simple geometrical form (Fig. 5.43).

An easy way to insure the symmetry of a title is first to count the letter and word spaces, then, working to the left and right from the middle space or letter on the vertical center line, to sketch the title lightly in

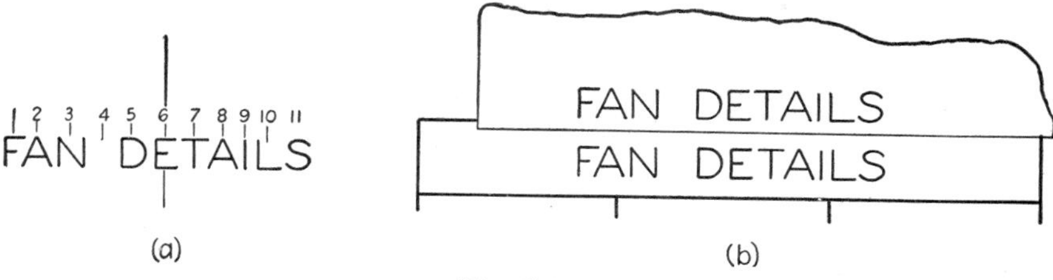

Fig. 5.44.

pencil, before lettering it in finished form (Fig. 5.44*a*). An alternate method is to letter a trial line along the edge of a piece of scrap paper and place it in a balanced position just above the location of the line to be lettered, as shown in Fig. 5.44(*b*).

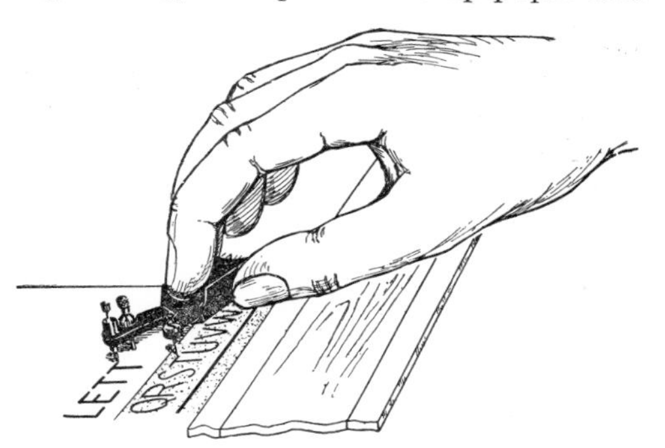

Fig. 5.45. Leroy lettering device.

5.42. Mechanical lettering devices and templates. Although mechanical lettering devices produce letters that may appear stiff to an expert, they are used in many drafting rooms for the simple reason that they enable even the unskilled to do satisfactory lettering. The average draftsman rightly prefers stiff uniformity to wavy lines and irregular shapes. One of the oldest instruments of this sort on the market is the *Wrico* outfit.

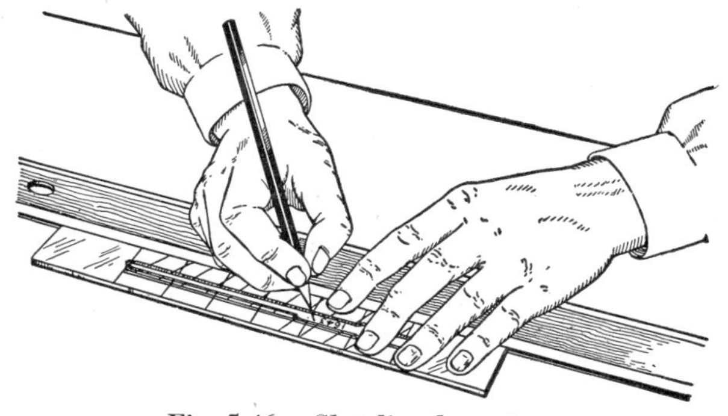

Fig. 5.46. Slot-line lettering.

With a satisfactory set of Wrico pens and templates, letters ranging in size from $\frac{3}{32}''$ to $\frac{1}{2}''$ in height may be executed. The letters are formed by a stylographic pen that is guided around the sides of openings in a template made of transparent pyralin.

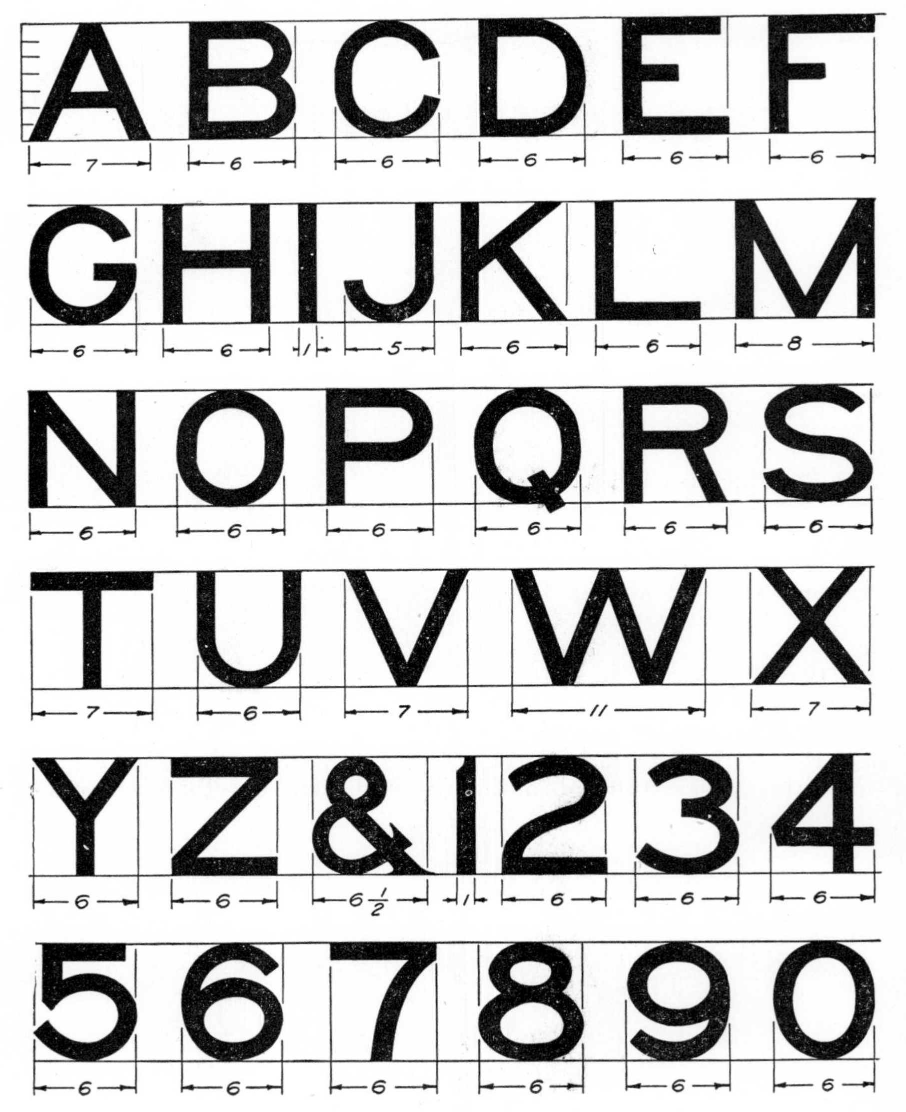

Fig. 5.47. Gothic letters.

The *Leroy* device, shown in Fig. 5.45, is possibly even more efficient than the Wrico, for it does not require the sliding of a template to complete a letter.

The slot-letter guide, shown in Fig. 5.46, is used in many commercial

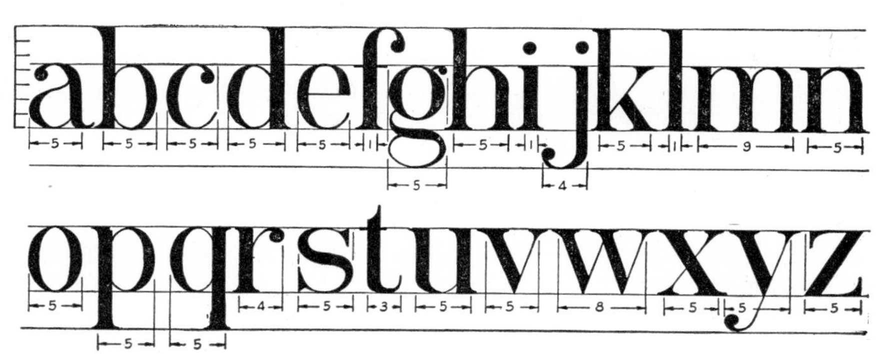

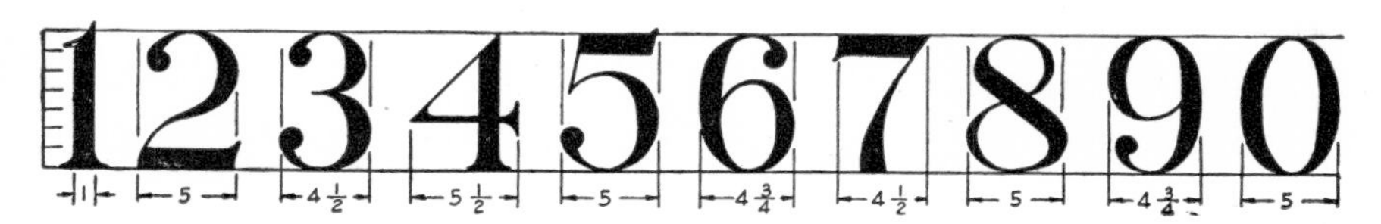

Fig. 5.48. Modern Roman letters.

drawing rooms. It enables the draftsman to letter speedily because the device eliminates the drawing of guide lines.

5.43. Commercial Gothic. All the letters in the commercial Gothic alphabet (see Fig. 5.47) are seven units high. Although the stems of the letters shown in the illustration are one unit thick, stem thickness may vary from one-tenth to one-fifth of a letter's height depending upon the effect desired. Since all their curves are circle arcs, Gothic letters are comparatively easy to construct. They are drawn first in outline, in skeleton form, and then are filled in with a ball-pointed pen. This style, from which the single-stroke engineering letters are derived, is used to some extent for titles on machine drawings, but more frequently it appears on maps, charts, and graphs that are prepared for display purposes.

5.44. Modern Roman. The Modern Roman letters shown in Fig. 5.48 are used extensively by engineers for names and titles on maps. Students should be familiar with this alphabet, for it appears in all modern publications. As in the case with the Gothic style, these letters must be drawn first in outline, in skeleton form, and then be filled in with a ball-pointed or wide-line pen. The straight lines are usually drawn with a ruling pen. The curved lines, except for the serifs, may be formed either mechanically or freehand. When attempting to construct this type of letter it is wise to bear in mind the following facts: (1) All vertical strokes are heavy except those forming the letters *M*, *N*, and *U*. (2) All horizontal strokes are light. (3) The serif extends about one unit on either side of the body of the stem. (4) The width of the heavy strokes may vary from one-eighth to one-sixth of the height of the letter.

Roman letters may be drawn either extended or compressed, depending upon the area to be covered or the space restrictions determined by other lettering, such as on maps. If a draftsman using the Roman-style letter would have his work look professional, he must pay particular attention to detail. Care must be taken to keep the proportions of a letter appearing more than once in a name or title identical. Most persons experienced at drawing should have little difficulty with these letters, if they follow carefully the details and proportions given in Fig. 5.48.

5.45. Problems. It should be noted that while these exercises are offered for the purpose of giving the student practice in letter forms and word composition, they also contain statements of important principles of drawing, shop notes, and titles with which every engineering draftsman should be familiar. Each lettering exercise should be submitted to the instructor for severe criticism before the student proceeds to the next. Sec. 5.2 should be reread before starting the first exercise.

TYPE 1 ABCDEFGHIJKLMNOP
QRSTUVWXYZ&
1234567890 $\frac{1}{2}$ $\frac{3}{4}$ $\frac{5}{8}$ $\frac{7}{16}$
TO BE USED FOR MAIN TITLES
& DRAWING NUMBERS

TYPE 2 ABCDEFGHIJKLMNOPQR
STUVWXYZ&
1234567890 $\frac{13}{64}$ $\frac{5}{8}$ $\frac{1}{2}$
TO BE USED FOR SUB-TITLES

TYPE 3 ABCDEFGHIJKLMNOPQRSTUVWXYZ&
1234567890 $\frac{1}{2}$ $\frac{3}{4}$ $\frac{5}{8}$ $\frac{7}{16}$
FOR HEADINGS AND PROMINENT NOTES

TYPE 4 ABCDEFGHIJKLMNOPQRSTUVWXYZ&
1234567890 $\frac{1}{2}$ $\frac{1}{4}$ $\frac{3}{8}$ $\frac{5}{16}$ $\frac{7}{32}$ $\frac{1}{8}$
FOR BILLS OF MATERIAL, DIMENSIONS & GENERAL NOTES

TYPE 5
OPTIONAL TYPE SAME AS TYPE 4 BUT USING TYPE 3 FOR FIRST LETTER OF PRINCIPAL WORDS. MAY BE USED FOR SUB-TITLES & NOTES ON THE BODY OF DRAWINGS.

TYPE 6 abcdefghijklmnopqrstuvwxyz
Type 6 may be used in place of
Type 4 with capitals of Type 3,
for Bills of Material and Notes
on Body of Drawing.

Fig. 5.49. Lettering—American Standard (inclined).

1. Letter the statement given in Fig. 5.50 in $\frac{5}{32}''$ capital letters using an appropriate pencil that is suited to the type of paper being used and one that will produce uniform opaque lines. The necessary guide lines should be drawn with a hard pencil.

2–3. Letter the statements given in Figs. 5.51–5.52 in $\frac{1}{8}''$ capital letters using an appropriate pencil that is suited to the type of paper being used and one that will produce uniform opaque lines. The necessary guide lines should be drawn with a hard pencil.

4. Letter the statement given in Fig. 5.53 in $\frac{5}{32}''$ capital letters using an appropriate pencil that is suited to the type of paper being used and one that will produce uniform opaque lines. The necessary guide lines should be drawn with a hard pencil.

POOR LETTERING DETRACTS FROM THE APPEARANCE OF A DRAWING

Fig. 5.50.

IN LEARNING TO LETTER CERTAIN DEFINITE RULES OF FORM & DESIGN MUST BE OBSERVED

Fig. 5.51.

WHEN LETTERING WITH INK, THE INK SHOULD BE WELL ABOVE THE TIP OF THE POINT

Fig. 5.52.

5–6. Letter the statements given in Figs. 5.54–5.55 in $\frac{1}{8}''$ capital letters using an appropriate pencil that is suited to the type of paper being used and one that will produce uniform opaque lines. The necessary guide lines should be drawn with a hard pencil. (See Fig. 5.8.)

#26 (.1470) DRILL AND REAM FOR #1 × 1 TAPER PIN WITH PC #41 IN POSITION

Fig. 5.53.

S.A.E. 1020 - COLD DRAWN STEEL BAR
1-14NF-3 1-8NC-2 1-5 SQUARE
BREAK ALL SHARP CORNERS UNLESS OTHERWISE SPECIFIED

Fig. 5.54.

$\frac{5}{16}$ DRILL-$\frac{3}{8}$-16NC-2 $\frac{21}{32}$ DRILL - C'BORE $\frac{29}{32}$D × $\frac{7}{8}$ DEEP -2 HOLES

Fig. 5.55.

7–16. Letter the following statements in $\frac{1}{8}''$ capital letters using an appropriate pencil that is suited to the type of paper being used and one that will produce uniform opaque lines. The necessary guide lines should be drawn with a hard pencil.

(7) A GOOD STUDENT REALIZES THE IMPORTANCE OF NEAT AND ATTRACTIVE LETTERING.

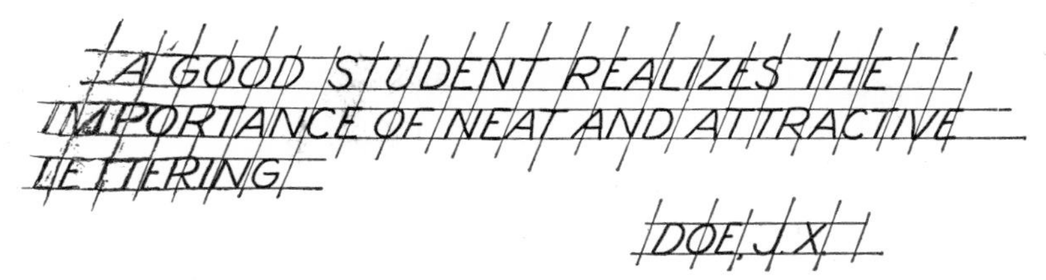

Fig. 5.56.

(8) THE CIRCUMFERENCE OF A CIRCLE MAY BE DIVIDED INTO TWENTY-FOUR EQUAL ARCS USING ONLY A T-SQUARE IN COMBINATION WITH THE 30–60° AND 45° TRIANGLES.

(9) A TRUE ELLIPSE MAY BE CONSTRUCTED BY THE TRAMMEL METHOD.

(10) THE POSITION OF THE VIEWS OF AN ORTHOGRAPHIC DRAWING MUST BE IN STRICT ACCORDANCE WITH THE UNIVERSALLY RECOGNIZED ARRANGEMENT ILLUSTRATED IN FIG. 7.4.

(11) THE VIEWS OF AN ORTHOGRAPHIC DRAWING SHOULD SHOW THE THREE DIMENSIONS, LENGTH, BREADTH, AND THICKNESS.

(12) AN INVISIBLE LINE SHOULD START WITH A SPACE WHEN IT FORMS AN EXTENSION OF A SOLID LINE.

(13) THE FRONT VIEW OF AN ORTHOGRAPHIC DRAWING SHOULD BE THE VIEW THAT SHOWS THE CHARACTERISTIC SHAPE OF THE OBJECT.

(14) AN AUXILIARY VIEW SHOWS THE TRUE SIZE AND SHAPE OF AN INCLINED SURFACE.

(15) A SECTIONAL VIEW SHOWS THE INTERIOR CONSTRUCTION OF AN OBJECT.

(16) #404 WOODRUFF KEY.

DRILL AND REAM FOR #2 TAPER PIN WITH PC#10 IN POSITION.

17–21. Using a hard pencil, draw two or more sets of horizontal and inclined guide lines for $\frac{5}{32}''$ letters, then execute directly with India ink the following exercises in lower-case letters:

(17) "The front and top views are always in line vertically."

(18) "The front and side views are in line horizontally."

(19) "The depth of the top view is the same as the depth of the side view."

(20) "If a line is perpendicular to a plane of projection, its projection will be a point."

(21) "If a line is parallel to a plane of projection, its projection on the plane is exactly the same length as the true length of the line."

22–26. Draw two or more sets of both horizontal and inclined guide lines, and letter the following series of words, whole numbers, and fractions, once in pencil and once in India ink. If a Braddock Lettering triangle is available, draw the seven guide lines shown in Fig. 5.8.

(22) $1\frac{1}{2}$, $3\frac{3}{4}$, $2\frac{7}{8}$, $1\frac{9}{16}$, $9\frac{17}{32}$, $4\frac{5}{8}$, $9\frac{13}{32}$, $7\frac{13}{64}$, $8\frac{1}{2}$, $\frac{11}{16}$, $5\frac{3}{8}$.

(23) $\frac{1}{2}'' \times 2\frac{3}{4}''$ HEX. HD. CAP SCREW, $\frac{3}{8} \times 1\frac{1}{4}$ UNC HEX. HD. BOLT & HEX. NUT.

(24) $\frac{3}{16}$ DRILL—$\frac{3}{8}$ DEEP, $\frac{1}{4}$ DRILL—4 HOLES, $\frac{1}{8} \times 45°$ CHAMFER.

(25) $\frac{1}{8}$ AM. STD. PIPE TAP, $\frac{1}{2}$—13 UNC—2B.

(26) 2 $\angle s$ $2\frac{1}{2} \times 2\frac{1}{2} \times \frac{1}{4} \times 8'$–$4''$, 10″ I 30#, 24″ WF74#.

27. Draw horizontal and inclined guide lines and letter the following detail titles. Use $\frac{5}{32}''$ capitals for the part names and $\frac{1}{8}''$ capitals for the remainder of the titles.

BASE		BUSHING		SPINDLE	
C.I.	1 REQ'D	BRO.	1 REQ'D	C.R.S.	1 REQ'D

28. Letter the following map title in Modern Roman. The letters of the first and third lines are to be $\frac{1}{2}''$ high, and those of the second line, which give the name of the county, are to be $\frac{3}{4}''$ high. Draw all necessary guide lines.

MAP OF

TIPPECANOE COUNTY

INDIANA

6 THE THEORY OF PROJECTION

6.1. Since engineering draftsmen are confronted with the task of recording the shapes and sizes of three-dimensional objects on the plane of a sheet of drawing paper, it is obvious that they must follow generally recognized procedures if their finished drawings are to be read easily. Size description and shape description are of equal importance, but, in order to simplify the presentation of the fundamentals underlying the making of working drawings, this chapter is concerned entirely with the methods commonly employed in describing shape. A later chapter will discuss size description.

Each of the different methods, axonometric, oblique, and orthographic, is based on some form of projection. The theory governing a method should be understood thoroughly before it is used to produce a drawing.

6.2. Perspective (scenographic) projection. In perspective projection, the projecting lines (visual rays) converge to a point, as shown in Fig. 6.1. The representation upon the transparent picture plane may be

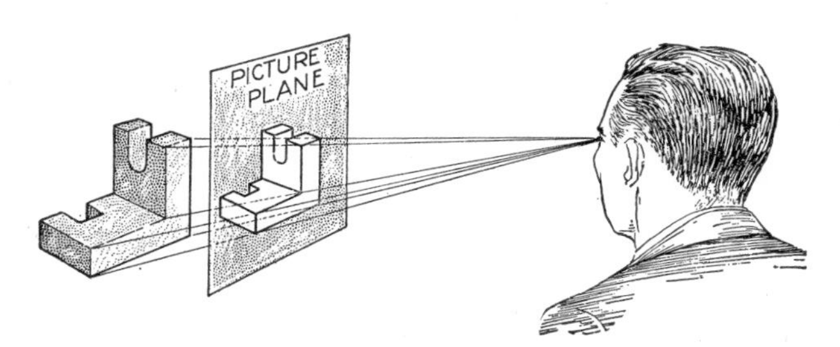

Fig. 6.1. Perspective projection.

considered the view that would be seen by one eye located at a definite point in space. The picture is established on the imaginary plane by the piercing points of the projecting lines from the eye to the object. The size of the view depends upon the distance from the observer to the plane and the distance from the plane to the object.

Perspective projection is not suitable for working drawings because a perspective view does not reveal exact size and shape. It is used mainly by architects in preparing preliminary sketches and display drawings of proposed houses and buildings.

6.3. Orthographic projection (parallel projection). If the observer in Fig. 6.1 moves straight back from the picture plane until he is an infinite distance from it, the projecting lines (projectors) from the eye to the object become parallel to each other and perpendicular to the picture plane. The resulting projection (see Fig. 6.2) will then be the same shape and size as the front surface of the object. From a practical viewpoint, the projection may be thought of as being formed by perpendicular projectors extended from the object to the plane. The view is called an orthographic projection.

Since the view shown in Fig. 6.2 does not reveal the thickness of the object, one or more additional projections (see Fig. 6.3) are necessary to

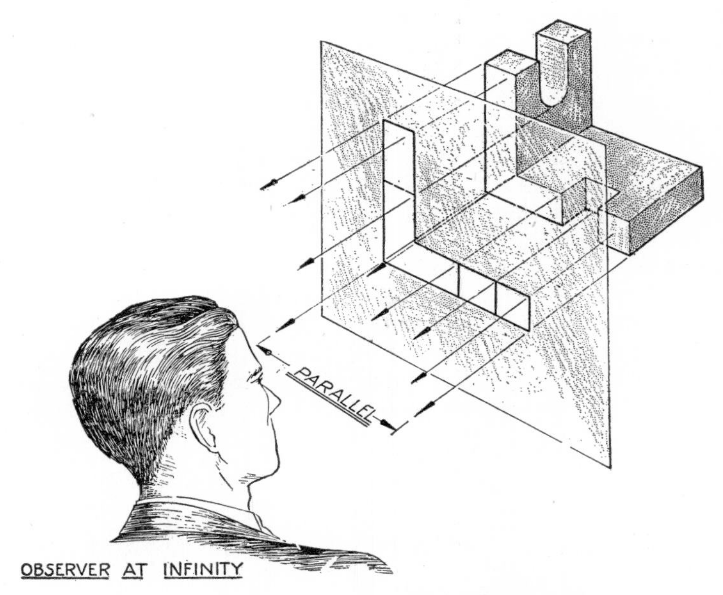

Fig. 6.2. Orthographic projection.

complete the description. Two projections are usually sufficient to describe simple objects, but three or more are necessary for complicated ones.

The picture planes are customarily called the principal or co-ordinate planes of projection, and the perpendiculars, projectors. In engineering drawing, the planes are usually arranged as shown in Fig. 6.4. Since all three are mutually perpendicular, they are called the horizontal, frontal, and profile co-ordinate planes. To maintain this mutual relationship when laying out views, it is the usual practice to consider the frontal plane as lying in the plane of the paper and the horizontal and profile planes as being revolved into position. Note in Fig. 6.5 the manner in which the planes are revolved. This theoretical treatment of the co-ordinate planes establishes an absolute relationship between the views. Visualizing an object would be considerably more difficult than it is, if it were not for this

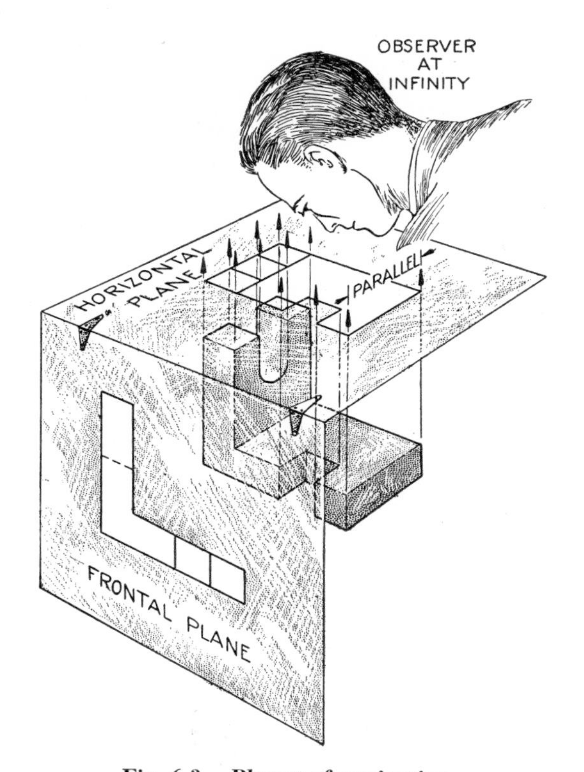

Fig. 6.3. Planes of projection.

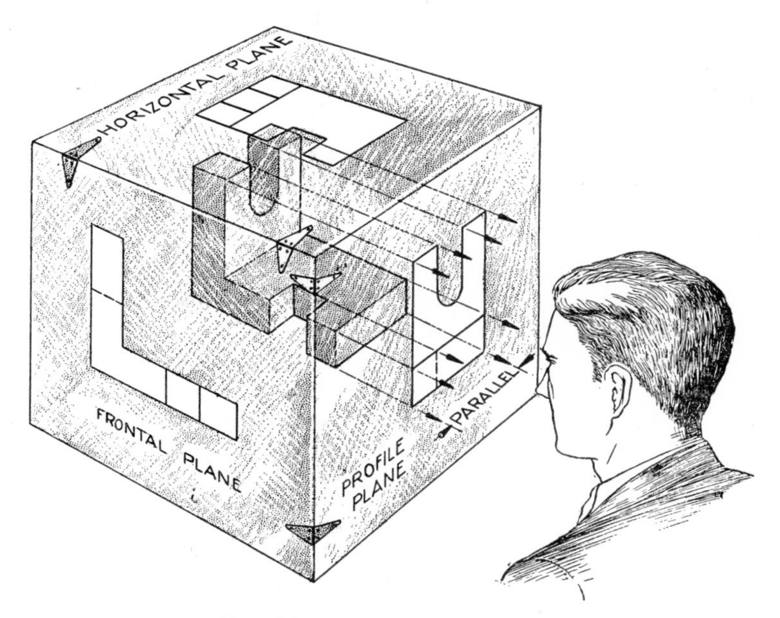

Fig. 6.4. Planes of projection.

fixed relationship, for it would be impossible to determine quickly the direction of sight for a particular view.

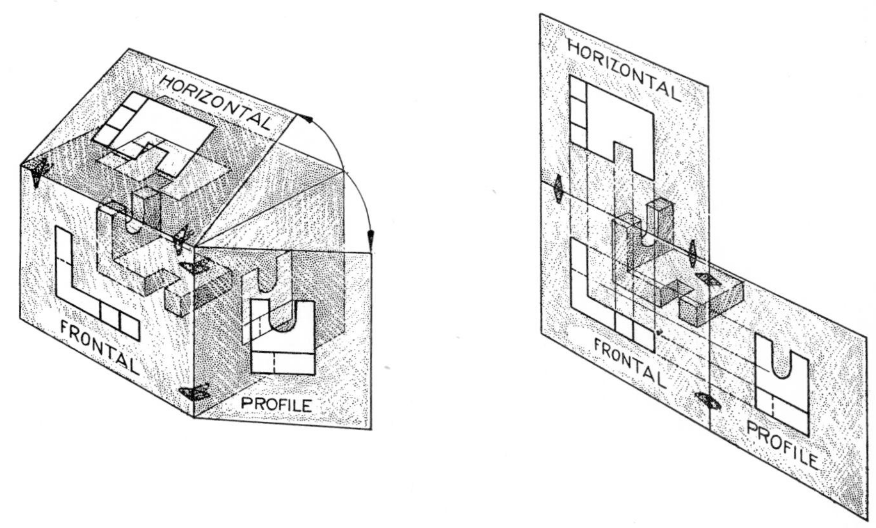

Fig. 6.5. The revolution of the planes of projection.

Fig. 6.6. The planes resolved into the plane of the paper.

6.4. One-plane projection. If the object is turned and then tilted so that three faces are inclined to the plane of projection, the resulting projection is a special type of orthographic projection known as axono-

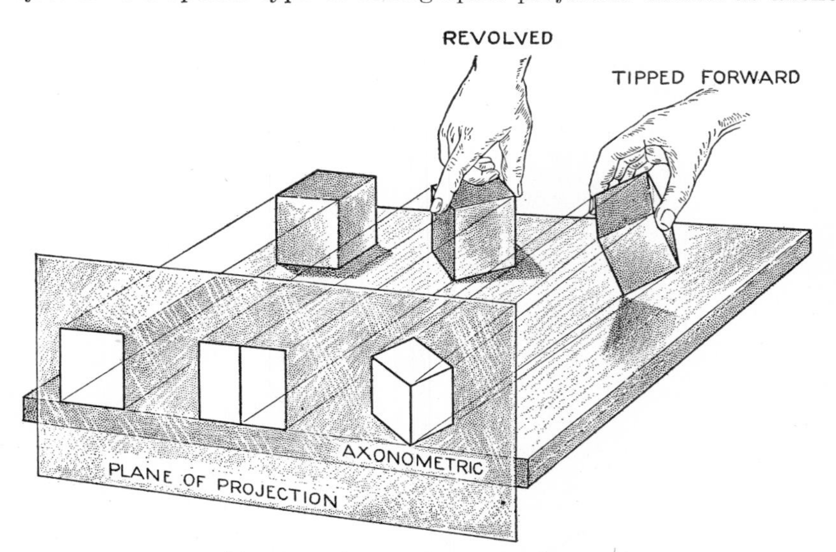

Fig. 6.7. Axonometric projection.

metric projection. Fig. 6.7 illustrates an axonometric projection of a cube. Note that the projectors from the object to the plane are perpendicular to the plane. The three recognized subdivisions of axonometric projection, namely, isometric, dimetric, and trimetric, are explained in Chapter 14.

Another form of one-plane projection is known as oblique projection. This form differs from orthographic projection in that, although one face is imagined to be parallel to the plane of projection, the projectors make an

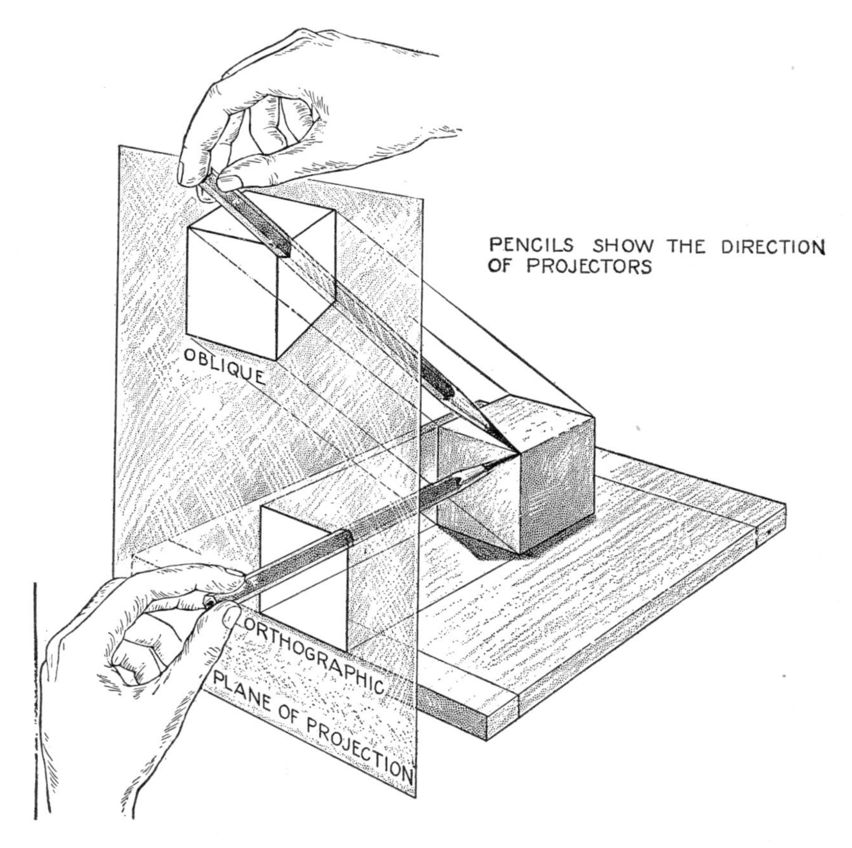

Fig. 6.8. Oblique projection.

angle other than 90° with it (Fig. 6.8). Obviously an infinite number of different views are possible, depending upon the angle the parallel projectors make with the plane of projection (picture plane). The various subdivisions are cavalier projection, cabinet projection, and clinographic projection (Chapter 14).

Axonometric projection, oblique projection, and perspective projection may all be classed together as one-plane pictorial projection.

6.5. First- and third-angle projection. If the horizontal and frontal planes are assumed to extend indefinitely on one side of the profile plane, four dihedral angles are formed and are designated as the *first, second, third,* and *fourth* angles (see Fig. 6.9). The lines of intersection of these planes are called co-ordinate axes. Their point of intersection is called the origin. In this discussion of first- and third-angle projection, it should be remembered that no matter in which angle the object is placed, the observer views it from in front of the frontal plane and from above the

Fig. 6.9. Planes of projection.

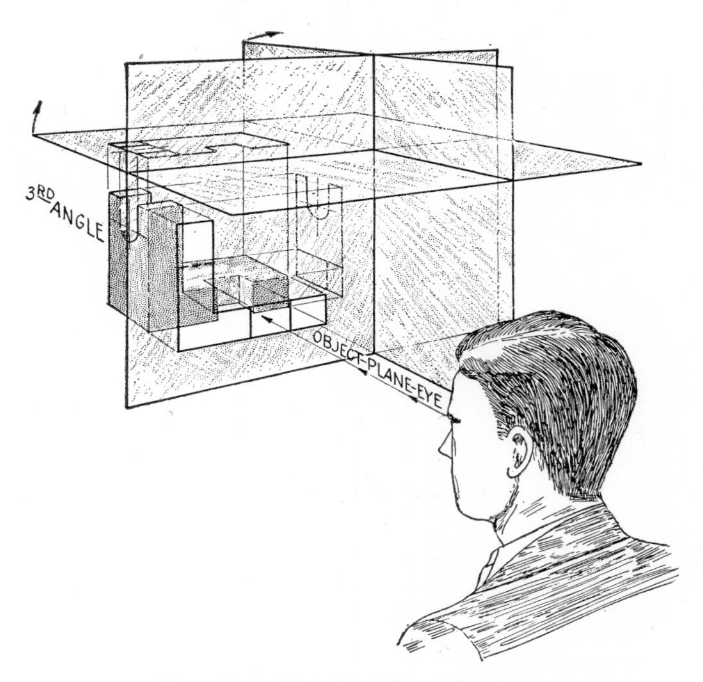

Fig. 6.10. Third-angle projection.

horizontal plane. To avoid misunderstandings, the directions for revolving the horizontal and profile planes into the frontal plane are illustrated in Fig. 6.10. Note that the first and third quadrants are "opened" and the second and fourth are "closed" in revolving the horizontal plane into the frontal plane.

If an object, such as the one shown in Fig. 6.10, is placed so that its main faces are parallel to the principal planes, the respective projection on each plane will show the true size and shape of all surfaces that are parallel to that principal plane. Theoretically, the object could have been shown in any one of the four quadrants. It has been placed in the third quadrant simply because engineering custom in the United States dictates the use of the third. This quadrant is used because the views, when revolved into the frontal plane, are in their natural positions. That is: the top view appears *above* the front view, as is expected, and the profile view, showing the *right side*, falls on the *right* of the front view.

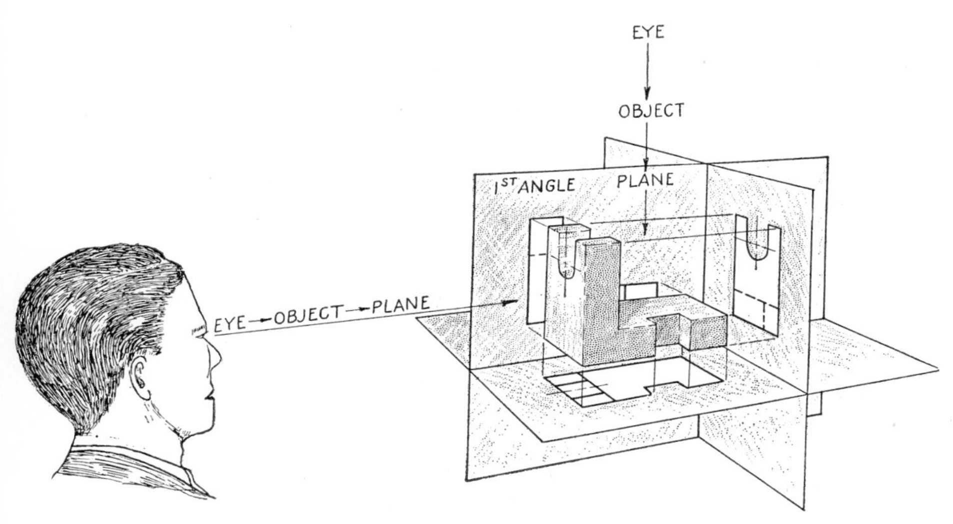

Fig. 6.11. First-angle projection.

In most foreign countries, "first-angle projection" is used for working drawings. (Study Fig. 6.11.) Observe that the top view is projected upon the horizontal plane and the front view upon the frontal plane. For this reason, the top view falls below the front view when the co-ordinate planes are revolved.

In this country, the use of first-angle projection for working drawings was abandoned by engineering draftsmen some fifty years ago, although it is still used by architects and structural designers.

The different systems of projection may be conveniently classified as follows:

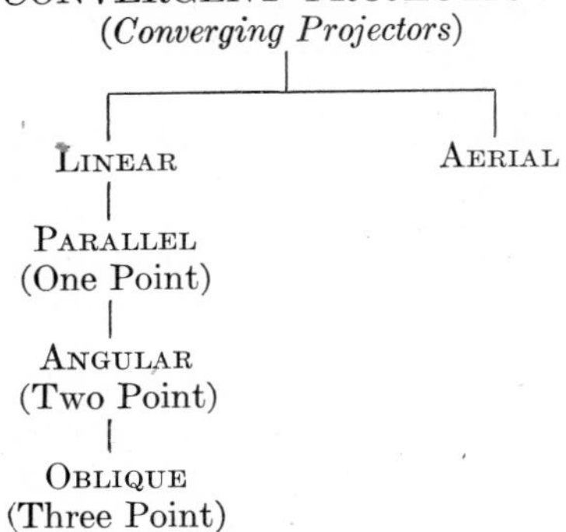
CONVERGENT PROJECTION
(Converging Projectors)
LINEAR
AERIAL
PARALLEL
(One Point)
ANGULAR
(Two Point)
OBLIQUE
(Three Point)

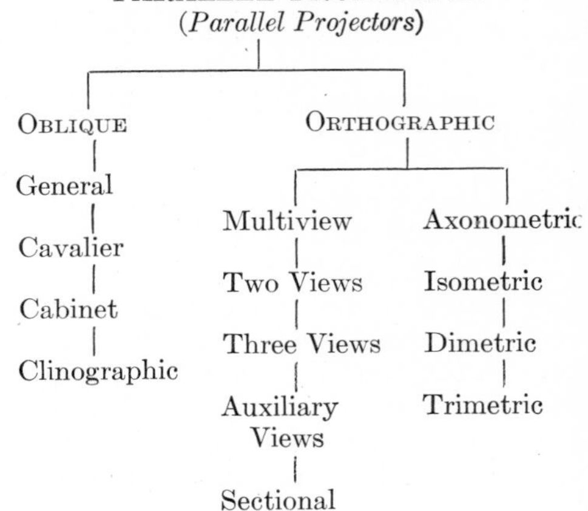
PARALLEL PROJECTION
(Parallel Projectors)
OBLIQUE
ORTHOGRAPHIC
General
Cavalier
Cabinet
Clinographic
Multiview
Axonometric
Two Views
Three Views
Auxiliary Views
Sectional Views
Isometric
Dimetric
Trimetric

7 MULTIVIEW DRAWING

7.1. Industrial draftsmen use the orthographic system of projection for describing the shape of machine parts and structures. Practical application of this method of describing an object results in a drawing consisting of a number of systematically arranged views that reproduce the object's exact shape. It was explained in the preceding chapter, Sec. 6.3, that a set of views showing the object from different positions is always taken.

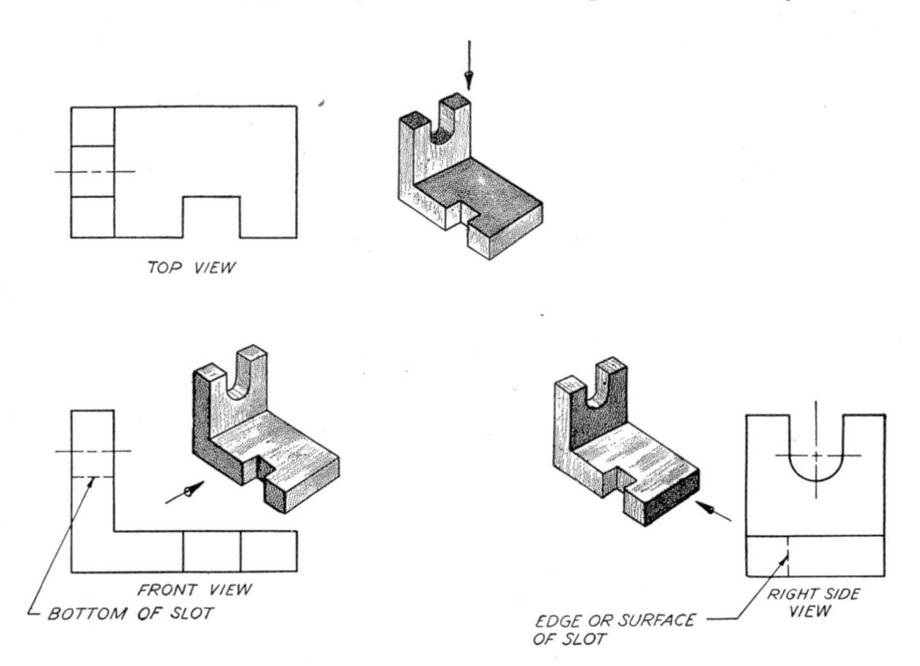

Fig. 7.1. Three views of an object.

The position of these views, in strict accordance with a universally recognized arrangement, must show the three dimensions, length, height, and depth. Although three views (Fig. 7.1) are usually required to describe an ordinary object, only two may be needed for a particularly simple one. A very complicated object may require four or more views. A view projected upon an auxiliary plane also may be desirable (see Chapter 8)

Such a view often makes possible the elimination of one of the principal views. Therefore, it is up to the draftsman to determine the number and type of views needed to produce a satisfactory drawing. He will soon develop a knack for this, if he bears in mind that the number of views required depends entirely upon the complexity of the shape to be described.

7.2. Definition. Multiview (multiplaner) projection is a method by means of which the exact shape of an object can be represented by two or more separate views produced upon projection planes that are usually at right angles to each other.

7.3. Methods of obtaining the views. The views of an object may be obtained by either of two methods:

(1) The natural method.

(2) The glass box method.

Since the resulting views will be the same in either case, the beginner should adopt the method he finds the easiest to understand. Both methods are explained here in detail.

7.4. The natural method. This method is commonly used by experienced commercial draftsmen. Each of the necessary views is obtained

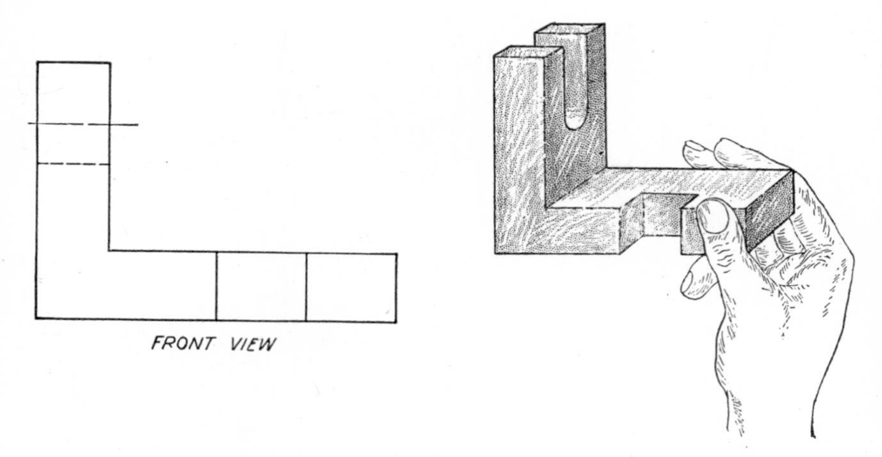

Fig. 7.2. Viewing an object (natural method).

looking directly at the particular side of the object the view is to represent. The front view in Fig. 7.2 represents the object as seen by an imaginary observer stationed directly in front of it at an infinite distance away.

Fig. 7.3 shows three of the principal views of an object, the front, top, and side views. They were obtained by looking directly at the front, top, and right side, respectively. In the application of this method, some draftsmen consider the position of the object as fixed and the position of the observer as shifted for each view; others find it easier to consider the observer's position as fixed and the position of the object as changed (Fig. 7.3) for each view. Regardless of which procedure is followed, the top

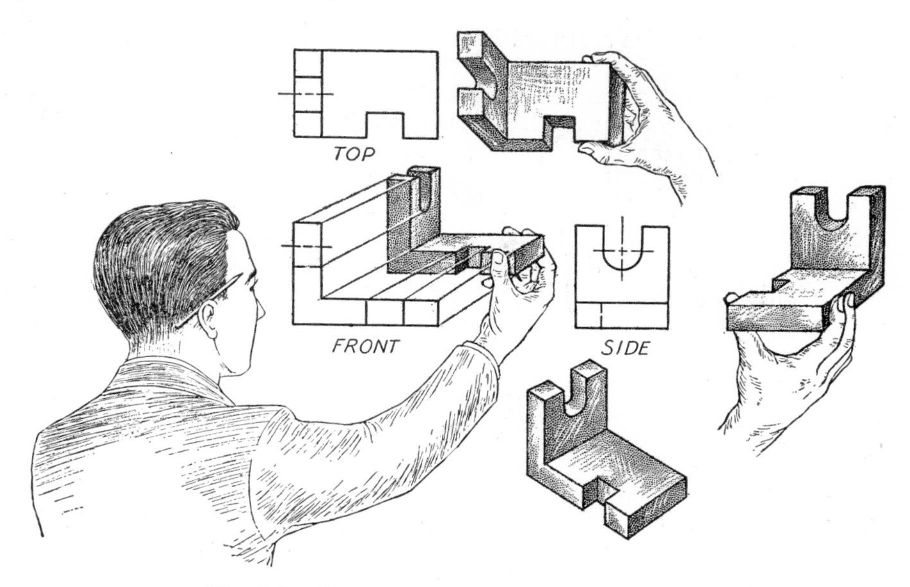

Fig. 7.3. Obtaining three views of an object.

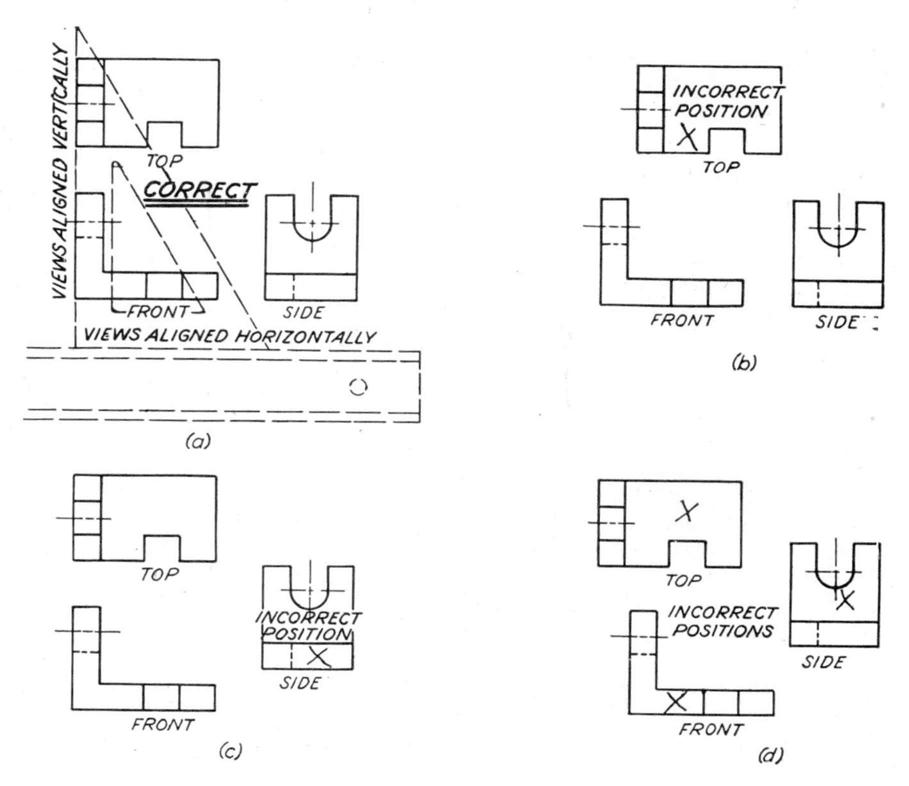

Fig. 7.4. Position of views.

and side views must be arranged in their natural positions relative to the front view.

Fig. 7.4 illustrates the natural relationship of views. Note that the top view is *vertically above* the front view, and the side view is *horizontally in line with* the front view. In both of these views the *front of the block is toward the front view.*

7.5. The "glass box" method. An imaginary "glass box" is used widely by drawing instructors to explain the arrangement of orthographic views. An explanation of this scheme can be best made by reviewing the use of planes of projection (Chapter 6). It may be considered that planes

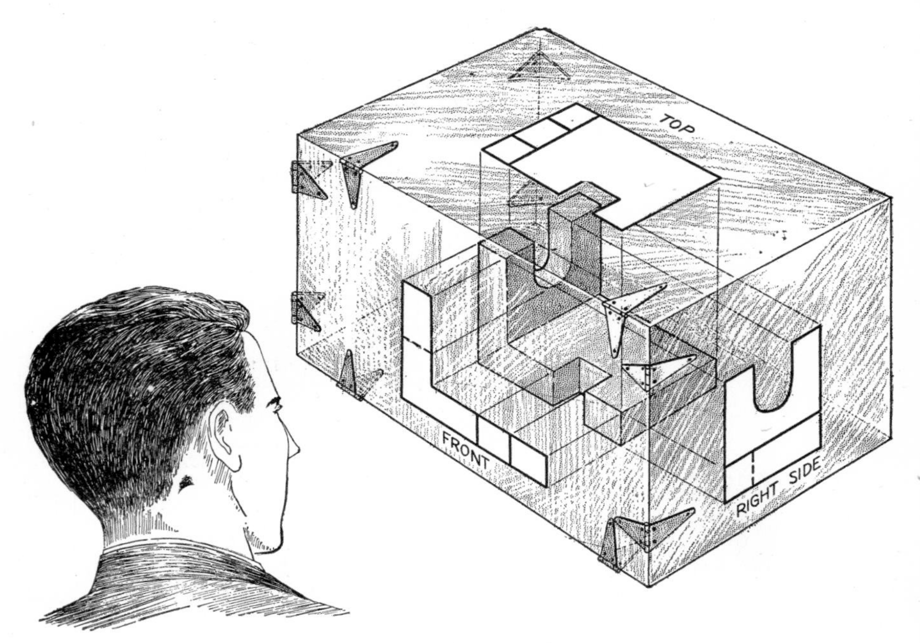

Fig. 7.5. The glass box.

of projection placed parallel to the six faces of an object form an enclosing "glass box" (see Fig. 7.5). The observer views the enclosed object from the outside. The views are obtained by running projectors from points on the object to the planes. This procedure is in accordance with the theory of orthographic projection explained in Sec. 6.3, as well as the definition in Sec. 7.2. The front, top, and right side of the box represent the H (horizontal), F (frontal), and P (profile) projection planes.

Since the projections on the sides of the three-dimensional transparent box are to appear on a sheet of drawing paper, it must be assumed that the box is hinged (see Fig. 7.6) so that, when it is opened outward into the plane of the paper, the planes assume the positions illustrated in Figs. 7.6 and 7.7. Note that all of the planes, except the back one, are hinged to the frontal plane. In accordance with this universally recognized assumption, the top projection must take a position directly above the front pro-

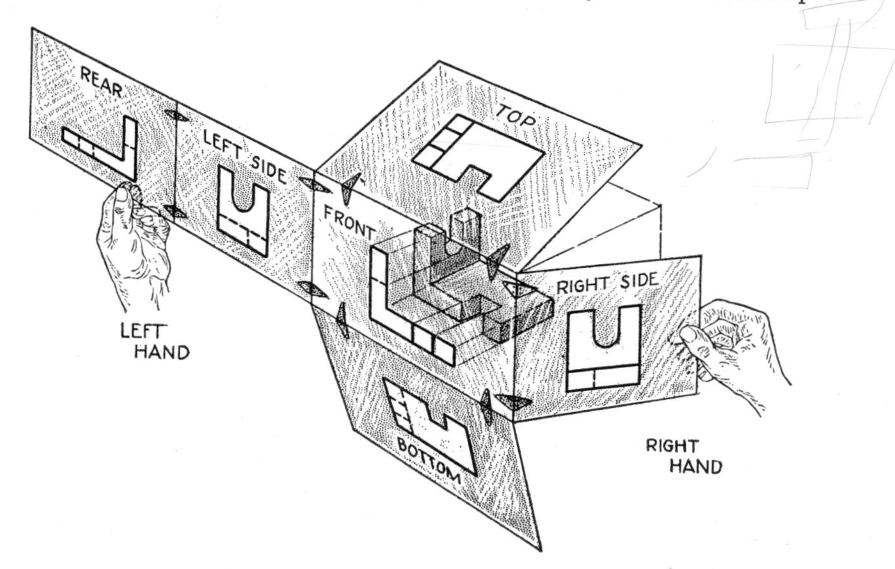

Fig. 7.6. Opening the glass box.

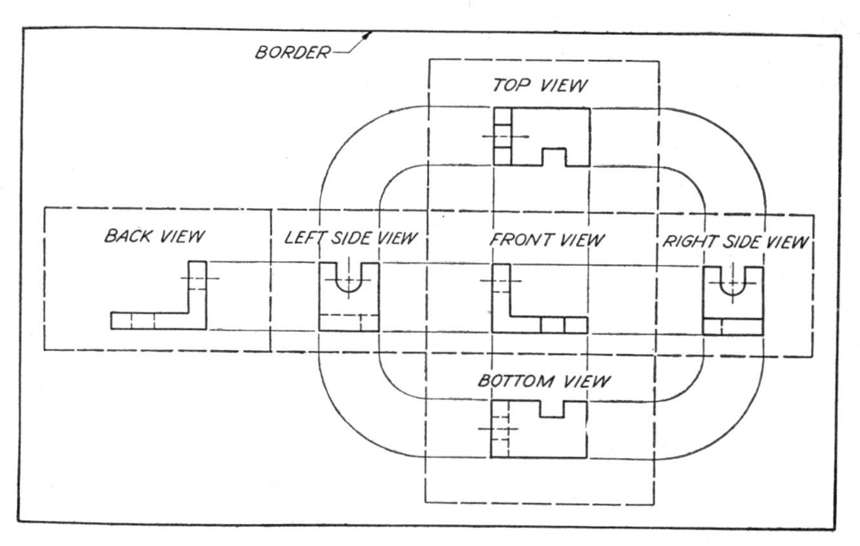

Fig. 7.7. Six views of an object on a sheet of drawing paper.

jection, and the right side projection must lie horizontally to the right of the front projection. To identify the separate projections, draftsmen call the one on the frontal plane the *front view* or *front elevation*, the one on the horizontal plane the *top view* or *plan*, and the one on the side or profile plane the *side view*, *side elevation*, or *end view*. Fig. 7.7 shows the six views of the same object as they would appear on a sheet of drawing paper. Ordinarily, only three of these views are necessary (front, top, and right side). A bottom or rear view will be required in comparatively few cases.

7.6. The "second position." Sometimes, especially in the case of a broad flat object, it is desirable to hinge the sides of the box to the hori-

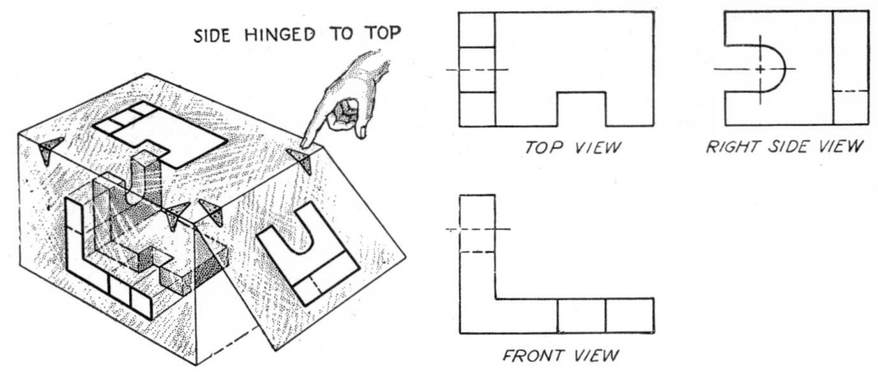

Fig. 7.8. The "second position" for the side view.

zontal plane so that the side view will fall to the right of the top view, as illustrated in Fig. 7.8. This arrangement conserves space on the paper and gives the views better balance.

7.7. The principles of multiview drawing. The following principles should be studied carefully and understood thoroughly before any attempt is made to prepare an orthographic drawing.

1. The front and top views are *always* in line vertically.

2. The front and side views are in line horizontally, except when the second position is used.

3. The front of the object in the top view faces the front view (Fig. 7.10).

4. The front of the object in the side view faces the front view (Fig. 7.10).

5. The depth of the top view is the same as the depth of the side view (or views).

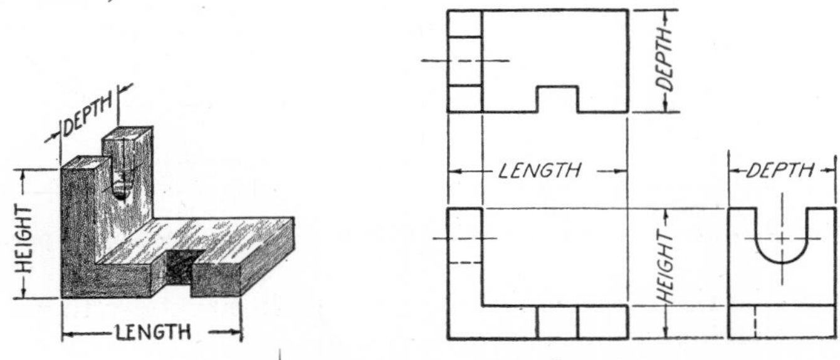

Fig. 7.9. View terminology.

6. The length of the top view is the same as the length of the front view.

7. The height of the side view is the same as the height of the front view.

8. If a line is parallel to a plane of projection, its projection on the plane is exactly the same length as the true length of the line (Fig. 7.11*a*, *b*, *c*).

9. If a line is inclined to a plane of projection, its projection on the plane will be shorter than the true length of the line (Fig. 7.11*d*).

10. If a line is perpendicular to a plane of projection, its projection will be a point.

11. If a surface is parallel to a plane of projection, its projection on the plane will show its true size and shape.

12. If a surface is inclined to a plane of projection, its projection on the plane will be foreshortened.

13. If a surface is perpendicular to a plane of projection, its projection on the plane will be a line.

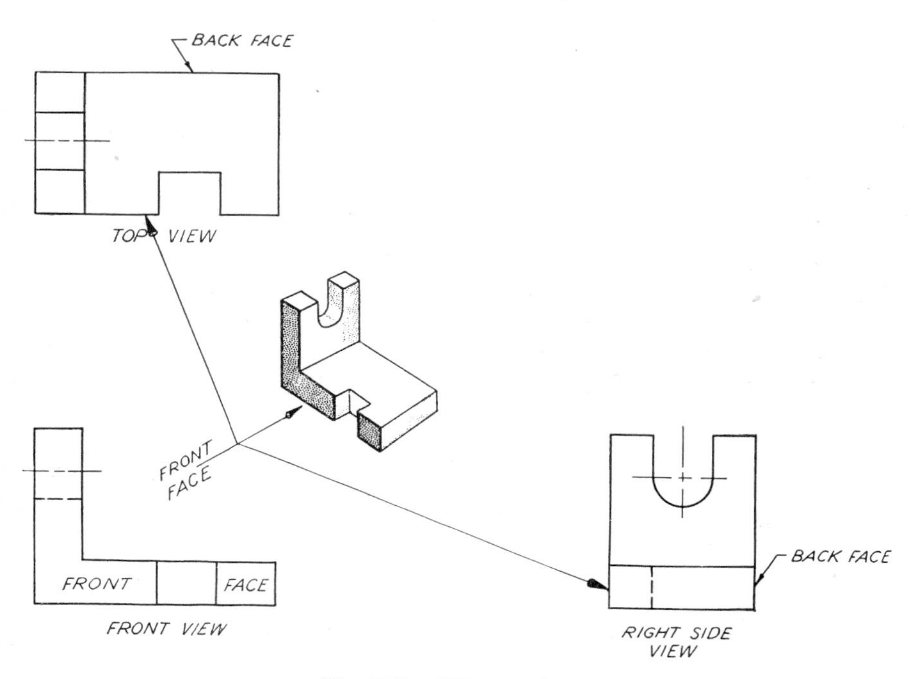

Fig. 7.10. View analysis.

The student should study Fig. 7.11 and attempt to visualize the space position of each of the given lines. It is very necessary both in preparing and reading graphical representations to recognize the position of a point, line, or plane and to know whether the projection of a line is true length or foreshortened or whether the projection of a plane shows the true size and

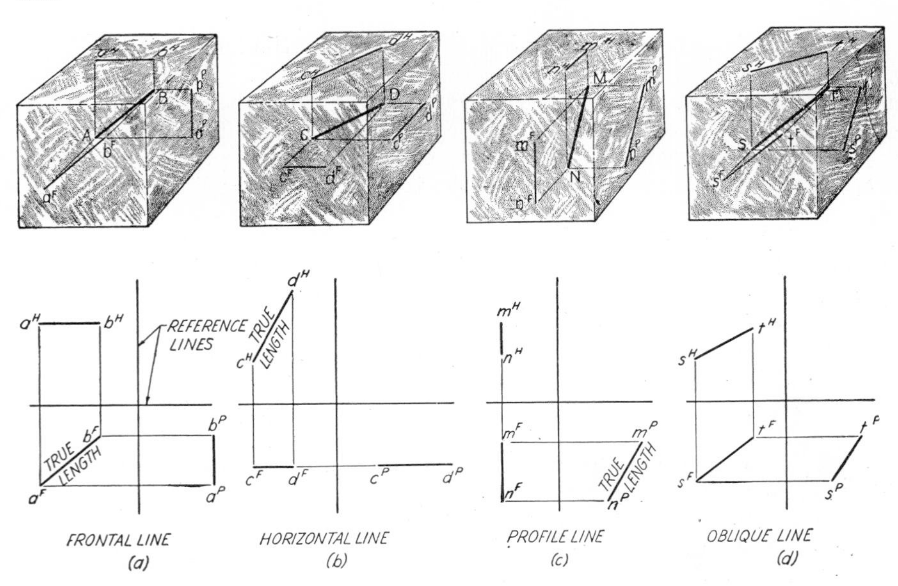

Fig. 7.11. Some typical line positions.

shape. The indicated reference lines may be thought of as representing the edges of the glass boxes shown. The projections of a line are identified as being on either a frontal, horizontal, or profile plane by the use of the letters F, H, or P with the lower-case letters that identify the end points of the line. For example, in Fig. 7.11(a), $a^{H}b^{H}$ is the horizontal projection of line AB, $a^{F}b^{F}$ is the frontal projection, and $a^{P}b^{P}$ is the profile projection.

7.8. Relationship of views. Following a recognized order in the relationship of views prevents confusion in reading drawings, just as fol-

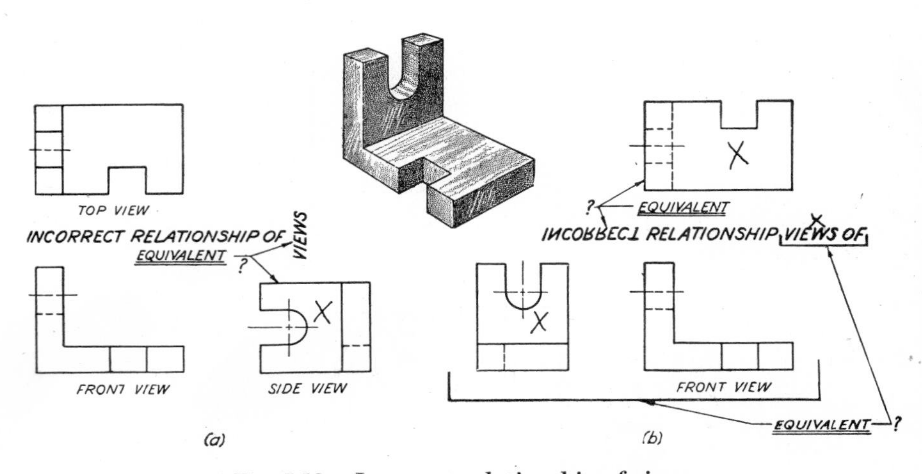

Fig. 7.12. Incorrect relationship of views.

lowing an expected order of words in statements leads to faster reading and interpretation. Fig. 7.12 illustrates this fact in a comparative manner. In (*a*), turning a view out of position confuses a trained person momentarily to the same extent as the turning of the word *views* confuses the reader of the associated statement. Locating views in the wrong relationship to the front view, such as drawing a bottom view above the front view (see *b*), and placing a right-side view to the left of the front view is equivalent to lettering a word of a statement upside-down and to having words out of an expected order. The following principles of the relationship of views should be carefully read and understood.

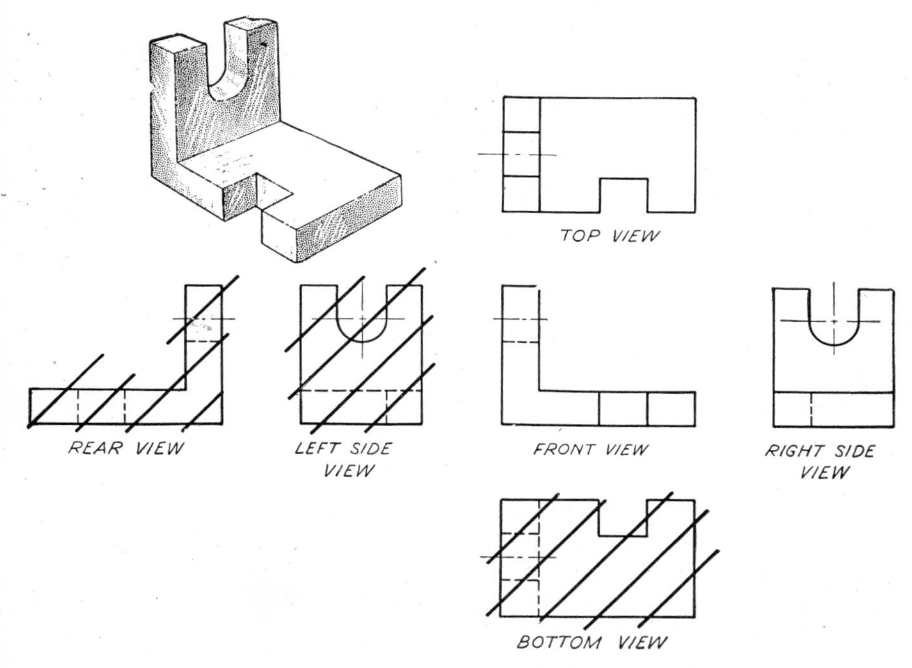

Fig. 7.13. Superfluous views.

1. A view taken from above is a top view and *must* be drawn above the front view and in line with it vertically.
2. A view taken from the right, in relation to the selected front, is a right-side view and *must* be drawn to the right of the front view and in line with it horizontally.
3. A view taken from the left is a left-side view and *must* be drawn to the left of the front view.
4. A view taken from below is a bottom view and *must* appear below the front view.

7.9. The selection of views. Careful study should be given to the outline of an object before the views are selected (Fig. 7.14). Otherwise there is no assurance that the object will be described completely from the reader's viewpoint (Fig. 7.15). Only those views that are necessary for a clear and complete description should be selected. Since the repetition

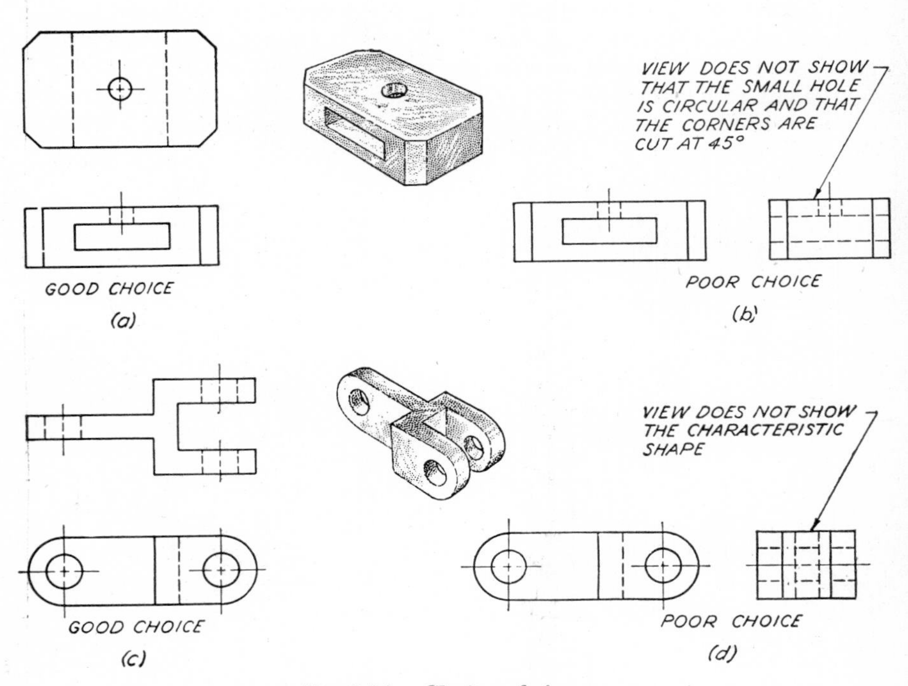

Fig. 7.14. Choice of views.

of information only tends to confuse the reader, superfluous views should be avoided. In Fig. 7.13, six views of a block are shown. Note that three views (front, top, and right side) describe the object fully. The other three views are unnecessary.

Although some objects, such as cylinders, bushings, bolts, and so forth, require only two views (front and side), more complicated pieces may require an auxiliary or sectional view in addition to the ordinary three views.

The space available for arranging the views often governs the choice between the use of a top or side view. The difference between the descriptive values of the two frequently is not great. For example, a draftsman often finds that the views of a long object will have better balance if a top view is used (see Fig. 7.16*a*); while, in the case of a short object (see *b*), the use of a side view may make possible a more pleasing arrangement. It should be remembered that the choice of views for many objects is definitely fixed by the contour alone, and no choice is offered as far as

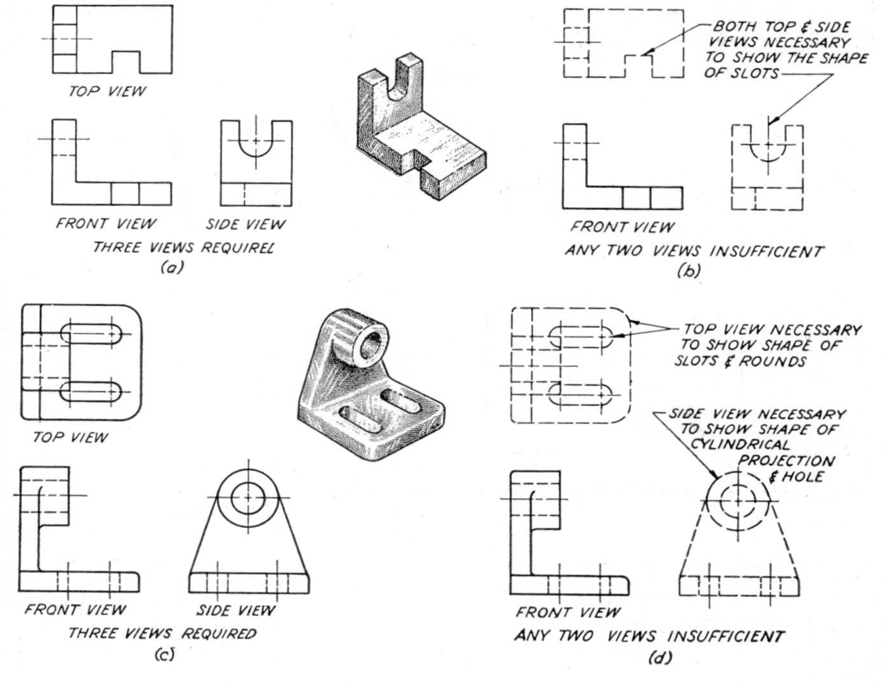

Fig. 7.15. Choice of views.

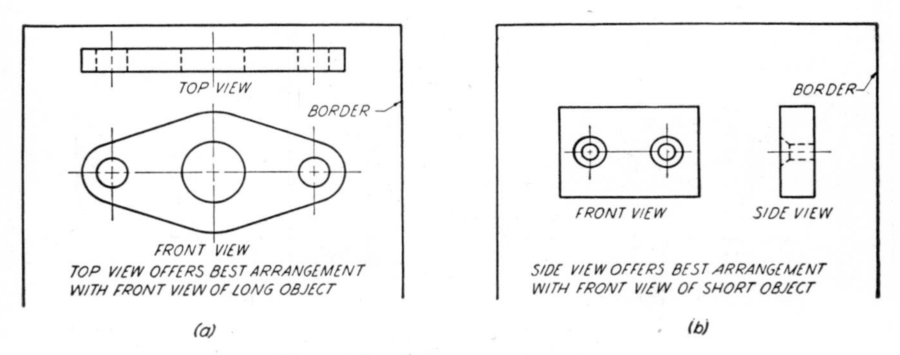

Fig. 7.16. Selection of views.

spacing is concerned. In commercial work, it is more important to have a set of views that describes an object clearly than one that is artistically balanced.

Often there is a choice between two equally important views, such as between a right-side and left-side view (Fig. 7.17) or between a top and bottom view (Fig. 7.18). In such cases, most commercial draftsmen adhere to the following rule: *A right-side view should be used in preference to a left-side view, and a top view in preference to a bottom view.* When this

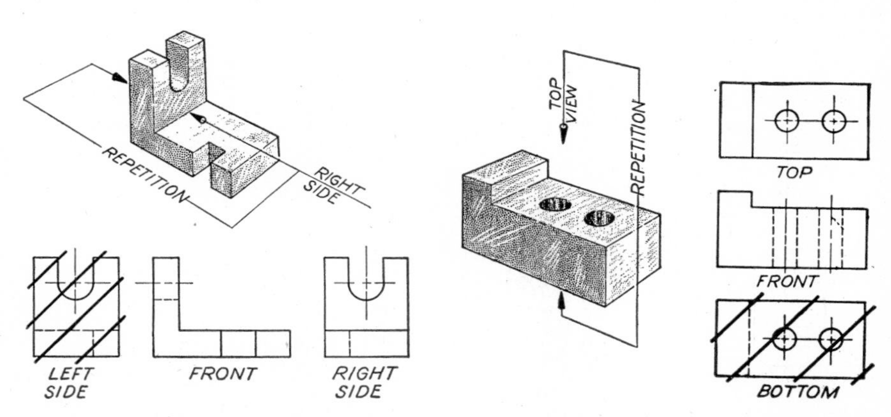

Fig. 7.17. The preferred side view.

Fig. 7.18. The preferred choice of a top view.

rule is applied to irregular objects, the front (contour) view should be drawn so that the most irregular outline is toward the top and right side.

Another rule, one that must be considered in selecting the front view, is as follows: *If possible, place the object so as to obtain the smallest number of hidden lines.*

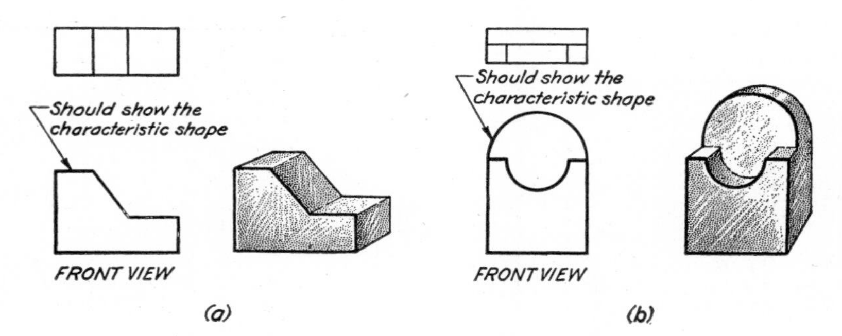

Fig. 7.19. The principal view of an object.

7.10. The principal (front) view. The principal view is the one that shows the characteristic contour of the object. See Fig. 7.19(*a*) and (*b*). Good practice dictates that this be used as the front view on a drawing. It should be clearly understood that the view of the natural front of an object is not always the principal view, because frequently it fails to show the object's characteristic shape. Therefore, another rule to be followed is: *Ordinarily, select the view showing the characteristic contour shape as the front view, regardless of the normal or natural front of the object.*

When an object does have a definite normal position, however, the front view should be in agreement with it. In the case of most machine parts, the front view can assume any convenient position that is consistent with good balance.

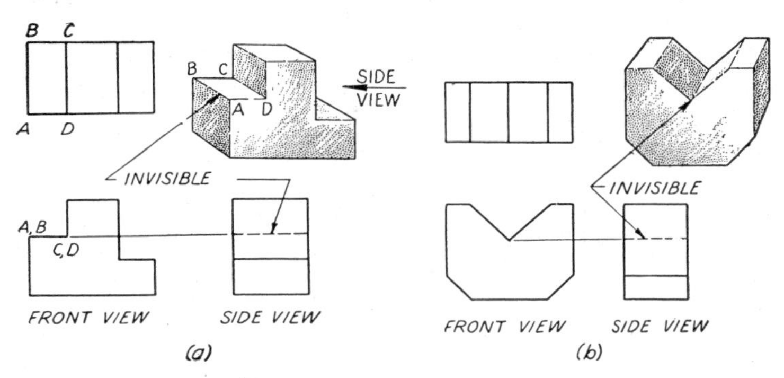

Fig. 7.20. Invisible lines.

7.11. Invisible lines. Dotted lines are used on an external view of an object to represent surfaces and intersections invisible at the point from which the view is taken. In Fig 7.20(a), the dotted line may be considered to represent the edge AB and the line of intersection CD, or it may represent the entire surface $ABCD$. In Fig. 7.20(b), the invisible line represents a line of intersection and not a plane.

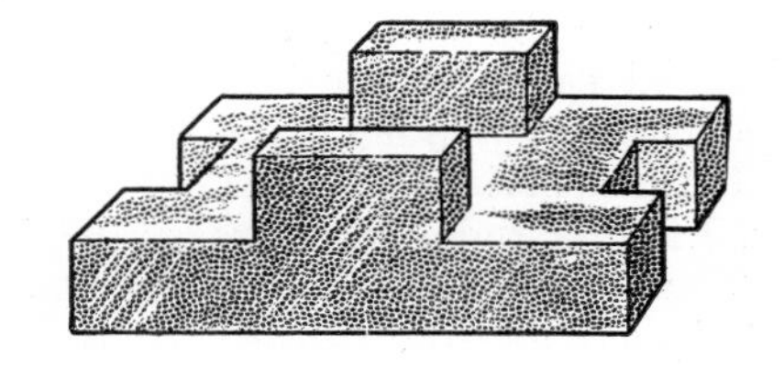

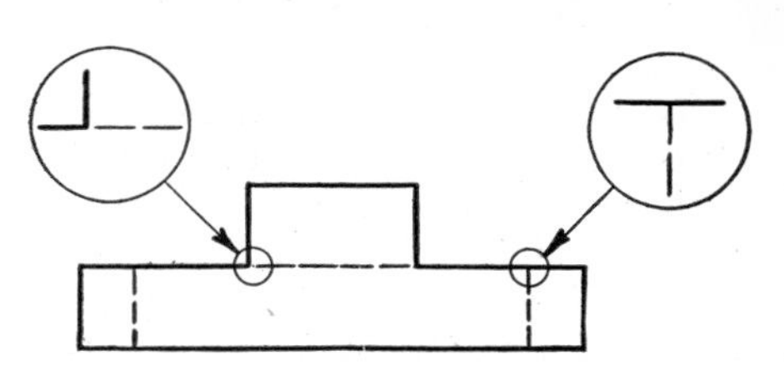

Fig. 7.21. Treatment of invisible lines.

7.12. Treatment of invisible lines. The short dashes that form an invisible line should be drawn carefully in accordance with the recommendations in Fig. 7.28. An invisible line always starts with a dash in contact with the object line from which it starts, unless it forms a continuation of a visible line. In the latter case, it should start with a space, in order to establish at a glance the exact location of the end point of the visible line. (See Fig. 7.21.) Correct and incorrect methods of starting and finishing invisible lines are illustrated in Fig. 7.22. Note that the effect of definite corners is secured at points A, B, E, and F, where, in each case, the end dash touches the intersecting line. Obviously this treatment is to be preferred to the treatment at points A', B', E', and F' in the column labeled "incorrect." When the point of intersection of an invisible line and another object line does not represent an actual intersection on the object, the intersection

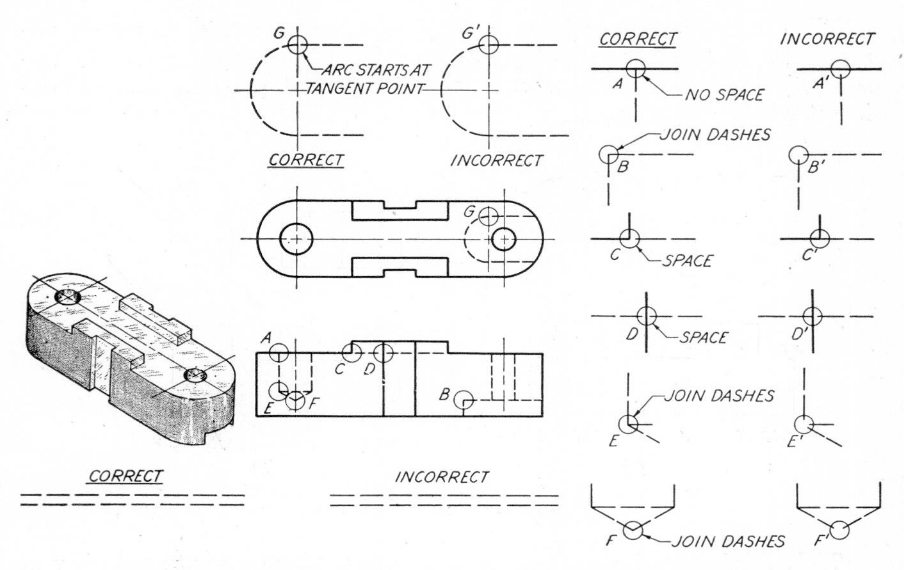

Fig. 7.22. Correct and incorrect junctures of invisible outlines.

should be open as at points C and D rather than closed as at C' and D'. An open intersection tends to make the lines appear to be at different distances from the observer.

In all cases similar to the one illustrated at C, the visible line will appear to be extended if the hidden line starts with a dash, as in C'.

Parallel invisible lines should have the breaks staggered, as shown in Fig. 7.22, for the sake of appearance.

The correct and incorrect treatment for starting invisible arcs is illustrated at G and G'. Note that an arc should start with a dash at the point of tangency. This treatment enables the reader to determine the exact end points of the curvature.

7.13. Omission of invisible lines. Although it is common practice for commercial draftsmen to omit hidden lines when their use tends to further confuse an already overburdened view or when the shape description of a feature is sufficiently clear in another view, it is not advisable for a beginning student to do so. The beginner, until he has developed the discrimination that comes with experience, will be wise to show all hidden lines.

7.14. To make an orthographic drawing. The location of all views should be determined before a drawing is begun. This will insure balance in the appearance of the finished drawing. The contour view is usually started first. After the initial start, the draftsman should construct his views simultaneously by projecting back and forth from one to the other. It is poor practice to complete one view before starting the others, as much more time will be required to complete the drawing.

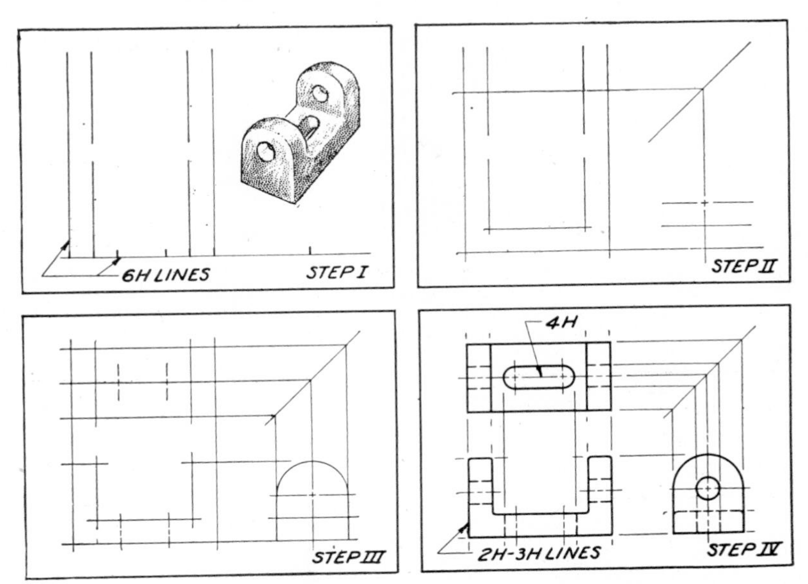

Fig. 7.23. Steps in making a three-view drawing of an object.

Fig. 7.23 shows the procedure for laying out a three-view drawing. The general outline of the views first should be drawn in lightly with a hard pencil and then heavied with a medium grade pencil. Although experienced draftsmen sometimes deviate from this procedure by drawing in the lines of known length and location in finished weight while constructing the views, it is not recommended that beginners do so. The graphic language must be learned by the painful process of trial and error, if individual technique is to be attained.

The common geometric methods for projecting from the top view to the side view, and vice versa, are shown in Fig. 7.24. The more accurate

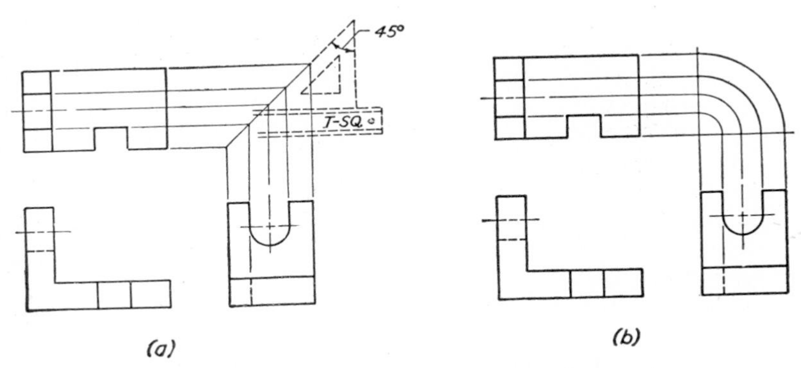

Fig. 7.24. Methods of projecting from the top view.

method is the one at the left, at (*a*), where only the T-square and triangles are required for construction. The location of the 45° measuring line, shown in (*a*), may be obtained by extending the construction lines representing the front edge of the top view and the front edge of the side view to an intersection. The center for the measuring arcs in (*b*) is found in the same manner.

When constructing a two-view drawing of a circular object, the pencil work must start with the drawing of the center lines, as shown in Fig. 7.25. This is necessarily the first step, because the construction of the circular (contour) view is based upon a horizontal and a vertical center line. The horizontal object lines of the rectangular view are projected from the circles.

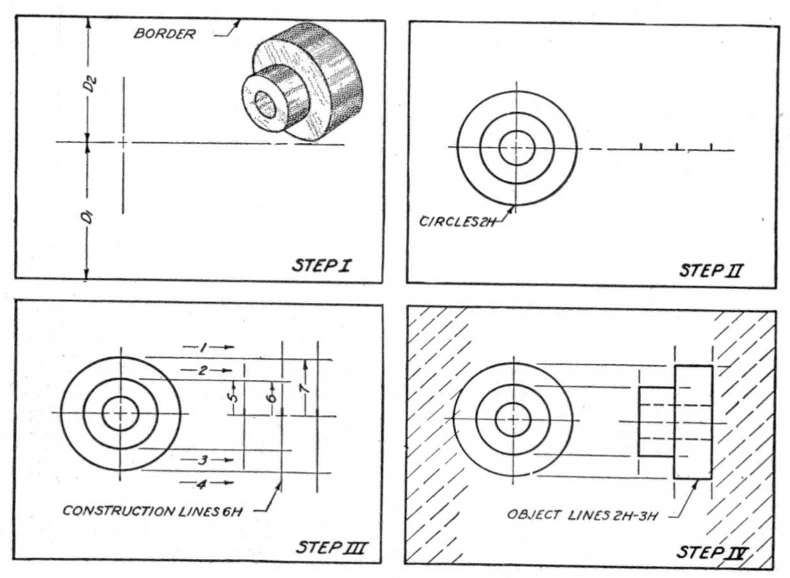

Fig. 7.25. Steps in making a two-view drawing of a circular object.

The vertical lines are drawn last. In order to space the views properly, the horizontal center line should be located so that the distances D_1 and D_2 are approximately equal; the vertical center line, so that the shaded areas appear to be balanced. In the case of complete working drawings, the spacing of the views must be modified to take into account notes, dimensions, titles, and so forth.

7.15. Penciling a drawing. The correct procedure for making a pencil drawing is shown in Fig. 7.26. Before any drawing can be done, it is necessary to select the scale to be used, care being taken that the one chosen is large enough to show all details to the best advantage. Ordinarily, the procedure of balancing the views on the sheet (see Sec. 7.14 and Fig. 7.26*a*) can be simplified by a preliminary freehand sketch showing their arrangement. When balancing views, it should be attempted

triangle, and so forth) is moved over it. After brushing, the amount of such soil may be still further reduced by raising the triangles and the T-square blade when moving them into new positions.

7.17. Visualizing an object from given views. Most students in elementary drawing courses find it difficult to visualize an object from two or more views. This trouble is largely due to the lack of systematic procedure for analyzing complex shapes.

The simplest method of determining shape is illustrated pictorially in Fig. 7.32. This method of "breaking down" may be applied to any

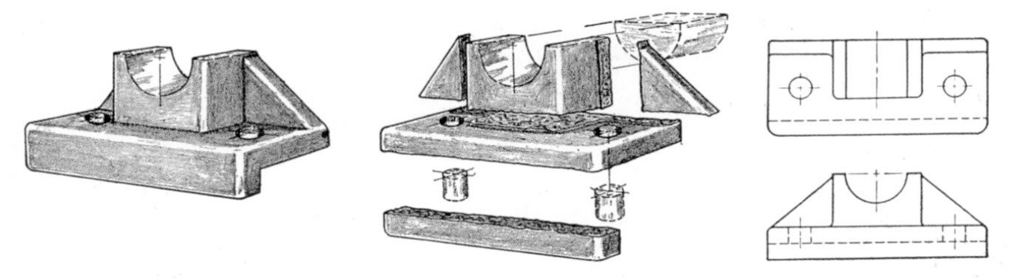

Fig. 7.33. "Breaking down" method.

object, since all objects may be thought of as consisting of elemental geometrical forms, such as prisms, cylinders, cones, and so on (Fig. 7.33). These imaginary component parts may be additions in the form of projections or subtractions in the form of cavities. Following such a detailed geometric analysis, a clear picture of an entire object can be obtained by mentally assembling a few easily visualized forms.

It should be realized, when analyzing component parts, that it is

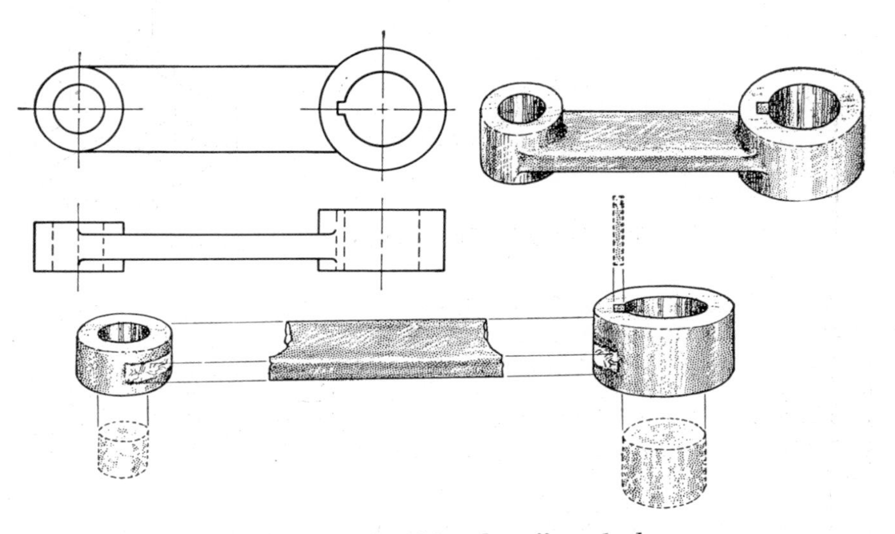

Fig. 7.34. "Breaking down" method.

impossible ordinarily to determine whether a form is an addition or a subtraction by looking at one view. For example, the small circles in the top view in Fig. 7.33 indicate a cylindrical form, but they do not reveal whether the form is a hole or a projection. By consulting the front view, however, the form is shown to be a hole (subtracted cylinder).

The graphic language is similar to the written language in that neither can be read at a glance. A drawing must be patiently read by referring systematically back and forth from one view to another. The reader at the same time must imagine a three-dimensional object and not a two-dimensional flat projection.

Fig. 7.34 illustrates further the scheme of "breaking down" objects into their component geometrical shapes.

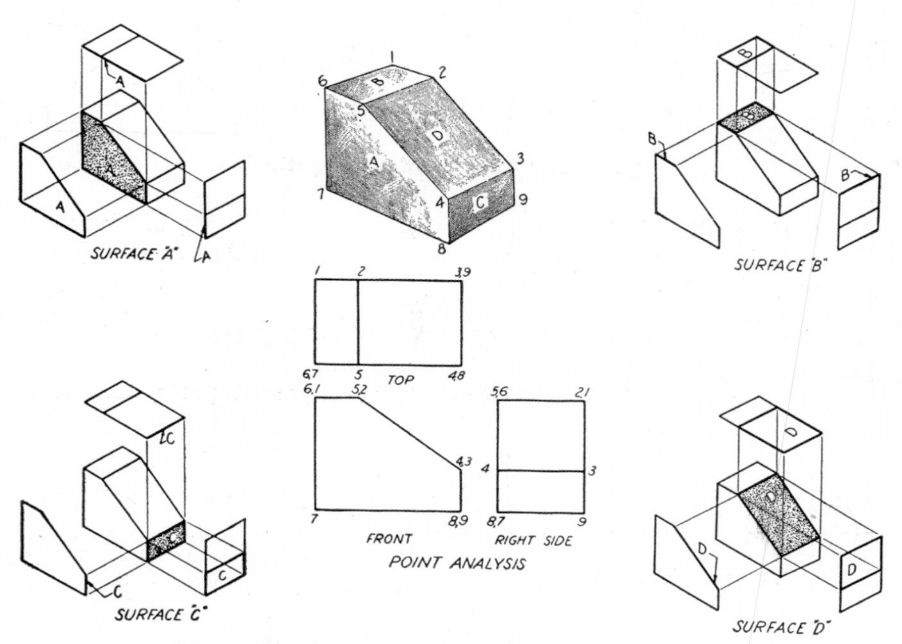

Fig. 7.35. Analysis of surfaces, lines, and points.

7.18. Analysis of surfaces, lines, and points in three principal views. An analysis of the representation of the surfaces of a multilated block is given pictorially in Fig. 7.35. It can be noted that each of the surfaces *A*, *B*, and *C* appears in true size and shape in one view, and as a line in each of the other two related views. Surface *D*, which is inclined, appears with foreshortened length in the top and side views, and as an inclined line in the front view.

Three views of each of the visible points are shown on the multiview drawing. At the very beginning of an elementary course in drawing, a student will often find it helpful to number the corners of an object in all views.

Fig. 7.36 shows a pictorial drawing and a three-view orthographic drawing of a mutilated block. The accompanying table gives an orderly analysis of the reading of the three views of the object. A table similar to this one may be prepared by a student to facilitate study of a particular drawing. Such a table, however, is never prepared by a commercial draftsman.

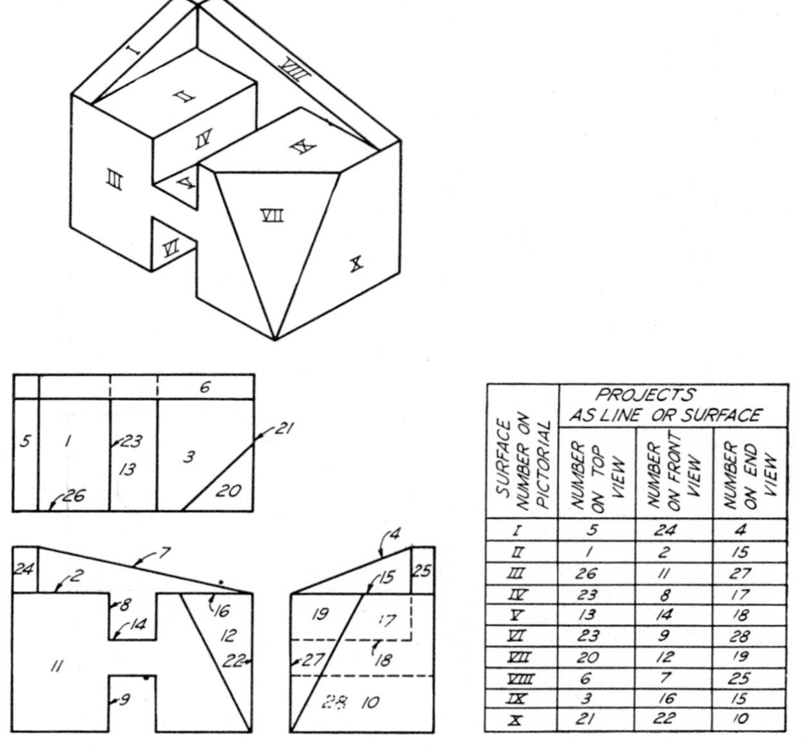

SURFACE NUMBER ON PICTORIAL	PROJECTS AS LINE OR SURFACE		
	NUMBER ON TOP VIEW	NUMBER ON FRONT VIEW	NUMBER ON END VIEW
I	5	24	4
II	1	2	15
III	26	11	27
IV	23	8	17
V	13	14	18
VI	23	9	28
VII	20	12	19
VIII	6	7	25
IX	3	16	15
X	21	22	10

Fig. 7.36. Lines and surfaces.

All lines and surfaces are numbered at random on the orthographic drawing so that the student may take each surface designated on the pictorial drawing and identify it by a different number on each of the three views. For example, surface *I* on the pictorial view appears as a surface in the top view and is identified by the number 5. The same surface appears as surface 24 in the front view, and as line 4 in the end view.

7.19. Problems. The problems that follow are intended primarily to furnish study in multiview projection through the preparation of sketches and instrumental drawings. Problems 1–12 (Fig. 7.39) are designed for

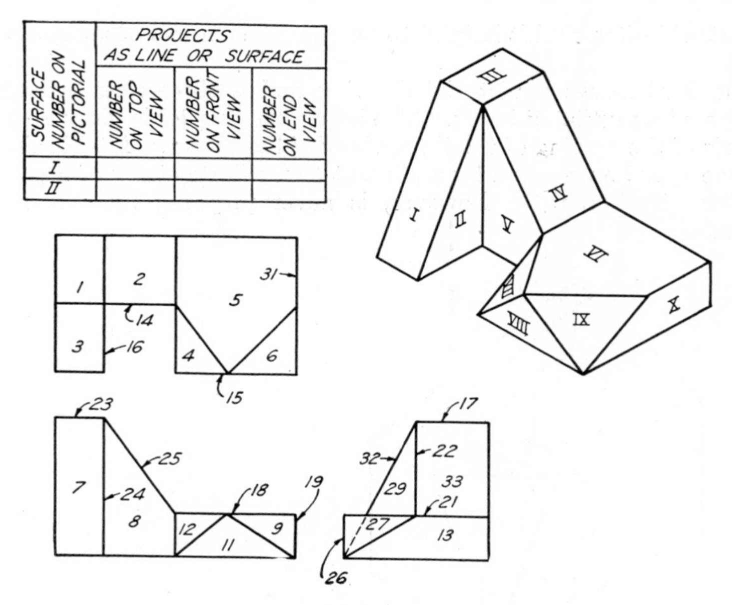

Fig. 7.37. Reading exercise.

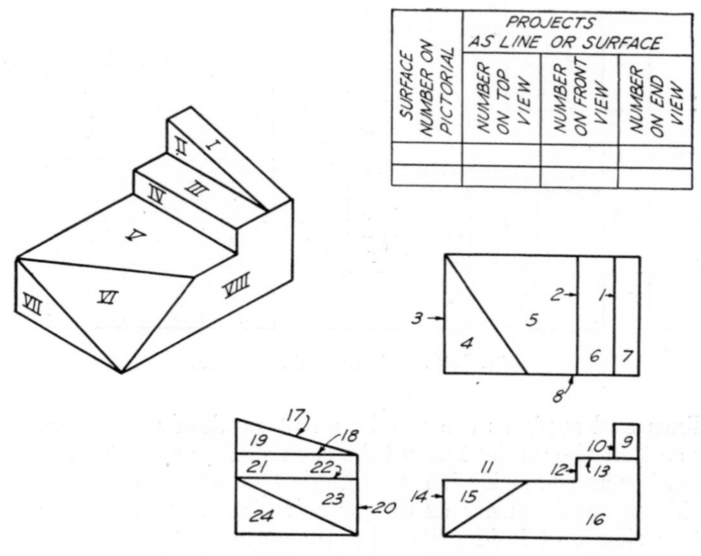

Fig. 7.38. Reading exercise.

the sketching of views alone. Many of the other problems in this chapter, however, may be prepared in more complete form. Their views may be dimensioned as are the views of working drawings, if the student will study carefully the beginning of the chapter on dimensioning before attempting

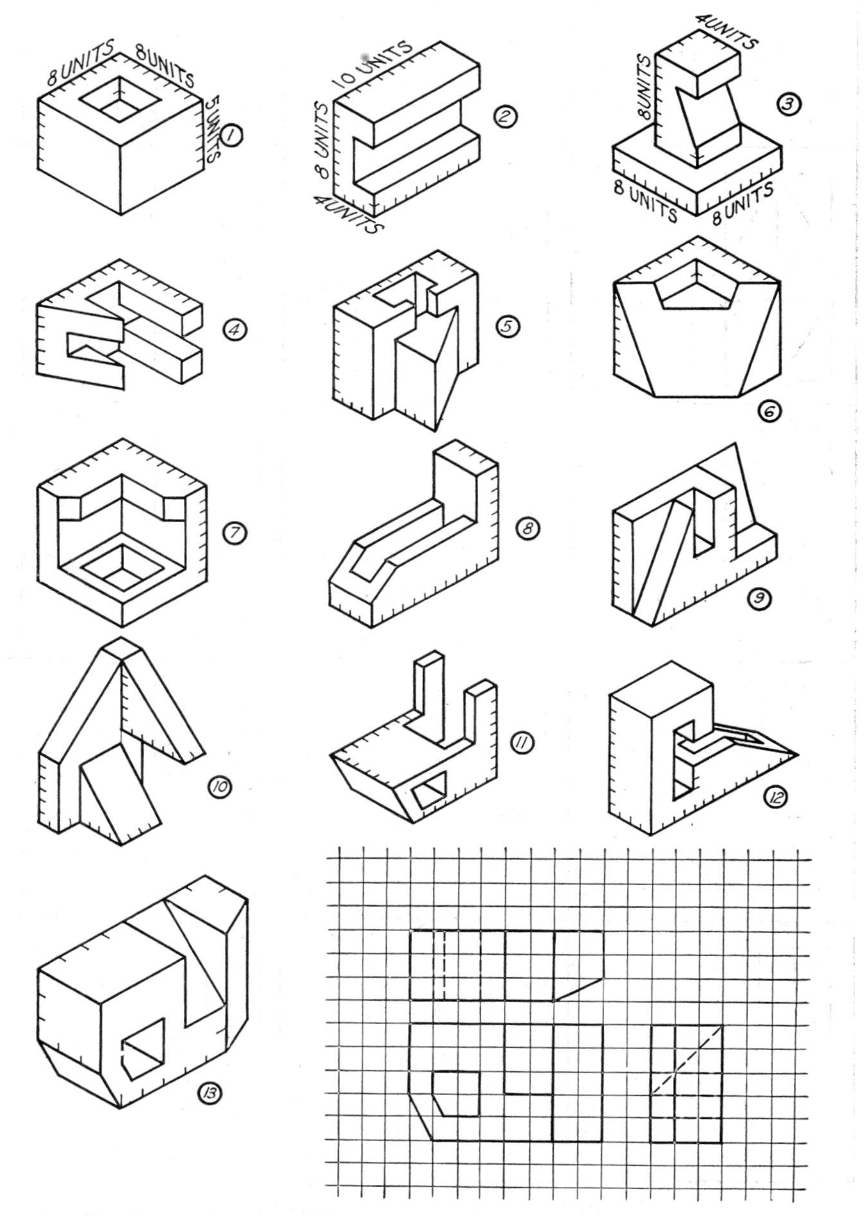

Fig. 7.39. Objects to be sketched in orthographic projection.

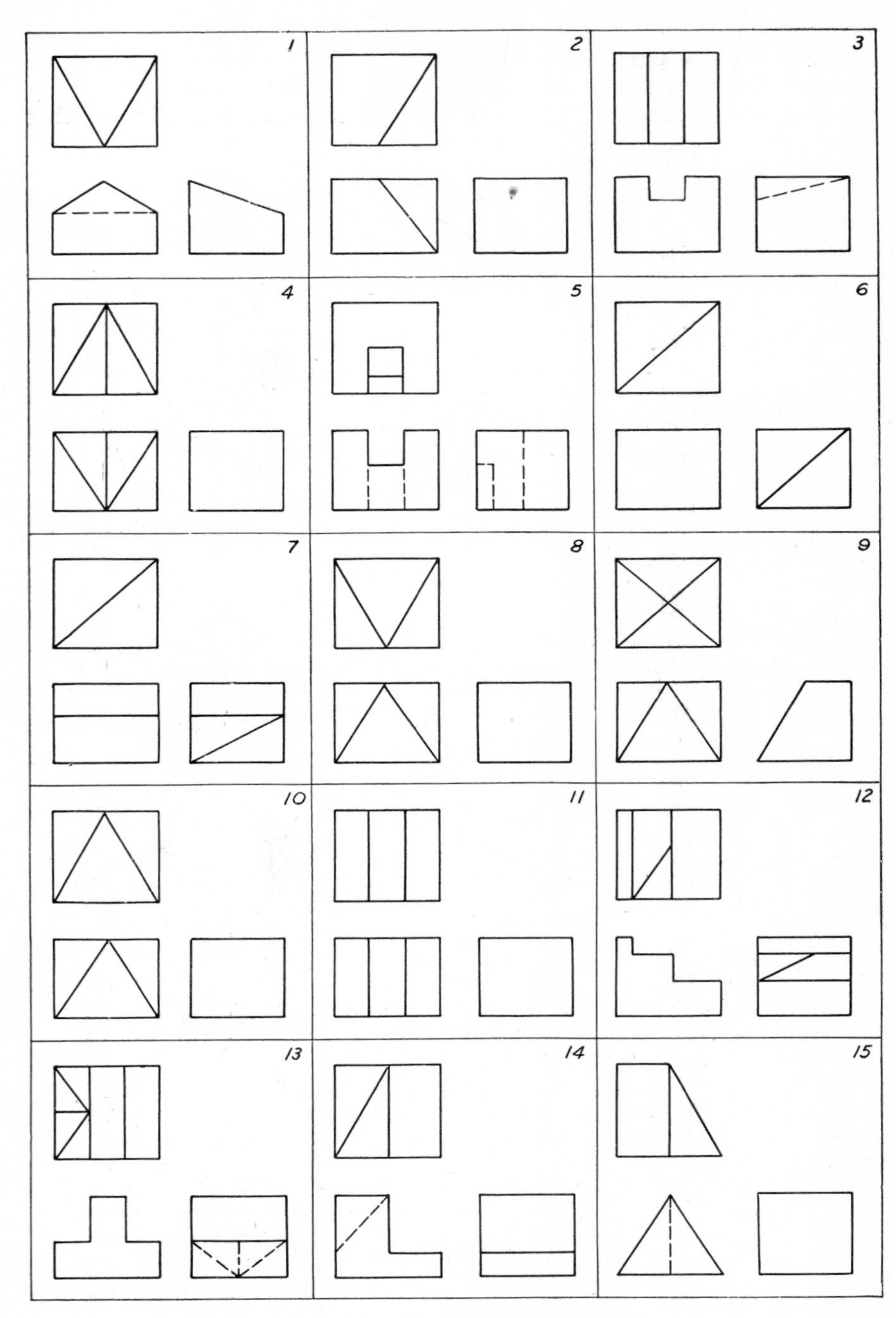

Fig. 7.40. Missing-line exercises.

to record size description (Chap. 16). All dimensions should be placed in accordance with the general rules of dimensioning.

The views shown in a sketch or drawing should be spaced on the paper with aim for balance within the border lines. Ample room should be allowed between the views for the necessary dimensions. If the views are not to be dimensioned, the distance between them may be made somewhat less than would be necessary otherwise.

Before starting to draw, the student should reread Sec. 7.15 and study Fig. 7.26, which shows the steps in making a multiview drawing. The preparation of a preliminary sketch, such as the one shown in this illustration, always proves helpful to the beginner.

All construction work should be done in light lines with a sharp hard pencil. A drawing should be checked by an instructor before the lines are "heavied in," unless the preliminary sketch was checked beforehand.

1–2. (Figs. 7.37, 7.38.) Draw a table similar to that shown in Fig. 7.36 and fill in the required information for each of the surfaces designated on the pictorial drawing by a Roman numeral. Draw the necessary guide lines and letter the column headings and information in $\frac{1}{8}''$ capitals.

3. (Fig. 7.39.) Sketch, *freehand*, the necessary views of each of the objects shown. Use cross-section paper if it is available. The selected length for the unit will determine the size of the drawing of each object. Read Chap. 12.

4. (Fig. 7.40.) A line is missing from each of the three-view drawings. When the correct missing line is found, the three views of each object will be consistent with one another. *Suggestion:* A good method of visualizing these objects is to sketch them pictorially or to cut a model from a piece of modeling clay, a cake of soap, or an ordinary potato.

5. (Fig. 7.41.) Add the missing line or lines in one view of each of the three-view drawings. When the missing line or lines have been determined, the three views of each object will be consistent with one another.

6. (Fig. 7.42.) Draw or sketch the third view for each of the given objects.

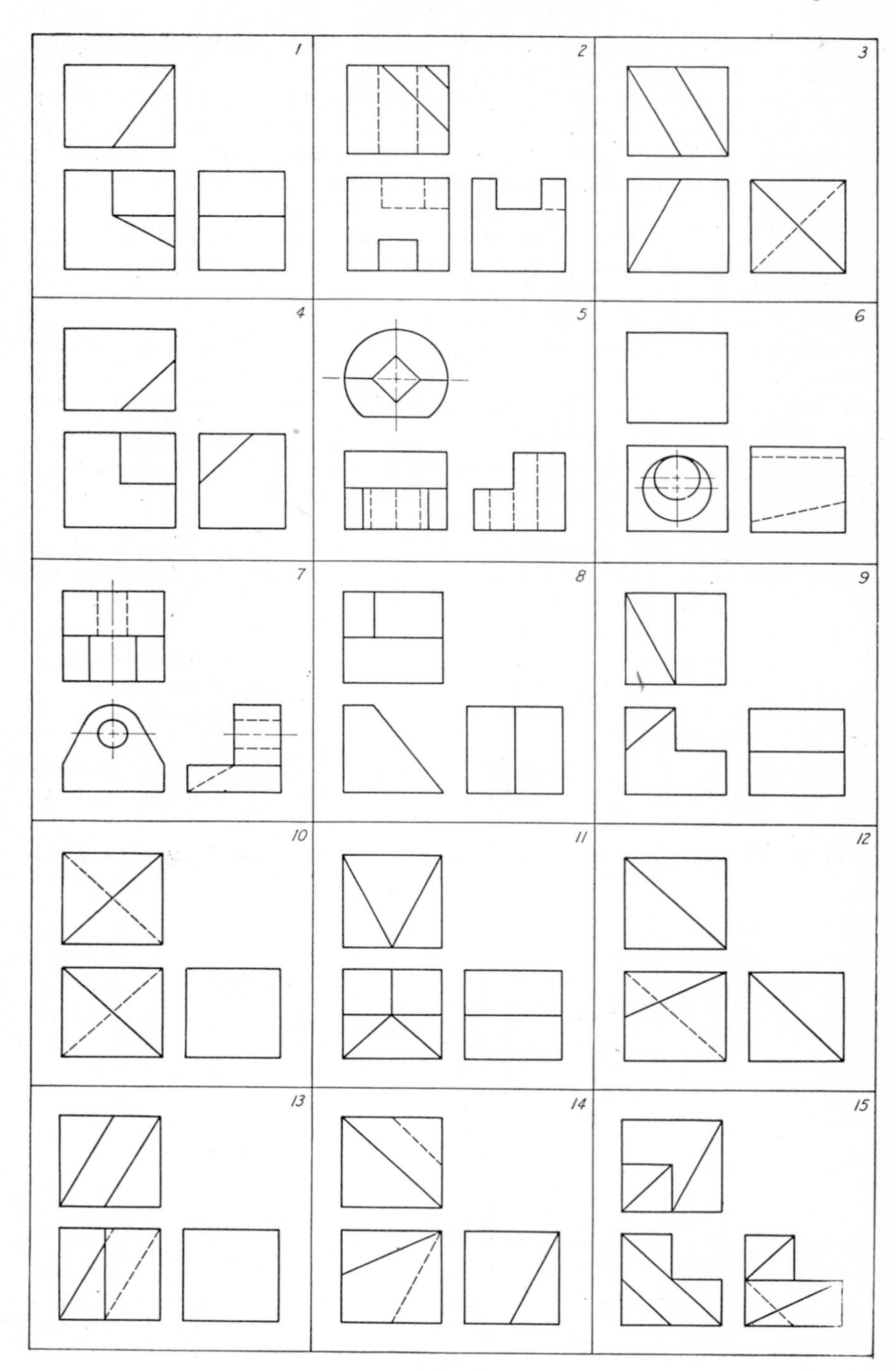

Fig. 7.41

Fig. 7.42

7–26. (Figs. 7.43–7.62.) Sketch, freehand, the necessary views of the given objects as assigned. The selected length for the unit will determine the size of the views. Assume any needed dimensions that are not given in units.

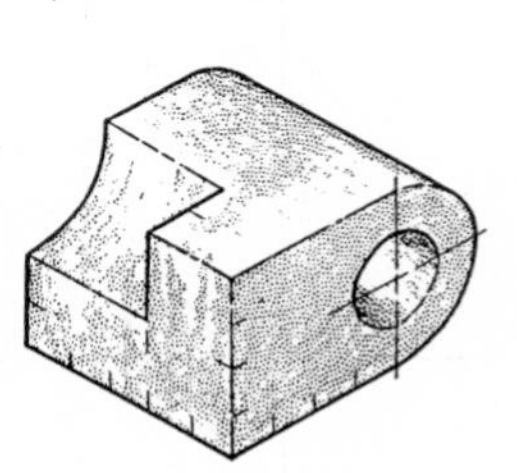

Fig. 7.43. Stop block.

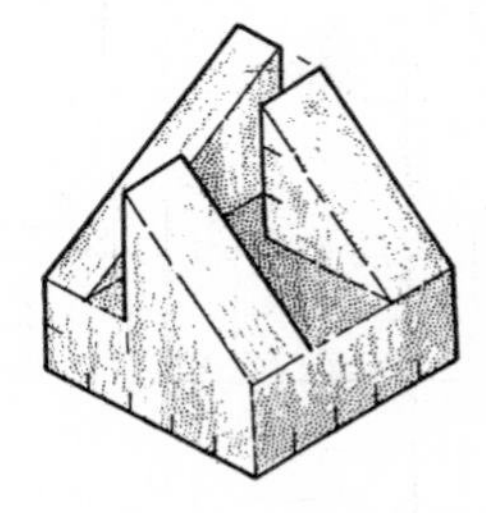

Fig. 7.44. Angle block.

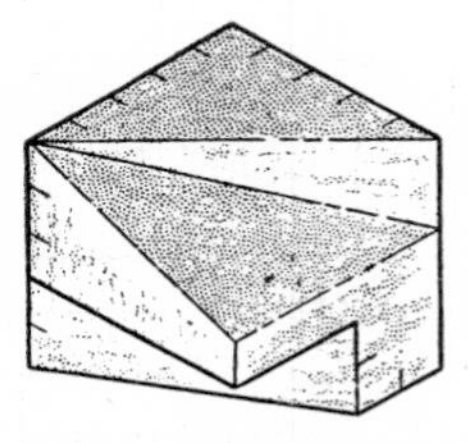

Fig. 7.45. Adjustment block.

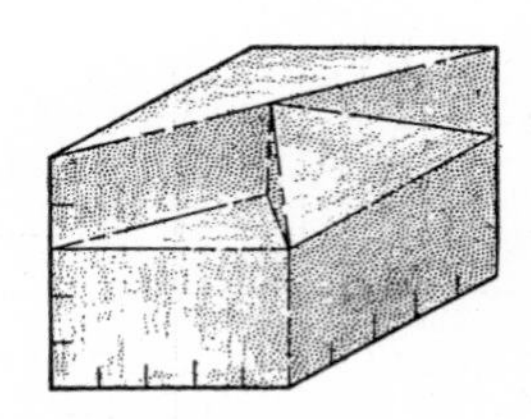

Fig. 7.46. Slip block.

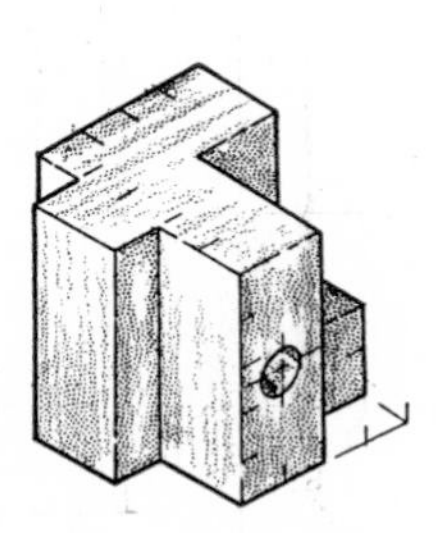

Fig. 7.47. Alignment block.

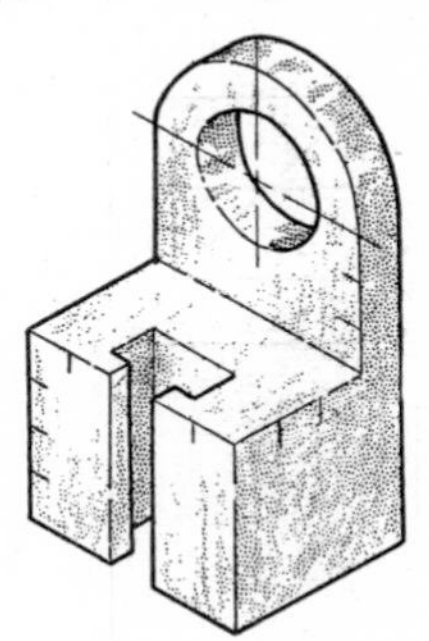

Fig. 7.48. Slide block.

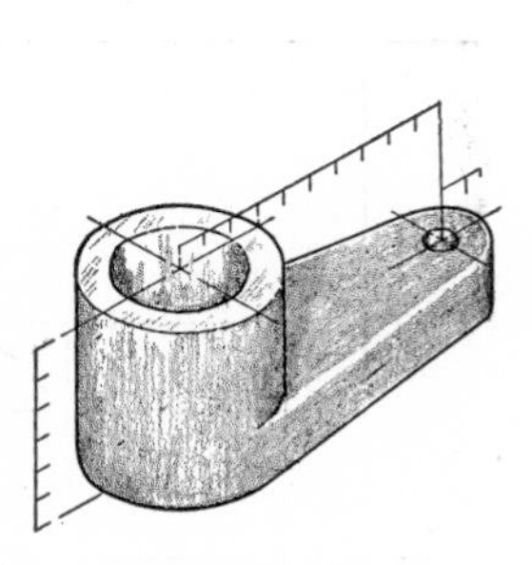

Fig. 7.49. Link.

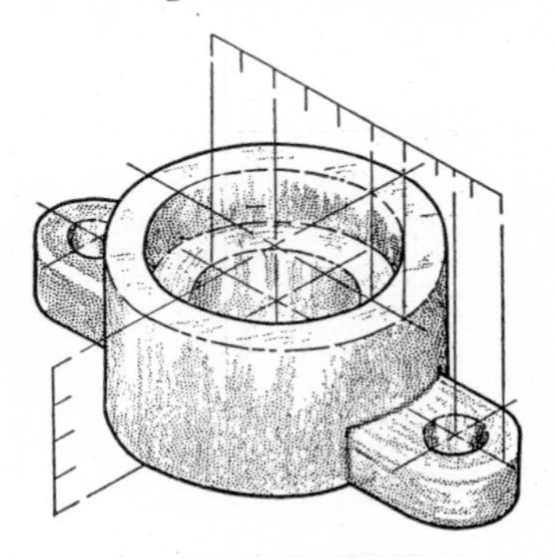

Fig. 7.50. Collar bracket.

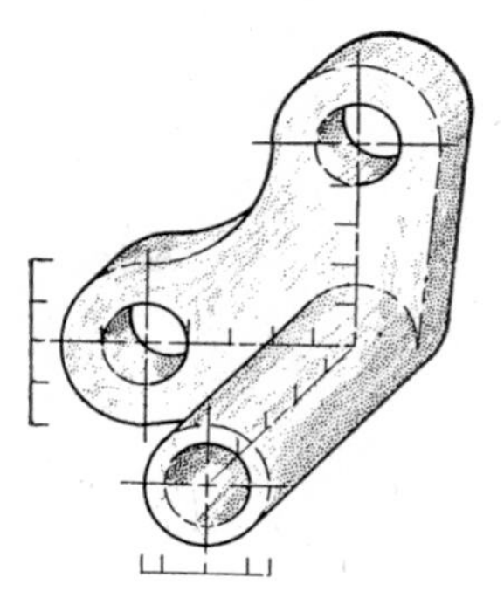

Fig. 7.51. Bell crank.

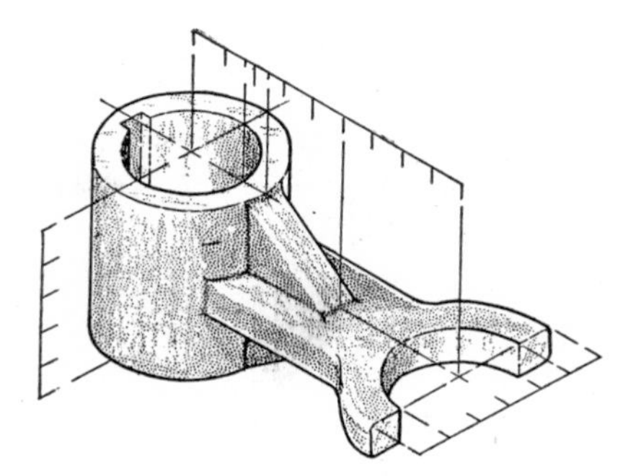

Fig. 7.52. Shifter.

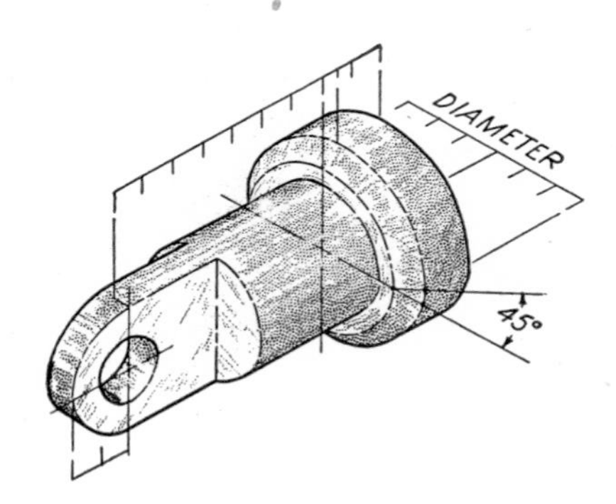

Fig. 7.53. Guide.

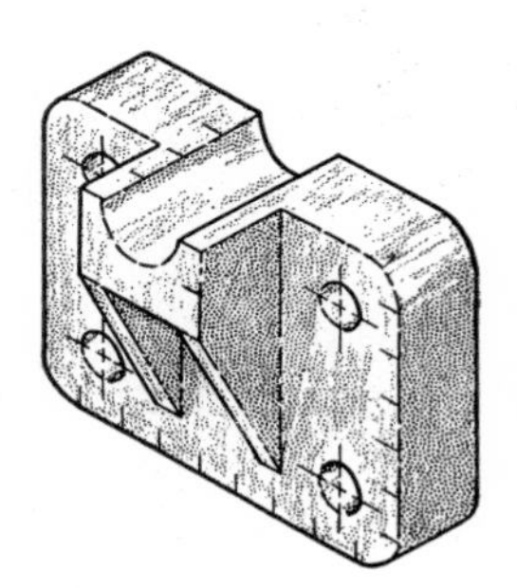

Fig. 7.54. Support bracket.

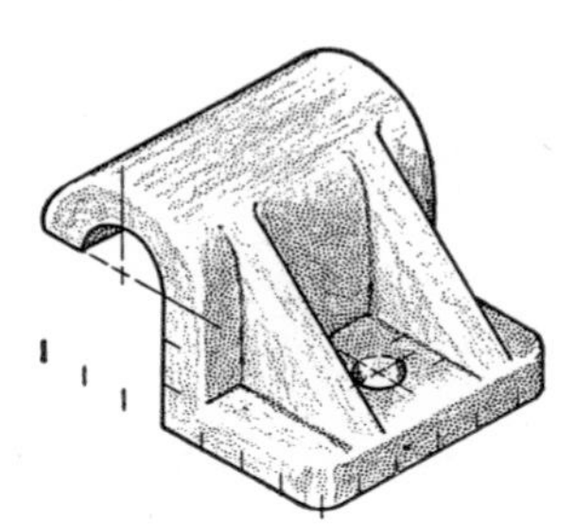

Fig. 7.55. Index bracket.

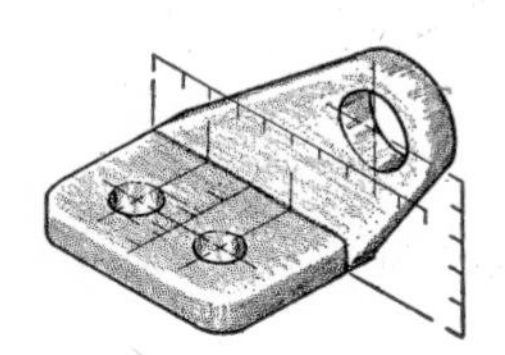

Fig. 7.56. Control bracket.

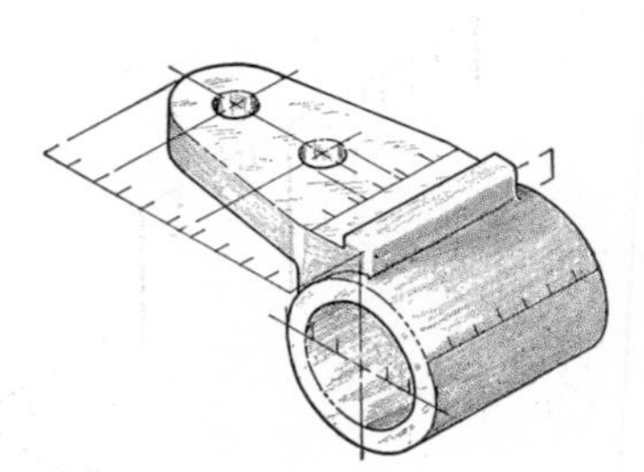

Fig. 7.57. Shaft bracket.

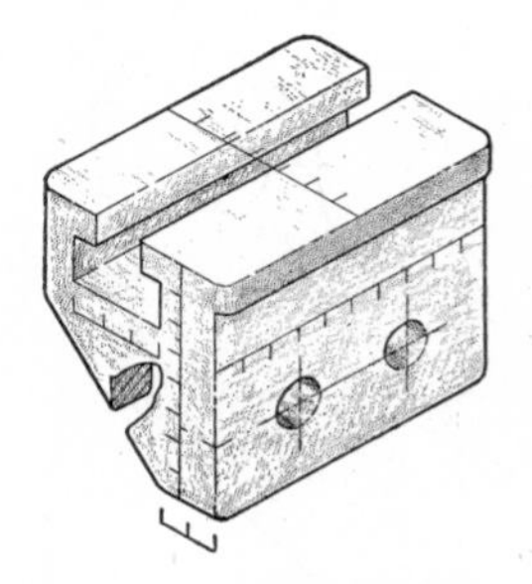

Fig. 7.58. Offset guide.

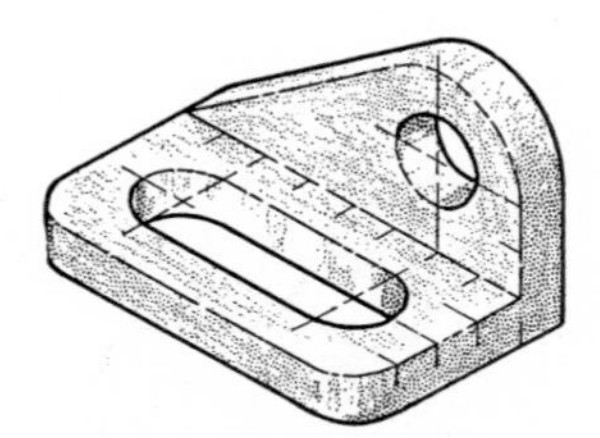

Fig. 7.59. Feed rod bracket.

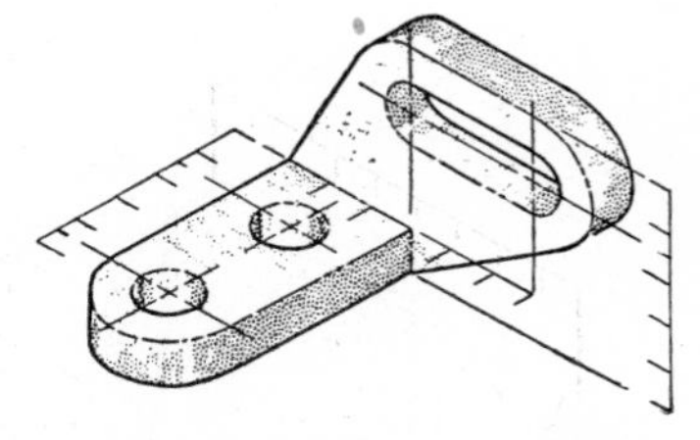

Fig. 7.60. Automatic feed bracket.

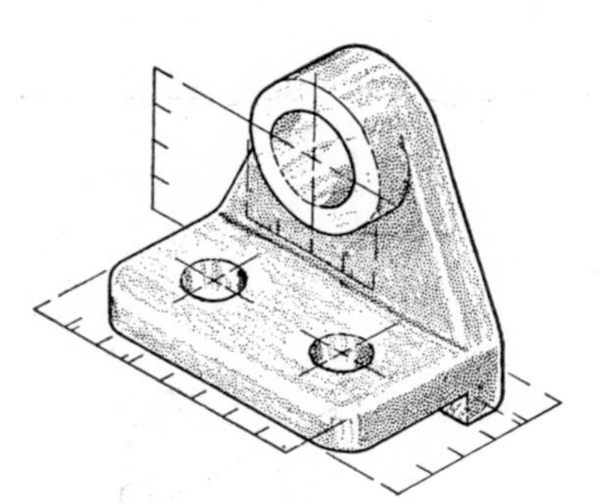

Fig. 7.61. Support bracket.

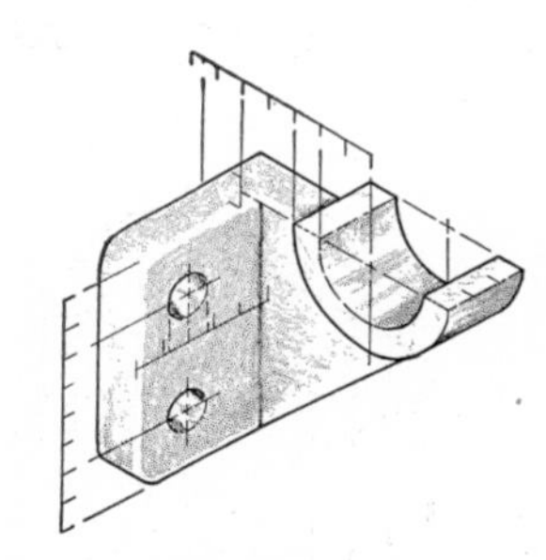

Fig. 7.62. Offset bracket.

27–36. (Figs. 7.63–7.72.) Reproduce the given views and draw the required view. Show all hidden lines.

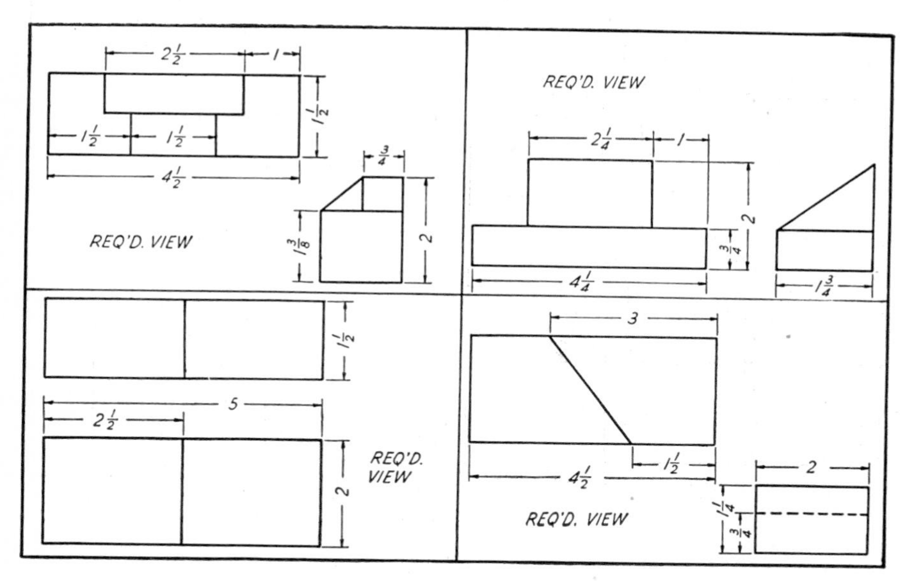

Fig. 7.63.

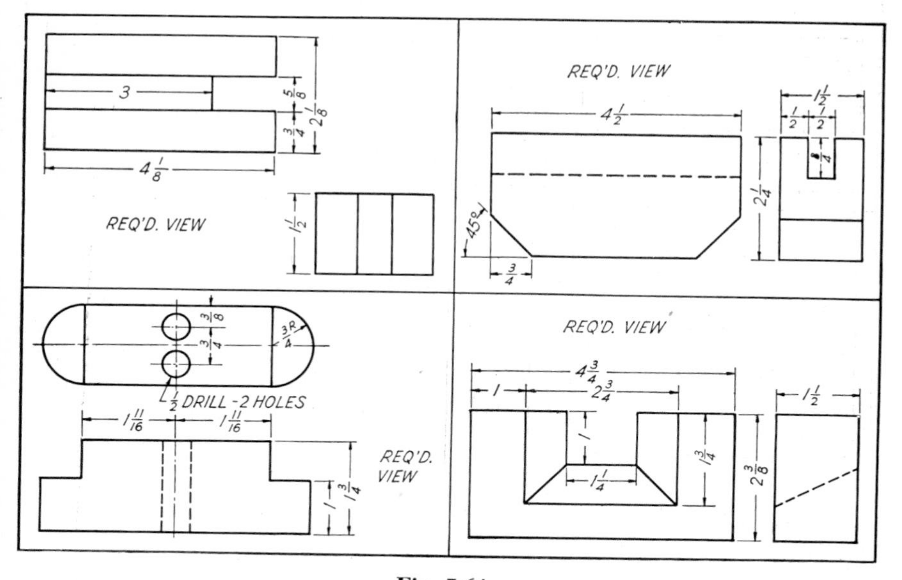

Fig. 7.64.

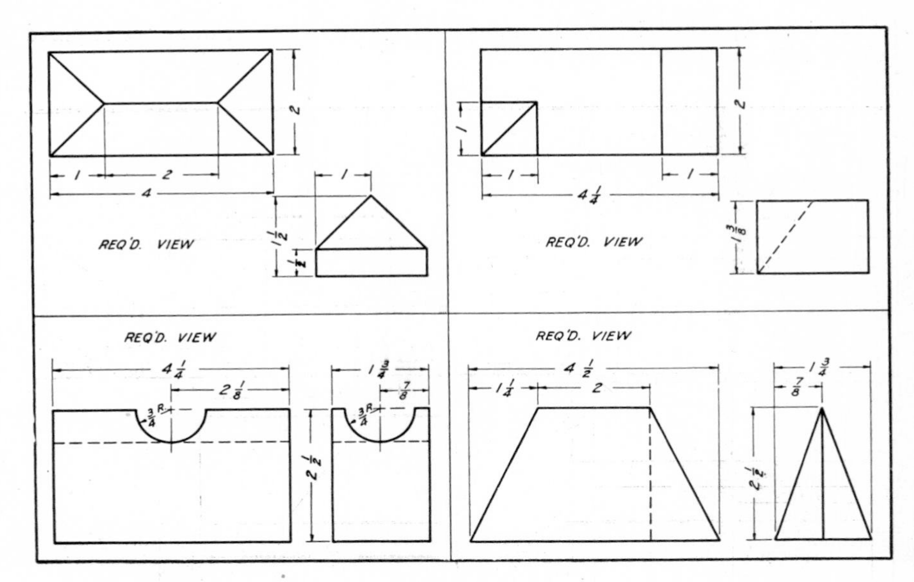

Fig. 7.65.

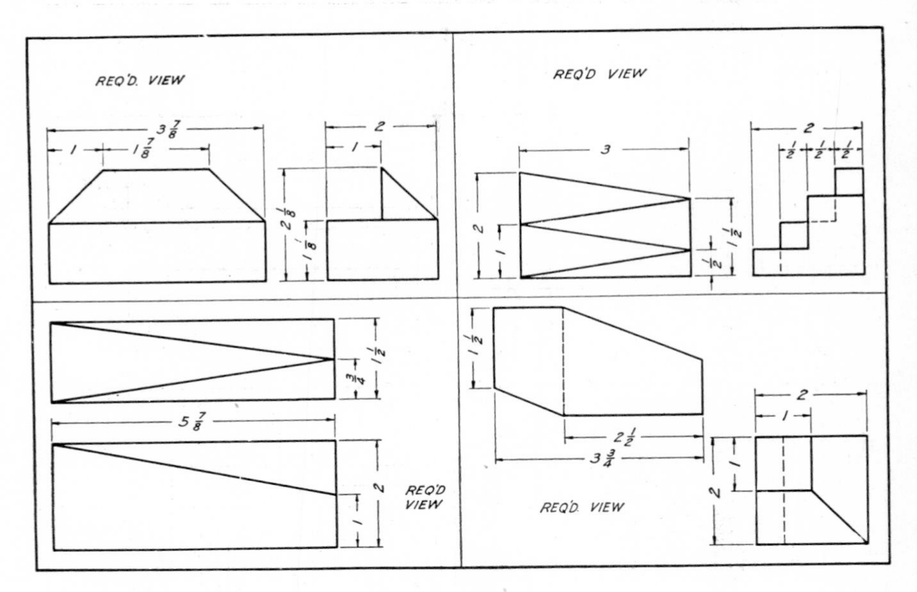

Fig. 7.66.

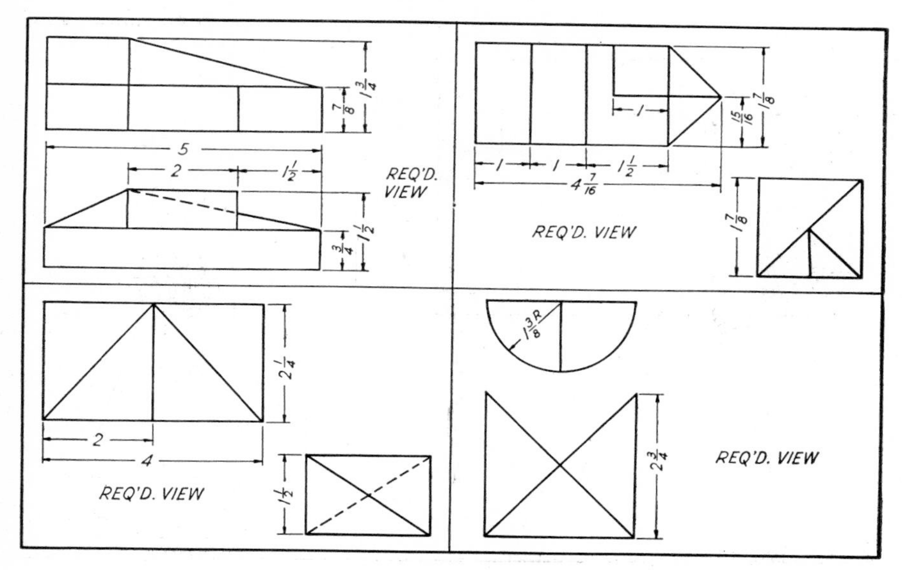

Fig. 7.67.

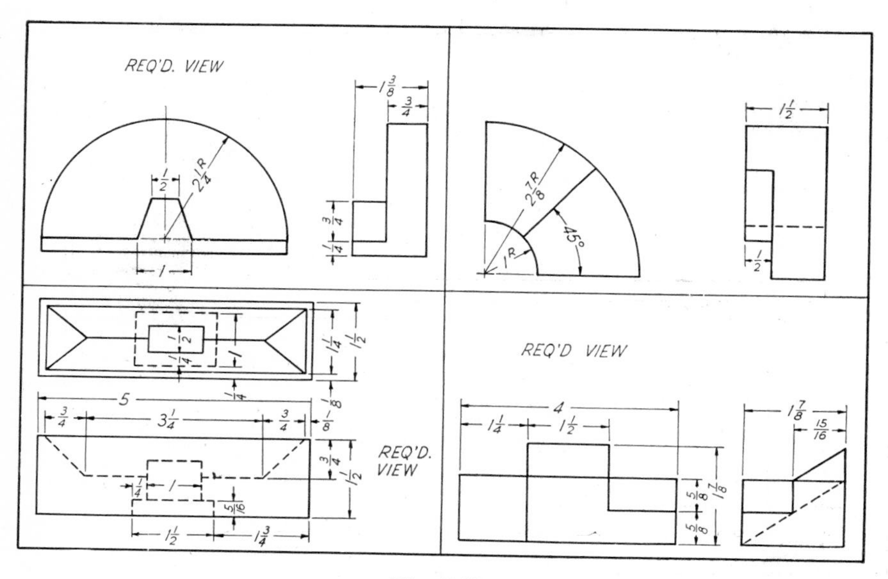

Fig. 7.68.

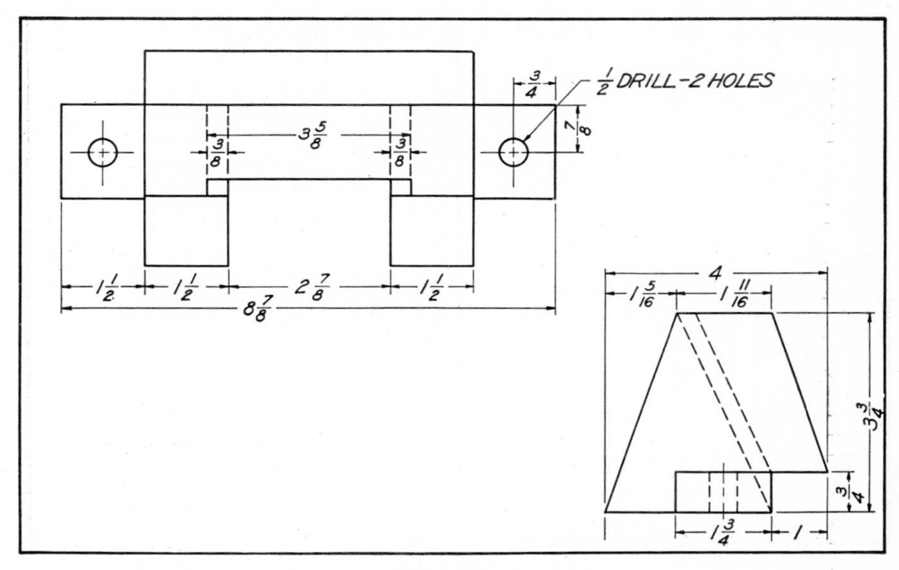

Fig. 7.69.

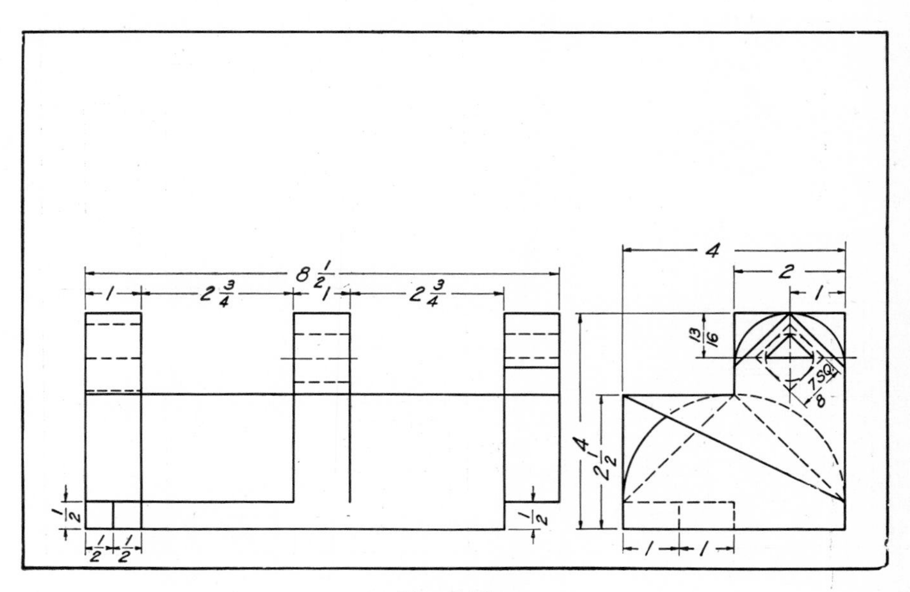

Fig. 7.70.

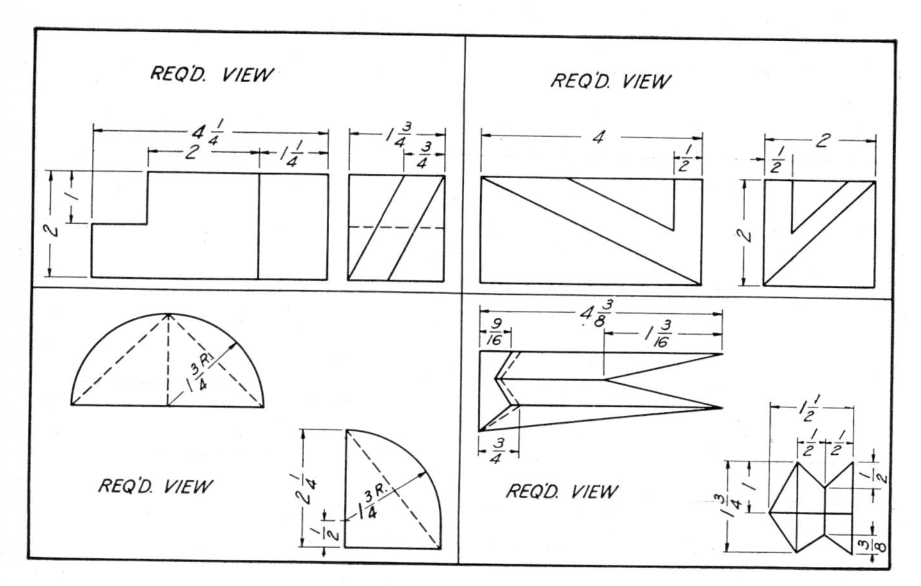

Fig. 7.71.

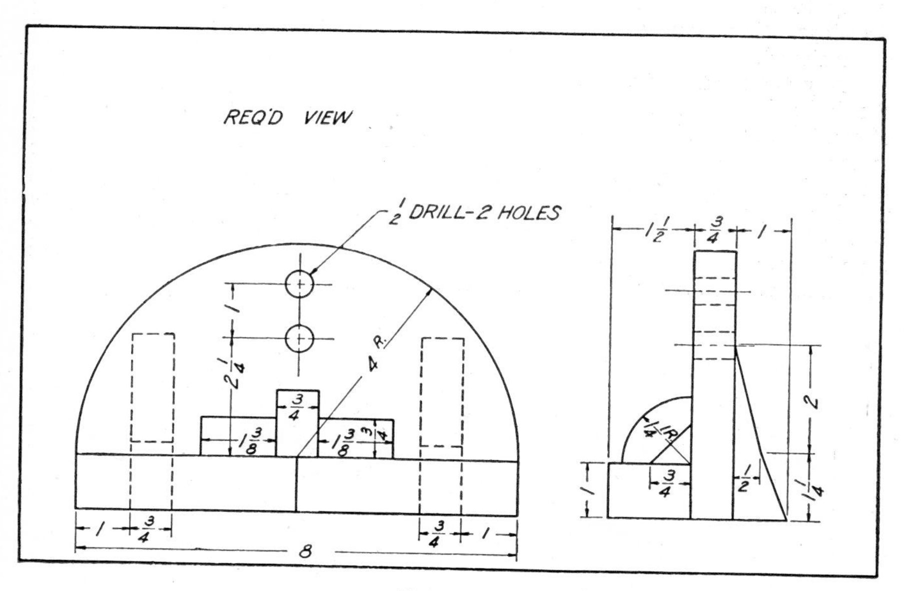

Fig. 7.72.

37. (Fig. 7.73.) Reproduce the front and side views of the mutilated block and draw the top view. Balance the drawing on the sheet. Show all hidden lines.

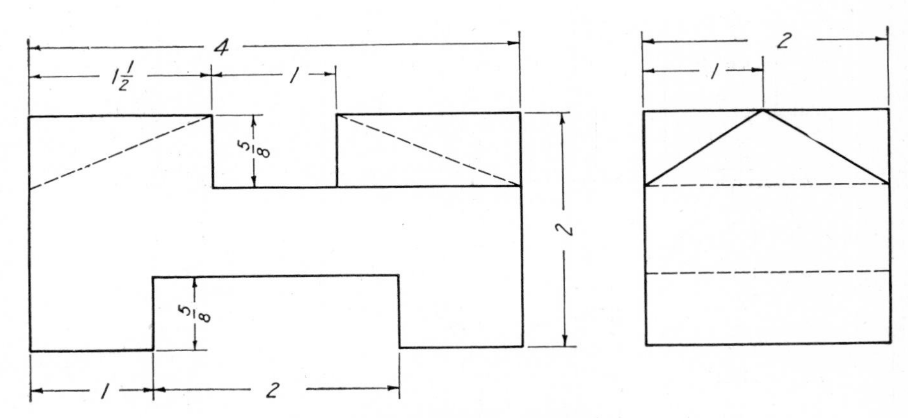

Fig. 7.73. Mutilated block.

38–86. (Figs. 7.74–7.122.) These problems are designed to give the student further study in multiview drawing and, at the same time, offer him the opportunity to apply good line technique to the preparation of elementary working drawings. The views of the drawings of the given objects may or may not be dimensioned.

Only the necessary views on which all of the hidden lines are to be shown should be drawn. It is suggested that a preliminary sketch be made on a piece of scratch paper before starting to draw. The sketch should show the proposed arrangement of the views and the calculated location of each view in relation to the border and the other views. The student should keep in mind the fact that the drawing is to be well balanced on the sheet and that the views are not to be crowded. If dimensions are to be given, ample space must be allowed between the views for their placement. It is usually wise for a student to consult his class instructor about the scale he has selected before reaching a final decision.

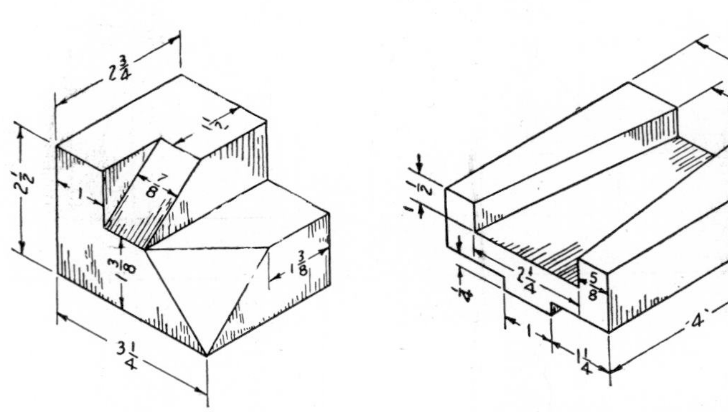

Fig. 7.74. Corner block. **Fig. 7.75. Wedge block.**

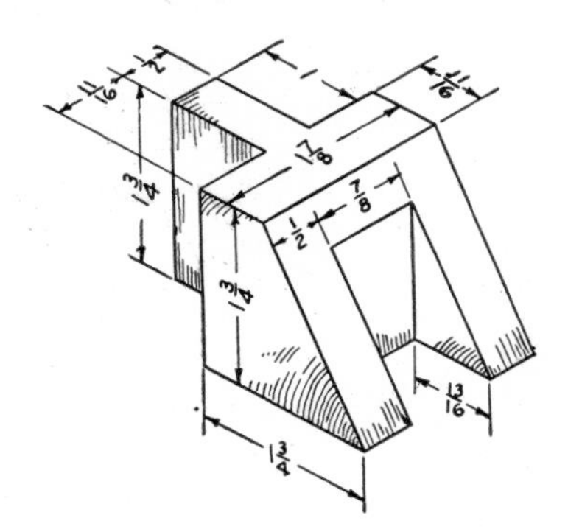

Fig. 7.76. Stop block.

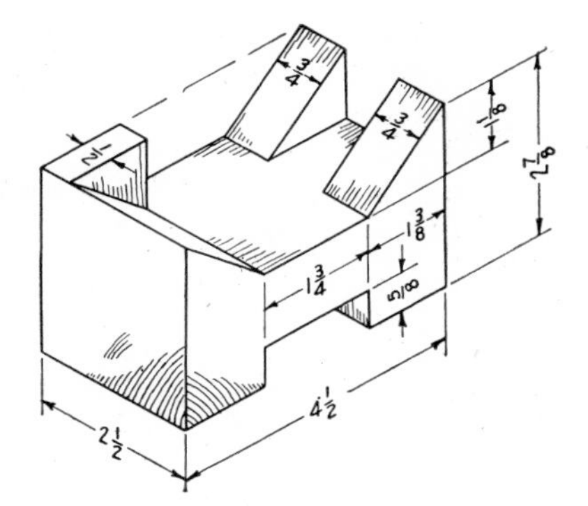

Fig. 7.77. Rest block.

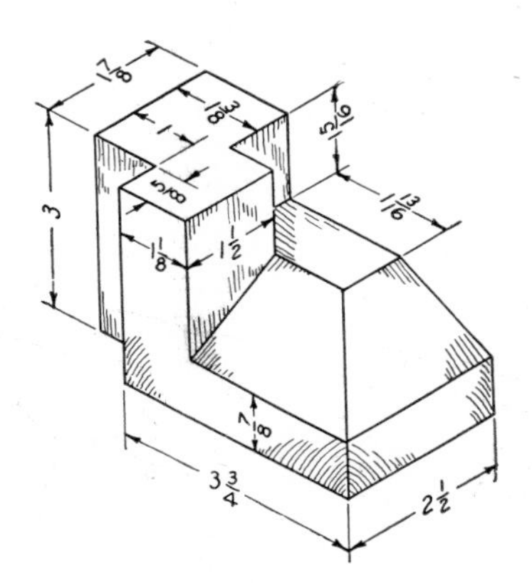

Fig. 7.78. Angle block.

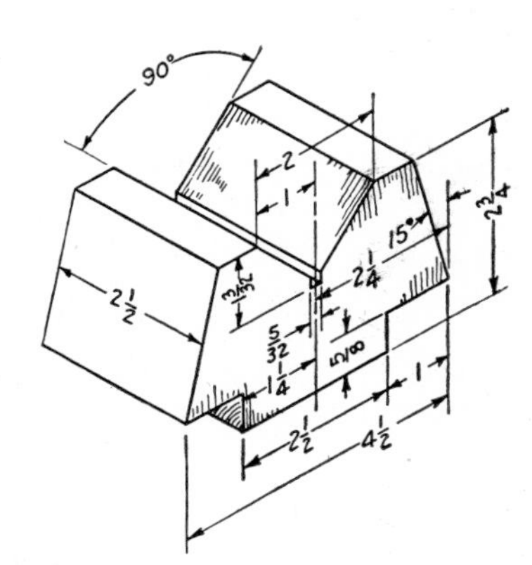

Fig. 7.79. V-rest.

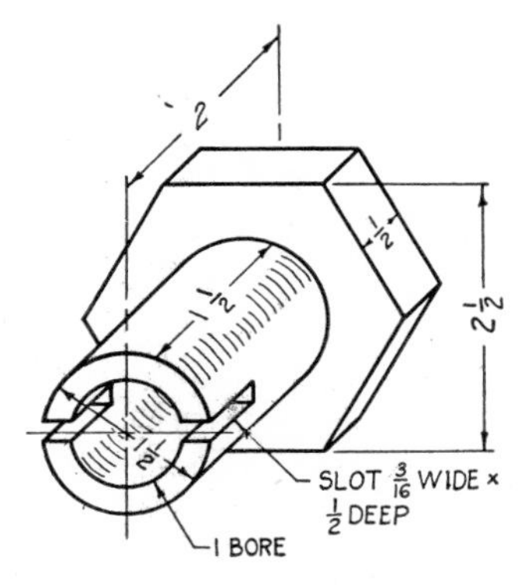

Fig. 7.80. Guide cap.

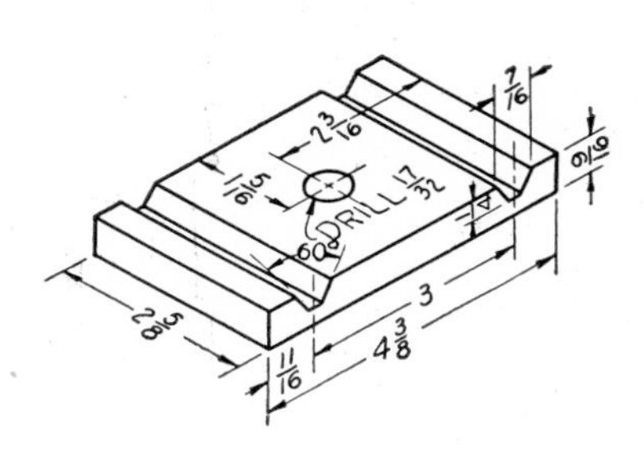

Fig. 7.81. Saddle block.

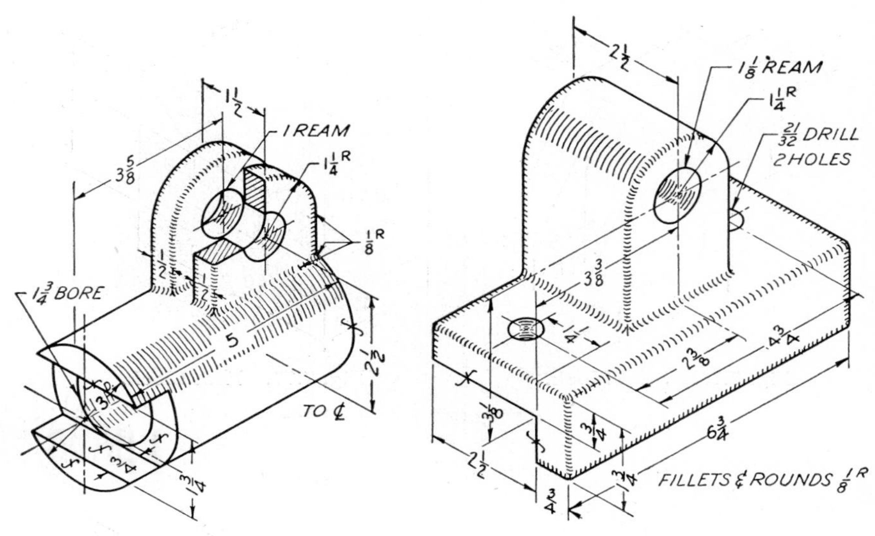

Fig. 7.82. Sliding link. Fig. 7.83. Guide.

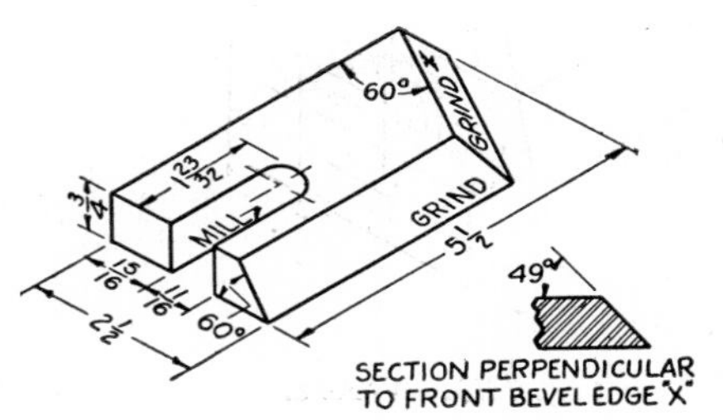

Fig. 7.84. Moulder knife.

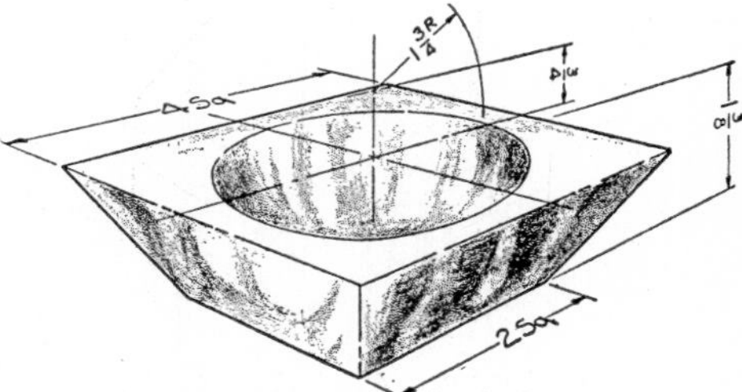

Fig. 7.85. Ash tray.

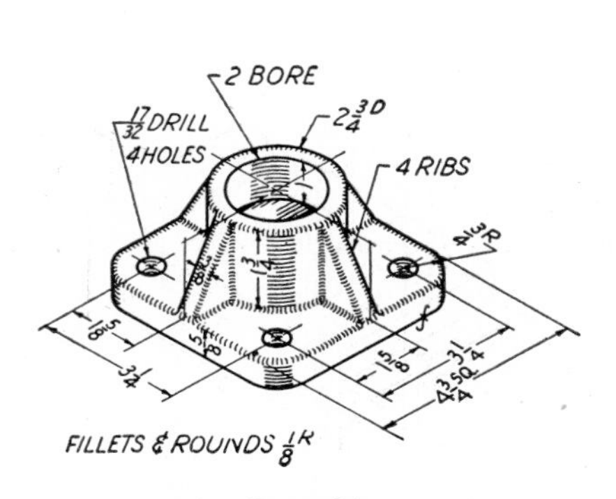

Fig. 7.86. Stanchion support.

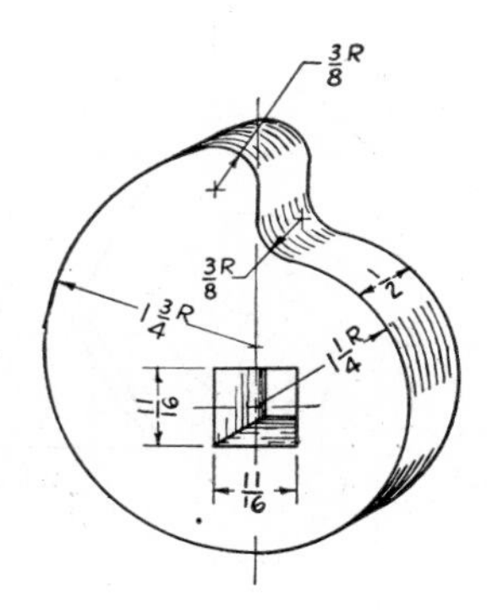

Fig. 7.87. Cam.

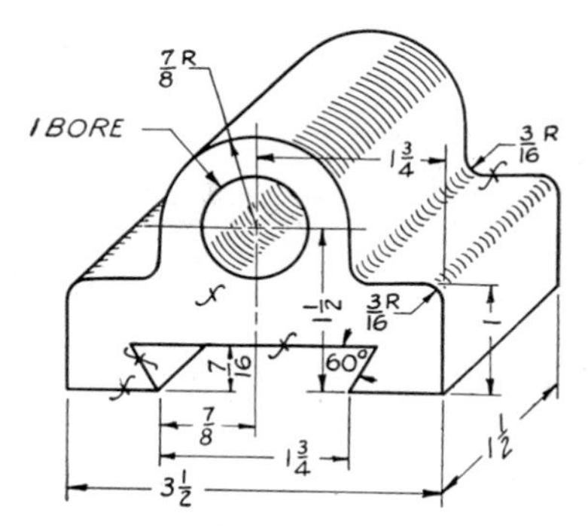

Fig. 7.88. Sliding guide.

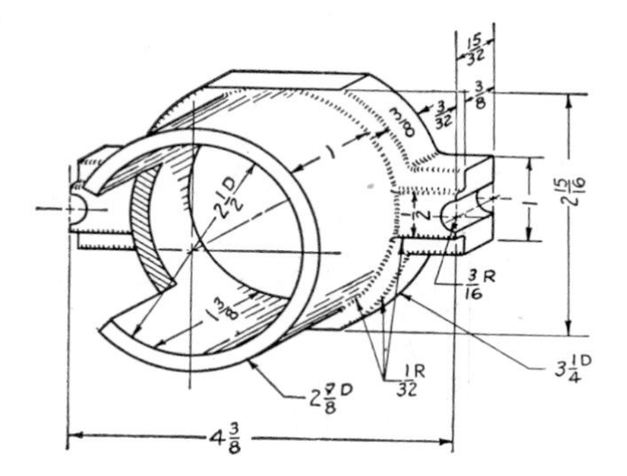

Fig. 7.89. Housing.

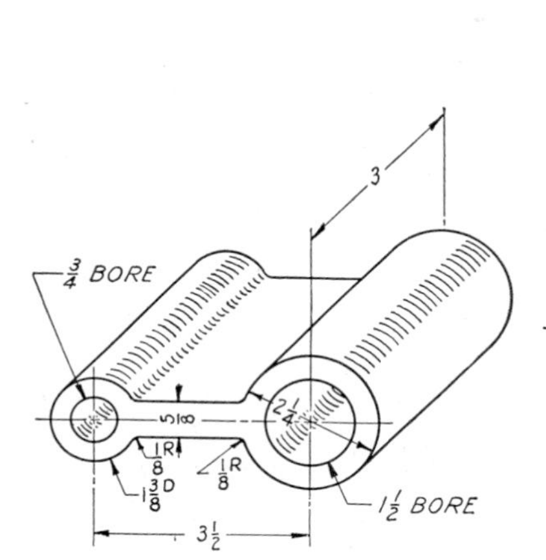

Fig. 7.90. Rod guide.

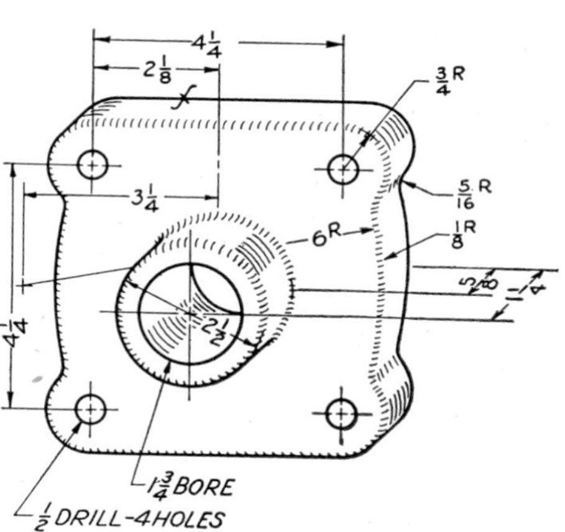

Fig. 7.91. Regulator body.

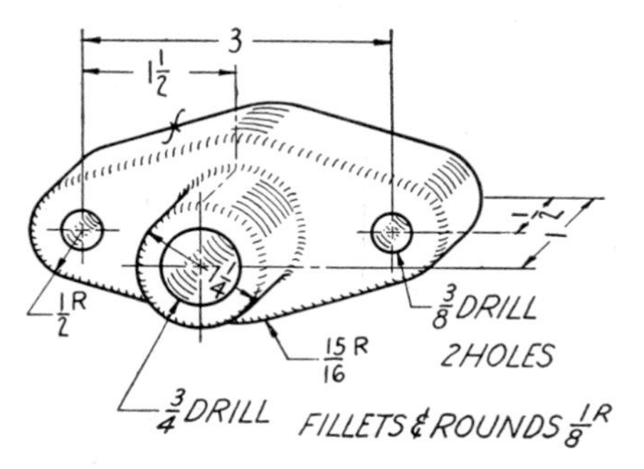

Fig. 7.92. Release bearing.

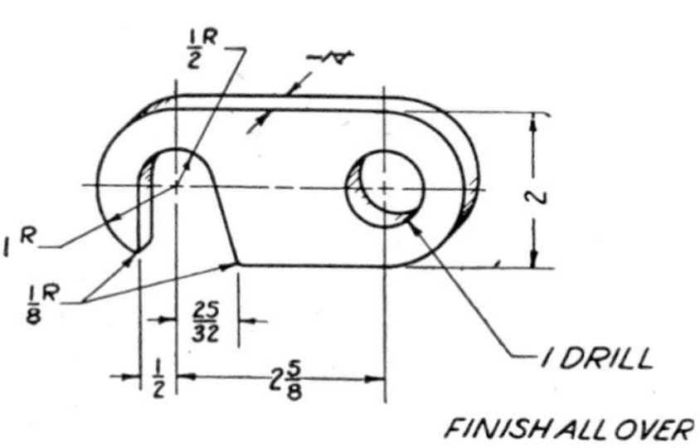

Fig. 7.93. Link.

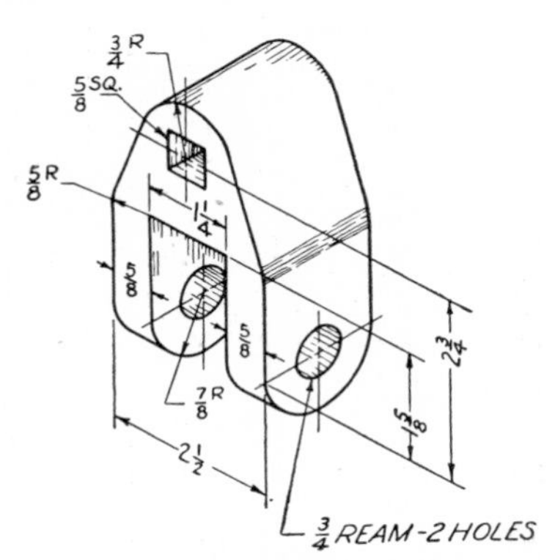

Fig. 7.94. Hinge link.

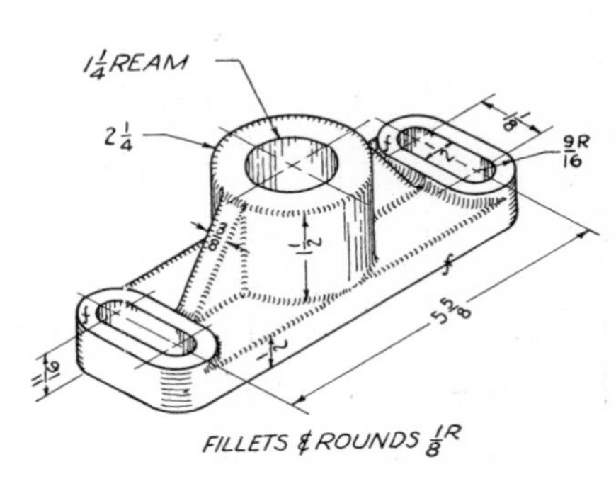

Fig. 7.95. Support base.

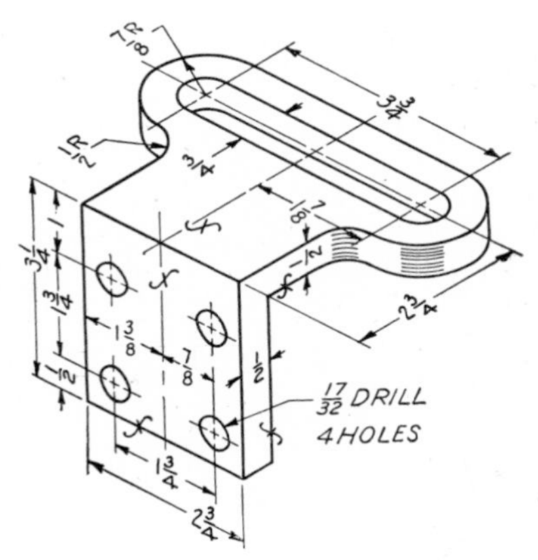

Fig. 7.96. Guide bracket.

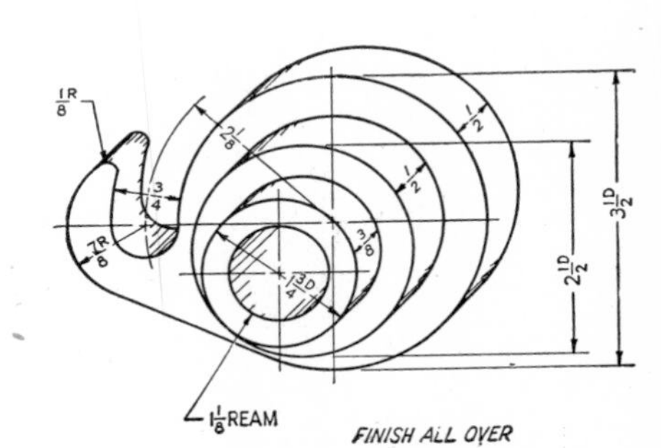

Fig. 7.97. Counter weight.

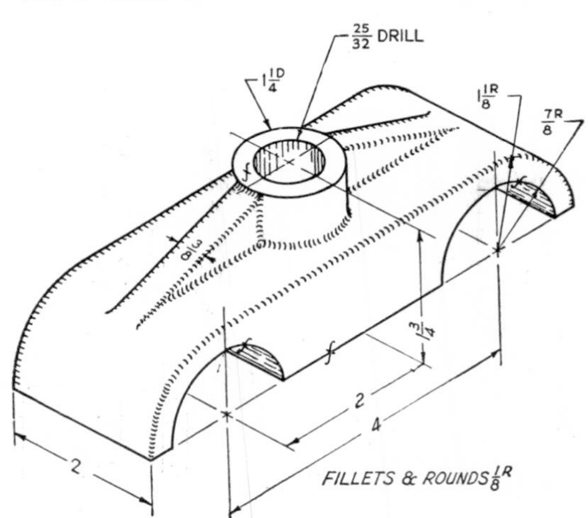

Fig. 7.98. Support stop.

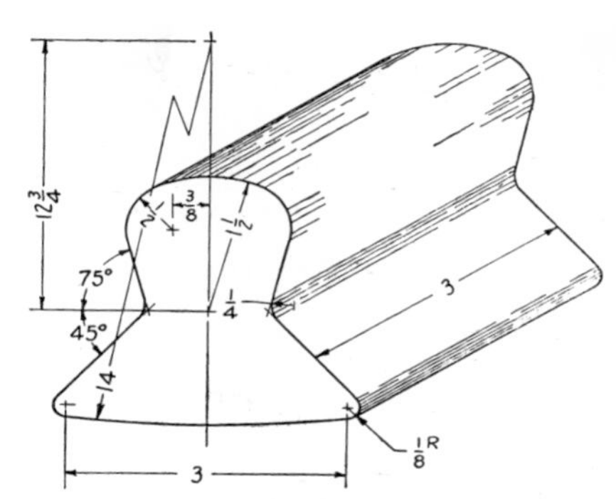

Fig. 7.99. Dolly block.

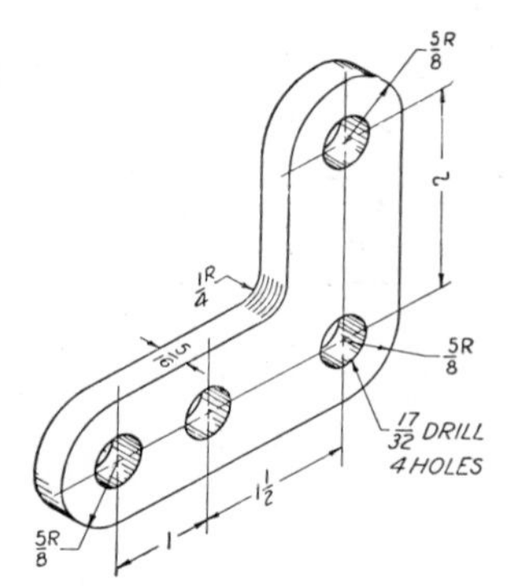

Fig. 7.100. End link.

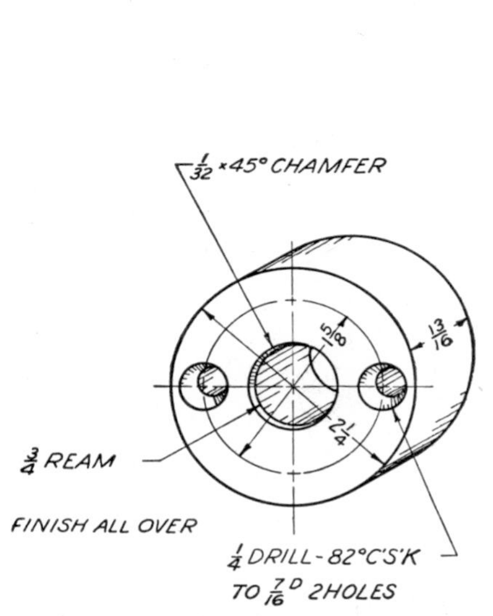

Fig. 7.101. Adjustment block.

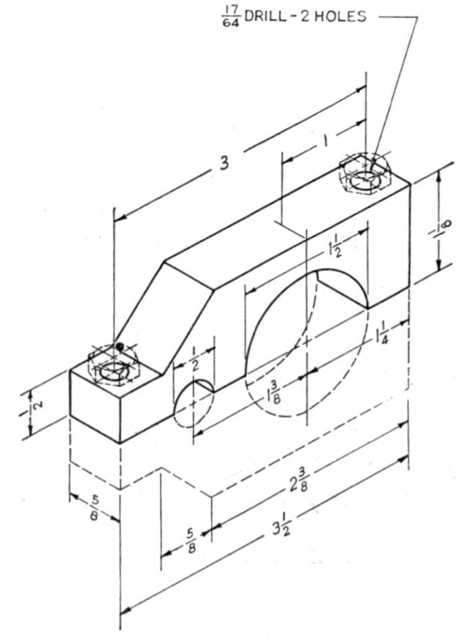

Fig. 7.102. Clamp spacer.

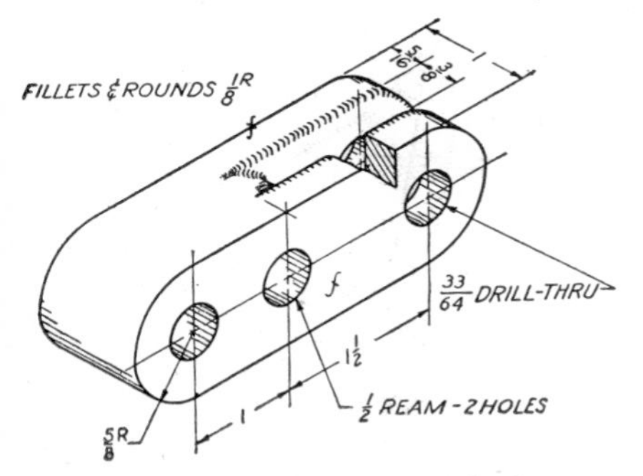

Fig. 7.103. Connecting link.

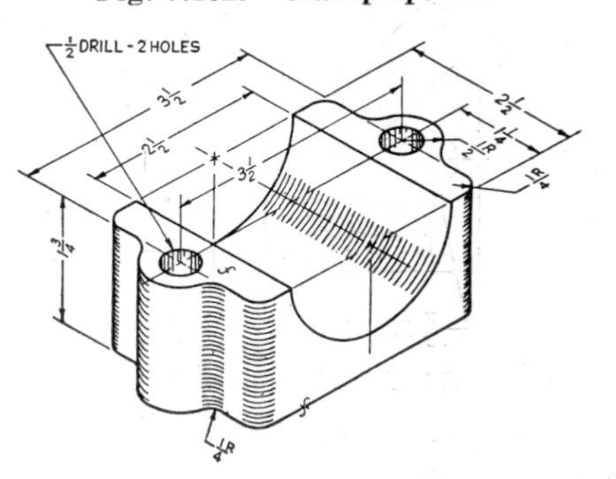

Fig. 7.104. Bearing block.

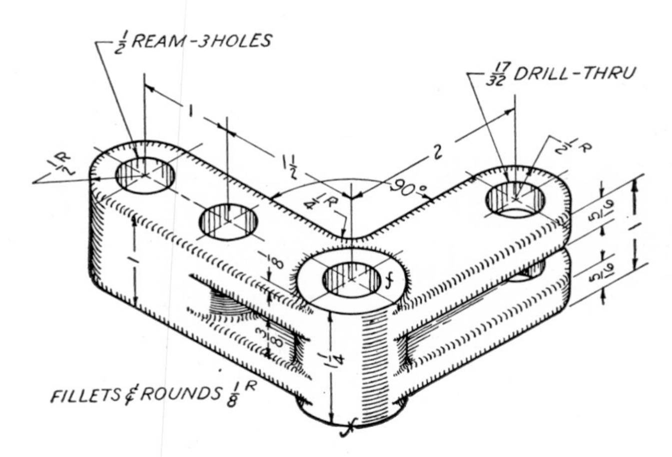

Fig. 7.105. Shifter link.

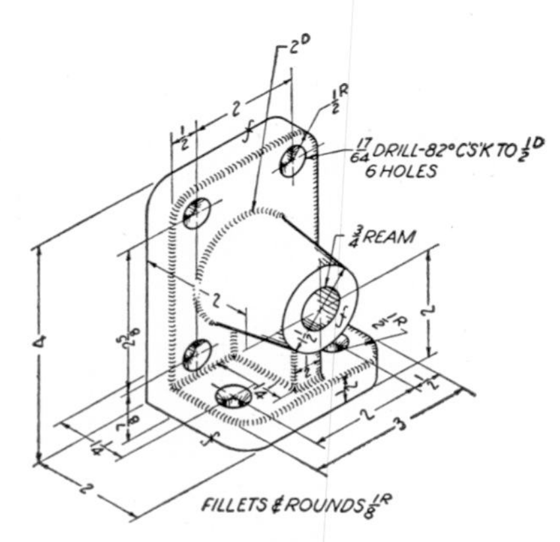

Fig. 7.106. Shaft bracket.

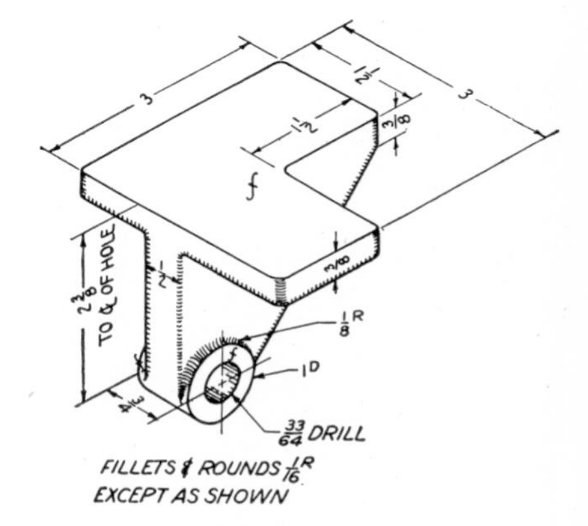

Fig. 7.107. Tool rest.

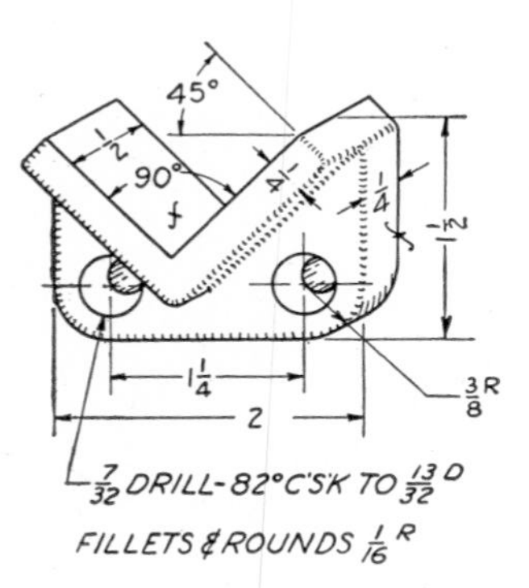

Fig. 7.108. Corner stop.

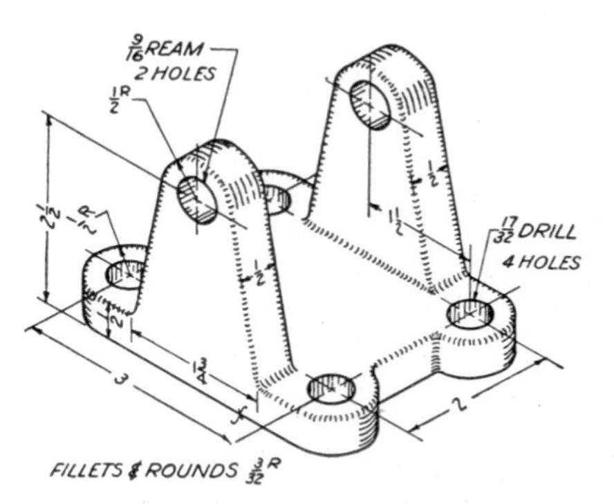

Fig. 7.109. Support bracket.

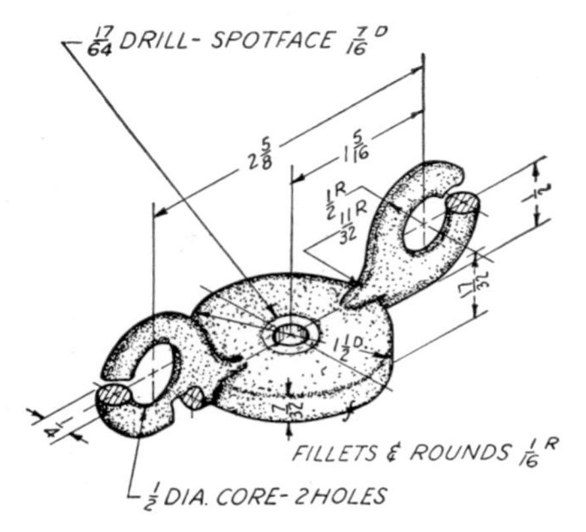

Fig. 7.110. Hanger.

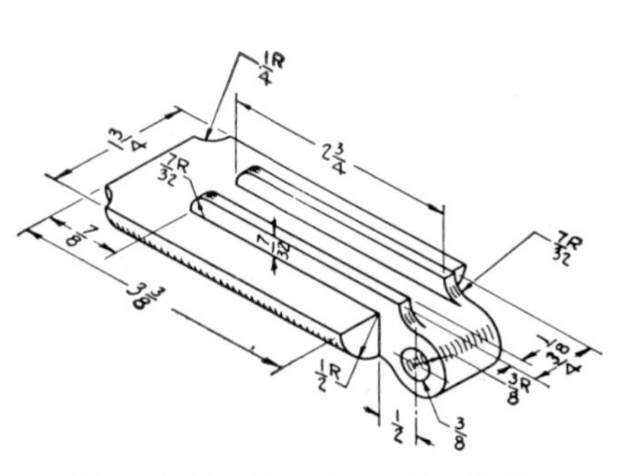

Fig. 7.111. Bearing oil well lid.

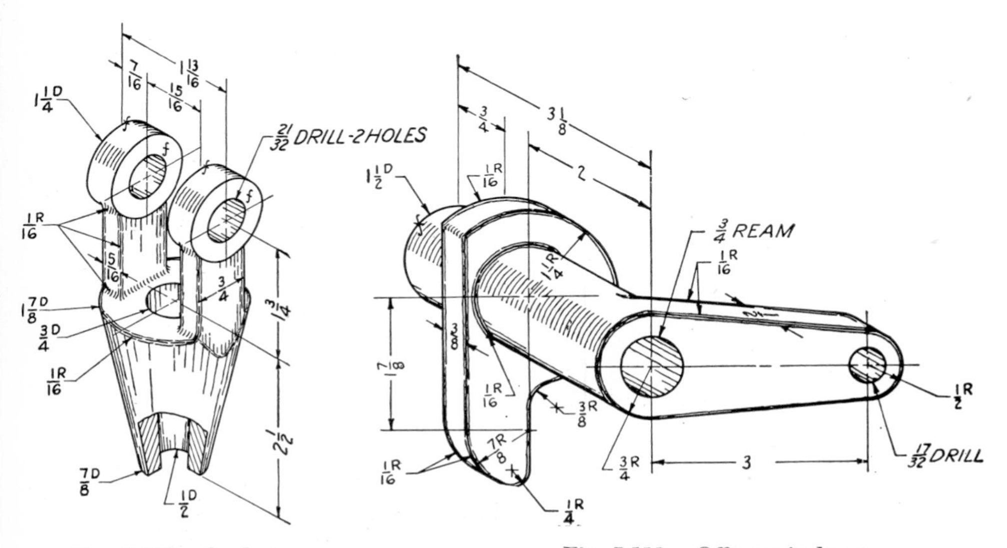

Fig. 7.112. Socket.

Fig. 7.113. Offset trip lever.

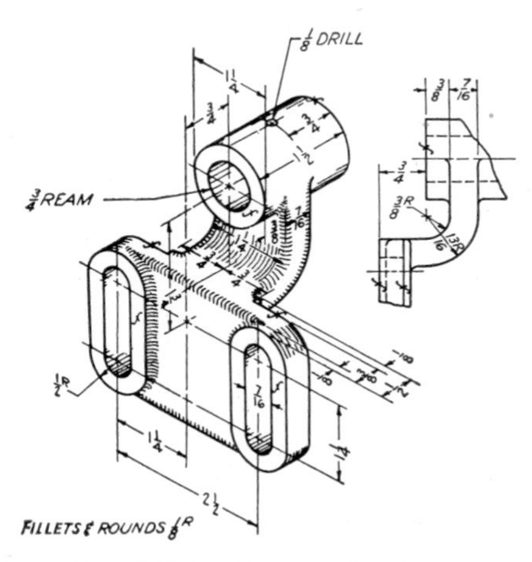

Fig. 7.114. Bearing bracket.

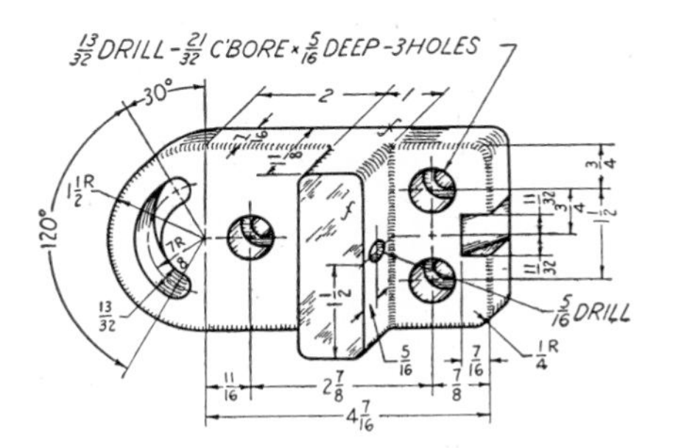

Fig. 7.115. Slotted base.

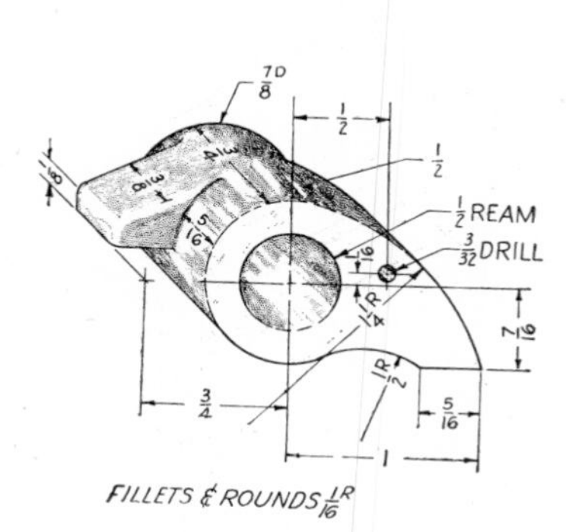

Fig. 7.116. Trip.

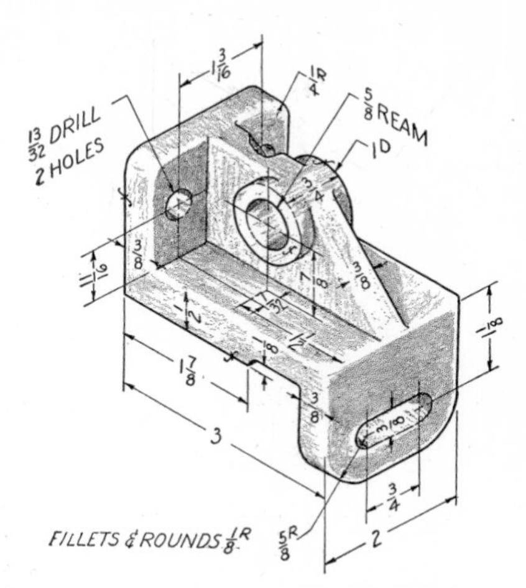

Fig. 7.117. Support bracket.

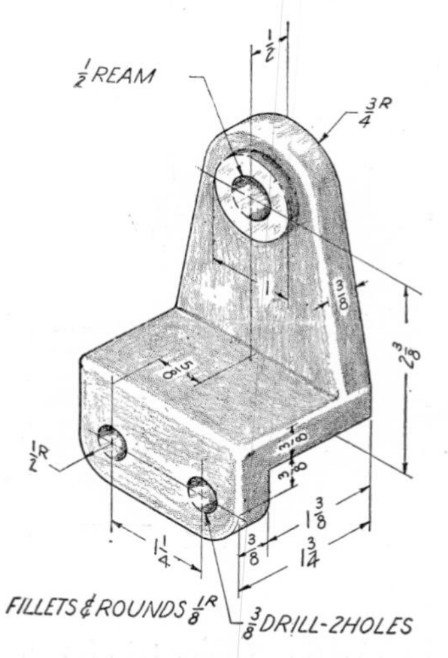

Fig. 7.118. Bearing bracket.

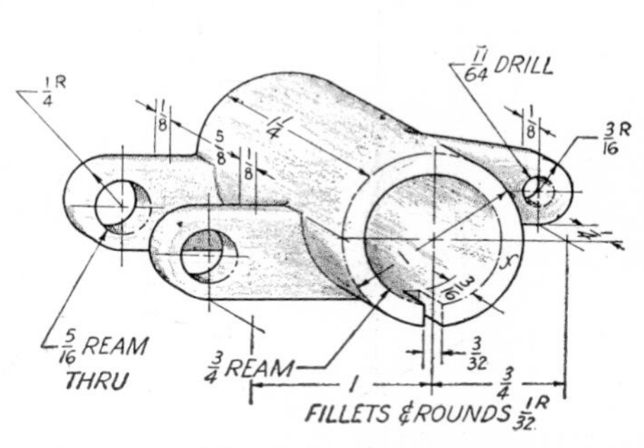

Fig. 7.119. Shaft guide.

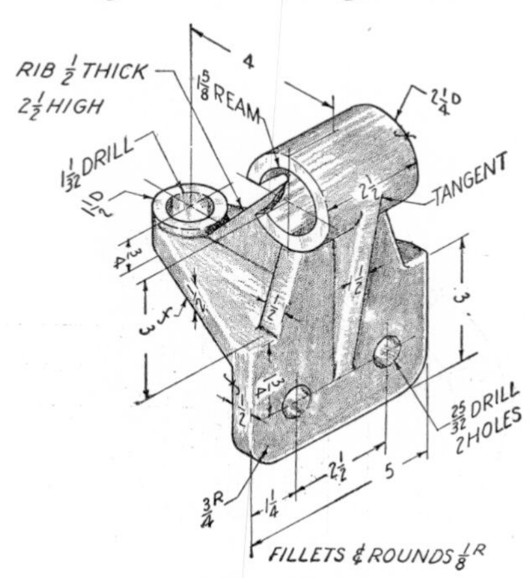

Fig. 7.120. Control bracket.

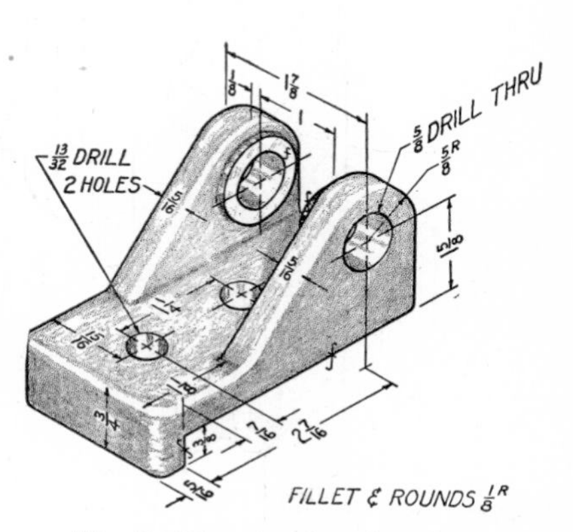

Fig. 7.121. Anchor bracket.

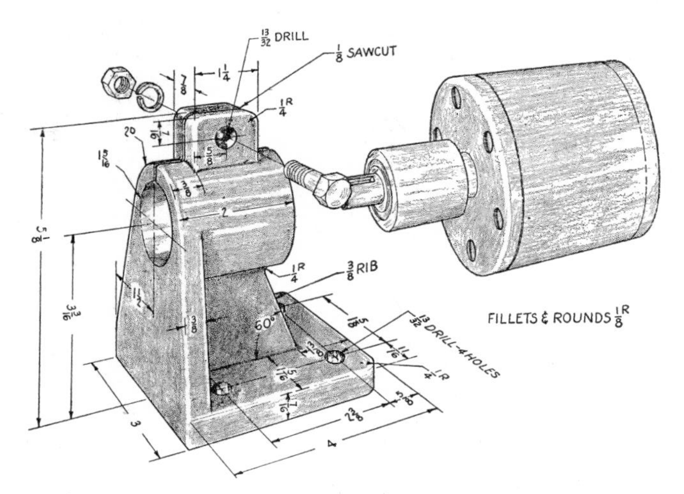

Fig. 7.122 Motor bracket.

87. (Fig. 7.123.) Make an orthographic drawing or sketch of the bench stop. The views may be dimensioned. The shaft portion that fits into the hole in the bench top is $\frac{3}{4}''$ in diameter and $2''$ long.

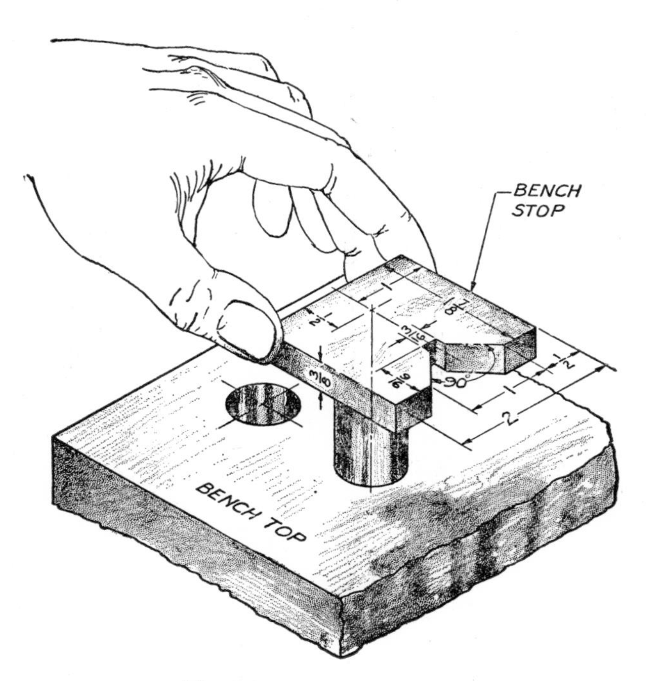

Fig. 7.123. Bench stop.

88. (Fig. 7.124.) Make a complete orthographic sketch or drawing of the trip. *Supplementary information:* (1) The diameter of the shaft is $1\frac{3}{8}''$. There should be a rather tight fit between the shaft and the broached hole. (2) The diameter of the hub is $2\frac{1}{4}''$. (3) The thickness of the rib is $\frac{5}{16}''$. (4) The rectangular surface shown in contact with the semi-spherical end of the trip pin is $\frac{7}{16}'' \times 1\frac{1}{2}''$. (5) The radius of the contact surface of the trip is $8''$. (6) Fillets and rounds $\frac{1}{8}''$ R. (7) Fillets and rounds have been purposely omitted from the pictorial drawing. They are to be shown by the student where necessary and desirable. (8) Mark all tangent points with a short dash across the line.

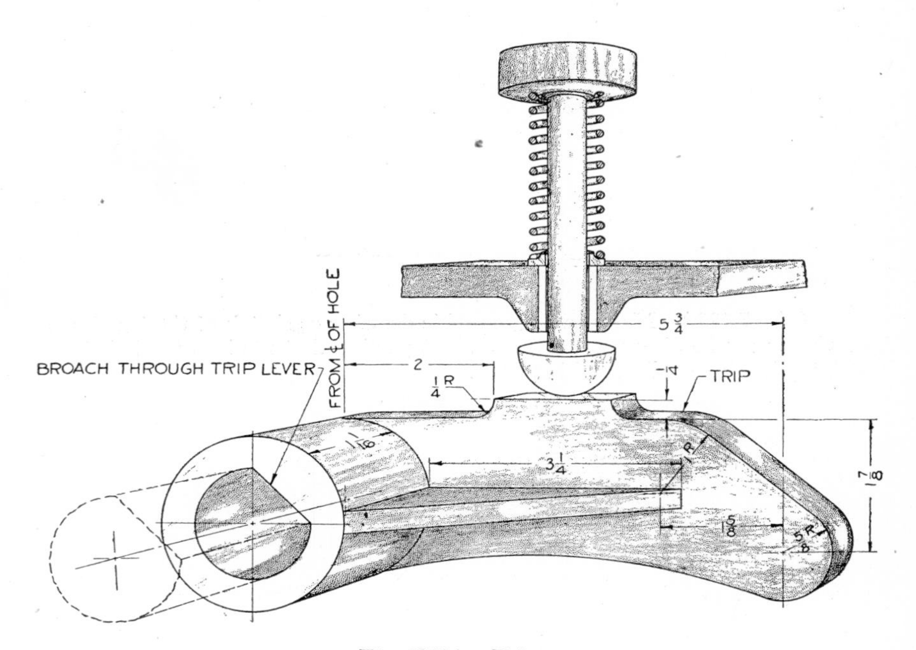

Fig. 7.124. Trip.

89. (Fig. 7.125.) Make a complete orthographic sketch or drawing of the bracket or link as assigned. *Supplementary information for bracket:* (1) The flat finished rectangular surface is $2\frac{1}{2}''$ above the centerline of the hole for the shaft. The over-all dimensions of this surface, which is fastened flush to a finished surface of the housing of the feed control, is $1\frac{1}{2}'' \times 2\frac{1}{2}''$. (2) The length of the cylindrical part is $2\frac{5}{16}''$. (3) The diameter of the shaft is $\frac{3}{4}''$. The hole in the bracket is to be reamed $\frac{1}{64}''$ larger for clearance. (4) The two small holes are drilled $\frac{1}{32}''$ over-size for $\frac{3}{8}''$ UNC bolts. They are $1\frac{1}{2}''$ apart center-to-center. (5) The ribs are $\frac{3}{8}''$ thick. The rib at the back of the plate is in a vertical plane and is tangent to the cylinder. (6) The *f* on the edge view of a surface indicates that the surface is to be finished. (7) The front face of the cylindrical portion to be finished contacts the surface of a collar which is not shown. (8) Fillets and rounds $\frac{1}{8}''$ R. Pay particular attention to fillets and rounds and their treatment. (9) Do not dimension. *Supplementary information for link:* (1) The three small holes are drilled over-size for a $\frac{3}{8}''$ rod as shown, and for $\frac{3}{8}''$ bolts. (2) The hole for the rod is $2\frac{1}{8}''$ above the center line of the hole for the shaft. (3) The holes for the bolts are $1\frac{1}{4}''$ apart. (4) The oil hole is to be drilled $\frac{1}{8}''$. (5) A control lever is attached to the boss side of the link by means of two $\frac{3}{8}''$ bolts. A positioning collar attached to the $\frac{3}{8}''$ rod comes in contact with the link.

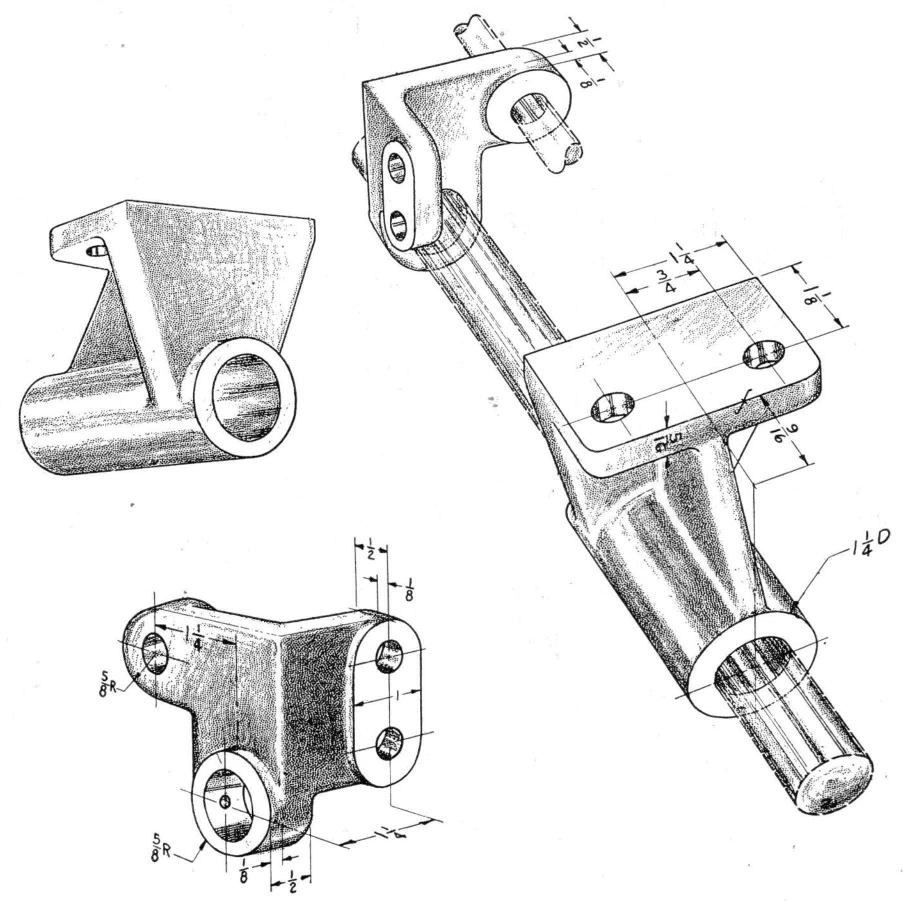

Fig. 7.125. Bracket and link.

90. (Fig. 7.126.) Make a complete orthographic drawing of the offset shaft bracket. *Supplementary information:* (1) The center line of the main shaft is $1\frac{3}{8}''$ above the finished surface of the pad. The hole in the bracket is to be reamed to accommodate a $1\frac{1}{4}''$ O.D. bushing as shown. (2) The length of the cylindrical part is $1\frac{1}{4}''$. Both faces, which are raised $\frac{1}{8}''$ on both sides, are contact faces. The O.D. is $1\frac{3}{4}''$. (3) The overall dimensions of the pad are to be $2\frac{3}{8}'' \times 2\frac{7}{8}''$. The $2\frac{3}{8}''$ dimension is in the direction parallel to the axis of the main shaft. (See bottom view.) (4) The small holes in the base are to be drilled oversize for $\frac{1}{2}''$-UNC cap screws. (5) The hole for the small shaft should be reamed larger for a $\frac{1}{2}''$ shaft. (6) The rib is to be $\frac{5}{16}''$ thick. It should finish tangent to the large cylinder. (7) Fillets and rounds are $\frac{1}{8}''$ R except as noted. (8) Pay particular attention to tangent runouts. (9) The near side of the $\frac{3}{8}''$ thick portion of the base is tangent to the $\frac{1}{2}$ R of the $\frac{7}{16}''$ thick base.

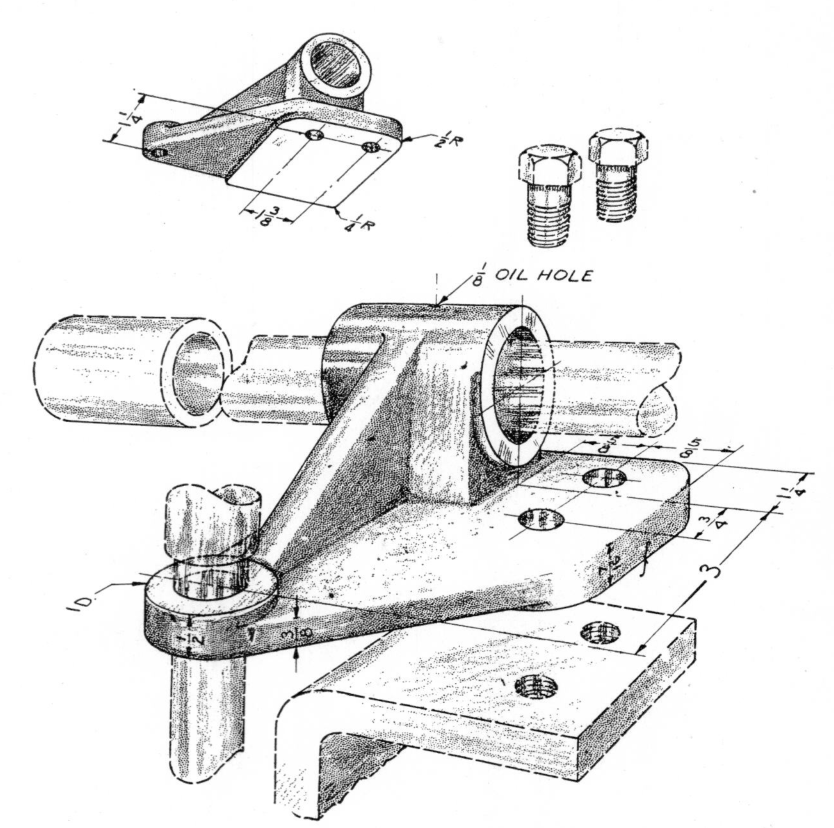

Fig. 7.126. Offset shaft bracket.

91. (Fig. 7.127.) Make a complete orthographic drawing of the cam or trip as assigned. The cam rotates, and with its irregular curved outline gives a predetermined vertical movement to the follower which provides automatic control for a barrel washer. Cams play an important part in the operation of many types of machines. *Supplementary information:* (1) The center hole of the guide cam is a pentagon inscribed in a circle $1\frac{1}{4}''$ in dia. (2) The cam track is $1\frac{1}{2}''$ thick. (3) The O.D. of both hubs is $1\frac{3}{4}''$. (4) The length of the front hub is $1\frac{15}{16}''$. (5) The overall dimension from the finished surface of one hub to the other is $6\frac{3}{32}''$. (6) The distance between the finished faces of the bosses around the curved slot is $1\frac{3}{4}''$. The purpose of a boss is to provide a raised surface for machining so that it will not be necessary to machine a larger area than is needed. When the cam and trip are in a particular position, the trip strikes a release pin which allows the barrel to move on to a conveyor. *Supplementary information for trip:* (1) The center for the $\frac{1}{4}$ R is in the plane of the $\frac{1}{2}'' \times \frac{1}{2}''$ plane surface. (2) The $1\frac{1}{2}''$ R and $2\frac{1}{2}''$ R arcs are tangent to the $1\frac{1}{2}''$ D cylinder.

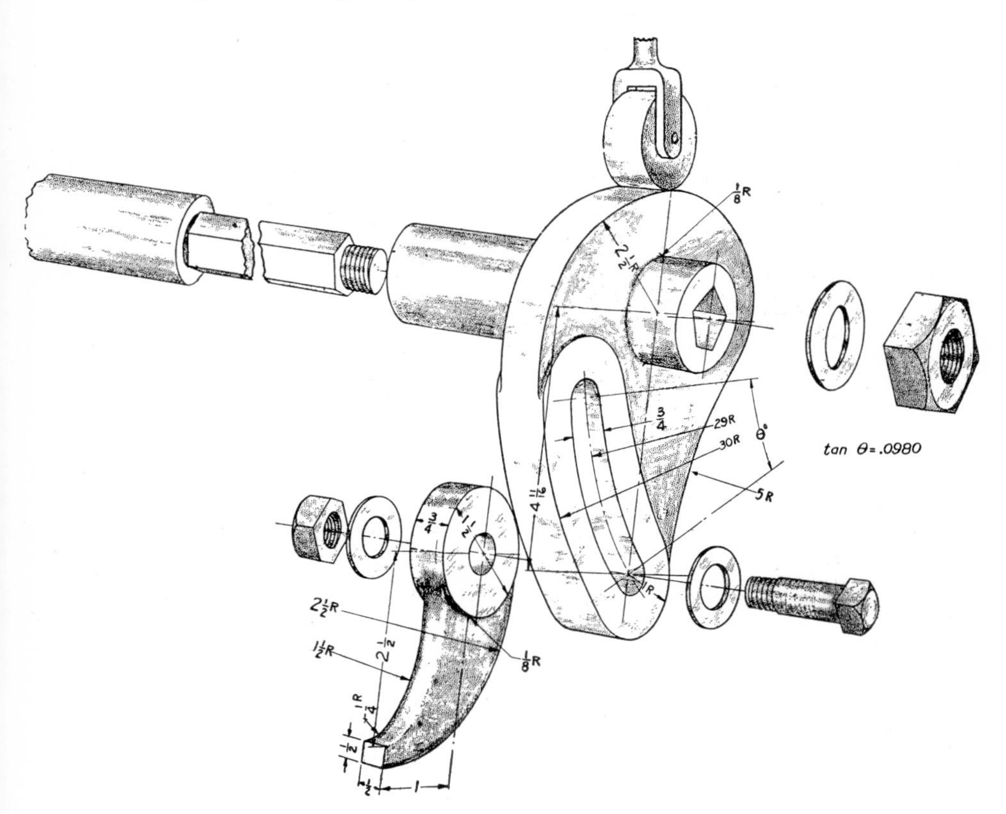

Fig. 7.127. Cam and trip (Barrel Washer).

92. (Fig. 7.128.) Make a complete orthographic drawing of the tube holder.

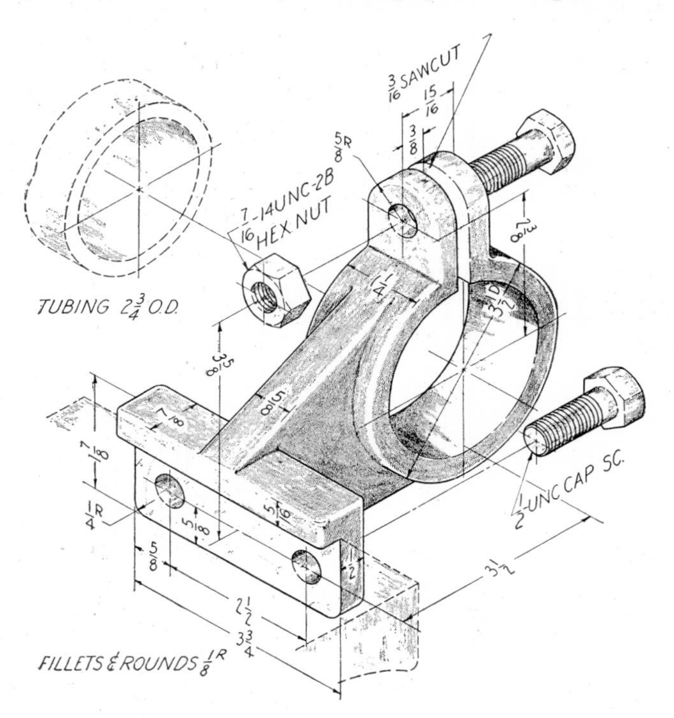

Fig. 7.128. Tube holder.

93. (Fig. 7.129.) Make a complete orthographic drawing of the anchor bracket.

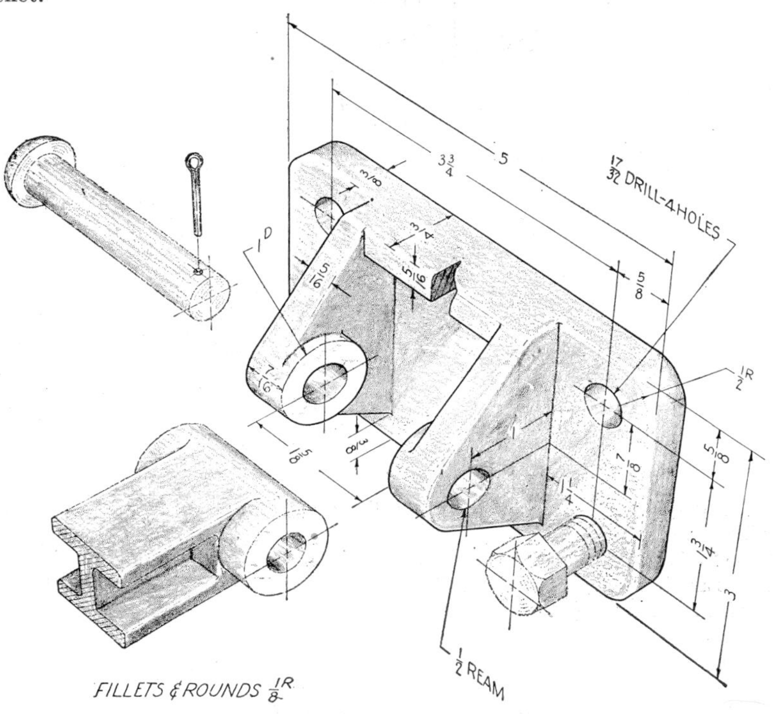

Fig. 7.129. Anchor bracket.

94. (Fig. 7.130.) Make a complete orthographic drawing of the stud guide.

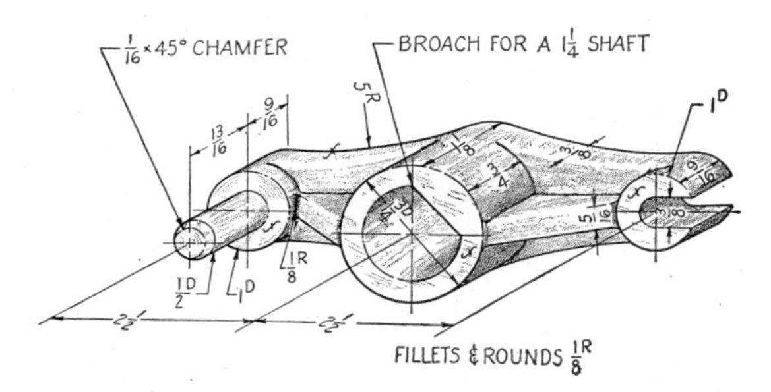

Fig. 7.130. Stud guide.

95. (Fig. 7.131.) Make a complete orthographic drawing of the shifter.

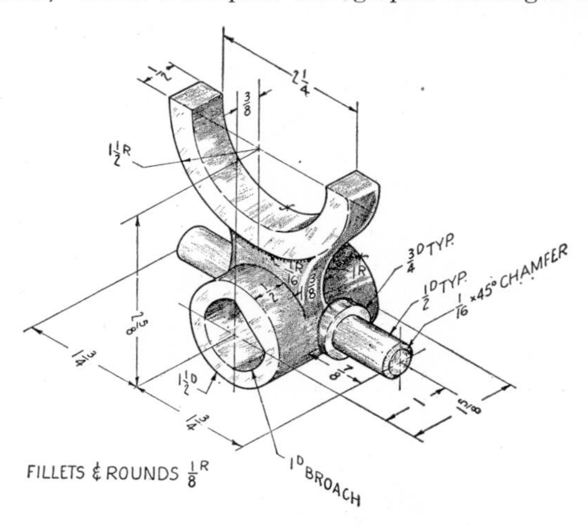

Fig. 7.131. Shifter.

96. (Fig. 7.132.) Make a complete three-view drawing of the motor base. The ribs are $\frac{3}{8}''$ thick. At points A, four holes are to be drilled for $\frac{1}{2}''$ bolts that are to be $2\frac{1}{2}''$ center to center in one direction and $3\frac{1}{8}''$ in the other. At points B, four holes are to be drilled for $\frac{1}{2}''$ bolts that fasten the motor base to a steel column. Fillets and rounds are $\frac{1}{8}^{R}$.

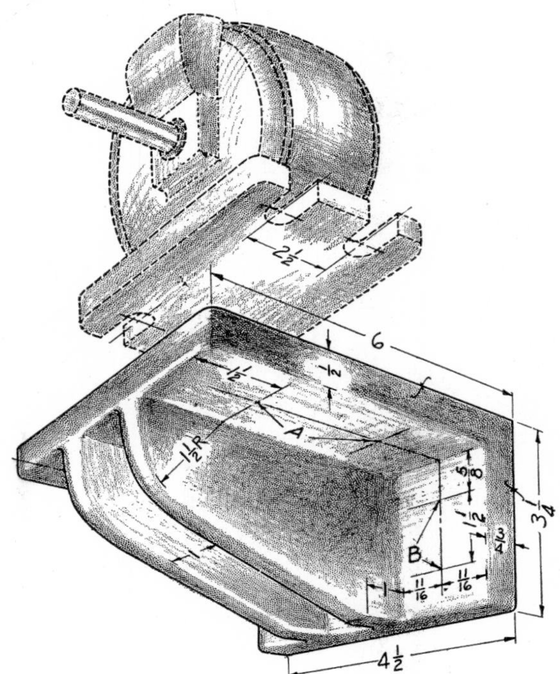

Fig. 7.132. Motor base.

97–98. (Fig. 7.133.) Make a complete three-view drawing of the tool rest and/or the tool rest bracket. The rectangular top surface of the tool rest is to be $1\frac{1}{8}''$ above the center line of the hole for the $\frac{7}{16}''$ bolt. The over-all dimensions of the top are $1\frac{1}{4}'' \times 2\frac{1}{2}''$. It is to be $\frac{1}{4}''$ thick. The over-all dimensions of the rectangular pad of the bracket are $1\frac{1}{4}'' \times 1\frac{7}{8}''$. The center line of the adjustment slot is $\frac{9}{16}''$ above the center line of the top holes in the rectangular pad and the distance from center line to center line of the slot is $1\frac{3}{8}''$. The bracket is to be fastened to a housing with $\frac{1}{4}''$ round head machine screws.

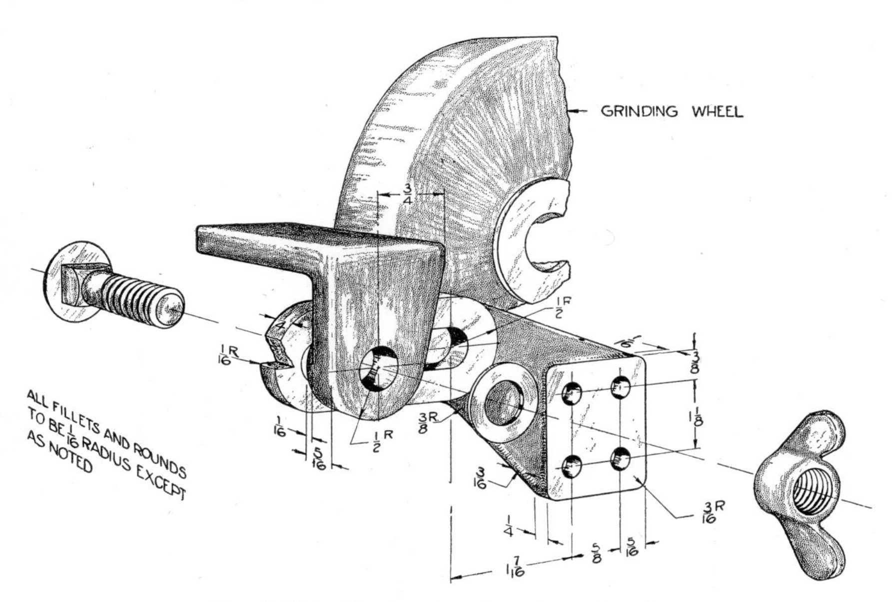

Fig. 7.133. Tool rest and tool rest bracket.

8 AUXILIARY VIEWS

8.1. When it is desirable to show the true size and shape of an irregular surface, which is inclined to two or more of the co-ordinate planes of projection, a view of the surface must be projected on a plane parallel to it. This imaginary projection plane is called an auxiliary plane, and the view obtained is called an auxiliary view (Fig. 8.1).

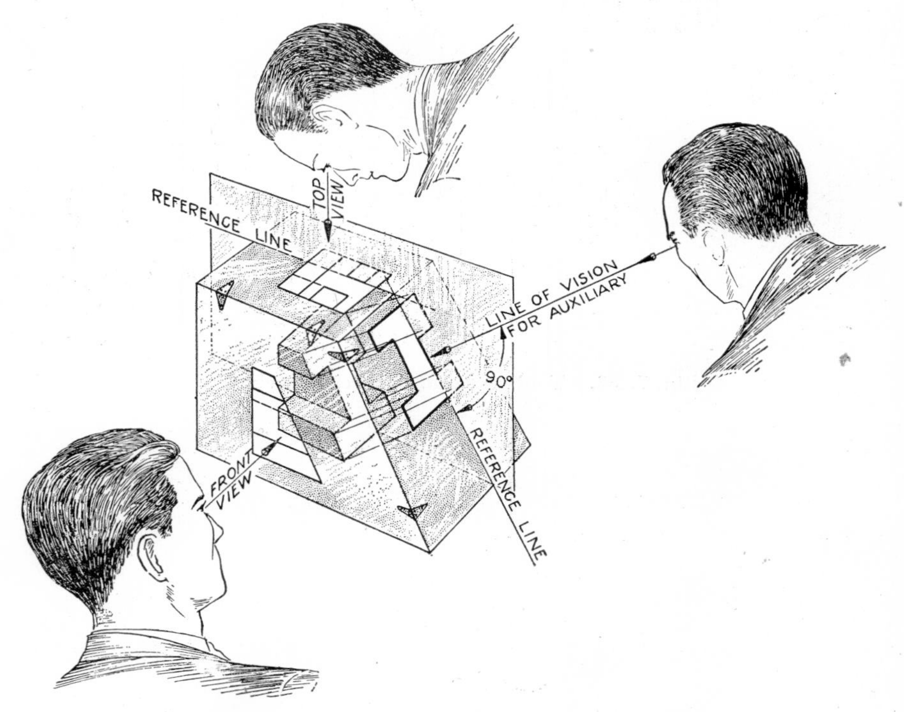

Fig. 8.1. Theory of projecting an auxiliary view.

The theory underlying the method of projecting principal views applies also to auxiliary views. In other words, an auxiliary view shows an inclined surface of an object as it would appear to an observer stationed an infinite distance away (Fig. 8.2).

8.2. The use of auxiliary views. In commercial drafting, an auxiliary view ordinarily is a partial view showing only an inclined surface. The reason for this is that a projection showing the entire object adds very little to the shape description. The added lines are likely to defeat the intended purpose of an auxiliary view. For example, a complete drawing

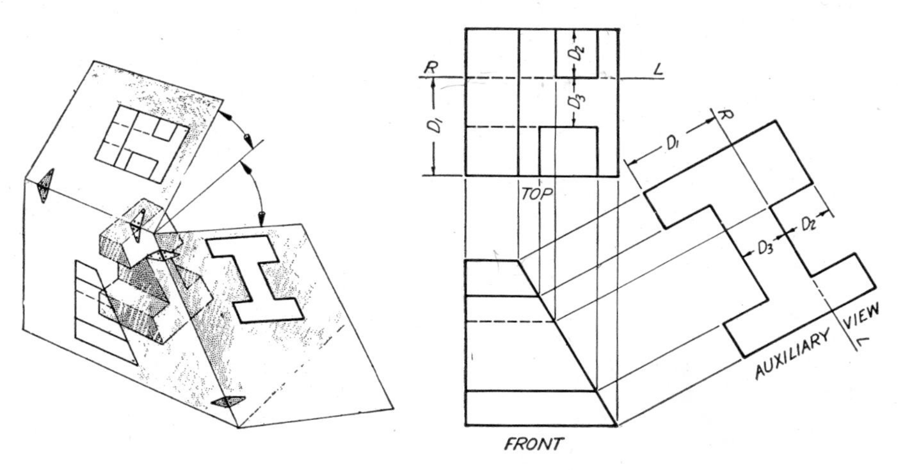

Fig. 8.2. An auxiliary view.

of the casting in Fig. 8.3 must include an auxiliary view of the inclined surface in order to show the true shape of the surface and the location of the holes. Compare the views in (*a*) and (*b*) and note the confused appearance of the view in (*b*). In technical schools, some instructors require

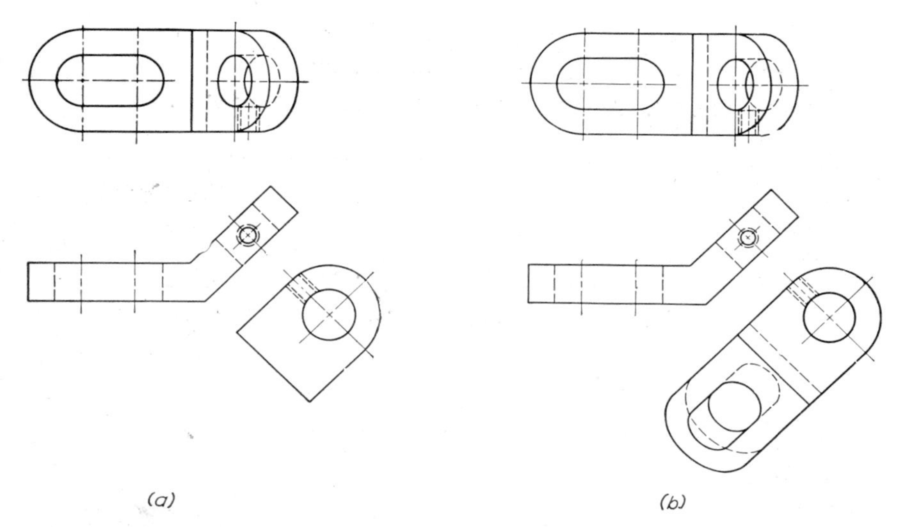

Fig. 8.3. Partial and complete auxiliary views.

that an auxiliary view show the entire object, including all invisible lines. Such a requirement, though impractical commercially, is justified in the classroom, for the construction of a complete auxiliary view furnishes excellent practice in projection.

A partial auxiliary view often is needed to complete the projection of a foreshortened feature in a principal view. This second important function of auxiliary views is illustrated in Fig. 8.15 and explained in Sec. 8.11.

8.3. Types of auxiliary views. Although auxiliary views may have an infinite number of positions in relation to the three principal planes of projection, primary auxiliary views may be classified into three general types in accordance with position relative to the principal planes. Fig. 8.4 shows the first type where the auxiliary plane is perpendicular to the frontal plane and inclined to the horizontal plane of projection. Here the

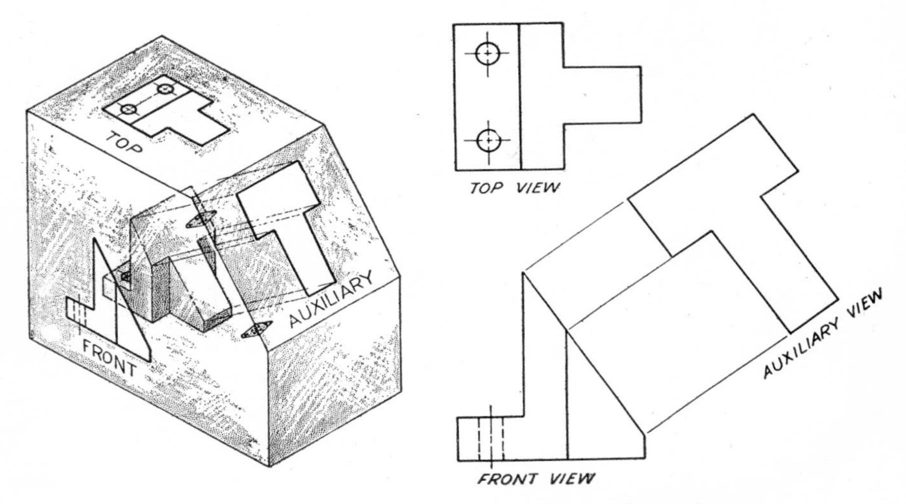

Fig. 8.4. Auxiliary view projected from front view.

auxiliary view and top view have one dimension that is common to both, the depth. Note that the auxiliary plane is hinged to the frontal plane, and that the auxiliary view is projected from the front view.

In Fig. 8.5 the auxiliary plane is perpendicular to the horizontal plane and inclined to the frontal and profile planes of projection. The auxiliary view is projected from the top view, and its height is the same as the height of the front view.

The third type of auxiliary view, as shown in Fig. 8.6, is projected from the side view and has a common dimension with both the front and top views. To construct it, distances may be taken from either the front or top view.

All three types of auxiliary views are constructed similarly. Each is projected from the view that shows the surface as an oblique line, and the distances for the view are taken from the other principal view that has a common dimension with the auxiliary. A careful study of the three illustrations will reveal the fact that the inclined auxiliary plane is always hinged to the principal plane to which it is perpendicular.

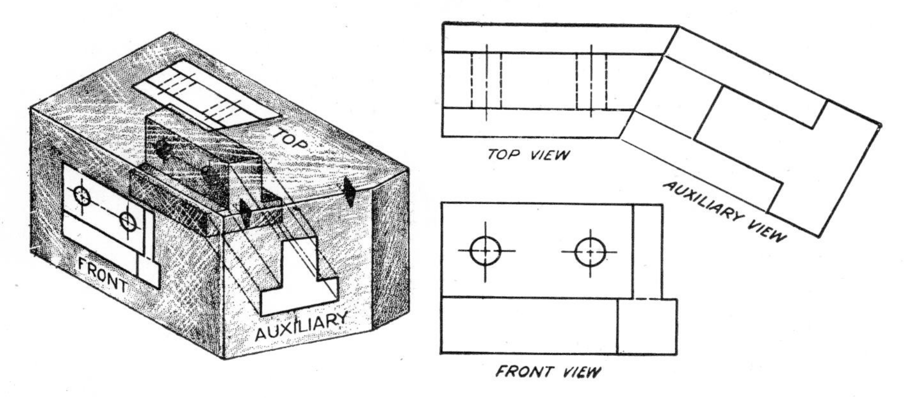

Fig. 8.5. Auxiliary view projected from top view.

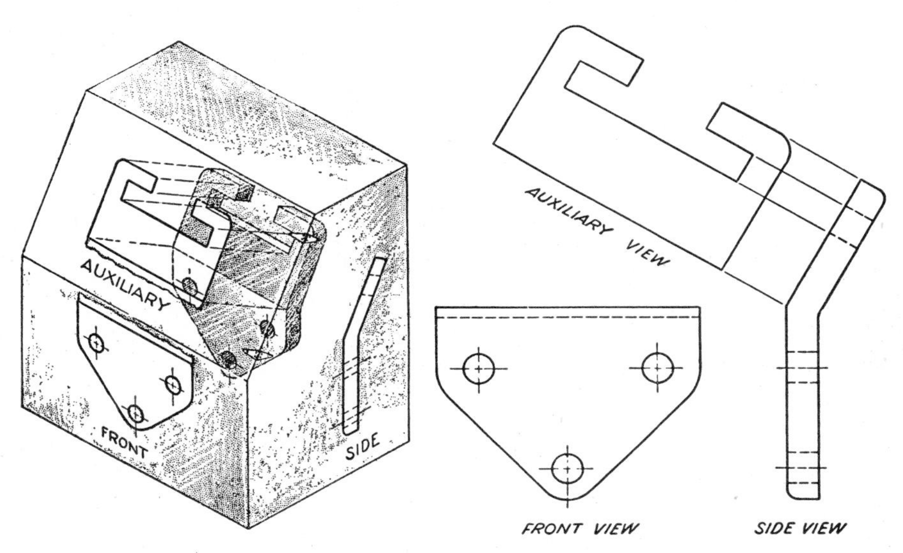

Fig. 8.6. Auxiliary view projected from side view.

8.4. Symmetrical and unsymmetrical auxiliary views. Since auxiliary views are either symmetrical or unsymmetrical about a center line or reference line, they may be termed (1) symmetrical, (2) unilateral, or (3) bilateral, according to the degree of symmetry. A symmetrical view is drawn symmetrically about a center line, the unilateral view entirely on one side of a reference line, and the bilateral view on both sides of a reference line.

8.5. To draw a symmetrical auxiliary view. When an inclined surface is symmetrical, the auxiliary view is "worked" from a center line (Fig. 8.7). The first step in drawing such a view is to draw a center line parallel to the oblique line that represents an edge view of the surface. If the object is assumed to be enclosed in a glass box, this center line may be considered the line of intersection of the auxiliary plane and an imaginary vertical center plane. There are professional draftsmen who, not acquainted with the "glass" box, proceed without theoretical explanation. Their method is simply to draw a working center line for the auxiliary view and a corresponding line in one of the principal views.

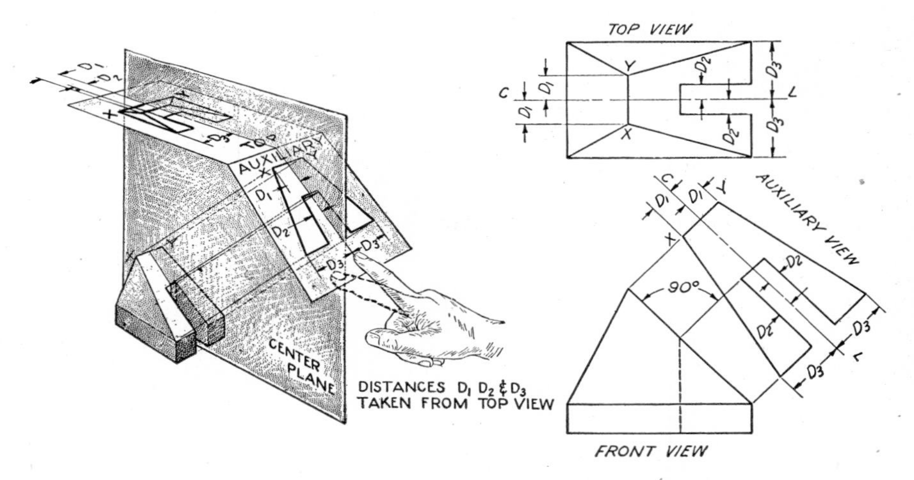

Fig. 8.7. A symmetrical auxiliary view of an inclined surface.

Although, theoretically, this working center line may be drawn at any distance from the principal view, actually it should be so located to give the whole drawing a balanced appearance. If not already shown, it also must be drawn in the principal view showing the true width of the inclined surface.

The next step is to draw projection lines from each point of the sloping face, remembering that the projectors make an angle of 90° with the inclined line representing the surface. With the projectors drawn, the location of each point in the auxiliary can be established by setting the dividers to each point's distance from the center line in the principal view and transferring the distance to the auxiliary view. For example, point X is projected to the auxiliary by drawing a projector from point X in the front view perpendicular to the center line. Since its distance from the center line in the top view is the same as it is from the center line in the auxiliary view, the point's location along the projector may be established by using the distance taken from the top view. In the case of point X, the distance is set off from the center line toward the front view. Point Y is set off from the center line away from the front view. A careful study of

Fig. 8.7 reveals the fact that if a point lies between the front view and the center line of the top view, it will lie between the front view and the center line of the auxiliary view, and, conversely, if it lies away from the front view with reference to the center line of the top view, it will lie away from the front view with reference to the center line of the auxiliary view.

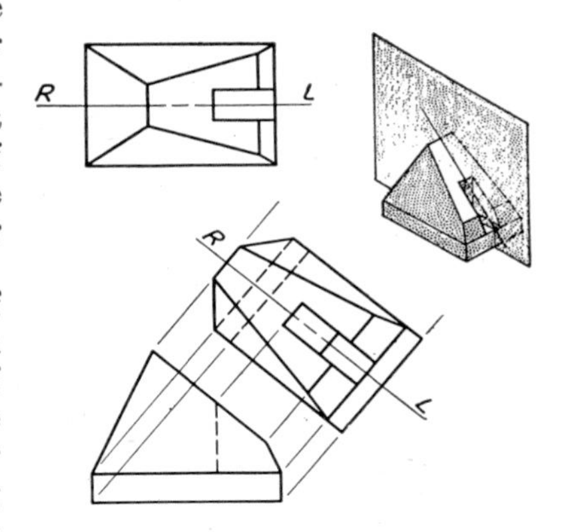

Fig. 8.8. An auxiliary view of an object.

Fig. 8.8 shows an auxiliary view of an entire object. In constructing such a view, the projectors from all points of the object must be perpendicular to the working center line, since the observer views the entire figure by looking directly at the inclined surface. The distances perpendicular to the auxiliary center line are taken from the top view.

8.6. Unilateral auxiliary views. When constructing a unilateral auxiliary view, it is necessary to work from a reference line that is drawn in a manner similar to the working center line of a symmetrical view. The reference line may be considered to represent the line of intersection

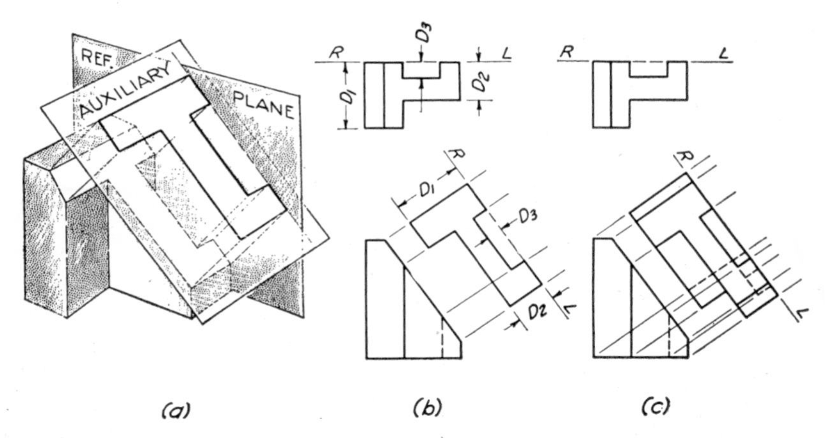

Fig. 8.9. A unilateral auxiliary view.

of a reference plane with the back edge of the inclined face (Fig. 8.9). The intersection of this plane with the top plane establishes the reference line in the top view. All the points are projected from the oblique line, as in a symmetrical view, and it should be noted in setting them off that they all fall on the same side of the reference line.

8.7. Bilateral auxiliary views. The method of drawing a bilateral view is similar to that of drawing a unilateral view, the only difference being that in a bilateral view the inclined face lies partly on both sides of the reference plane, as shown in Fig. 8.10.

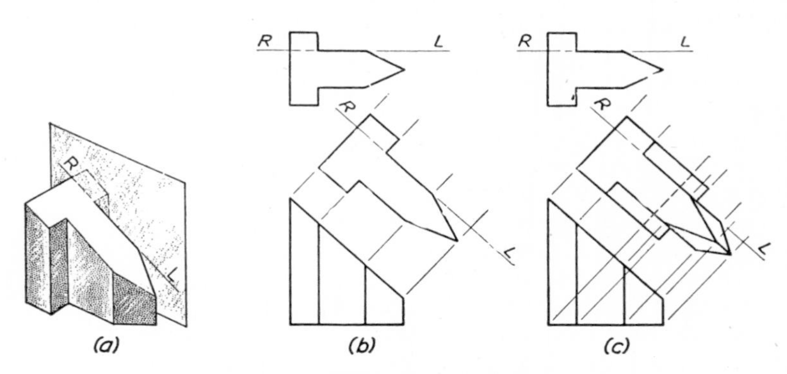

Fig. 8.10. A bilateral auxiliary view.

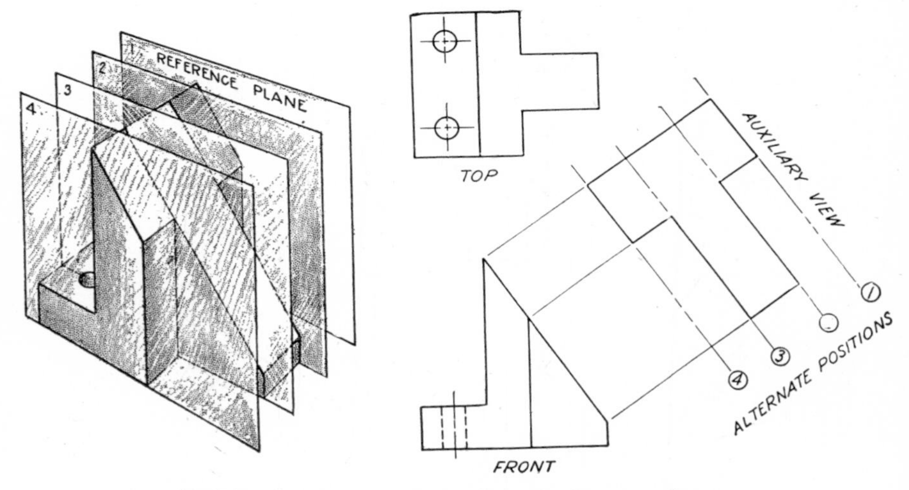

Fig. 8.11. Choice of position of reference plane.

8.8. Curved lines in auxiliary views. To draw a curve in an auxiliary view, the draftsman must plot a sufficient number of points to insure a smooth curve (see Fig. 8.12). The points are projected first to the oblique line representing the surface in the front view and then to the auxiliary view. The distance of any point from the center line in the auxiliary view is the same as its distance from the center line in the end view.

8.9. To construct an auxiliary view, practical method. The usual steps in constructing an auxiliary view are shown in Fig. 8.13. The illustration should be studied carefully, as each step is explained on the drawing.

8.10. Often the use of an auxiliary view allows the elimination of one of the principal views (front, top, or side) or makes possible the use of a partial principal view. The shape description furnished by the partial views shown in Fig. 8.14 is sufficient for a complete understanding of the

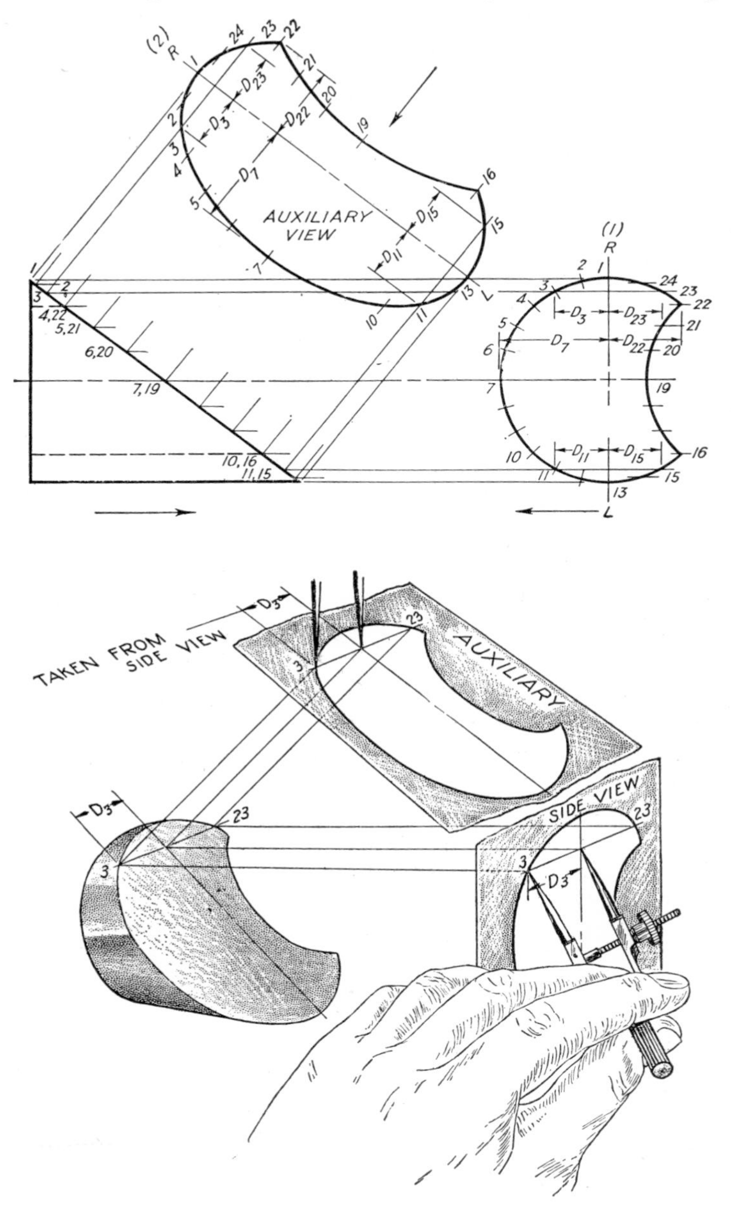

Fig. 8.12. Curved line auxiliary view.

shape of the part. The use of partial views simplifies the drawing, saves valuable drafting time, and tends to make the drawing easier to read.

A break line is used at a convenient location to indicate an imaginary break for a partial view.

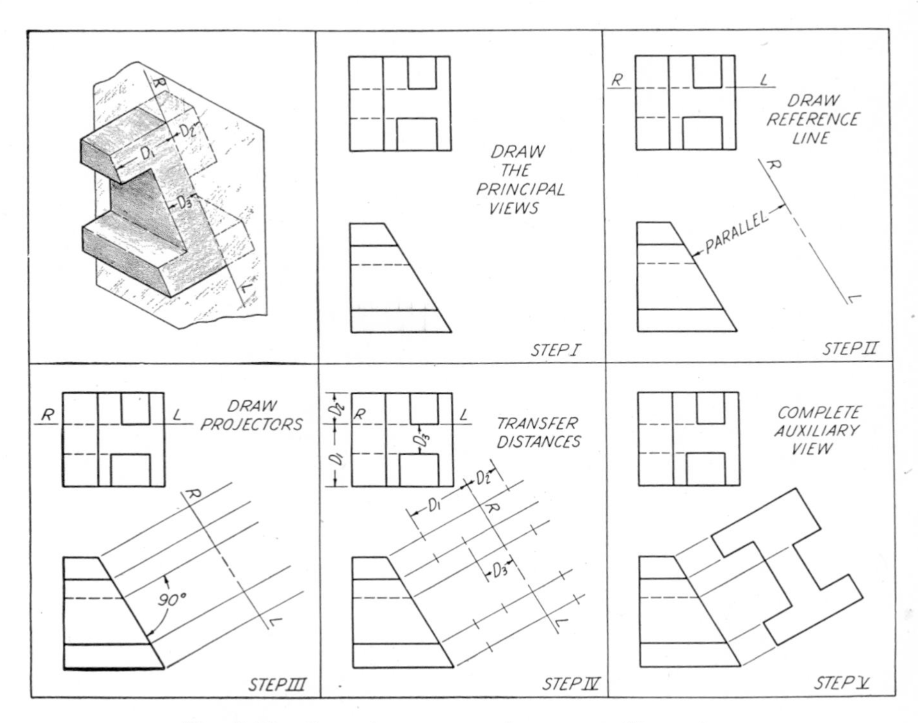

Fig. 8.13. Steps in constructing an auxiliary view.

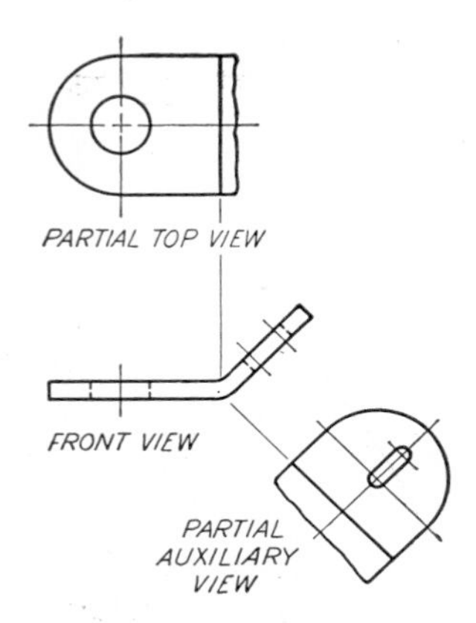

Fig. 8.14. Partial views.

8.11. The use of an auxiliary view to complete a principal view. As previously stated, it is frequently necessary to project a foreshortened feature in one of the principal views from an auxiliary view. In the case of the object shown in Fig. 8.15, the foreshortened projection of the in-

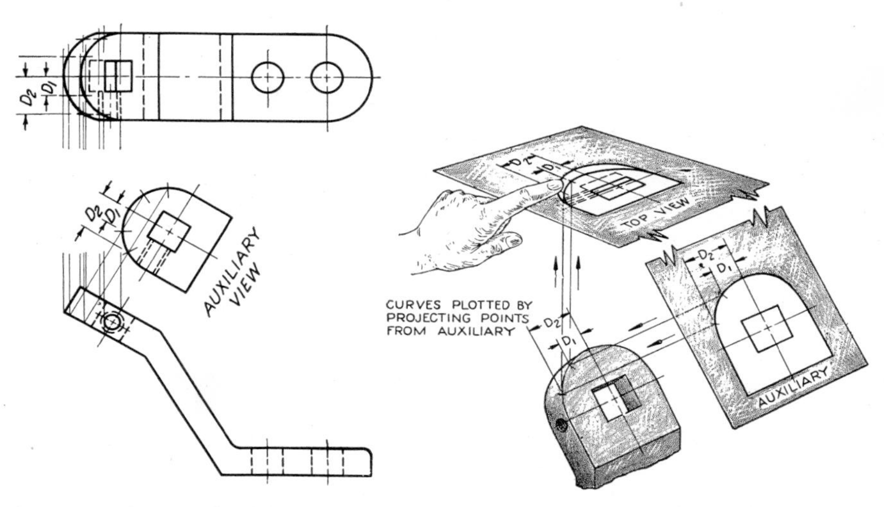

Fig. 8.15. Use of auxiliary to complete a principal view.

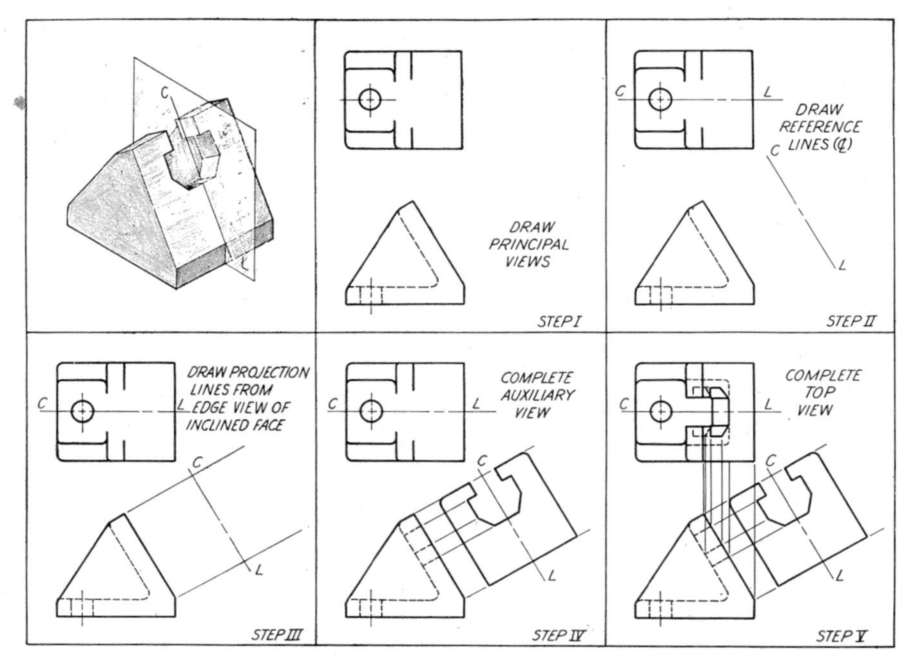

Fig. 8.16. Steps in preparing an auxiliary view and completing a principal view.

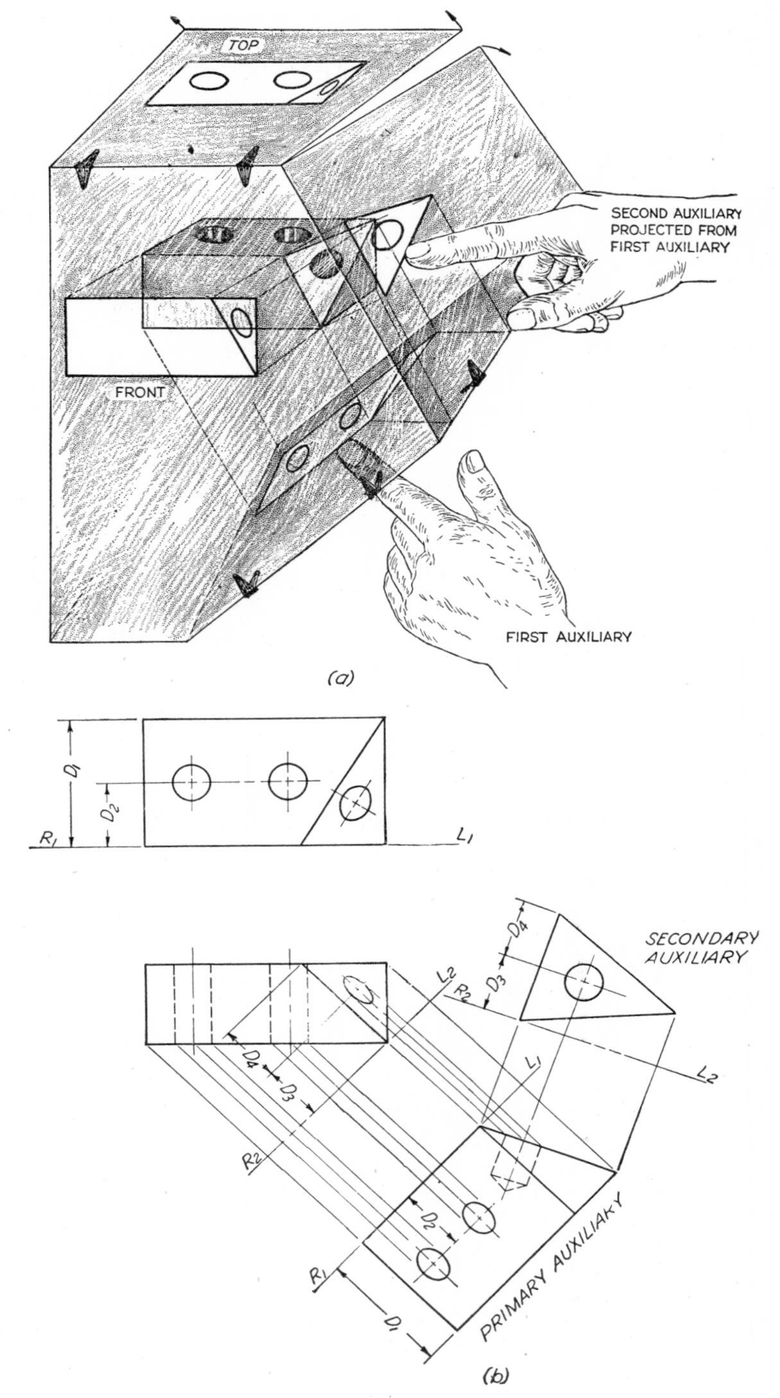

Fig. 8.17. A secondary auxiliary view of an oblique face.

clined face in the top view can be projected from the auxiliary view. The elliptical curves are plotted by projecting points from the auxiliary view to the front view and from there to the top view. The location of these points in the top view with respect to the center line is the same as their location in the auxiliary view with respect to the auxiliary center line. For example, the distance D_1 from the center line in the top view is the same as the distance D_1 from the auxiliary center line in the auxiliary view.

The steps in preparing an auxiliary view and using it to complete a principal view are shown in Fig. 8.16.

8.12. Secondary (oblique) auxiliary views. Frequently an object will have an inclined face that is not perpendicular to any one of the principal planes of projection. In such cases it is necessary to draw two auxiliary views (Fig. 8.17). The primary auxiliary view is constructed by projecting the figure upon a primary auxiliary plane that is perpendicular to the inclined surface and one of the principal planes. This plane may be at any convenient location. In the illustration, the primary auxiliary plane is perpendicular to the frontal plane. Note that the inclined face appears as a straight line in the primary auxiliary view. Using this view as a regular view, the secondary auxiliary view may be projected upon a plane parallel to the inclined face. Fig. 8.17(*b*) shows a practical application of the theoretical principles shown pictorially in (*a*).

Fig. 8.18 shows the progressive steps in preparing and using a secondary auxiliary view of an oblique face to complete a principal view. Reference planes have been used as datum planes from which to take the necessary

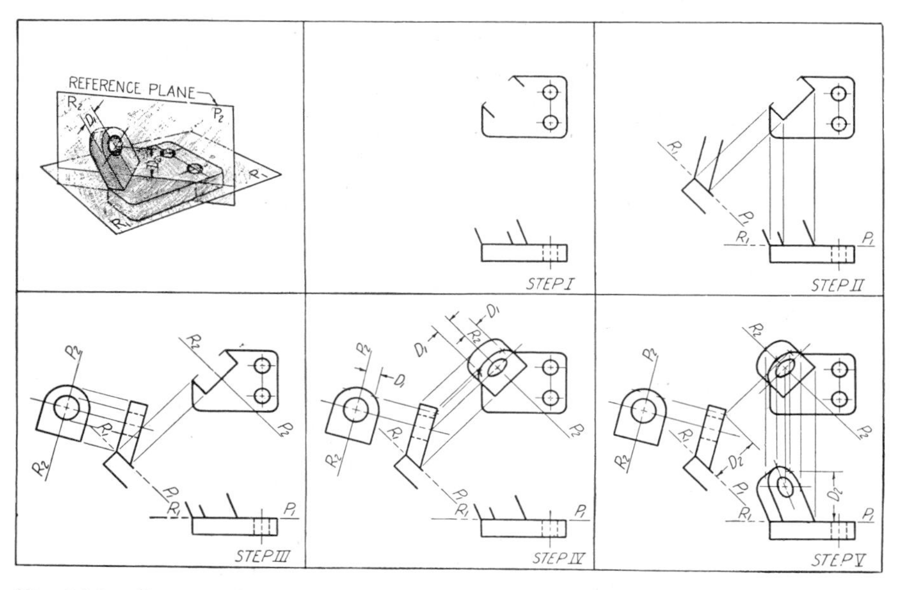

Fig. 8.18. Steps in drawing a secondary auxiliary view and using it to complete a principal view.

measurements. Step II shows the partial construction of the primary auxiliary view in which the inclined surface appears as a line. Step III shows the secondary auxiliary view projected from the primary view and completed, using the known measurements of the lug. The primary auxiliary view is finished by projecting from the secondary auxiliary view. Step IV illustrates the procedure for projecting from the secondary auxiliary view to the top view through the primary auxiliary in order to complete the foreshortened view of the lug. It should be noted that distance D_1 taken from reference plane R_2P_2 in the secondary auxiliary is transferred to the top view because both views show the same width distances in true length. A sufficient number of points should be obtained to allow the use of an irregular curve. Step V shows the projection of these points on the curve to the front view. In this case the measurements are taken from the primary auxiliary view because the height distances from reference plane R_1P_1 are the same in both views.

8.13. Line of intersection. It is frequently necessary to represent a line of intersection between two surfaces when making a multiview drawing involving an auxiliary view. Fig. 8.19 shows a method for drawing the line of intersection on a principal view. In this case the scheme

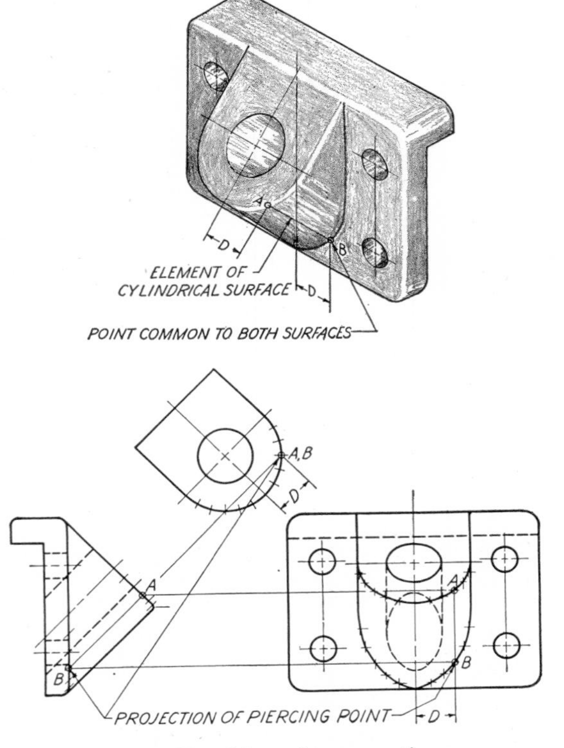

Fig. 8.19. Line of intersection.

commonly used for determining the intersection involves the use of elements drawn on the surface of the cylindrical portion of the part as shown on the pictorial drawing. These elements such as AB, are common to the cylindrical surface. Point B where the element pierces the flat surface, is a point that is common to both surfaces and, therefore, lies on the line of intersection.

On the orthographic views, element AB appears as a point on the auxiliary view and as a line on the front view. The location of the projection of the piercing point on the front view is visible upon inspection. Point B is found in the other principal view by projecting from the front view and setting off the distance D taken from the auxiliary view. The distance D of point B from the center line is a true distance for both views. The center line in the auxiliary view and side view can be considered as the edge view of a reference plane or datum plane from which measurements can be made.

8.14. Problems. The problems shown in Figs. 8.20 and 8.21 are designed to give the student practice in constructing auxiliary views of the inclined surfaces of simple objects formed mainly by straight lines. They will provide needed drill in projection if, for each of the objects in Fig. 8.21, an auxiliary is drawn showing the entire object. Complete drawings may be made of the objects shown in Figs. 8.22–8.25 and 8.27–8.37. If the views are to be dimensioned, the student should adhere to the rules of dimensioning given in Chapter 16 and should not take too seriously the locations for the dimensions on the pictorial representations.

1. (Fig. 8.20.) Using instruments, reproduce the given views and draw an auxiliary view of the inclined surface of each of the given objects.

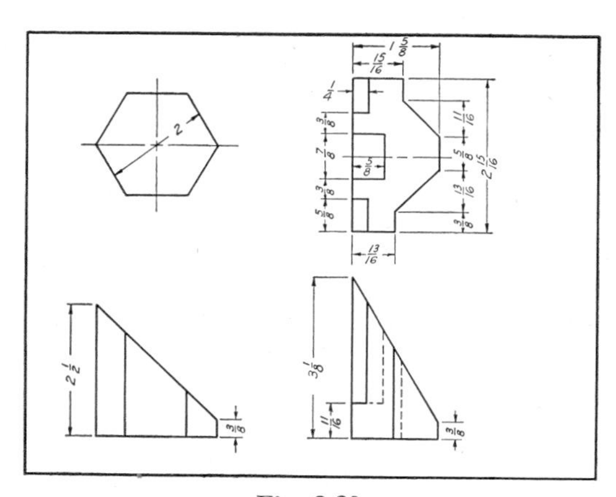

Fig. 8.20.

2. (Fig. 8.21.) Using instruments, reproduce the given views of an assigned object and draw an auxiliary view of its inclined surface.

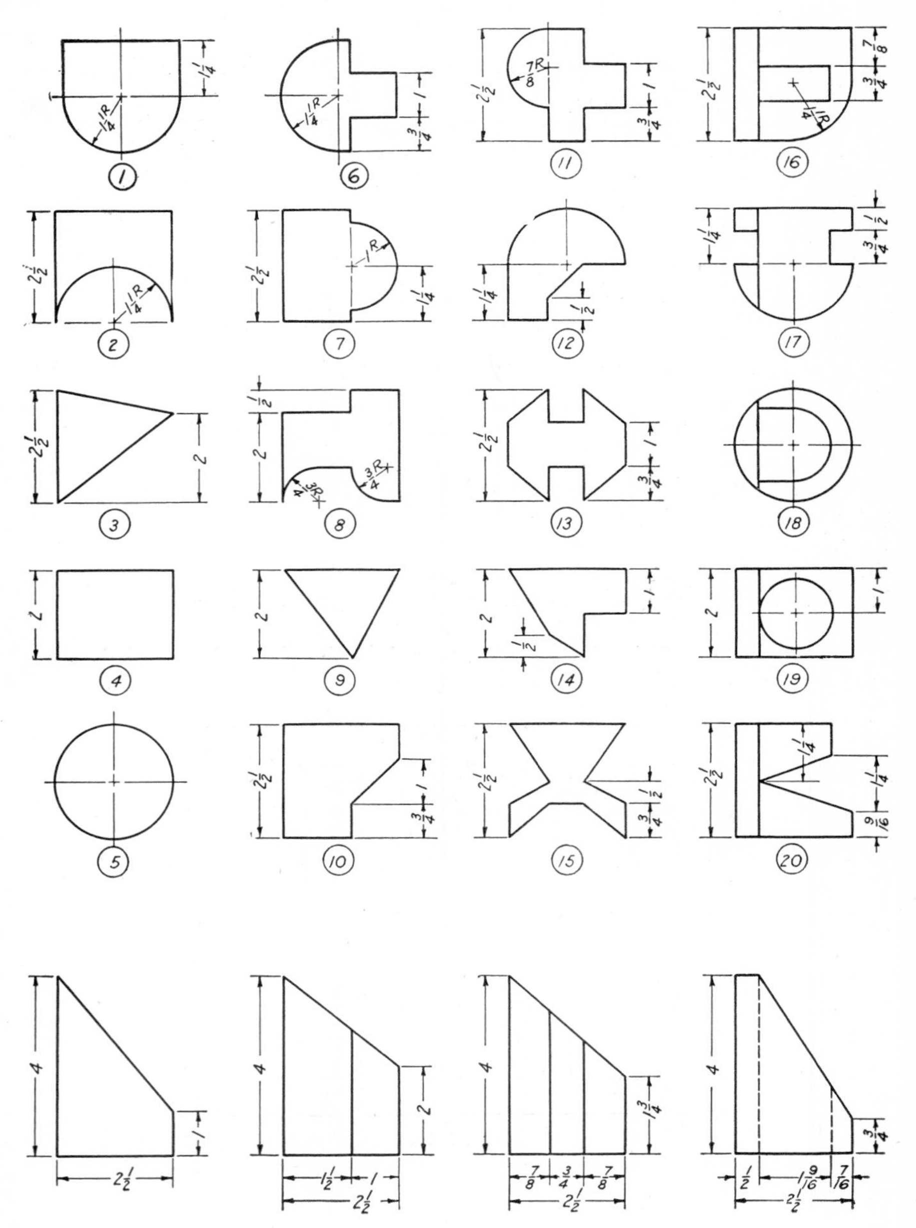

Fig. 8.21.

3. (Fig. 8.22.) Draw the views that are necessary to describe fully the *sliding guide.* The auxiliary view should show only the inclined surface.

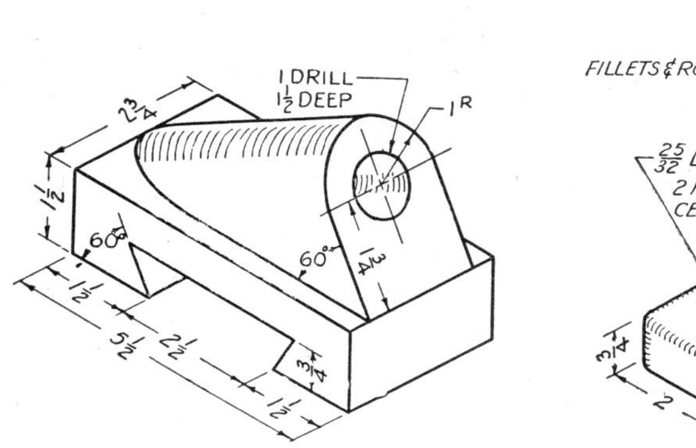

Fig. 8.22. **Sliding guide.**

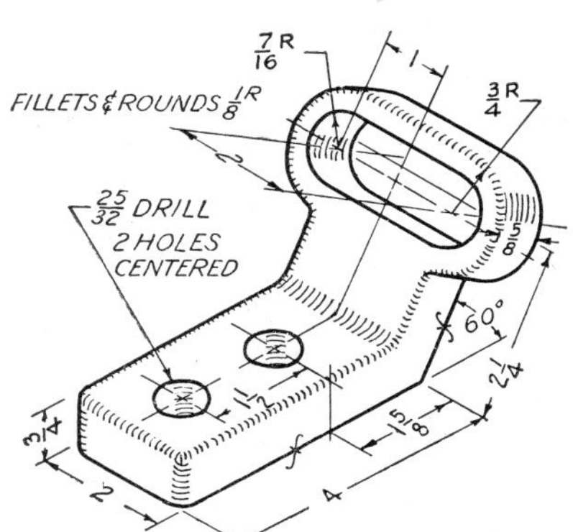

Fig. 8.23. **Guide bracket.**

4. (Fig. 8.23.) Draw the necessary views of the *guide bracket.* It is suggested that the top view be a partial one and that the auxiliary view show only the inclined surface.

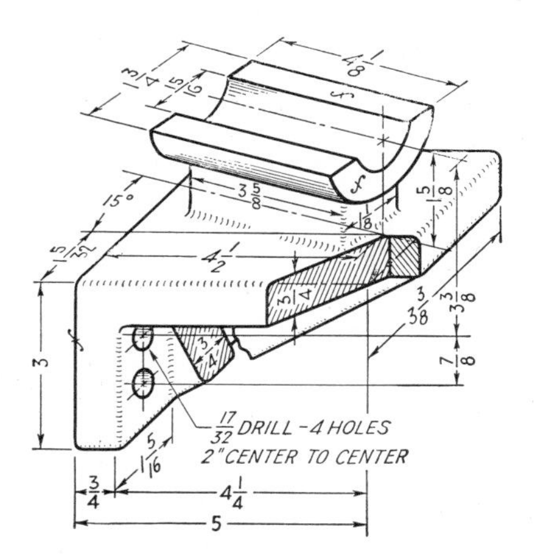

Fig. 8.24. **Angle bearing.**

5. (Fig. 8.24.) Draw the views that would be necessary on a working drawing of the *angle bearing.*

6. (Fig. 8.25.) Draw the views that would be necessary on a working drawing of the *boiler bracket.*

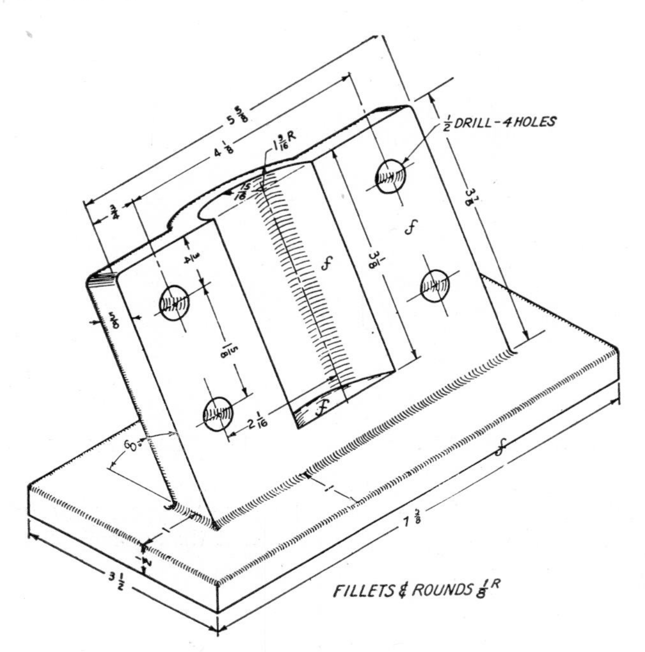

Fig. 8.25. Boiler bracket.

7. (Fig. 8.26.) Using instruments, reproduce the given views of an assigned object and draw a secondary auxiliary view that will show the true size and shape of the inclined surface.

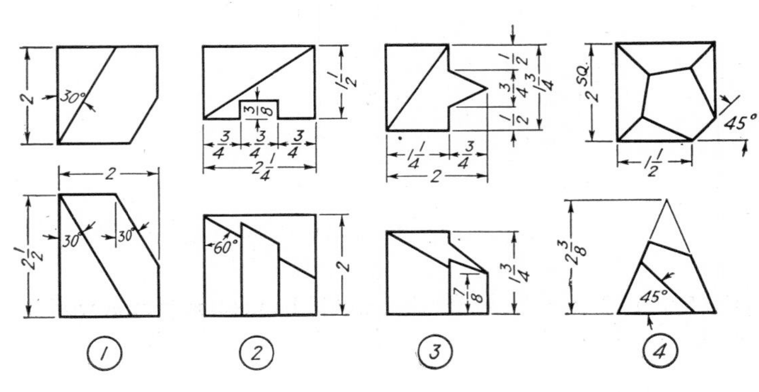

Fig. 8.26.

8. (Fig. 8.27.) Draw the views that would be necessary on a working drawing of the *feeder bracket.*

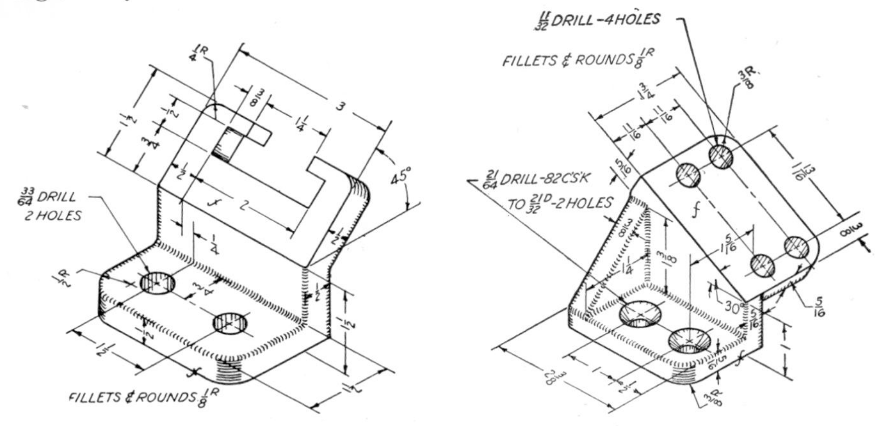

Fig. 8.27. Feeder bracket. **Fig. 8.28. Offset bracket.**

9. (Fig. 8.28.) Draw the necessary views of the *offset bracket.* It is suggested that partial views be used, except in the view where the inclined surface appears as a line.

10. (Fig. 8.29.) Draw the necessary views of the *hinge bracket.*

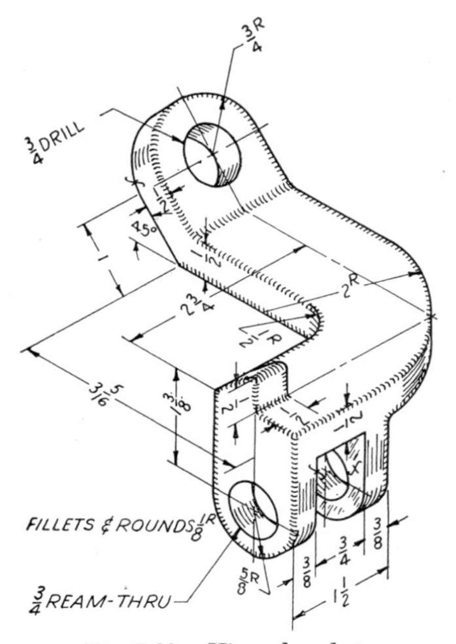

Fig. 8.29. Hinge bracket.

11. (Fig. 8.30.) Draw the necessary views of the *anchor bracket.* Make partial views for the top and end views.

12. (Fig. 8.31.) Draw the views that would be necessary on a working drawing of the *angle bracket*. Note that two auxiliary views will be required.

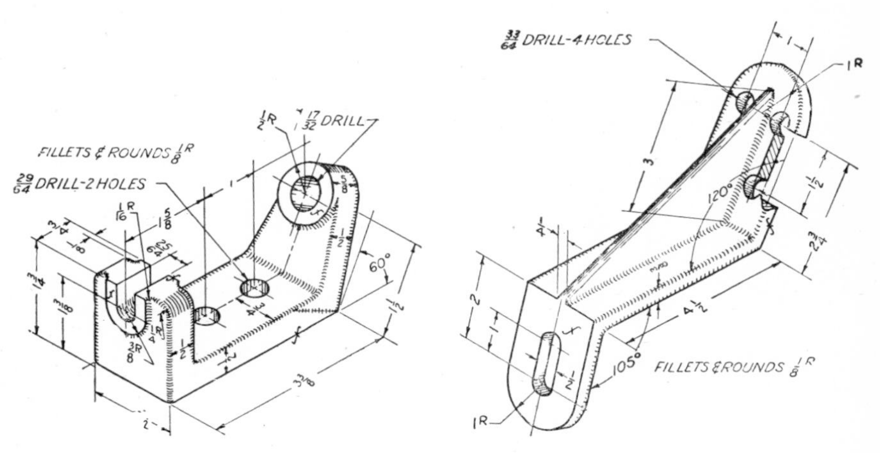

Fig. 8.30. Anchor bracket.

Fig. 8.31. Angle bracket.

13. (Fig. 8.32.) Draw the views that would be needed on a working drawing of the *gear cover*. The opening on the inclined face is circular. The pictorial drawing shows an unfinished casting. Show finished surfaces where necessary.

14. (Fig. 8.33.) Draw the views that would be necessary on a working drawing of the 45° *elbow*.

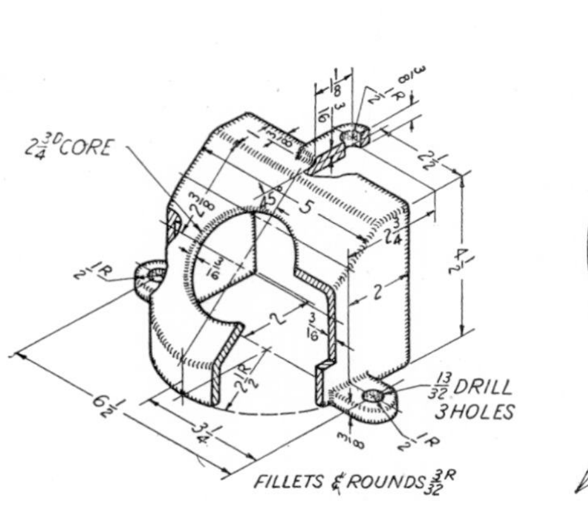

Fig. 8.32. Gear cover.

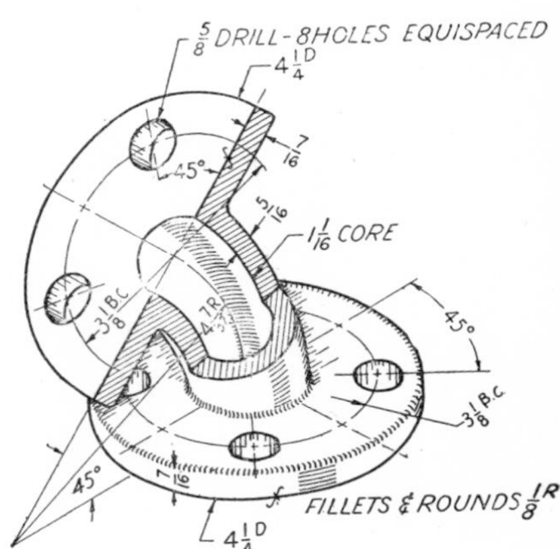

Fig. 8.33. 45° elbow.

15. (Fig. 8.34.) Draw the views as given. Complete the auxiliary view and the front view.

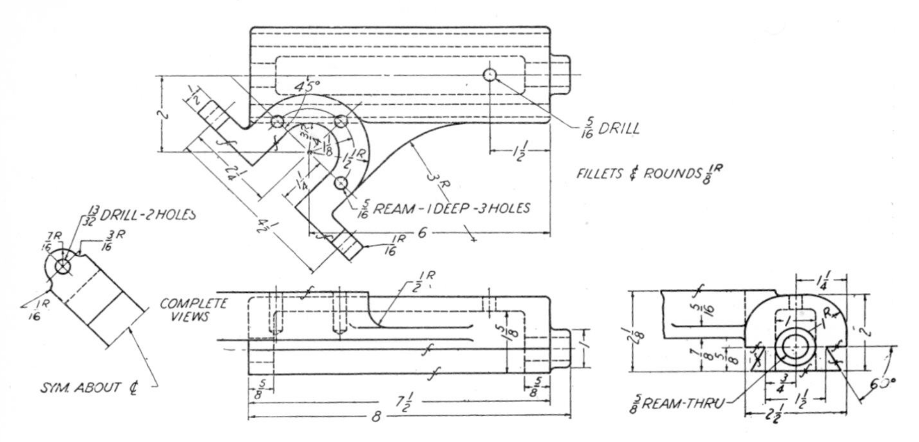

Fig. 8.34. Sliding tool base.

16. (Fig. 8.35.) Draw the views as given. Complete the top view.

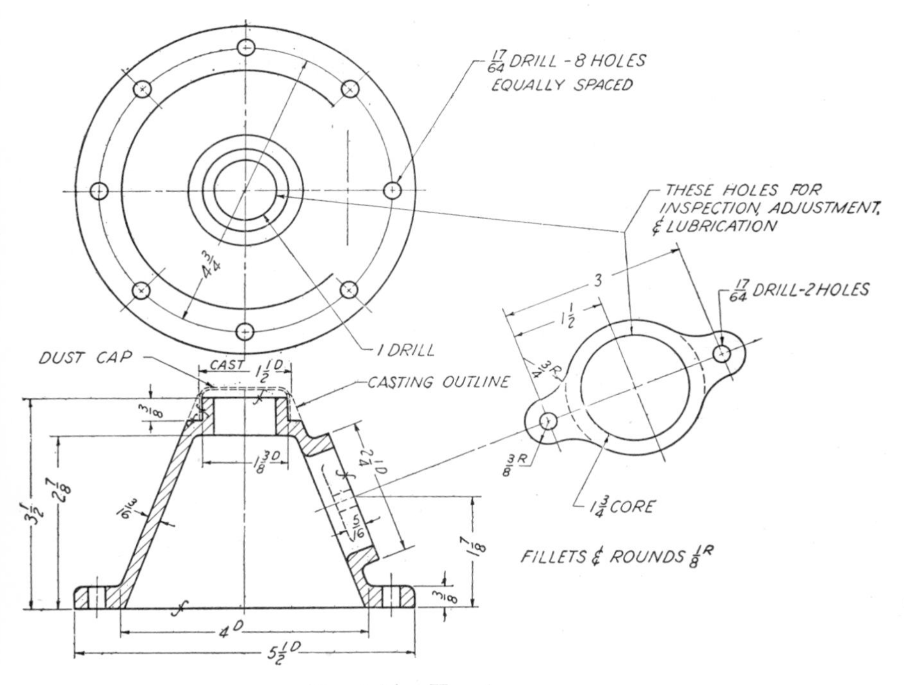

Fig. 8.35. Housing cover.

17. (Fig. 8.36.) Draw the layout for the *support anchor* as given and then, using the double auxiliary view method, complete the views as required.

The plate and cylinder are to be welded. Since the faces of the plate show as oblique surfaces in the front and top views, double auxiliary views are necessary to show the thickness and the true shape.

Start the drawing with the auxiliary views that are arranged horizontally on the paper, then complete the principal views. The inclined face of the cylinder will show as an ellipse in top and front views; but do not show this in the auxiliary view that shows the true shape (4″ square) of the plate.

How would you find the view that shows the true angle between the inclined face and the axis of the cylinder?

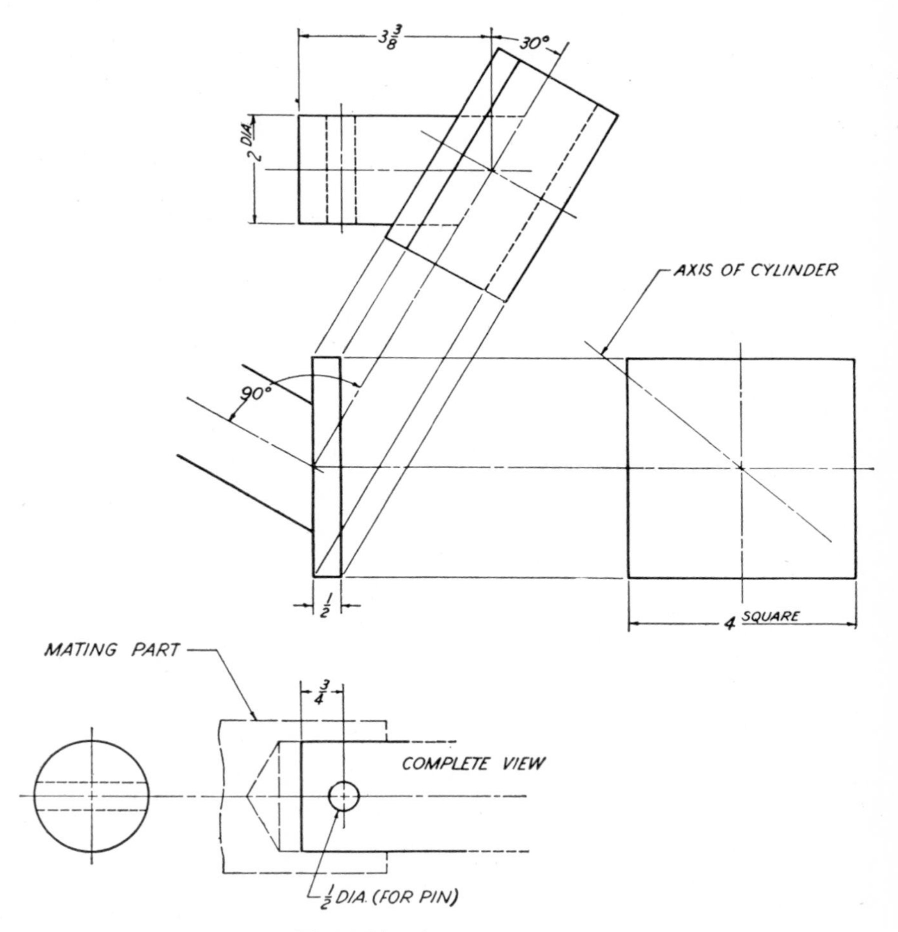

Fig. 8.36. Support anchor.

18. (Fig. 8.37.) Draw the views as given and add the required primary and secondary auxiliary views.

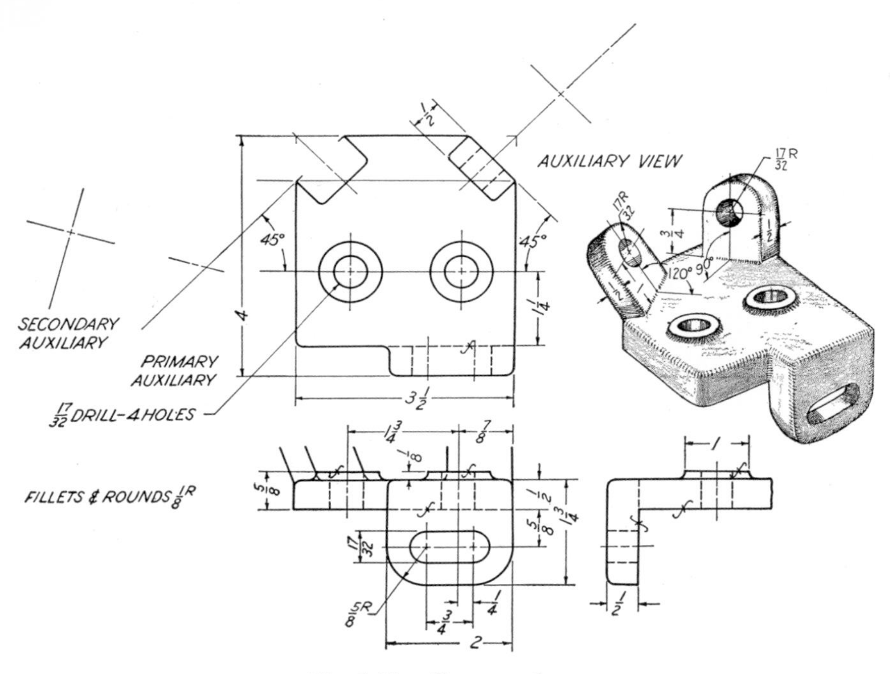

Fig. 8.37. Cross anchor.

9 REVOLUTION

9.1. Revolution. Although in general the views on a working drawing represent satisfactorily an object in a fixed natural position, in order to improve the representation or to reveal the true size and shape of a principal surface, it sometimes is desirable to revolve an elemental part until it is parallel to a co-ordinate plane.

The distinguishing difference between this method and the method of auxiliary projection is that, in the procedure of revolution, the observer turns the object with respect to himself instead of shifting his viewing position with respect to an oblique surface of the object.

Despite the fact that the revolution of an entire object, as illustrated in Fig. 9.1, rarely has a practical application in commercial drafting, the making of such a drawing provides excellent drill in projection. Therefore, since the following related articles are intended primarily to aid in the training of embryo engineers and drafting students, the practical applications of revolution purposely have been ignored, while the procedures for making simple and successive revolutions of entire objects are explained in detail.

9.2. Simple (single) revolution. When the regular views are given, an object may be drawn in any oblique position by imagining it to be revolved about an axis perpendicular to one of the principal co-ordinate

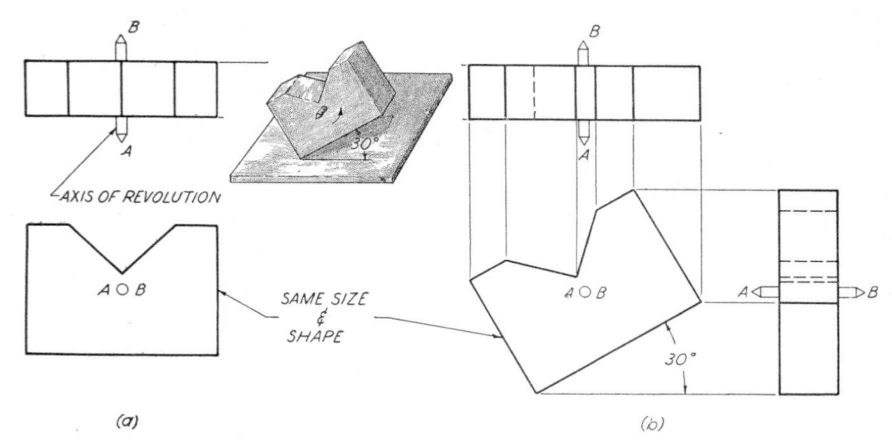

Fig. 9.1. A single revolution about an axis perpendicular to the frontal plane.

(frontal, horizontal, or profile) planes. A single revolution about such an axis is known as a "simple revolution." Figs. 9.1, 9.2, and 9.3 illustrate the three general cases.

9.3. Revolution about a horizontal axis perpendicular to the frontal plane. A simple revolution about an axis perpendicular to the frontal plane is illustrated in Fig. 9.1. The object is first revolved about an imaginary assumed axis, AB, until it is in the desired position. The views of it then are obtained by orthographic projection, as in the case of any ordinary multiview drawing. Because the front face revolves parallel to the frontal plane, the projection on that plane will change in position but

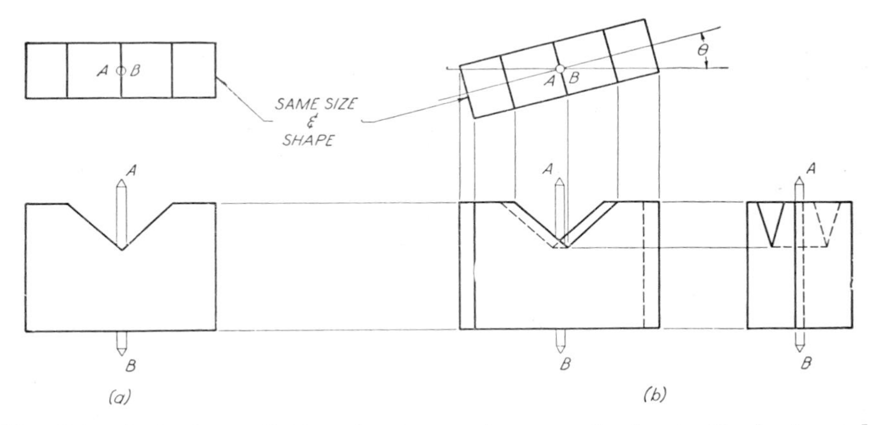

Fig. 9.2. A single revolution about an axis perpendicular to the horizontal plane.

will retain its true size and shape. For this reason, the most convenient drawing procedure is to first copy the front view, as it is shown in (*a*), in its new revolved position (say at 30°). Then, since the depth of the top view is unchanged by the revolution of the object, the required top view can be drawn easily by projecting each point horizontally from the top view in (*a*) to a projection line drawn upward through the corresponding point on the revolved front view in (*b*). The side view may be constructed by regular projection.

The front view may be drawn directly in a revolved position, without first drawing the normal orthographic front view. If this procedure is followed, the depth of the top and side views may be set off to the known dimensions.

9.4. Revolution about a vertical axis perpendicular to the horizontal plane. If an object is revolved about an imaginary axis perpendicular to the horizontal plane, as shown in Fig. 9.2, the top view changes in position but not in size and shape. The top view, therefore, should be drawn first in its revolved position, and the front and side views should be projected from it. The height of the front view and the side view is the same as the height of the normal front view in (*a*) and, for this reason, vertical dimensions can be conveniently projected from the initial views.

9.5. Revolution about a horizontal axis perpendicular to the profile plane. A single revolution of an object about an axis perpendicular to the profile plane is illustrated in Fig. 9.3. Since in this case it is the side view that is perpendicular to the axis and that revolves parallel to a co-ordinate plane, it is the side view that remains unchanged in size and shape. The length of the top and front views is not affected by the revolution. Therefore, horizontal dimensions for these views may be set off by measurement.

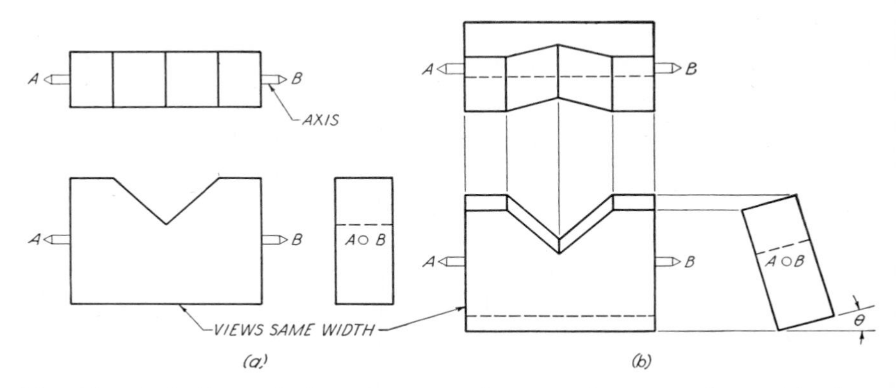

Fig. 9.3. A single revolution about an axis perpendicular to the profile plane.

From these general cases of simple revolution, two principles have appeared that can be stated as follows:

1. The view that is perpendicular to the axis of revolution changes only in position.
2. The lengths of the lines parallel to the axis do not change during the revolution and, therefore, may be either measured or projected from the normal views of the object.

9.6. Clockwise and counterclockwise revolution. An object may be revolved either clockwise or counterclockwise about an axis of revolution. The direction is indicated by the view to which the axis is perpendicular. For example, front views, when revolved as in Fig. 9.4(*b*), show a clockwise revolution. When revolved as in Fig. 9.4(*a*), their revolution is counterclockwise. Top views show a clockwise revolution when revolved to the right. Right-side views indicate a clockwise direction of revolution when they have been revolved to the right, and a counterclockwise direction when revolved to the left.

9.7. Successive (multiple) revolution. Since it is possible to draw an object in any oblique position relative to the co-ordinate planes, it is possible to show it revolved through a series of successive simple revolutions. Usually such a series is limited to three or four stages. Fig. 9.5 shows an object revolved successively about three separate axes. The normal orthographic view is shown in space I. In space II, the object has been revolved clockwise through an angle of 30 degrees about an axis perpendicular to the frontal plane. A system of numbers by which each corner is identified, as shown, is not necessary in the case of a simple object. If the object is in the least complex, however, possible confusion is avoided by the use of identification symbols of some type. In space III, the object has been revolved counterclockwise from its position in space II through an angle of 15 degrees about an axis perpendicular to the horizontal plane. From this position, represented in space III, the object is revolved clockwise through 15 degrees into the position shown in space IV. This last simple revolution completes a series of three simple revolutions involving the three general cases previously discussed.

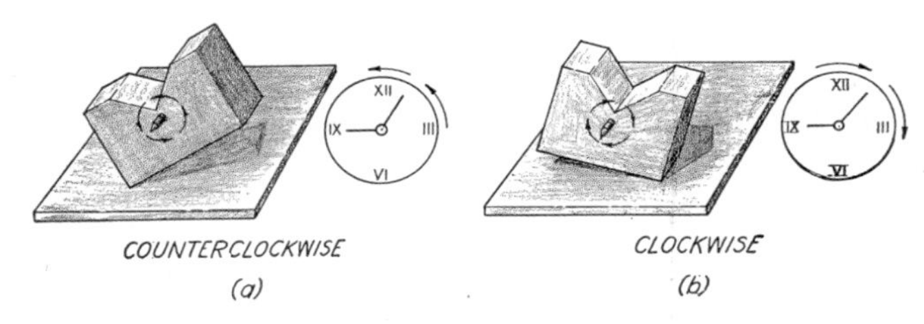

Fig. 9.4. Direction of revolution.

9.8. To find the true length of a line by revolution. In engineering drafting, it frequently is necessary to determine the true length of a line when constructing the development of a surface (Chapter 22). The true lengths must be found of those lines that are not parallel to any co-ordinate plane and, therefore, appear foreshortened in all the principal views. (See Sec. 7.7, "Principles of multiview drawing.") The practical as well as the theoretical procedure is to revolve any such oblique line into a position parallel to a co-ordinate plane so that its projection on that particular plane will be the same length as the line. In Fig. 9.6(a), this is illustrated by the edge AB on the pyramid. AB is oblique to the co-ordinate planes and its projections are foreshortened. If this edge line is imagined to be revolved until it becomes parallel to the frontal plane, then the projection ab_r in the front view will be the same length as the true length of AB.

A practical application of this method is shown in Fig. 9.6(c). The true length of the edge AB, in Fig. 9.6(a), would be found by revolving its top projection into the position ab_r representing AB revolved parallel to the frontal plane, and then projecting the end point b_r down into its new position along a horizontal line through b. The horizontal line represents the horizontal plane of the base in which the point B travels as the line AB is revolved.

Commercial draftsmen who are unfamiliar with the theory of co-ordinate planes find the true length projection of a line by visualizing the line's revolution. They think of an edge as being revolved until it is in

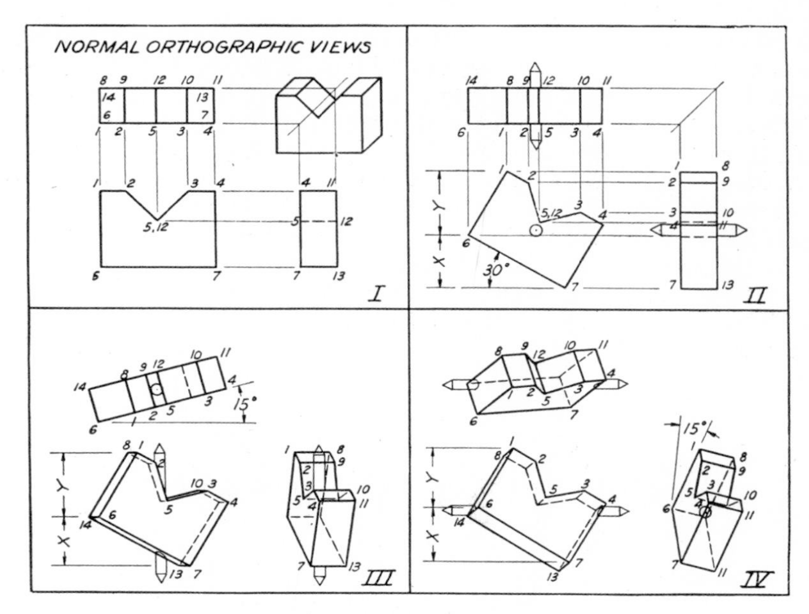

Fig. 9.5. Successive revolution.

a plane perpendicular to the line of sight of an observer stationed an infinite distance away (Figs. 22.11, 22.12, and 22.13). The process corresponds to that used in drawing regular orthographic views (see Sec. 7.4). Usually this method is more easily understood by a student.

Note in Fig. 9.6(*a* and *b*) that the true length of a line is equal to the hypotenuse of a right triangle whose altitude is equal to the difference in the elevation of the end points and whose base is equal to the top projec-

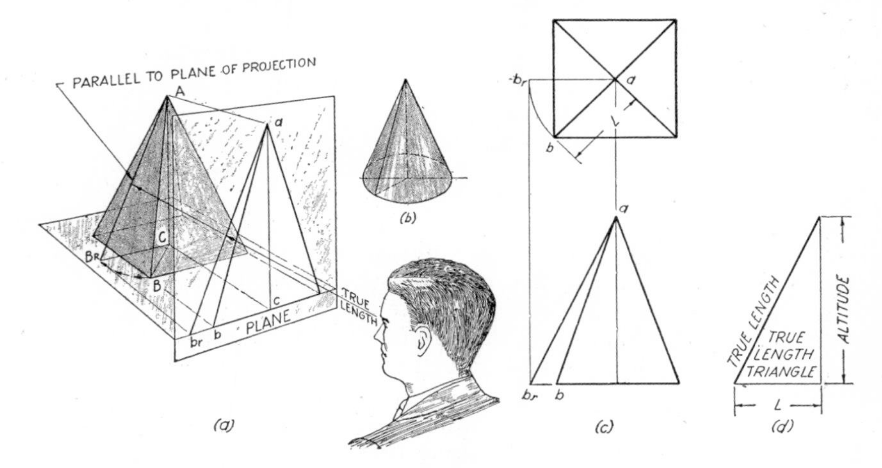

Fig. 9.6. True length of a line, revolution method.

tion of the line. With this fact in mind, many draftsmen determine the true length of a line by constructing a true-length triangle similar to the one illustrated in Fig. 9.6(*d*).

9.9. True-length lines. Students who, lacking a thorough understanding of the principles of projection (Sec. 7.7), find it difficult to determine whether or not a projection of a line in one of the principal views shows the true length of the line, should study carefully the following facts:

1. If the projection of a line shows the true length of a line, one of the other projections must appear as a horizontal line, a vertical line, or a point on one of the other views of the drawing.
2. If the top and front views of a line are horizontal, then both views show the true length.
3. If the top view of a line is a point, the front and side views show the true length.
4. If the front view of a line is a point, the top and side views show the true length.
5. If the top and front views of a line are vertical, the side view shows the true length.
6. If the side projection of a line is a point, the top and front views show the true length.
7. If the front view of a line is horizontal and the top view is inclined, the top inclined view shows the true length.

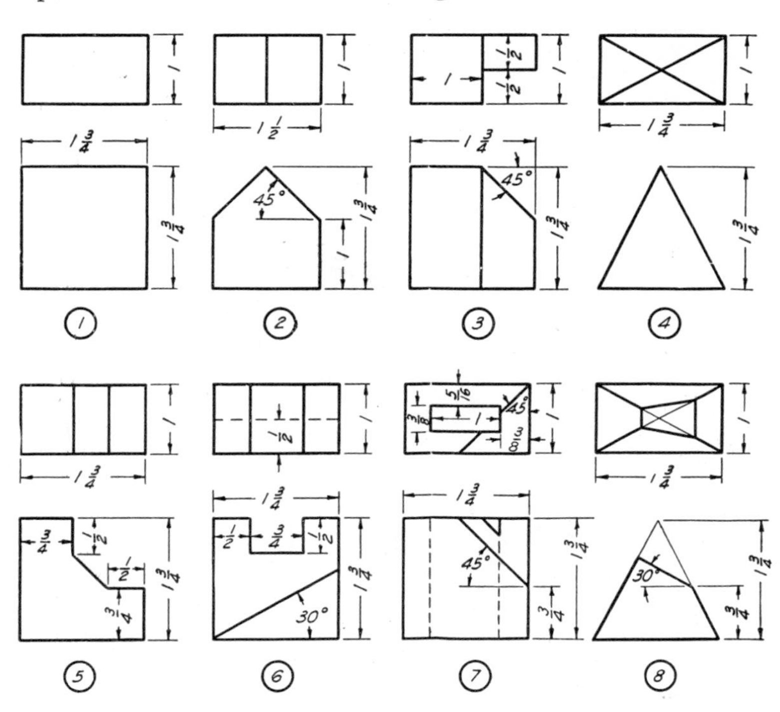

Fig. 9.7.

8. If the top view of a line is horizontal and the front view is inclined, the front inclined view shows the true length.

9.10. Problems. The following problems in revolution furnish excellent drill in projection and offer the student a chance to develop further his imagination and ability to visualize in three dimensions. It will be found worth while to number all the corners of each object used, both on the normal views and on the views of the successive stages.

1–8. Divide, into four equal areas, the space inside the border line of a sheet of drawing paper. In the upper left-hand space, draw the normal orthographic views of an object assigned from Fig. 9.7. In the lower left-hand space, show the object revolved through an angle of 30° about an axis perpendicular to the front plane (see Fig. 9.1). In the upper right-hand space, show a simple revolution from the normal orthographic view about an axis perpendicular to the top plane (see Fig. 9.2). Revolve the object through an angle of 30°. Complete the drawing by making a simple revolution about an axis perpendicular to the side or profile plane (see Fig. 9.3). Revolve the object from the original normal position through an angle of 30°.

9–16. Divide a sheet of drawing paper into four equal areas and make a series of successive revolutions of an object assigned from Fig. 9.7. Revolve the object through the three stages shown in Fig. 9.5. Make the revolutions in the following order: (1) in the lower left-hand space, revolve the object through an angle of 30° about an axis perpendicular to the front plane; (2) in the lower right-hand space, revolve the object from its previous position through an angle of 15° about an axis perpendicular to the top plane; (3) in the upper right-hand space, make a revolution through an angle of 15° about an axis perpendicular to the side or profile plane.

10 SECTIONAL VIEWS

10.1. Sectional views (Fig. 10.1). Although the invisible features of a simple object usually may be described on an exterior view by the use of hidden lines, it is unwise to depend upon a perplexing mass of such lines to adequately describe the interior of a complicated object or an assembled

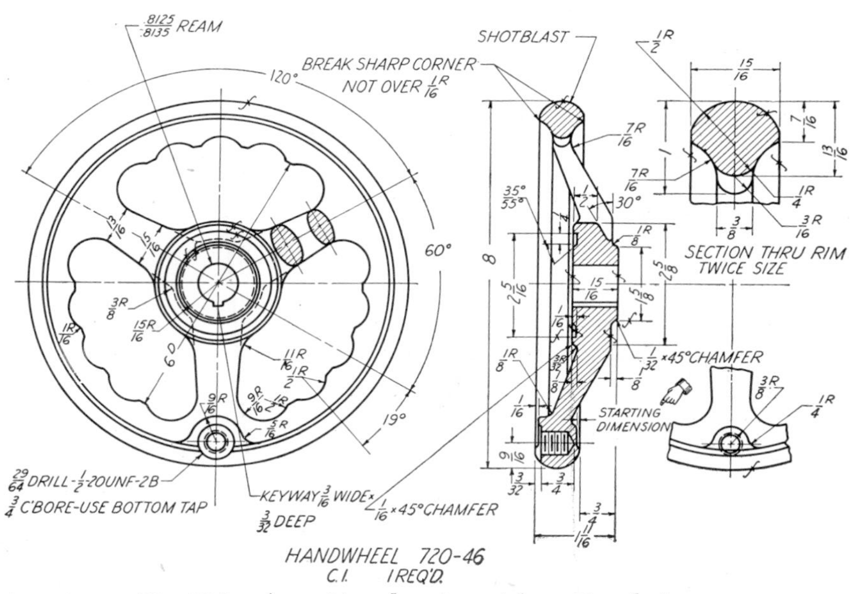

Fig. 10.1. A working drawing with sectional views.

Courtesy Warner & Swasey Co.

mechanism. Whenever a representation becomes so confused that it is difficult to read, it is customary to make one or more of the views "in section" (Fig. 10.2). A view "in section" is one obtained by imagining the object to have been cut by a cutting plane, the front portion being removed so as to clearly reveal the interior features. Fig. 10.3(*c*) illustrates the use of an imaginary cutting plane. The resulting sectional (front) view, accompanied by a top view, is shown in Fig. 10.3(*f*). At this point it should be understood that a portion is shown removed only in a sectional view, not in any of the other views. (See Fig. 10.3*f*.)

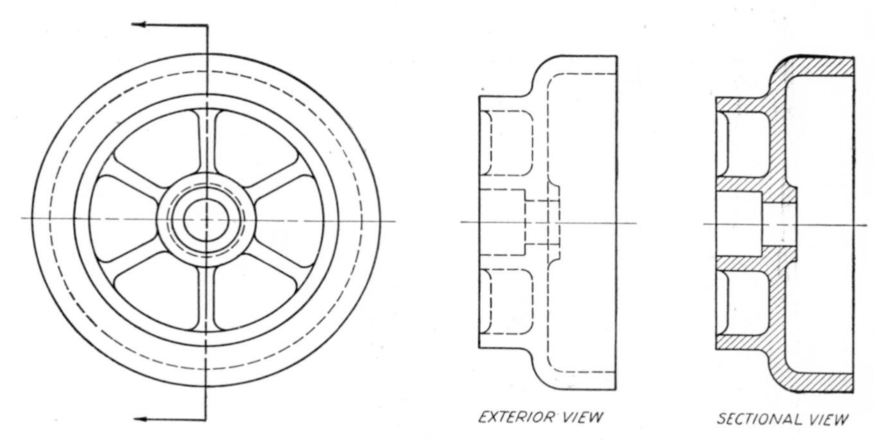

Fig. 10.2. A sectional view.

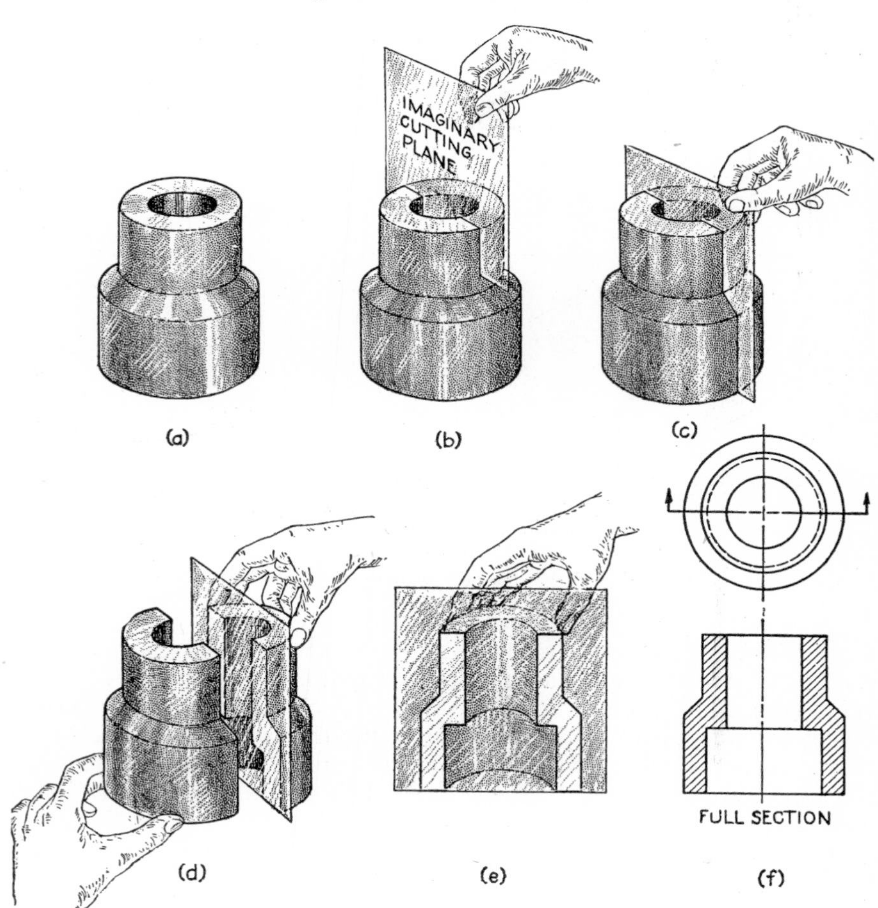

Fig. 10.3. The theory of the construction of a sectional view.

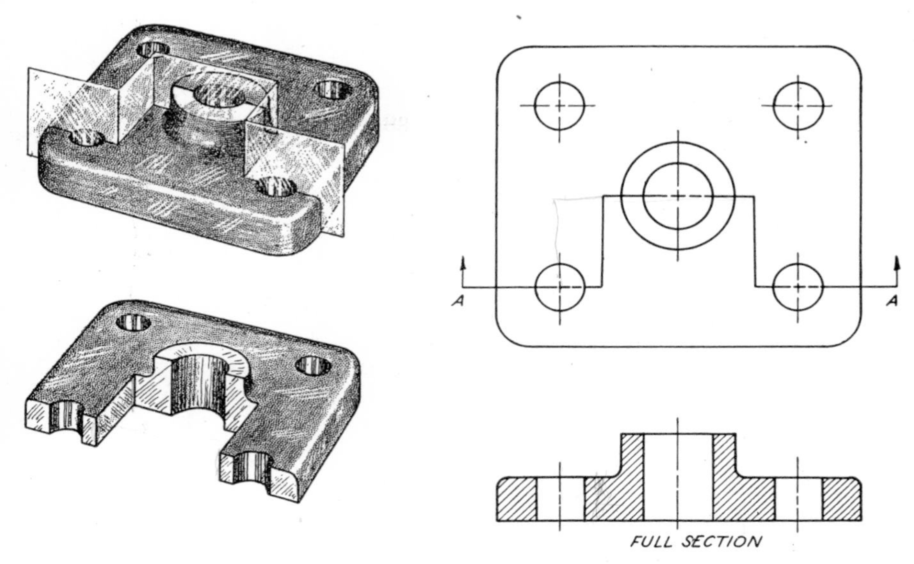

Fig. 10.4. An offset cutting plane.

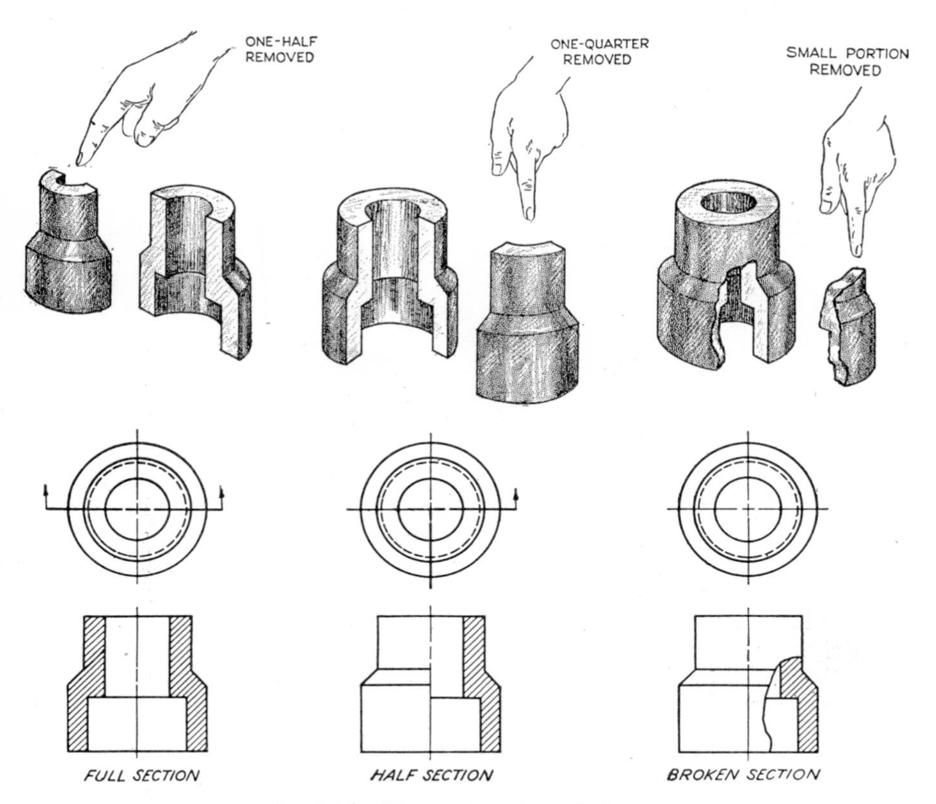

Fig. 10.5. Types of sectional views.

When the cutting plane cuts an object lengthwise, the section obtained is commonly called a longitudinal section; when crosswise, it is called a cross section. It is designated as being either a full section, a half section, or a broken section. If the plane cuts entirely across the object, the section represented is known as a full section. If it cuts only halfway across a symmetrical object, the section is a half section. A broken section is a partial one which is used when less than a half section is needed.

On a completed sectional view, fine section lines are drawn across the surface cut by the imaginary plane, to emphasize the contour of the interior (see Sec. 10.8).

10.2. A full section. Since a cutting plane that cuts a full section passes entirely through an object, the resulting view will appear as illustrated in Fig. 10.3(*f*). Although the plane usually passes along the main axis, it may be offset (see Fig. 10.4) to reveal important features.

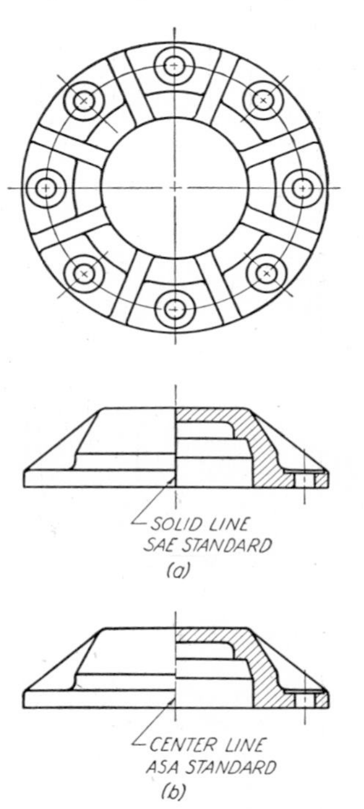

Fig. 10.6. A half section.

A full sectional view, showing an object's characteristic shape, usually replaces an exterior front view; however, one of the other principal views, side or top, may be converted into a sectional view if some interior feature thus can be shown to better advantage or if such a view is needed in addition to a sectioned front view.

The procedure in making a full sectional view is simple, in that the sectional view is an orthographic one. The imaginary cut face of the object simply is shown as it would appear to an observer looking directly at it from a point an infinite distance away. In any sectional view, it is considered good practice to omit all invisible lines unless such lines are necessary to clarify the representation. Even then they should be used sparingly.

10.3. A half section. The cutting plane for a half section removes one quarter of an object. The plane cuts halfway through to the axis or center line so that half the finished sectional view appears in section and half appears as an external view. (See Fig. 10.5.) This type of sectional view is used when a view is needed showing both the exterior and interior construction of a symmetrical object. Good practice dictates that hidden lines be omitted from both halves of the view unless they are absolutely necessary for dimensioning purposes or for explaining the construction. Although the use of a solid line object line to separate the two halves of a half section has been approved by the Society of Automotive Engineers in the new SAE Drafting Standards (Fig. 10.6*a*), many draftsmen prefer to use a center line as shown in 10.6(*b*). They reason that the removal of a quarter of the object is theoretical and imaginary and that an actual edge, which would be implied by a solid line, does not exist. The center line is taken as denoting a theoretical edge.

10.4. A broken section. A broken or partial section is used mainly to expose the interior of objects so constructed that less than a half section is required for a satisfactory description (Fig. 10.7). The object theoretically is cut by a cutting plane and the front portion is removed by breaking it away. The "breaking away" gives an irregular boundary line to the section.

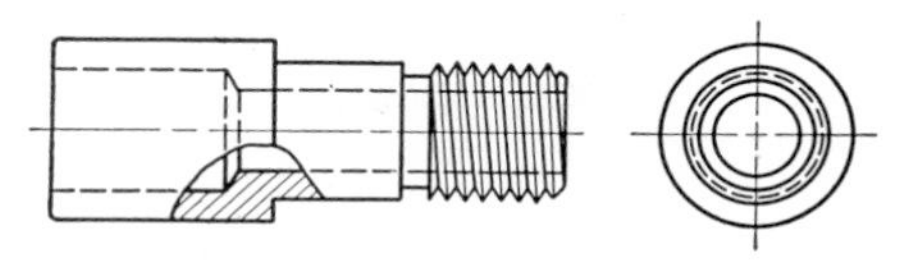

Fig. 10.7. A broken section.

10.5. A revolved section. A revolved section is useful for showing the true shape of the cross section of some elongated object, such as a bar, or some feature of an object, such as an arm, spoke, or rib (Figs. 10.1 and 10.8).

To obtain such a cross section, an imaginary cutting plane is passed through the member perpendicular to its axis, and then is revolved through 90° to bring the resulting view into the plane of the paper (Fig. 10.9). When revolved, the section should show in its true shape and in its true revolved position, regardless of the location of the lines of the exterior view. If any lines of the view interfere with the revolved section, they should be omitted (Fig. 10.10). It sometimes is advisable to provide an open space for the section by making a break in the object (see Fig. 10.8).

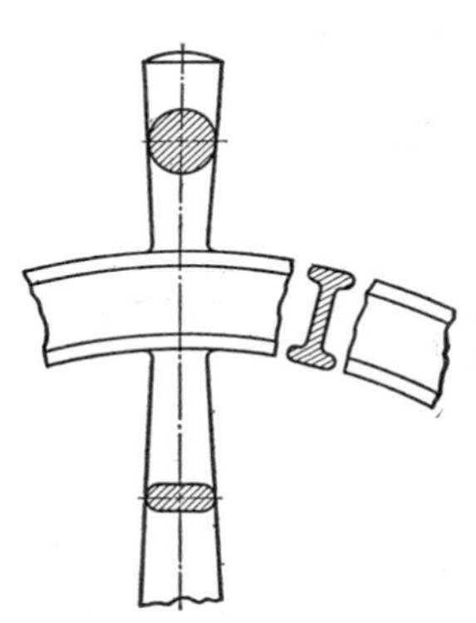

Fig. 10.8. A revolved section.*

10.6. Detail or removed sections. A detail section is similar to a revolved section, except that it does not appear on an external view but, instead, is drawn "out of place," and appears adjacent to it (Fig. 10.11). There are two good reasons why detail sections frequently are desirable. First, their use may prevent a principal view of an object, the cross section of which is not uniform, from being cluttered with numerous revolved sections (Fig. 10.11). Second, they may be drawn to an enlarged scale in order to emphasize detail and allow for adequate dimensioning (Fig. 10.12).

Whenever a detail section is used, there must be some means of identifying it. Usually this is accomplished by showing the cutting plane on the principal view and then labeling both the plane and the resulting view, as shown in Fig. 10.11.

10.7. Phantom sections. A phantom or hidden section is a regular exterior view upon which the interior construction is emphasized by crosshatching an imaginary cut surface with dotted section lines (see Fig. 10.13).

---

* ASA Z14.1–1946.

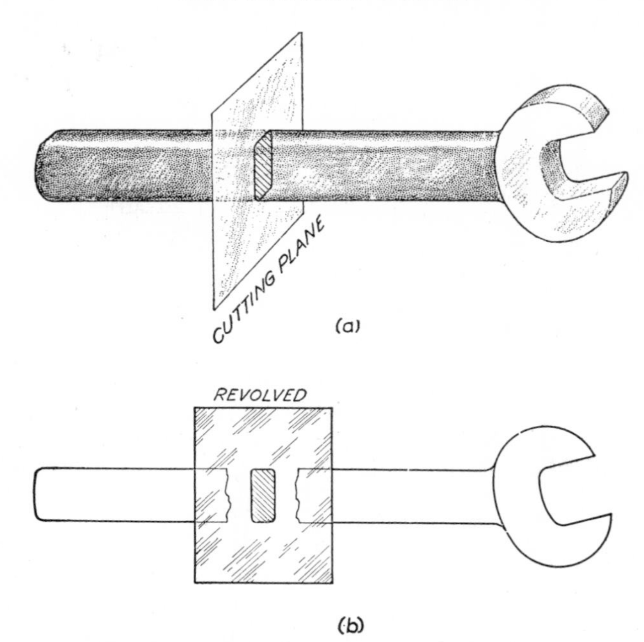

Fig. 10.9. A revolved section and cutting plane.

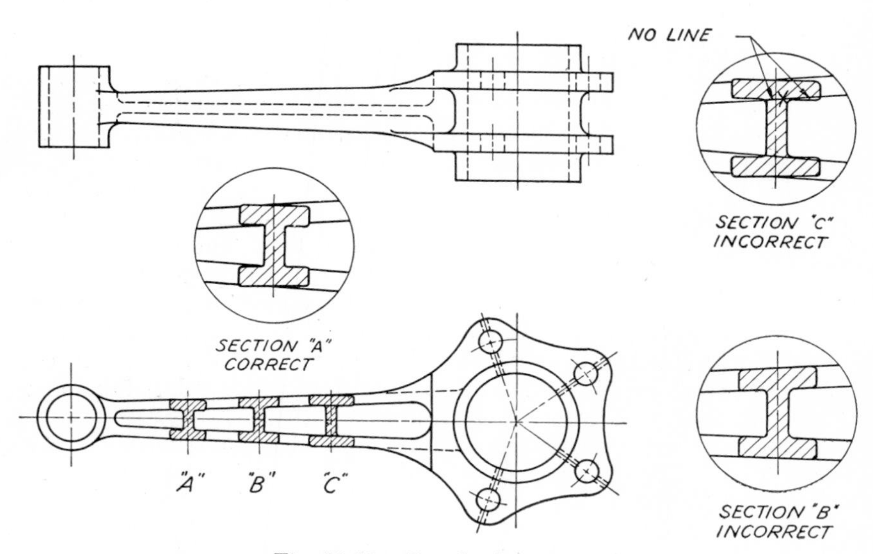

Fig. 10.10. Revolved sections.

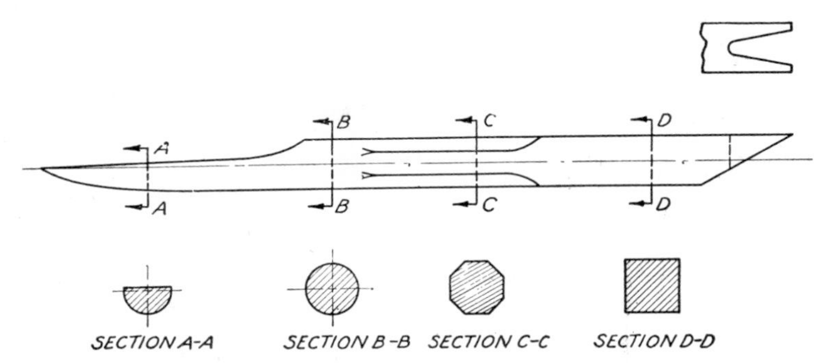

Fig. 10.11. Detail sections.

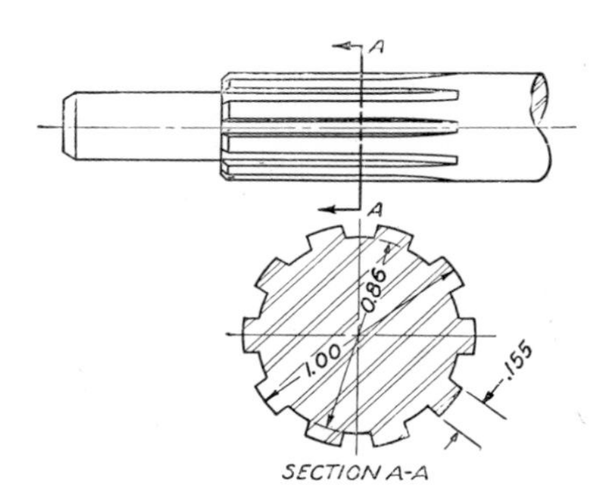

Fig. 10.12. A detail section.

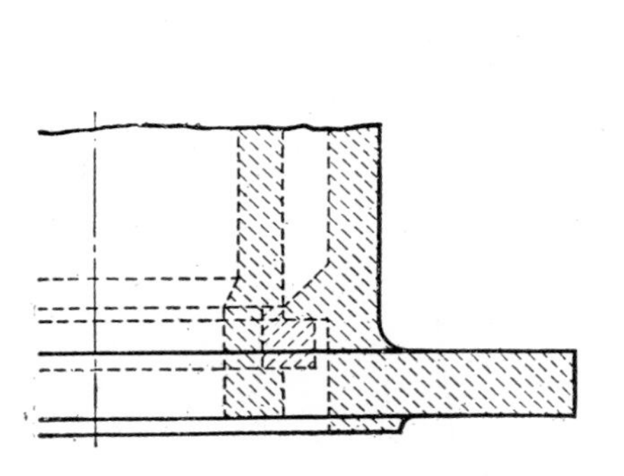

Fig. 10.13. A phantom section.*

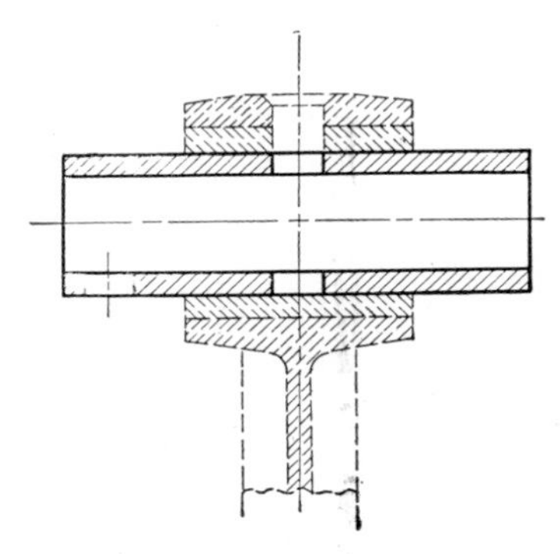

Fig. 10.14.

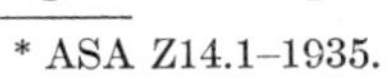

* ASA Z14.1–1935.

This type of section is used only when a regular section or a broken section would remove some important exterior detail, or, in some instances, to show an accompanying part in its relative position with regard to a particular part (Fig. 10.14). Instead of using a broken line with dashes of equal length, the phantom line shown in Fig. 3.32 could have been used to represent the outline of the adjacent parts shown in Fig. 10.14.

10.8. Section lining. Section lines are light continuous lines drawn across the imaginary cut surface of an object for the purpose of emphasizing the contour of its interior. Usually they are drawn at an angle of 45° except in cases where a number of adjacent parts are shown assembled. (See Fig. 10.18.)

To be pleasing in appearance, these lines must be correctly executed. While on ordinary work they are spaced about $\frac{3}{32}''$ apart, there is no set rule governing their spacing. They simply should be spaced to suit the drawing and the size of the areas to be crosshatched. For example, on small views having small areas, the section lines may be as close as $\frac{1}{32}''$, while on large views having large areas they may be as far apart as $\frac{1}{8}''$. In the case of very thin plates, the cross section is shown "solid black" (Fig. 10.15).

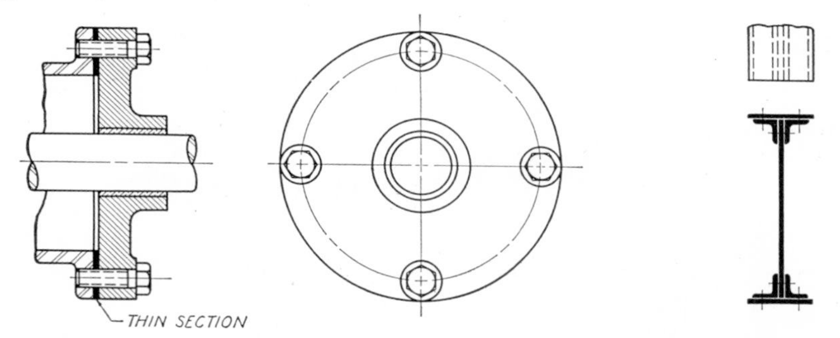

Fig. 10.15. Thin sections.

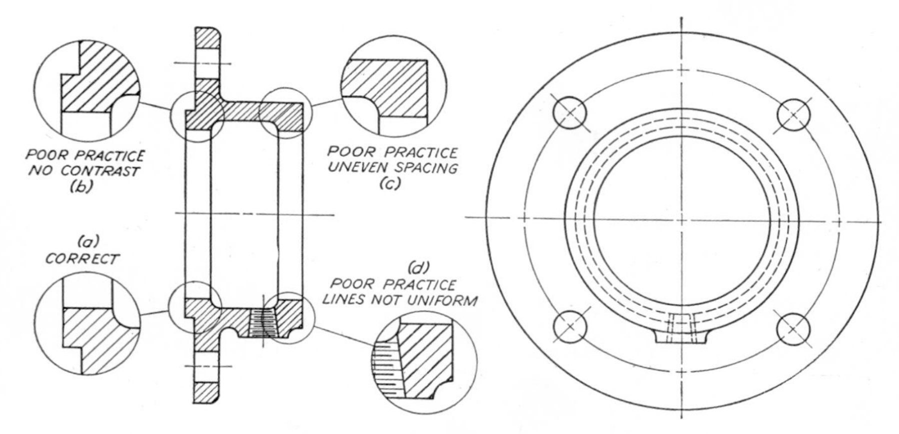

Fig. 10.16. Faults in sectional lining.

The usual mistake of the beginning student is to draw the lines too close together. This, plus the unavoidable slight variations, causes the section lining to appear streaked. Although several forms of mechanical section liners are available, most draftsmen do their spacing by eye. The student is advised to do likewise, being careful to see that the initial pitch, as set by the first few lines, is maintained across the area. To accomplish this, he should check back from time to time to make sure there has been no slight general increase or decrease in the spacing. An example of correct section lining is shown in Fig. 10.16(a), and, for comparison, examples of faulty practice may be seen in Fig. 10.16(b), (c), and (d). Experienced draftsmen realize that nothing will do more to ruin the appearance of a drawing than carelessly executed section lines.

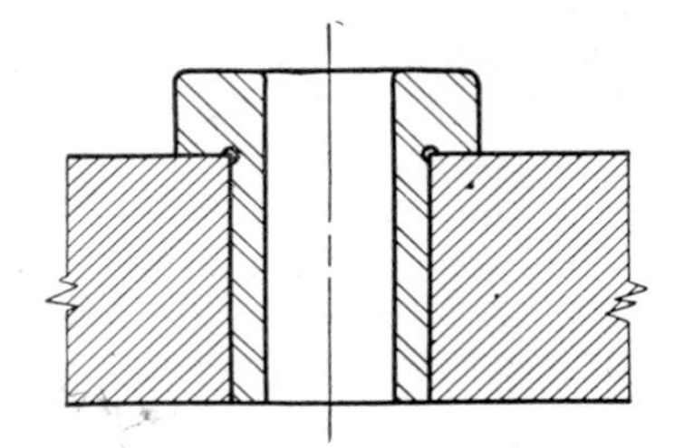

Fig. 10.17. Two adjacent pieces.

As shown in Fig. 10.17, the section lines on two adjacent pieces should slope at 45 degrees in opposite directions. If a third piece adjoins the two other pieces, as in Fig. 10.18(a), it ordinarily is section-lined at 30 degrees. An alternate treatment, which might be used, would be to vary the spacing without changing the angle. On a sectional view showing an assembly of related parts, *all portions of the cut surface of any part must be section-lined in the same direction, for a change would lead the reader to consider the portions as belonging to different parts. Furthermore, to allow quick identification, each piece (and all identical pieces) in every view of the assembly drawing should be section-lined in the same direction.*

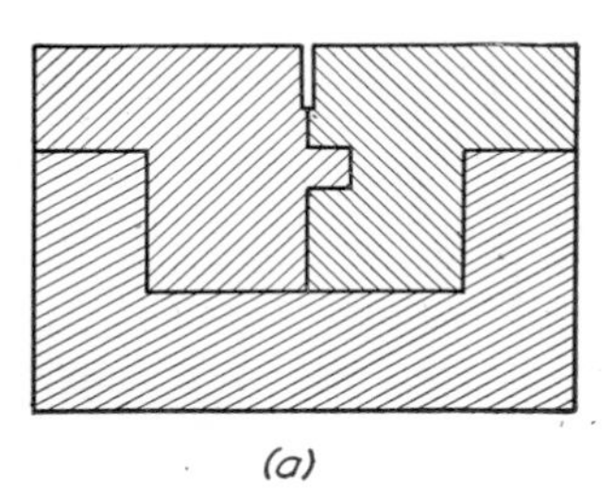

(a)

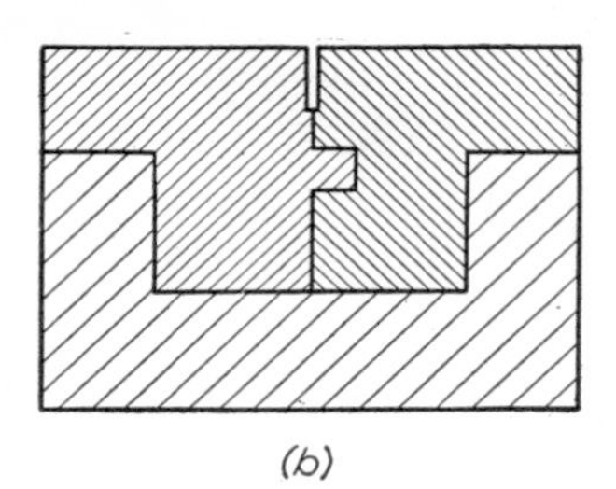

(b)

Fig. 10.18. Three adjacent pieces.

Shafts, bolts, pins, rivets, balls, and so on, whose axes lie in the plane of section are not treated the same as ordinary parts. Having no interior construction to be shown, they are drawn in full and thus tend to make the adjacent sectioned parts stand out to better advantage (Fig. 10.19).

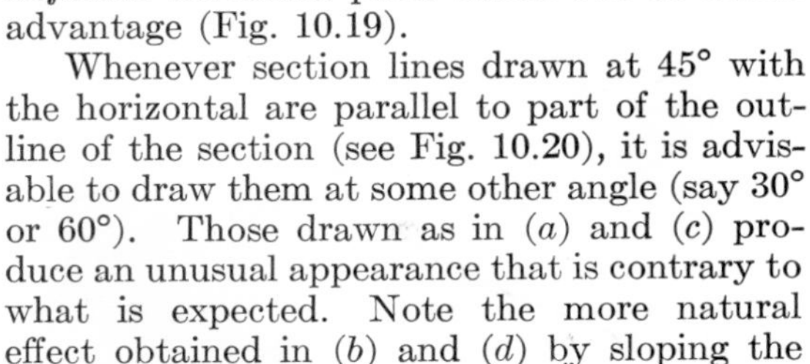

Whenever section lines drawn at 45° with the horizontal are parallel to part of the outline of the section (see Fig. 10.20), it is advisable to draw them at some other angle (say 30° or 60°). Those drawn as in (a) and (c) produce an unusual appearance that is contrary to what is expected. Note the more natural effect obtained in (b) and (d) by sloping the lines at 30°. Note also the lines shown in (e), and the recommended remedial treatment illustrated in (f).

10.9. Outline sectioning. Very large surfaces may be section-lined around the bounding outline only, as illustrated in Fig. 10.21.

10.10. The symbolic representation for a cutting plane. The symbolic lines that are used to represent the edge view of a cutting plane are shown in Fig. 10.22. The line is as heavy as an object line and is composed of either alternate long and short dashes or a series of dashes of equal length. The latter form is used in the automobile industry and has been approved by the SAE (Society of Automotive Engineers). On drawings of ordinary size, when alternate long and short dashes are used for the cutting plane line, the long dashes are $\frac{3}{4}''$ long, the short dashes $\frac{1}{8}''$ long, and the spaces $\frac{1}{16}''$ wide. When drawn in ink, the dashes are $\frac{1}{40}''$ to $\frac{1}{32}''$

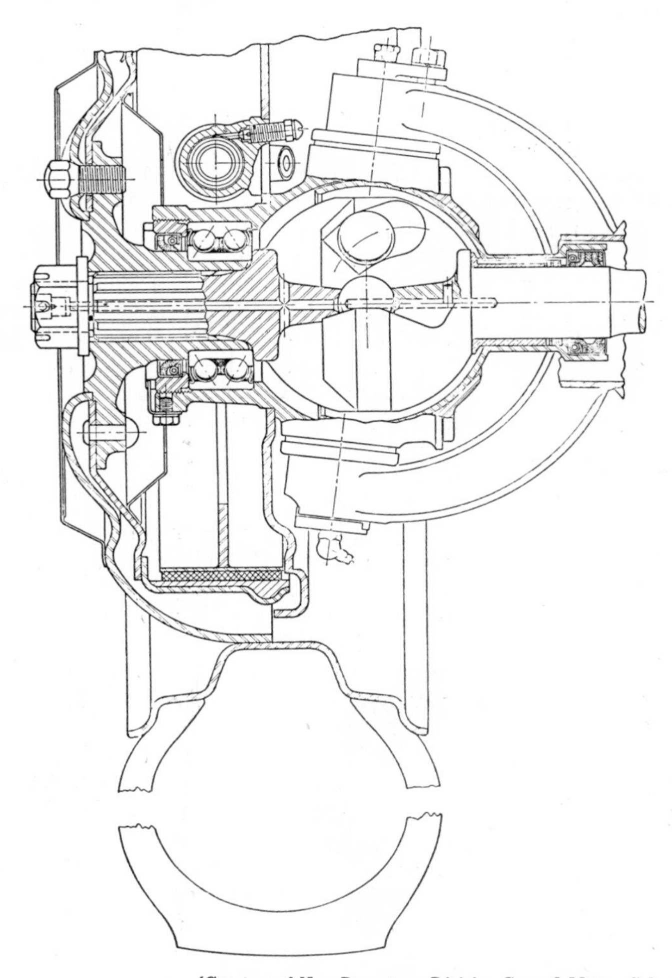

(Courtesy of New Departure, Division General Motors Sales Corporation)

Fig. 10.19. Treatment of shafts, fasteners, ball bearings, and so forth.

wide, depending on the size of the drawing. When drawn in pencil on manila paper, they are made with a medium pencil.

Arrowheads are used to show the direction in which the imaginary cut surface is viewed, and reference letters are added to identify it (Fig. 10.25).

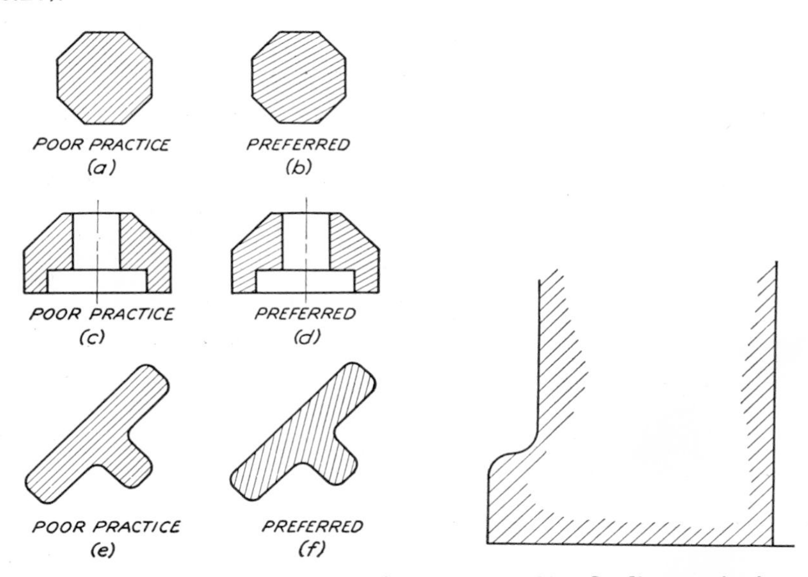

Fig. 10.20. Section lining at 30°, 60°, and 75°.

Fig. 10.21. Outline sectioning.

Whenever a sectional view is not on the same sheet as the principal view showing the cutting plane line, the section may be identified by a letter placed in a circle as the numerator of a fraction with a number as the denominator. The number is the sheet number on which the sectioned view will be found. In Fig. 10.23 section *B-B* would not appear with the top view as shown because it would be drawn on a different sheet.

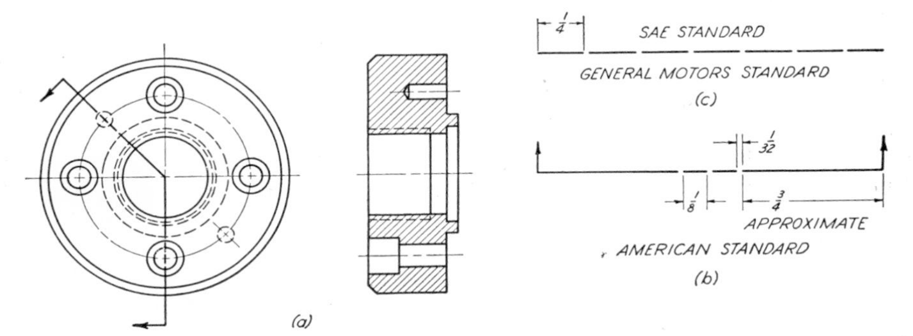

Fig. 10.22. Cutting plane lines.

Whenever the location of the cutting plane is obvious, it is common practice to omit the edge-view representation, particularly in the case of symmetrical objects. If it is shown, however, and coincides with a center line, it takes precedence over the center line.

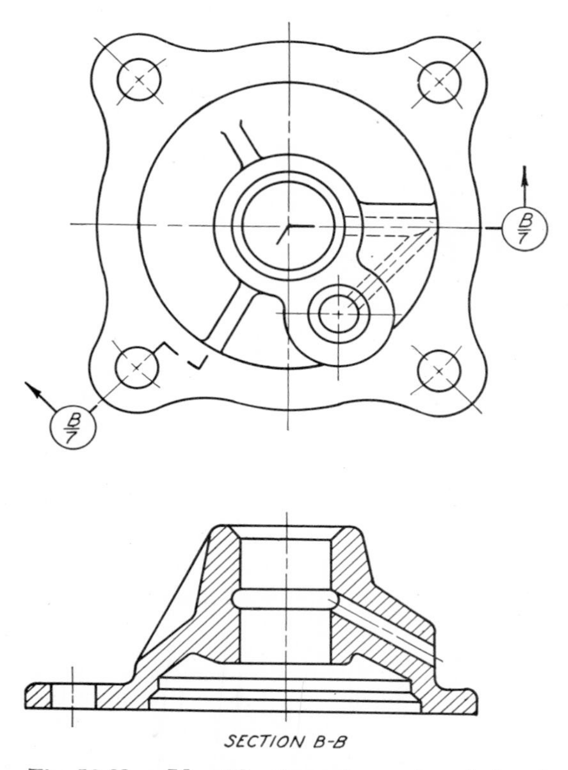

Fig. 10.23. Identification of a sectional view.*

10.11. Summary of the practices of sectioning.

1. A cutting plane may be offset in order to cut the object in such a manner as to reveal an important detail that would not be shown if the cutting plane were continuous.

2. All visible lines beyond the cutting plane for the section are usually shown.

3. Invisible lines beyond the cutting plane for the section are usually not shown, unless they are absolutely necessary to clarify the construction of the piece. In a half section, they are omitted in the unsectioned half, and either a center line or a solid line is used to separate the two halves of the view (Figs. 10.5 and 10.6).

4. On a view showing assembled parts, the section lines on adjacent pieces are drawn in opposite directions at an angle of 45° (Fig. 10.17).

* ASA Z14.1–1946.

5. On an assembly drawing, the portions of the cut surface of a single piece in the same view or different views always should be section-lined in the same direction, with the same spacing (Fig. 10.19).

6. The symbolic line indicating the location of the cutting plane may be omitted if the location of the plane is obvious (Fig. 10.1).

7. On a sectioned view showing assembled pieces, an exterior view is preferred for shafts, rods, bolts, nuts, rivets, and so forth, whose axes are in the plane of section (Fig. 10.19).

10.12. Auxiliary sections. A sectional view, projected upon an auxiliary plane, is sometimes necessary to show the shape of a surface cut by a plane, or to show the cross-sectional shape of an arm, rib, and so forth, inclined to any two or all three of the principal planes of projection (Fig. 10.24). When a cutting plane cuts an object, as in Fig. 10.24, arrows should show the direction in which the cut surface is viewed. Auxiliary sections are drawn by the usual method for drawing auxiliary views. When the bounding edge of the section is a curve, it is necessary to plot enough points to obtain a smooth one. Sec. 8.9 explains in detail the method for constructing the required view. A section view of this type usually shows only the inclined cut surface.

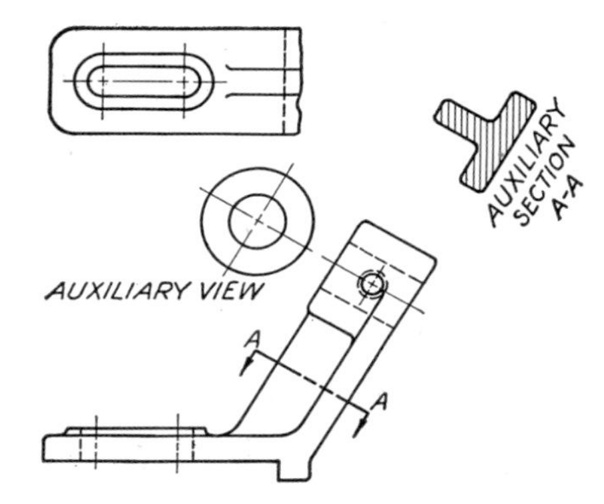

Fig. 10.24. An auxiliary section.

10.13. Conventional sections. Sometimes a less confusing sectioned representation is obtained if certain of the strict rules of projection as explained in Chapter 11 are violated. For example, an unbalanced and confused view results when the sectioned view of the pulley shown in Fig. 10.26 is drawn in true projection, as in (*a*). It is better practice to preserve symmetry by showing the spokes as if they were aligned into one plane, as in (*c*). Such treatment of unsymmetrical features is not misleading, since their actual arrangement is revealed in the circular view. The spokes are not sectioned in the preferred view. If they were, the first impression would be that the wheel had a solid web (*b*). (See Fig. 10.27.)

The holes in a flange should be shown in a sectioned view at their true distance apart, across the bolt circle, even though their axes do not fall in the plane of section. (See Fig. 10.28.) The unbalanced view in (*b*) conveys no impression of symmetry, nor does it reveal the true location of the holes with reference to rim. The view in (*a*), showing the upper hole as if it had been swung into the plane of section, is less misleading and is therefore to be preferred.

In Fig. 10.29 is shown another example of conventional representation. The sectional view is drawn as if the upper projecting lug had been swung until the portion of the cutting plane through it formed a continuous plane

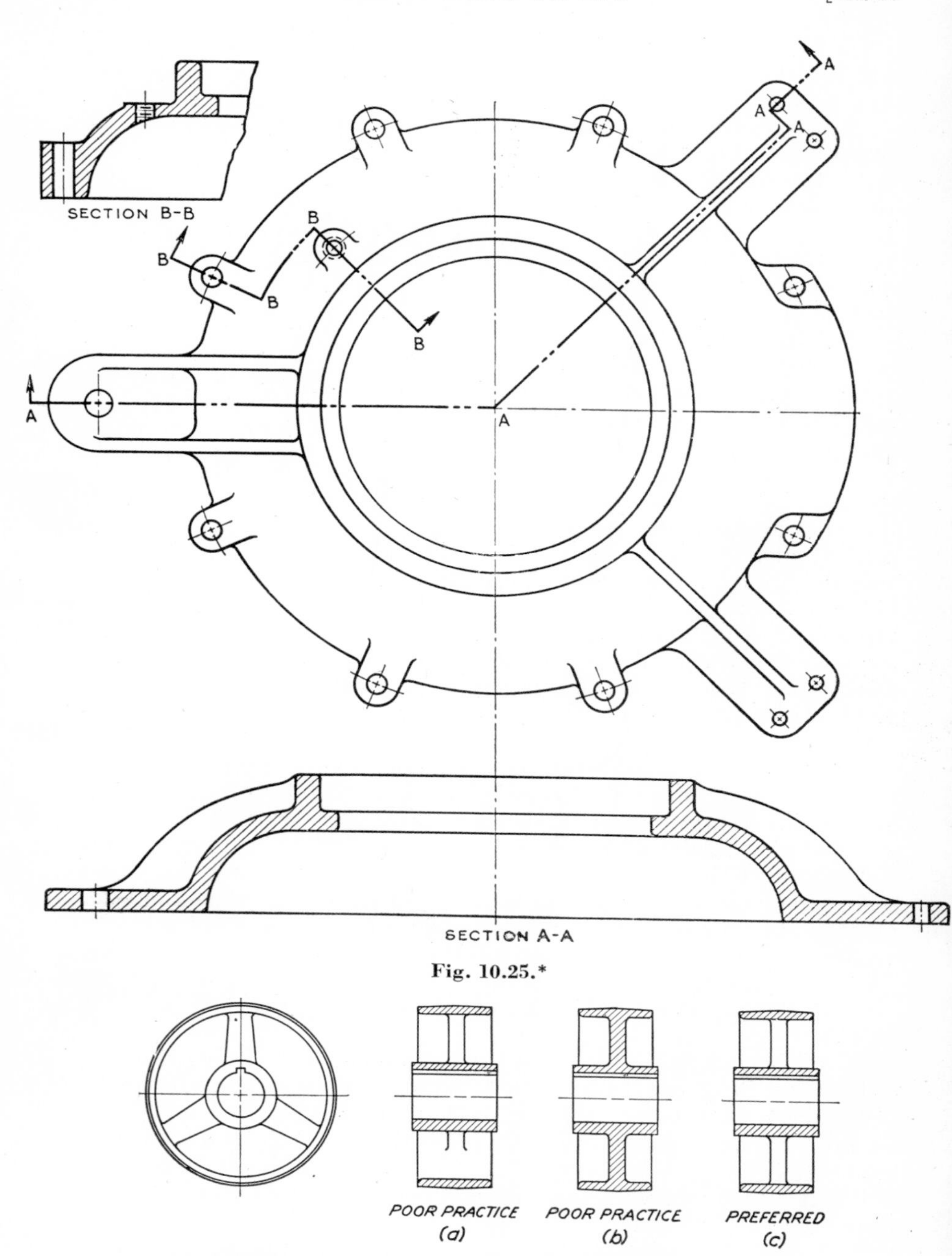

Fig. 10.25.*

Fig. 10.26. Conventional treatment of spokes in section.

---

* ASA Z14.1–1946.

with the other portion. (See Sec. 11.3.) It should be noted that the hidden lines in the sectioned view are necessary for a complete description of the construction of the lugs.

10.14. Ribs in section. When a machine part has a rib cut by a plane of section (Fig. 10.30), a "true" sectional view taken through the rib proves false and misleading, because the crosshatching on the rib causes the object to appear "solid." The preferred treatment is to omit arbitrarily the section lines from the rib, as illustrated by Fig. 10.30(a). The resulting sectional view may be considered the view that would be obtained if the plane were offset to pass just in front of the rib (b).

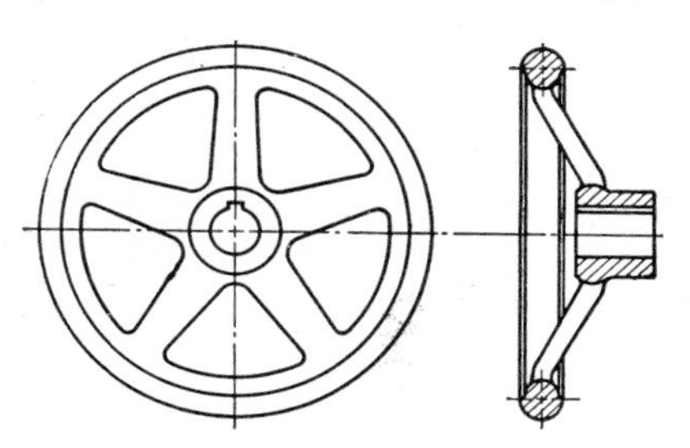

Fig. 10.27. Spokes in section.*

An alternate conventional method, approved but not used as frequently as the one above, is illustrated in Fig. 10.31. This practice of omitting alternate section lines sometimes is adopted when it is necessary to emphasize a rib that might otherwise be overlooked.

10.15. Material symbols. The section-line symbols recommended by the American Standards Association for indicating various materials are shown in Fig. 10.32. Code section lining ordinarily is not used on a working (detail) drawing of a separate part. It is considered unnecessary to indicate a material symbolically, when its exact specification must also

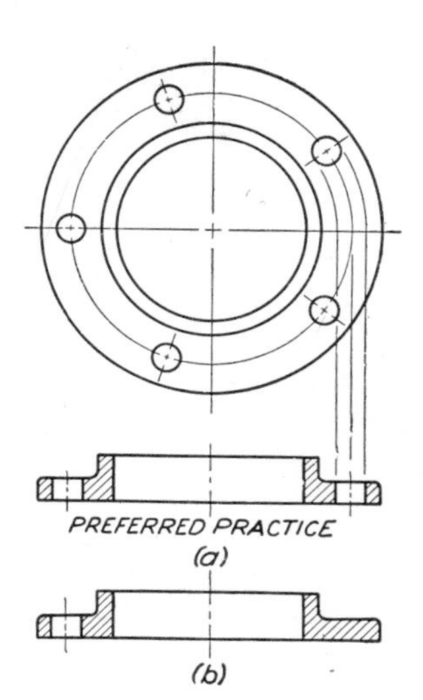

Fig. 10.28. Drilled flanges.

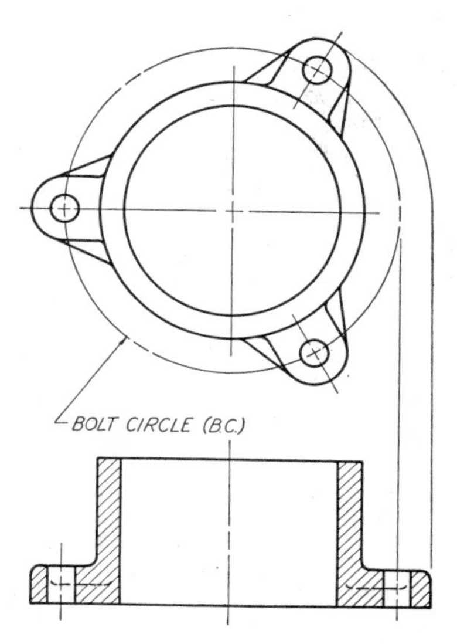

Fig. 10.29. Revolution of a portion of an object.

* ASA Z14.1–1946.

be given as a note. For this reason, and in order to save time as well, the easily drawn symbol for cast iron is commonly used on detail drawings for all materials. Contrary to this general practice, however, some few chief draftsmen insist that symbolic section lining be used on all detail drawings prepared under their supervision.

Code section lining usually is employed on an assembly section showing the various parts of a unit in position, because a distinction between the materials causes the parts to "stand out" to better advantage. Furthermore, a knowledge of the type of material of which an individual part is composed often helps the reader to identify it more quickly and understand its function.

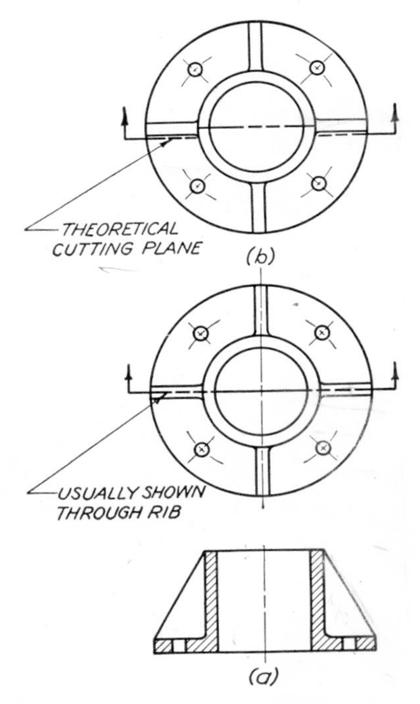

Fig. 10.30. **Conventional treatment of ribs in section.**

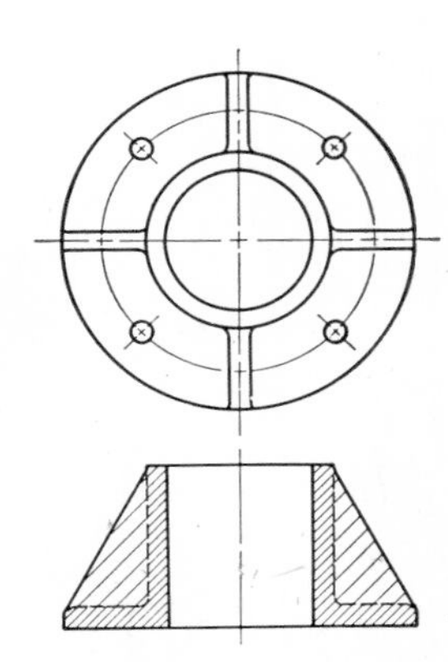

Fig. 10.31. **Alternate treatment of ribs in section.**

Symbols and conventions which are commonly used to represent materials and manufactured items on the working drawings of a structure are shown in Fig. 23.15.

10.16. Problems. The following problems were designed to emphasize the principles of sectioning. It is not recommended that a great amount of time be spent on them, as more practice in applying the fundamentals of sectioning is offered the student by problems at the end of the chapter on working drawings. Those orthographic drawings that are prepared from the pictorials of objects may be dimensioned if the elementary principles of dimensioning (Chapter 16) are carefully studied.

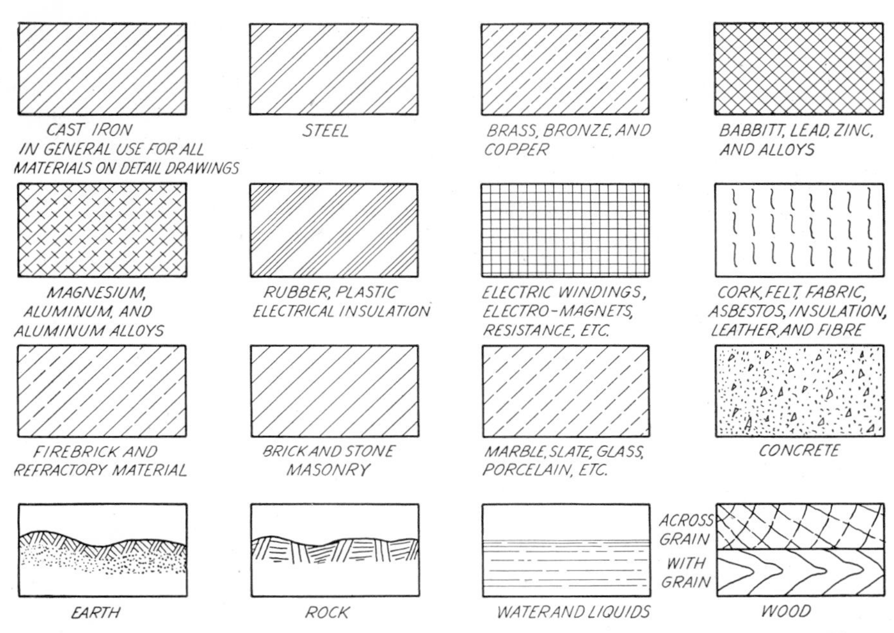

Fig. 10.32. Material symbols.

1. (Fig. 10.33.) Reproduce the top and side views and change the front view into a sectional view that will be in accordance with the indicated cutting plane.

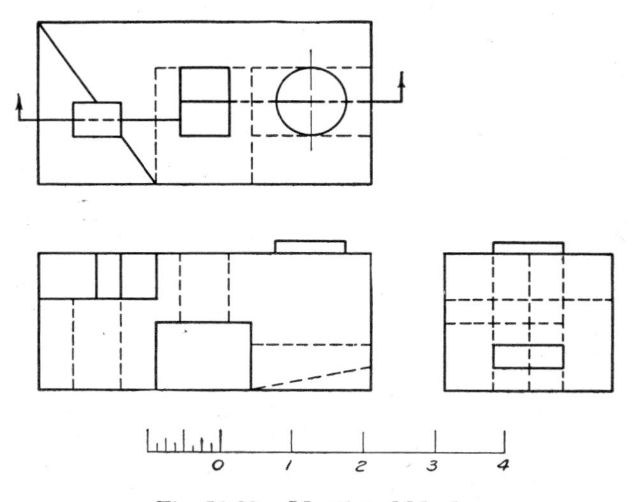

Fig. 10.33. Mutilated block.

2. (Fig. 10.34.) Reproduce the top view and change the front view into a full section view in accordance with the indicated cutting plane.

3. (Fig. 10.35.) Reproduce the top view and change the front and side views into sectional views that will be in accordance with the indicated cutting planes.

4. (Fig. 10.36.) Draw a front view of the pulley (circular view) and a side view in full section.

5. (Fig. 10.37.) Reproduce the top view of the rod support and draw the front view in full section. Read Sec. 11.5 before starting to draw.

6. (Fig. 10.38.) Draw a front view of the "*V*" pulley (circular view) and a side view in full section.

7. (Fig. 10.39.) Draw a full sectional view of the fluted column. Reproduce the circular view.

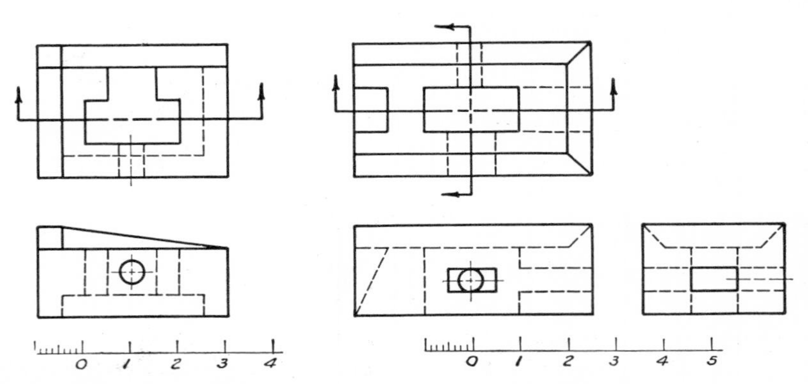

Fig. 10.34. Mutilated block.

Fig. 10.35. Mutilated block.

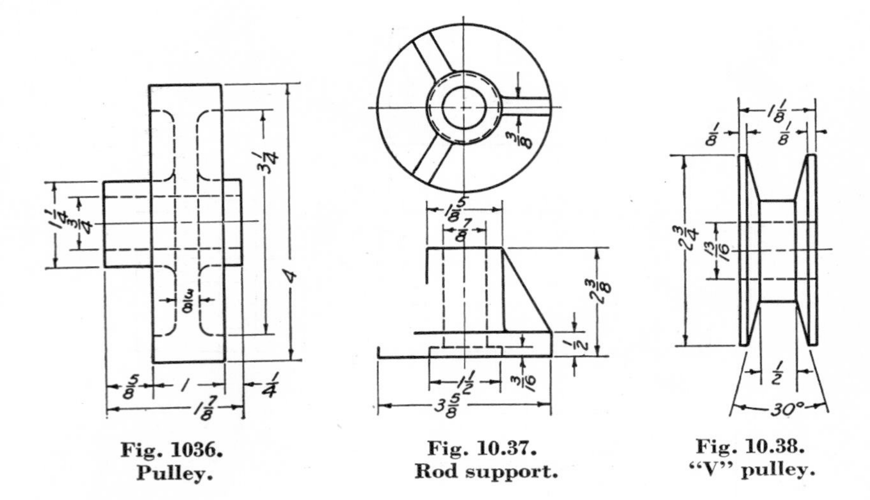

Fig. 1036. Pulley.

Fig. 10.37. Rod support.

Fig. 10.38. "V" pulley.

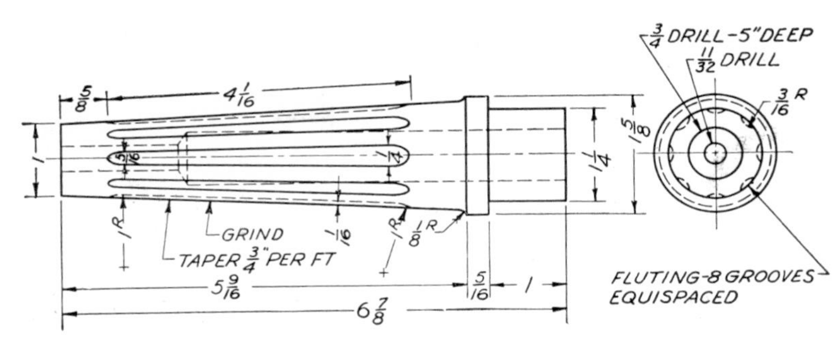

Fig. 10.39. **Fluted column.**

8. (Fig. 10.40.) Make a full sectional view of the "rectangular view" of the piston head. Reproduce the circular view.

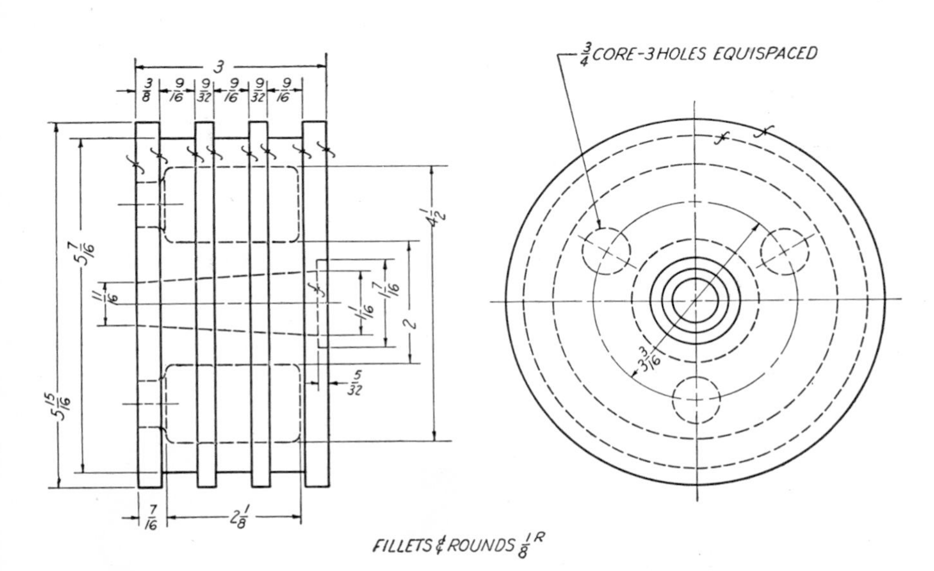

Fig. 10.40. Piston head.

9. (Fig. 10.41.) Reproduce the two views of the hand wheel and change the right-side view into a full section.

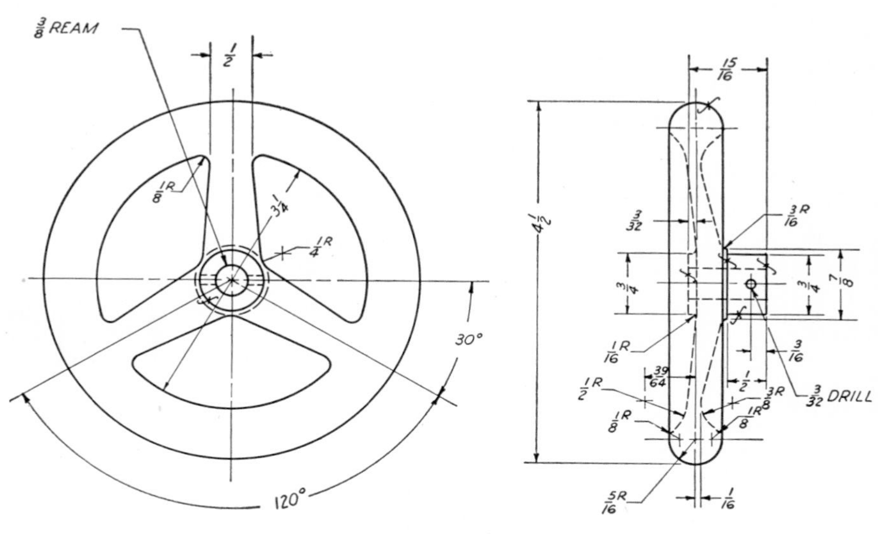

Fig. 10.41. Hand wheel.

10. (Fig. 10.42.) Reproduce the circular front view of the pump cover and convert the right-side view to a full section.

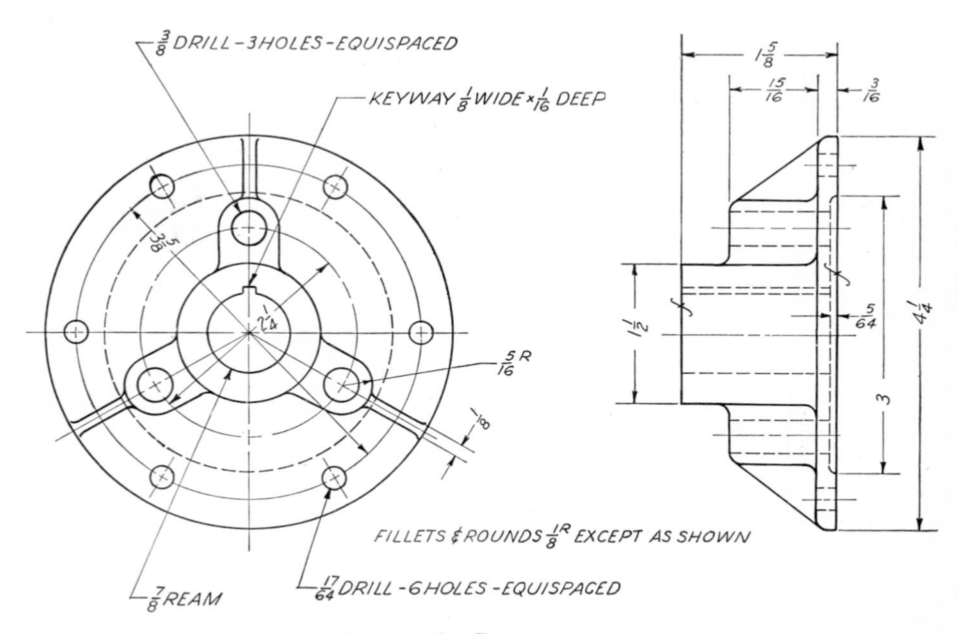

Fig. 10.42. Pump cover.

11. (Fig. 10.43.) Reproduce the top view of the control housing cover and convert the front view to a full section.

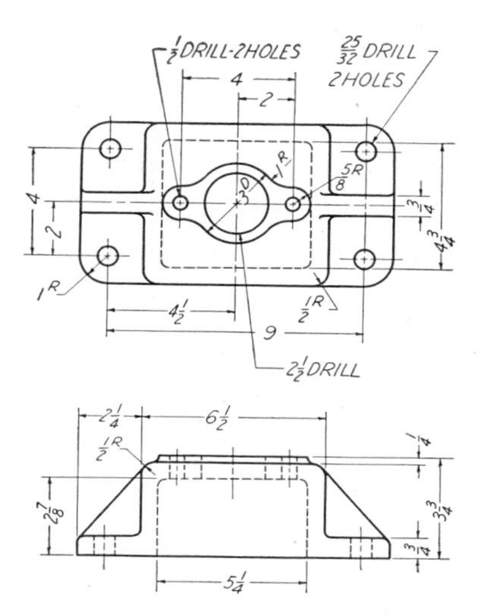

Fig. 10.43. Control housing cover.

12. (Fig. 10.44.) Reproduce the views of the crank and draw a detail (removed) section *A-A* in the position indicated.

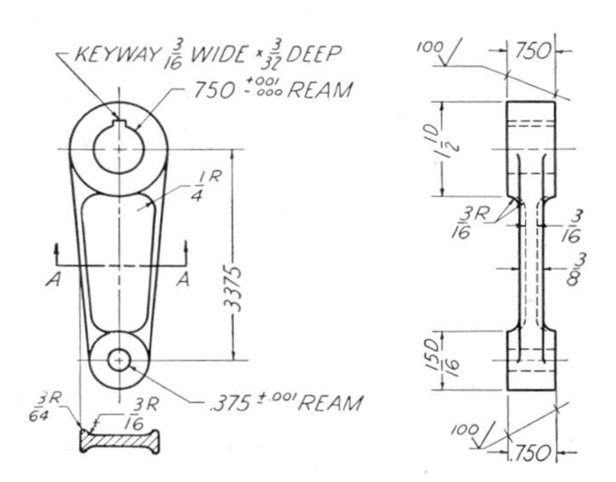

Fig. 10.44. Crank.

13. (Fig. 10.45.) Draw the necessary views of the link and use a revolved or detail section to show the cross section through the rib.

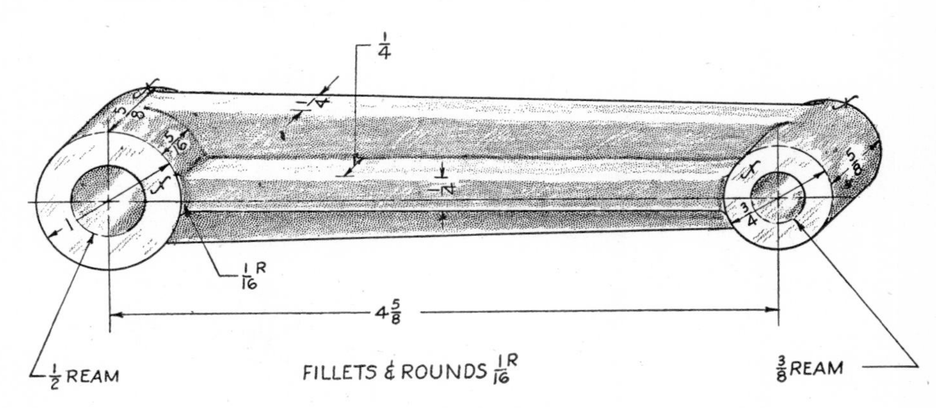

Fig. 10.45. Link.

14–23. (Figs. 10.46–10.55.) These problems may be dimensioned, as are working drawings. For each object, the student should draw all the views necessary for a working drawing of the part. Good judgment should be exercised in deciding whether the sectional view should be a full section or a half section. After the student has made his decision, he should consult his class instructor.

The end guide has five ribs (Fig. 10.55).

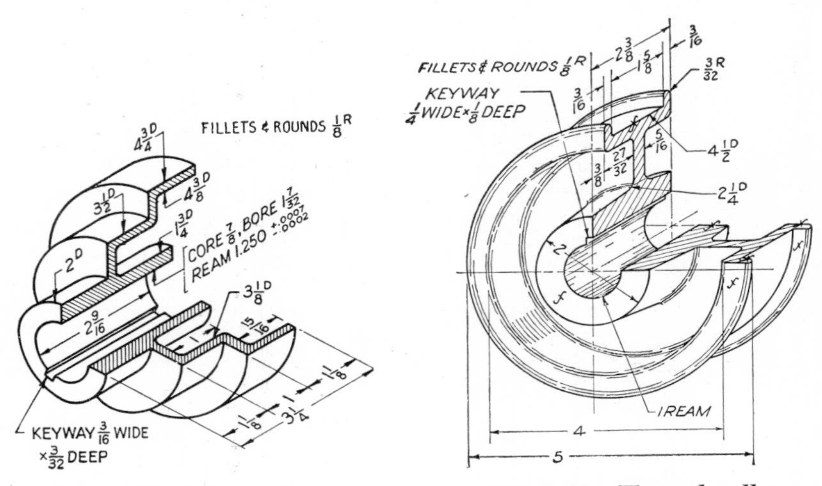

Fig. 10.46. Cone pulley. **Fig. 10.47. Flanged pulley.**

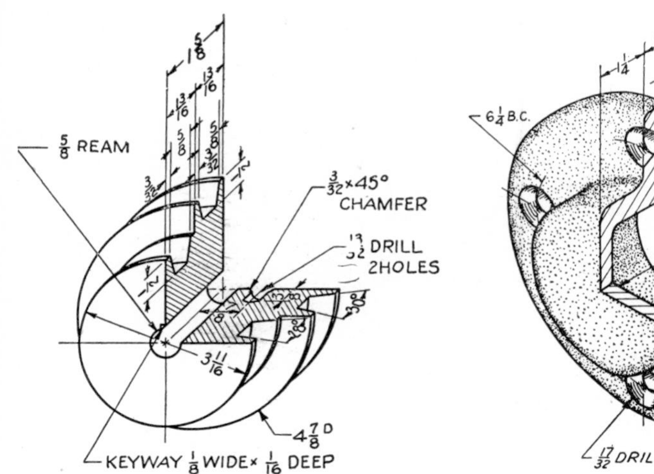

Fig. 10.48. "V" motor pulley.

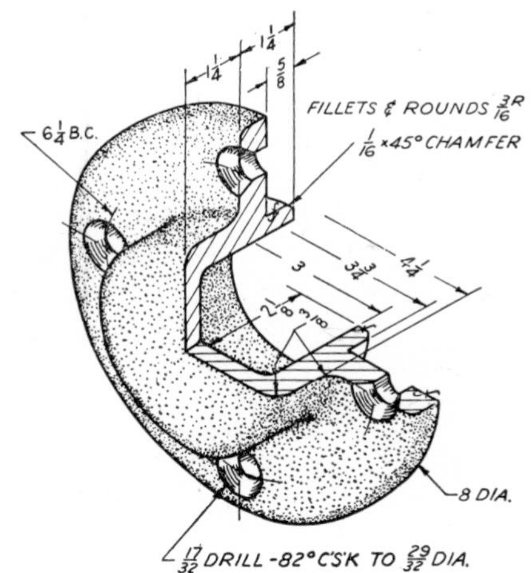

Fig. 10.49. Cover.

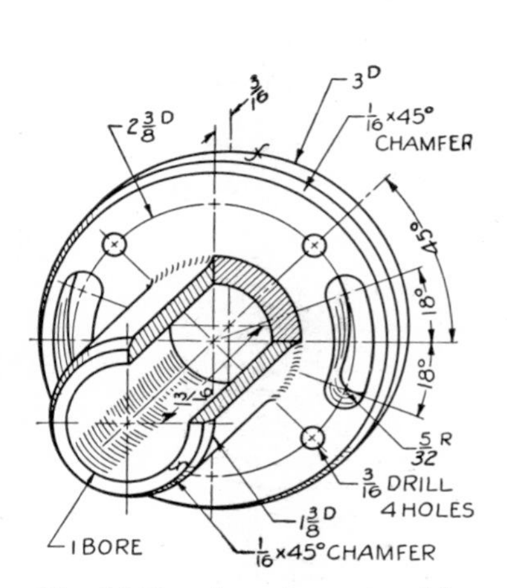

Fig. 10.50. Attachment guide.

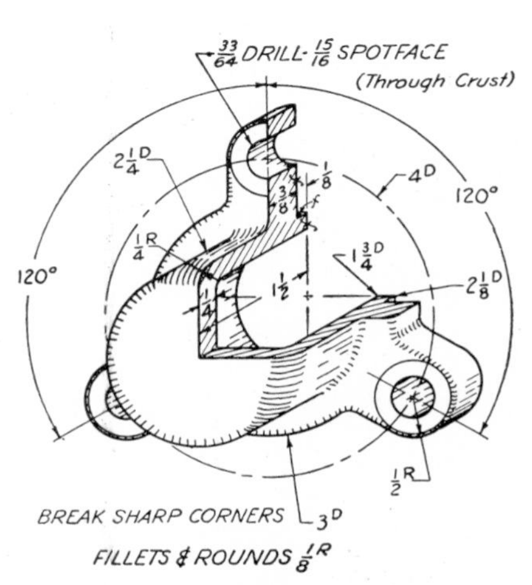

Fig. 10.51. End cap.

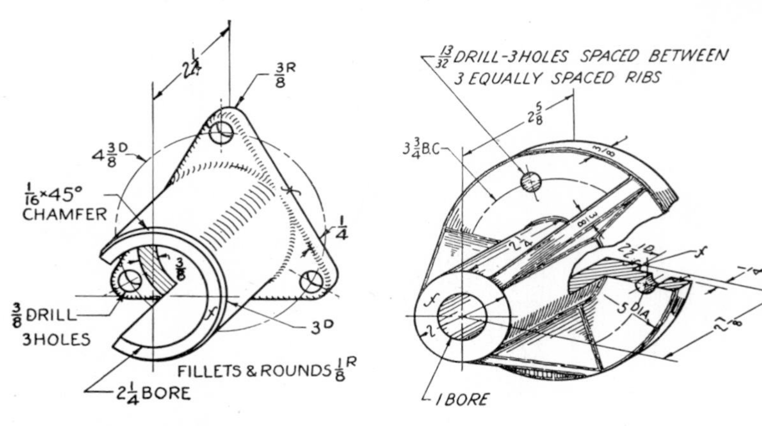

Fig. 10.52. Radiator outlet.

Fig. 10.53. Rod yoke.

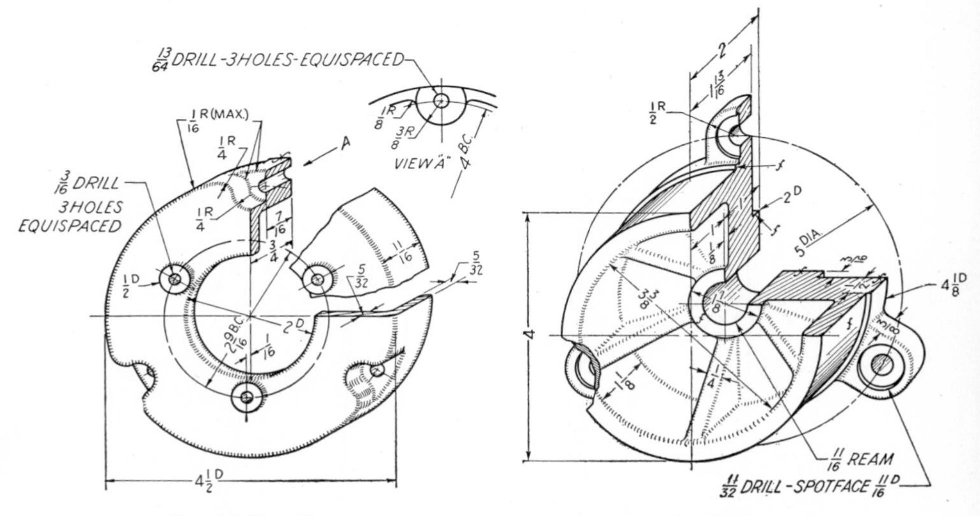

Fig. 10.54. Cover.

Fig. 10.55. End guide.

11 CONVENTIONAL PRACTICES AND REPRESENTATIONS IN ORTHOGRAPHIC DRAWING

11.1. In commercial drafting, certain conventional practices have been adopted in order to obtain added clearness. Many of them eliminate particularly awkward conditions that arise from strict adherence to the rules of projection. These idioms of drawing have slowly developed with the graphic language until at the present time they are universally recognized and observed.

11.2. The treatment of unimportant intersections. The conventional methods of treating various unimportant intersections are shown in Fig. 11.1. To show the true line of intersection in each case would add little to the value of the drawing. Therefore, in the views designated as preferred, true projection has been ignored in the interest of simplicity. On the front views, in (*a*) and (*b*) for example, there is so little difference between the descriptive values of the true and approximate representations of the hole that the extra labor necessary to draw the true representation is unwarranted.

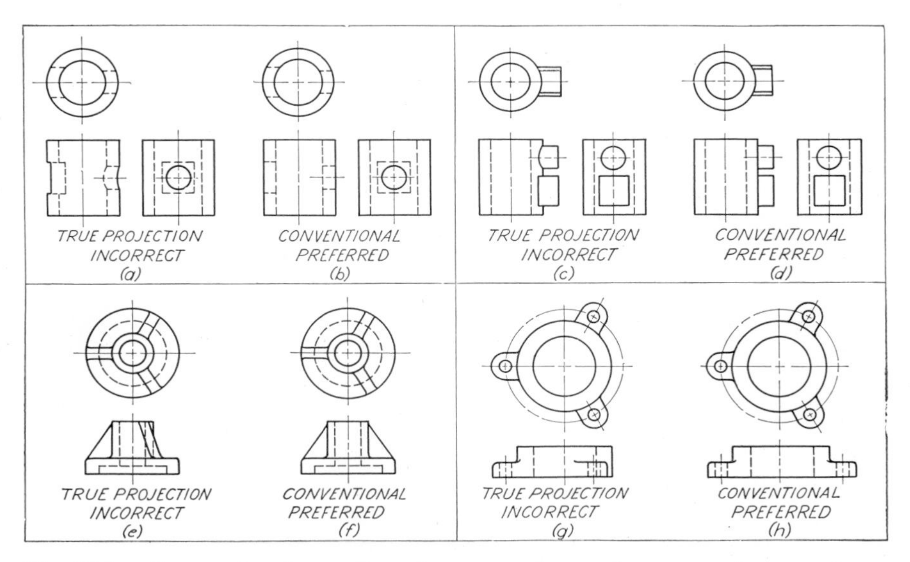

Fig. 11.1. Conventional practice of representing unimportant intersections, ribs, and lugs.

11.3. Aligned views. Pieces that have arms, ribs, lugs, or other parts at an angle are often shown aligned or "straightened out" in one view, as illustrated in Fig. 11.2. By this method, it is possible to show the true shape as well as the true position of such features.

11.4. Developed views. Bent pieces, similar to the piece shown in Fig. 11.3, are often drawn so that one view is a developed view of the blank from which the piece is to be formed, and the other is a true view showing the characteristic contour.

In laying out the developed view extra metal must be allowed for bends. The empirical formula used for computing the bend allowance (arc length) for a bend is shown in (*b*).

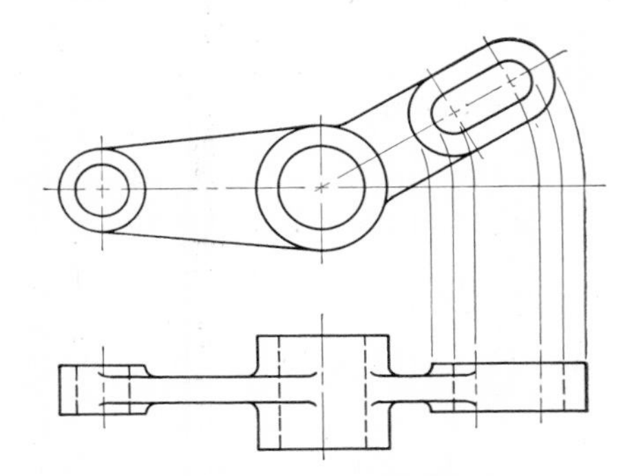

Fig. 11.2. Aligned views.

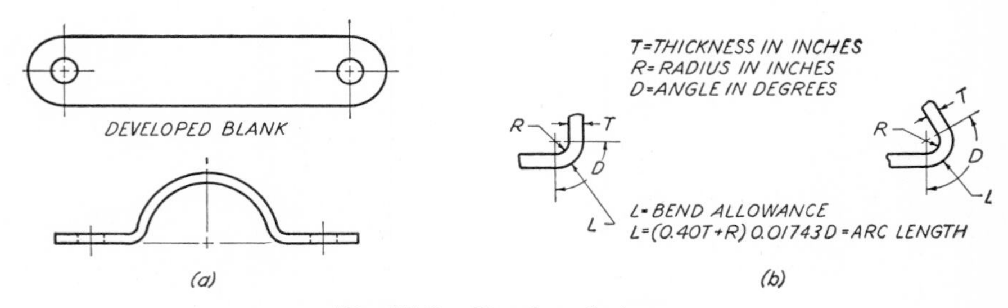

Fig. 11.3. Developed views.

11.5. Conventional treatment of radially arranged features. Many objects that have radially arranged features may be shown more clearly if true projection is violated (Fig. 11.4). Violation of true projection in such cases consists of intentionally showing such features swung out of position in one view so as to present the idea of symmetry and show the true relationship of the features at the same time. For example, while the radially arranged holes in a flange (see Fig. 11.5) should always be shown in their true position in the circular view, they should be shown in a revolved position in the other view in order to show their true relationship with the rim. The conventional treatment for drilled flanges in section is explained in Sec. 10.13.

Radial ribs and radial spokes are similarly treated. The true projection of such features may create representations that are unsymmetrical and misleading. The preferred conventional method of treatment, by preserving symmetry, produces representations that are more easily understood and that at the same time are much simpler to draw. Fig. 11.6

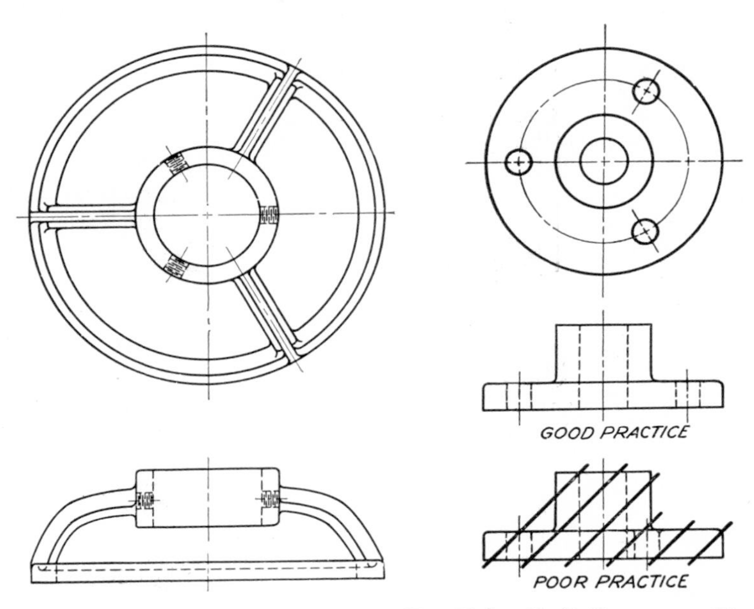

Fig. 11.4. Symmetry.

Fig. 11.5. Radially arranged holes.

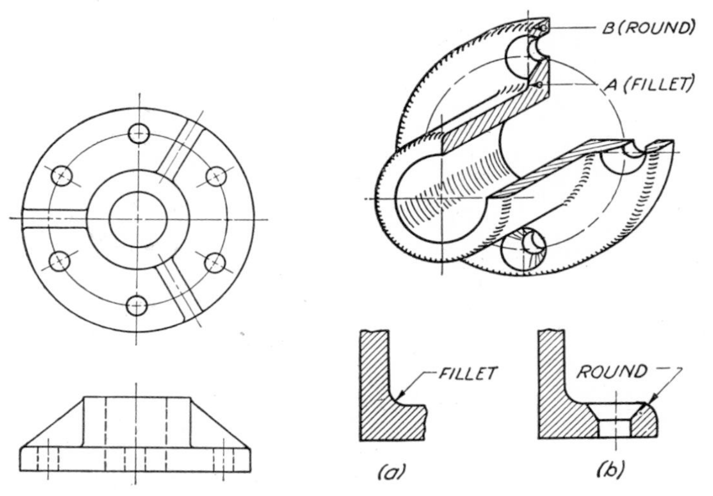

Fig. 11.6. Conventional treatment of radially arranged ribs.

Fig. 11.7. Fillets and rounds. (a) Fillet (internal); (b) round (external).

illustrates the preferred treatment for radial ribs. The proper method for treating radial ribs and radial spokes in sectioned views is explained in Secs. 10.13 and 10.14.

11.6. Representation of fillets and rounds. Interior corners, which are formed on a casting by unfinished surfaces, always are filled in (filleted) at the intersection, in order to avoid possible fracture at that point. Sharp corners are also difficult to obtain and are avoided for this reason as well (Fig. 11.7). Exterior corners are rounded for appearance and for the comfort of persons who must handle the part when assembling or repairing the machine on which the part is used. A rounded internal corner is known as a "fillet"; a rounded external corner is known as a "round."

When two intersecting surfaces are machined, however, their intersection will become a sharp corner. For this reason, all corners formed by unfinished surfaces should be shown "broken" by small rounds, and all corners formed by two finished surfaces or one finished surface and one unfinished surface should be shown "sharp." Although in the past it has been the practice to allow pattern makers to use their judgment about the size of fillets and rounds, many present-day companies require their designers and draftsmen to specify their size even though their exact size may not be important.

Since fillets and rounds eliminate the intersection lines of intersecting surfaces, they create a special problem in orthographic representation.

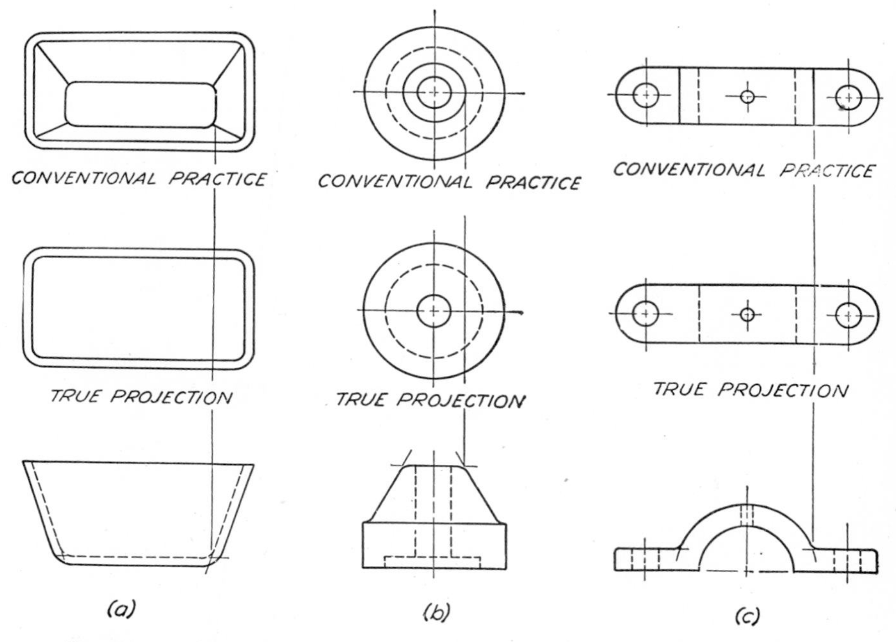

Fig. 11.8. Conventional practice of representing nonexisting lines of intersection.

To treat them in the same manner as they would be treated if they had large radii results in views that are misleading. For example, the true projection view in Fig. 11.8(*a*) confuses the reader, because at a first glance it does not convey the idea that there are abrupt changes in direction. To prevent such a probable first impression and to improve the descriptive value of the view, it is necessary to represent these theoretically nonexisting lines. These characteristic lines are projected from the approximate intersections of the surfaces, with the fillets disregarded.

Fig. 11.9 illustrates the accepted conventional method of representing the "run-out" intersection of a fillet in cases where a plane surface is tangent to a cylindrical surface. Although run-out arcs such as these are usually drawn freehand, a French curve or a bow instrument may be used.

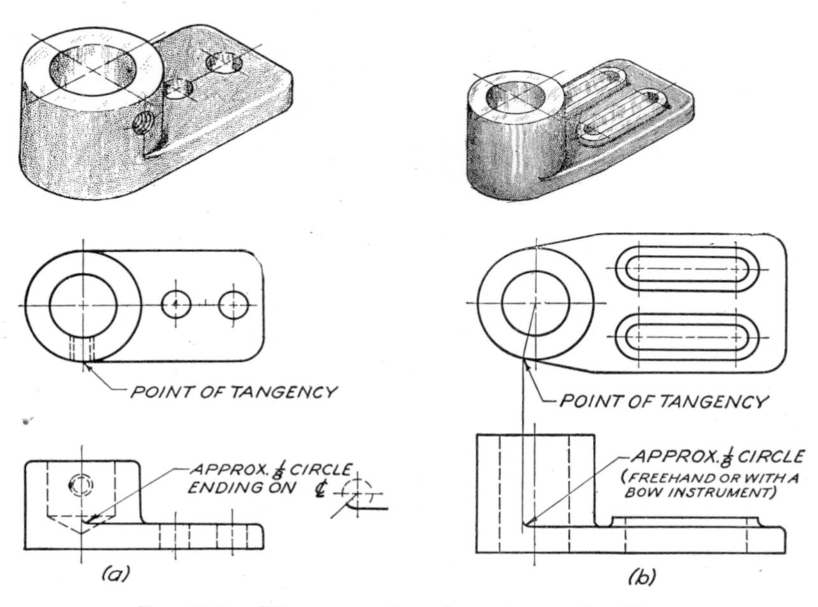

Fig. 11.9. The conventional treatment for fillets.

If they are drawn with the latter type of instrument, a radius should be used that is equal to the radius of the fillet, and the completed arc should form approximately one-eighth of a circle.

The generally accepted methods of representing intersecting fillets and rounds are illustrated in Fig. 11.10. The treatment, in each of the cases shown, is determined by the relationship existing between the sizes of the intersecting fillets and rounds. Fig. 11.10 shows several illustrations of accepted conventional methods used to represent run-outs.

11.7. Accepted violations of true projection in the representation of boltheads, slots, and holes for pins. Another departure from true projection is encountered in representing a bolthead. For example, on a working drawing, it is considered to be the best practice to show the head across corners in both views, regardless of the fact that in true projection one view would show "across flats." (See Fig. 11.11.) This method of treatment eliminates the possibility of a reader interpreting a hexagonal head to be a square head. Furthermore, the showing of a head the "long way" in both views clearly reveals the space needed for proper clearance.

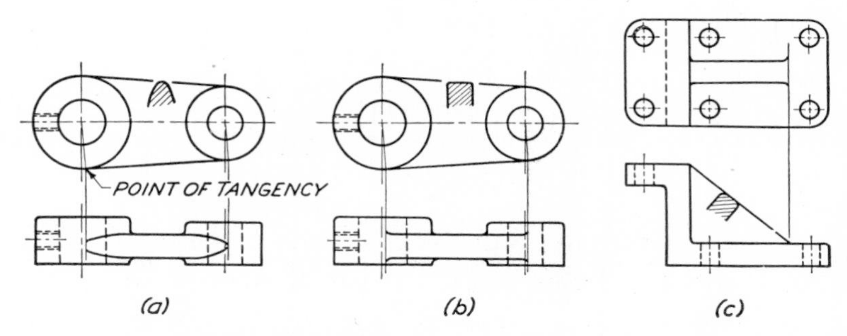

Fig. 11.10. The approximate methods of representing intersecting fillets, rounds.

Fig. 11.11 also shows several illustrations of the correct method of representing slots and holes for pins. In the case of the slotted head fasteners the slots are shown at 45° in the end views in order to avoid placing a slot on a center line where it is usually difficult to draw so that the center line passes accurately through the center. This practice does not affect the descriptive value of the drawing, because the true size and shape of the slot is shown in the front view. The hole for a pin is shown at 45° for the same reason. In such a position it may be more quickly observed.

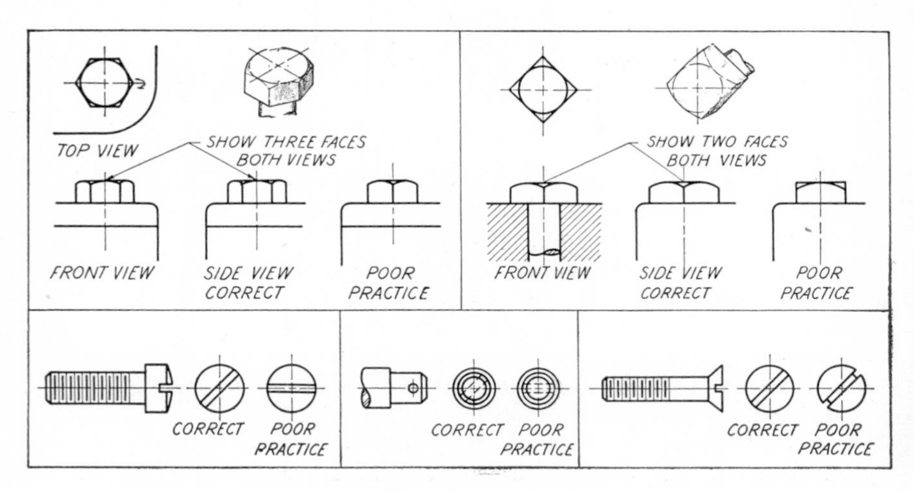

Fig. 11.11. Treatment of bolt heads, slots, and holes for pins.

11.8. Half views. When the space available is insufficient to allow a satisfactory scale to be used for the representation of a symmetrical piece, it is considered good practice to make one view a half view, as shown in Fig. 11.12. The half view, however, must be the top or side view and not the front view, which shows the characteristic contour. When the front

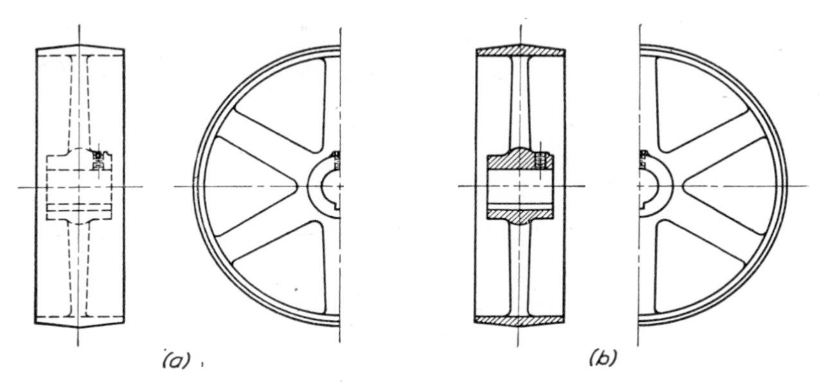

Fig. 11.12. A half view.

view is an exterior view, the half view should be the front half of the top or side view; when the front view is a sectional view, it should be the rear half.

11.9. Conventional breaks. A relatively long piece of uniform section may be shown to a larger scale, if a portion is broken out so that the ends can be drawn closer together (Fig. 11.13). When such a scheme is employed, a conventional break is used to indicate that the length of the

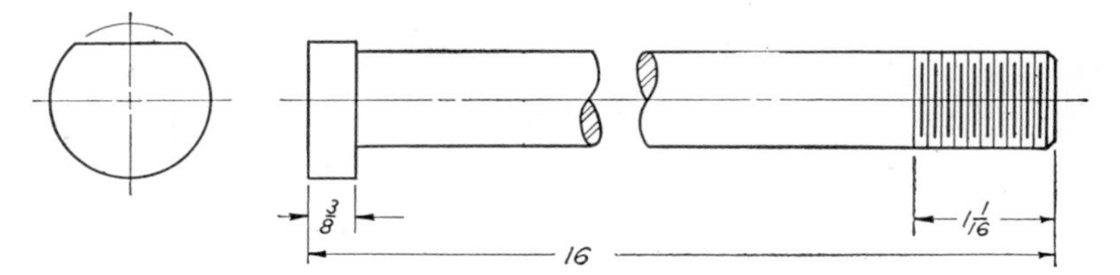

Fig. 11.13. A broken-out view.

representation is not to scale. The American Standard conventional breaks, shown in Fig. 11.14, are used on either detail or assembly drawings. The breaks representation for indicating the broken ends of rods, shafts, tubes, and so forth, are designed to reveal the characteristic shape of the cross section in each case. Although break lines for round sections may be drawn freehand, particularly on small views, it is better practice to draw them with either an irregular curve or a bow instrument. The breaks for wood sections, however, always should be drawn freehand.

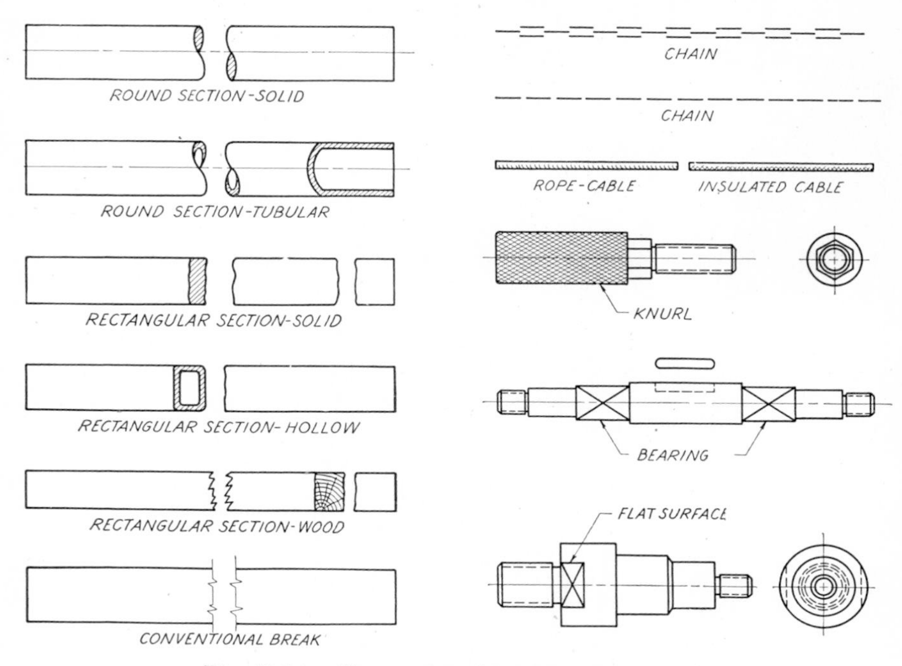

Fig. 11.14. Conventional breaks and symbols.

Fig. 11.15 shows the steps for drawing the break lines for the broken end of a solid round section. The small connecting curves may be drawn freehand.

Other recognized symbolic representations that are commonly used are shown in Fig. 11.14.

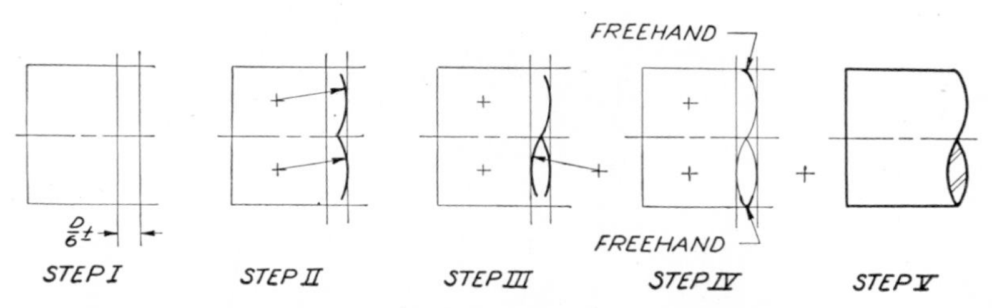

Fig. 11.15. Steps in drawing break lines for a round section.

11.10. Ditto lines. When it is desirable to minimize labor in order to save time, ditto lines may be used to indicate a series of identical features. For example, the threads on the shaft shown in Fig. 11.16 are just as effectively indicated by ditto lines as by a completed profile representa-

Fig. 11.16. Ditto lines.

tion. When ditto lines are used, a long shaft of this type may be shortened without actually showing a conventional break.

11.11. A conventional method for showing a part in alternate positions. A method frequently used for indicating an alternate position

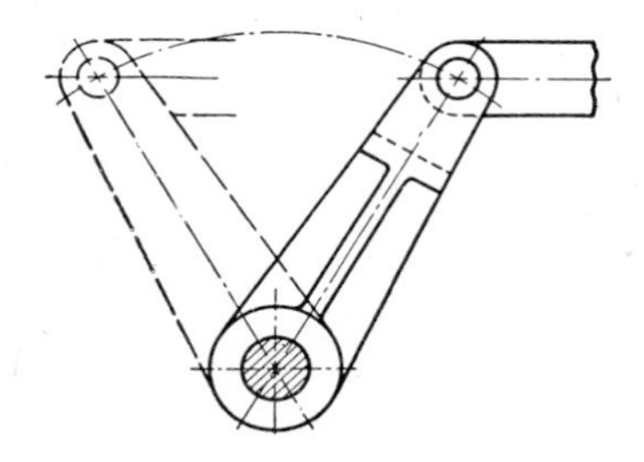

Fig. 11.17. Alternate positions.*

of a part or a limiting position of a moving part is shown in Fig. 11.17. The long dashes forming the object lines of the view showing the alternate position should be of medium weight. The phantom line shown in Fig. 3.32 is recommended in the SAE Automotive Drafting Standards and may be used for representing the alternate position of a part.

* ASA Z14.1–1946.

12 FREEHAND DRAFTING

12.1. Value of freehand drafting. Freehand technical drafting is primarily the language of those in responsible charge of the development of technical designs and plans. Chief engineers, chief draftsmen, designers, and squad bosses have found that the best way to present their ideas for either a simple or complex design is through the medium of sketches. Sketches may be schematic, as are those that are original expressions of

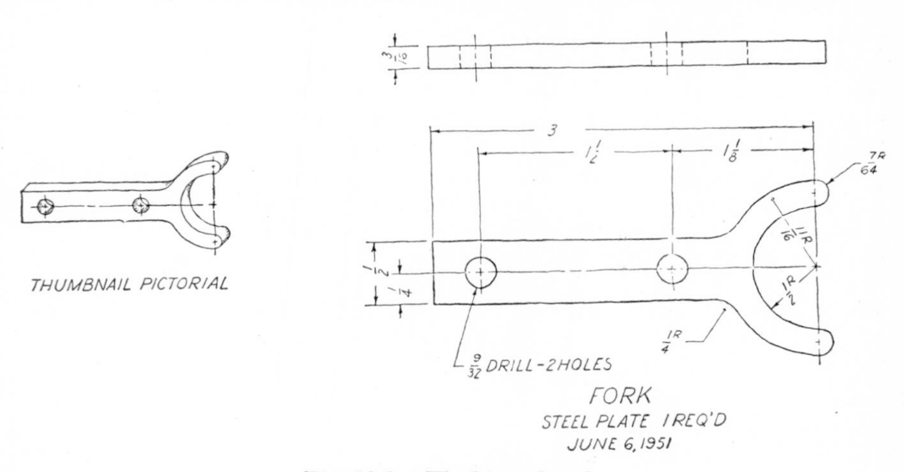

Fig. 12.1. Working sketch.

new ideas, or they may be instructional, their purpose being to convey ideas to draftsmen or shopmen. Some sketches, especially those prepared for the manufacture of parts that are to replace worn or broken parts on existing machines, may resemble complete working drawings.

Since the importance of freehand drafting very often is underestimated, the purpose of this discussion is to amplify training in this phase. The young prospective engineer should understand, when beginning his studies, that sketching and not mechanical drafting will be his ultimate form of expression and that he must be able to prepare complete sketches that will present his ideas and decisions to subordinates in an understandable manner. Fig. 12.1 is an example of a working sketch.

12.2. Sketching materials. For the type of sketching discussed here, the required materials are an *F* pencil, a soft eraser, and some paper. In the industrial field, men who have been improperly trained in sketching often use straight-edges and cheap pocket compasses that they could well dispense with if they would adopt the correct technique. Preparing sketches with instruments consumes much unnecessary time.

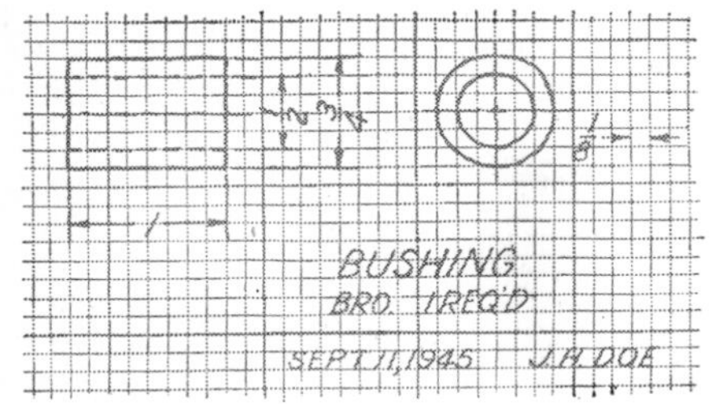

Fig. 12.2. Sketches on cross-section paper.

For the person who cannot produce a satisfactory sketch without guide lines, cross-section paper is helpful. Ordinarily, the ruling on this paper forms one-inch squares which are subdivided into one-eighth or one-tenth inch squares. Such paper is especially useful when sketching to scale is desirable (Fig. 12.2).

A specially ruled paper, shown in Fig. 12.3, is used in making isometric sketches.

12.3. Projections. Although freehand drafting lacks the refinement given by mechanical instruments, it is based upon the same principles of projection and conventional practices that apply to multiview, pictorial, and the other divisions of mechanical drawing. For this reason, one must be thoroughly familiar with projection, in all of its many forms, before he is adequately trained to prepare sketches.

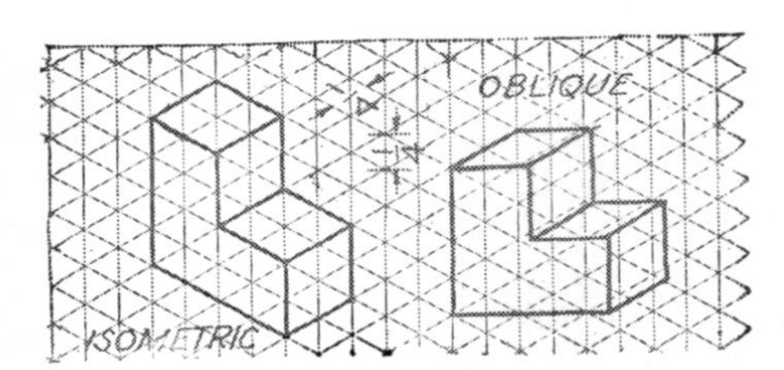

Fig. 12.3. Sketches on isometric paper

12.4. Technique of lines. Freehand lines quite naturally will differ in their appearance from mechanical ones. A well-executed freehand line will never be perfectly straight and absolutely uniform in weight, but an effort should be made to approach *exacting uniformity.* As in the case of mechanical lines, they should be black and clear and not broad and fuzzy. (See Fig. 12.4.)

12.5. Sharpening the sketching pencil. A sketching pencil should be sharpened, on a file or piece of sandpaper, to a conical point. The point then should be rounded slightly, on the back of the sketch pad or on another sheet of paper, to the correct degree of dullness. When rounding the point, the pencil should be rotated to prevent the formation of sharp edges.

12.6. Straight lines. The pencil should rest on the second finger and be held loosely by the thumb and index finger about 1 to $1\frac{1}{2}$ inches above the point.

Horizontal lines are sketched from left to right with an easy arm motion that is pivoted about the muscle of the forearm. The straight line thus becomes an arc of infinite radius.

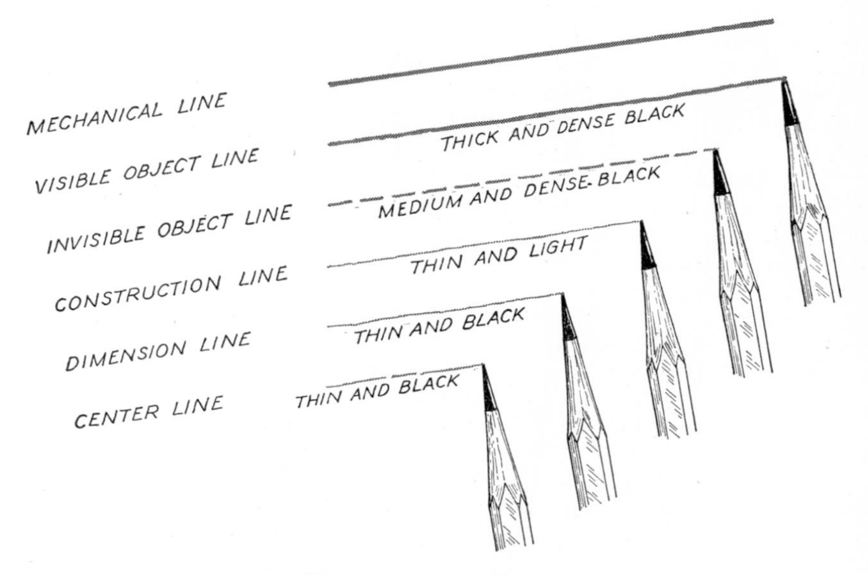

Fig. 12.4. Sketch lines.

When sketching a straight line, it is advisable to first mark the end points with light dots or small crosses (Fig. 12.5). The complete procedure for sketching a straight line is as follows:

1. Mark the end points.

2. Make a few trial motions between the marked points to adjust the eye and hand to the contemplated line.

3. Sketch a *very* light line between the points by moving the pencil in two or three sweeps. When sketching the trial line, the eye should be on the point toward which the movement is directed. With each stroke, an attempt should be made to correct the most obvious defects of the stroke preceding, so that the finished trial line will be relatively straight.

4. Darken the finished line, keeping the eye on the pencil point on the trial line.

The final line, replacing the trial line, should be distinct, black, uniform, and straight.

It is helpful to turn the paper through a *convenient angle* so that the horizontal and vertical lines assume a slight inclination (Fig. 12.6). A horizontal line, when the paper is in this position, is sketched to the right and upward, thus allowing the arm to be held slightly away from the body and making possible a free arm motion.

Short vertical lines may be sketched either downward or upward,

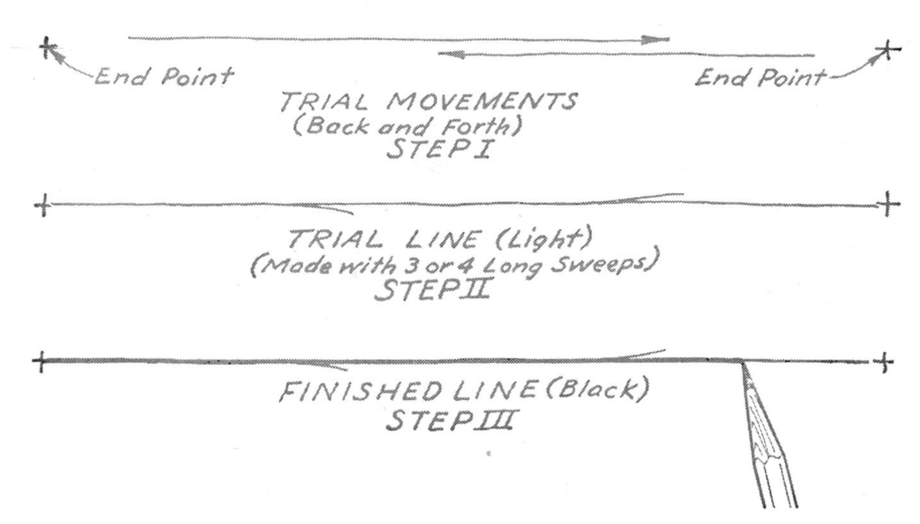

Fig. 12.5. Steps in sketching a straight line.

without changing the position of the paper. When sketching downward, the arm is held slightly away from the body and the movement is toward the sketcher (see Fig. 12.7). To sketch vertical lines upward, the arm is held well away from the body.

By turning the paper, a long vertical line may be made to assume the position of a horizontal line and can be sketched with the same general movements used for the latter.

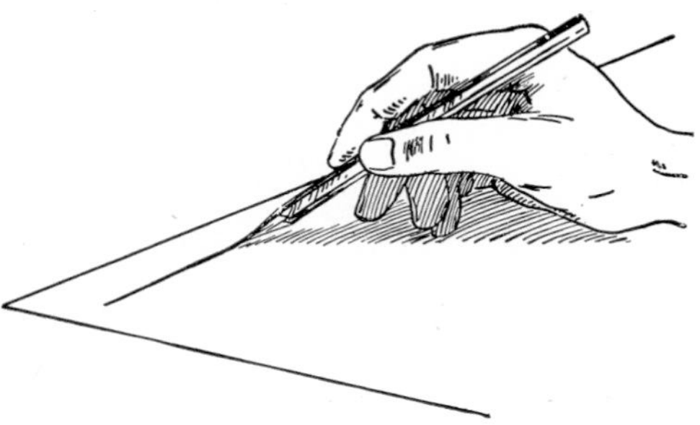

Fig. 12.6. Sketching horizontal lines.

Inclined lines running upward from lower left to upper right may be sketched upward with the same movements used for horizontal lines, but those running downward from upper left to lower right are sketched with the general movements used for either horizontal or vertical ones, depending upon their inclination (Fig. 12.8). Inclined lines may be more easily sketched by turning the paper to make them conform to the direction of horizontal lines.

12.7. Circles. Small circles may be sketched by marking radial distances on perpendicular center lines (Fig. 12.9). These distances can be marked off either by eye or by measuring with a marked strip of paper (see Fig. 12.10). Larger circles may be constructed more accurately by sketching two or more diagonals, in addition to the center lines, and by sketching short construction lines perpendicular to each, equidistant from the center.

Tangent to these lines, short arcs are drawn perpendicular to the radii. The circle is completed with a light construction line, and all defects are corrected before darkening (Fig. 12.11).

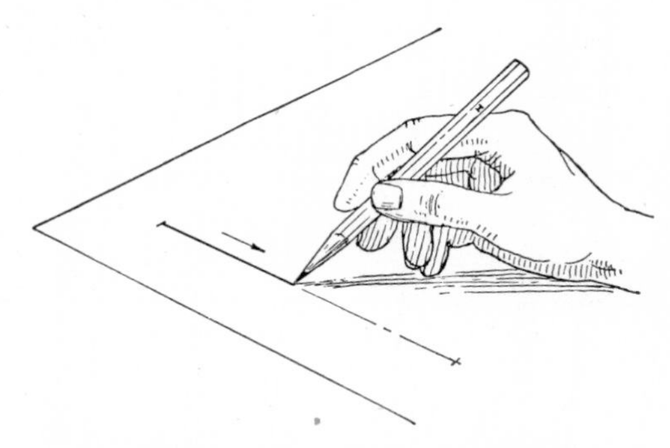

Fig. 12.7. Sketching vertical lines.

12.8. Ellipses. An ellipse of good proportion may be sketched within an enclosing rectangle. The rectangle, since it is used merely as an aid in forming the ellipse, should be drawn with very light lines, and the required ellipse should be sketched tangent to the sides.

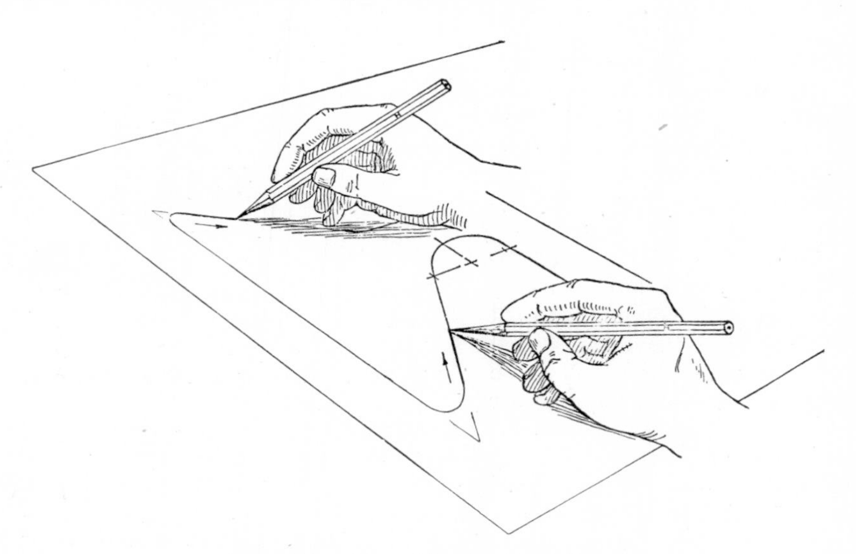

Fig. 12.8. Sketching inclined lines.

12.9. Making a sketch. When making orthographic working sketches, a systematic order should be followed and all the rules and conventional practices used in making working drawings should be applied. The following procedure is recommended:

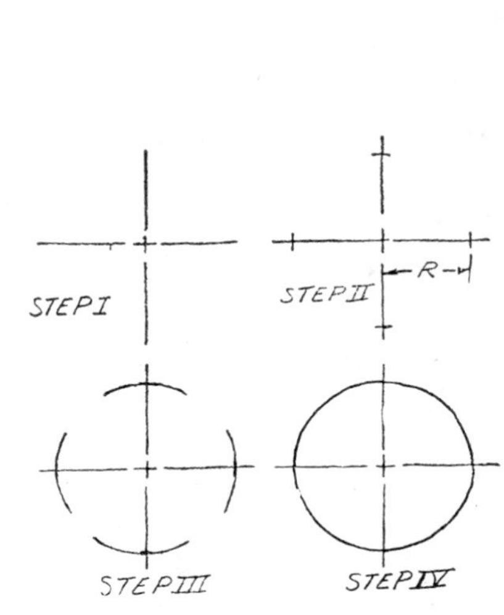

Fig. 12.9. Sketching small circles.

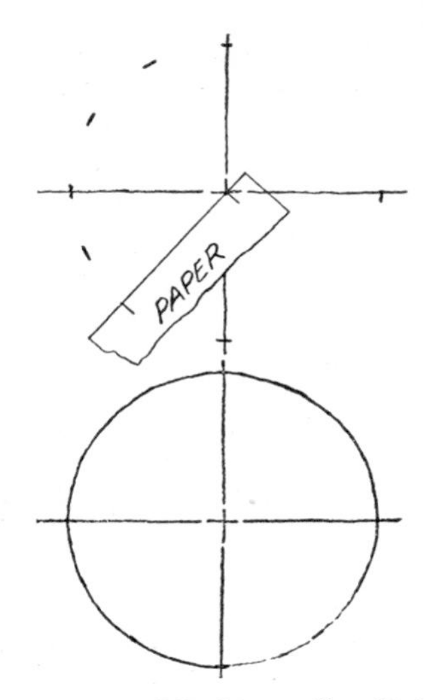

Fig. 12.10. Marking off radial distances.

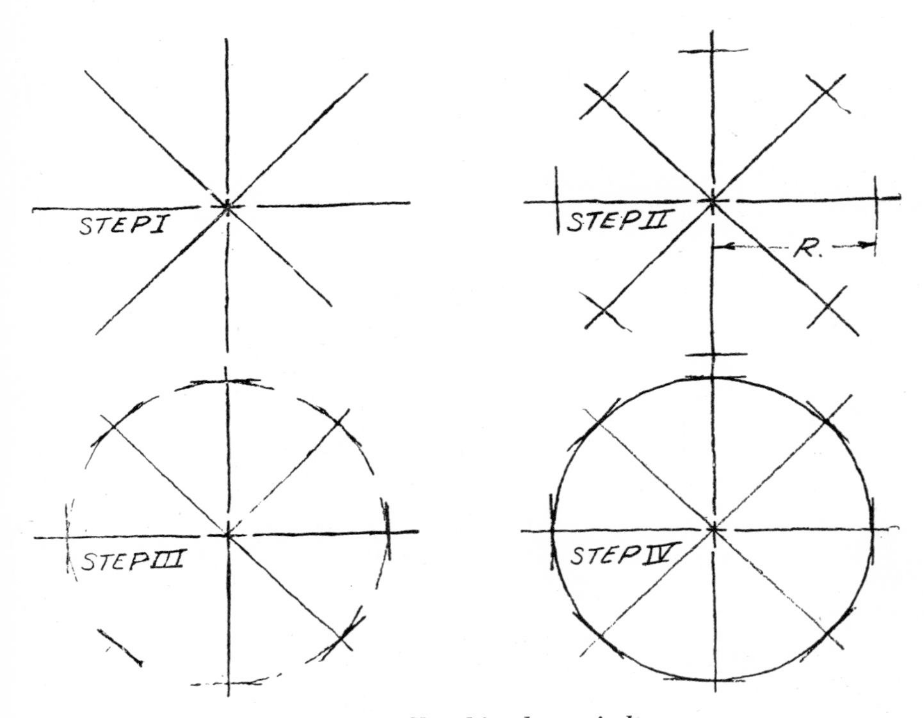

Fig. 12.11. Sketching large circles.

1. Examine the object, giving particular attention to detail.
2. Determine which views are necessary.
3. "Block in" the views, using light construction lines.
4. Complete the detail and darken the object lines.
5. Sketch extension lines and dimension lines, including arrowheads.
6. Complete the sketch by adding dimensions, notes, title, date, sketcher's name or initials, and so on.
7. Check the entire sketch carefully to see that no dimensions have been omitted.

The progressive steps in making a sketch of an object are shown in Fig. 12.12.

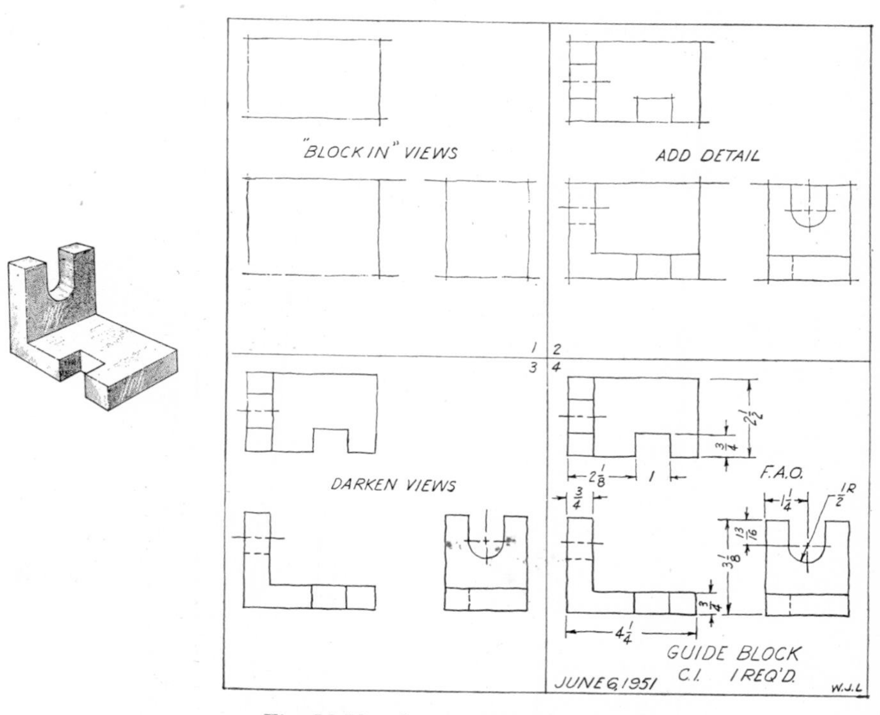

Fig. 12.12. Steps in sketching.

12.10. Making sketches of parts for the purpose of replacement and repair. It quite frequently is necessary to make working-drawing sketches of broken or worn parts. Such sketches are used instead of mechanical drawings because they can be made and sent to the shop in a much shorter time. The procedure given in Sec. 12.9 should be followed carefully when making sketches to be used by workmen in the shops.

12.11. Measurements and measuring instruments. If a sketch is to serve as a working drawing, it must contain all the necessary dimen-

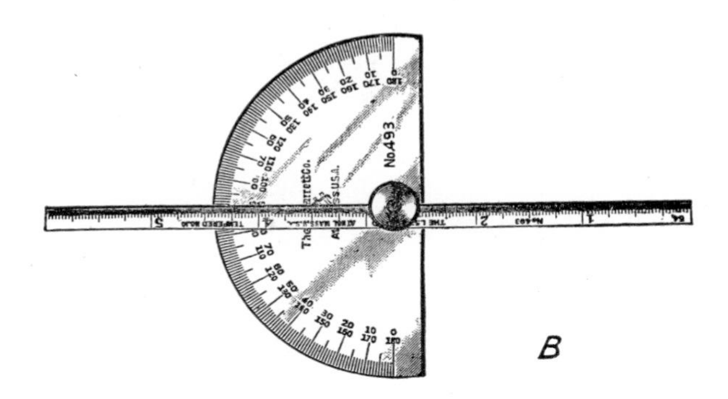

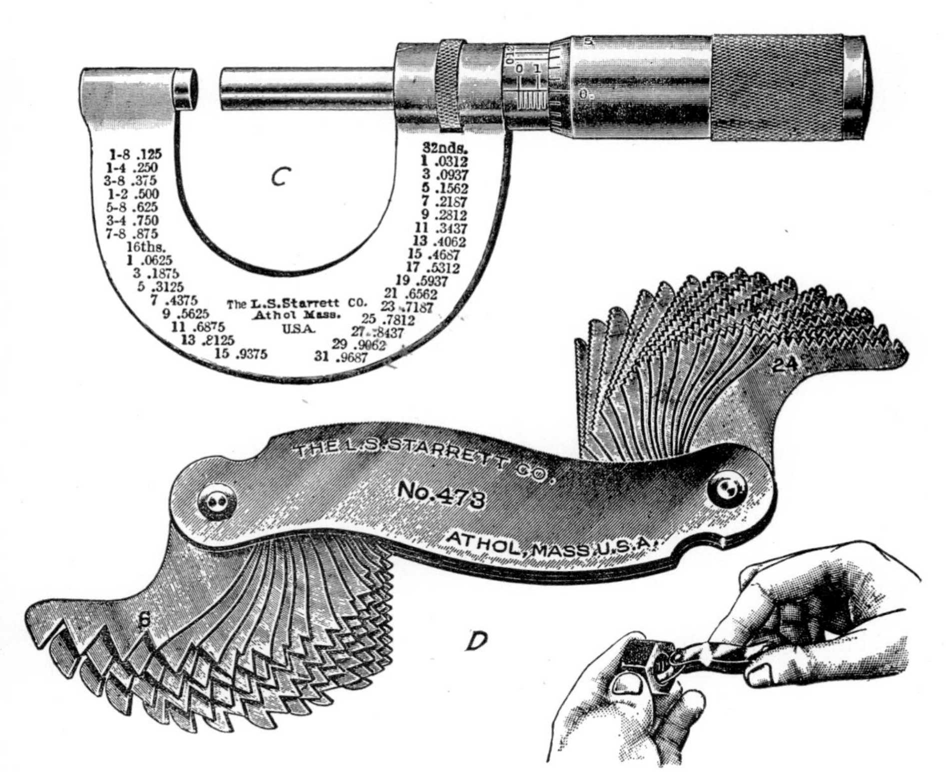

Fig. 12.13. A, steel scale; B, protractor; C, micrometer calipers; D, thread-pitch gage.

sions and instructional notes needed by the workmen. If a sketch is for the manufacture of a part that is to replace a worn or broken part in an existing machine, measurements must be taken from the original part with the same general types of measuring devices to be used in manufacturing the new part (Fig. 12.13). The instrument selected for each particular detail should be of a type that will allow measurements to be made with the correct degree of accuracy. For most machine parts, a steel scale and a set of inside and outside calipers will prove sufficient. When more accurate measurements are necessary, a micrometer must be used. In any case, the selection of the instrument for a measurement should be determined by exercising good judgment backed by practical shop experience. Fig. 12.14 shows how the outside calipers are used to take measurements from an object. Fig. 12.15 shows the use of the inside calipers for measuring the diameter of a hole.

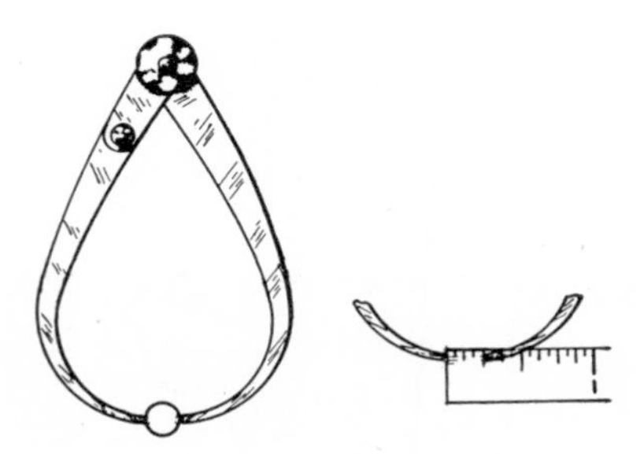

Fig. 12.14. Outside calipers.

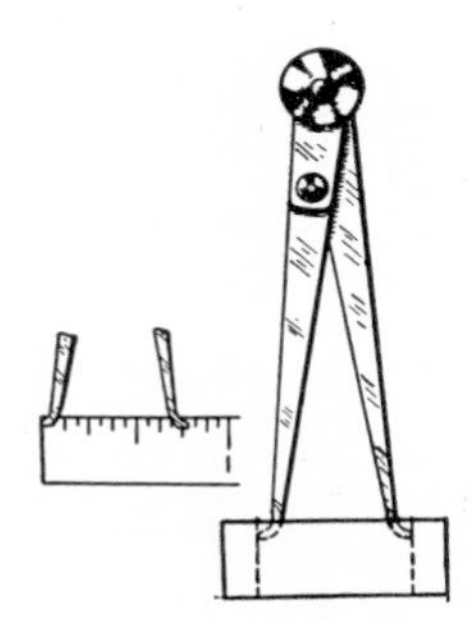

Fig. 12.15. Inside calipers.

When taking measurements, certain practices are recommended. For example, to obtain the distance between holes (shown on the sketch as between centers), measure the distance between corresponding edges. To locate other features and to take off size dimensions, measure from a finished surface whenever possible, for a finished surface is usually a mating surface. The man in the shop must work from such a surface if he is to produce a part accurate enough to function in the existing machine.

12.12. The title. A title is far more important on a sketch than many persons realize. It serves to identify the sketch and usually contains additional valuable information such as (1) the type of material, (2) the number required, (3) the name or initials of the sketcher, and (4) the date.

12.13. Pictorial sketching. Often an engineer or draftsman must sketch an object pictorially, freehand, in order to present an idea to another who has not been trained to read a multiview (orthographic) drawing. In design work, a pictorial view frequently is placed on a preliminary sketch along with the dimensioned views, so that anyone assisting in the development of the design may be able quickly to grasp an idea of the pictorial form visualized by the designer.

Truthfully, most engineers are not artists, but, any engineer can and should become able to make skillfully a satisfactory pictorial sketch by using one of the so-called "mechanical methods" explained briefly in this discussion and in detail in Chapter 14.

A student having difficulty in interpretating a multiview drawing usually will find that a pictorial sketch, prepared as explained in Fig. 12.16, will clarify the form that he is trying to visualize, even before the last lines of the sketch have been drawn.

The practices presented in Chapter 14 for the mechanical methods, isometric, oblique, and perspective, are followed generally in pictorial sketching, except that angles are assumed and lengths are estimated.

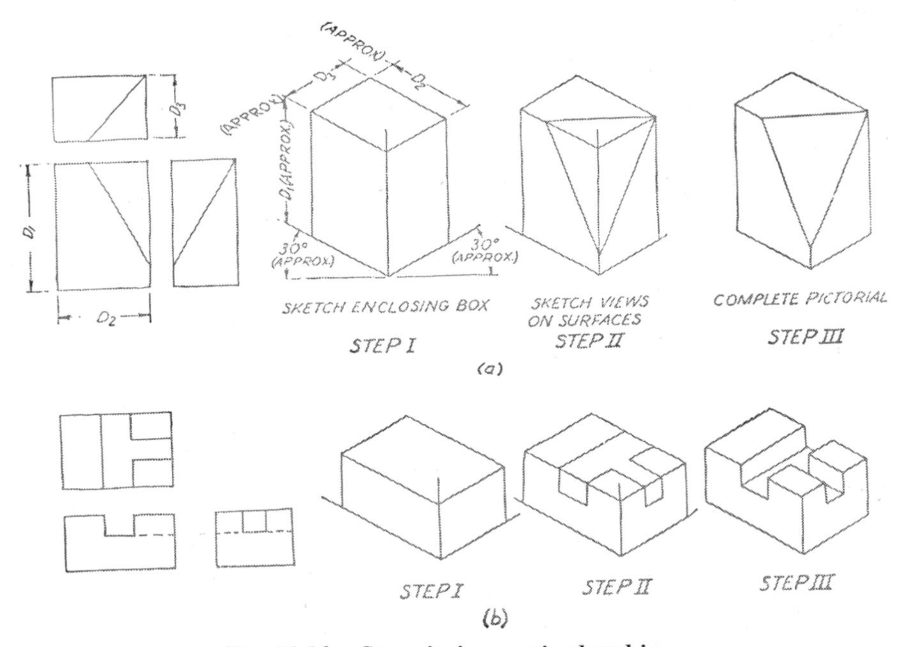

Fig. 12.16. Steps in isometric sketching.

For this reason, one must develop an eye for good proportion before he will be able to create a satisfactory pictorial sketch that will be in no way misleading.

12.14. Isometric sketching. Isometric sketching starts with three isometric lines, called axes, which represent three mutually perpendicular lines. One of these axes is sketched vertically, the other two at 30° with the horizontal. In Fig. 12.16 (step I), the near front corner of the enclosing box lies along the vertical axis, while the two visible receding edges of the base lie along the axes receding to the left and to the right.

If the object is of simple rectangular form as in Fig. 12.16, it may be sketched by drawing an enclosing isometric box (step I) upon the surfaces of which the orthographic views may be sketched (step II). Care must be taken in assuming lengths and distances so that the finished view (step III) will have relatively correct proportions. In constructing the enclosing box (step I), the vertical edges are parallel to the vertical axis, and edges receding to the right and to the left are parallel to the right and left axes, respectively.

Objects of more complicated construction may be "blocked in" as shown in Fig. 12.17. Note that the projecting cylindrical features are enclosed in "isometric" prisms, and that the circles are sketched within isometric squares. The procedure in Fig. 12.17 is the same as in Fig. 12.16,

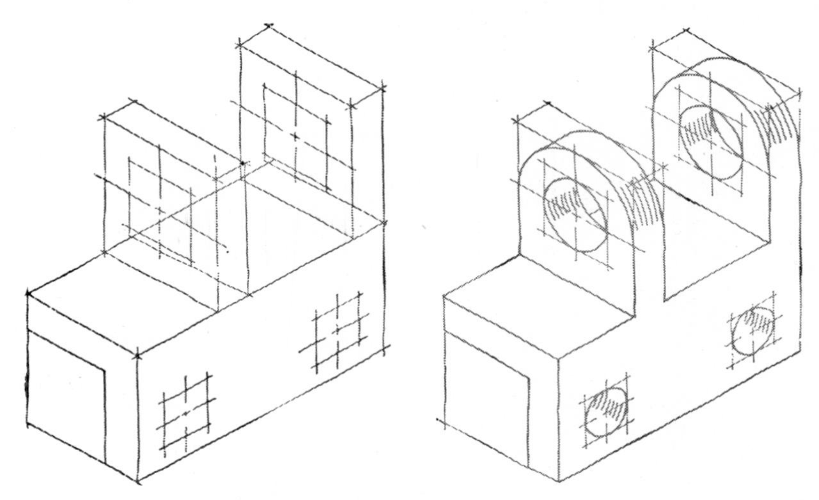

Fig. 12.17. Blocking in an isometric sketch.

except that three enclosing isometric boxes are needed in the formation of the final representation instead of one.

In sketching an ellipse to represent a circle pictorially, an enclosing "isometric square" (rhombus) is drawn having sides equal approximately to the diameter of the true circle (step I, Fig. 12.18). The ellipse is formed

Fig. 12.18. Isometric circles.

by first drawing arcs tangent to the mid-points of the sides of the isometric square in light sketchy pencil lines (step II). In finishing the ellipse (step III) with a dark heavy line, care must be taken to obtain a nearly elliptical shape.

Fig. 12.19 shows the three positions for an isometric circle. Note that the major axis is horizontal for an ellipse on a horizontal plane (I).

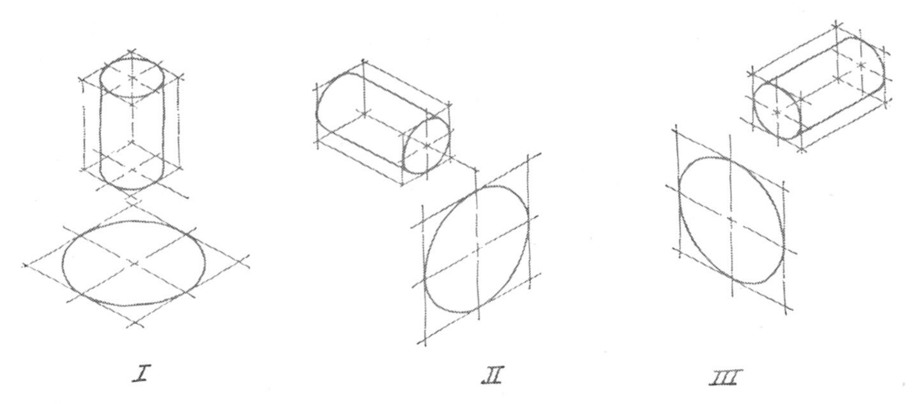

Fig. 12.19. Isometric circles.

12.15. Oblique projection. A sketch in oblique projection shows the front face without distortion, in its true shape. It has this one advantage over isometric projection, even though the final result usually will not present so pleasing an appearance. It is not recommended for objects having circular or irregularly curved features on any but the front plane or in a plane parallel to it.

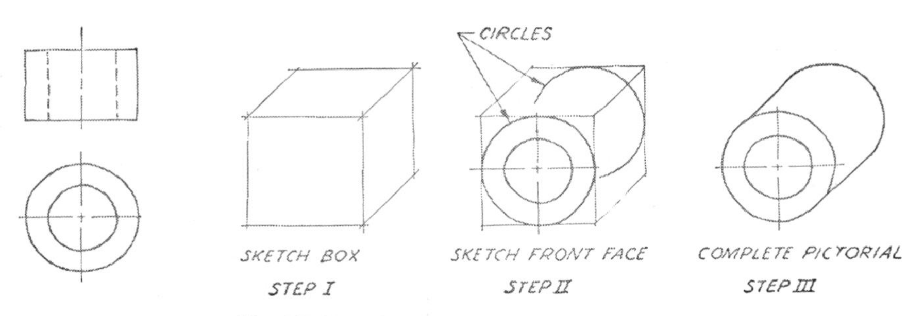

Fig. 12.20. Steps in oblique sketching.

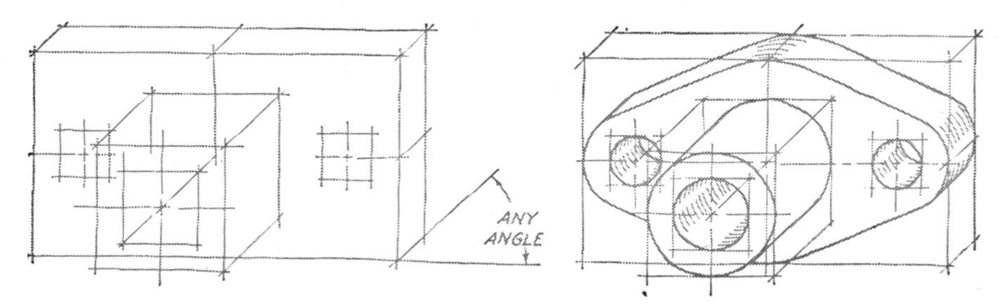

Fig. 12.21. Blocking in an oblique sketch.

Fig. 12.20 shows the steps for making an oblique sketch. The receding lines of the enclosing box (step I) are parallel and may be drawn at any angle.

Fig. 12.22 illustrates how the illusion of extreme elongation in the direction of the receding axis may be minimized by foreshortening to obtain proportions more pleasing to the eye.

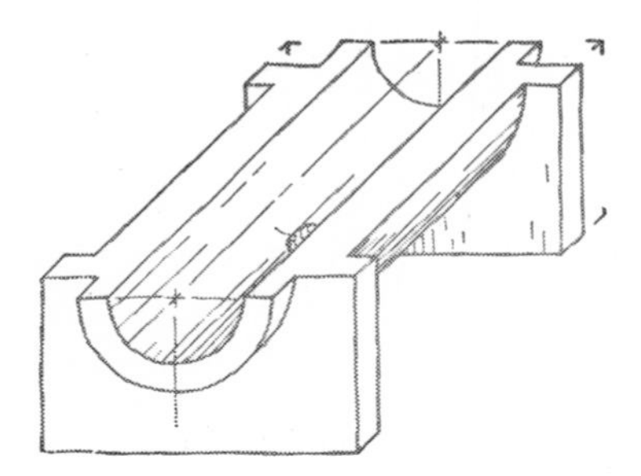

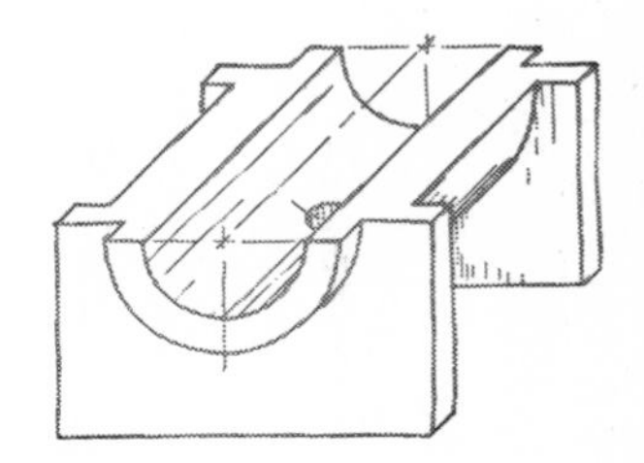

Fig. 12.22. Oblique sketches.

12.16. Perspective sketching. A sketch that has been prepared in accordance with the concepts of perspective will present a somewhat more pleasing and realistic effect than one in oblique or isometric projection. A perspective sketch actually presents an object as it would appear when observed from a particular point. The recognition of this fact, along with an understanding of the concepts that an object will appear smaller at a distance than when it is close, and that horizontal lines converge as they recede until they meet at a vanishing point, should enable one to produce sketches having a perspective appearance. In sketching an actual object, a position should be selected that will show it to the best advantage. When the object exists only in one's mind or

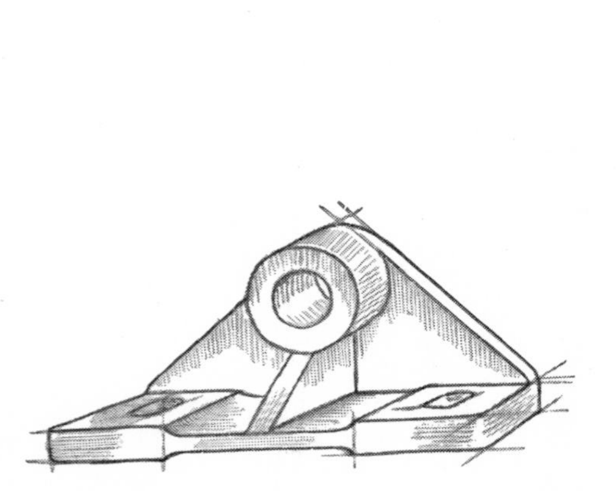

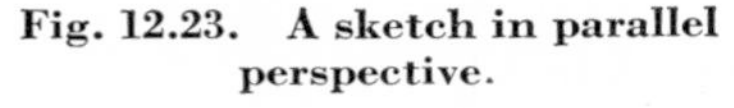

Fig. 12.23. A sketch in parallel perspective.

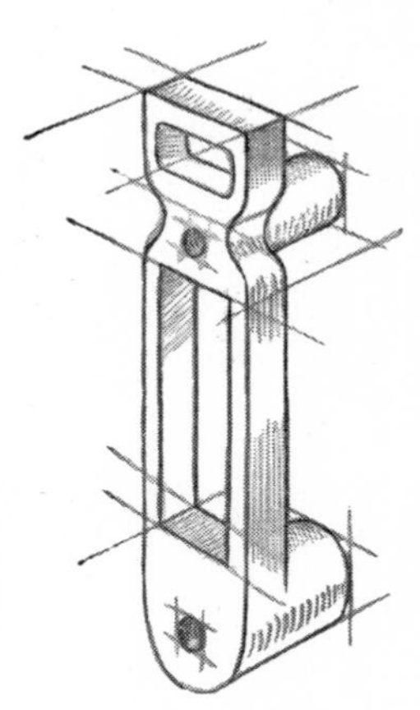

Fig. 12.24. A sketch in angular perspective.

on paper in orthographic form, then the object must be visualized and the viewing position assumed.

At the start, the principal lines should be sketched in lightly, extending each line for some length toward its vanishing point. After this has been accomplished, the enclosing perspective squares for circles should be blocked in and the outline for minor details added. When the object lines have been darkened, the construction lines extending beyond the figure may be erased.

Fig. 12.23 shows a parallel or one-point perspective that bears some resemblance to an oblique sketch. All faces in planes parallel to the front show their true shape. All receding lines should meet at a single vanishing point. Fig. 12.24 is an angular perspective. All horizontal lines receding upward to the right extend toward a vanishing point at the right, and those receding to the left extend toward a vanishing point at the left.

12.17. Problems. The following practical one-view working sketches were selected to provide practice in lettering and sketching. The pictorial representations of practical machine parts offer the opportunity for practice in sketching and further study of multi-view projection.

1–6. (Figs. 12.25–12.30.) Reproduce an assigned one-view sketch on a sheet of sketching paper.

7–26. (Figs. 12.31–12.50.) Make a multi-view sketch of an assigned machine part. Show only the necessary views. For convenience, important distances have been marked off in units. The selected length for the unit in each case will determine the size dimensions of the part.

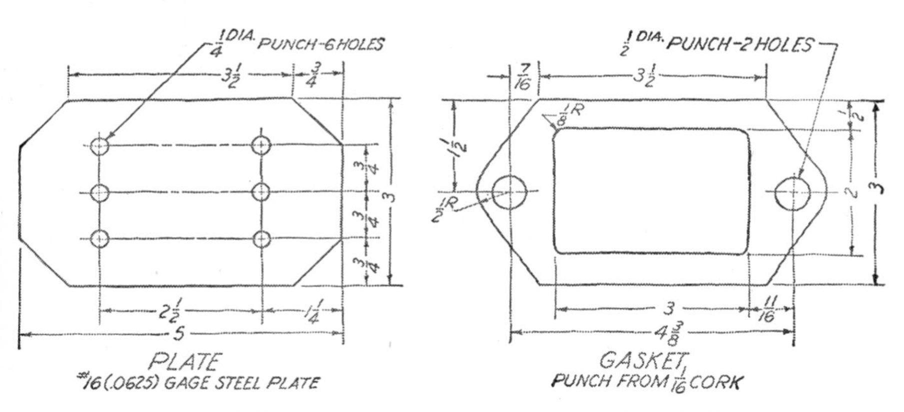

Fig. 12.25.

Fig. 12.26.

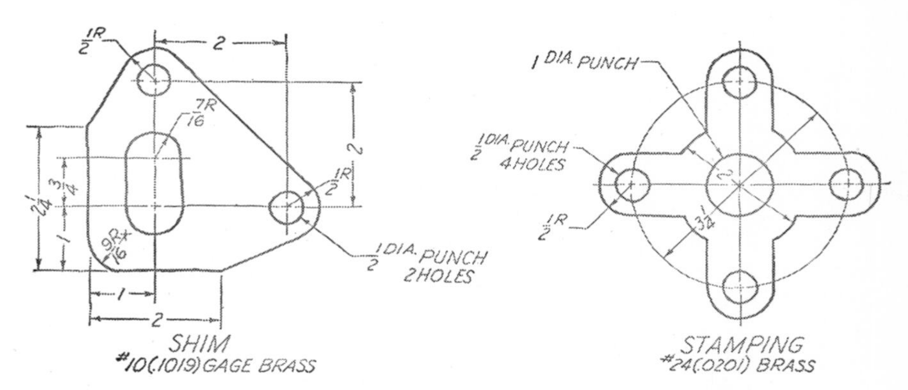

Fig. 12.27. Fig. 12.28.

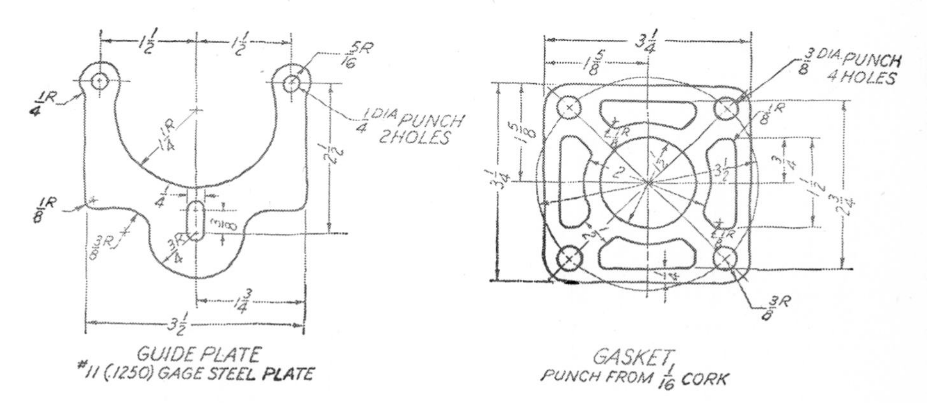

Fig. 12.29. Fig. 12.30.

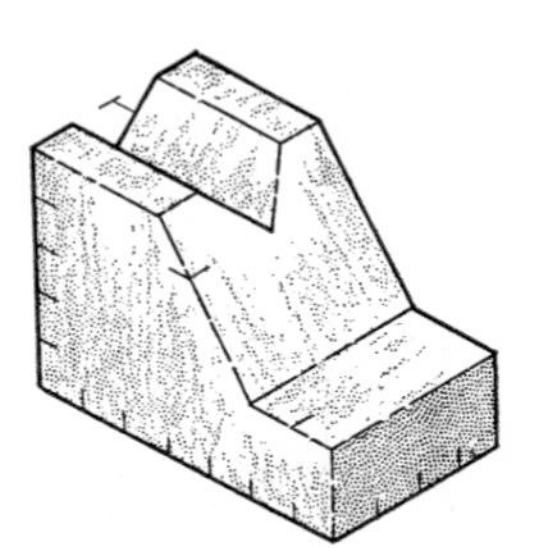

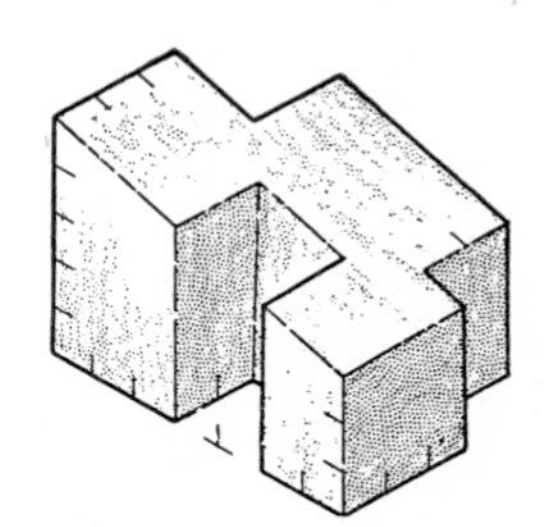

Fig. 12.31. Fig. 12.32.

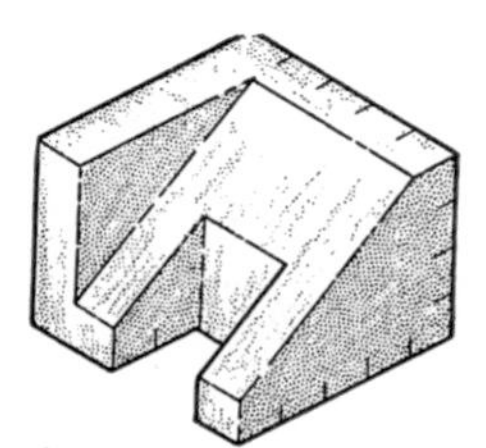

Fig. 12.33.

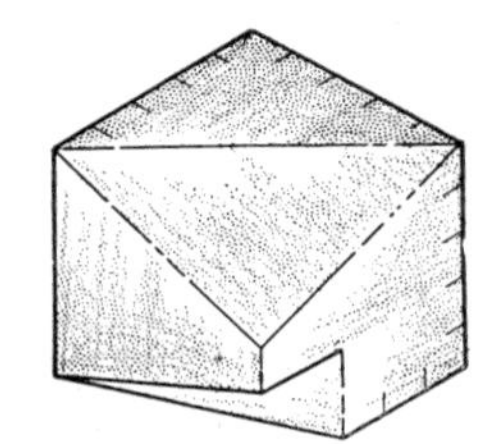

Fig. 12.34.

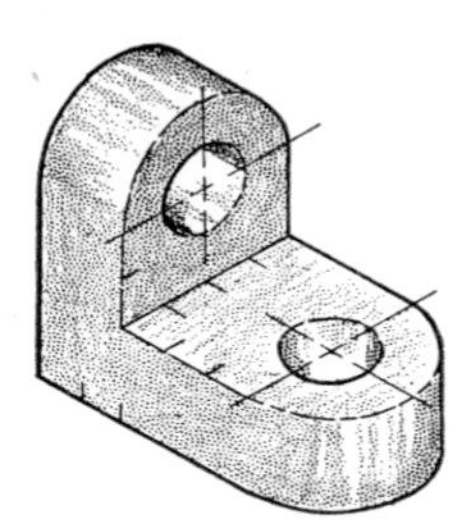

Fig. 12.35.

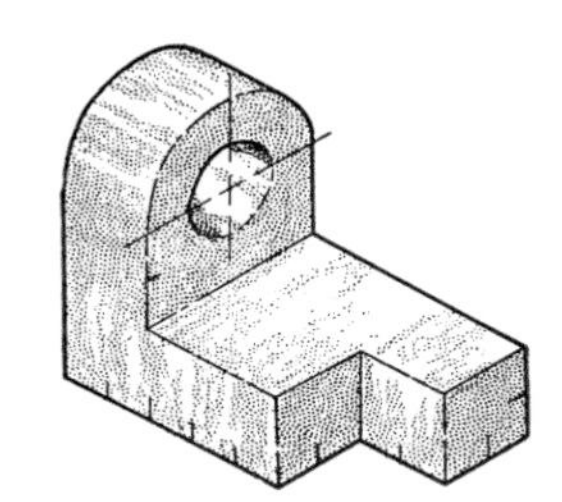

Fig. 12.36.

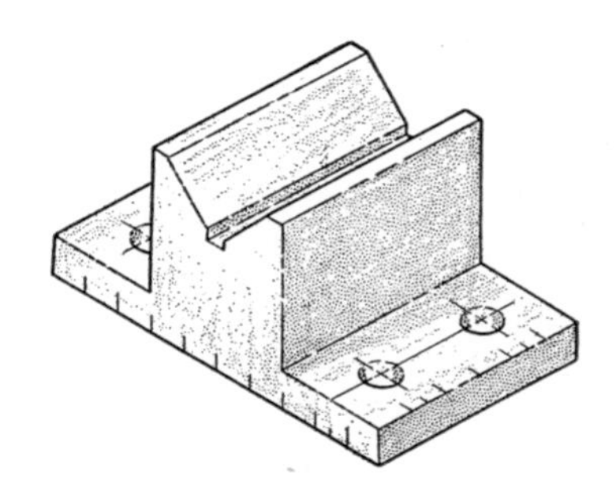

Fig. 12.37.

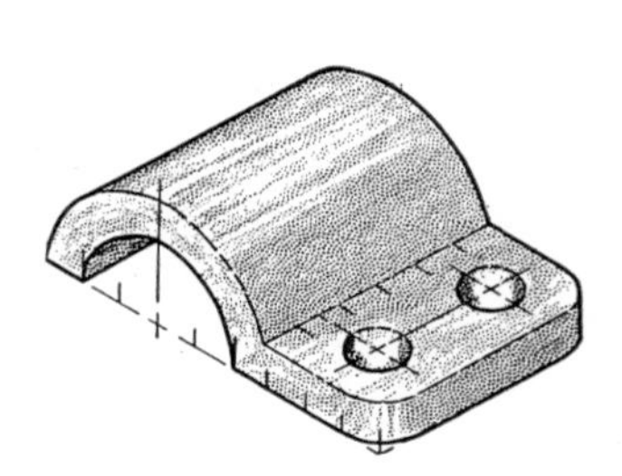

Fig. 12.38.

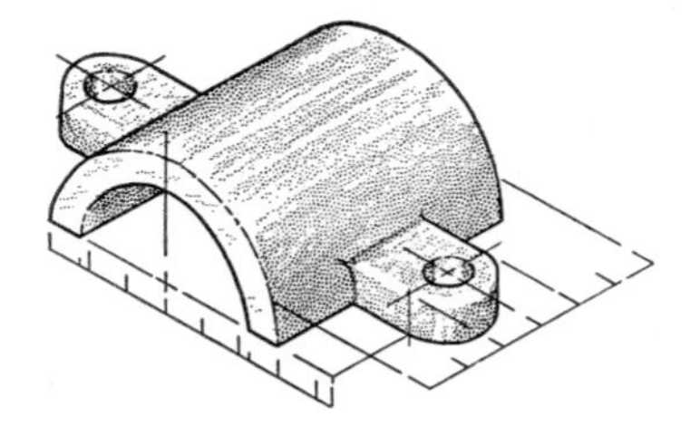

Fig. 12.39.

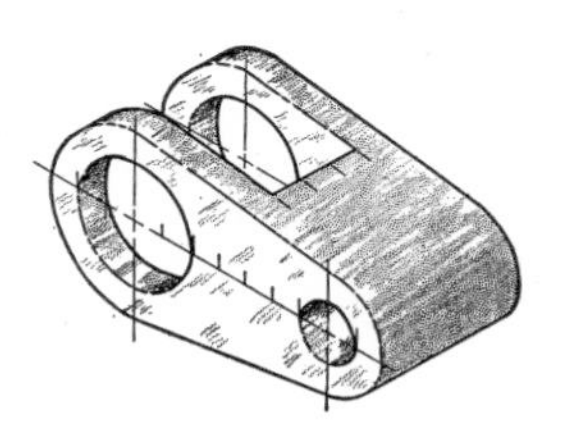

Fig. 12.40.

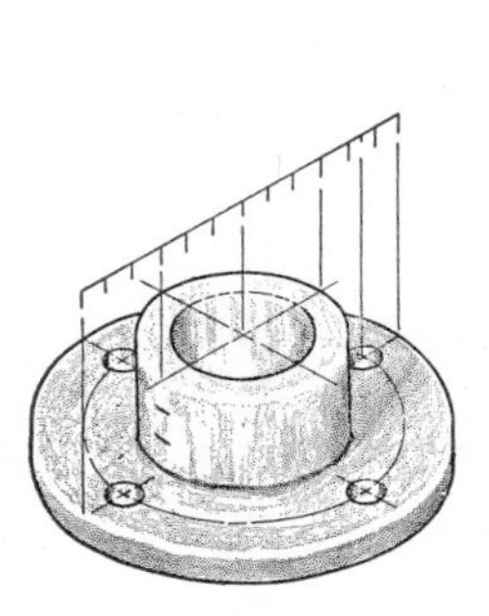

Fig. 12.41.

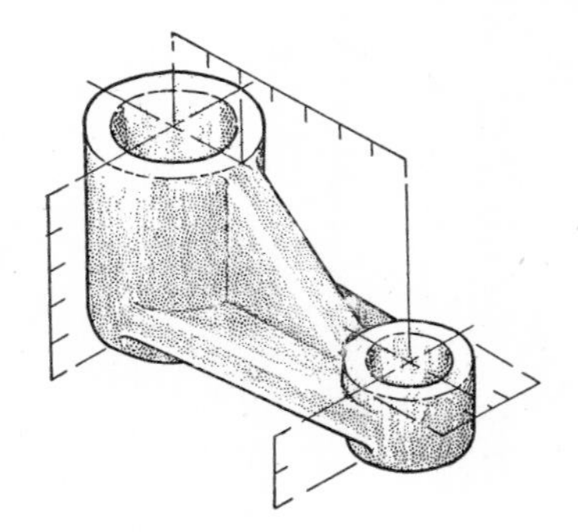

Fig. 12.42.

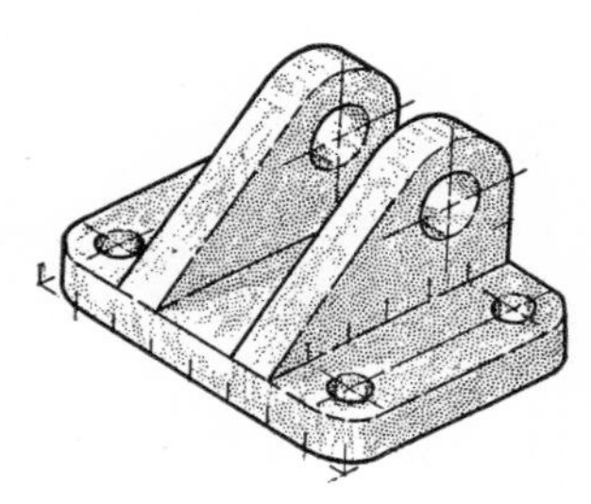

Fig. 12.43.

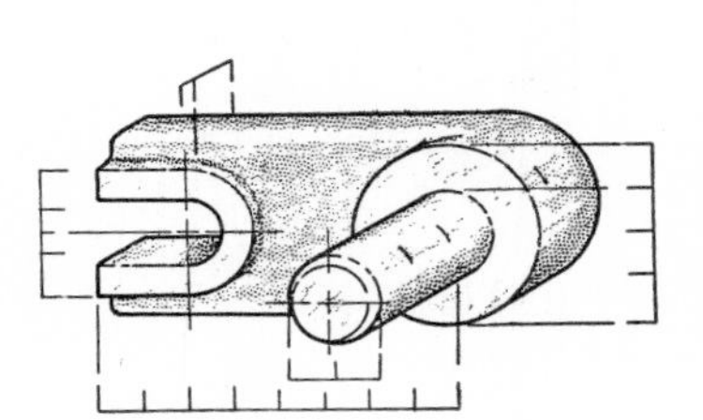

Fig. 12.44.

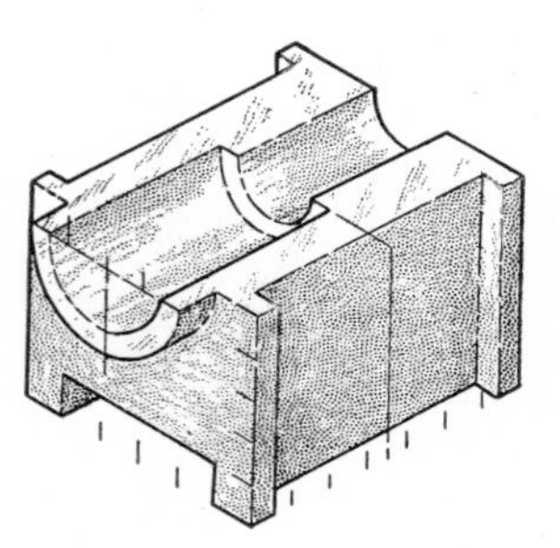

Fig. 12.45. Bearing block.

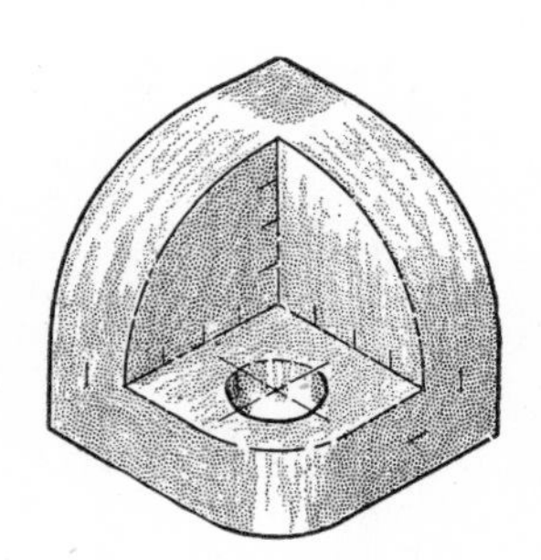

Fig. 12.46. Corner block.

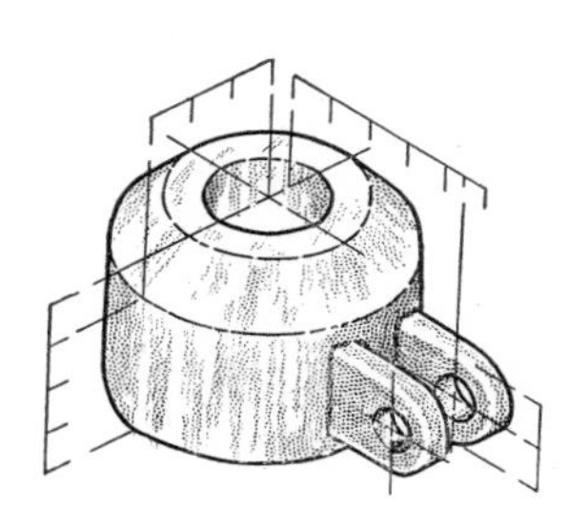

Fig. 12.47. Feeder cone.

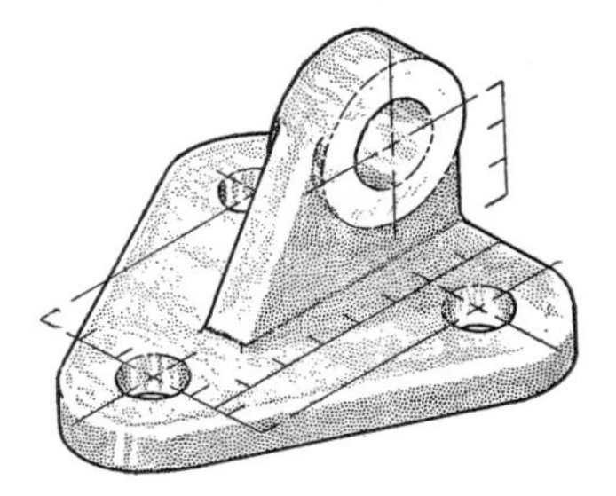

Fig. 12.48. Bracket.

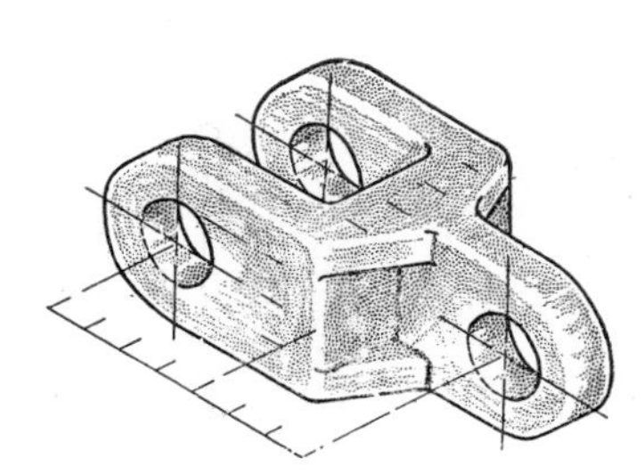

Fig. 12.49. Link.

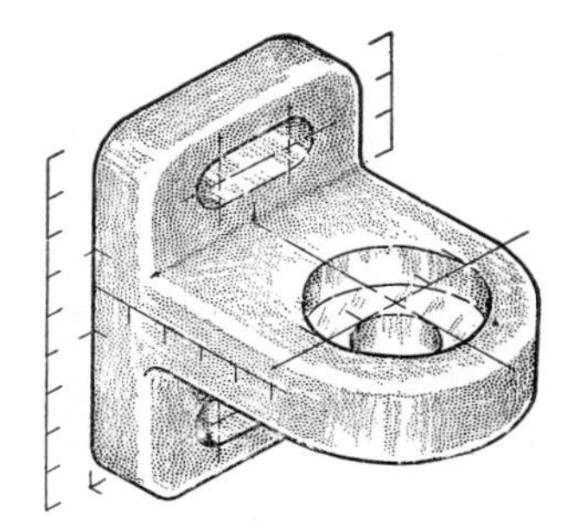

Fig. 12.50. Bearing bracket.

13 INK WORK AND TRACING

13.1. Inking a working drawing. An original working drawing is never sent to the shop. Instead, it is safely filed away in the engineering department. The shop gets a blueprint. Prints may be made from pencil drawings that have been executed on light bond tracing paper or pencil cloth, or from inked tracings done on cloth.

13.2. Use of the ruling pen. The ruling pen is used to ink mechanical lines. It is always guided by the working edge of a T-square, triangle, or French curve, and is never used freehand (Fig. 13.1).

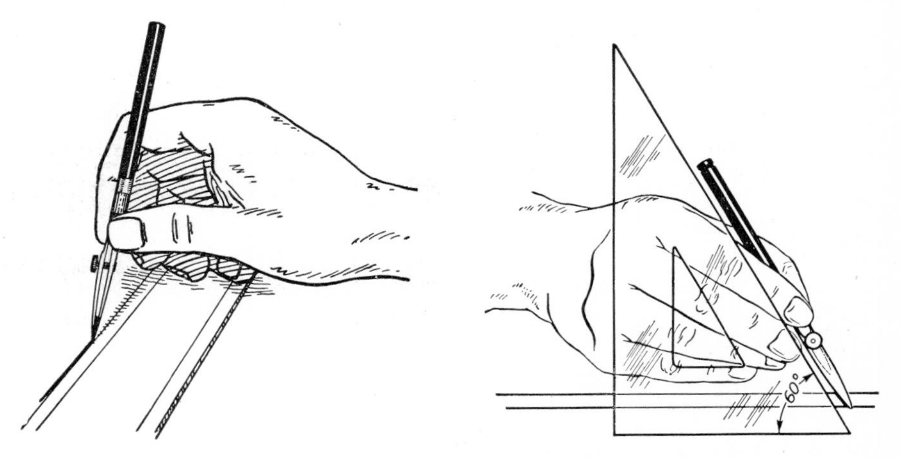

Fig. 13.1. Using the ruling pen.

Fig. 13.2. Holding the pen.

When ruling a line, the pen should be in a vertical plane and inclined slightly (approximately 60°) in the direction of the movement. It is held by the thumb and forefinger, as illustrated in Fig. 13.2, with the blade against the second finger and the adjusting screw on the outside away from the ruling edge. The third and fourth fingers slide along the T-square blade and help control the pen. Short lines are drawn with a hand movement; long lines with a free arm movement that finishes with a finger movement. While drawing, the angle of inclination and speed must remain constant to obtain a line of uniform width and straightness. Particular attention should be given to the position of the pen, as practically all faulty lines are due to incorrect inclination or to leaning the pen so that the point is too close to the straightedge or too far away from it. The correct position of the pen for drawing a satisfactory line is illustrated in Fig. 13.2.

If the pen is held so that it leans outward, as shown in Fig. 13.3(*a*), the point will be against the straightedge, and ink will run under and cause a blot; or, if it leans inward, as in Fig. 13.3(*b*), the outer nib will not touch the paper and the line will be ragged.

Unnecessary pressure against the straightedge changes the distance between the nibs, which in turn may either reduce the width of the line along its entire length or cause its width to vary as in Fig. 13.3(*d*).

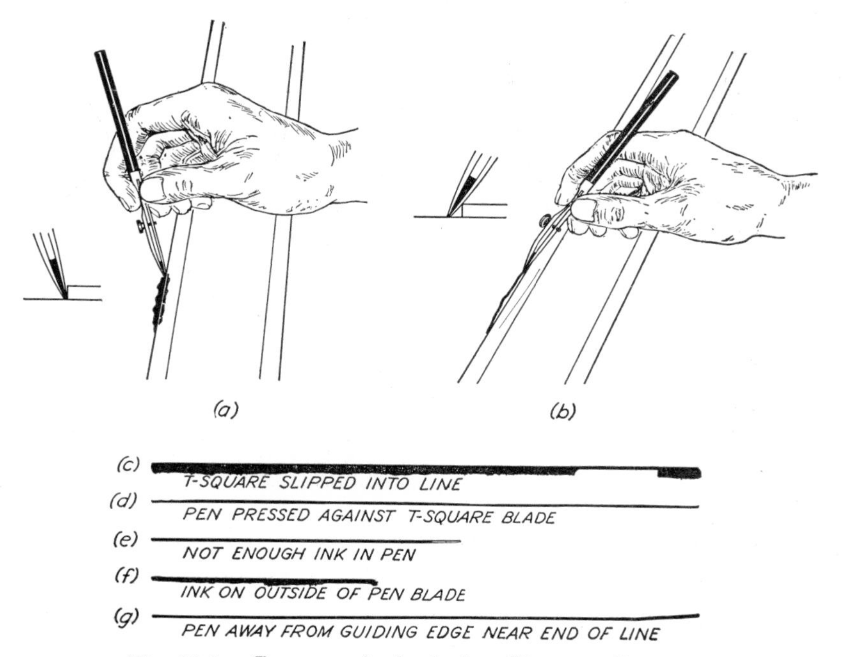

Fig. 13.3. Common faults in handling a ruling pen.

It will not take any beginner long to discover that care must be taken when removing a T-square or triangle away from a wet ink line.

The ruling pen is filled by inserting the quill or dropper device between the nibs, as shown in Fig. 13.4. Care must be taken, while filling, to see that there is enough ink to finish the line and that none of the ink from the filler gets on the outside of the blades. No more than $\frac{1}{4}$ inch should ever be put in; there is a danger of blotting if the pen is used with a greater amount.

The width of a line is determined by the distance between the nibs, which is regulated by the adjusting screw. When setting the pen, a series of test lines should be drawn with a straightedge on a small piece of the same kind of paper or cloth to establish the setting for the desired width of the line (Fig. 13.6). The draftsman's line gauge, shown in Fig. 13.5, is convenient for testing the widths of trial lines as illustrated in

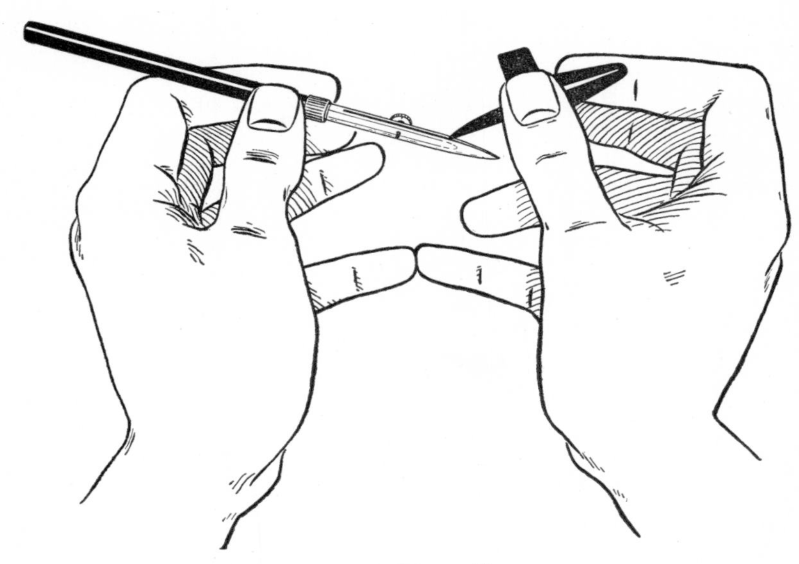

Fig. 13.4. Inking a line pen.

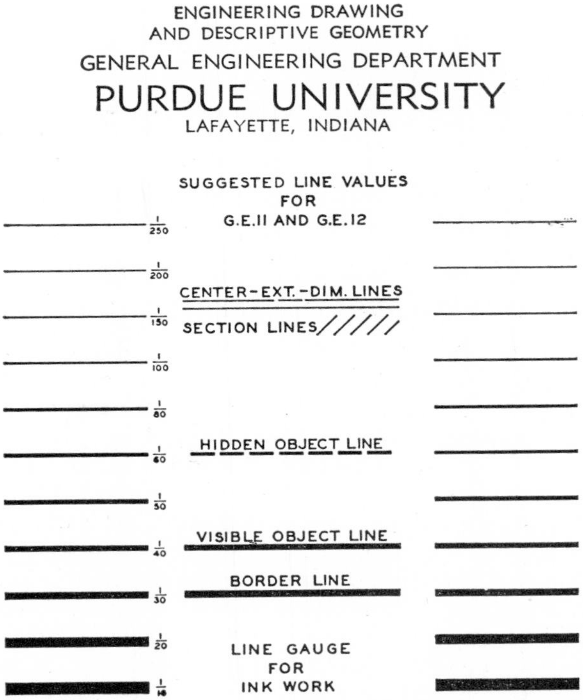

ENGINEERING DRAWING
AND DESCRIPTIVE GEOMETRY
GENERAL ENGINEERING DEPARTMENT
PURDUE UNIVERSITY
LAFAYETTE, INDIANA

SUGGESTED LINE VALUES
FOR
G.E.11 AND G.E.12

$\frac{1}{250}$

$\frac{1}{200}$

CENTER-EXT.-DIM. LINES

$\frac{1}{150}$ SECTION LINES//////

$\frac{1}{100}$

$\frac{1}{80}$

$\frac{1}{60}$ HIDDEN OBJECT LINE

$\frac{1}{50}$

$\frac{1}{40}$ VISIBLE OBJECT LINE

$\frac{1}{30}$ BORDER LINE

$\frac{1}{20}$

$\frac{1}{10}$

LINE GAUGE
FOR
INK WORK

Fig. 13.5. Gauge for determining widths of lines.

Fig. 13.6. If the first trial line is not of the desired width, another and another should be drawn until the final one agrees with the selected width as given on the gauge.

Ruling pens will not perform satisfactorily unless kept clean. For the best results, the ruling pen or any inking instrument *always* must be wiped before each refilling, and before laying it down, so that it will be ready

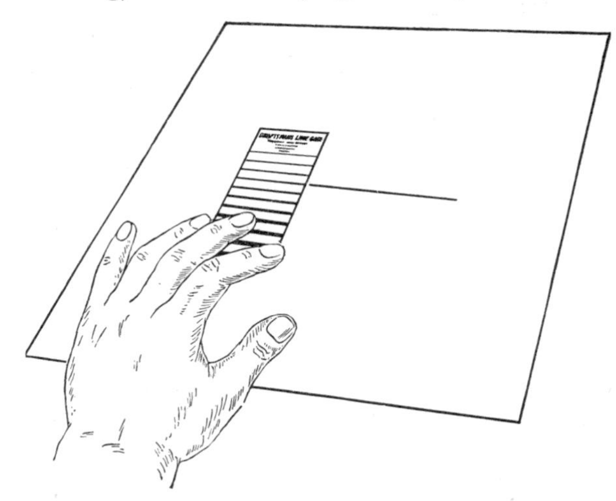

Fig. 13.6. Testing a trial line on a "try sheet."

for use again. A dirty pen in which the ink has been allowed to thicken will not draw any better than a dull one. To avoid changing the setting of the pen when cleaning it, fold the pen wiper twice at 90° (see Fig. 13.7) and draw the corner of the fold between the ends of the blades. After a few lines have been drawn, a small speck of ink frequently lodges on the outside of the tip of one or both blades and increases the width of the lines being drawn or makes the drawing of fine lines impossible. These specks may be removed by inclining the pen at a slight angle and rubbing the sides of the tips of the blades on a piece of paper laid on a flat surface. Either a speck of ink or a small piece of loose dirt or lint will cause the width of a line to change suddenly for no apparent reason, or will cause the second of two consecutively drawn lines to be broader than the first, even though the setting of the pen has not been changed.

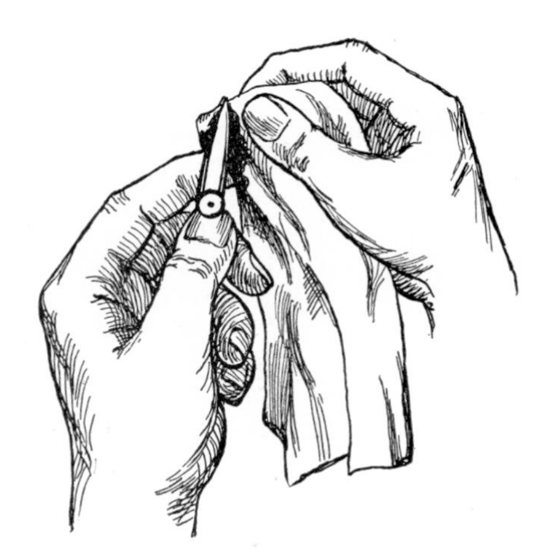

Fig. 13.7. Cleaning the ruling pen.

If the ink refuses to flow when the pen is touched to the paper, either the ink has thickened or the opening between the nibs has become clogged. To start it flowing, draftsmen often touch the point to the back of a finger or pinch the blades together. Whenever this fails to produce an immediate flow, the pen should be cleaned and refilled.

13.3. Conventional ink lines. The American Standards Association conventional symbols for ink lines for different purposes are shown in Fig. 3.32. They have been reproduced full width so that they appear as required for a well-executed ink tracing. Recommended line widths have been given in Fig. 13.5 for the conventional lines most commonly used, such as the visible object line, invisible object line, center line, etc.

13.4. Tracing. Often, when it is necessary to make duplicate copies (blueprints) of important drawings for a machine or structure, the original pencil drawings are traced in ink on a tracing medium, usually tracing cloth. Contrary to the practice of old-time draftsmen and the intention of the early manufacturers of this medium, the dull side is now almost universally used for the inking surface instead of the slick side because it produces less light glare, it will take both pencil and ink lines better, and it will withstand more erasing. The fact that the dull side will take pencil lines is important because, on some occasions, in order to save time, drawings are made directly on the cloth and then traced. Upon completion of the tracing, all pencil lines including the guide lines and slope lines for the lettering may be removed by wiping the surface of the cloth with a rag moistened with a small amount of gasoline, benzine, or cleaning fluid.

When the tracing cloth has been fastened down over the drawing, a small quantity of tracing cloth powder may be sprinkled over the surface to make it take the ink evenly and smoothly. After it has been well rubbed in, the excess must be thoroughly removed by wiping with a clean cloth, for even a small amount of loose powder left on the surface can cause clogging of the pen. Powder is also used by some persons over a spot where an erasure has been made; but a better practice is to use a piece of soapstone, which will put a smooth, slick finish over the damaged area. In applying the soapstone, rub the spot and then wipe a finger over it a few times. Following this treatment, the erased area will take ink almost as well as the original surface.

Since ink lines are made much wider than pencil lines, in order to get a good contrast on a blueprint, they should be carefully centered over the pencil lines when tracing. The center of an ink line should fall directly on the pencil line as shown correctly in Fig. 13.8. For ink work it might be said that ink lines are tangent when their center lines touch. In this same illustration, note the poor junctures obtained when ink lines are not centered so that their center lines are tangent.

Fig. 13.9(*a*) shows the filled-in corner effect that frequently appears to the disgust of the draftsman, when an ink line is drawn from or to another previously drawn line that is still wet.

When a working drawing is traced in ink on either paper or cloth, the lines should be "inked" in a definite order. Otherwise, the necessity of waiting for the ink to dry after every few lines not only wastes time, but often results in a line here and there being left out. Furthermore, hit-and-miss inking may produce lines of unequal width. It is therefore recommended that the student make a conscientious attempt to follow the order of inking suggested in this chapter.

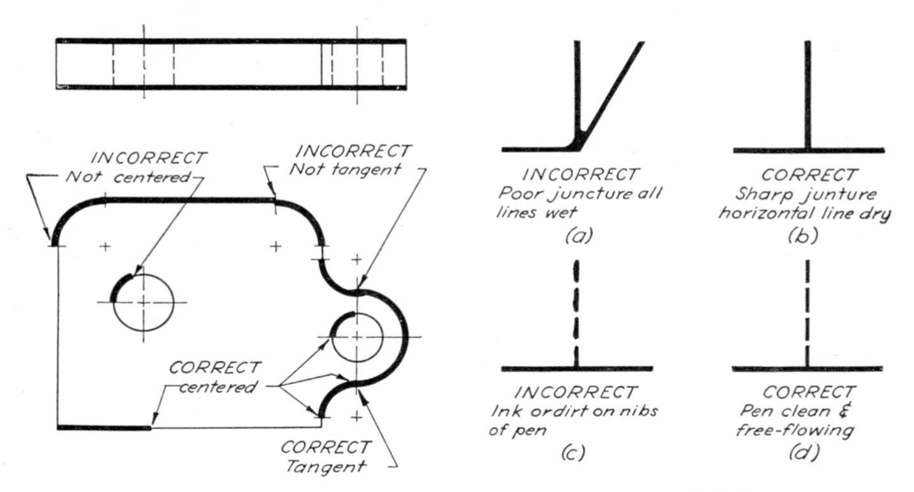

Fig. 13.8. Inking over pencil lines. **Fig. 13.9. Ink lines.**

After the paper or cloth has been fastened down over the drawing, and before the inking is begun, each tangent point should be marked and all centers should be indented.

ORDER OF INKING

I. Curved Lines:
  1. Circles and circle arcs (small circles first) in the order of (*a*), (*b*), and (*c*)
     (*a*) Visible.
     (*b*) Invisible.
     (*c*) Circular center lines and dimension lines.
  2. Irregular curves.
     (*a*) Visible.
     (*b*) Invisible.

II. Straight Lines:
  1. Visible.
     (*a*) Horizontal, from the top of the sheet down.
     (*b*) Vertical, from the left side of the sheet to the right.
     (*c*) Inclined, from the left to the right.
  2. Invisible.
     (*a*) Horizontal.
     (*b*) Vertical.
     (*c*) Inclined.
  3. Auxiliary (center, extension, and dimension lines, etc.).
     (*a*) Horizontal.

   (*b*) Vertical.
   (*c*) Inclined.
   (*d*) Section lines.

III. Arrowheads and Dimension Figures.
IV. Notes and Titles.
V. Border.

Fig. 13.10 illustrates the application of this order of inking.

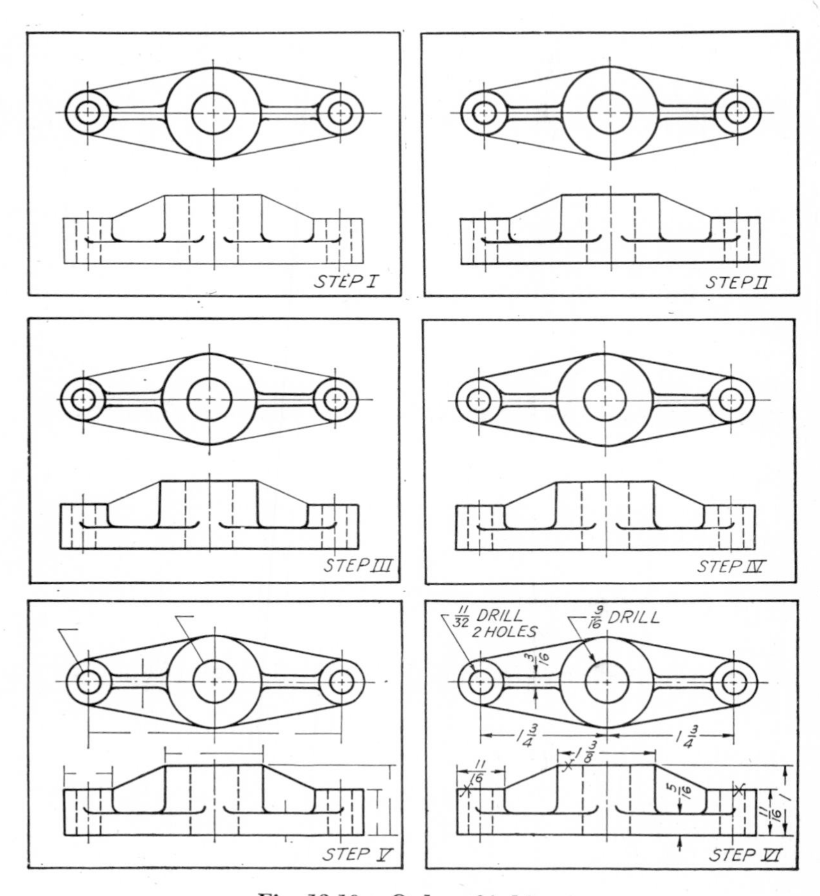

Fig. 13.10. Order of inking.

13.5. Use of the drawing ink. All pens are filled by means of a quill or dropper, and *never* by dipping them in the ink.

The ink bottle should always set off the board and to the right so that it will be handy and yet not be accidentally upset. When the ink is to be used, the cork may be removed with very little effort by twisting it out with the thumb and forefinger while holding the neck of the bottle between the third and fourth fingers of the same hand.

The bottle should be kept tightly corked at all times when not in use to prevent the ink from thickening and evaporating. Fig. 13.11 shows a handy ink bottle holder.

Fig. 13.11. Special ink bottle holder and filler.

13.6. Sharpening a ruling pen. Ruling pens, whether they have been used continuously or intermittently, eventually show signs of wear. When a pen's nibs have lost their elliptical shape and have become so dull that the ink spreads under their tips, fine lines cannot be drawn until the pen has been sharpened. The way to detect this condition is to examine the tips. If bright spots may be seen on the tips, the pen is too dull for satisfactory work. Examples of worn points are illustrated in Fig. 13.12(*a*) and (*b*).

Since even new pens are seldom sharpened properly and often require retouching, every draftsman should be able to reshape and sharpen his

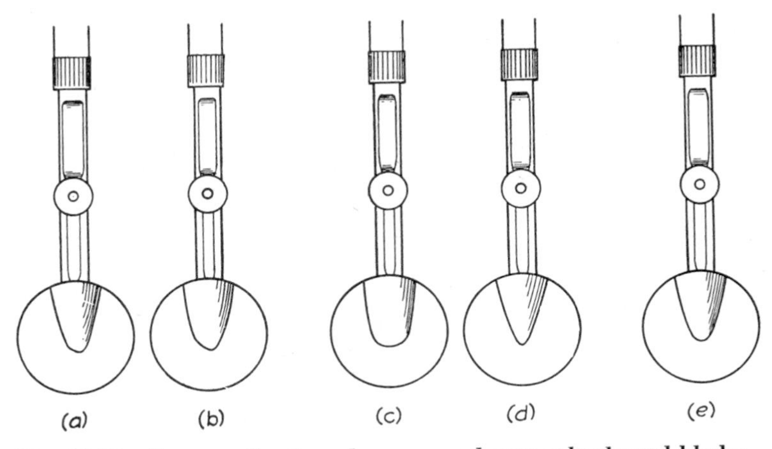

Fig. 13.12. Incorrectly shaped, worn, and correctly shaped blades.

own pen. A beginner should consult his instructor or an experienced draftsman regarding the condition of his pens before attempting to use them.

Incorrectly sharpened points are illustrated in Fig. 13.12(*c*) and (*d*). Points shaped as shown in either (*c*) or (*d*) are aggravating, because if a point is rounded as in (*c*), the ink flows too freely; if it is too pointed as in (*d*), the ink cups up and the flow is difficult to start. Only a pen that is correctly shaped and sharpened, as shown in Fig. 13.12(*e*), will give the results that should be expected.

Although blades should be sharpened to a thin edge, care should be taken not to make them sharp enough to cut the surface of the paper. A pen should never be sharpened, even the slightest amount, on the inside of the blades. Such treatment causes the blades to flare at the point and prevents the ink from feeding down to the paper, making it difficult or impossible to start a line.

Fig. 13.13. Shaping the points.

A fine-grained Arkansas oilstone is the best all-purpose stone for sharpening a ruling pen. The first step in sharpening is to equalize the length of the nibs and correct their shape. This may be done by bringing the blades together so that they barely touch, and then drawing them lightly back and forth across the stone while swinging the pen through an arc of approximately 120 degrees each stroke. (See Fig. 13.13.) During this operation, it is essential that the pen be held in a vertical plane and that an even pressure be maintained against the stone. When an inspection, under a magnifying glass, reveals that the nibs have been restored to their correct shape, the blades should be opened and each nib sharpened all around the outside to a thin edge. A blade is sharpened by holding the pen as shown in Fig. 13.14 and sliding it back and forth across the stone with a slight rolling motion to preserve its original convex shape. The pen should be examined from time to time so that the sharpening can be stopped as soon as the bright point disappears.

Finally, a test should be made by filling the pen and drawing a series of lines of various weights on a piece of tracing paper or tracing cloth. If

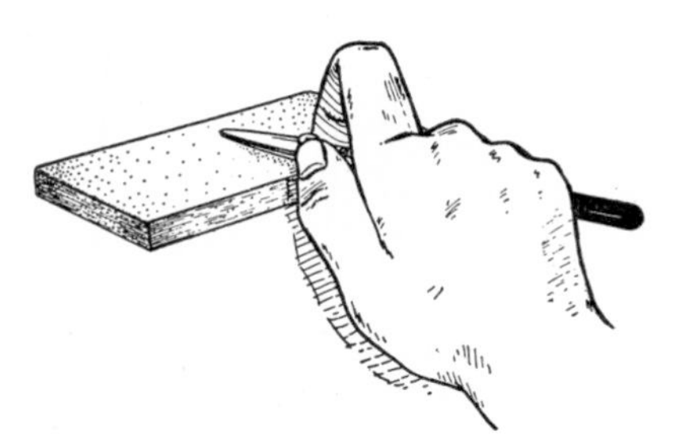

Fig. 13.14. Sharpening the blades.

the instrument is capable of drawing satisfactory lines of any weight, particularly very fine lines, it has been correctly sharpened. If the ink feeds too freely, however, the nibs are too rounded, as shown in Fig. 13.12(*c*); or if the ink cups high in the point, the nibs are too pointed, as in Fig. 13.12(*d*). In either case, the entire sharpening process must be repeated.

If the blades cut the paper, even when the usual light working pressure is applied, the nibs should be slightly dulled and brought to an edge that is not quite so sharp.

Occasionally, if the pen has not been correctly sharpened, a feather-edge or burr appears on the inside edge of a nib. It may be removed by laying the inside of the blade flat on the stone and grinding it lightly.

14 PICTORIAL DRAWING

14.1. An orthographic drawing of two or more views describes an object accurately in form and size but, since each of the views shows only two dimensions without any suggestion of depth, such a drawing can convey information only to those who are familiar with graphic representation. For this reason, multiview drawings are used mainly by engineers, draftsmen, contractors, and shopmen.

Frequently, however, engineers and draftsmen find they must use

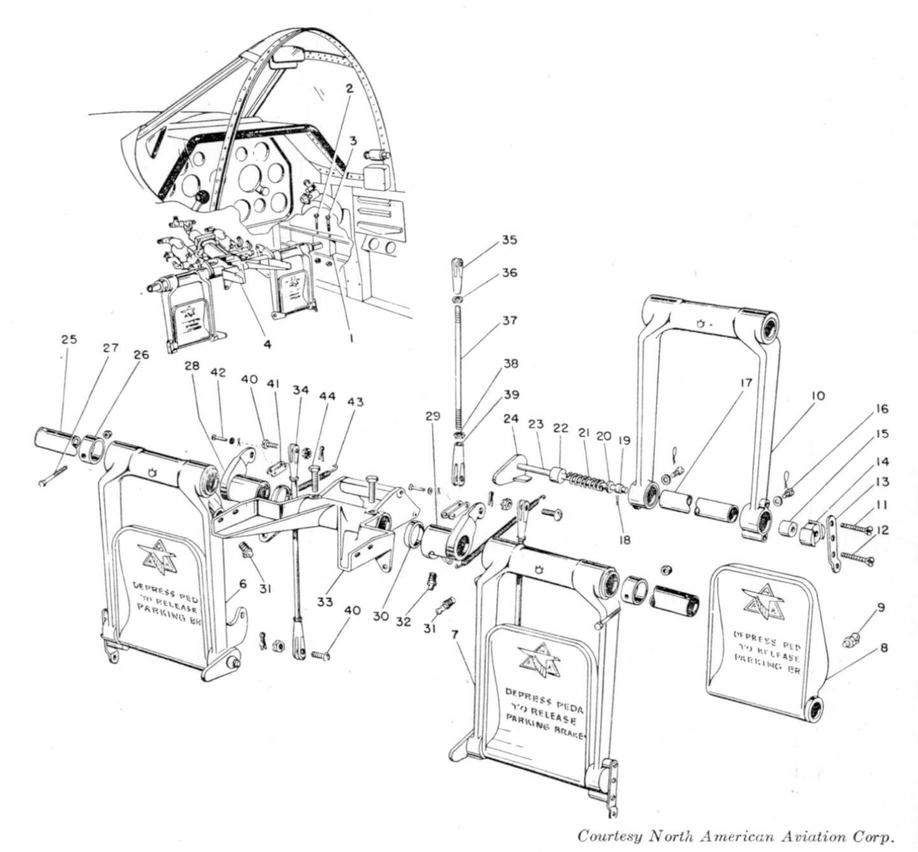

Courtesy North American Aviation Corp.

Fig. 14.1. Pictorial presentation for a manual.

conventional picture drawings to convey specific information to persons who do not possess the trained imagination necessary to construct mentally an object from views. To make such drawings, several special schemes of one-plane pictorial drawing have been devised that combine the pictorial effect of perspective with the advantage of having the principal dimensions to scale. But pictorial drawings, in spite of certain advantages, have disadvantages that limit their use. A few of these are as follows:

1. Some drawings frequently have a distorted, unreal appearance that is disagreeable.
2. The time required for execution is, in many cases, greater than for an orthographic drawing.
3. They are difficult to dimension.
4. Some of the lines cannot be measured.

Even with these limitations, pictorial drawings are used extensively for catalogs, Patent Office records, piping diagrams, and furniture designs. Occasionally they are used, in one form or another, to supplement and clarify machine and structural details which would be difficult to visualize. (See Fig. 14.1.)

14.2. Divisions of pictorial drawing. Single-plane pictorial drawings are classified in three general divisions: (1) axonometric projection, (2) oblique projection, and (3) perspective projection. (See Fig. 14.2.)

Perspective methods produce the most realistic drawings, but the necessary construction is more difficult and tedious than the construction required for the conventional methods classified under the other two

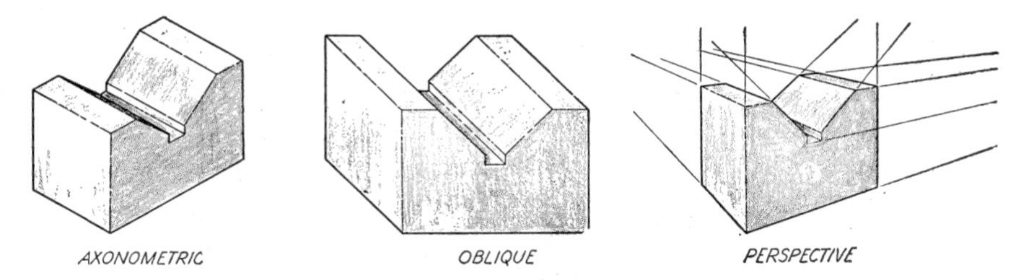

Fig. 14.2. Axonometric, oblique, and perspective projection.

divisions. For this reason, engineers customarily use some form of either axonometric or oblique projection. Modified methods, which are not theoretically correct, are often used to produce desired effects.

14.3. Divisions of axonometric projection. Theoretically, axonometric projection is a form of orthographic projection. The distinguishing difference is that only one plane is used instead of two or more, and the object is turned from its customary position so that three faces are displayed (Fig. 14.3). Since an object may be placed in a countless number of positions relative to the picture plane, an infinite number of views may be drawn which will vary in general proportions, lengths of edges, and sizes of angles. For practical reasons, a few of these possible positions have been classified in such a manner as to give the recognized divisions of axonometric projection: (1) isometric, (2) dimetric, and (3) trimetric.

Isometric projection is the simplest of these, because the principal axes make equal angles with the plane of projection and the edges are therefore foreshortened equally.

14.4. Isometric projection. If the cube in Fig. 14.3 were revolved through an angle of 45 degrees about an imaginary vertical axis, as shown in II, and is then tilted forward until its body diagonal is perpendicular to the vertical plane, the edges would be foreshortened equally and the cube would be in the correct position to produce an isometric projection.

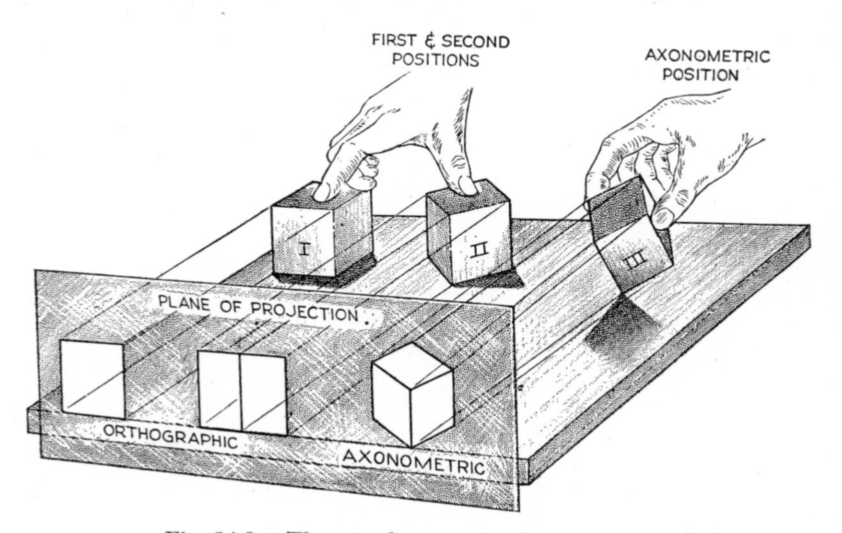

Fig. 14.3. Theory of axonometric projection.

The three front edges, called isometric axes, make angles of approximately 35° 16′ with the vertical plane of projection or picture plane. In this form of pictorial, the angles between the projections of these axes are 120°, and the projected lengths of the edges of an object, along and parallel to these axes, are approximately 81 per cent of their true lengths. It should be observed that the 90° angles of the cube appear in the isometric projection as either 120° or 60°.

It was stated in Sec. 9.1 (Chapter 9) that the distinguishing difference between revolution projection and auxiliary projection is that, in the procedure of revolution, the observer turns the object with respect to himself, while in auxiliary projection he shifts his position in relation to it. Therefore, since axonometric projection is a form of orthographic projection, both methods will produce the same final pictorial representation when applied to axonometric projection.

In Fig. 14.3, the object (cube) was turned and tilted until the body diagonal was in a position perpendicular to the plane of projection. Now, if instead of turning and tilting the object in relation to a principal plane of projection, an auxiliary plane is used that will be perpendicular to the body diagonal, the view projected on the plane will be an axonometric projection. Since the auxiliary plane will be inclined to the principal planes upon which the front, top, and side views would be projected, the auxiliary view, taken in a position perpendicular to the body diagonal, will be a secondary auxiliary view, as shown in Fig. 14.4.

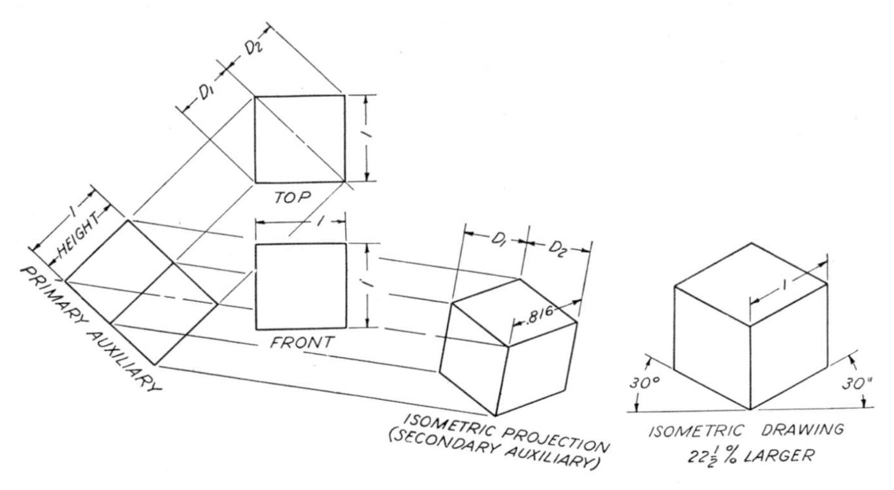

Fig. 14.4. Comparison of isometric projection and isometric drawing.

14.5. Isometric scale. An isometric scale (proportional scale) for laying off distances parallel to isometric axes may be made by the simple graphical method shown in Fig. 14.5. Usually, the scale is drawn along the edge of a strip of paper or cardboard. Its use is illustrated in Fig. 14.6.

14.6. Isometric drawing. Objects seldom are drawn in true isometric projection, the use of an isometric scale being inconvenient and impractical. Instead, a conventional method is used in which all foreshortening is ignored, and actual true lengths are laid off along isometric

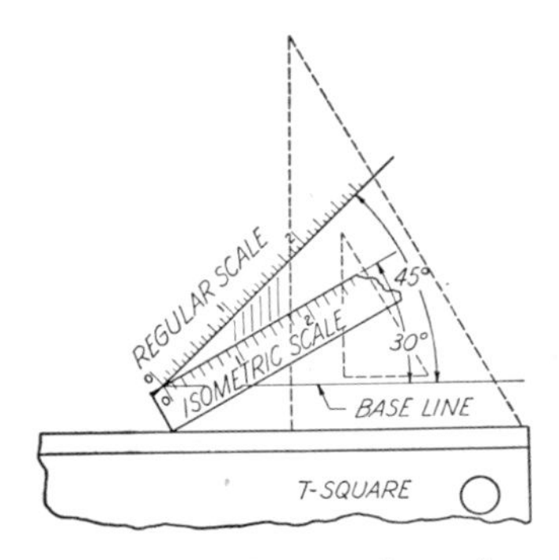

Fig. 14.5. Isometric scale.

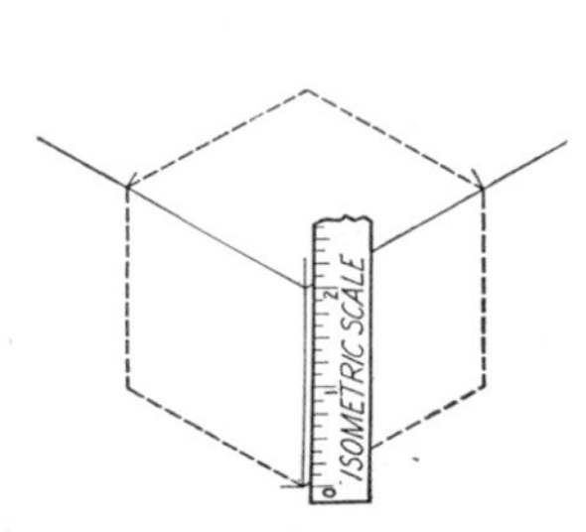

Fig. 14.6. Use of an isometric scale.

axes and isometric lines. To avoid confusion and to set this method apart from true isometric projection, it is called isometric drawing.

The isometric drawing of a figure is slightly larger (approximately $22\frac{1}{2}$ per cent) than the isometric projection, but, since the proportions are the same, the increased size does not affect the pictorial value of the representation. (See Fig. 14.4.) The use of a regular scale makes it possible for a draftsman to produce a satisfactory drawing with a minimum expenditure of time and effort.

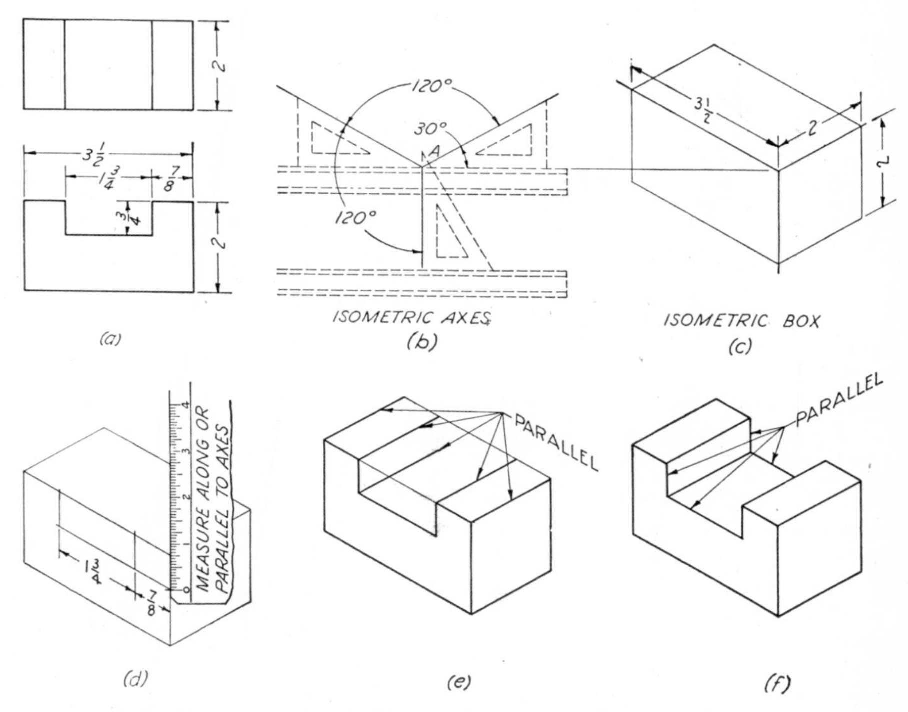

Fig. 14.7. Procedure for constructing an isometric drawing.

In isometric drawing, lines that are parallel to the isometric axes are called *isometric lines*.

14.7. To make an isometric drawing of a rectangular object. The procedure followed in making an isometric drawing of a rectangular block is illustrated in Fig. 14.7. The three axes that establish the front edges, as shown in (*b*), should be drawn through point *A* so that one extends vertically downward and the other two upward to the right and left at an angle of 30° from the horizontal. Then the actual lengths of the edges may be set off, as shown in (*c*) and (*d*), and the remainder of the view completed by drawing lines parallel to the axes through the corners thus located, as in (*e*) and (*f*).

Hidden lines, unless absolutely necessary for clearness, always should be omitted on a pictorial representation.

The same object may be drawn by starting with point B. (See Fig. 14.8.) Often it is more convenient to start at a lower corner.

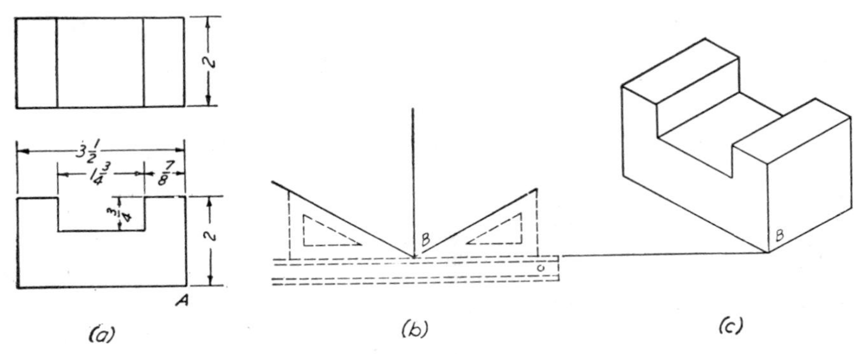

Fig. 14.8. Alternate procedure construction.

14.8. Nonisometric lines. In a pictorial view, the lines that are oblique to the isometric axes are called nonisometric lines. Since a line of this type does not appear in its true length and cannot be measured directly, its position and projected length must be established by locating its extremities. In Fig. 14.9, AB and CD, which represent the edges of the block, are nonisometric lines. The location of AB is established in the

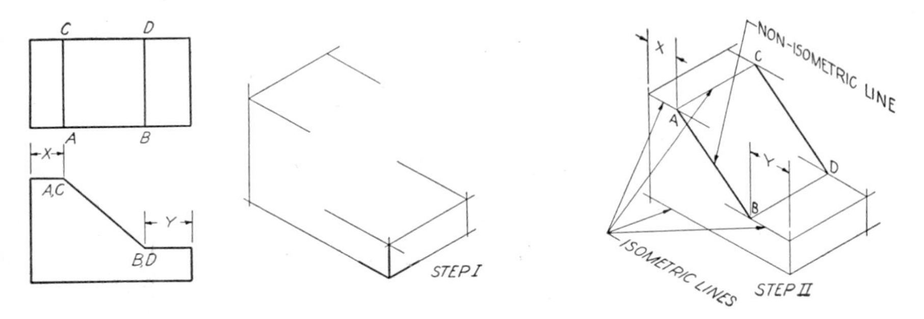

Fig. 14.9. Nonisometric lines.

pictorial view by locating points A and B. Point A is on the top edge, X distance from the left side surface. Point B is on the upper edge of the base, Y distance from the right side surface. All other lines coincide with or are parallel to the axes, and therefore may be measured off with the scale.

The pictorial representation of an irregular solid containing a number of nonisometric lines mav be conveniently constructed by the box method; that is, the object may be enclosed in a rectangular box so that both isometric and nonisometric lines may be located by points of contact with its surfaces and edges. (See Fig 14.10.)

A study of Figs 14.9 and 14.10 reveals the important fact that lines that are parallel on an object are parallel in the pictorial view, and, conversely, lines that are not parallel on the object are not parallel on the view. It is often possible to eliminate much tedious construction work by the practical application of this principle of parallel lines.

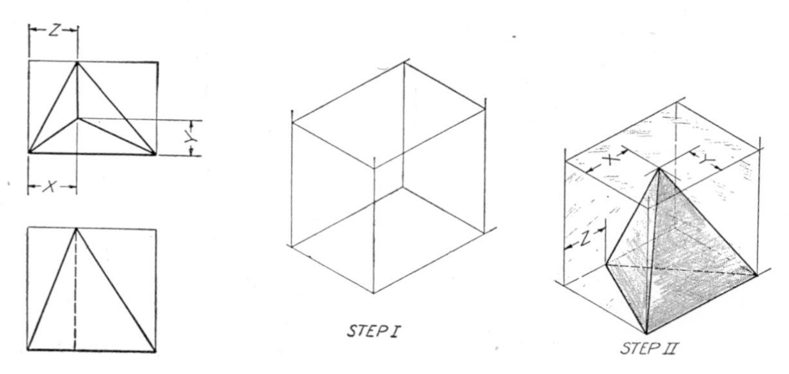

Fig. 14.10. Box construction.

14.9. Co-ordinate construction method. When an object contains a number of inclined surfaces, such as the one shown in Fig. 14.11, the use of the co-ordinate construction method is desirable. In this method, the end points of the edges are located in relation to an assumed isometric base line located upon an isometric reference plane. For example, the line RL is used as a base line from which measurements are made along isometric lines, as shown. The distances required to locate point A are taken directly from the orthographic views.

Irregular curved edges are most easily drawn in isometric by the offset method, which is a modification of the co-ordinate construction method

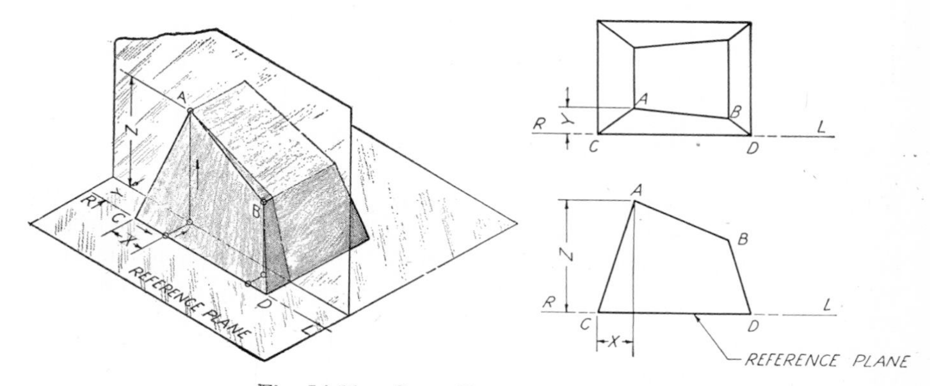

Fig. 14.11. Co-ordinate construction.

(Fig. 14.12). The position of the curve readily can be established by plotted points that may be located by measuring along isometric lines.

14.10. Angles in isometric drawing. When nonisometric lines are located by angular measurements (Fig. 14.13), it is necessary to draw at least a partial orthographic view of the object and take off the dimensions.

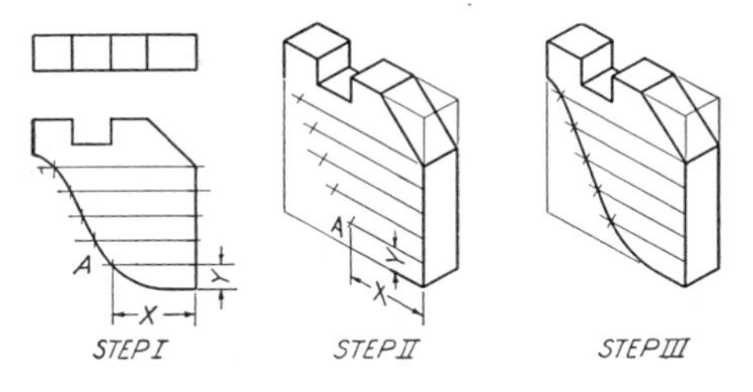

Fig. 14.12. Offset construction.

The scale should be the same as that of the pictorial view (*a*). A practical application of this principle, to the construction of an isometric drawing of a 60° angle, is shown in (*b*). By making this construction at the place where the angle is to appear on the isometric drawing, the position of the required line is obtained graphically.

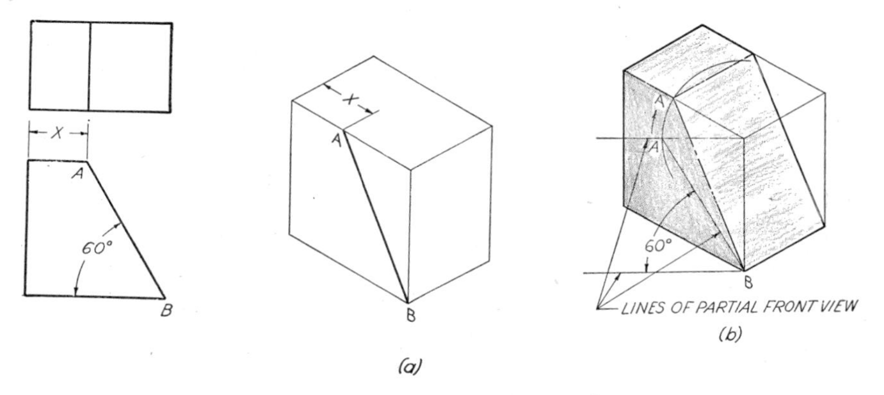

Fig. 14.13. Angles in isometric.

14.11. Circle and circle arcs in isometric drawing. In isometric drawing, a circle appears as an ellipse. The tedious construction required for plotting an ellipse accurately (Figs. 14.14 and 14.15) often is avoided by using some approximate method of drawing. The representation thus obtained is accurate enough for most work, although the true ellipse, which is slightly narrower and longer, is more pleasing in shape. For an approximate construction, a four-center method is generally used.

To draw an ellipse representing a pictorial circle, a square is conceived to be circumscribed about the circle in the orthographic projection. When transferred to the isometric plane in the pictorial view, the square becomes a rhombus (isometric square) and the circle an ellipse tangent to the rhombus at the mid-points of its sides. If the ellipse is to be drawn by the four-center method (Fig. 14.16), the points of intersection of the perpendicular bisectors of the sides of the rhombus will be centers for the four arcs forming the approximate ellipse. The two intersections that

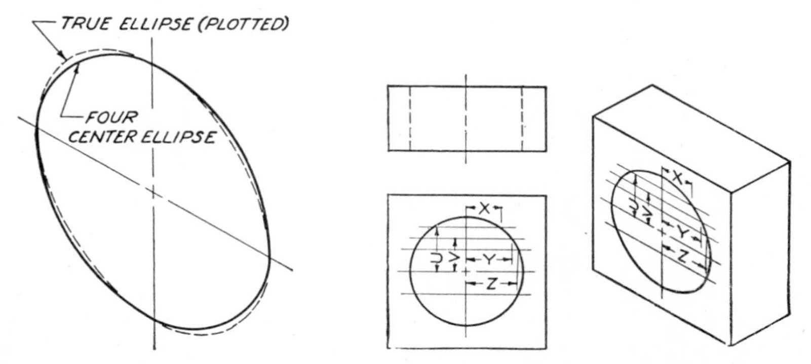

Fig. 14.14. Pictorial ellipses. **Fig. 14.15. To plot an isometric circle.**

lie on the corners of the rhombus are centers for the two large arcs, while the remaining intersections are centers for the two small arcs. Furthermore, the length along the perpendicular from the center of each arc to the point at which the arc is tangent to the rhombus (mid-point) will be the radius. All construction lines required by this method may be made with a T-square and a 30 × 60° triangle.

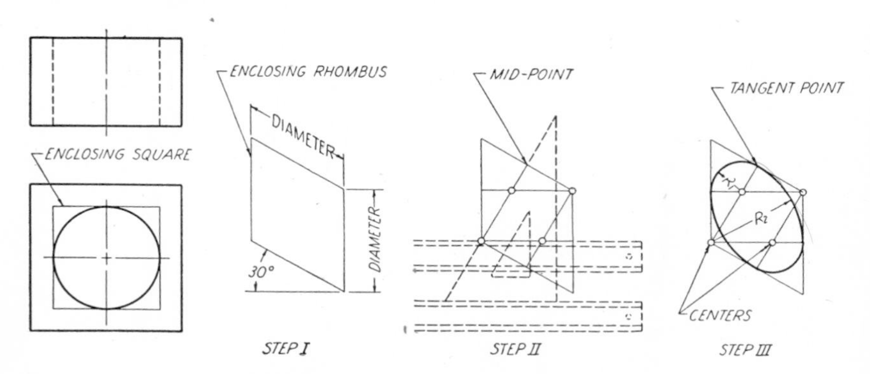

Fig. 14.16. Four-center approximation.

The amount of work may be still further shortened, and the accuracy of the construction improved, by following the procedure shown in Fig. 14.17. The steps in this method are:

Step I. Draw the isometric center lines of the required circle.

Step II. Using a radius equal to the radius of the circle, strike arcs across the isometric center lines.

Steps III–IV. Through each of these points of intersection erect a perpendicular to the other isometric center line.

Steps V–VI. Using the intersection points of the perpendiculars as centers and the lengths of the perpendiculars as radii, draw the four arcs that form the ellipse.

A circle arc will appear in pictorial representation as a segment of an

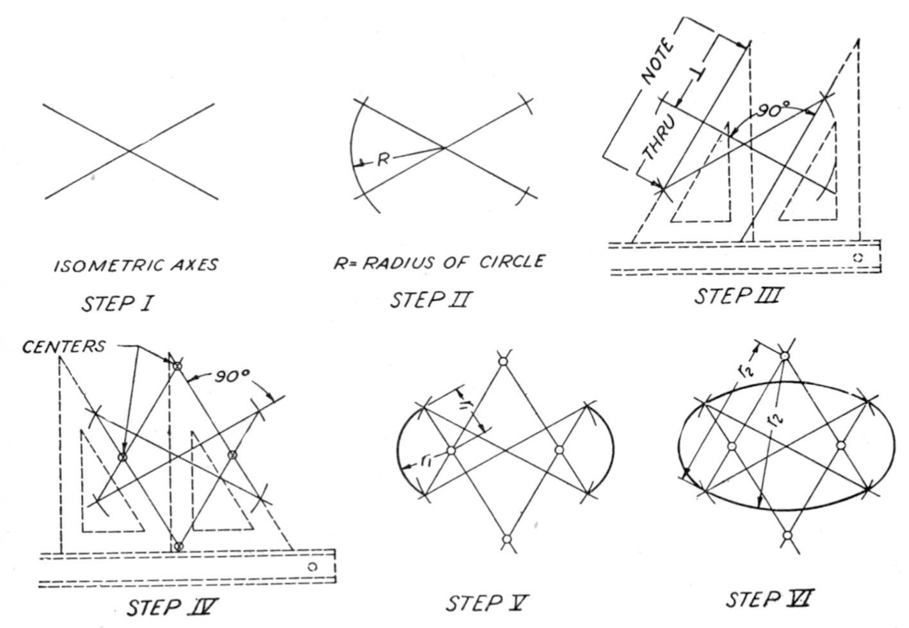

Fig. 14.17. Steps in drawing a four-center isometric circle (ellipse).

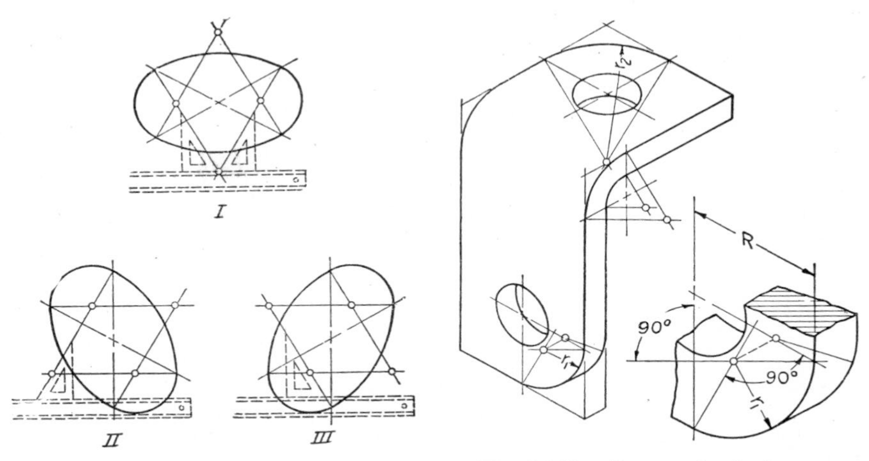

Fig. 14.18. Isometric circles.

Fig. 14.19. Isometric circle arcs.

ellipse. Therefore, it may be drawn by using as much of the four-center method as is required to locate the needed centers. (See Fig. 14.19.) For example, to draw a quarter circle, it is only necessary to lay off the true radius of the arc along isometric lines drawn through the center and to draw intersecting perpendiculars through these points.

To draw isometric concentric circles by the four-center method, a set of centers must be located for each circle (Fig. 14.20).

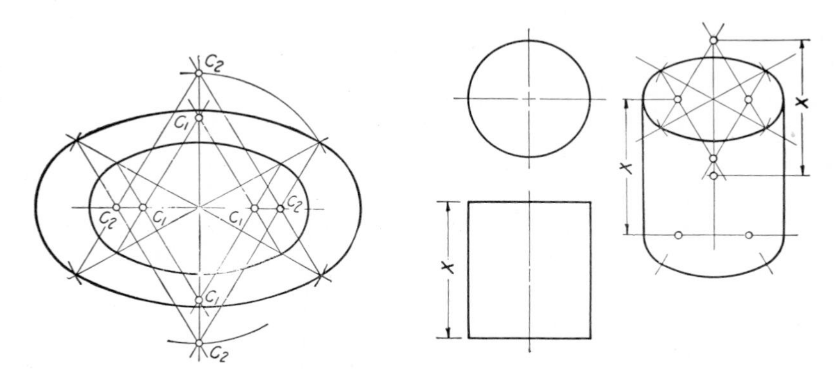

Fig. 14.20. Isometric concentric circles.

Fig. 14.21. Isometric parallel circles.

When several circles of the same diameter occur in parallel planes, the construction may be simplified. Fig. 14.21 shows two views of a cylinder and its corresponding isometric drawing. The centers for the ellipse representing the upper base are found in the usual way, while the four centers for the lower base are located by moving the centers for the upper base a distance equal to the height of the cylinder. It should be noted that corresponding centers lie along an isometric line parallel to the axis of the cylinder.

Circles and circle arcs in nonisometric planes are plotted by using the

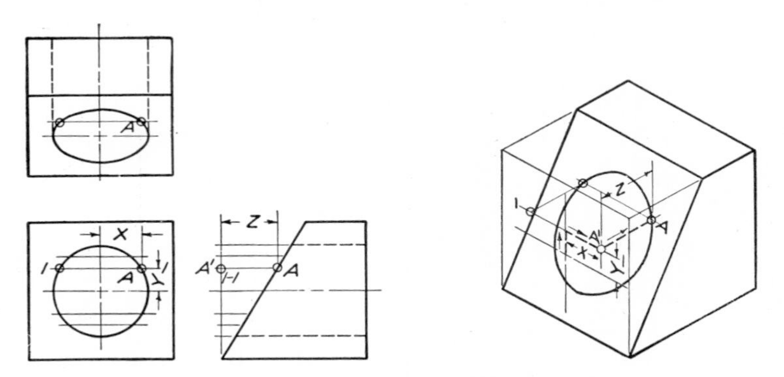

Fig. 14.22. Circles in nonisometric planes.

a dimetric projection may be drawn by using the auxiliary view method. Fig. 14.30 shows the front, top, primary auxiliary, and secondary auxiliary of a part. The secondary auxiliary is the dimetric projection. The procedure is the same as for an isometric projection (see Fig. 14.4), except that the line of sight, instead of being in the direction of a body diagonal,

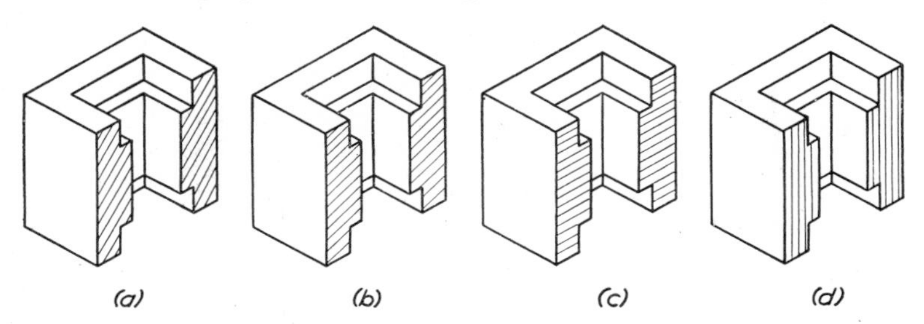

Fig. 14.29. Section lining.

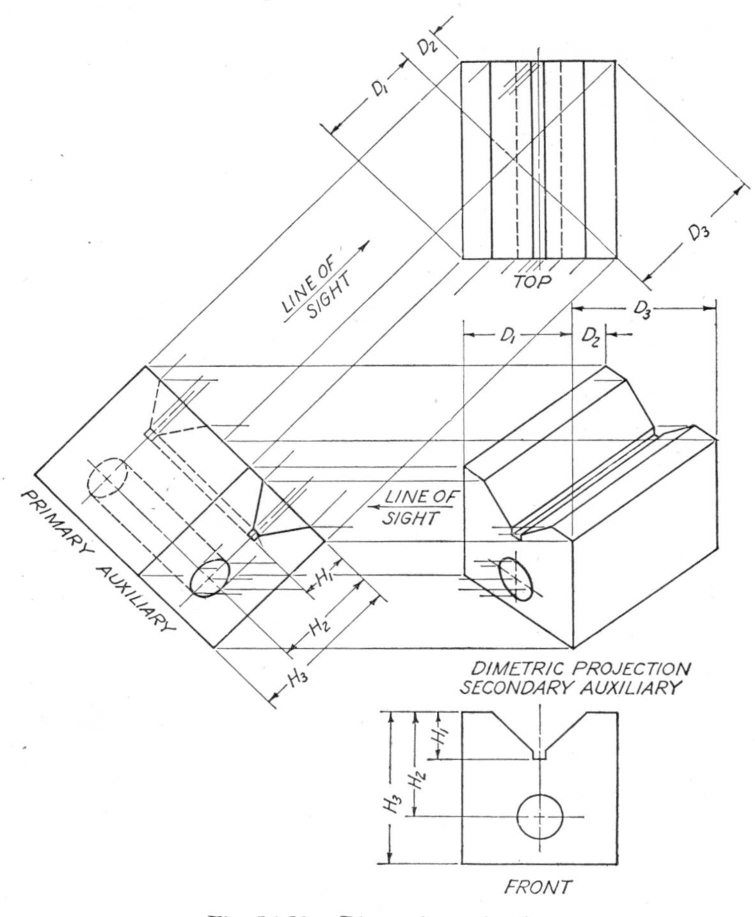

Fig. 14.30. Dimetric projection.

is in a direction to satisfy the conditions of dimetric projection. Obviously, an infinite number of dimetric projections are possible.*

In practical application, dimetric projection is sometimes modified so that regular scales can be used to lay off measurements to assumed ratios. This is called dimetric drawing (Fig. 14.31*a*).

The angles and scales may be worked out† for any ratios such as $1:1:\frac{1}{2}$ (Full size: Full size: Half size), $1:1:\frac{3}{4}$ (Full size: Full size: Three-fourths size). For example, the angles for the ratios $1:1:\frac{1}{2}$ are 7° 11′ and 41° 25′. After the scales have been assumed and the angles computed, an enclosing box may be drawn in conformity to the angles and the view completed by following the general procedure used in isometric drawing, except that two scales must be used. The positions commonly used, along with the scale ratios and corresponding angles, are shown in (*b*). The first scale given in each ratio is for the vertical axis. Since obviously two of the axes are foreshortened equally, while the third is foreshortened in different ratio, two scales must be used. This is an effective method of representation.

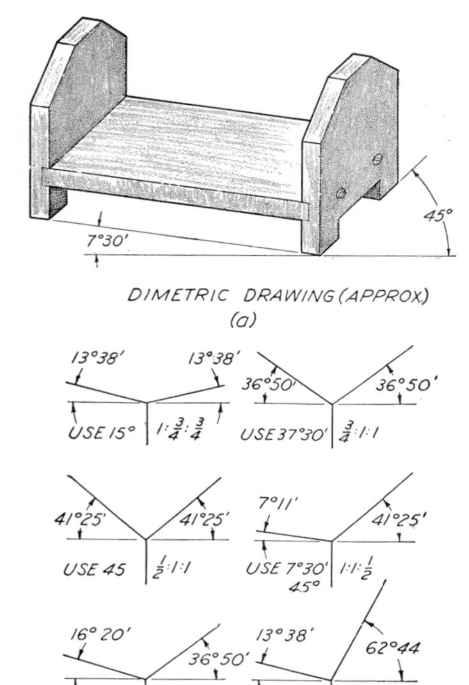

Fig. 14.31. Approximate dimetric drawing.

14.15. Trimetric projection. A trimetric projection of an object is the view obtained when each of the three axes makes a different angle with the plane of projection. Fig. 14.32 illustrates the application of the auxiliary view method to the construction of a trimetric projection. This form of pictorial representation has been used to some extent by certain aircraft companies for the preparation of production illustrations.

14.16. Oblique projection. In oblique projection, the view is produced by using parallel projectors that make some angle other than 90° with the plane of projection. Generally, one face is placed parallel to the picture plane

* At Texas Agricultural and Mechanical College, the auxiliary view method for constructing pictorial representations is associated directly with principal views and working drawings. (*A New Approach to Axonometric Projection and Its Application to Shop Drawings*, by J. G. McGuire.)

† Formula: $\cos \alpha = -\frac{\sqrt{2s_1^2s_2^2 - s_2^4}}{2s_1s_2}$. In this formula, α is one of the equal angles; s_1 is one of the equal scales; s_2 is the third scale.

and the projection lines are taken at 45°. This gives a view that is pictorial in appearance, as it shows the front and one or more additional faces of an object. In Fig. 14.33, the orthographic and oblique projections of a cube are shown. When the angle is 45°, as in this illustration, the representation is sometimes called cavalier projection. It is generally known, however, as an oblique projection or an oblique drawing.

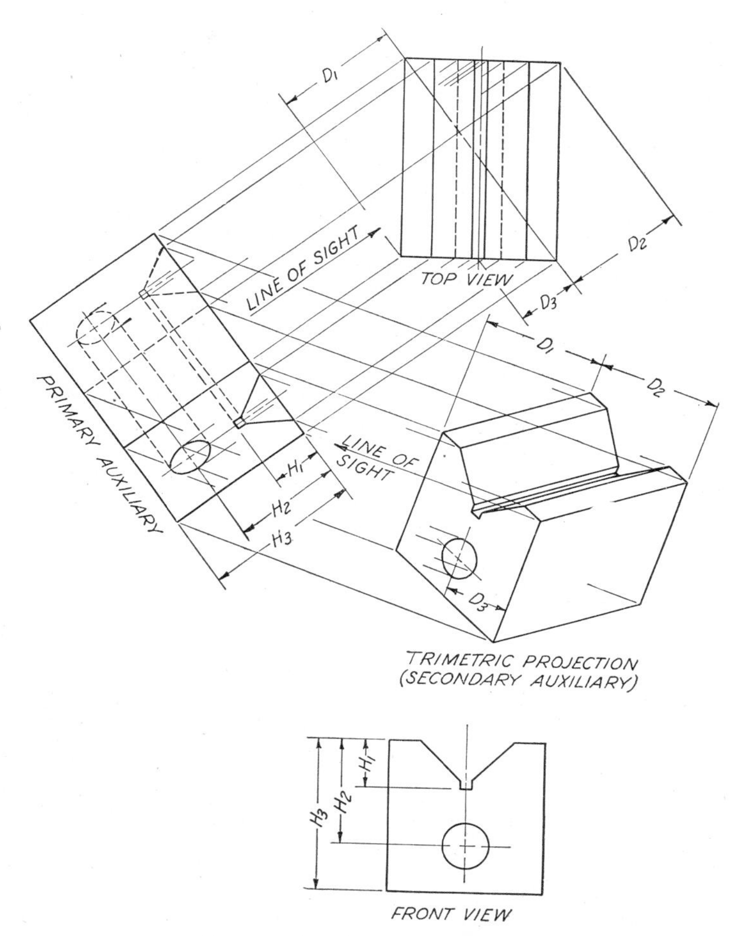

Fig. 14.32. Trimetric drawing.

14.17. Principle of oblique projection. The theory of oblique projection can be explained by imagining a vertical plane of projection in front of a cube parallel to one of its faces (Fig. 14.33). When the projectors make an angle of 45° in any direction with the picture plane, the length of any oblique projection $A'B'$ of the edge AB is equal to the true length of AB. Note that the projectors could be parallel to any element of a 45° cone having its base in the plane of projection. With projectors at this particular angle (45°), the face parallel to the plane is projected in its true size and shape and the edges perpendicular to the picture plane are projected in their true length. If the projectors make a greater angle, the oblique projection will be shorter, while if the angle is less, the projection will be longer.

14.18. Oblique drawing. This form of drawing is based upon three mutually perpendicular axes along which, or parallel to which, the neces-

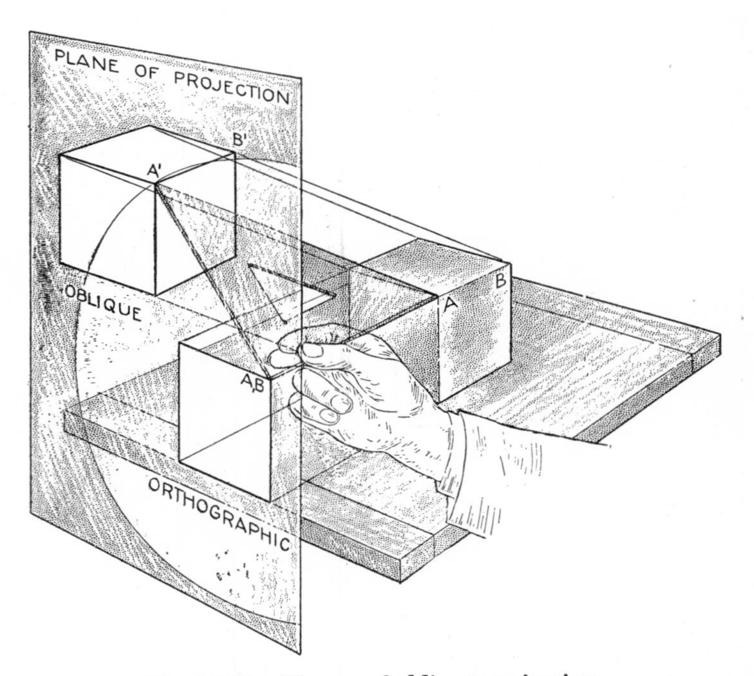

Fig. 14.33. Theory of oblique projection.

sary measurements are made for constructing the representation. Oblique drawing differs from isometric drawing principally in that two axes are always perpendicular to each other while the third (receding axis) is at some convenient angle, such as 30°, 45°, or 60° with the horizontal. (See

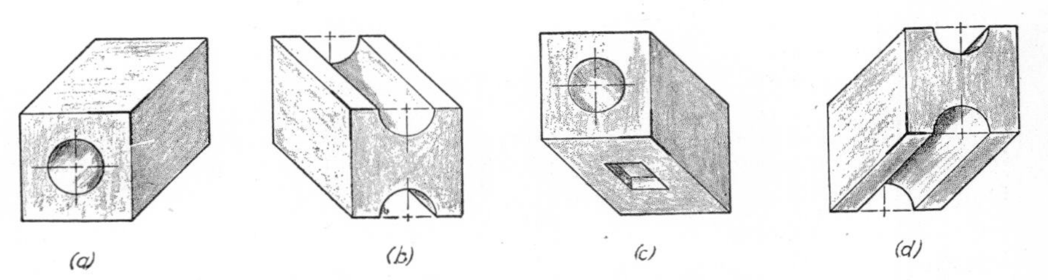

Fig. 14.34. Various positions of the receding axis.

Fig. 14.35.) It is somewhat more flexible and has the following advantages over isometric drawing: (1) circular or irregular outlines on the front face show in their true shape; (2) distortion can be reduced by foreshortening along the receding axis; and (3) a greater choice is permitted in the selection of the positions of the axes. A few of the various views that can be obtained by varying the inclination of the receding axis are illustrated in Fig. 14.34. Usually, the selection of the position is governed by the character of the object.

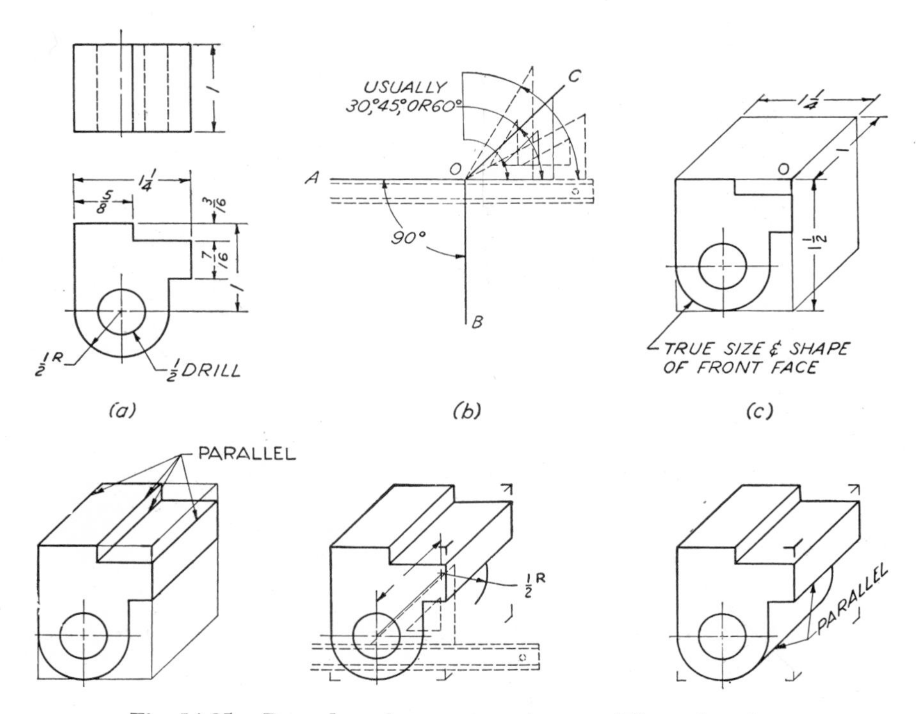

Fig. 14.35. Procedure for constructing an oblique drawing.

14.19. To make an oblique drawing. The procedure followed in constructing an oblique drawing of an adjustable guide is illustrated in Fig. 14.35. The three axes that establish the perpendicular edges in (*b*) are drawn through point *O* representing the front corner. *OA* and *OB* are perpendicular to each other and *OC* is at any desired angle (say 45°) with the horizontal. After the length, height, and depth have been set off, as in (*c*), the front face may be laid out in its true size and shape and the view can be completed by drawing lines parallel to the receding axes through the established corners. The circle and semicircle are shown parallel to the picture plane in order to avoid distortion and because, from the draftsman's standpoint, it is easier to draw a circle than to construct an ellipse.

In general, the procedure for constructing an oblique drawing is the same as for an isometric drawing.

14.20. Rules for placing an object. Generally, the most irregular face, or the one containing the most circular outlines, should be placed parallel to the picture plane, in order to minimize distortion and simplify construction. By following this practice, all or most of the circles and circle arcs can be drawn with a compass, and the tedious construction that would be required to draw their elliptical representations in a receding plane is eliminated. In selecting the position of an object, two rules should be followed. The first is to place the face having the most irregular contour, or the most circular outlines, parallel to the picture plane. Note in Fig. 14.36 the advantage of following this rule.

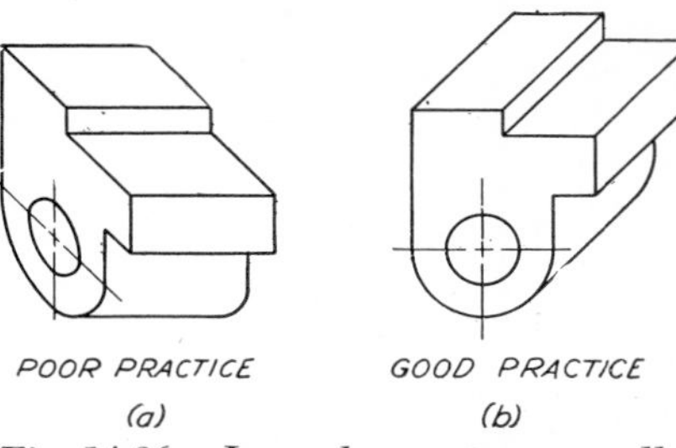

Fig. 14.36. Irregular contour parallel to picture plane.

When the longest face of an object is used as the front face, the pictorial view will be distorted to a lesser degree and, therefore, will have a more realistic and pleasing appearance. Hence, the second rule is to place the longest face parallel to the picture plane. Compare the views shown in Fig. 14.37 and note the greater distortion in (*a*) over (*b*).

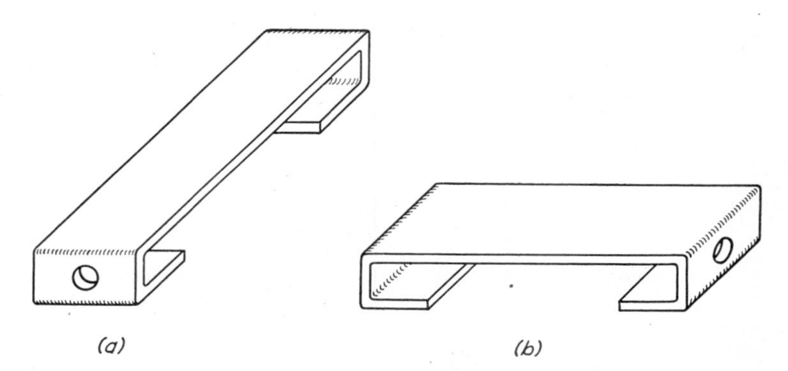

Fig. 14.37. Long axis parallel to picture plane.

If these two rules clash, the first should govern. It is more desirable to have the irregular face show its true shape than it is to lessen the distortion in the direction of the receding axis.

14.21. Use of a basic plane. If the front face of an object is in one plane, it will appear in the oblique drawing exactly the same as in orthographic drawing. Note this fact in Fig. 14.35. But the front of many objects is composed of two or more parallel planes whose relationship must be carefully established. The convenient way to accomplish this is to use one of the planes as a basic (starting) plane and work from it in the direction of the receding axis, as illustrated in Fig. 14.38. Since the front surface A presents the contour shape, it should be selected as the basic plane and drawn first as the front of the oblique projection, as shown in (c). The center P of the circles for surface B may be located easily by measuring along the axis of the hole from O, in plane A, a distance X equal to the distance between the planes. The measurement must be made forward along the axis from O, because surface B is in front of A. The centers of the arcs on the surface C are located in a similar manner, except that the direction of making the measurements is from the basic plane toward the back.

When an object has an inclined front surface with a curved outline, it may be drawn by constructing a right section and making offset measurements as shown in Fig. 14.39.

14.22. Angles, circles, and circle arcs in oblique. As previously stated, angles, circles, and irregular outlines on surfaces parallel to the plane of projection show in true size and shape. When located on receding faces, the construction methods used in isometric drawing usually may be applied. Fig. 14.40 shows the method of drawing the elliptical representation of a circle on an oblique face. Note that the method is identical with that used for constructing isometric circles, except for the slight change in the position of the axes.

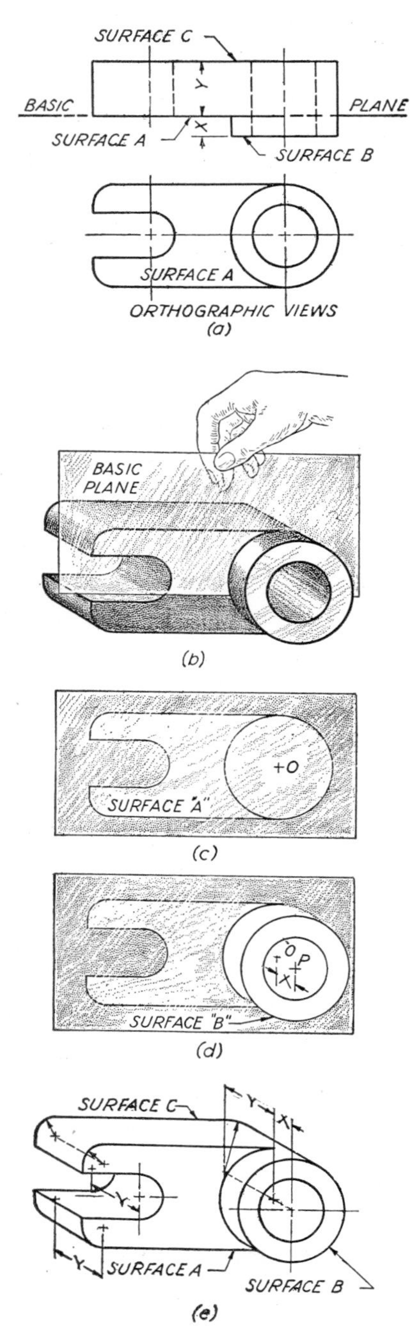

Fig. 14.38. Basic plane theory of construction.

14.23. Reduction of measurements in the direction of the receding axis. An oblique drawing often presents a distorted appearance that is unnatural and disagreeable to the eye. In some cases the view constructed by this scheme is so misleading in appearance that it is unsatisfactory for any practical purpose. As a matter of interest, the effect of distortion is due to the fact that the receding lines are parallel and do not

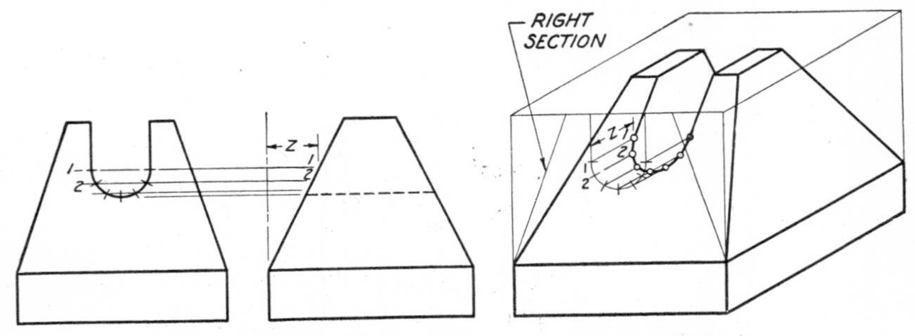

Fig. 14.39. Curved outlines on an inclined plane.

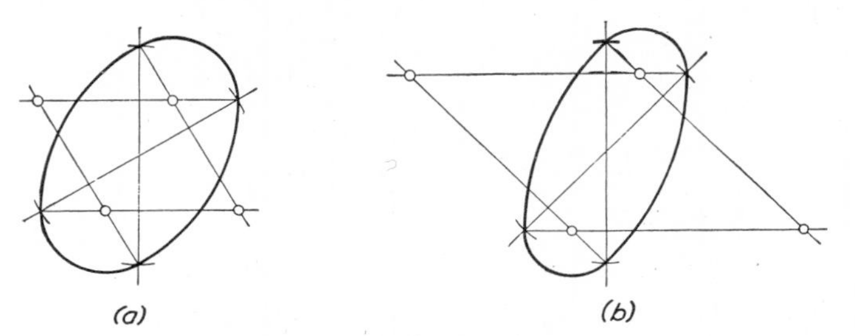

Fig. 14.40. Oblique circles.

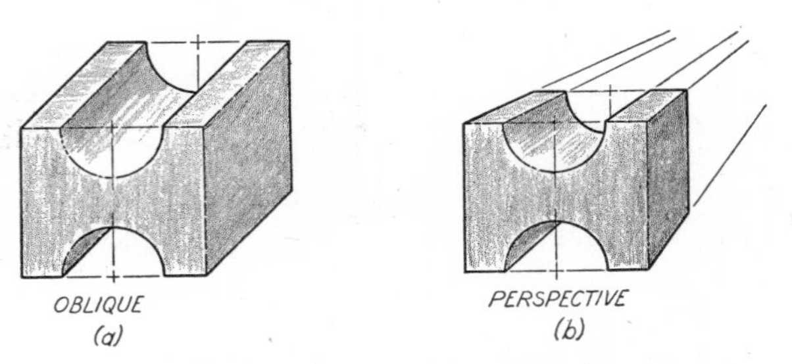

Fig. 14.41. Comparison of oblique and perspective.

appear to converge as the eye is accustomed to anticipating. Note the comparison between oblique and perspective drawing in Fig. 14.41. The perspective view in (*b*) has a natural appearance because the receding lines appear to converge.

The appearance of excessive thickness can be overcome somewhat by reducing the length of the receding lines. For practical purposes, measurements usually are reduced one-half, but any scale of reduction may be arbitrarily adopted if the view obtained will be more realistic in

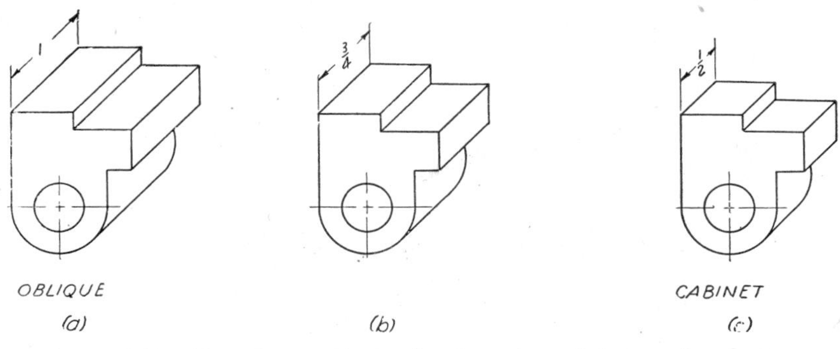

Fig. 14.42. Foreshortening in the direction of the receding axis.

appearance. When the receding lines are drawn one-half their actual length, the resulting pictorial view is called a cabinet drawing. Fig. 14.42 shows an oblique drawing (*a*) and a cabinet drawing (*c*) of the same object, for the purpose of comparison.

14.24. Oblique sectional views. Oblique sectional views are drawn to show the interior construction of objects. The construction procedure is the same as for an isometric sectional view, except that oblique planes are used for cutting the object. An oblique half section is illustrated in Fig. 14.43.

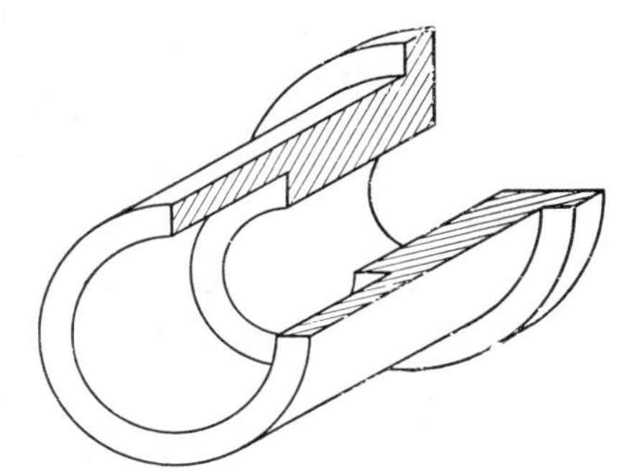

Fig. 14.43. Oblique half section.

14.25. Pictorial dimensioning. The dimensioning of isometric and other forms of pictorial working drawings is done in accordance with the following rules:

1. Draw extension and dimension lines (except those dimension lines applying to cylindrical features) parallel to the pictorial axes in the plane of the surface to which they apply (Fig. 14.44).

2. If possible, apply dimensions to visible surfaces.

3. Place dimensions on the object, if, by so doing, better appearance, added clearness, and easy readings result.

4. Notes may be lettered either in pictorial or as on ordinary drawings. When lettered as on ordinary drawings the difficulties encountered in forming pictorial letters are avoided (Fig. 14.44).

5. Make the figures of a dimension appear to be lying in the plane of the surface whose dimension it indicates, by using vertical figures drawn

in pictorial (Fig. 14.44). (Note: Guide lines and slope lines are drawn parallel to the pictorial axes.)

14.26. Conventional treatment of pictorial drawings. When it is desirable for an isometric or an oblique drawing of a casting to present a somewhat more or less realistic appearance, it becomes necessary to

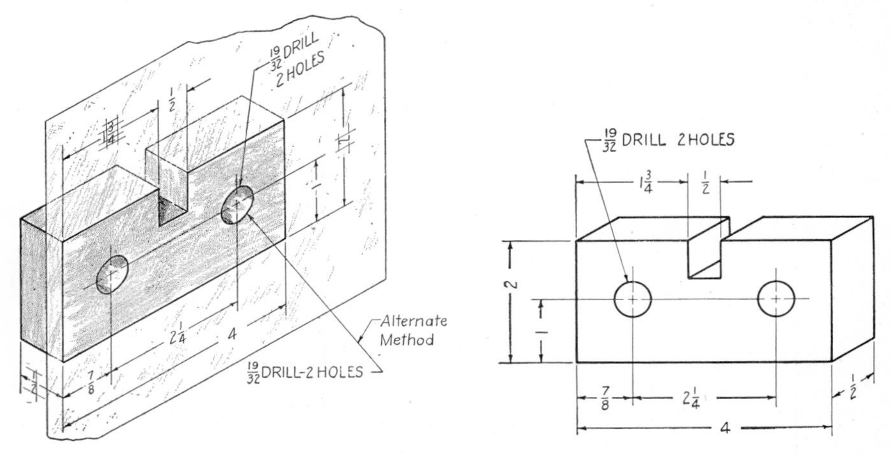

Fig. 14.44. Extension and dimension lines in isometric (left); numerals, fractions, and notes in oblique (right).

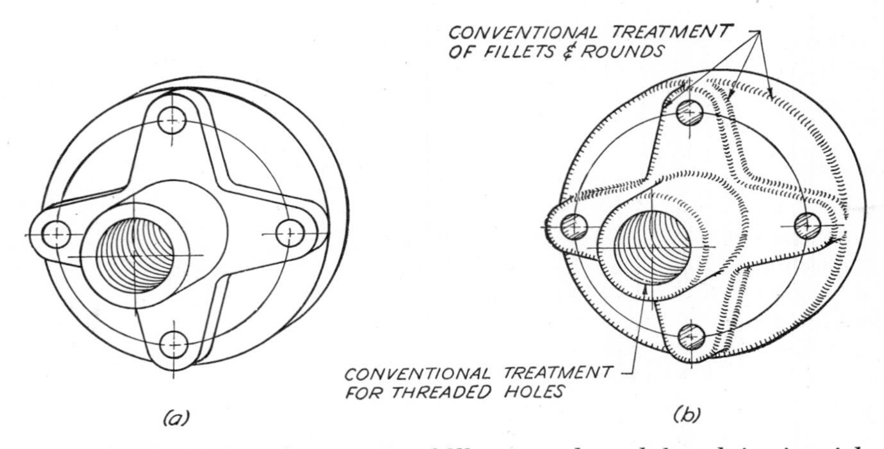

Fig. 14.45. Conventional treatment of fillets, rounds, and threads in pictorial.

represent the fillets and rounds on the unfinished surfaces. One method, commonly used by draftsmen, is shown in Fig. 14.45(*b*). On the drawing in (*a*), all of the edges have been treated as if they were sharp. The conventional treatment for threads in pictorial is illustrated in (*b*).

Fig. 14.46 shows a pictorial diagram.

14.27. Perspective. In perspective projection, an object is shown much as the human eye or camera would see it at a particular point. Actually, it is a geometrical method by which a picture can be projected upon a picture plane in much the same way as in photography. Perspective drawing differs from the methods previously discussed in that, although the projectors or visual rays are oblique to the picture plane, they intersect at a common point known as the station point. (See Fig. 14.50.)

Since perspective shows an object as it appears instead of showing its true shape and size, it is rarely used by engineers. It is more extensively employed by architects to show the appearance of proposed buildings, by artist-draftsmen for production illustrations, and by illustrators in preparing advertising drawings.

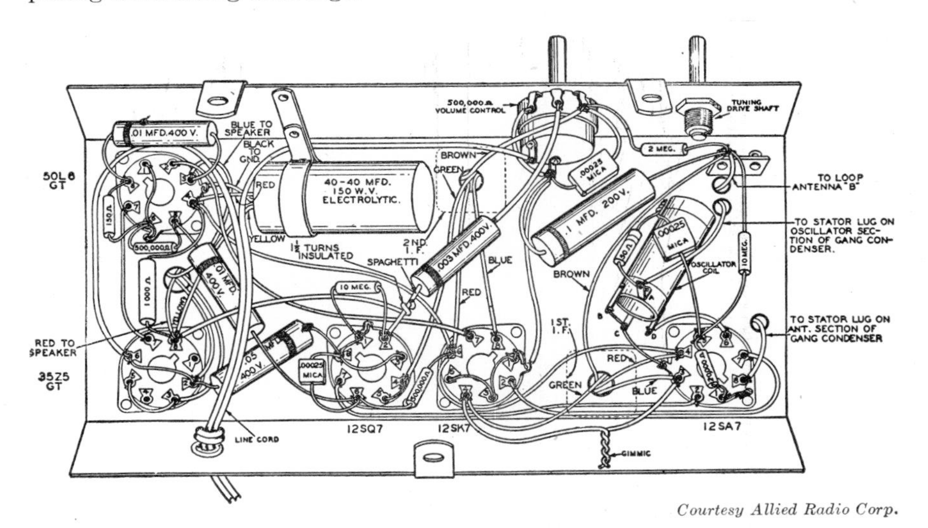

Courtesy Allied Radio Corp.

Fig. 14.46. Pictorial diagram.

Fig. 14.1 shows a type of production illustration that has been widely used in assembly departments as an aid to those persons who find it difficult to read an orthographic assembly. This form of presentation, which shows the mechanism both exploded and assembled, has made it possible for industrial concerns to employ semitrained personnel. Fig. 14.47 shows a type of industrial drawing made in perspective that has proved useful in aircraft plants. Because of the growing importance of this type of drawing, and also because engineers frequently will find perspective desirable for other purposes, its elementary principles should be discussed logically in this text. Other books on the subject, some of which are listed in the bibliography, should be studied by architectural students and those interested in a more thorough discussion of the various methods.

The fundamental concepts of perspective can be explained best if the

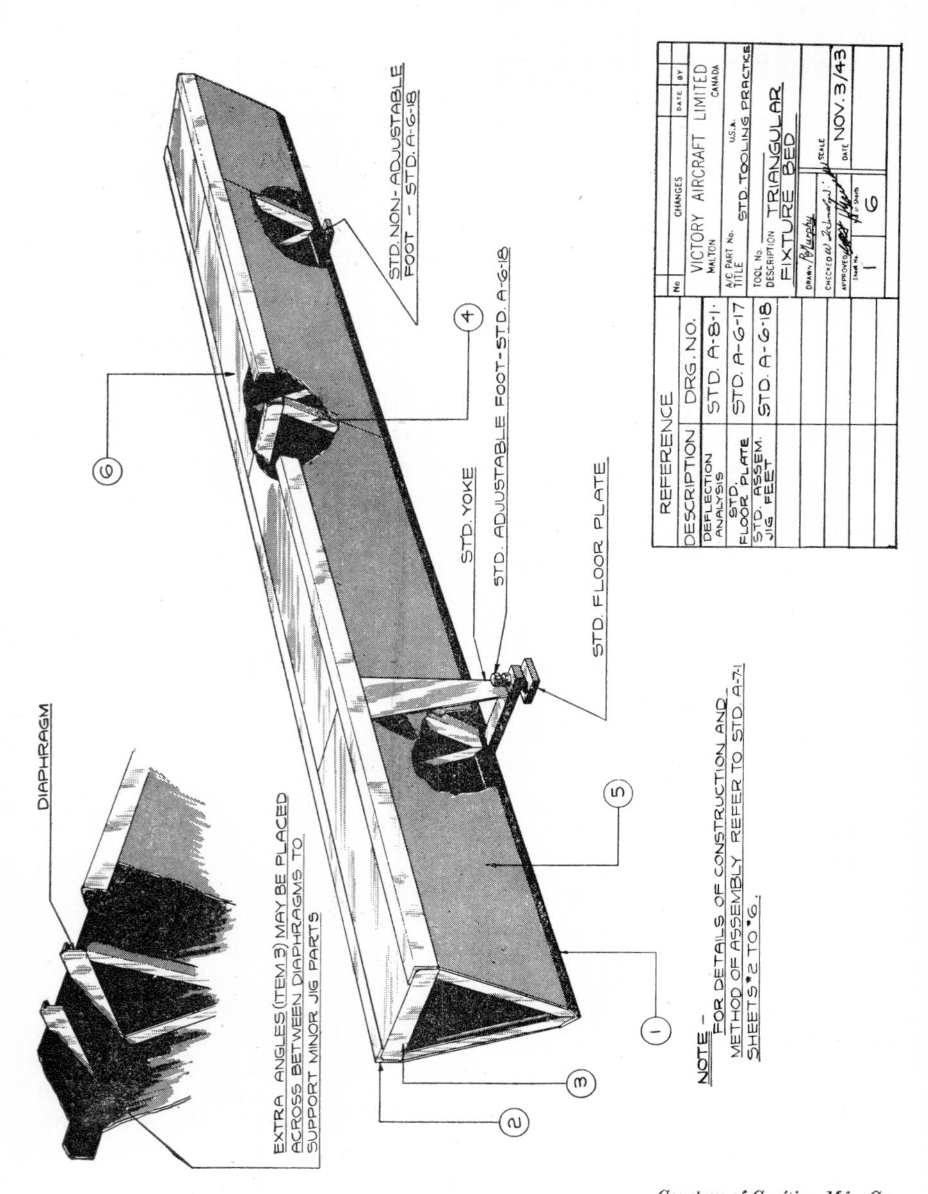

Courtesy of Crafting Mfg. Co.

Fig. 14.47. A production illustration.

reader will imagine himself looking through a picture plane at a formal garden with a small pool flanked by lamp posts, as shown in Fig. 14.48. The point of observation, at which the rays from the eye to the objects in the scene meet, is called the *station point*, and the plane upon which the view is formed by the piercing points of the visual rays is known as the

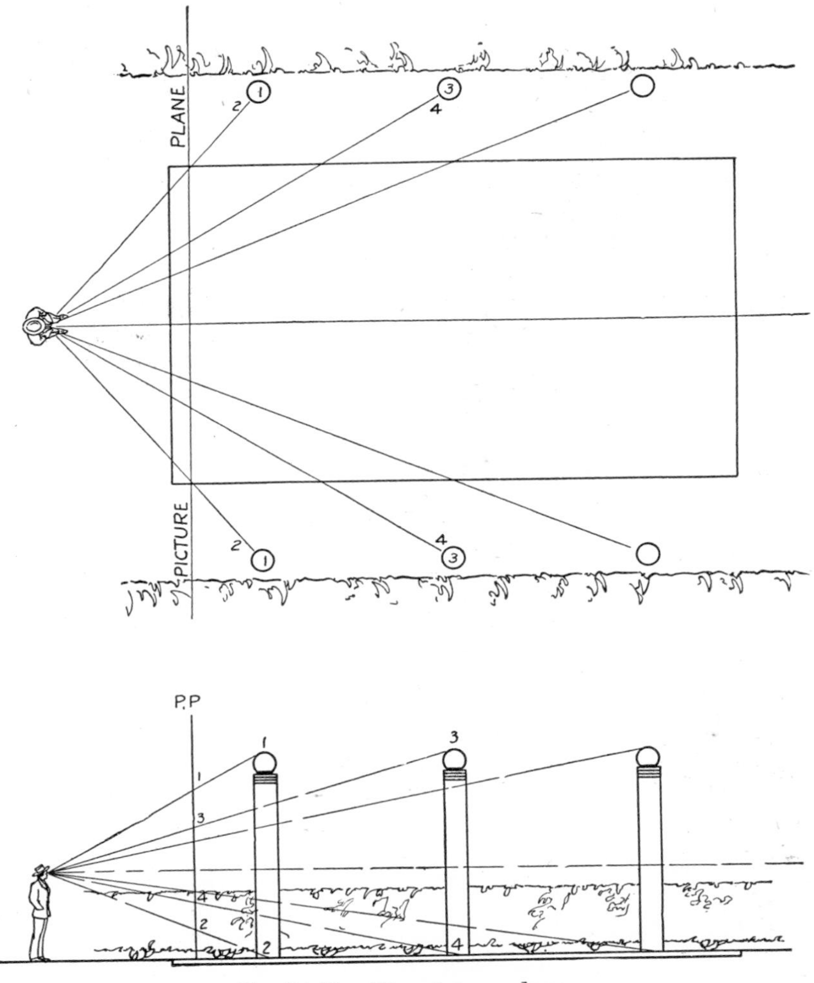

Fig. 14.48. The picture plane.

picture plane (*PP*). The piercing points reproduce the scene, the size of which depends upon the location of the picture plane.

It should be noted that objects of the same height intercept a greater distance on the picture plane when close to it than when farther away. For example, rays from the lamp post at 2 intercept a distance 1–2 on the picture plane, while the rays from the pole at 4, which actually is the same height, intercept the lesser distance 3–4. From this fact it should be observed that the farther away an object is, the smaller it will appear,

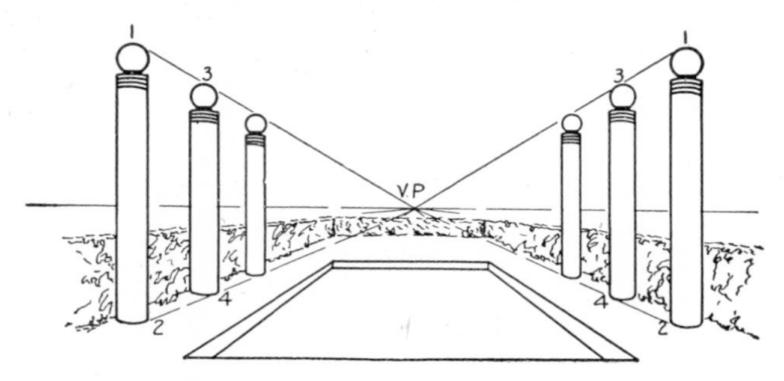

Fig. 14.49. The picture (perspective).

until a point is reached at which there will be no distance intercepted at all. This happens at the horizon.

Fig. 14.49 shows the scene observed by the man in Fig. 14.48 as it would be formed on the picture plane. The posts farther from the picture plane

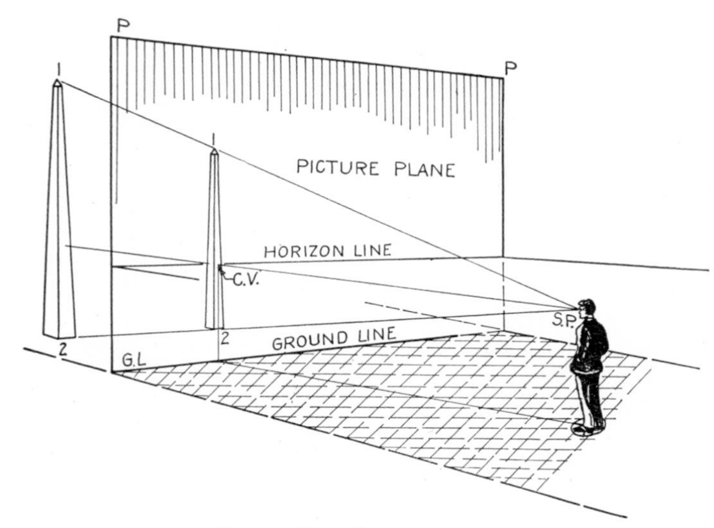

Fig. 14.50. Nomenclature.

diminish in height, as each one has a height on the picture plane equal to the distance it intercepts, as shown in Fig. 14.48. The lines of the pool and hedge converge to the center of vision or vanishing point, which is located directly in front of the observer, on the horizon.

14.28. Perspective nomenclature. Fig. 14.50 illustrates pictorially the accepted nomenclature of perspective drawing. The horizon line is the line of intersection of the horizontal plane through the observation point (eye of the observer) and the picture plane. The horizontal plane is known as the *plane of the horizon.* The ground line is the line of intersection of the ground plane and the picture plane. The *CV* point is the center of vision of the observer. It is located directly in front of the eye in the plane of the horizon on the horizon line.

14.29. Location of picture plane. The picture plane is usually placed between the object and the *SP* (station point). In parallel perspective (Sec. 14.34) it may be passed through a face of the object in order to show the true size and shape of the face.

14.30. Location of the station point. The station point should be located in front of the object, where the object can be viewed to the best advantage. It is desirable that it should be at a distance from the picture plane equal to at least twice the height or width of the object, in order to avoid distortion, for at such distance, or greater, the entire object can be viewed without moving the head.

14.31. Position of the object in relation to the horizon. When making a perspective of a tall object, such as a building, the horizon usually is assumed to be at a height above the ground plane equal to the height of a man's eye ($5\frac{1}{2}$ feet). A small object may be placed above or below the horizon, depending upon the view desired.

14.32. Lines. The following facts should be recognized concerning the perspective of lines:

1. Parallel horizontal lines vanish at a single *VP* (vanishing point). Usually the *VP* is at the point where a line parallel to the system through the *SP* pierces the *PP* (picture plane).

2. A system of horizontal lines has its *VP* on the horizon.

3. Vertical lines, since they pierce the picture plane at infinity, will appear vertical in perspective.

4. When a line lies in the picture plane, it will show its true length because it will be its own perspective.

5. When a line lies behind the picture plane, its perspective will be shorter than the line.

14.33. Types of perspective. In general, there are two types of perspective: *parallel perspective* and *angular perspective.* In parallel perspective, one of the principal faces is parallel to the picture plane and is its own perspective. All vertical lines are vertical, and the receding horizontal lines converge to a single vanishing point. In angular perspective, the object is placed so that the principal faces are at an angle with the picture plane. The horizontal lines converge at two vanishing points.

14.34. Parallel perspective. Fig. 14.51 shows the parallel perspective of a rectangular block. The *PP* line is the top view of the picture plane, SP_H is the top view of the station point, and *CV* is the center of vision. The receding horizontal lines vanish at *CV*. The front face, since it lies in the picture plane, is its own perspective and shows in its true size. The lines representing the edges back of the picture plane are found by projecting downward from the points at which the visual rays pierce the picture plane, as shown by the top views of the rays. Fig. 14.52 shows a parallel perspective of a cylindrical machine part.

14.35. Angular perspective. Fig. 14.53 shows pictorially the graphical method for the preparation of a two-point perspective drawing of a cube. To visualize the true layout on the surface of a sheet of drawing paper, it is necessary to revolve mentally the horizontal plane downward into the vertical or picture plane. Upon completion of Sec. 14.35, it is

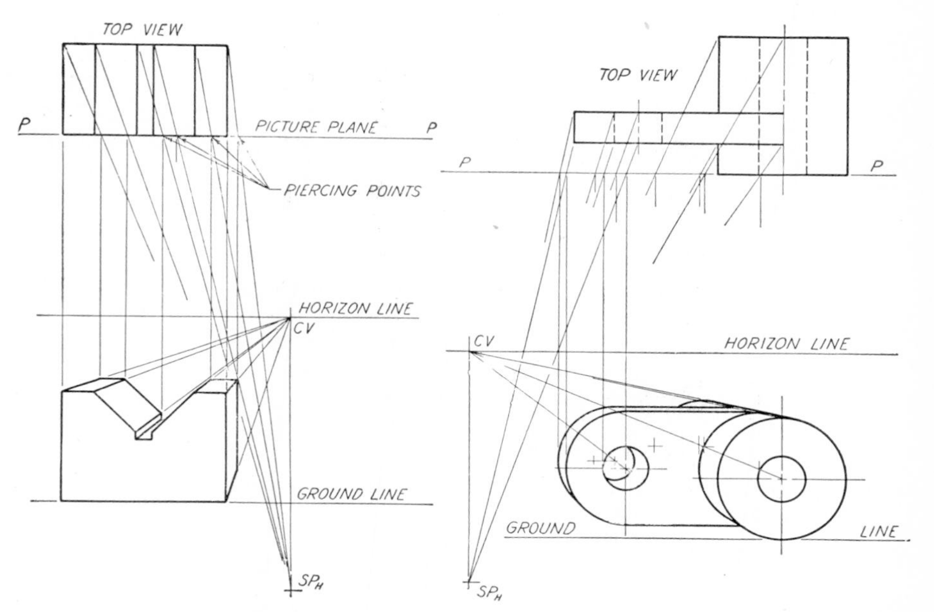

Fig. 14.51. Parallel perspective.

Fig. 14.52. Circles in parallel perspective.

suggested that the reader turn back and endeavor to associate the development of the perspective in Fig. 14.54 with the pictorial presentation in Fig. 14.53. For a full understanding of the construction in Fig. 14.54, it is necessary to differentiate between the lines that belong to the horizontal plane and those that are on the vertical or picture plane. In addition, it must be fully realized that there is a top view for the perspective that is a line, and that in this line view lie the points that must be projected downward to the perspective representation (front view).

Fig. 14.54 shows an angular perspective of a mutilated block. The block has been placed so that one vertical edge lies in the picture plane. The other vertical edges are parallel to the plane, while all of the horizontal lines are inclined to it so that they vanish at the two vanishing points, VPL and VPR, respectively.

In constructing the perspective shown in this illustration, an ortho-

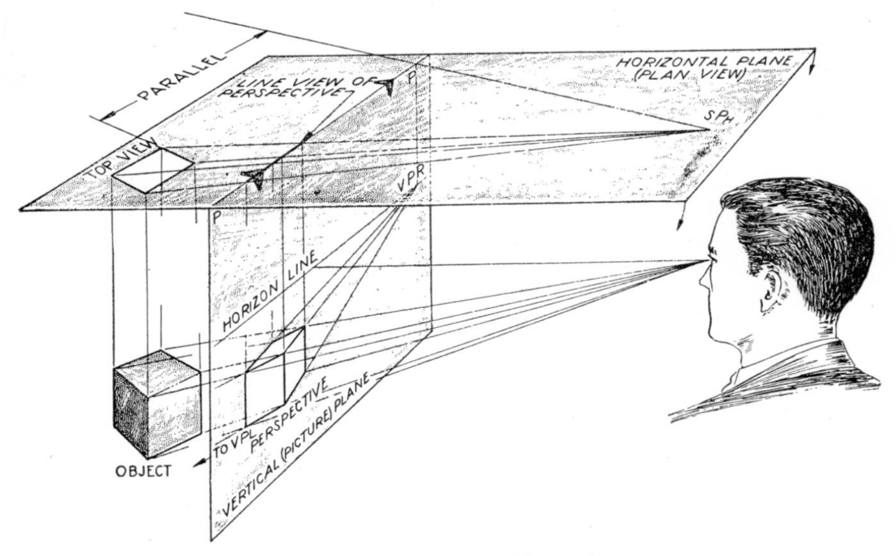

Fig. 14.53. Angular perspective.

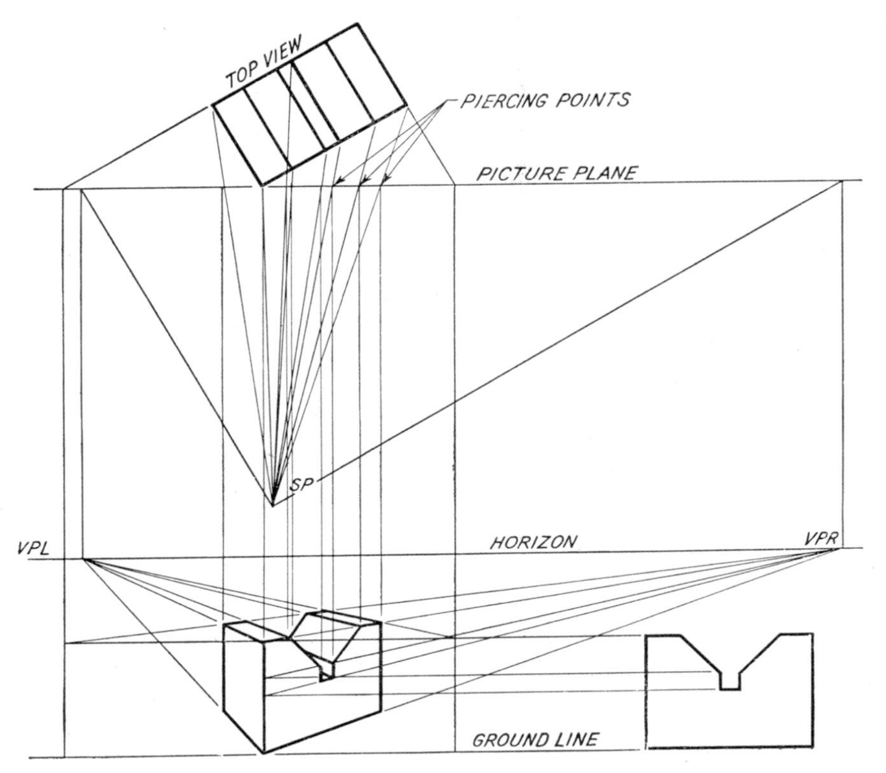

Fig. 14.54. Angular perspective.

graphic top view was drawn in such a position that the visible vertical faces made angles of 30° and 60° with the picture plane. Next, the location of the observer was assumed and the horizon line was established. The vanishing points *VPL* and *VPR* were found by drawing a 30° line and a 60° line through the *SP*. Since these lines are parallel to the two systems of receding horizontal lines, each will establish a required vanishing point at its intersection with the picture plane. The vertical line

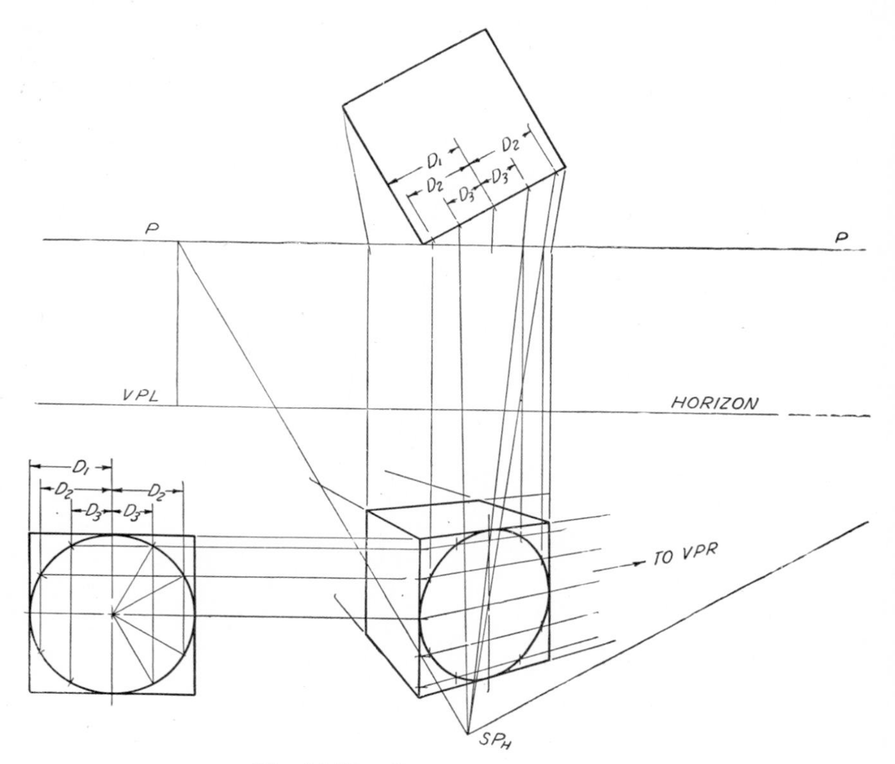

Fig. 14.55. Circles in perspective.

located in the picture plane, which is its own perspective, was selected as a measuring line on which to project vertical measurements from the orthographic front view. The lines shown from these division points along this line to the vanishing points (*VPL-VPR*) established the direction of the receding horizontal edge lines in the perspective. The position of the back edges was determined by projecting downward from the points at which the projectors from the station point (*SP*) to the corners of the object pierced the picture plane, as shown by the top view of the object and projectors.

14.36. Circles in perspective. If a circle is on a surface that is inclined to the picture plane (*PP*), its perspective will be an ellipse. It is the usual practice to construct the representation within an enclosing square by finding selected points along the curve in the perspective as shown in Fig. 14.55. Any points might be used, but it is recommended that points be located on 30°, 45°, and 60° lines.

14.37. Problems. The student will find that a preliminary sketch will facilitate the preparation of isometric and oblique drawings of the problems of this chapter. On such a sketch he may plan the procedure of construction. Since many engineers frequently find it necessary to prepare pictorial sketches during discussions with untrained persons who cannot read orthographic views, it is recommended that some problems be sketched freehand on either plain or pictorial grid paper. (See Fig. 12.3.)

1. (Fig. 14.56.) Prepare instrumental isometric drawings or freehand sketches of the objects as assigned.

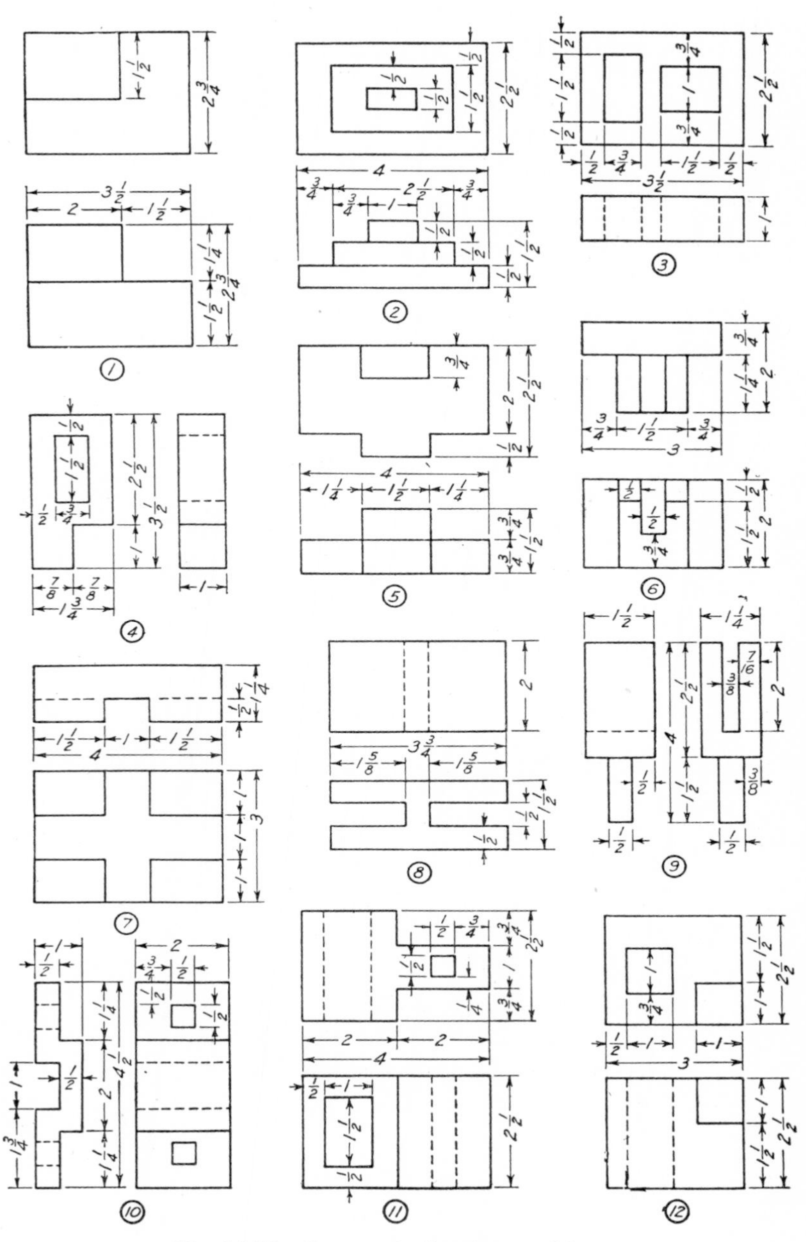

Fig. 14.56. Isometric drawing problems.

2. (Fig. 14.57.) Prepare instrumental isometric drawings or freehand sketches of the objects as assigned.

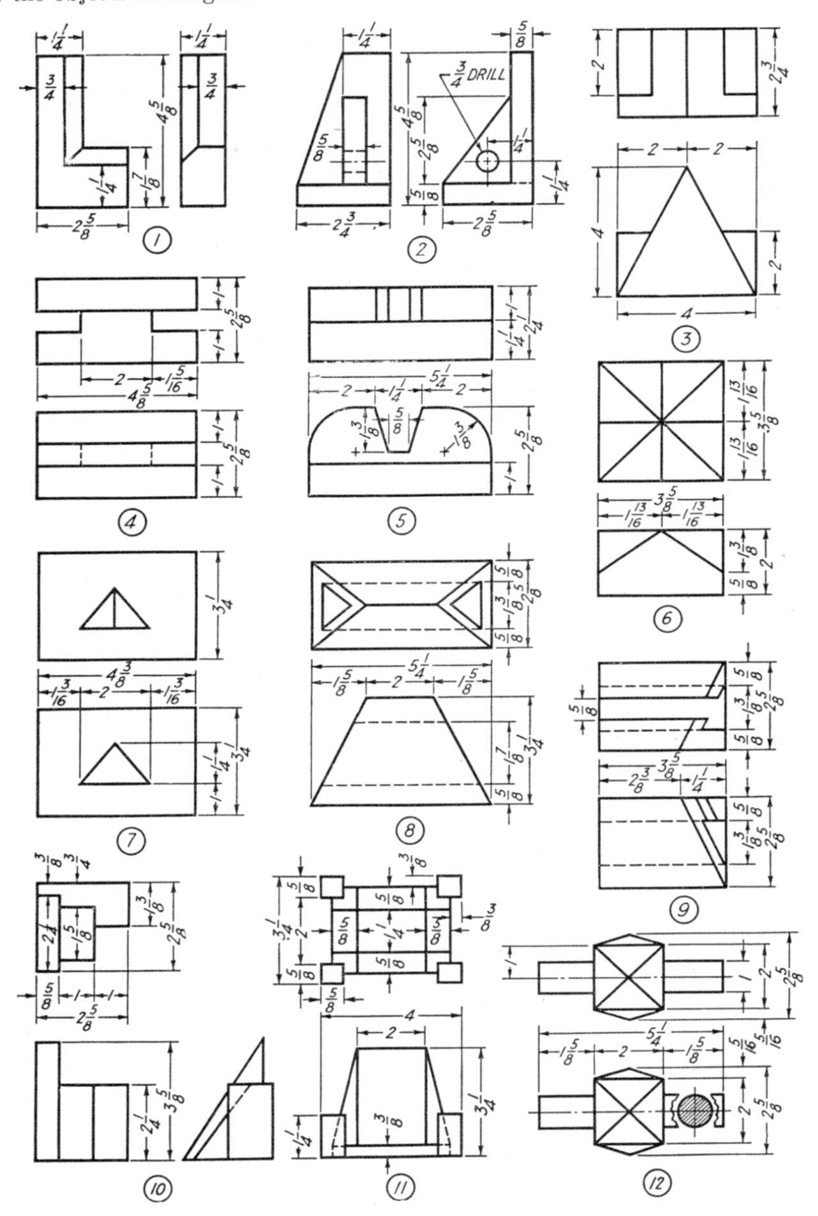

Fig. 14.57. Isometric drawing problems.

3. (Fig. 14.58.) Prepare instrumental oblique drawings or freehand sketches of the objects as assigned.

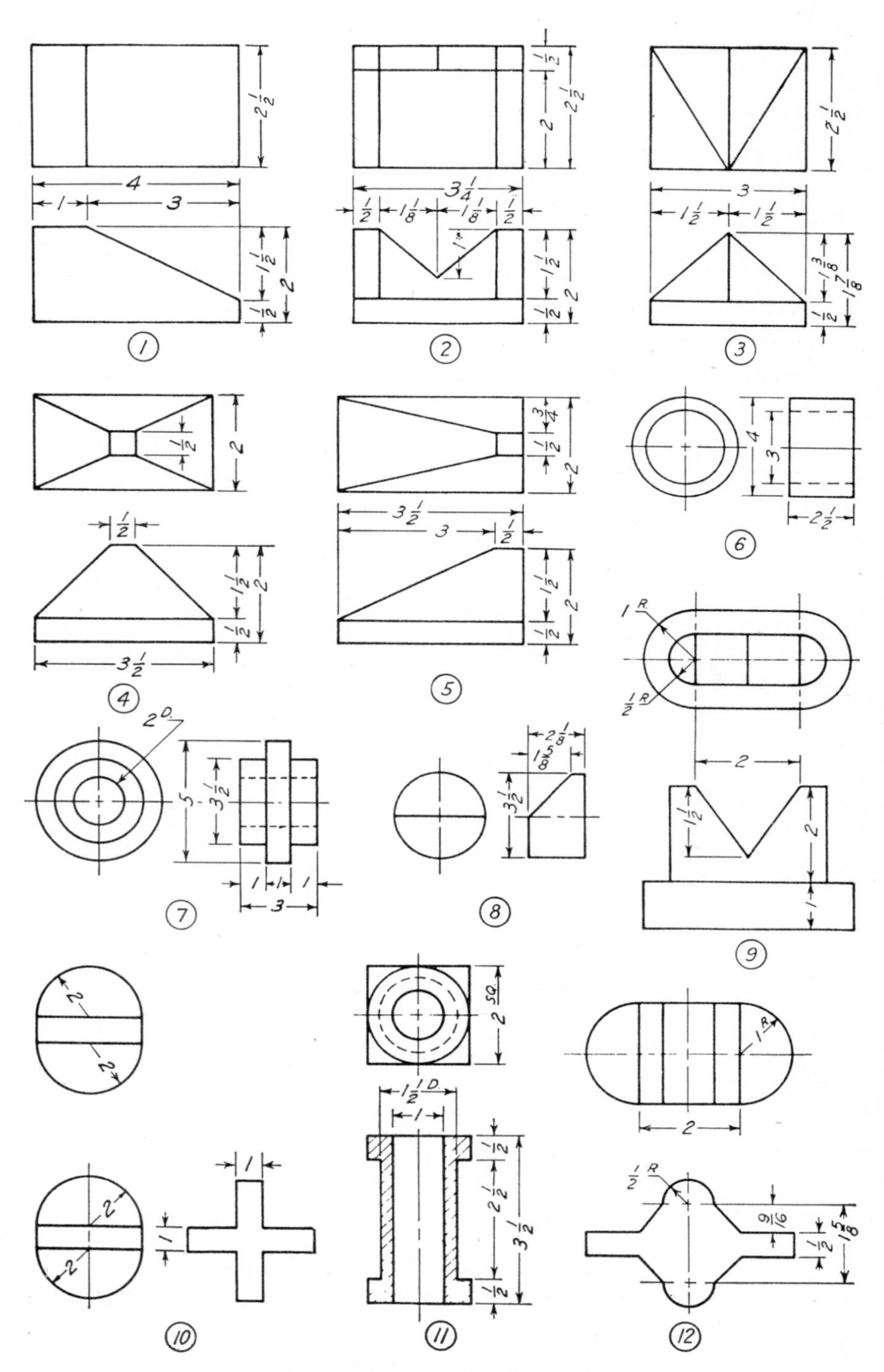

Fig. 14.58. Oblique drawing problems.

4. (Fig. 14.59.) Prepare instrumental oblique drawings or freehand sketches of the objects as assigned.

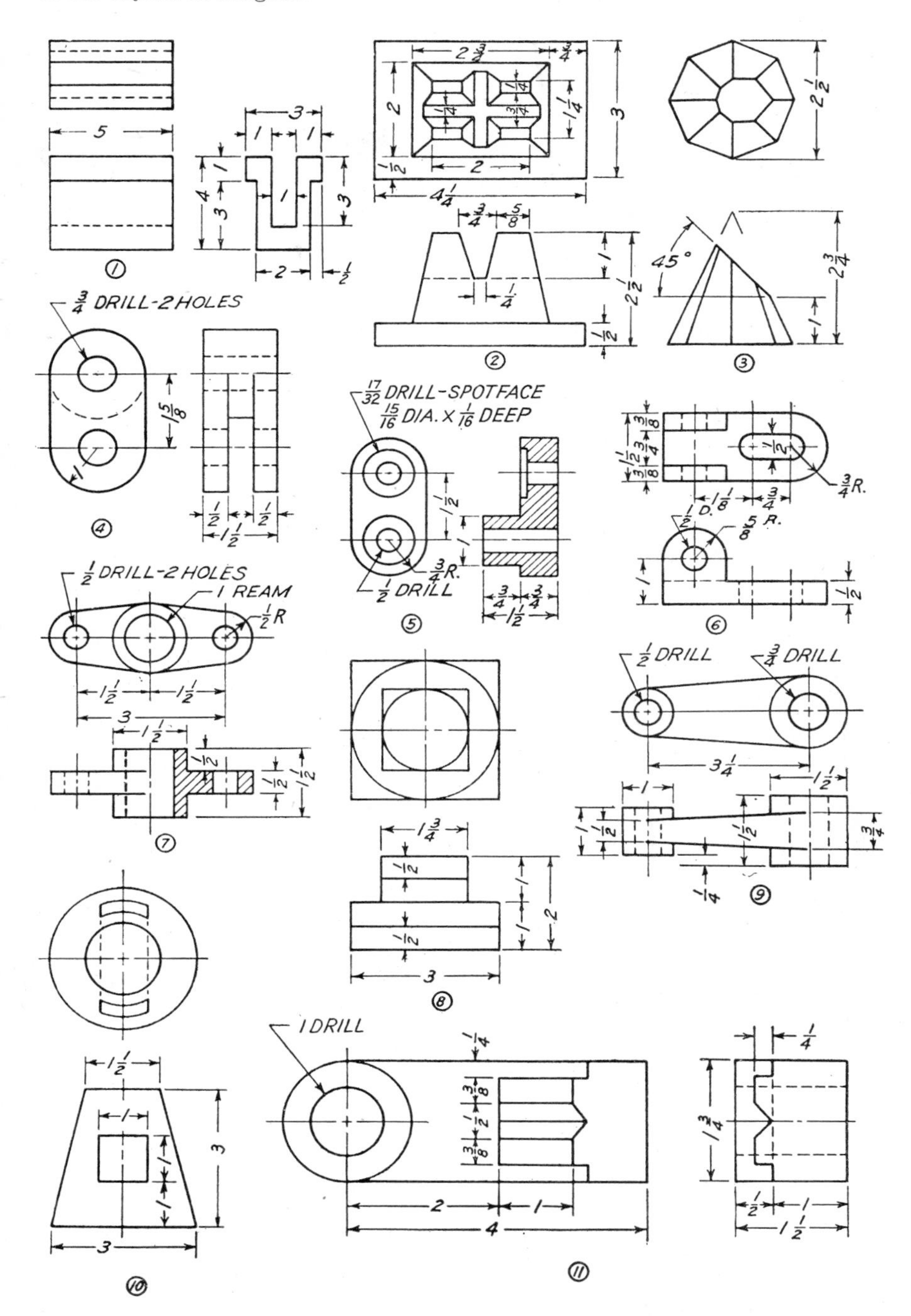

Fig. 14.59. Oblique drawing problems.

5. (Fig. 14.60.) Make an isometric drawing of the sawhorse. Select a suitable scale.

6. (Fig. 14.61.) Make an oblique drawing of the locomotive driver nut.

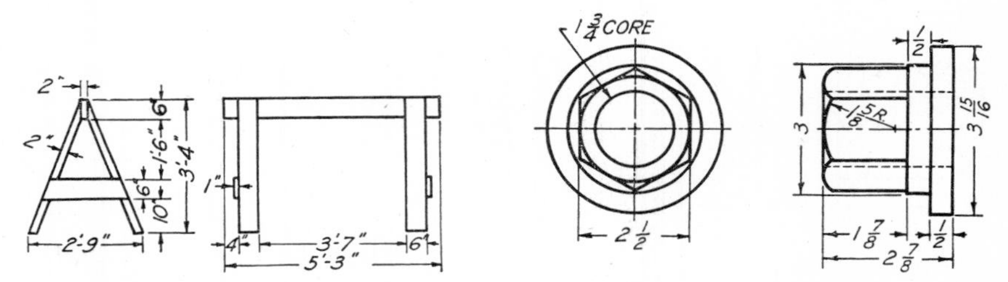

Fig. 14.60. Sawhorse. **Fig. 14.61. Locomotive driver nut.**

7. (Fig. 14.62.) Make an isometric drawing of the stepladder. Select a suitable scale.

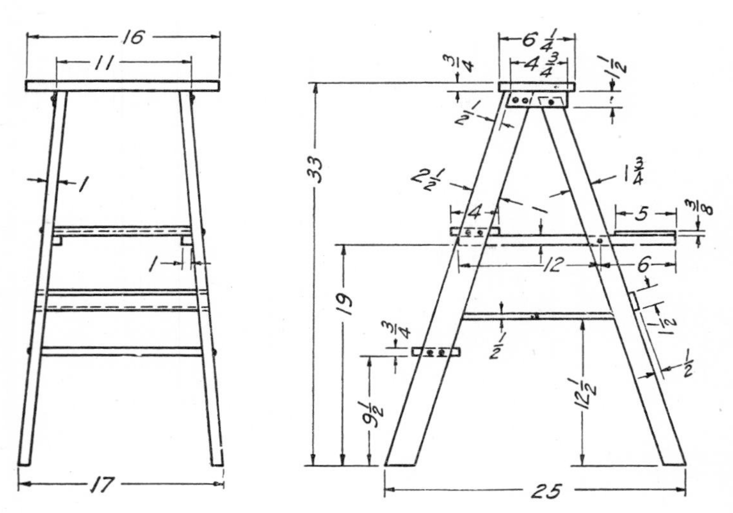

Fig. 14.62. Stepladder.

8. (Fig. 14.63.) Make an oblique drawing of the adjustment cone.

9. (Fig. 14.64.) Make an oblique drawing of the fork.

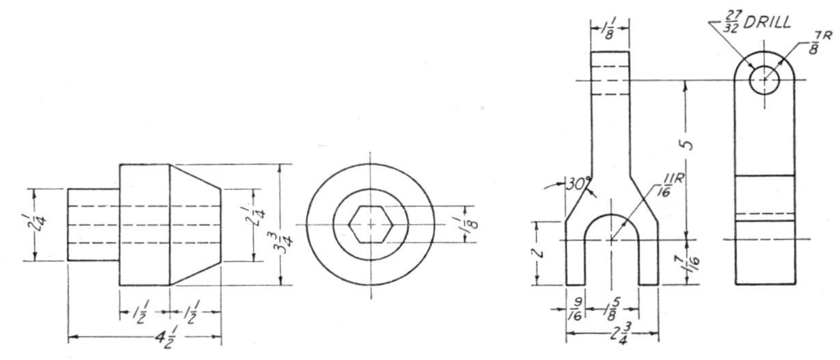

Fig. 14.63. Adjustment cone.

Fig. 14.64. Fork.

10. (Fig. 14.65.) Make an oblique drawing of the feeder guide.

11. (Fig. 14.66.) Make an isometric drawing of the hinge bracket.

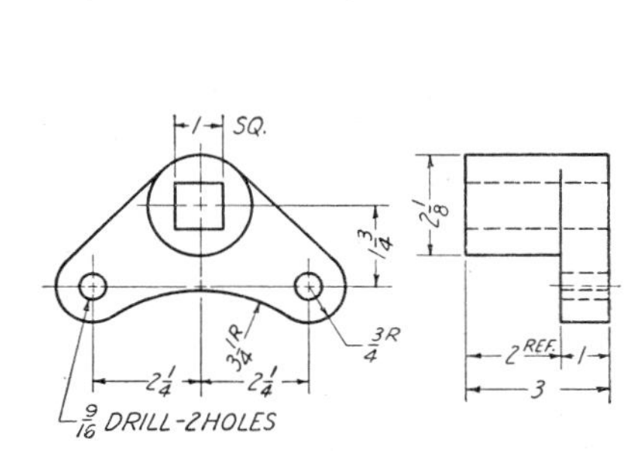

Fig. 14.65. Feeder guide.

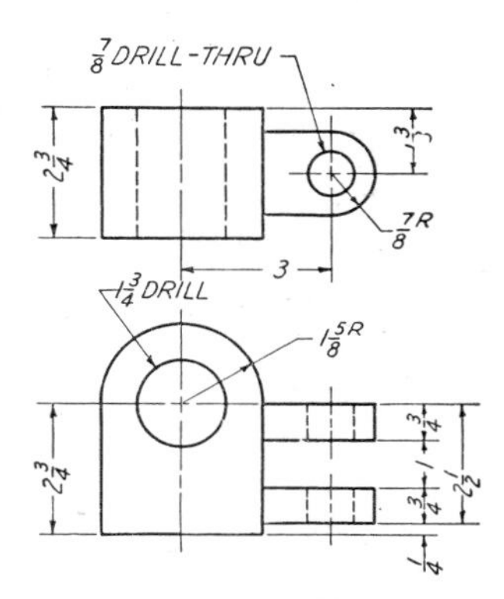

Fig. 14.66. Hinge bracket.

12. (Fig. 14.67.) Make an isometric drawing of the alignment bracket.

13. (Fig. 14.68.) Make an isometric drawing of the stop block.

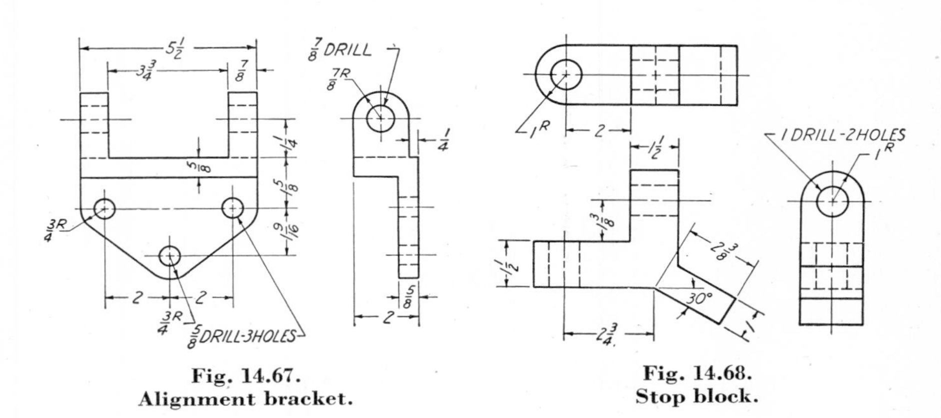

Fig. 14.67.
Alignment bracket.

Fig. 14.68.
Stop block.

14. (Figs. 14.63–14.65.) Make a parallel perspective drawing as assigned.

15. (Figs. 14.66–14.68.) Make an angular perspective drawing as assigned.

15 SHOP PROCESSES

15.1. Shop processes. An engineering draftsman must be thoroughly familiar with the fundamental shop processes before he is qualified to prepare drawings that will fulfill the requirements of the production shops. In preparing working drawings, he must consider each and every individual process involved in the production of a piece, and then specify the processes in terms that the shopman will understand. All too frequently, drawings that specify impractical methods and impossible operations are sent to the shops. Most of these impractical specifications are the result of a lack of knowledge, on the draftsman's part, of what can or cannot be done by skilled craftsmen using modern machines and tools.

Although an accurate knowledge of the shop processes can be acquired only through actual experience in the various shops, it is possible for an apprentice draftsman to obtain a working knowledge of the fundamental operations through study and observation. This chapter presents and explains the principal operations in the pattern shop, foundry, forge shop, and machine shop.

15.2. Castings. Castings are formed by pouring molten metal into a mold or cavity. In sand molding, the molten metal assumes the shape of the cavity that has been formed in a sand mold by ramming a prepared moist sand around a pattern and then removing the pattern. Although a casting shrinks somewhat in cooling, the metal hardens in the exact shape of the pattern used (Fig. 15.1).

A sand mold consists of at least two sections. The upper section, called the *cope*, and the lower section, called the *drag*, together form a box-shaped structure called a *flask*.

When large holes ($\frac{3}{4}''$ and over) or interior passageways and openings are needed in a casting, dry sand cores are placed in the cavity. Cores exclude the metal from the space they occupy and thus form desired openings. Large holes are cored in order to avoid an unnecessary boring operation. A dry sand core is formed by ramming a mixture of sand and a binding material into a core box that has been made in the pattern shop. To make a finished core rigid, the coremaker places it in a core oven where it is baked until it is hard.

The molder when making a mold inserts in the sand a sprue stick that he removes after the cope has been rammed. This resulting hole, known as the *sprue*, conducts the molten metal to the *gate*, which is a passageway cut to the cavity. The adjacent hole called the *riser* provides an outlet for excess metal.

15.3. The pattern shop. The pattern shop prepares patterns of all pieces that the foundry is to cast. Although special pattern drawings are frequently submitted, the pattern maker ordinarily uses a drawing of the finished piece that the draftsman has prepared for both the pattern shop and the machine shop. The finish marks on such a drawing are just as important to him as to the machinist, for he must allow, on each surface to be finished, extra metal, the amount of which depends upon the method of machining and the size of the casting. In general, this amount varies from $\frac{1}{16}''$, in very small castings, to as much as $\frac{3}{4}''$, in large castings.

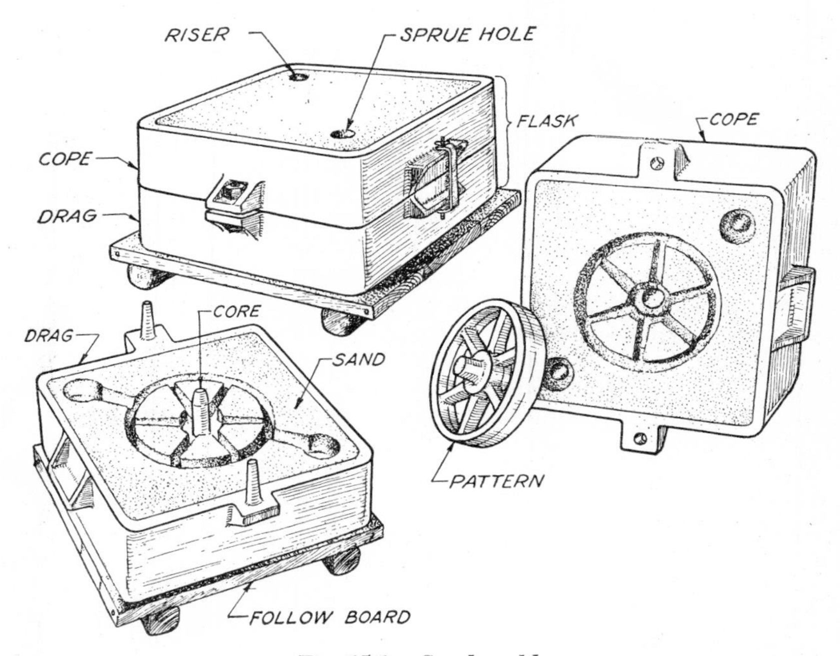

Fig. 15.1. Sand mold.

It is not necessary for the draftsman to specify on his drawing the amount to be allowed for shrinkage, for the pattern maker has available a "shrink rule," which is sufficiently oversize (approximately $\frac{1}{8}''$ per foot) to take care of the shrinkage.

A pattern usually is first constructed of light strong wood, such as white pine or mahogany, which, if only a few castings are required, may be used in making sand molds. In quantity production, however, where a pattern must be used repeatedly, the wooden one will not hold up, so a metal pattern (aluminum, brass, and so on), is made from it and is used in its place.

Every pattern must be constructed in such a way that it can be withdrawn from each section of the sand mold. If the pattern consists of two halves (split), the plane of separation should be so located that it will coincide with the plane of separation of the cope and the drag (Fig. 15.1). Each portion of the pattern must be slightly tapered, so that it can be withdrawn without leaving a damaged cavity. The line of intersection, where the dividing plane cuts the pattern, is called the *parting line*. Although this line is rarely shown on a drawing, the draftsman should make certain that his design will allow the pattern maker to establish it. Ordinarily, it is not necessary to specify the slight taper, known as *draft*, on each side of the parting line, for the pattern maker assumes such responsibility when constructing the pattern.

A "filled-in" interior angle on a casting is called a *fillet*, to distinguish it from a rounded exterior angle, which is known as a *round* (Fig. 15.2). Sharp interior angles are avoided for two reasons: They are difficult to cast; and they are likely to be potential points of failure because the crystals of the cooling metal arrange themselves at a sharp corner in a weak pattern. Fillets are formed by nailing quarter rounds of wood or strips of leather into the sharp angles, or by filling the angles with wax.

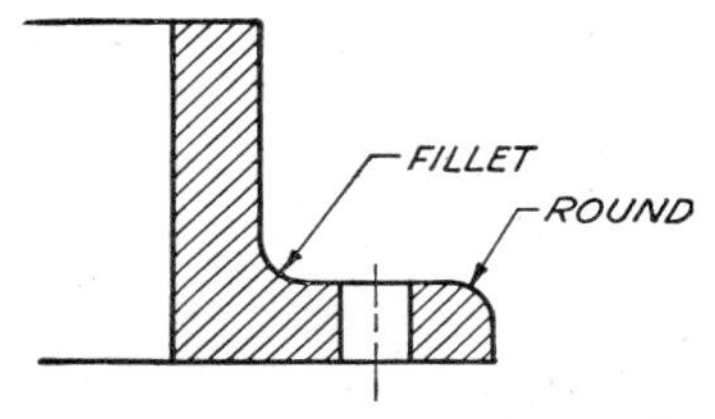

Fig. 15.2. Fillets and rounds on a casting.

15.4. The foundry. Although a draftsman is not directly concerned with the foundry, since the pattern maker takes his drawing and prepares all patterns and core boxes for the molder, it is most important that he be familiar with the operations in making a sand mold and a casting. Otherwise, he will find it difficult to prepare an economical design, the cost of which depends upon how simple it is to mold and cast.

15.5. Die casting. Die casting is an inexpensive method for producing certain types of machine parts, particularly those needing no great strength, in mass production. The castings are made by forcing molten metal or molten alloy into a cavity between metal dies in a die-casting machine. Parts thus produced usually require little or no finishing.

15.6. The forge shop. Many machine parts, especially those that must have strength and yet be light, are forged into shape, the heated metal being forced into dies with a drop hammer. Drop forging, since heated metal is made to conform to the shape of a cavity, might be considered a form of casting. However, because dies are difficult to make and are expensive, this method of production is used principally to make parts having an irregular shape that would be costly to machine and could not be made from casting material. Forgings are made of a high-grade steel. Dies are made by expert craftsmen who are known simply as diemakers.

Generally, special drawings, giving only the dimensions needed, are made for the forge shop.

15.7. Standard stock forms. Many types of metal shapes, along with other materials that are used in the shops for making parts for structures, are purchased from manufacturers in stock sizes. They are made available from the stock department, where rough stock, such as rods, bars, plates, sheet metal, and so on, is cut into sizes desired by the machine shop.

15.8. The machine shop. In general, the draftsman is more concerned with machine-shop processes than with the processes in other shops, as all castings and forgings that have been prepared in accordance with his drawings must receive their final machining in the machine shop. Since all machining operations must be considered in the design and then properly specified, a draftsman must be thoroughly familiar with the limitations as well as the possibilities of such common machines as the lathe, drill press, boring machine, shaper, planer, milling machine, and grinder. An explanation of the operation and capabilities of each machine will be given in the following sections.

15.9. The lathe. Many common operations, such as turning, facing, boring, reaming, knurling, threading, and so on, may be performed with

Fig. 15.3. Lathe operation—turning.

this widely used machine. In general, however, it is used principally for machining (roughing-out) cylindrical surfaces to be finished on a grinding machine. Removing metal from the exterior surfaces of cylindrical objects is known as turning and is accomplished by a sharp cutting tool that removes a thin layer of metal each time it travels the length of a cylindrical surface on the revolving work (Fig. 15.3). The piece, which is supported in the machine between two aligned centers, known as the *dead center* and the *live center*, is caused to rotate about an axis by power transmitted through a lathe dog, chuck, or a face plate. The work revolves against the cutting tool, held in a tool post, as the tool moves parallel to the longitudinal axis of the piece being turned. Cutting an interior surface is known as *boring* (Fig. 15.4). A note is not necessary on a drawing to indicate that a surface is to be turned on a lathe.

When a hole is reamed, it is finished very accurately with a fluted reamer of the exact required diameter. If the operation is performed on a lathe, the work revolves as the nonrotating reamer is fed into the hole by turning the handwheel on the tail stock. (See Fig. 15.5.)

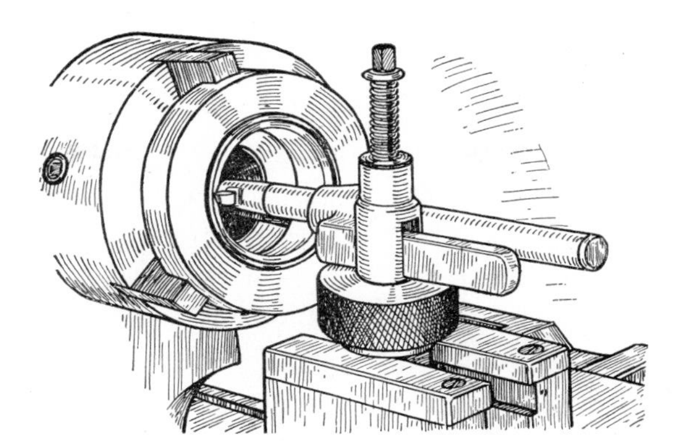

Fig. 15.4. Boring on a lathe.

Screw threads may be cut on a lathe by a cutting tool that has been ground to the shape required for the desired thread. The thread is cut as the tool travels parallel to the axis of the revolving work at a fixed speed (Fig. 15.6).

Fig. 15.5. Reaming on the lathe.

Knurling is the process of roughening or embossing a cylindrical surface. This is accomplished by means of a knurling tool containing knurl rollers that press into the surface of the work as it is fed across them (Fig. 15.7).

Fig. 15.6. Cutting threads on a lathe.

Fig. 15.7. Knurling.

15.10. The drill press. A drill press is a necessary piece of equipment in any shop because, although it is used principally for drilling, as the name implies (Fig. 15.8), other operations, such as reaming, counterboring, countersinking, and so on, may be performed on it by merely using the proper type of cutting tool. The cutting tool is held in position in a chuck and is made to revolve, through power from a motor or line shafting, at a particular speed suitable for the type of metal being drilled. The most flexible drill press, especially for large work, is the radial type, which is so designed that the spindle is mounted on a movable arm that can be revolved into any desired position for drilling. With this machine, holes may be drilled at various angles and locations without shifting the work, which may be either clamped to the horizontal table or held in a drill vise or drill jig. The ordinary type of drill press without a movable arm is usually found in most shops along with the radial type. A multiple-spindle drill is used for drilling a number of holes at the same time.

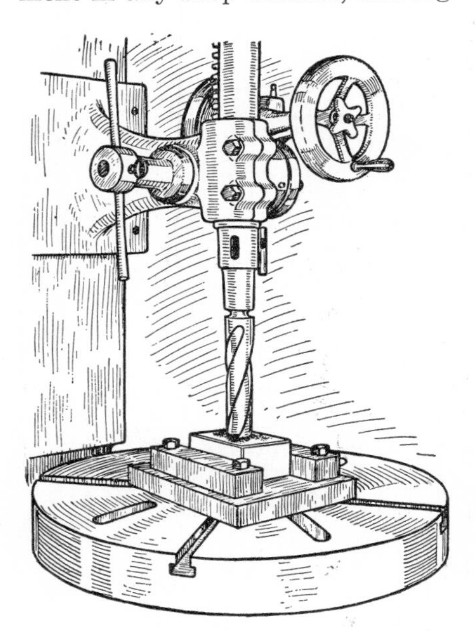

Fig. 15.8. A drill press.

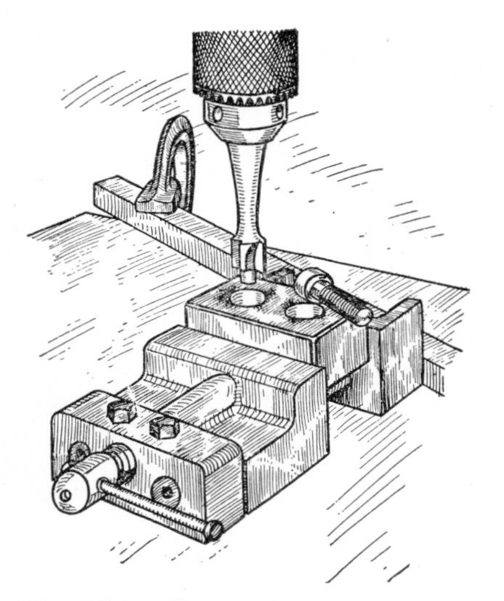

Fig. 15.9. Counterboring on a drill press.

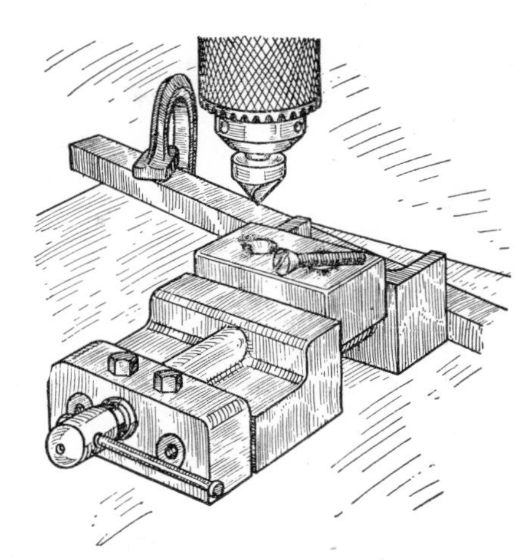

Fig. 15.10. Countersinking on a drill press.

Fig. 15.9 shows a setup on a drill press for performing the operation of counterboring. A counterbore is used to enlarge a hole to a depth that will allow the head of a fastener, such as a fillister-head cap screw, to be brought to the level of the surface of the piece through which it passes. A counterbore has a piloted end having approximately the same diameter as the drilled hole.

Fig. 15.10 shows a setup for the operation of countersinking. A countersink is used to form a tapering depression that will fit the head of a flat-head machine screw or cap screw and allow it to be brought to the level of the surface of the piece through which it passes.

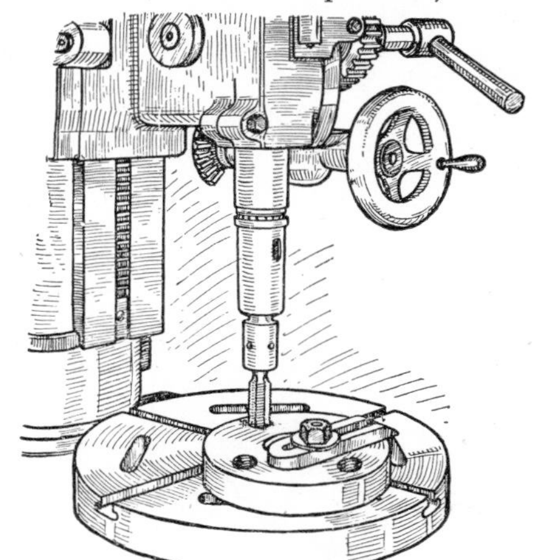

Fig. 15.11. Tapping on a drill press.

A plug tap is used to cut threads in a drilled hole (Fig. 15.11).

A spotfacer is used to finish a round spot that will provide a good seat for the head of a screw or bolt on the unfinished surface of a casting.

15.11. Hand reaming. A hole may be finished to an accurate size by hand reaming, as shown in Fig. 15.13. The reamer in this illustration is of a special type known as a *line reamer*.

15.12. Boring (Fig. 15.14). Boring is the operation of enlarging a

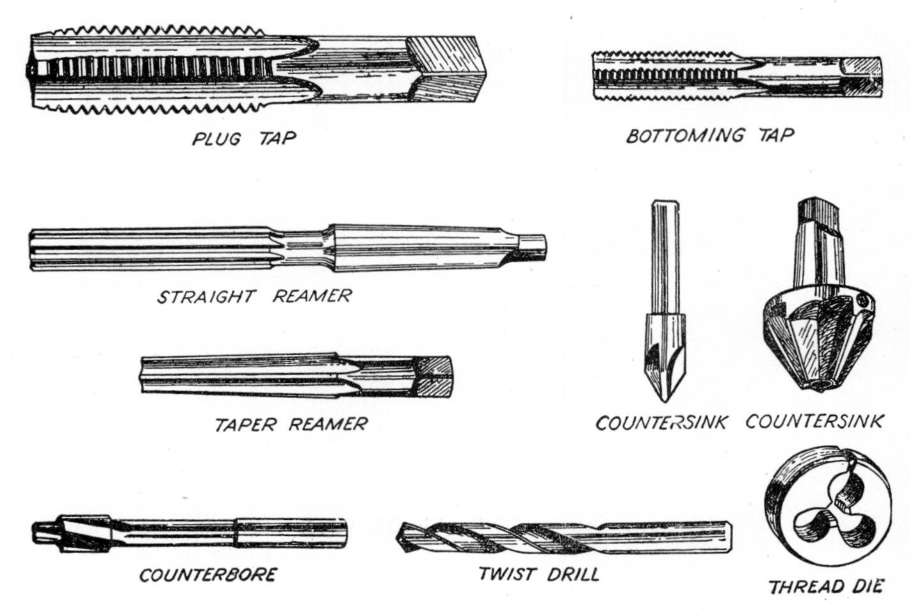

Fig. 15.12. Various cutting tools.

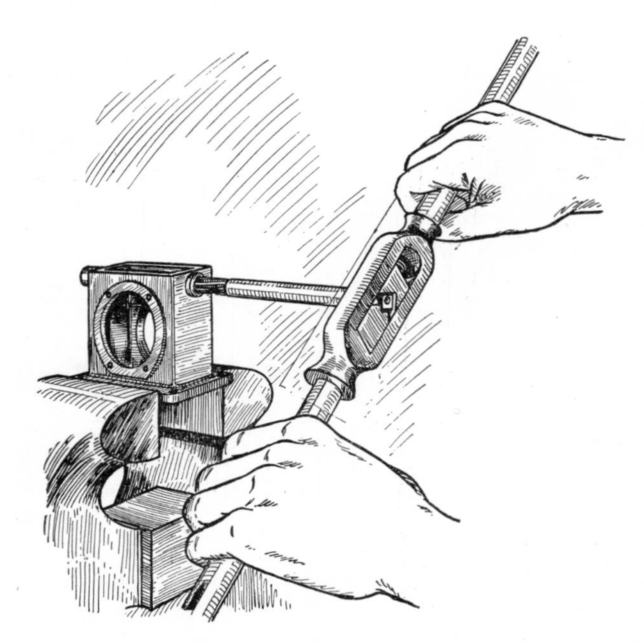

Fig. 15.13. Hand reaming.

circular hole for accuracy in roundness or straightness, and may be accomplished on a lathe, drill press, milling machine, or boring mill. When the hole is small and of considerable length, the operation may be performed on a lathe. If the hole is large, the work is usually done on a boring mill, of which there are two types—the vertical and the horizontal. On a vertical boring machine, the work is fastened on a horizontal revolving table, and the cutting tool or tools, which are stationary, advance vertically into it as the table revolves. On a horizontal boring machine, the tool revolves and the horizontal table upon which the work is fastened is stationary.

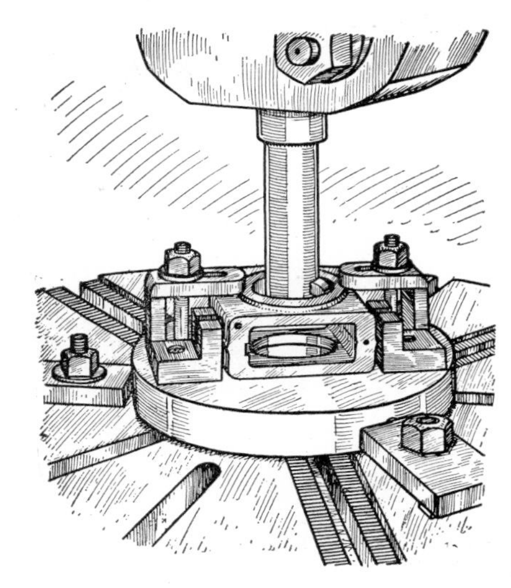

Fig. 15.14. Boring on a boring mill.

15.13. The milling machine. A milling machine is used for finishing plane surfaces and for milling gear teeth, slots, keyways, and so on. In finishing a plane surface, a rotating circular cutter removes the metal for a desired cut as the work, fastened to a moving horizontal bed, is automatically fed against it. Fig. 15.16 shows a setup for milling gear

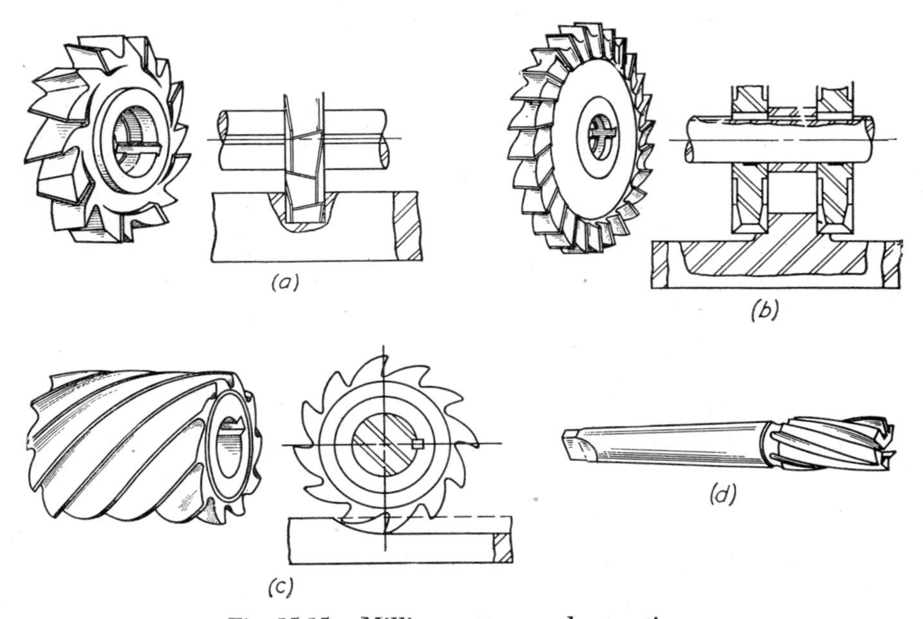

Fig. 15.15. Milling cutters and operations.

teeth in a gear blank. Note the form of this particular type of cutter. Several other types of milling cutters are shown in Fig. 15.15.

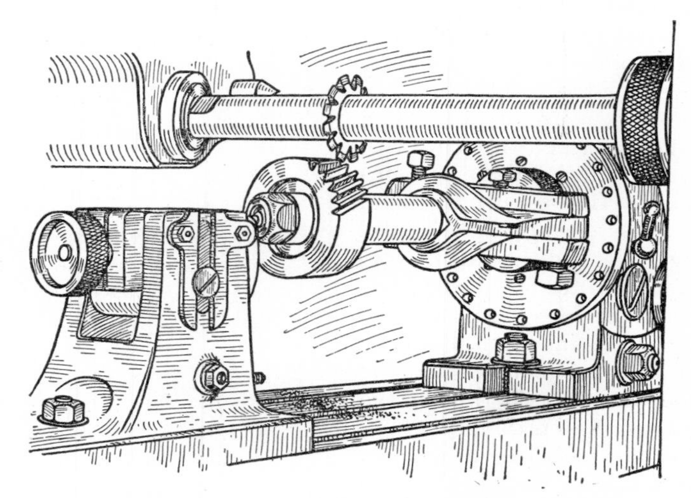

Fig. 15.16. Cutting gear teeth on a milling machine.

15.14. The shaper (Fig. 15.17). A shaper is used for finishing small plane surfaces and for cutting slots and grooves. In action, a fast-moving reciprocating ram carries a tool across the surface of the work, which is fastened to an adjustable horizontal table. The tool cuts only on the forward stroke.

Fig. 15.17. Shaper.

15.15. The planer. The planer is a machine particularly designed for cutting down and finishing large flat surfaces. The work is fastened to a long horizontal table that moves back and forth under the cutting tool. In action, the tool cuts as the table moves the surface against it. Unlike the cutter on the shaper, it is stationary except for a slight movement laterally for successive cuts.

15.16. The grinding machine. A grinding machine has a rotating grinding wheel that, ordinarily, is either an emery wheel (fine or coarse) or some type of high-speed wheel made of carborundum. Grinding consists in bringing the surface to be ground into contact with the wheel. Although grinding machines are often used for "roughing" and for grinding down projections and surfaces on castings, their principal use, as far as a draftsman is concerned, is for the final finishing operation to bring a piece of work down to accurate dimensions. Internal grinders are available for various purposes.

15.17. Polishing. Polishing consists of bringing a ground surface into contact with a revolving disc of leather or cloth, thus producing a lustrous smoothness that would be impossible to obtain by using even the finest grinding wheel. The operation is specified on a drawing by a note, "polish" or "grind and polish."

15.18. Broaching. A broach is a tool used to cut keyways and to form square, rectangular, hexagonal, or irregular-shaped holes. It is a hard, tempered steel shaft with serrated cutting edges that enlarge a drilled, punched, or cored hole to a required shape. Broaches are either pushed or pulled through the work. A special broaching machine is used for pulling broaches. Some form of press, hydraulic or otherwise, is required for push broaches.

15.19. Jigs and fixtures. Often, when an operation must be performed many times in making a part in quantities on a general machine, one of two devices, a *jig* or a *fixture*, may be used to facilitate production and insure accuracy without making repeated measurements. Although both jigs and fixtures fulfill the same general purpose, there is a distinguishing difference between them. A jig, for example, holds the work as it guides the tool and, ordinarily, is not fixed to the machine. A fixture, on the other hand, is rigidly fastened to a machine and holds the work in position without acting as a guide for the cutting tools.

Since most large manufacturing concerns have special departments for designing jigs and fixtures, the ordinary draftsman is not directly concerned with these auxiliary devices when he is preparing working drawings.

15.20. Special production machines. In large industrial concerns, most mechanical parts are made on specialized machines by semiskilled operators. A discussion of even a few of these, however, is beyond the scope of a general drawing text in which each subject is limited to a few pages. Since most specialized mass-production machines operate on the same general principles as the general-purpose machines, a young engineering draftsman should be able to determine their limitations and capabilities through observation, if he has a general knowledge of such machines as the lathe, shaper, drill press, milling machine, and so on. No prospective designer or draftsman should ever forego an opportunity to observe special production machines. He must have a thorough understanding of all shop machines and methods, if his drawings are to be satisfactory for the shops.

15.21. Measuring tools. Figs. 15.18, 15.19, and 15.20 show a few of the measuring tools commonly available in shops. When great accuracy is not required, calipers are used (Fig. 15.19). The outside calipers are suited for taking external measurements, as for example from a shaft. They are adjusted to fit the piece, and then the setting is applied to a rule to make a reading. The inside calipers have out-turned toes, which fits them for taking internal measurements, as for example in measuring either a cylindrical or a rectangular hole. When extreme accuracy is required, some form of micrometer calipers may be used (Fig. 15.20).

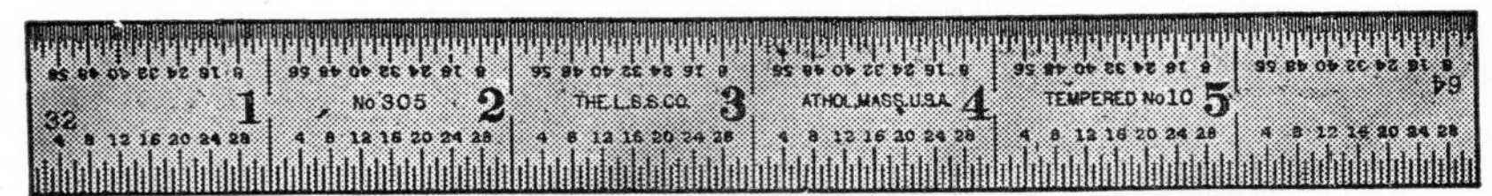

Quick Reading with Decimal Equivalents

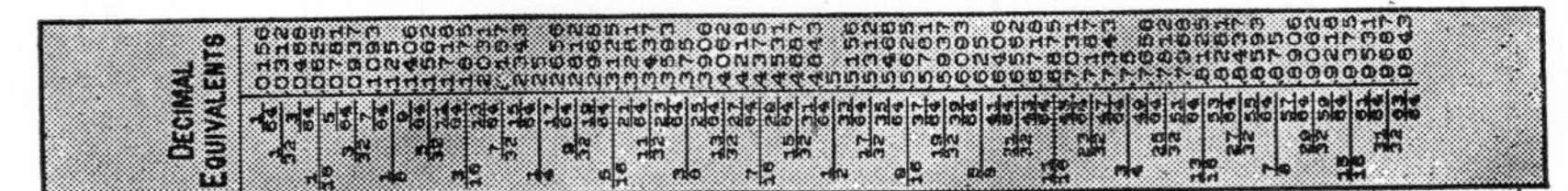

Fig. 15.18. The steel rule.

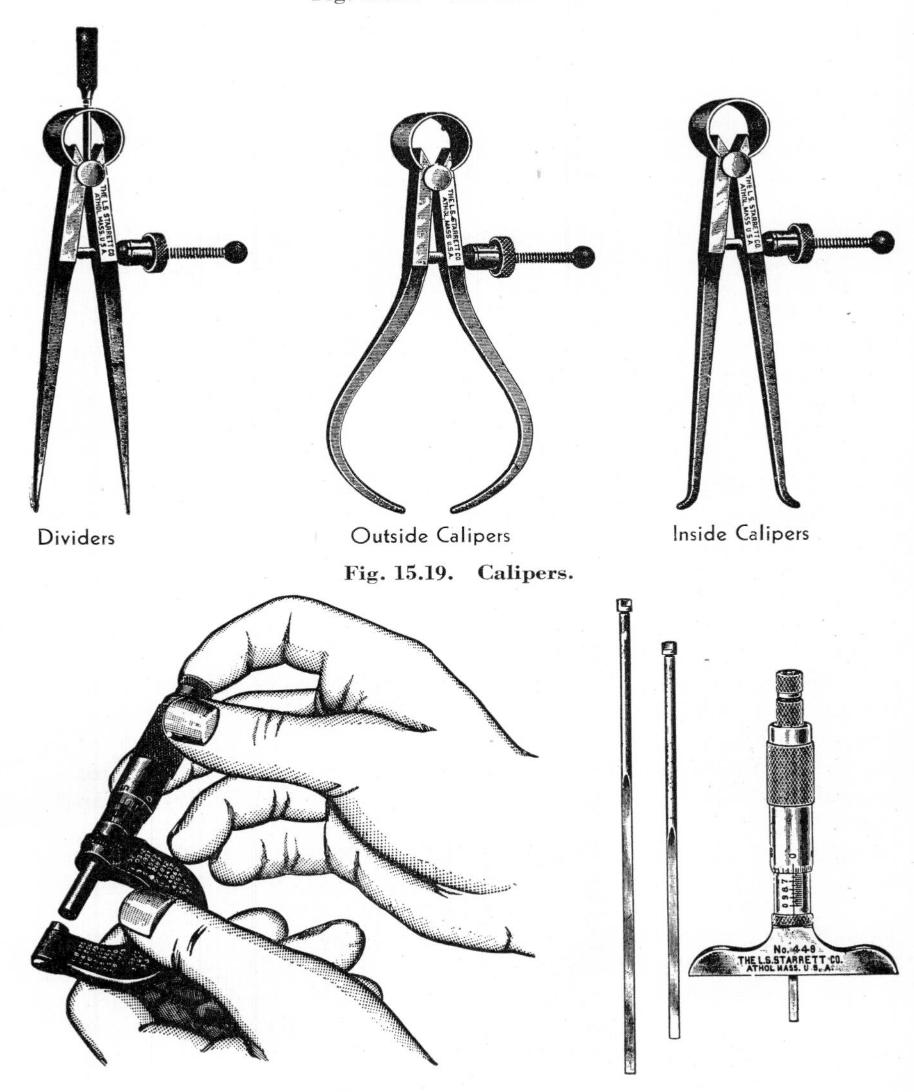

Fig. 15.19. Calipers.

Fig. 15.20. Micrometers.

16 DIMENSIONING

16.1. A detail drawing, in addition to giving the shape of a part, must furnish the workman with information on the distances between surfaces, locations of holes, kind of finish, type of material, number required, and so forth. The expression of this information on a drawing by the use of lines, symbols, figures, and notes is known as dimensioning.

Intelligent dimensioning requires engineering judgment and a thorough knowledge of the practices of pattern making, forging, and machining. It should be remembered that the shopman must be able to produce the part exactly as it is designed and shown on the blueprint. He should not be required to seek additional information, add or subtract dimensions, or use his judgment about a class of fit. The dimensions given are not those used in the design or in making the drawing. Instead, they are the ones required by the shopman and should be placed with that in mind.

In order to satisfy each craftsman's demands, the draftsman must first review the object represented and decide upon the production procedures necessary to create the part. Then, he mentally should follow it through all of these processes in order to determine the required dimensions, being careful to locate each dimension where the mechanic or pattern maker will expect to find it. In brief, a drawing should be so dimensioned that the work may be done as economically and conveniently as possible.

16.2. Theory of dimensioning. Any part may be dimensioned easily and systematically by dividing it into simple geometrical solids. Even complicated parts, when analyzed, usually are found to be composed principally of cylinders and prisms and, frequently, frustums of pyramids and cones. The dimensioning of an object may be accomplished by dimensioning each elemental form to indicate its size and relative location from a center line, base line, or finished surface. A machine drawing requires two types of dimensions: *size dimensions* and *location dimensions.*

16.3. Size dimensions (Figs. 16.2 and 16.3). Size dimensions give the size of a piece, component part, hole, or slot.

Fig. 16.1 should be carefully analyzed, as the placement of dimensions shown is applicable to the elemental parts of almost every piece.

The rule for placing the three principal dimensions (length, height, and depth) on the drawing of a prism or modification of a prism is: *Give two dimensions on the principal view and one dimension on one of the other views.*

The circular cylinder, which appears as a boss or shaft, requires only *the diameter and length, both of which are shown preferably on the rectangular view.* It is better practice to dimension a hole (negative cylinder) by giving the diameter and operation as a note on the contour view with a leader to the circle (Figs. 16.5 and 16.60).

Cones are dimensioned by giving the diameter of the base and the altitude on the same view. A taper is one example of a conical shape found on machine parts (Fig. 16.57).

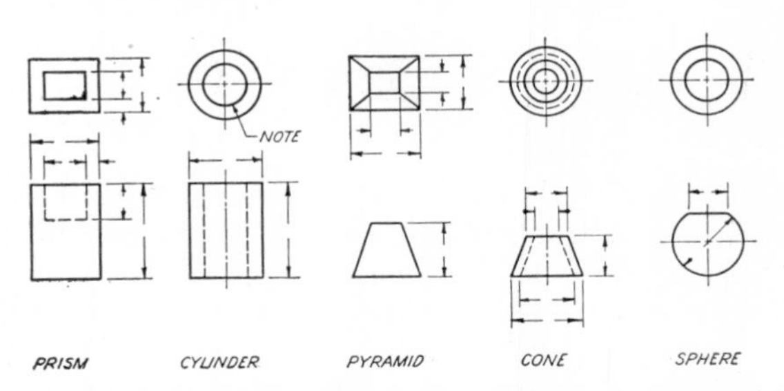

Fig. 16.1. Dimensioning geometrical shapes.

Pyramids, which frequently form a part of a structure, are dimensioned by giving two dimensions on the view showing the shape of the base. A sphere requires only the diameter.

16.4. Location dimensions. Location dimensions fix the relationship of the component parts (projections, holes, slots, and other significant forms) of a piece or structure. Particular care must be exercised in their selection and placing, because upon them depend the accuracy of the operations in making a piece and the proper mating of the piece with other parts. To select location dimensions intelligently, the draftsman should determine the contact surfaces, finished surfaces, and center lines of the

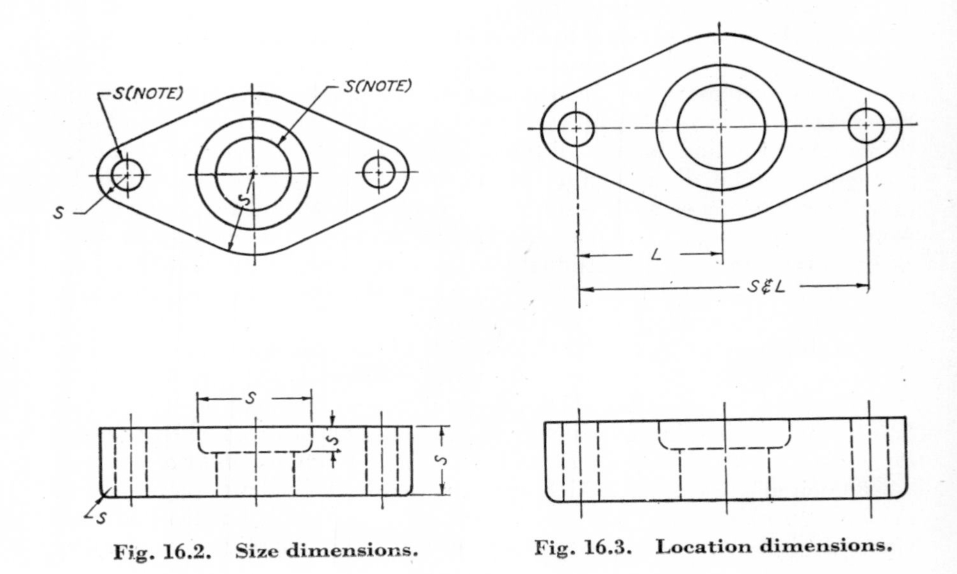

Fig. 16.2. Size dimensions. **Fig. 16.3. Location dimensions.**

elementary geometrical forms and, with the accuracy demanded and the method of production in mind, decide from what other surface or center line each should be located. Mating location dimensions must be given from the same center line or finished surface on both pieces.

Location dimensions are given center to center, surface to center, or surface to surface. Fig. 16.4 illustrates each of these cases.

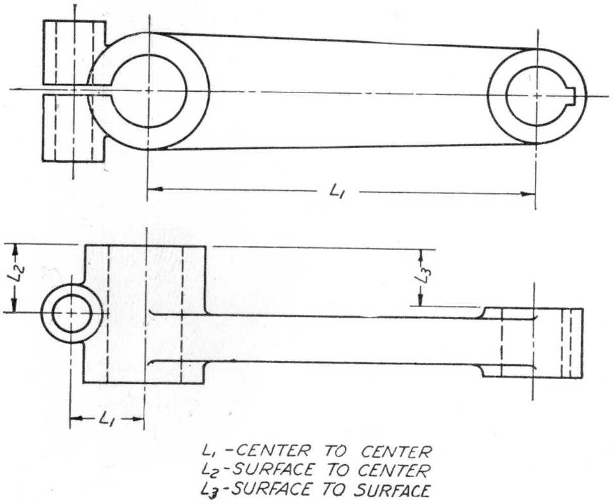

L_1 -CENTER TO CENTER
L_2-SURFACE TO CENTER
L_3-SURFACE TO SURFACE

Fig. 16.4. Types of location dimensions.

16.5. Procedure in dimensioning. The theory of dimensioning may be applied in six steps, as follows:

1. Mentally divide the object into its component geometrical shapes.
2. Place the size dimensions on each form.
3. Select the locating center lines and surfaces after giving careful consideration to mating parts and to the processes of manufacture.
4. Place the location dimensions so that each geometrical form is located from a center line or finished surface.
5. Add the over-all dimensions. (These are usually the summation of the included dimensions in the direction of the length, height, and depth.)
6. Complete the dimensioning by adding the necessary notes.

If the foregoing procedure is followed in the order stated, all required dimensions will have been given. Its application to the *rod support* (Fig. 16.5) gives the following results:

1. The piece is analyzed as a positive cylinder, three negative cylinders, and three positive prisms.
2. The size dimensions required on the component geometrical forms are designated by the letter *S*. Observe that a note serves as the size dimension for the hole (negative cylinder)
3. The finished surface of the base was selected as a locating surface.
4. From this surface, a location dimension designated by the letter *L*

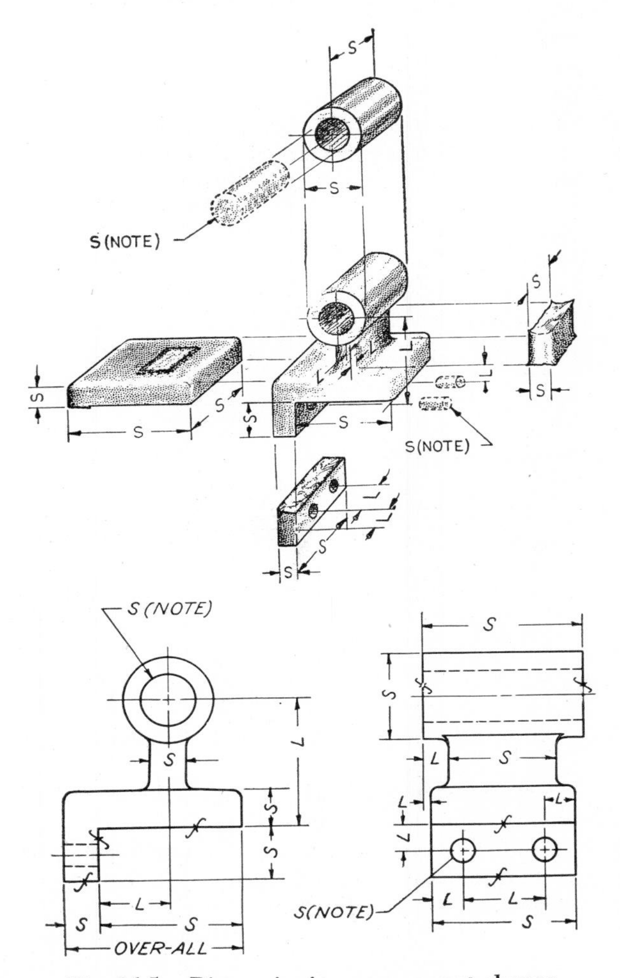

Fig. 16.5. Dimensioning component shapes.

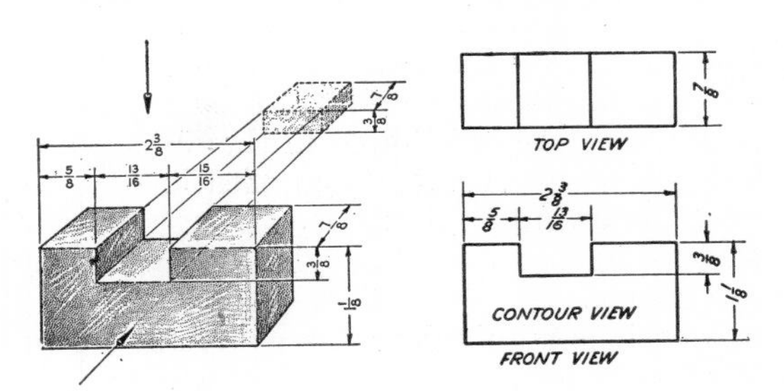

Fig. 16.6. Placing dimensions.

is placed as shown, in order to locate accurately the axis of the hole in relation to this contact surface.

5. Over-all dimensions and size dimensions (length and depth) are the same for the piece. Since the top of the object is cylindrical, no over-all height dimension should be shown. (See rule 16, Sec. 16.8.)

6. The notes complete the dimensioning of the drawing.

16.6. Placing dimensions. Dimensions must be placed where they will be most easily understood—in the locations where the shopman will expect to find them. They generally are attached to the view that shows the contour of the features to which they apply, and a majority of them usually will appear on the principal view (Fig. 16.6). Except in cases where special convenience and ease in reading are desired, or when a dimension would be so far from the form to which it referred that it might be misinterpreted, dimensions should be placed outside a view. They should appear directly on a view only when clarity demands.

All extensions and dimension lines should be drawn before the arrowheads have been filled in or the dimensions, notes, and titles have been lettered. Spacing dimension lines $\frac{1}{2}''$ from the view and $\frac{3}{8}''$ from each other provides an ample distance to satisfy the one rule to which there is no exception: *Never crowd dimensions.* Although it sometimes may be necessary to reduce the distance between dimension lines to a minimum of $\frac{1}{4}''$, the spacing should be uniform throughout. If the location of a dimension forces a poor location on other dimensions, its shifting may allow all to be placed more advantageously without sacrificing clearness. Important location dimensions should be given where they will be conspicuous, even if a size dimension must be moved.

DIMENSIONING PRACTICES

16.7. A generally recognized system of lines, symbols, figures, and notes is used to indicate size and location. Fig. 16.8 illustrates dimensioning terms and notation.

Fig. 16.7. A dimension line.

A *dimension line* is lightweight and continuous, broken only near the center to receive the figure giving the distance that it indicates. It is terminated at each end by an arrowhead whose point touches the extension line (Fig. 16.8).

Extension lines are light continuous lines extending from a view to indicate the extent of a measurement given by a dimension line that is located outside of a view. They start $\frac{1}{16}''$ from the view and extend $\frac{1}{8}''$ beyond the dimension line (Fig. 16.8).

Arrowheads are drawn for each dimension line, before the figures are lettered. They are made with the same pen or pencil used for the letter-

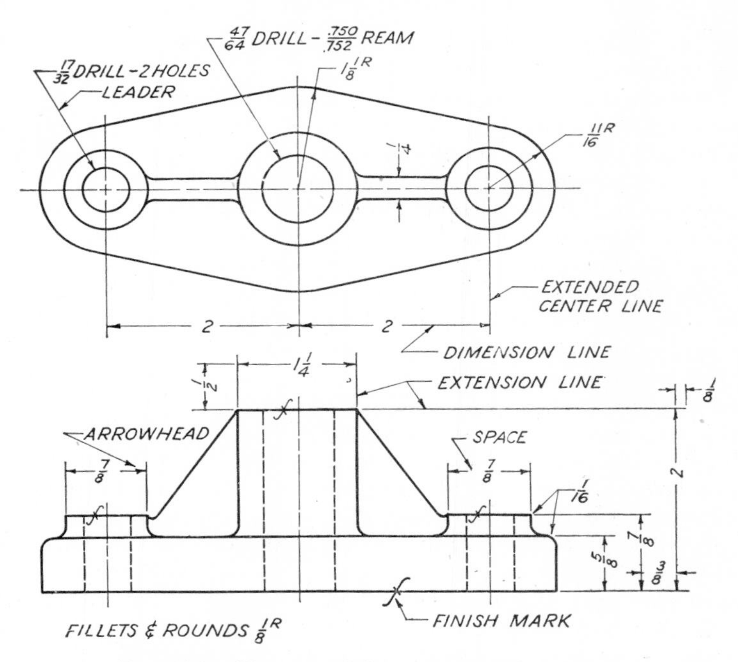

Fig. 16.8. Term and dimensioning notation.

ing. The size of an arrowhead, although it may vary with the size of a drawing, should be uniform on any one drawing. To have the proper proportions, the length of an arrowhead must be approximately three times its spread (American Standard). This length for average work is usually

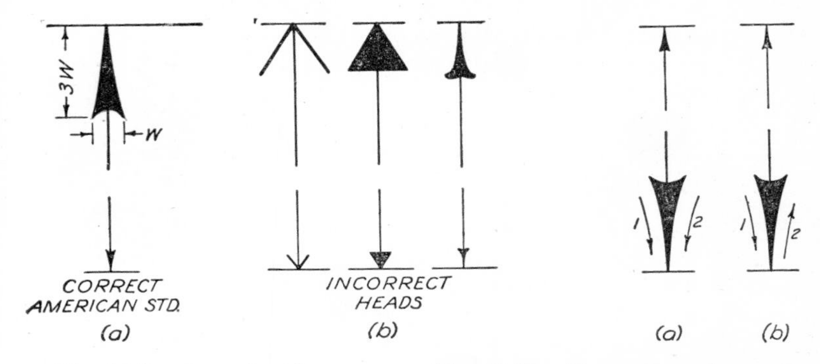

Fig. 16.9. Arrowheads. **Fig. 16.10. Formation of arrowheads.**

$\frac{1}{8}''$. Fig. 16.9 shows enlarged drawings of both correct and incorrect heads. Use of any one of the incorrect shapes should be avoided, for it may ruin what otherwise would be a well-executed drawing. Although many draftsmen draw an arrowhead with one stroke, the beginner will get better results by using two slightly concaved strokes drawn toward the point (Fig. 16.10*a*) or, as shown in Fig. 16.10(*b*), one stroke drawn to the point and one away from it.

A *leader* or *pointer* is a light continuous line (terminated by an arrowhead) that extends from a note to the feature of a piece to which the note applies (Fig. 16.11). It should be made with a straightedge and should not be curved or made freehand (American Standard's recommen dation).

A leader pointing to a curve should be radial, and the first $\frac{1}{8}''$ of it should be in line with the note (Fig. 16.11).

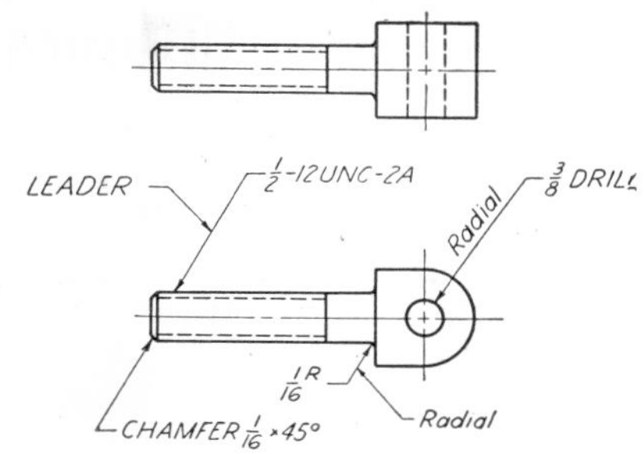

Fig. 16.11. A leader.

Finish marks indicate the particular surfaces of a rough casting or forging that are to be machined or "finished." They are placed in all views, across the visible or invisible lines that are the edge views of surfaces to be machined (Fig. 16.13).

The modified italic *f*, shown in Fig. 16.12(*a*), is still widely used in spite of the fact that new forms have been recommended by the American Standards Association. The student will find that careful adherence to the dimensions illustrated here will improve the appearance of those on his drawing.

Fig. 16.12(*b*) shows the ASA recommended 60 degree *V* with its point touching the line view of the surface to be machined. In commercial practice a code letter oftentimes is used to indicate the type of machining required. The code letter or letters are placed in the *V* as shown in (*c*).

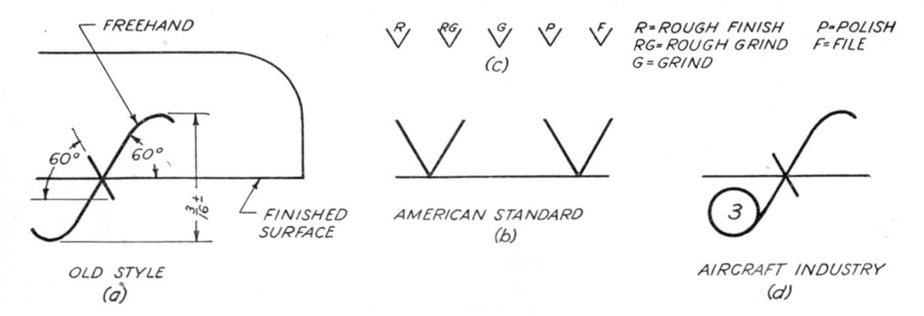

Fig. 16.12. Finish marks.

Fig. 16.12(*d*) shows the type of finish mark used by some aircraft companies. The numeral in the circle expresses the type of finish.

It is not necessary to show finish marks on drilled or reamed holes, when the finish is specified as an operation in a note, such as $\frac{3}{4}''$ Drill or 1″ Ream. They are also omitted, and a title note, "finish all over," is substituted, if the piece is to be completely machined. Finish marks are not required when decimal dimensions are used.

Dimension figures should be lettered either horizontal or vertical with the whole numbers equal in height to the capital letters in the notes. Guide lines and slope lines must be used and should be drawn with the Braddock Triangle, as shown in Fig. 5.8. The holes illustrated in this figure give $\frac{1}{8}''$ whole numbers and $\frac{1}{4}''$ fractions, the usual heights for

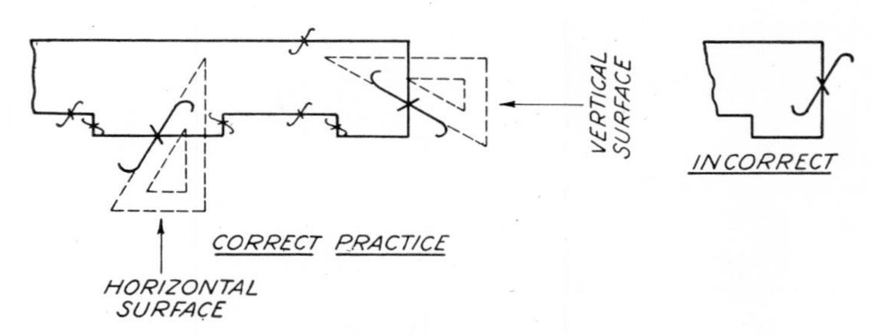

Fig. 16.13. Placing *f* marks.

ordinary working drawings. Figures must be legible; otherwise, they might be misinterpreted in the shop and cause errors which would be embarrassing to the draftsman.

16.8. General dimensioning practices.

The reasonable application of the selected dimensioning practices that follow should enable a student to dimension acceptably. The practices in

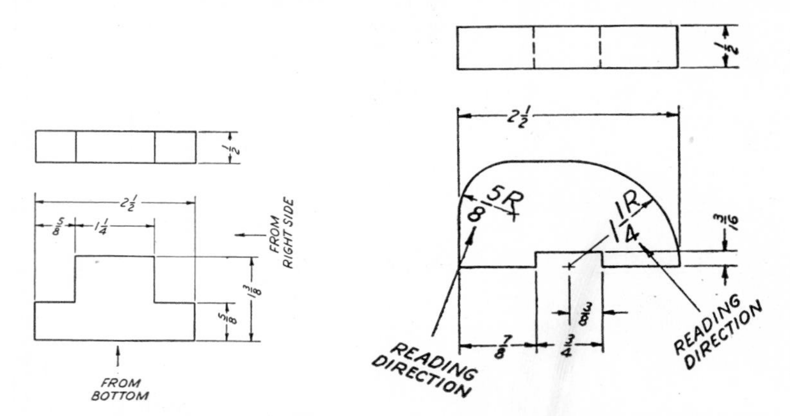

Fig. 16.14. Reading dimensions.

Fig. 16.15. Reading oblique directions.

boldfaced type should never be violated. In fact, these have been so definitely established by practice that they might be called rules.

1. Place dimensions so that they can be read from the bottom and right side of the drawing (Figs. 16.14 and 16.15). An exception to this rule should be made in the preparation of drawings in the aircraft and automotive fields. These industries, along with a few manufacturing firms in other fields, use the unidirectional system under which all dimensions are made to read from the bottom of the sheet (Fig. 16.16). This system is also suitable for very large drawings.

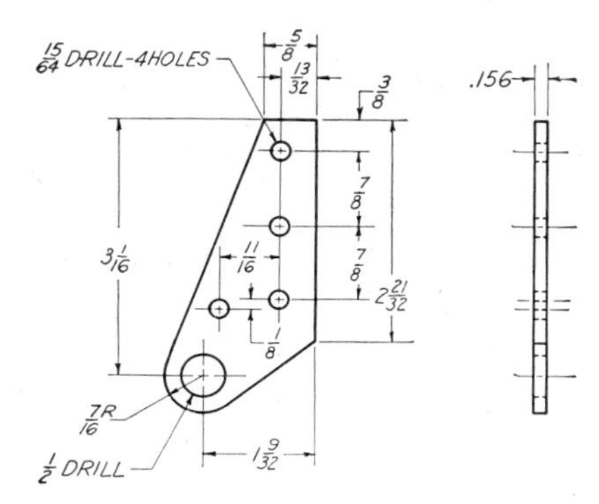

Fig. 16.16. Unidirectional system.

2. Place dimensions outside a view, unless they will be more easily and quickly understood if shown on it (Fig. 16.17).

3. Place dimensions between views unless the rules such as the contour rule, the rule against crowding, and so forth, prevent their being so placed.

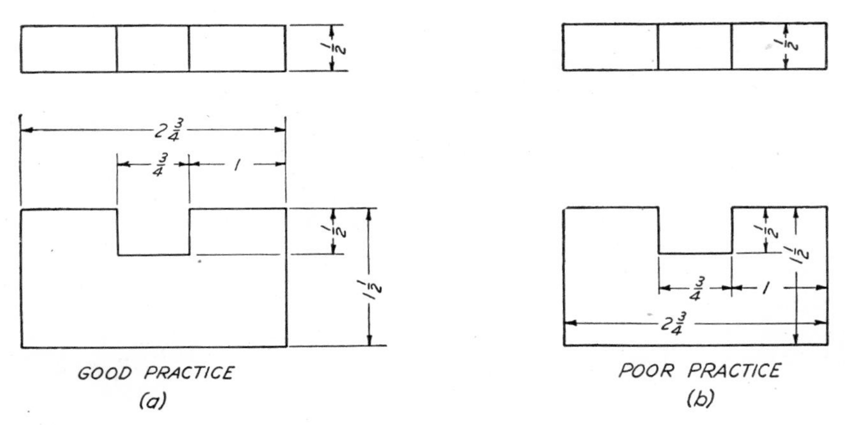

Fig. 16.17. Placing dimensions.

4. **Do not use an object line or a center line as a dimension line.**

5. Locate dimension lines so that they will not cross extension lines.

6. If possible, avoid crossing two dimension lines.

7. A center line may be extended to serve as an extension line (Fig. 16.18).

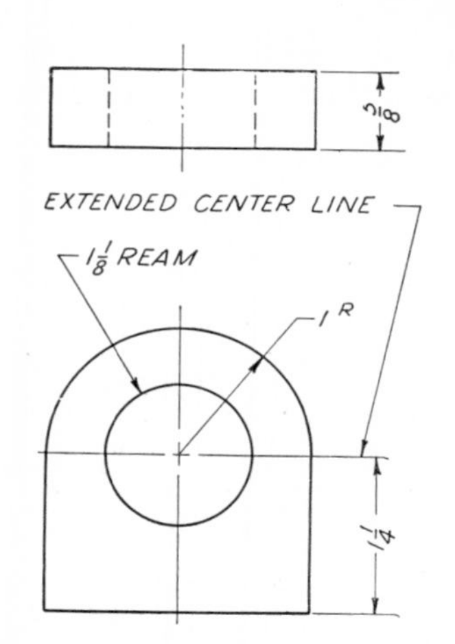

Fig. 16.18. Extended center line.

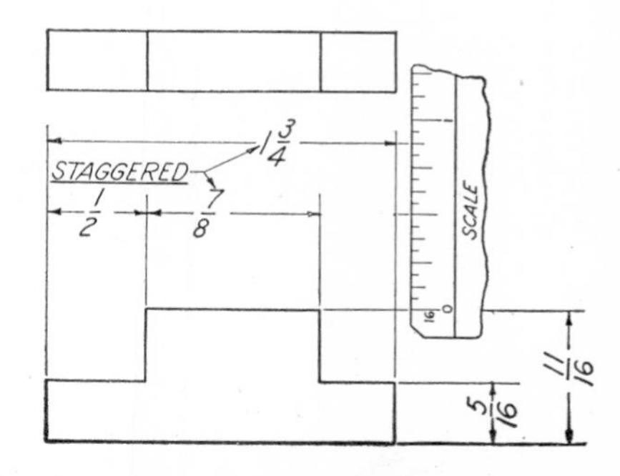

Fig. 16.19. Spacing dimension lines.

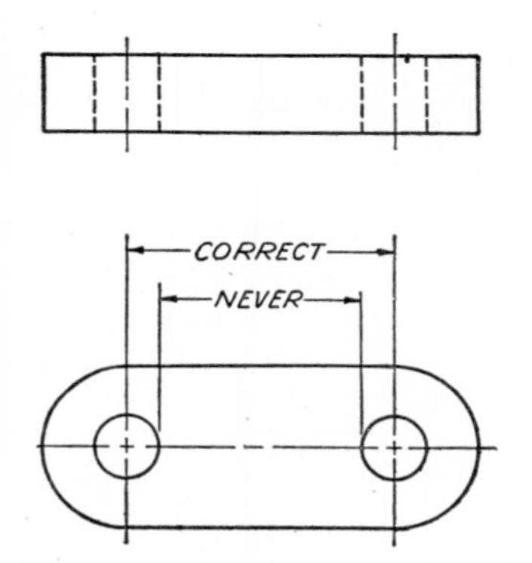

Fig. 16.20. Locating holes.

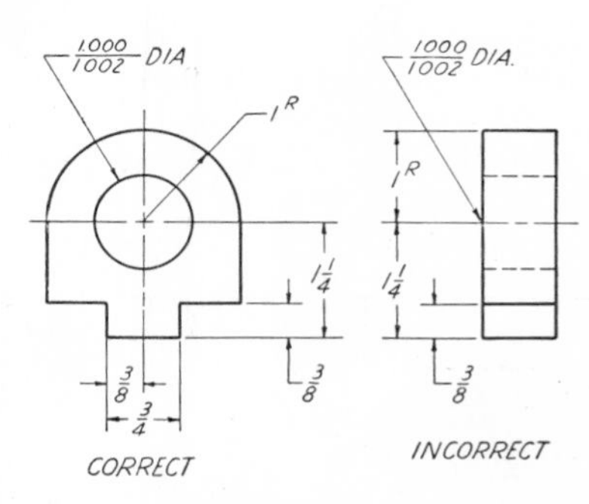

Fig. 16.21. Contour principle of dimensioning.

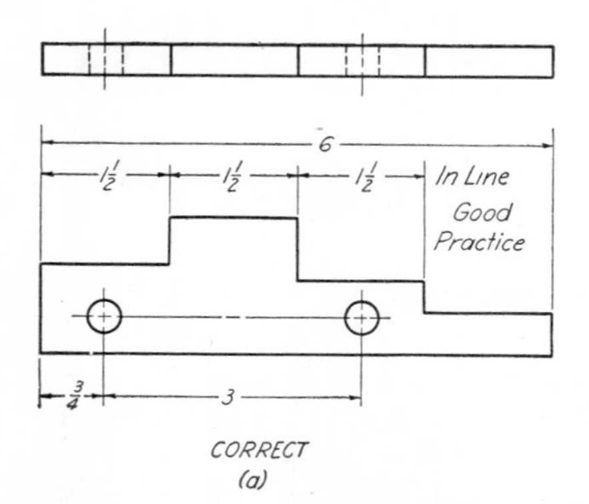

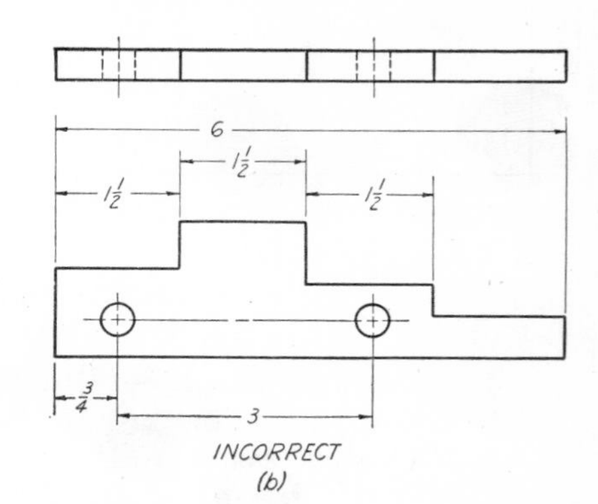

Fig. 16.22. Consecutive dimensions.

8. Keep parallel dimensions equally spaced (usually $\frac{3}{8}''$ apart) and the figures staggered (see Fig. 16.19).

9. Always give locating dimensions to the centers of circles that represent holes, cylindrical projections, or bosses (Fig. 16.20).

10. If possible, attach the location dimensions for holes to the view upon which they appear as circles.

11. Group related dimensions on the view showing the contour of a feature (Fig. 16.21).

12. Arrange a series of dimensions in a continuous line (Fig. 16.22).

13. Dimension from a finished surface, center line, or base line that can be readily established (Fig. 16.23).

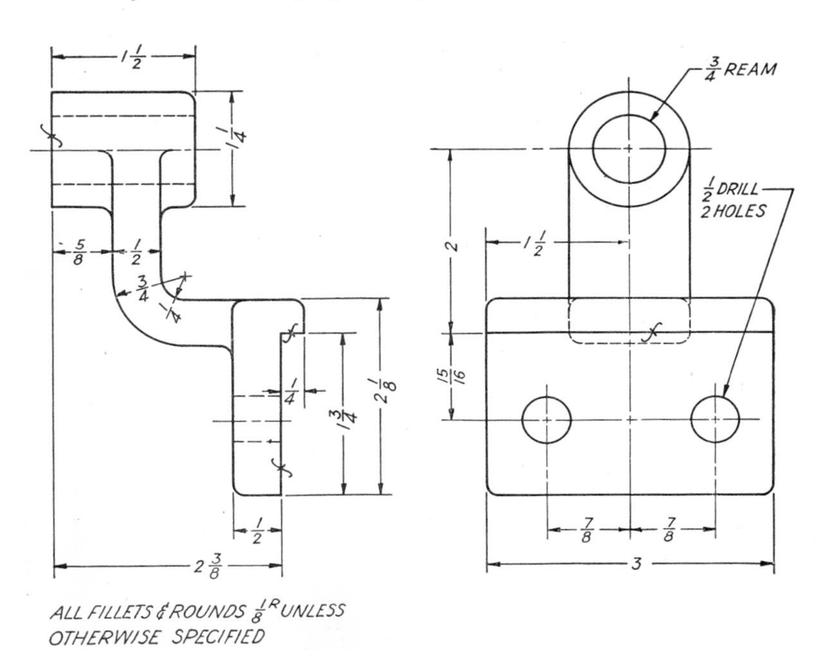

Fig. 16.23. Dimensioning a bracket.

14. Stagger the figures in a series of parallel dimension lines to allow sufficient space for the figures and to prevent confusion (Fig. 16.24).

15. Place longer dimensions outside shorter ones so that extension lines will not cross dimension lines (Fig. 16.25).

16. Give three over-all dimensions located outside any other dimensions (unless the piece has cylindrical ends).

17. When an over-all is given, one intermediate distance should be omitted unless noted (REF.) as being given for reference (Fig. 16.26).

18. Do not repeat a dimension. One of the duplicated dimensions may be missed if a change is made. Give only those dimensions that are necessary to produce or inspect the part.

19. Make decimal points of a sufficient size so that dimensions cannot be misread.

20. When dimension figures appear on a sectional view, show them in a small uncrosshatched portion so that they may be easily read. This may be accomplished by doing the section lining after the dimensioning has been completed (Fig. 16.27).

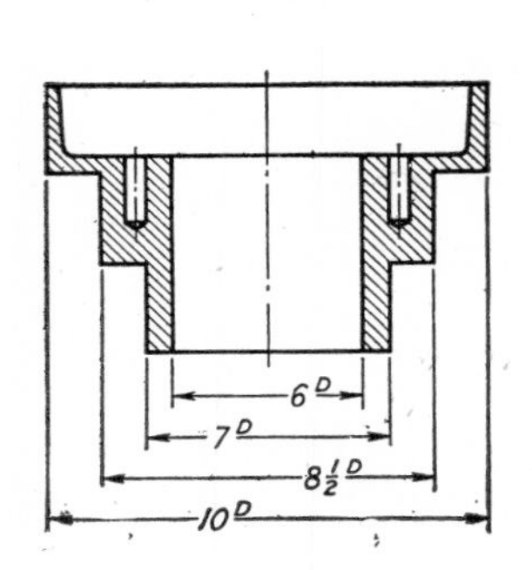

Fig. 16.24. Parallel dimensions.

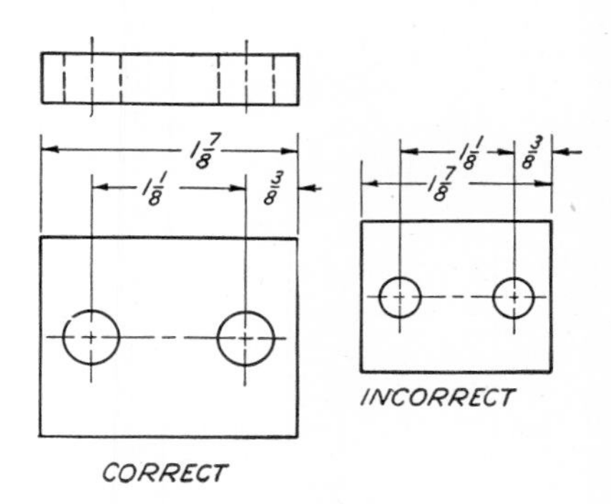

Fig. 16.25. Long and short dimensions.

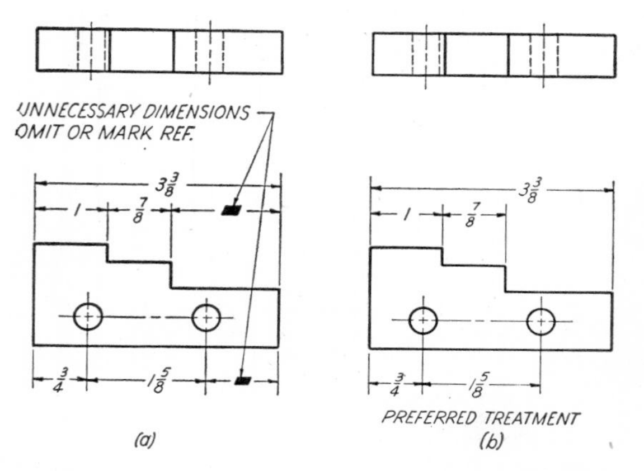

Fig. 16.26. Omit unnecessary dimensions.

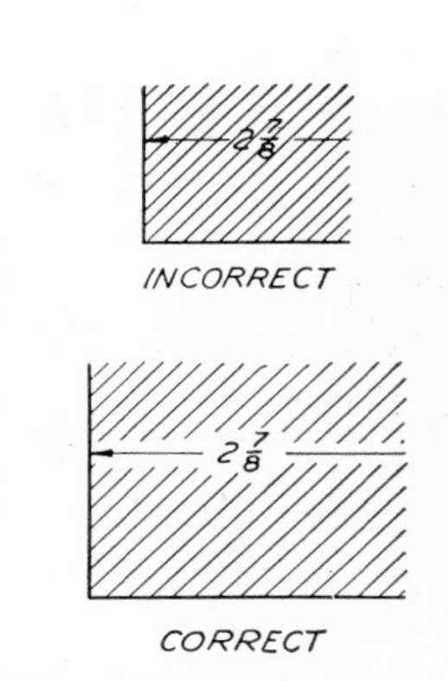

Fig. 16.27. Dimension figures on a section view.

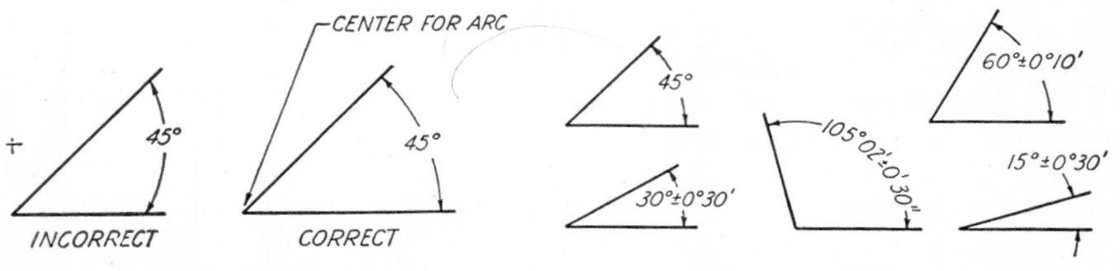

Fig. 16.28. To dimension an angle.

Fig. 16.29. Angular dimensions.

21. When an arc is used as a dimension line for an angular measurement, use the vertex of the angle as the center (Fig. 16.28).

22. Place the figures of angular dimensions so they will read from the bottom of a drawing, except in the case of large angles (Fig. 16.29).

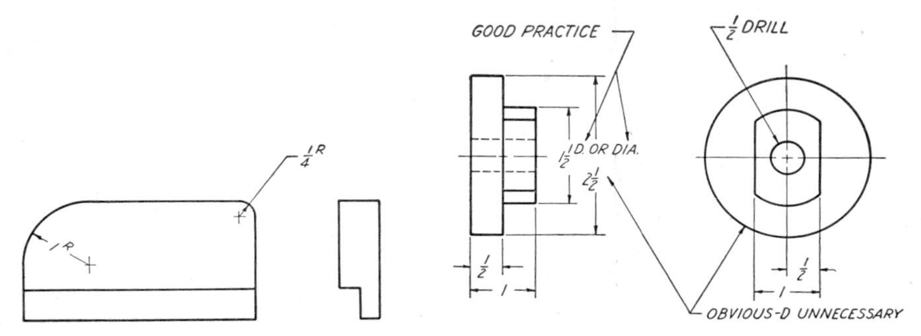

Fig. 16.30. Dimensioning radii. **Fig. 16.31. Dimensioning a cylindrical piece.**

23. Always dimension an arc by giving its radius followed by the abbreviation *R*, and indicate the center with a small cross. (Note that the arrowhead is omitted at the center (Fig. 16.30).)

24. Show the diameter of a circle, never the radius. If it is not clear that the dimension is a diameter, the figures should be followed by the abbreviation *D* (Figs. 16.31 and 16.32). Often this will allow the elimination of one view.

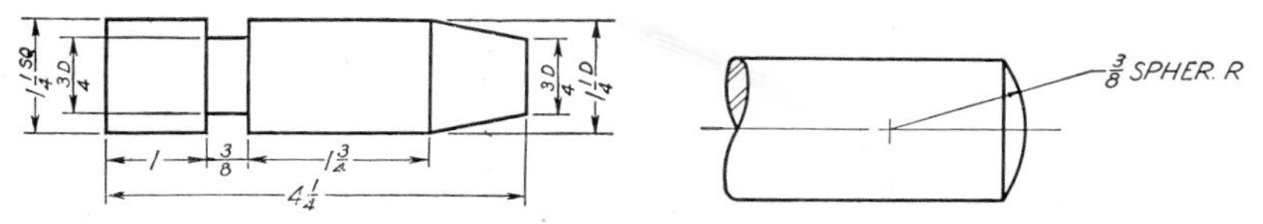

Fig. 16.32. Use of "D" in dimensioning cylindrical shapes.* **Fig. 16.33. Dimensioning a piece with a spherical end.**

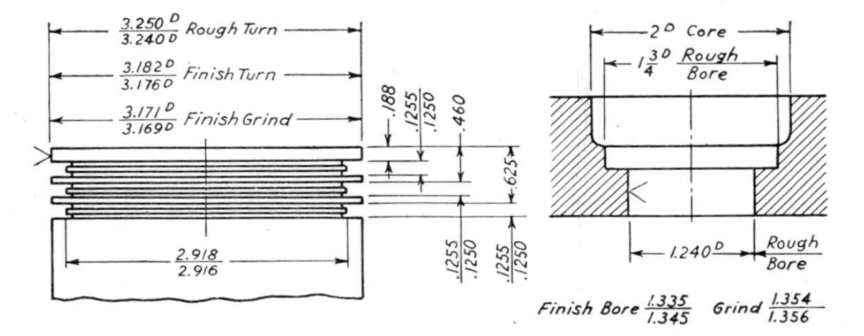

Fig. 16.34. Dimensioning machined holes and cylinders.*

* ASA Z14.1–1946.

25. When dimensioning a portion of a sphere with a radius the term SPHER. R is added (Fig. 16.33).

26. Letter all notes horizontally.

27. Make dimensioning complete, so that it will not be necessary for a workman to add or subtract to obtain a desired dimension or to scale the drawing.

28. Letter the word *bore* or *core* with the diameter of bored or cored holes (Fig. 16.34).

29. Give the diameter of a circular hole, never the radius, because all hole-forming tools are specified by diameter. If the hole does not go through the piece, the depth may be given as a note (Fig. 16.35).

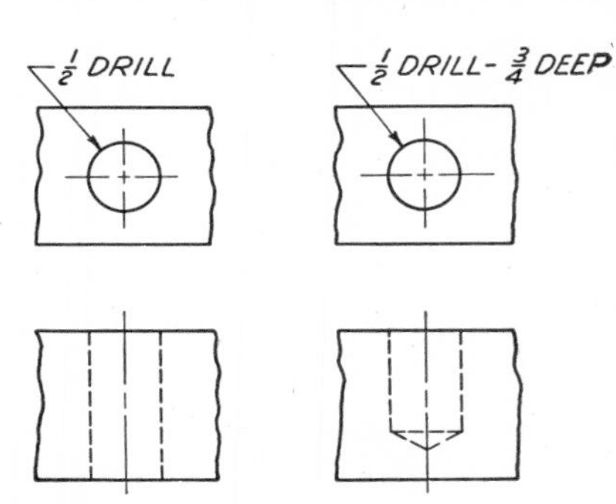

Fig. 16.35. Dimensioning holes.

30. Never crowd dimensions into small spaces. Use the practical methods suggested in Fig. 16.36.

31. Avoid placing inclined dimensions in the shaded areas shown in Fig. 16.37. Place them so that they may be conveniently read from the right side of the drawing. If this is not desirable, make the figures read from the left in the direction of the dimension line (Fig. 16.38(*a*)). The unidirectional method is shown in (*b*)

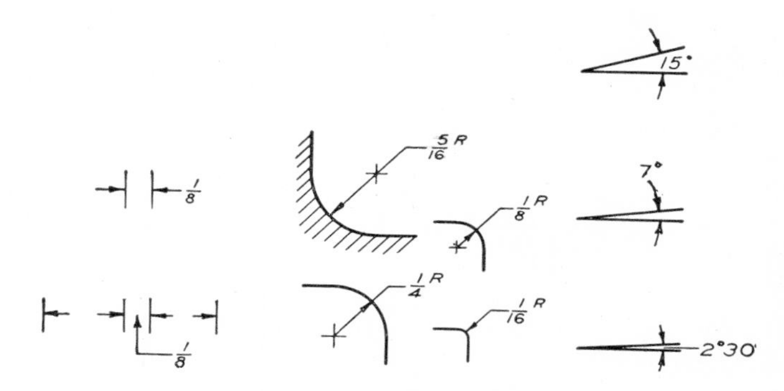

Fig. 16.36. Dimensioning in limited spaces.

32. Omit superfluous dimensions. Do not supply dimensional information for the same feature in two different ways (Fig. 16.39).

33. Give dimensions up to 72″ in inches, except on structural and architectural drawings (Fig. 16.40). Omit the inch marks when all dimensions are in inches.

34. Show dimensions in feet and inches as illustrated in Fig. 16.41. Note that the use of the hyphen in (*a*) and (*b*), and the cipher in (*b*), eliminates any chance of uncertainty and misinterpretation.

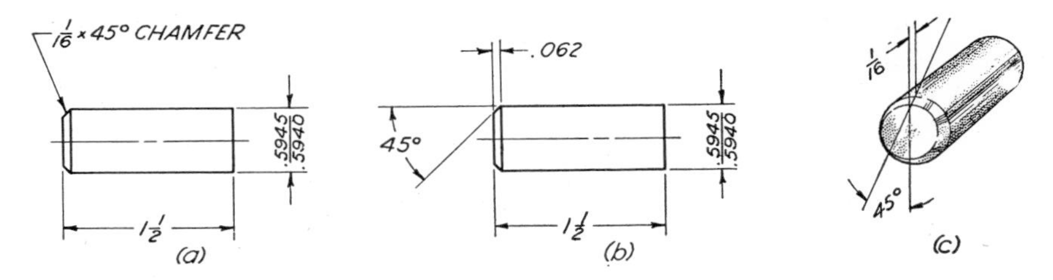

Fig. 16.42. Dimensioning a chamfer.

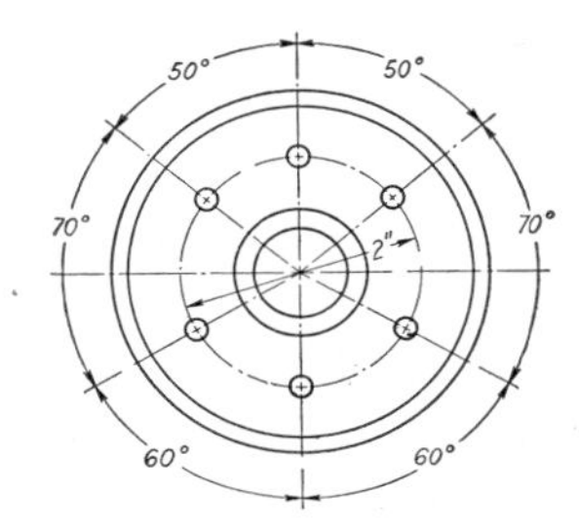

Fig. 16.43. Unequally spaced holes.*

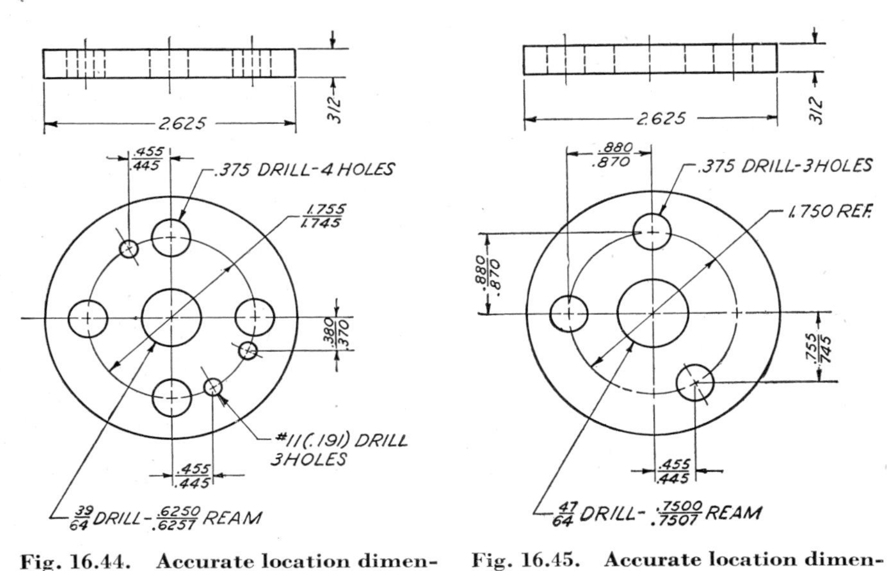

Fig. 16.44. Accurate location dimensioning of holes.

Fig. 16.45. Accurate location dimensioning of holes.

* ASA Z14.1–1946.

42. Dimension, as required by the method of production, a piece with rounded ends. (See Figs. 16.49–16.51.)

(a) Give radii and center-to-center distance on parts that would be laid out by using centers and radii. Do not show an over-all dimension. It is not required. (See Fig. 16.49.)

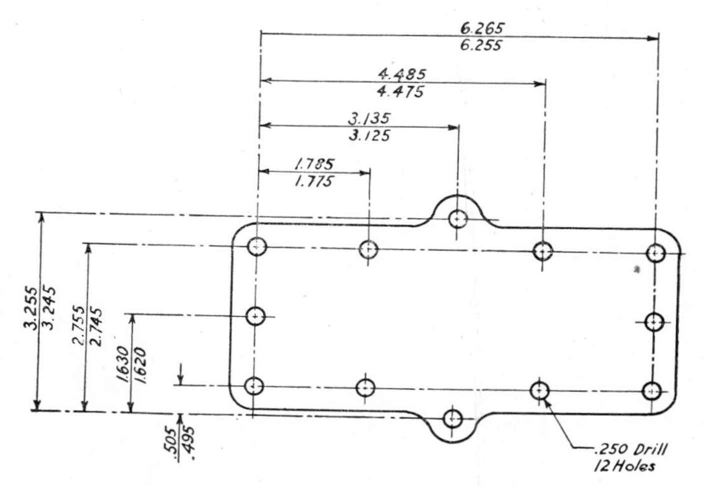

Fig. 16.46. Location dimensioning of holes.*

(b) Slots that are to provide for adjustment are dimensioned by over-all length and width dimensions and are located by dimensions given to their center lines. (See Fig. 16.50.)

(c) Slots that are to perform a mechanical function are dimensioned from center-to-center as two partial holes. The R is given to indicate a true radius. Slots of this type are subject to gage inspection. (See Fig. 16.51.)

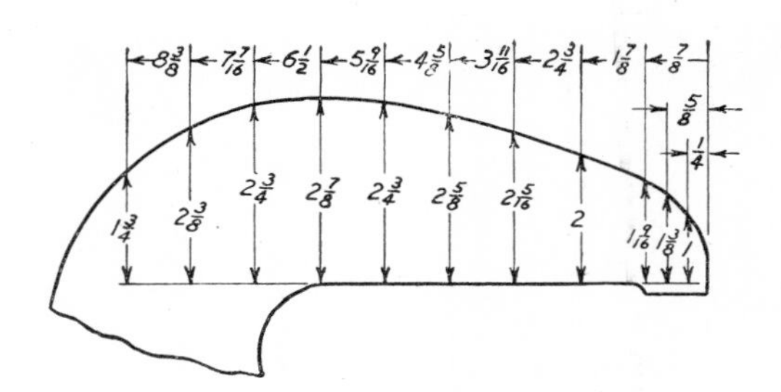

Fig. 16.47. Dimensioning curves by offsets.*

* ASA Z14.1–1946.

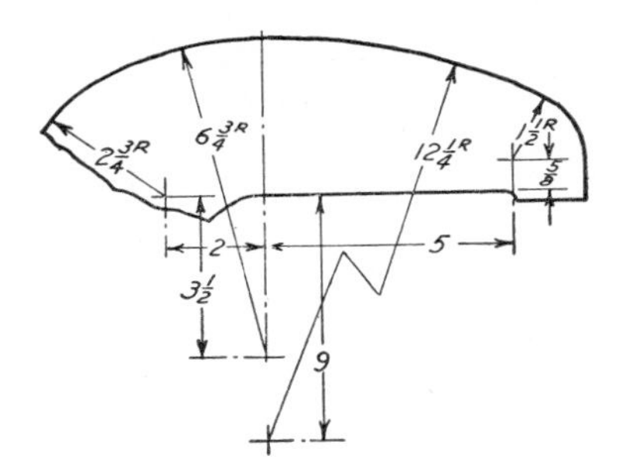

Fig. 16.48. Dimensioning curves by radii.*

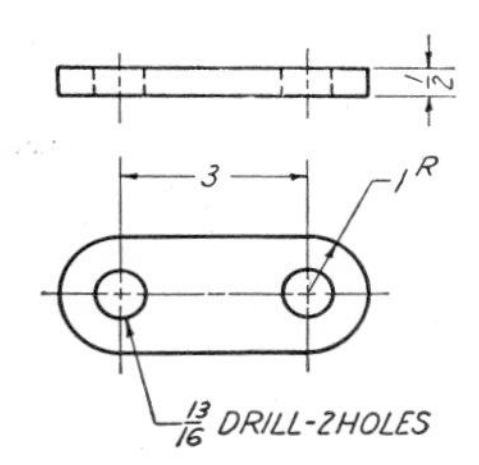

Fig. 16.49. Dimensioning a piece with rounded ends.

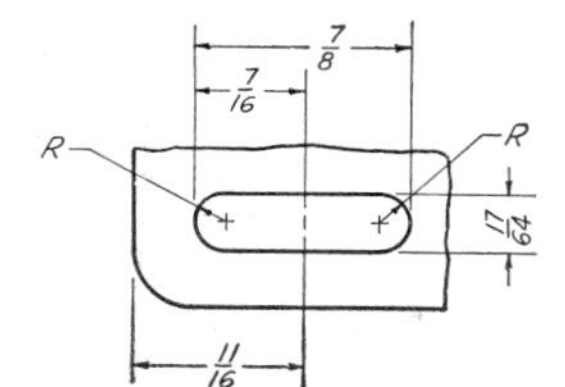

Fig. 16.50. Slot to provide for adjustment.

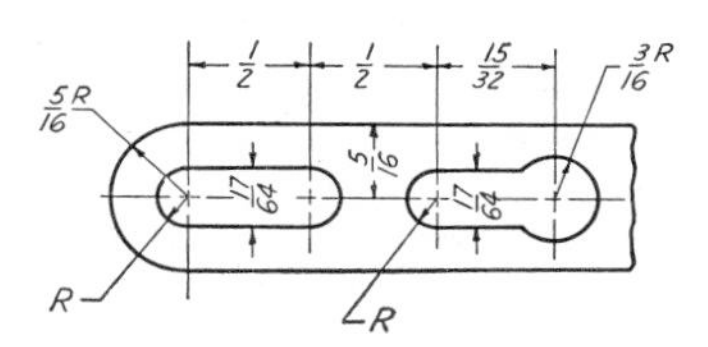

Fig. 16.51. Slots performing a mechanical function.

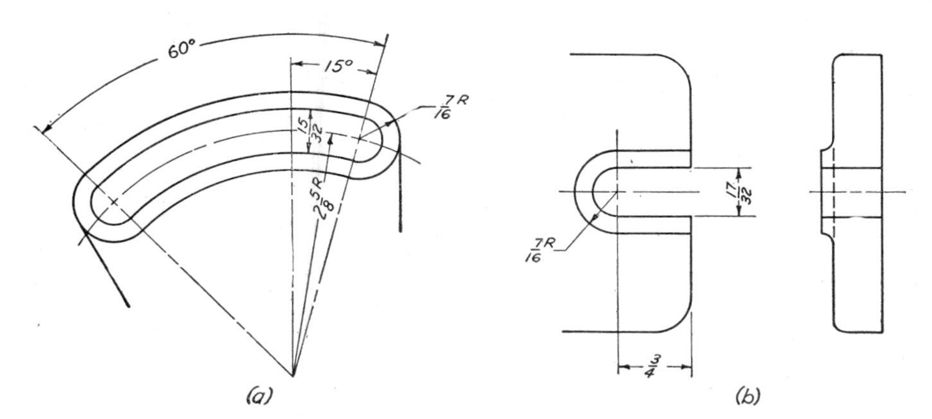

Fig. 16.52. Dimensioning semicircular features.

---

* ASA Z14.1–1946.

(d) Give the width and over-all length for Pratt and Whitney keyways because this is the manner in which the keys are specified.

43. A keyway on a shaft should be dimensioned as shown in Fig. 16.53(*a*). If the keyway is in a hub it is dimensioned as shown in (*b*).

44. When knurls are to provide a rough surface for better grip it is necessary to specify the pitch and kind of knurl as shown in Fig. 16.54.

45. Snug fitting dovetailed parts should be dimensioned with tolerances

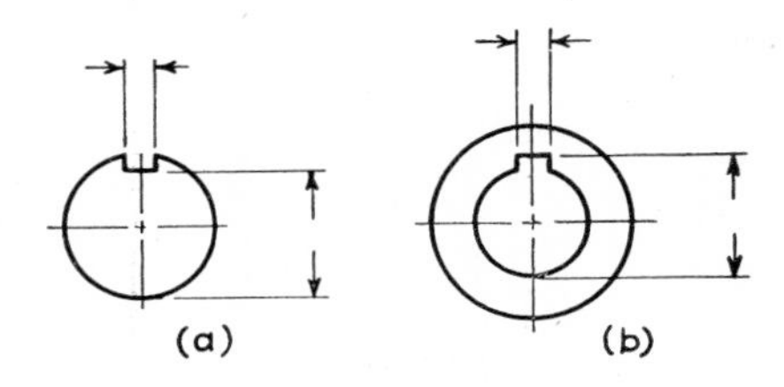

Fig. 16.53. Dimensioning keyways.*

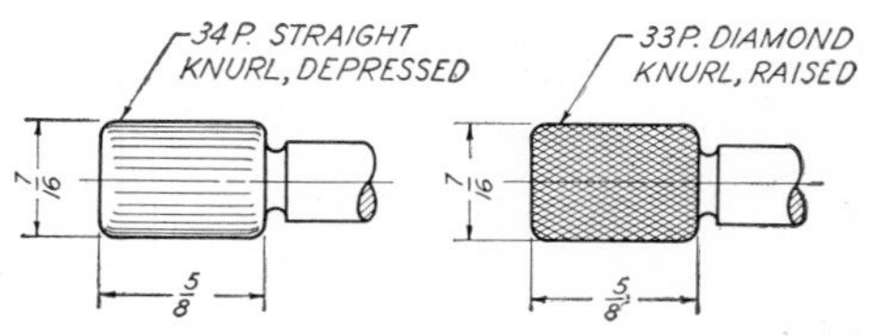

Fig. 16.54. Dimensioning knurls to provide grip.*

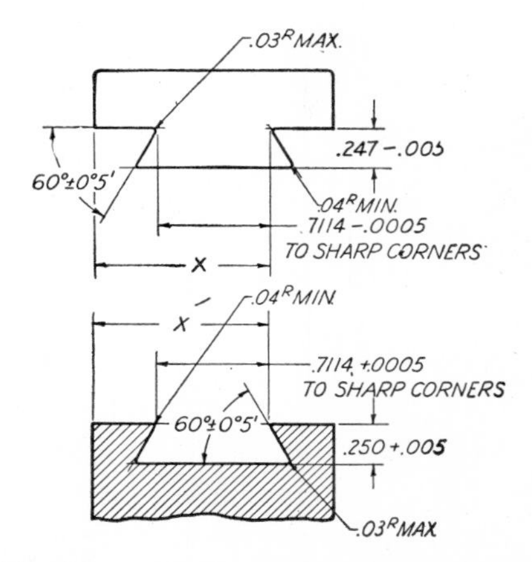

Fig. 16.55. Dimensioning a dovetail slot and tongue.

* ASA Z14.1–1946.

as shown in Fig. 16.55. Dimensions are given to sharp corners. Flats may be substituted for rounded corners if desired.

46. In sheet metal work mold lines are used in dimensioning instead of the centers of the arcs. (See Fig. 16.56.) A mold line (construction line) is the line at the intersection of the plane surfaces adjoining a bend. The formula for bend allowance is given in Fig. 11.3.

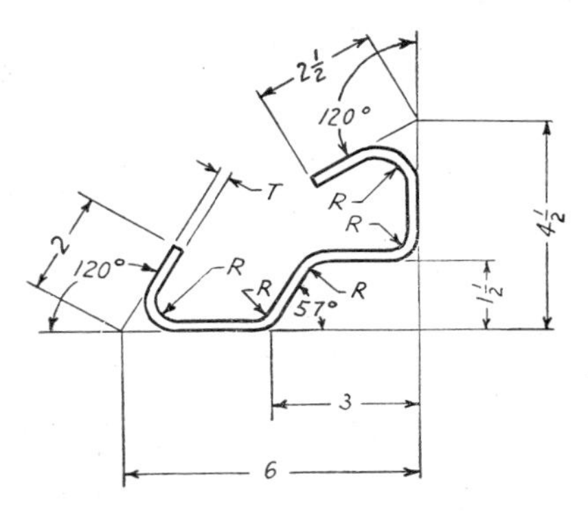

Fig. 16.56. Profile dimensioning.*

47. Dimension standard and special tapers as illustrated in Fig. 16.57.

(a) Special tapers may be dimensioned by giving one diameter, the length, and a note.

(b) Standard tapers require one diameter, the length, and a note specifying the taper by number.

(c) Tapers may be dimensioned with tolerances by giving a diameter with its location as shown in (c).

48. A half section may be dimensioned through the use of hidden lines on the external portion of the view (Fig. 16.58).

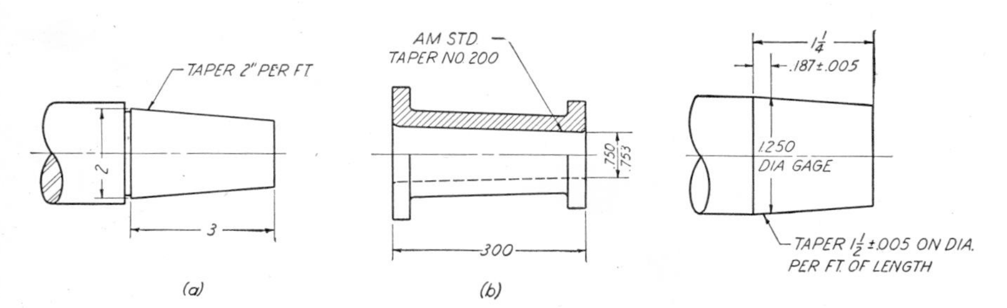

Fig. 16.57. Dimensioning tapers.

* ASA Z14.1–1946.

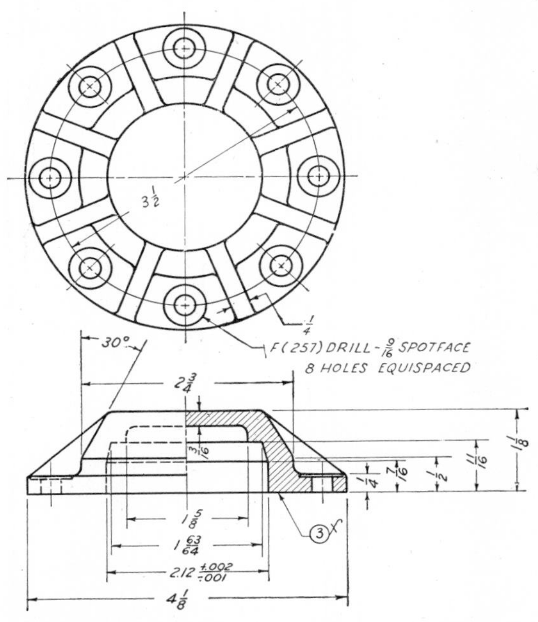

Fig. 16.58. Dimensioning a half-section.

16.9. Base-line dimensioning. In certain types of precision work, principally diemaking, all dimensions are given from base lines. These may be finished surfaces at right angles or important center lines. The use of this method prevents cumulative errors, as each dimension is independent of the others (Fig. 16.59).

16.10. Notes. The use of properly composed notes often adds clarity to the presentation of dimensional information involving specific operations. Notes also are used to convey supplementary instructions about the kind of material, kind of fit, degree of finish, and so forth. It is good practice to specify a dimension representing a tool operation or a

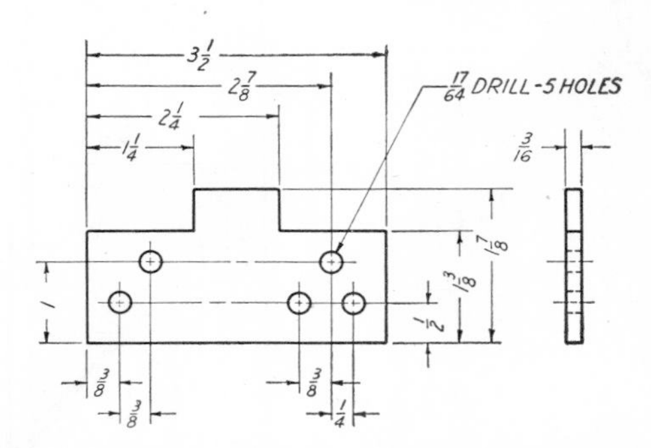

Fig. 16.59. Base-line dimensioning.

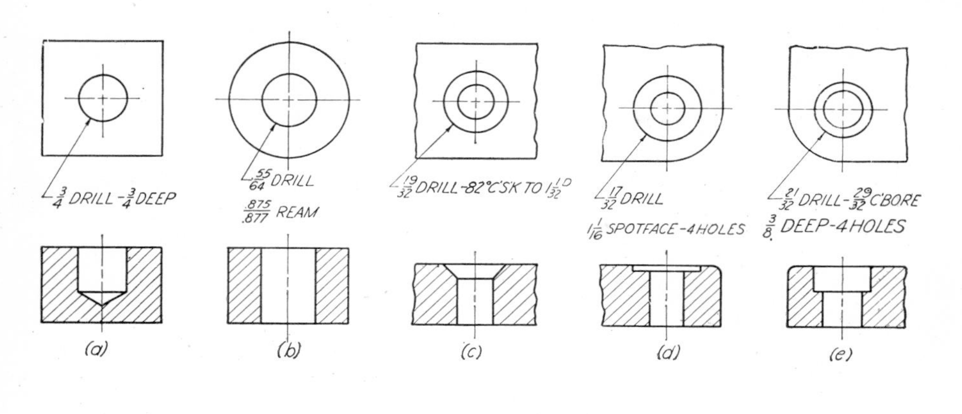

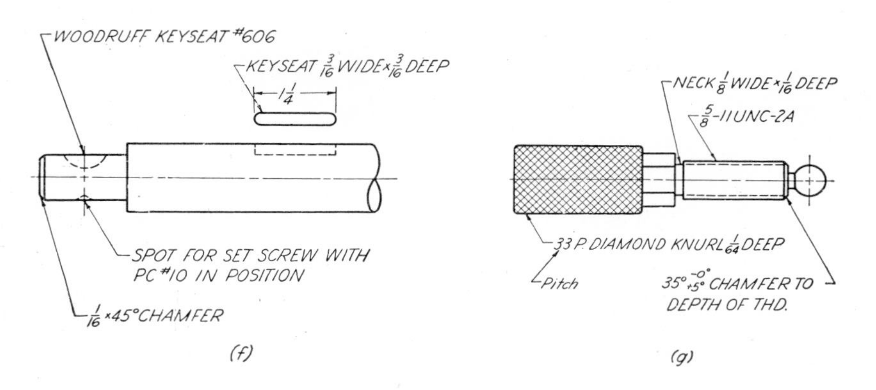

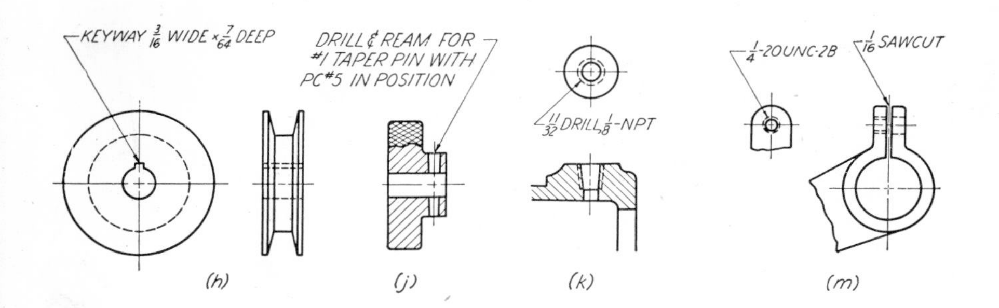

FILLETS AND ROUNDS 1/8 R EXCEPT AS SHOWN
FINISH ALL OVER
SANDBLAST
PEEN OVER IN ASSEMBLY
POLISH TO REMOVE ALL TOOL MARKS

3/8 DRILL-3 HOLES EQUALLY SPACED
BREAK ALL SHARP EDGES
ALL DRAFT ANGLES 7° UNLESS OTHERWISE SPECIFIED
GRIND
2 REQ'D

UNDERCUT 1/4 WIDE × 1/8 DEEP
BROACH
HEAT-TREAT
PICKLE
TUMBLE

(n)

Fig. 16.60. Shop notes.

series of tool operations by a note rather than by figured dimensions. Brevity in form is desirable for notes of general information or specific instruction.

RULES FOR THE FORMULATION AND PLACEMENT OF SHOP NOTES

1. Give the size first, then the machining operation.

EXAMPLE: $\frac{17}{32}$ *Drill.*

2. In the case of threaded parts, use the terminology recommended by the ASA for the American-British unified thread.

EXAMPLE: $\frac{1}{2}$–13UNC–2A.

3. Where there are several holes alike in a group, use one note and indicate the number of holes.

EXAMPLE: $\frac{1}{2}$ *Drill–4 Holes.*

4. Where there are two or more similar groups, repeat the entire note for each group.

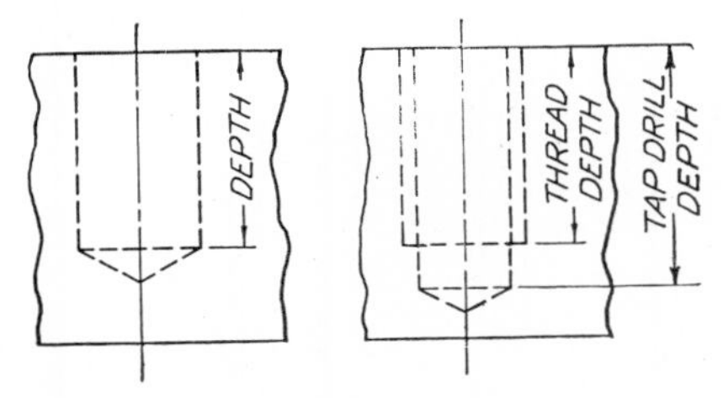

Fig. 16.61. Depth of drilled and tapped holes.

5. For drilled holes and reamed holes, give the diameter, the operation required, and the depth. If the hole goes all the way through the piece, the depth should be omitted.

6. For a tapped (threaded) hole, give the tap-drill size, the diameter of the screw, the number of threads per inch, the kind of thread, and the class of fit. (See Fig. 17.19.) The depth is omitted if the hole goes all the way through the piece. Depth measurements for drilled and tapped holes are shown in Fig. 16.61.

7. Locate the notes for a piece in such a way that they will not overlap the adjacent views of another piece on the same drawing.

8. Notes should not be placed on views or near the lines of a drawing. Use leaders to clarify their purpose.

9. When putting a shop note for a hole on a drawing, if possible, make the leader point to the circular view.

10. If a single note is applicable to similar holes on two adjacent pieces on the same drawing, it should not be used as a common reference but should be repeated for each piece.

11. *Good practice.* In the formulation of shop notes, it is good practice to supply all necessary information. For example, although $\frac{1}{4}$–20UNC–2B is considered by many to be a satisfactory note, it is much better to add the tap-drill size thus: #7(.2010) DRILL, $\frac{1}{4}$–20UNC–2B.

In the case of reamed holes, the drill should accompany the note, as for example: $\frac{31}{64}$ DRILL $\frac{.5000}{.5010}$ REAM. This will relieve the engineering department of any responsibility in case the wrong drill should be used.

16.11. Fractional and decimal dimensioning. For ordinary work, where accuracy is relatively unimportant, shopmen work to nominal dimensions given as common fractions of an inch, as $\frac{1}{2}$, $\frac{1}{4}$, $\frac{1}{8}$, $\frac{1}{16}$, $\frac{1}{32}$, $\frac{1}{64}$. When dimensions are given in this way, many large corporations specify the required accuracy through a note on the drawing that reads as follows: *Permissible variations on common fraction dimensions to machined surfaces to be plus or minus .010 unless otherwise specified.* It should be understood that the allowable variations will differ among manufacturing concerns because of the varying degrees of accuracy required for different types of work.

When greater accuracy is required, the American Standards Association recommends a complete decimal system of dimensioning in their American Standard for Drawings and Drafting Room Practice (Z14.1–1946). (See Fig. 16.62.) The recommendation is as follows:

> The fundamental basis of the complete decimal system is the use of a two place decimal, i.e., a decimal consisting of two figures after the decimal point. In all dimensions where a fraction would ordinarily be used, the two-place decimal can be applied. The figures after the decimal point, where applicable, should be in fiftieths (e.g., .02, .04, .08, .84) so that when halved (e.g., diameters to radii) two-place decimals will result. Exceptions, of course, will have to be made, but they should be kept to a minimum.

Fig. 16.62 shows the application of the complete decimal system in dimensioning a plate. In Fig. 16.63 a drawing is shown that was obtained

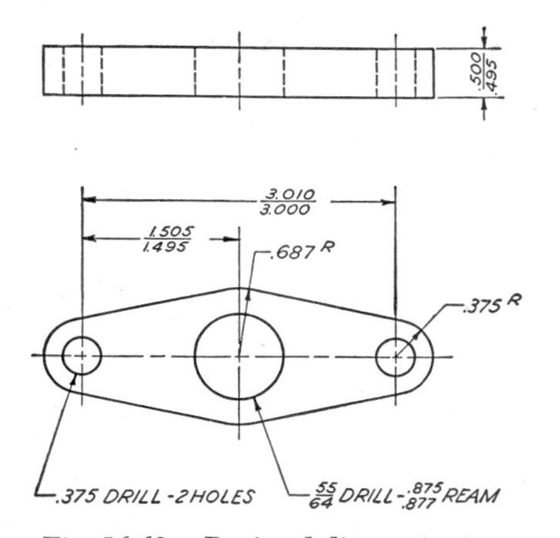

Fig. 16.62. Decimal dimensioning.

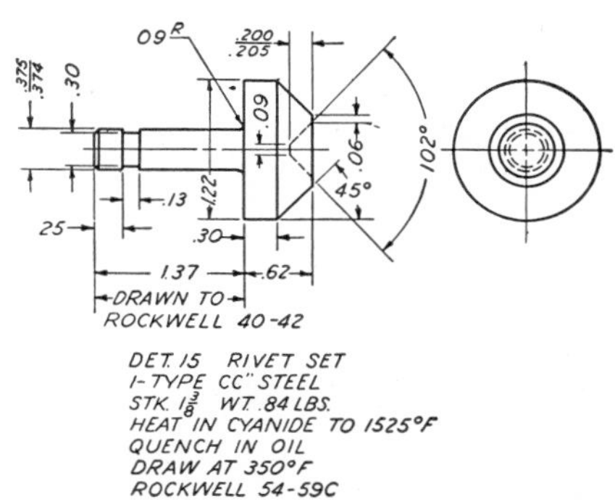

Fig. 16.63. Ford Motor Company decimal system.

from the Ford Motor Co., where some years ago, the decimal system was adopted principally for precision work. In the fabricating department, where measurements are fairly large, the fractional system is used.

16.12. Limit dimensions. Present-day competitive manufacturing requires quantity production and interchangeability for many closely mating parts. The production of each of these mating parts to an exact decimal dimension, although theoretically possible, is economically unfeasible, since the cost of a part rapidly increases as an absolute correct size is approached. For this reason, the commercial draftsman specifies an allowable error (tolerance) between decimal limits (Fig. 16.64). The determination of these limits depends upon the accuracy and clearance required for the moving parts to function satisfactorily in the machine. Although manufacturing experience is often used to determine the proper limits for the parts of a mechanism, it is better and safer practice to adhere

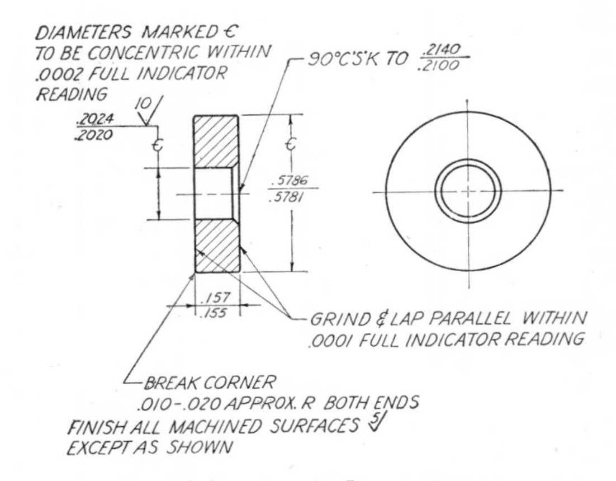

Fig. 16.64. Limit dimensioning.

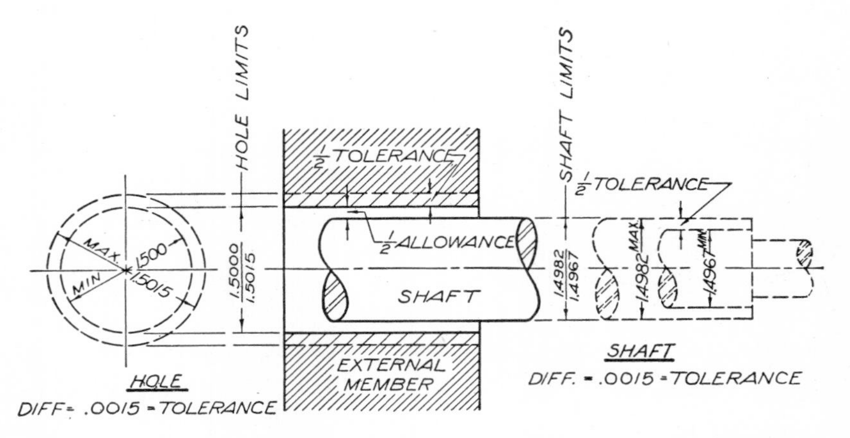

Fig. 16.65. Limit dimensions.

to the eight classes of fits recommended by the American Standards Association in ASA–B4a–1925.* To select proper classes of fits and to compute limit dimensions, it is necessary to understand the following associated terms.

Nominal Size. A designation given to the subdivision of a unit of length having no specific limits of accuracy but indicating a close approximation to a standard size.

Basic Size. The exact theoretical size from which all limiting variations are made.

Allowance. An intentional difference in the dimensions of mating parts, or, the minimum clearance space that is intended between mating parts. It represents the condition of the tightest permissible fit, or the largest internal member mated with the smallest external member. It is to provide for the different classes of fit.

Tolerance. The amount of variation permitted in the size of a part.

Limits. The extreme permissible dimensions of a part.

CLASSIFICATION OF FITS†

Loose Fit (Class 1)—Large Allowance. This fit provides for considerable freedom and embraces certain fits where accuracy is not essential.

EXAMPLES: Machined fits of agricultural and mining machinery; control apparatus for marine work; textile, rubber, candy, and bread machinery; general machinery of a similar grade; some ordnance material.

Free Fit (Class 2)—Liberal Allowance. For running fits with speeds of 600 r.p.m. or over, and journal pressures of 600 lb. per sq. in. or over.

EXAMPLES: Dynamos, engines, many machine-tool parts, and some automotive parts.

Medium Fit (Class 3)—Medium Allowance. For running fits under 600 r.p.m. and with journal pressures less than 600 lb. per sq. in.; also for sliding fits; and the more accurate machine-tool and automotive parts.

Snug Fit (Class 4)—Zero Allowance. This is the closest fit that can be assembled by hand and necessitates work of considerable precision. It should be used where no perceptible shake is permissible and where moving parts are not intended to move freely under a load.

Wringing Fit (Class 5)—Zero to Negative Allowance. This is also known as a "tunking fit" and it is a practically metal-to-metal fit. Assembly is usually selective and not interchangeable.

Tight Fit (Class 6)—Slight Negative Allowance. Light pressure is required to assemble these fits, and the parts are more or less permanently assembled, such as the fixed ends of studs for gears, pulleys, rocker arms, etc. These fits are used for drive fits in thin sections or extremely long fits in other sections and also for shrink fits on very light sections. Used in automotive, ordnance, and general machine manufacturing.

Medium Force Fit (Class 7)—Negative Allowance. Considerable pressure is required to assemble these fits, and the parts are considered permanently assembled. These fits are used in fastening locomotive wheels, car wheels, arma-

* This standard is now under revision.

† Classification of Fits. ASA–B4a–1925 (under revision).

tures of dynamos and motors, and crank discs to their axles or shafts. They are also used for shrink fits on medium sections, or long fits. These fits are the tightest that are recommended for cast iron holes or external members, as they stress cast iron to its elastic limit.

Heavy Force and Shrink Fit (Class 8)—Considerable Negative Allowance. These fits are used for steel holes where the metal can be highly stressed without exceeding its elastic limit. These fits cause excessive stress for cast iron holes. Shrink fits are used where heavy-force fits are impractical, as on locomotive wheel tires, heavy crank discs of large engines, and so forth.

16.13. Computation of limit dimensions. To obtain the correct fit between two engaging parts, limit dimensions are computed that modify the nominal size of both. Numerical values of the modifications necessary to obtain the proper allowance and tolerances for various diameters for all classes of fits are given in Table XXXI in the Appendix. The allowance for moving parts (classes 1–4) must produce a clearance; the allowance for fast fits (classes 5–8) must create an interference.

The two systems in common use for computing limit dimensions under the unilateral method adopted by the American Standards Association are (1) the basic hole system, and (2) the basic shaft system.

16.14. Basic hole system. Because most limit dimensions are computed on the basic hole system, the tables in this book are made especially to facilitate figuring limits according to this system. If, as is the usual case, the nominal size is given, all that is necessary to determine the limits is to convert the nominal size to basic hole size and apply the figures given under "limits," adding or subtracting (according to their signs) to or from the basic size to obtain the limits for both the hole and the shaft.

EXAMPLE: *Basic Hole System.*

To illustrate the terms, suppose that a $\frac{1}{2}''$ shaft is to have a class 2 fit in a $\frac{1}{2}''$ hole (Fig. 16.66*a*). The nominal size of the hole is $\frac{1}{2}''$. The basic hole size (smallest hole) is the exact theoretical size 0.5000.

From the table given here, it is found that the hole may vary between plus 0.0000 and plus 0.0010, and the shaft between −0.0009 and −0.0019. The tolerance on both mating parts is 0.0010, and the allowance (tightest fit) is 0.0009.

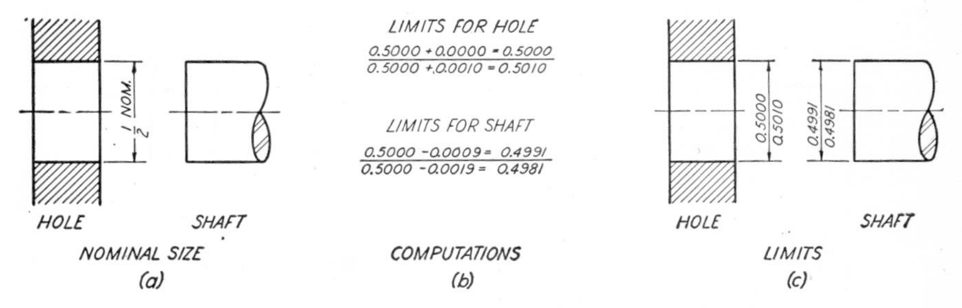

Fig. 16.66. Computation of limits (basic hole system).

FREE FIT (CLASS 2)—LIBERAL ALLOWANCE, INTERCHANGEABLE

For running fits with speeds of 600 r.p.m. or over, and journal pressures of 600 lb. per sq. in. or over.

Size		Limits				Tightest Fit	Loosest Fit
From	*Up to and Including*	*Hole or External Member*		*Shaft or Internal Member*		*Allowance*	*Allowance + Tolerances*
		+		−	−	+	+
0	$\frac{3}{16}$	0.0007	0.0000	0.0004	0.0011	0.0004	0.0018
$\frac{3}{16}$	$\frac{5}{16}$	0.0008	0.0000	0.0006	0.0014	0.0006	0.0022
$\frac{5}{16}$	$\frac{7}{16}$	0.0009	0.0000	0.0007	0.0016	0.0007	0.0025
$\frac{7}{16}$	$\frac{9}{16}$	0.0010	0.0000	0.0009	0.0019	0.0009	0.0029
$\frac{9}{16}$	$\frac{11}{16}$	0.0011	0.0000	0.0010	0.0021	0.0010	0.0032
$\frac{11}{16}$	$\frac{13}{16}$	0.0012	0.0000	0.0012	0.0024	0.0012	0.0036
$\frac{13}{16}$	$\frac{15}{16}$	0.0012	0.0000	0.0013	0.0025	0.0013	0.0037
$\frac{15}{16}$	$1\frac{1}{16}$	0.0013	0.0000	0.0014	0.0027	0.0014	0.0040

The limits on the hole are: $\dfrac{(0.5000 + 0.0000)}{(0.5000 + 0.0010)} = \dfrac{0.5000}{0.5010}$.

The limits on the shaft are: $\dfrac{(0.5000 - 0.0009)}{(0.5000 - 0.0019)} = \dfrac{0.4991}{0.4981}$.

The limits are placed in the order in which they will be approached when the part is machined (Fig. 16.66). For this reason, the minimum limit should appear above the line for an internal dimension, and the maximum dimension above for an external dimension.

16.15. Basic shaft system. When in some instances a number of parts requiring different fits but having the same nominal size must be mounted upon a shaft, the basic shaft system is used, because it is much easier to adjust the limits for the holes than it is to machine a shaft of one nominal diameter to a number of different sets of limits required by different fits.

The basic shaft size can be easily converted into basic hole size by adding the allowance to or subtracting the allowance from the given shaft size. The formula in this instance is:

$$\text{Basic Shaft} \pm \text{Allowance} = \text{Basic Hole Size.}$$

Example: Suppose two No. 3208 New Departure ball bearings, having a bore diameter of 1.5748, are to be fitted along with a spacer and two dust caps to the same shaft, which is stationary. The limit dimensions must be computed by the basic shaft system. From Table XXXIII (Appendix), which gives the mounting fits for ball bearings, the basic shaft size (largest shaft) is found to be 1.5744.

The first step in the computation of the limits for the spacer using a class 5 fit involves the use of the formula for converting the basic shaft system to the basic hole system.

$$1.5744 \text{ (Basic Shaft)} - 0.0005 \text{ (Allowance)} = 1.5739 \text{ (Basic Hole)}.$$

Using the values found in Table XXXI (Appendix), class 5, the limits on the hole are

$$\frac{(1.5739 + 0.0000)}{(1.5739 + 0.0007)} = \frac{1.5739}{1.5746}.$$

16.16. Tolerances. Necessary tolerances may be expressed by general notes printed on a drawing form or they may be given with definite values for specific dimensions (Fig. 16.64). When expressed in the form of a printed note, the wording might be as follows: *Allowable variation on all fractional dimensions is ±.010 unless otherwise specified.* A general note for tolerance on decimal dimensions might read: *Allowable variation on decimal dimensions is ±.001.* This general note would apply to all decimal dimensions where limits were not given.

The general notes on tolerances should be allowed to apply to all dimensions where it is not necessary to use specific tolerances.

16.17. Unilateral and Bilateral Tolerances. Unilateral tolerances may be expressed in any one of several ways as shown in Fig. 16.67.

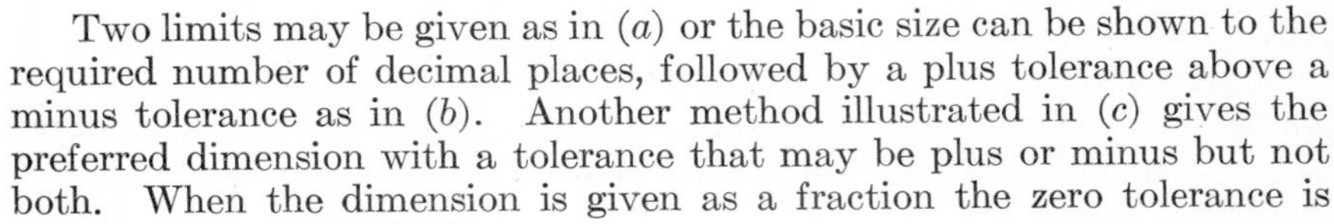

Fig. 16.67. Unilateral tolerances.

Two limits may be given as in (*a*) or the basic size can be shown to the required number of decimal places, followed by a plus tolerance above a minus tolerance as in (*b*). Another method illustrated in (*c*) gives the preferred dimension with a tolerance that may be plus or minus but not both. When the dimension is given as a fraction the zero tolerance is expressed by a 0 (cipher).

Bilateral tolerances are expressed with a divided tolerance (Fig. 16.68).

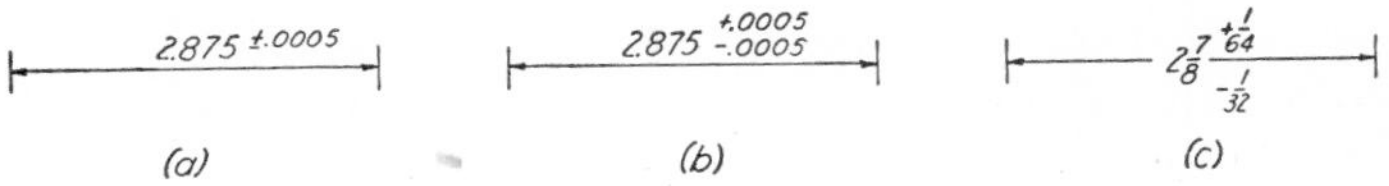

Fig. 16.68. Bilateral tolerances.

Whenever the plus and minus values are unequal as in (*c*) the plus value is placed above the dimension line.

16.18. Cumulative tolerances. An undesirable condition may result when either the location of a surface or an over-all dimension is affected by more than one tolerance dimension. When this condition exists as illustrated in Fig. 16.69(*a*) the tolerances are said to be cumulative. It can be noted in (*a*) where the dimensions are continuous from surface-to-surface that there is a permissible variation of only 0.005 in the over-all length of the piece while at the same time it is not unreasonable to expect all dimensions to vary between either the extreme high or low limits. If minimum tolerances are obtained between all surfaces, the length of the part could be 3.980 as against a minimum specified length of 3.995. If it is necessary to maintain the over-all dimension within the specified limits, the allowable variation of 0.005 must be distributed among the four dimensions. This would increase manufacturing costs because the machinist would find it necessary to work to limits closer than those that are specified. In order to avoid this situation, it is the preferred practice to locate the surfaces from a datum plane as shown in (*b*), so that each surface is affected by only one dimension. The use of a datum plane makes it possible to take full advantage of permissible variations in size and still satisfy all requirements for the proper functioning of the part.

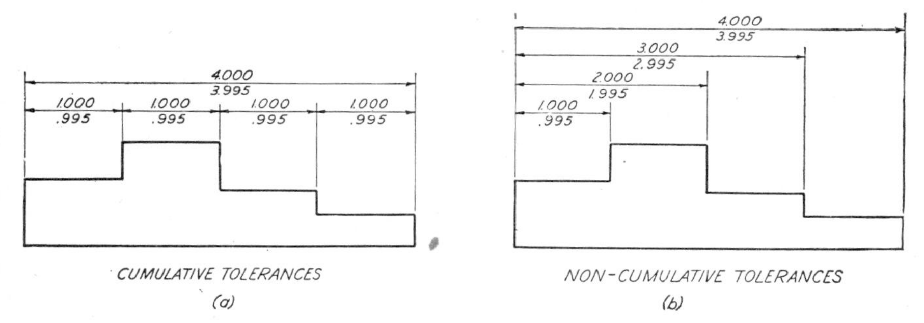

Fig. 16.69. Cumulative tolerances.

16.19. Production tolerances. Whenever extreme accuracy is required for the production of parts it becomes necessary to specify tolerances for concentricity, squareness, parallelism, and flatness. The tolerances for these features are usually expressed in notes. See Figs. 16.64 and 16.70.

16.20. Concentricity tolerances. A note expressing the permissible variation in concentricity for mating coaxial cylindrical surfaces on closely fitted precision parts is necessary if the parts are to be produced with an exactness that will permit assembly. A note specifying the tolerance for concentricity might read as follows: *Diameters marked must be concentric within ■ total indicator reading.* If this is a general note, given without leaders to the cylindrical surfaces to which the note applies, a letter or the symbol ∈ may be used to identify the diameters as shown in Fig. 16.70.

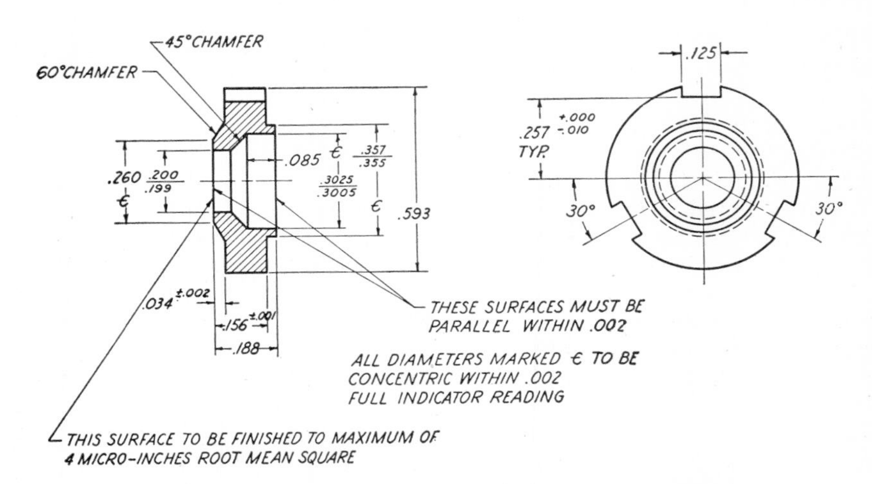

Fig. 16.70. Tolerance of concentricity and parallelism.

16.21. Squareness tolerances. A note is used to specify the tolerance governing the squareness of one surface to another. Such a note might read as follows: *This surface must be square with axis of hole within ■ total indicator reading at X radius.*

16.22. Parallelism tolerances (Fig. 16.70). A tolerance for parallelism is expressed in a note in terms of the linear deviation from parallel per inch. A note for parallelism tolerance might read as follows: *These surfaces must be parallel within .002 per inch.*

16.23. Flatness tolerances. A note is used to express the tolerance relating to flatness. The note should specify the direction (concave or convex) and give the permitted amount of deviation from flat. Such a note might read: *This surface must be flat to ■ concave.*

16.24. Surface quality. The improvement in machining methods within recent years coupled with a strong demand for increased life for machined parts has caused engineers to give more attention to the quality of the surface finish. Not only the service life but also the proper functioning of the part as well may depend upon obtaining the needed smoothness quality for contact surfaces.

On an engineering drawing a surface may be represented by line if shown in profile or it may appear as a bounded area in a related view. Machined and ground surfaces, however, do not have the perfect smoothness represented on a drawing. Actually a surface has three dimensions, namely, length, breadth, and curvature (waviness) as illustrated in Fig. 16.71(*a*). In addition there will be innumerable peaks and valleys of differing lengths, widths, and heights. An exaggerated profile of surface roughness is shown in (*b*). Combined waviness and roughness is illustrated in (*c*).

The following terms must be understood before the surface symbol shown in Fig. 16.72(*a*) can be properly applied.

Roughness. Roughness is the relatively finely spaced surface irregularities that are produced by the cutting action of tool edges and abrasive grains on surfaces that are machined.

Waviness. Waviness is the surface undulations that are of much greater magnitude than the roughness irregularities. Waviness may result from machine or work deflections, vibrations, warping, strains, or similar causes.

Lay. Lay is the predominate direction of the tool marks of the surface pattern. See Fig. 16.72(*b*).

Microinch. A microinch is one millionth (0.000001) of an inch.

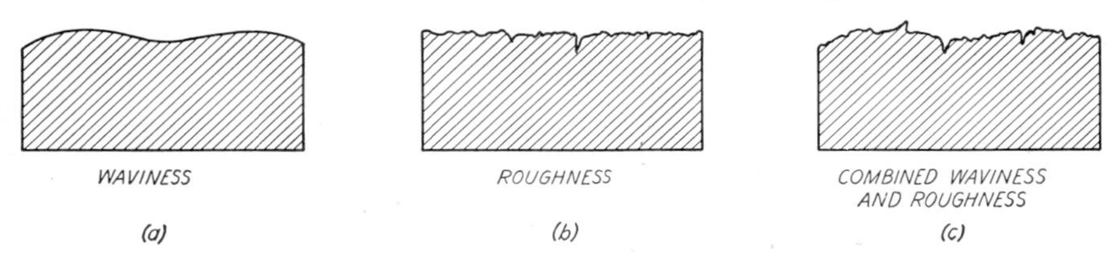

Fig. 16.71. Surface definitions illustrated.

The following was abstracted from the American Standard Publication "Drawings and Drafting Room Practice" (ASA Z14.1–1946):

A surface whose finish is to be specified should be marked with the finish mark having the general form of a check mark (√) so that the point of the symbol is

(a) On the line indicating the surface,

(b) On a leader pointing to the surface (Fig. 16.73).

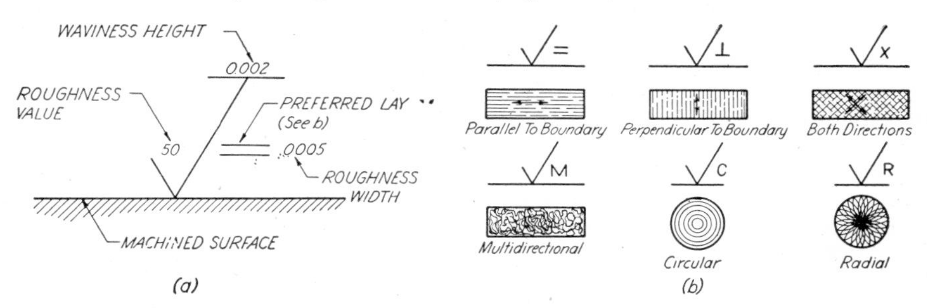

Fig. 16.72. Surface quality symbols.

Where it is desired to specify only the surface roughness height, and the width of roughness or direction of tool marks is not important, the simplest form of the symbol should be used. See Fig. 16.64. This height may be either maximum peak to valley height, average peak to valley height, or average deviation from the mean (RMS or arithmetical). The numerical value is placed in the √ as shown.

Where it is desired to specify waviness height in addition to roughness height a straight horizontal line should be added to the top of the simple symbol. See Fig. 16.72(*a*). The numerical value of height of waviness would be shown above this line.

Then, if the nature of the preferred lay is to be shown in addition to these two characteristics, it will be indicated by the addition of a combination of lines as shown in Fig. 16.72(*a*) and (*b*). The parallel and perpendicular part of the symbol indicates that the dominant lines on the surface are parallel or perpendicular to the boundary line of the surface in contact with the symbol.

The complete symbol, including the roughness width placed to the right of the lay symbol, is shown in Fig. 16.72(*a*).

The use of only one number to specify the height or width of roughness or waviness shall indicate the maximum value. Any lesser degree of roughness will be satisfactory. When two numbers are used separated by a dash, they indicate the maximum and minimum permissible values.

Surface finish should be specified only by experienced personnel because the function of many parts does not depend upon the smoothness quality of a surface or surfaces. In addition, surface quality need not be necessarily indicated for many parts that are produced to close dimensional tolerances because a satisfactory surface finish may result from the required

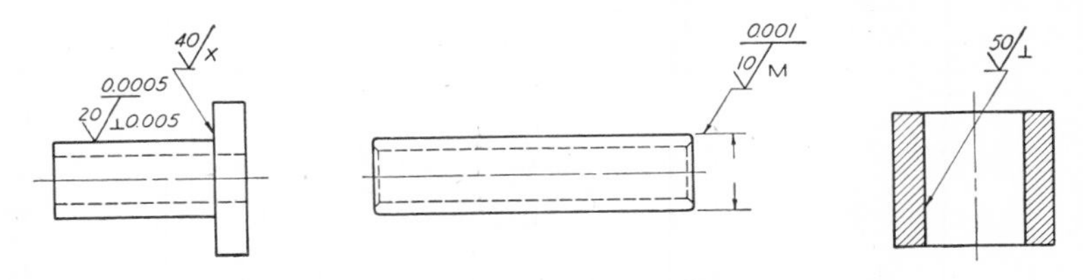

Fig. 16.73. Application of surface finish symbols.

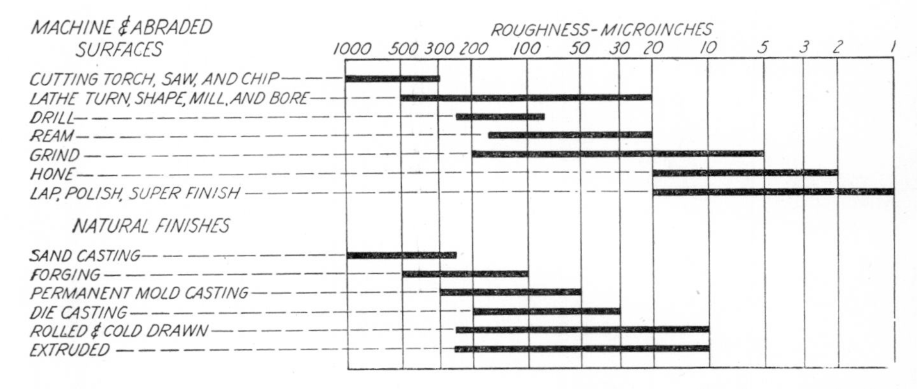

Fig. 16.74. Surface finishes expected from common production methods.

machining processes. It should be remembered that the cost of producing a part will generally become progressively greater as the specification of surface finish becomes more exacting.

The chart in Fig. 16.74 shows the expected surface roughness in microinches for surfaces produced by common production methods.

The surface-quality symbol, which is used only when it is desirable to specify surface smoothness, should not be confused with a finish mark that indicates the removal of material. A surface-quality symbol might be used for a surface on a die-casting, forging, or extruded shape where the surface is to have a natural finish and no material is to be removed.

16.25. Problems. The following problems offer the student the opportunity to apply the rules of dimensioning given in this chapter.

1–2. (Figs. 16.75 and 16.76.) Reproduce the given views of an assigned part. Determine the dimensions by transferring them from the drawing to the open-divided scale, by means of the dividers.

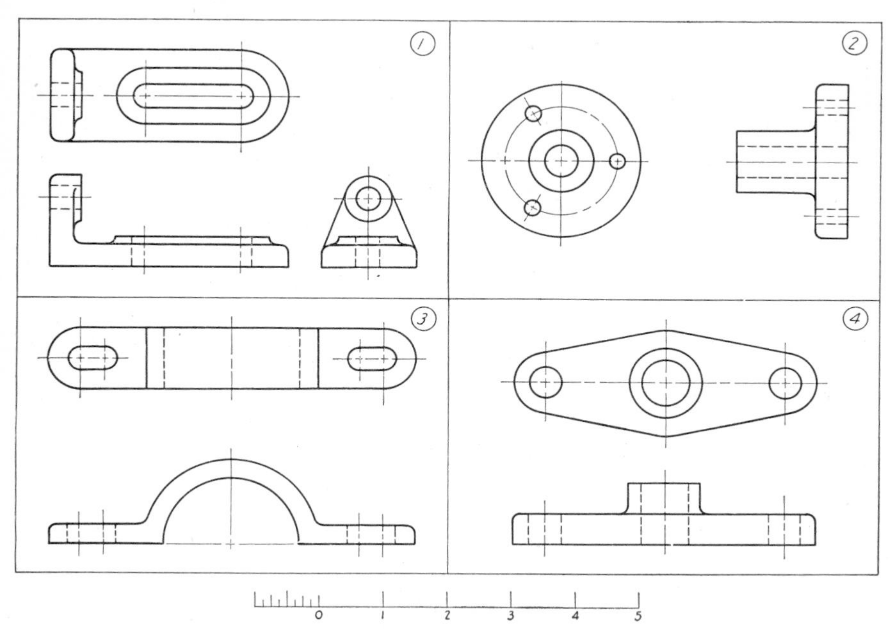

Fig. 16.75. Dimensioning problems.

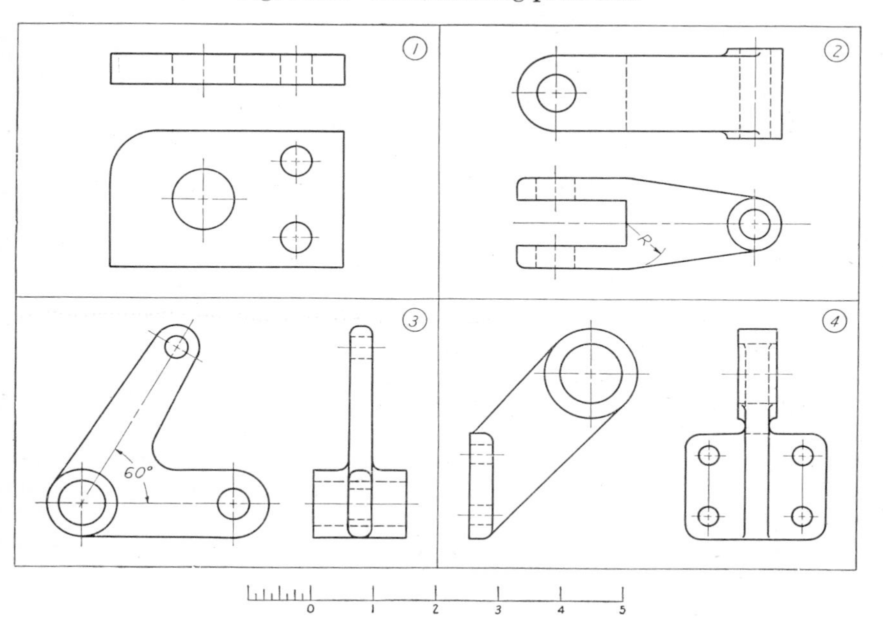

Fig. 16.76. Dimensioning problems.

17 SCREW THREADS AND FASTENERS

17.1. In the commercial field,where the practical application of engineering drawing takes the form of working drawings, knowledge of screw threads and fasteners is important. There is always the necessity for assembling parts together either with permanent fastenings, such as rivets, or with bolts, screws, and so forth, which may be removed quite easily.

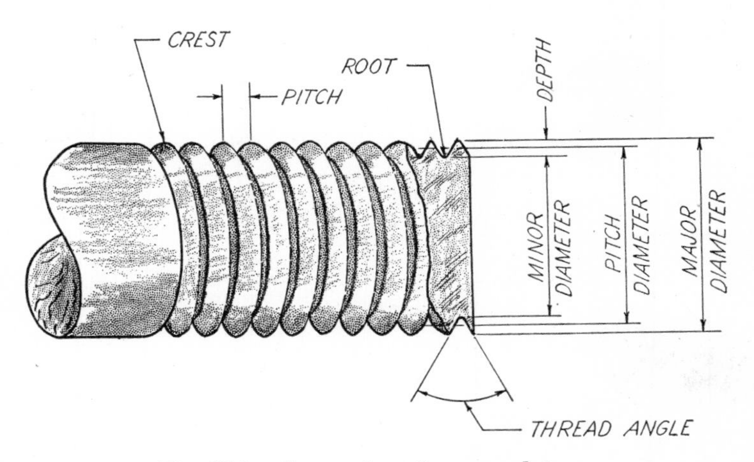

Fig. 17.1. Screw thread nomenclature.

Engineers, detailers, and draftsmen must be completely familiar with the common types of threads and fastenings, as well as with their use and correct methods of representation, because of the frequency of their occurrence in structures and machines. Information concerning special types of fasteners may be obtained from manufacturers' catalogues.

The beginner should study Fig. 17.1 to acquaint himself with the terms commonly associated with screw threads.

17.2. Threads. The principal uses of threads are: (1) for fastening,

(2) for adjusting, and (3) for transmitting power. To satisfy most of the requirements of the engineering profession, the different forms of threads shown in Fig. 17.2 are used.

The American Standard form (National Form N) thread which is being replaced by the new unified thread form is still widely used in the

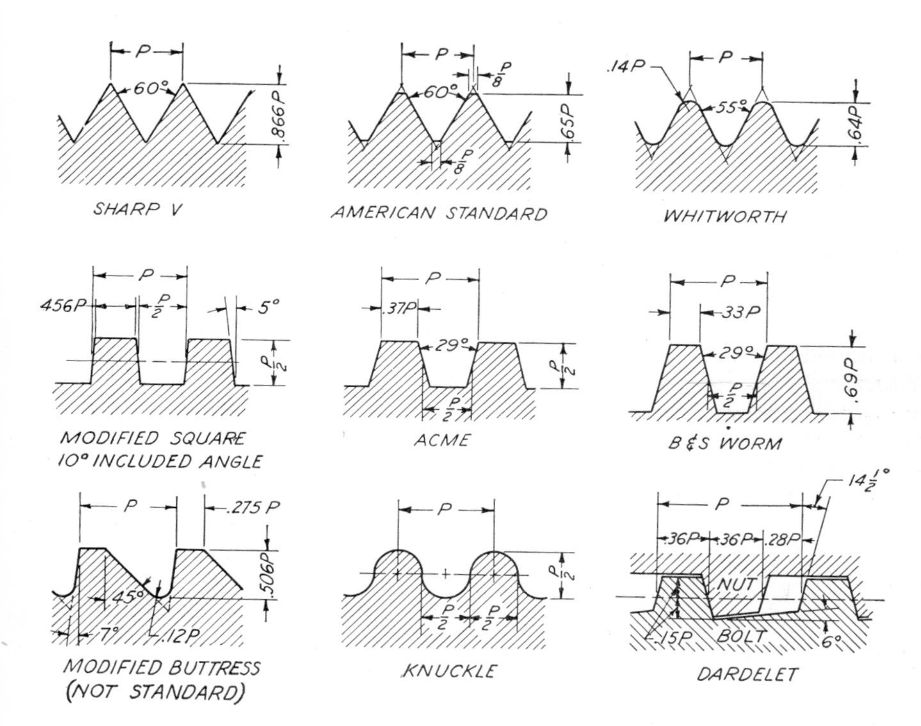

Fig. 17.2. Screw threads.*

United States. The sharp V is used to some extent where adjustment and holding power are essential.

For the transmission of power and motion, the modified square, Acme, and Brown and Sharpe worm threads have been adopted. The modified square thread which is now rarely used transmits power parallel to its axis. A still further modification of the square thread is the stronger Acme, which is easier to cut and more readily disengages split nuts (as lead screws on lathes). The Brown and Sharpe worm thread, with similar proportions but with longer teeth, is used for transmitting power to a worm wheel.

---

* ASA B1.3–1941.
Handbook H-28 (1944) National Bureau of Standards.

The knuckle thread, commonly found on incandescent lamps, plugs, and so on, can be cast or rolled.

The Whitworth and buttress threads are not often encountered by the average engineer. The former, which fulfills the same purpose as the American Standard thread, is used in England but is also frequently found in this country. The buttress or breech-block thread, which is designed to take pressure in one direction, is used for breech mechanisms of large guns and for airplane propeller hubs. The thread form has not been standardized and appears in different modified forms.

The Dardelet thread is self-locking in assembly.

17.3. American-British unified thread. A new Unified Thread Standards (ASA BI. 1–1949) came into existence after the representatives of the United States, Great Britain, and Canada signed a unification agreement on Nov. 18, 1948 in Washington, D. C. This accord, which made possible the interchangeability of threads for these countries, created a new thread form (Fig. 17.3) that is a compromise between our own American Standard design and the British Whitworth. The external thread of the new form has a rounded root and may have either a flat or rounded crest.

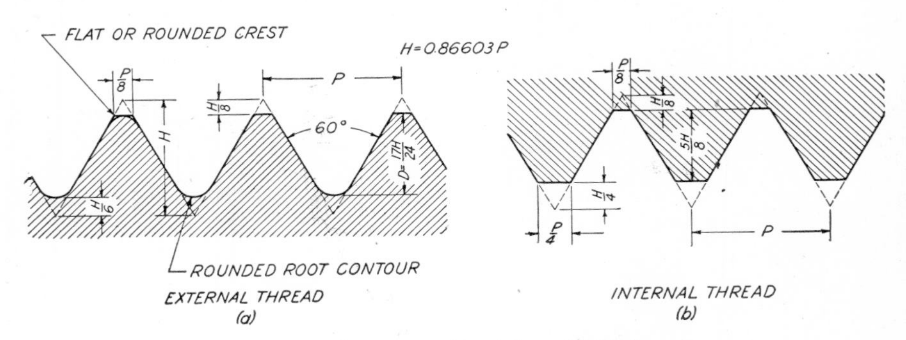

Fig. 17.3. American-British unified thread.

17.4. Right-hand and left-hand threads. A right-hand thread advances into a threaded hole when turned clockwise; a left-hand thread advances when turned counter-clockwise. They can be easily distinguished by the thread slant. A right-hand thread on a horizontal shank always slants upward to the left and a left-hand upward to the right (Fig. 17.4). A thread is always considered to be right-hand if it is not otherwise specified. A left-hand thread is always marked *L.H.* on a drawing.

17.5. Multiple threads. Whenever a quick advance is desired, as on fountain pens, valves, and so on, two or more threads are cut side by side. Two threads form a double thread, three a triple thread, and so on. A thread that is not otherwise designated is understood to be a single thread.

Fig. 17.5 shows heavy strings wound around a rod for the purpose of demonstrating single and double threads. The center line of the single

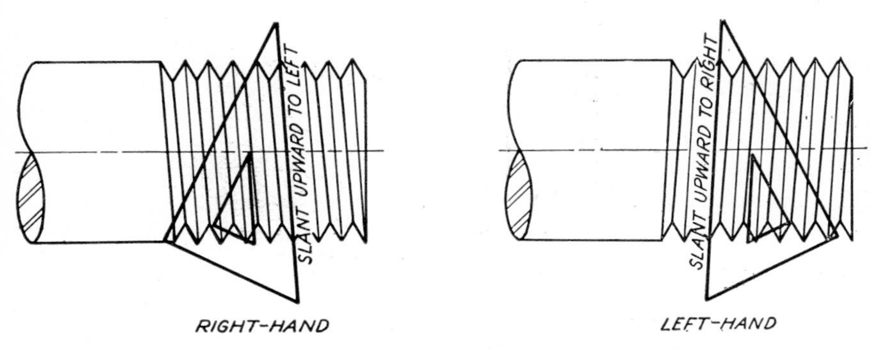

Fig. 17.4. Right-hand and left-hand threads.

string, representing the single thread, assumes the form of a helix. In the case of the double thread, it should be noted that there are two strings side-by-side that are shaded differently for clarity. On a double thread, each thread starts diametrically opposite the other one.

17.6. Pitch. The pitch of a thread is the distance from any point on a thread to the corresponding point on the adjacent thread, measured parallel to the axis as shown in Fig. 17.1.

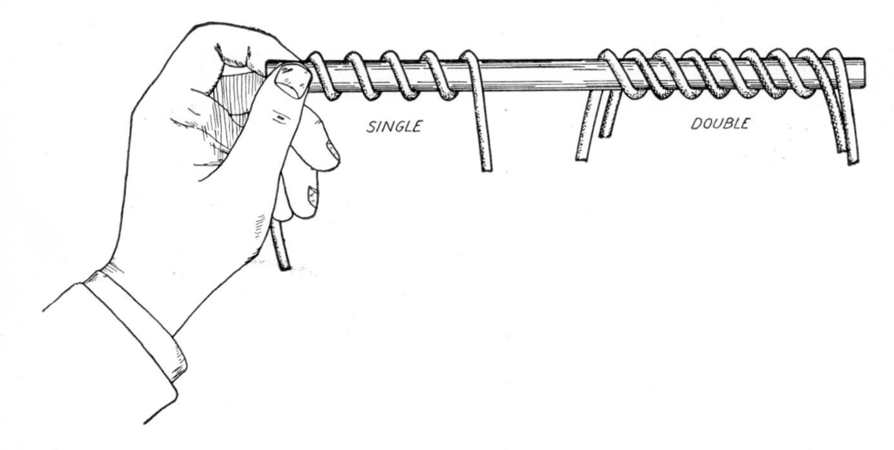

Fig. 17.5. Demonstration of a helix as related to a single and double screw thread.

17.7. Lead. The lead of a screw may be defined as the distance advanced parallel to the axis when the screw is turned one revolution. (See Fig. 17.6.) For a single thread, the lead is equal to the pitch; for a double thread, the lead is twice the pitch; for a triple thread, the lead is three times the pitch, and so on.

17.8. Semiconventional screw-thread representation. The true representation of screw threads by helical curves, requiring unnecessary time and laborious drafting, is rarely used. The semiconventional method, which consists of drawing the true profile of the thread and the helical curves as straight lines, is preferred in commercial practice (Fig. 17.7).

The steps in drawing a sharp V-thread are shown in Figs. 17.8 and 17.9.

The flattened roots and crests are disregarded in the representation of American Standard threads and they are drawn as sharp V's. An effective relief and finish is given by drawing all lines fine except root lines.

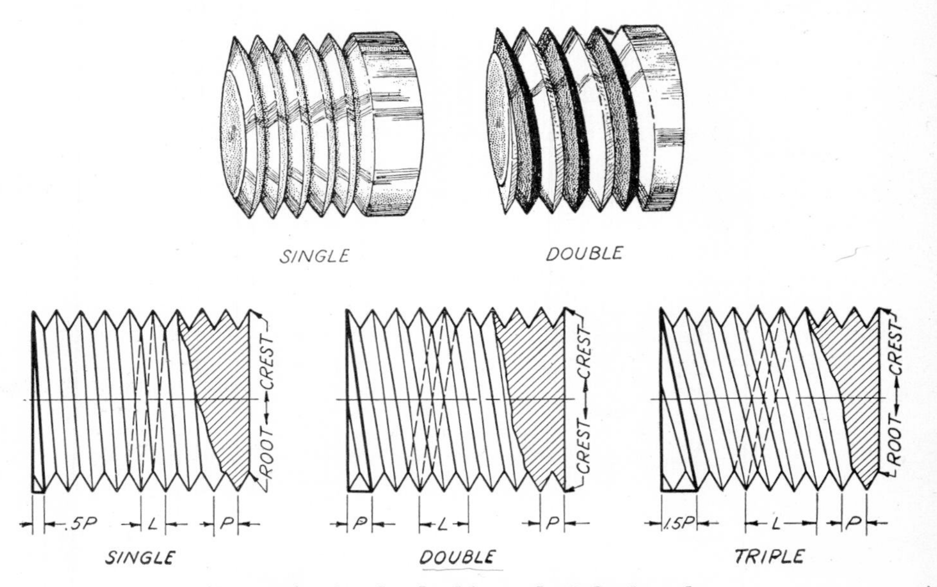

Fig. 17.6. Single, double, and triple threads.

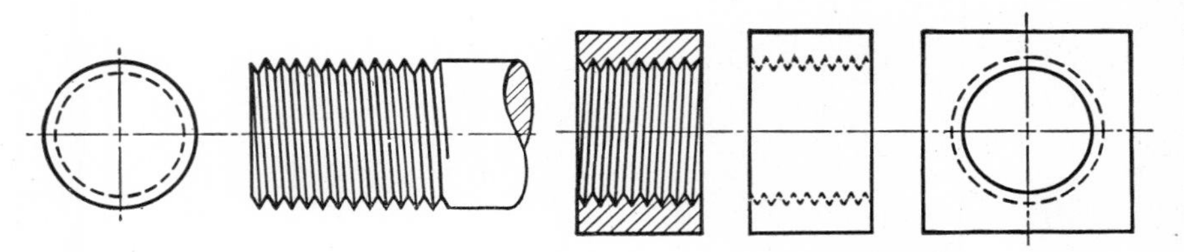

Fig. 17.7. Thread representation.*

In drawing a single, triple, or an odd-number multiple thread, a crest is always diametrically opposite a root; in a double or even-number multiple thread, a crest is opposite a crest and a root opposite a root.

The stages in drawing semiconventional modified square and Acme threads are shown in Figs. 17.11, 17.12, and 17.13. All lines of the finished square thread are made the same weight. The root lines of the Acme thread are made heavier than the other lines.

* ASA Z14.1–1935.

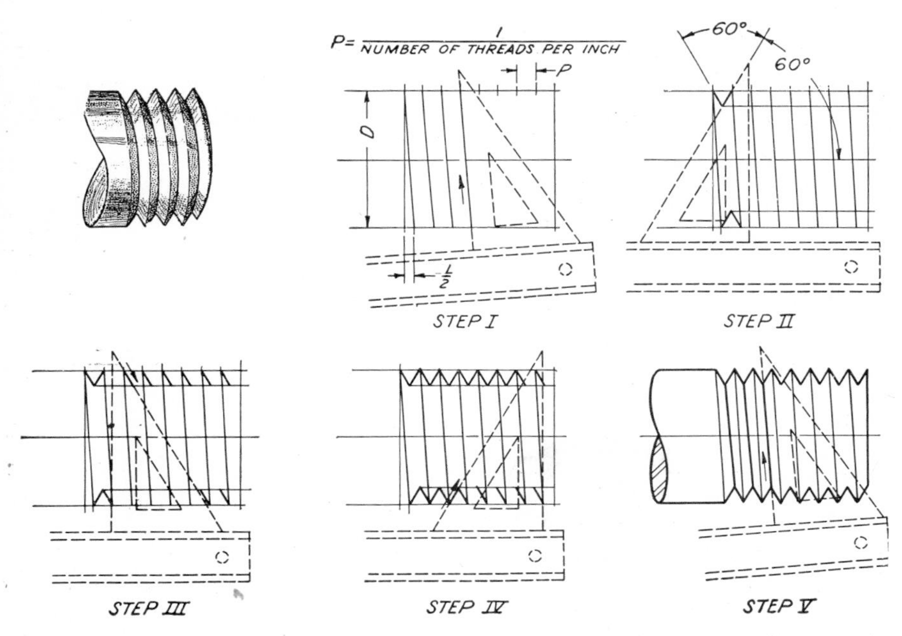

Fig. 17.8. **Semiconventional Unified-American and sharp V threads (external).**

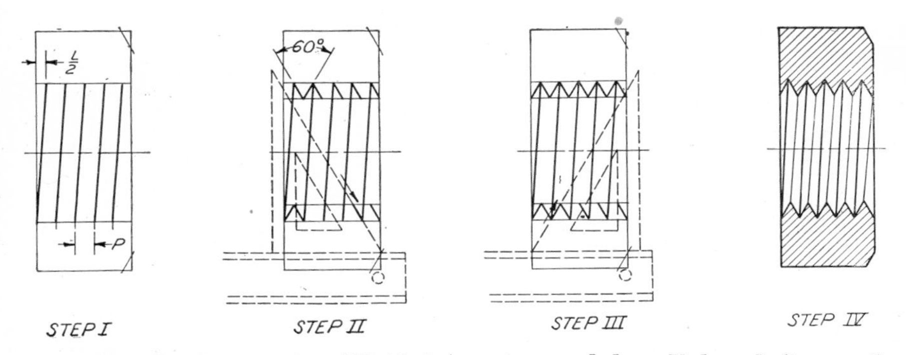

Fig. 17.9. **Semiconventional Unified-American and sharp V threads (internal).**

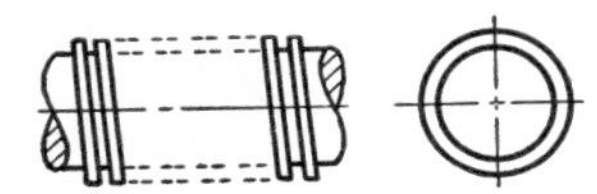

Fig. 17.10. Simplified representation of a square thread.*

* ASA Z14.1–1946.

Fig. 17.10 shows a simplified method of representation for square threads.

17.9. Conventional thread symbols. Recognizing the necessity for saving time and expense in the preparation of drawings, the American

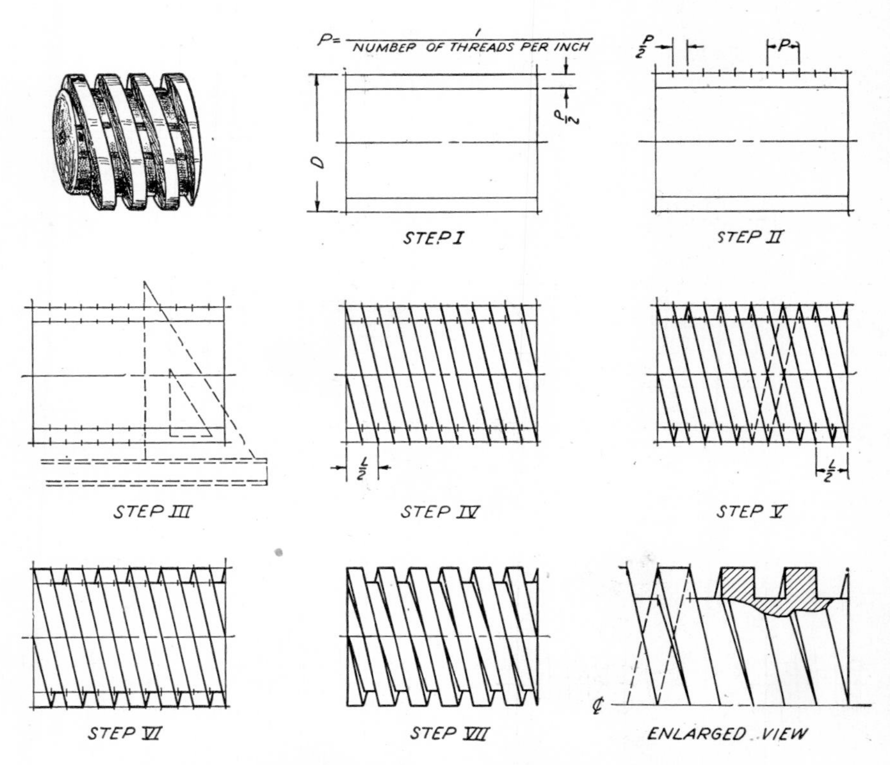

Fig. 17.11. Semiconventional (modified) square threads.

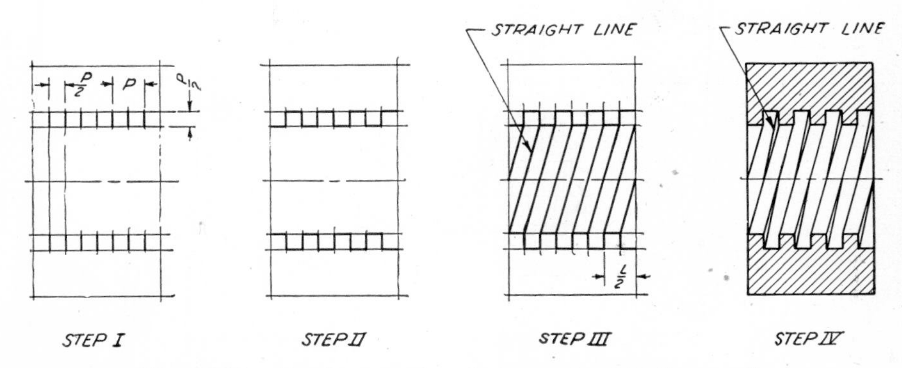

Fig. 17.12. Semiconventional square threads (internal).

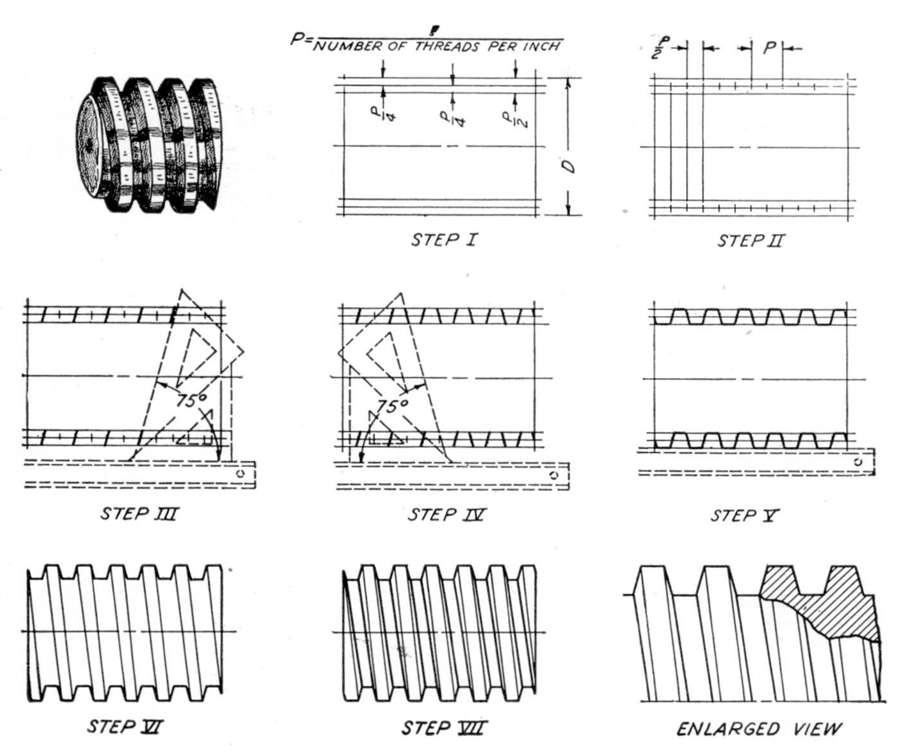

Fig. 17.13. Semiconventional Acme thread.

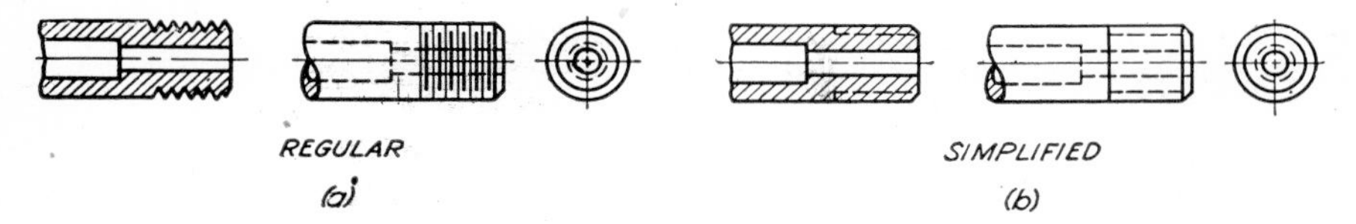

Fig. 17.14. External thread symbols.*

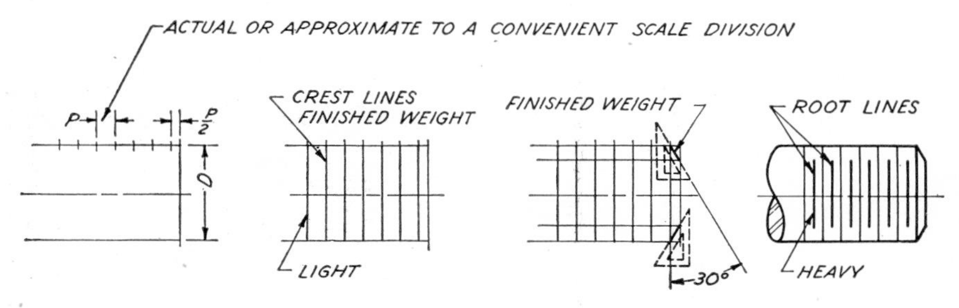

Fig. 17.15. Drawing conventional threads.

* ASA Z14.1–1946.

Standards Association has adopted the "regular" and "simplified" series of conventional thread symbols to be used to represent threads having a diameter of one inch or less.

The simplified symbols were adopted to simplify drafting on drawings. The root of the thread is represented by invisible lines drawn parallel to the axis.

The regular symbols consist of alternate long and short lines perpendicular to the axis. Although these lines, representing the crests and roots of the thread, are not spaced to actual pitch, their spacing should indicate noticeable differences in the number of threads per inch of different threads on the same working drawing or group of drawings. The root lines are made heavier than the crest lines.

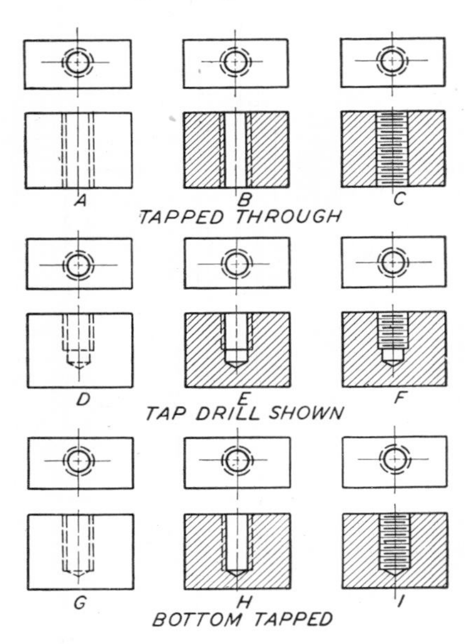

Fig. 17.16. Internal thread symbols. American Standards (ASA Z14.1–1946).

Before a hole can be tapped (threaded), it must be drilled to permit the tap to enter. See Tables II and IV for tap drill sizes for standard threads. Since the last of the thread cut is not well formed or usable, the hole must be shown drilled and tapped deeper than the screw will enter. (See Fig. 17.16*D*, *E*, *F*.) To show the threaded portion extending to the bottom of the drilled hole indicates the use of a bottoming tap to cut full threads at the bottom. This is an extra and expensive operation not justified except in cases where the depth of the hole and the distance the screw must enter are limited. (See Fig. 17.16*G*, *H*, *I*.)

17.10. Threads in section. The semiconventional representation of threads in section, which is used for large diameters only, is shown in Fig. 17.9. Since the far side of an internal thread in section is visible, the crest and root lines incline in the opposite direction to those of an external thread having the same specifications.

Regular and simplified symbols for threads of small diameter are shown in Figs. 17.14 and 17.16.

Sectional assembly drawings from the American Standards Association publication, ASA Z14.1–1946, are shown in Fig. 17.17. When assembled pieces are both sectioned, the semiconventional representation is used, and the thread form is drawn as in Fig. 17.17.

17.11. American Standard thread series. The profile of the American Standard Thread (Fig. 17.2) is similar to a 60° V, except that the crest is flattened and the root is built up so that the depth of the American

Standard thread is $\frac{3}{4}$ the depth of a V thread of the same pitch. This results in a much stronger screw for a given outside diameter and pitch. The American Standard form is the same as the United States Standard form and was adopted by the American Standards Association in 1935.†

The American Standard, consisting of five series of screw threads, uses the same form or profile in each series but not the same number of threads per inch for any given diameter.

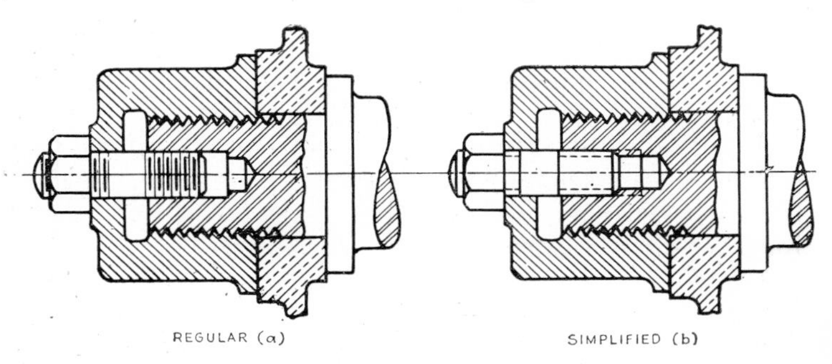

Fig. 17.17. Threads in section.*

1. *The coarse thread series* is recommended for general industrial use.

2. *The fine thread series* has four principal advantages over the coarse thread series:

(*a*) Greater strength for a given outside diameter.
(*b*) More ability to resist vibration.
(*c*) More easily tightened.
(*d*) Less weight for a given strength.

3. *The 8-pitch thread series*, having 8 threads per inch for all diameters from 1 to 6 inches, is used on bolts for high-pressure flanges and for cylinder head studs that require a proper initial tension so that joints will not open up. It is now used for many other classes of engineering work.

4. *The 12-pitch thread series*, having 12 threads per inch for diameters from $\frac{1}{2}$ inch to 6 inches, is used in boiler work, railroad work, and in machine construction for thin nuts on shafts and sleeves.

5. *The 16-pitch series*, having 16 threads per inch for all diameters from $\frac{3}{4}$ inch to 4 inches, is used mainly for threaded adjusting collars and bearing-retaining nuts.

17.12. Screw-thread fits. The American Standards Association has also adopted four classes of fits between mating threads (as between a bolt and nut). Each class of fit has a definite purpose and use in the field of commercial design. It is neither sound economics nor good practice to employ higher quality of fit than is required for satisfactory performance.

Class 1 fit. Recommended only for screw-thread work where clear-

† ASA B1.1–1935.
* ASA Z14.1–1946.

ance between mating parts is essential for rapid assembly and where shake or play is not objectionable.*

Class 2 fit. Represents a high quality of commercial thread product and is recommended for the great bulk of interchangeable screw-thread work.*

Class 3 fit. Represents an exceptionally high quality of commercially threaded product and is recommended only in cases where the high cost of precision tools and continual checking is warranted.*

Class 4 fit. Intended to meet very unusual requirements more exacting than those for which class 3 is intended. It is a selective fit if initial assembly by hand is required. It is not, as yet, adaptable to quantity production.*

17.13. Identification symbols for American Standard threads. American Standard threads are specified on drawings, in specifications,

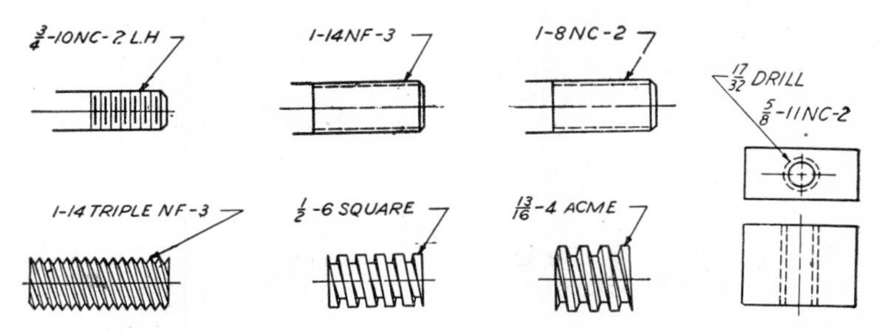

Fig. 17.18. Thread identification symbols.

and in stock lists by the thread information given in the following order:

1. Diameter in inches (or screw number).
2. Number of threads per inch.
3. Initial letters of the series. (*NC* for National Coarse, *NF* for National Fine, and *N* for National Form with a special pitch.)
4. Class of fit.

If the thread is left hand, the letters *L.H.* should appear at the end of the specification.

17.14. Unified and American screw thread series. The Unified and American screw thread series as given in ASA B1.1–1949 consists of six series and a selection of special threads that cover special combinations of diameter and pitch. Each series differs from the other by the number of threads per inch for a specific diameter.

The coarse thread series (UNC and NC) is designated UNC for sizes above $\frac{1}{4}''$ in diameter. This series is recommended for general industrial use.

The fine thread series (UNF and NF) designated UNF for sizes above $\frac{1}{4}''$, was prepared for use when a fine thread is required and for general use in the automotive and aircraft fields.

* ASA B1.1–1935.

The extra-fine thread series, designated NEF is used for automotive and aircraft work when a maximum number of threads is required for a given length. A few specific sizes of this series are designated UN.

The 8, 12, and 16 thread series, designated 8N or 8UN, 12N or 12UN, and 16N or 16UN are used for the same purposes as the 8, 12, and 16 pitch thread series of the old American Standard series.

17.15. Unified and American screw thread fits. Classes of fits are determined by the amounts of tolerance and allowance specified. Under the new unified system classes 1A, 2A, and 3A apply only to external threads; classes 1B, 2B, and 3B apply to internal threads. Classes 2 and 3 from the former American Standard have been retained without change in the new Unified and American Thread Standard for use in the United States only, but they are not among the Unified classes even though the thread forms are identical. These fits are used with the American thread series (NC, NF, and N series) which covers sizes from size 0 (.060) to 6″.

Class 1A and Class 1B replace class 1 of the old American Standard.

Class 2A and Class 2B were adopted as the recognized standards for screws, bolts, and nuts.

Class 3A and class 3B invoke new classes of tolerances. These classes along with class 2A and class 2B should eventually replace class 2 and class 3 now retained from the American Standard.

17.16. Identification symbols for Unified screw threads. Threads are specified under the new unified system by giving the diameter, number of threads per inch, initial letters (UNC, UNF, etc.), and class of fit (1A, 2A, and 3A; or 1B, 2B, and 3B). See Fig. 17.19.

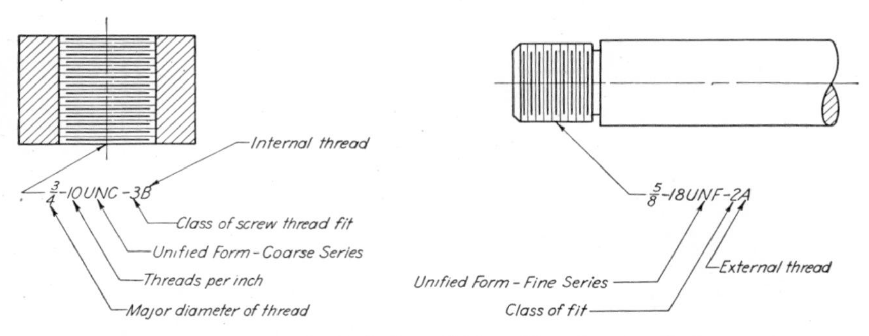

Fig. 17.19. Unified thread identification symbols.

17.17. American Standard bolts and nuts. Commercial producers of bolts and fasteners manufacture their products in accordance with the standard specifications given in the American Standard entitled "Wrench-Head Bolts and Nuts, and Wrench Openings (Revised 1941)." *
The specifications cover three series, which are:

1. *Regular series.* The regular series was adopted for general use. The new standard is more economical in the use of material than the old

* ASA B18.2–1941.

United States Standard, but there is an ample factor of safety with the new dimensions. Some deviations were made from the theoretical dimensions to reduce the number of wrench openings. It is generally understood that this series should be used unless otherwise specified.

2. *Heavy series.* Heavy boltheads and nuts are designed to satisfy the special commercial need for greater bearing surface.

3. *Light-series nuts.* Light nuts are used under conditions requiring a substantial savings in weight and material. They are usually supplied with a fine thread.

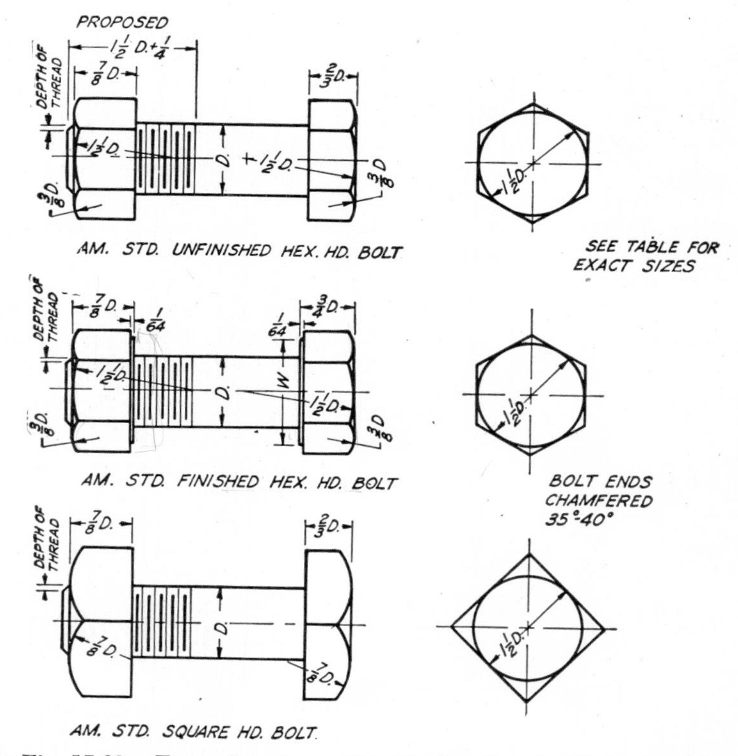

Fig. 17.20. Formula proportions for American Standard bolts.

The amount of machining is the basis for further classification of hexagonal bolts and nuts in both the regular and heavy series as unfinished, semifinished, and finished. Square-head bolts and nuts are supplied as unfinished and semifinished.

Unfinished heads and nuts are not washer-faced, nor are they machined on any surface.

Semifinished bolt heads and nuts are machined or treated on the bearing surface to provide a washer face for bolt heads and either a washer face or a circular bearing surface for nuts. Nuts, not washer-faced, have the circular bearing surface formed by chamfering the edges.

Finished heads and nuts are washer-faced and are machined on all surfaces. The washer face is $\frac{1}{64}''$ thick and has a diameter equal to the distance across flats.

Formula dimensions for unfinished and finished hexagonal head and unfinished square-head bolts and nuts (Regular Series) are given in Fig. 17.20. The width across flats and height of head for any given American Standard bolt, as well as the corresponding dimensions for the nut, may be obtained from American Standard tables.

Bolts and nuts should be drawn across corners in all views. This recognized commercial practice, which violates the principles of true projection, prevents confusion of square and hexagonal forms on drawings.

All semifinished hexagonal heads and nuts have the same distance across flats as the unfinished, but, since the finishing of the bearing surface requires the removal of metal, the height of heads and the thickness of nuts are less.

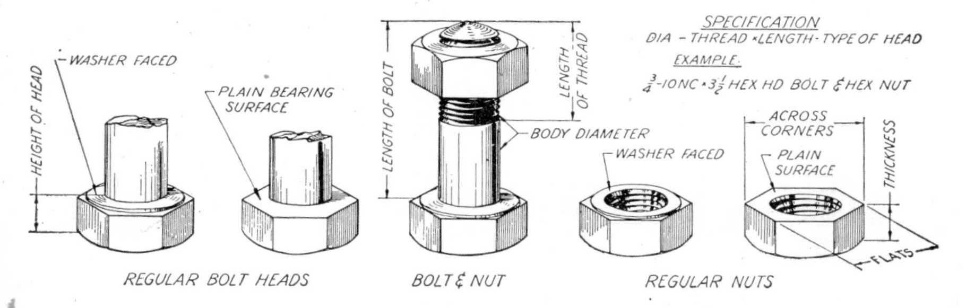

Fig. 17.21. American Standard bolts and nuts.

All finished heads and nuts on bolts $\frac{3}{4}''$ in diameter or over have the same distance across flats as the corresponding unfinished and semifinished ones, but the height dimension of the head is somewhat greater in every case. The thickness of a finished nut is the same as the thickness of an unfinished nut of the same diameter, in all sizes.

The chamfer angle on the tops of heads and nuts is 30° on hexagons and 25° on squares, but both are drawn at 30° on bolts greater than 1″ in diameter. Since it is difficult in drawing small bolts to show the 30° contour lines representing the chamfer, they should be omitted for diameters of 1″ or less.

Bolt lengths have not been standardized in construction practice, because of the varied requirements in engineering design. There is a proposed standard for minimum thread lengths for bolts, but it has not been approved. See Table VI (Appendix). Standard length increments for length under the head to the end of a hexagonal bolt are: $\frac{1}{8}''$ for bolts $\frac{1}{4}''$ to $\frac{3}{4}''$ in length, $\frac{1}{4}''$ for bolts $\frac{3}{4}''$ to 3″ in length, and $\frac{1}{2}''$ for bolts 3″ to 6″ in length. Length increments for square head bolts are: $\frac{1}{8}''$ for bolts $\frac{1}{4}''$ to $\frac{3}{4}''$ in length, and $\frac{1}{4}''$ for bolts $\frac{3}{4}''$ to $4\frac{3}{4}''$ in length.

Bolts are specified in parts lists and elsewhere by giving the diameter, number of threads per inch, series, class of fit, length, finish, and type of head.

EXAMPLE: $\frac{1}{2}$-13UNC-2A × $1\frac{3}{4}$ SEMI-FIN. HEX. HD. BOLT.

Frequently it is advantageous and practical to abbreviate the specification thus:

EXAMPLE: $\frac{1}{2}$ × $1\frac{3}{4}$ UNC SEMI-FIN. HEX. HD. BOLT.

17.18. To draw boltheads and nuts. Using the dimensions given in Fig. 17.20 or taken from the tables, draw the lines representing the top and contact surface of the head or nut and the diameter of the bolt. Lay out a hexagon about an inscribed chamfer circle equal to $1\frac{1}{2}$D (Fig. 17.22) and project the necessary lines to block in the view. Draw in the arcs after finding the centers as shown in Fig. 17.22.

A square-head bolt or nut may be drawn by following the steps indicated in Fig. 17.23.

17.19. Studs. Studs, or stud bolts, which are threaded on both ends, as shown in Fig. 17.24, are used where bolts would be impractical and for parts that must be frequently removed (cylinder heads, steam chest covers, pumps, and so on). They are first screwed permanently into the tapped holes in one part before the removable member with its corresponding clearance holes is placed in position. Nuts are used on the projecting ends to hold the parts together.

Since studs are not standard they must be produced from specifications given on a detail drawing. In dimensioning a stud, the length of thread must be given for both the stud end and nut end along with an over-all dimension. The thread information is given by note.

In a bill of material, studs may be specified as follows:

EXAMPLE: $\frac{1}{2}$-13UNC-2A × $2\frac{3}{4}$ STUD.

It is good practice to abbreviate the specification thus:

EXAMPLE: $\frac{1}{2}$ × $2\frac{3}{4}$ STUD.

17.20. Cap screws (Fig. 17.26). Cap screws are similar to machine screws. They are available in four standard heads, usually in finished

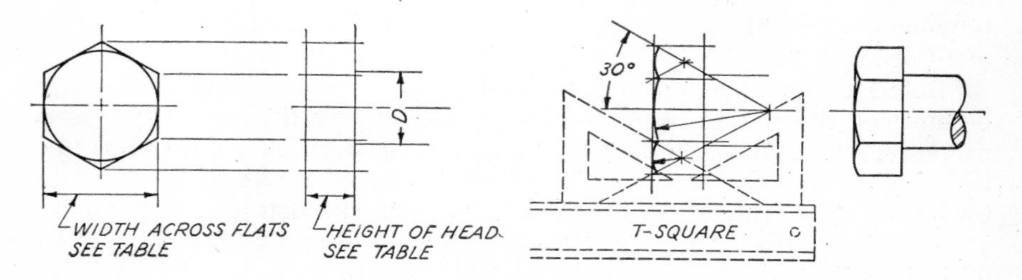

Fig. 17.22. Steps in drawing a hexagonal bolt head.

form. When parts are assembled, the cap screws pass through clear holes in one member and screw into threaded holes in the other (Fig. 17.25). Hexagonal cap screws have a washer face $\frac{1}{64}''$ thick with a diameter equal to the distance across flats. All cap screws 1″ or less in length are threaded to the head.

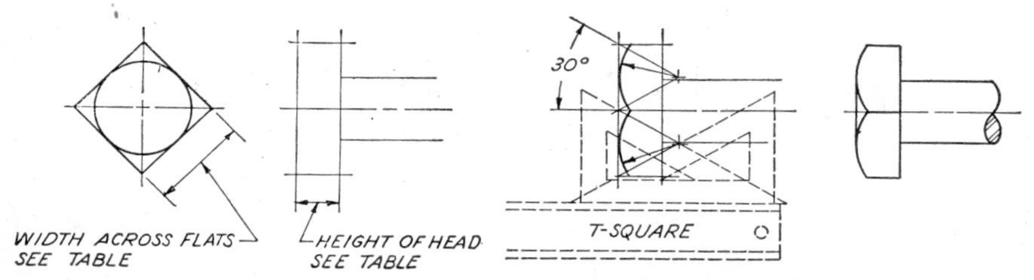

Fig. 17.23. Steps in drawing a square bolt head.

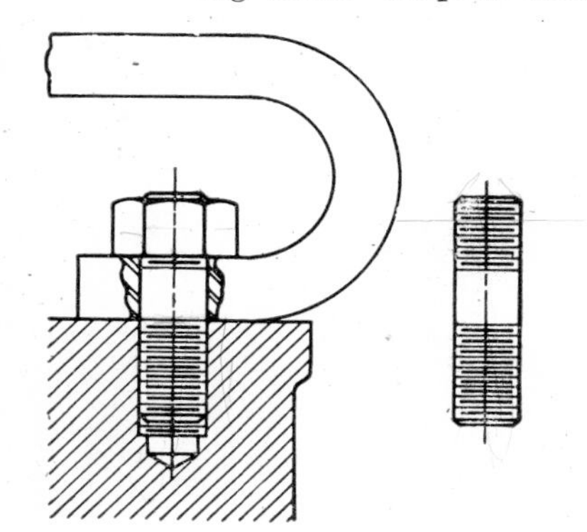

Fig. 17.24. Stud bolt.

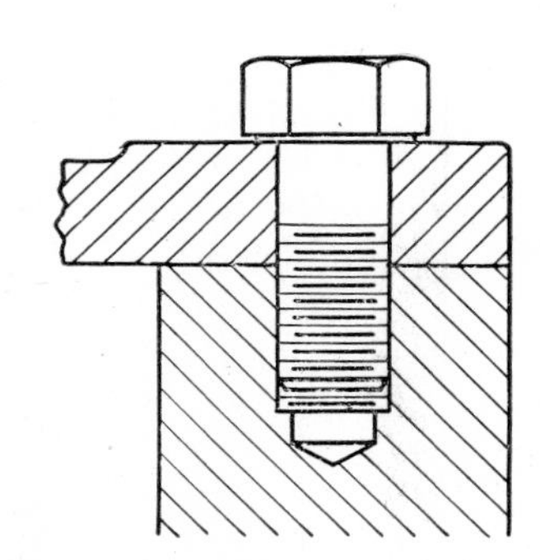

Fig. 17.25. Hexagonal-head cap screw.

Cap screws are specified by giving the diameter, number of threads per inch, series, class of fit, length, and type of head.

EXAMPLE: $\frac{5}{8}$-11UNC-2A × 2 FIL. HD. CAP SC.

It is good practice to abbreviate the specification thus:

EXAMPLE: $\frac{5}{8}$ × 2 UNC FIL. HD. CAP SC.

17.21. Machine screws. Machine screws, which fulfill the same purpose as cap screws, are used chiefly for small work having thin sections (Fig. 17.27). Under the approved American Standard, they range from No. 0 (0.060″ dia.) to $\frac{3}{4}''$ (0.750 dia.) and are available in either the American Standard Coarse or Fine-Thread Series. The four forms of heads shown in Fig. 17.28 have been standardized. A

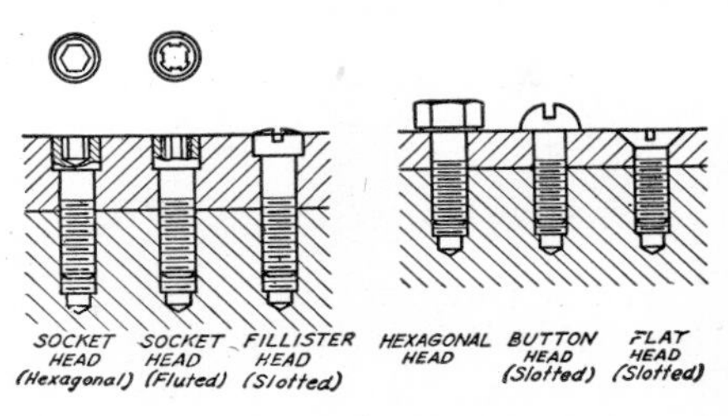

Fig. 17.26. Cap screws.

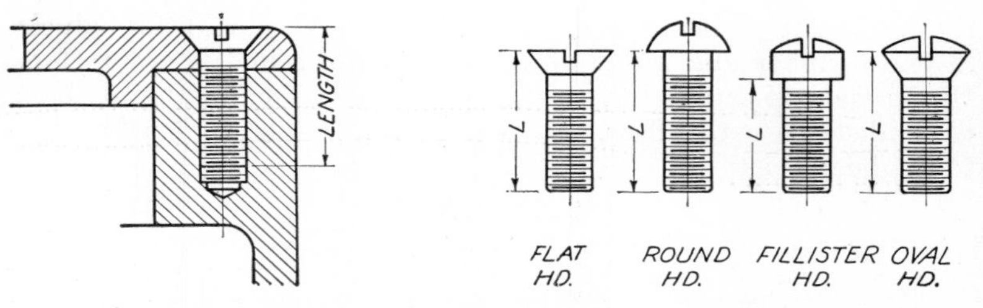

Fig. 17.27. Use of a machine screw. **Fig. 17.28. Types of machine screws.**

machine screw $1\frac{1}{4}''$ or less in length is threaded to the underneath side of the head.

To specify machine screws, give the diameter, threads per inch, thread series, fit, length, and type of head.

EXAMPLE: No. 12–24*NC*–**3** × $\frac{3}{4}''$ FIL. HD. MACH. SC.

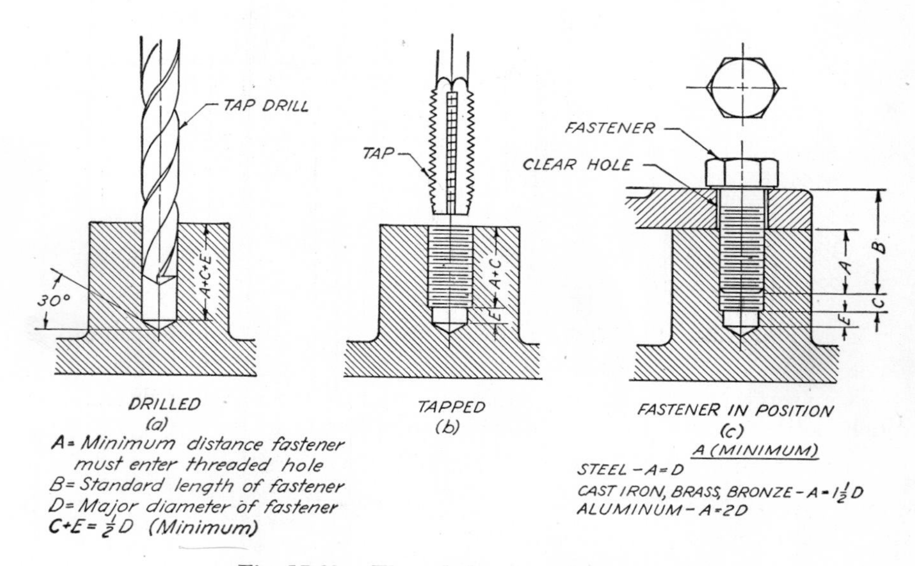

Fig. 17.29. Threaded hole and fastener.

It is good practice to abbreviate by omitting the thread series and class of fit.

EXAMPLE: No. 12–24 × $\frac{3}{4}''$ FIL. HD. MACH. SC.

17.22. Commercial lengths: studs, cap screws, machine screws. Unless a fastening of any of these types carries a constant and appreciable fatigue stress, the usual practice is to have it enter a distance related to its nominal diameter (Fig. 17.29). If the depth of the hole is not limited, it should be drilled to a depth of 1 diameter beyond the end of the fastener to permit tapping to a distance of ½ diameter below the fastener.

The length of the fastening should be determined to the nearest commercial length that will allow it to fulfill minimum conditions. In the case of a stud, care should be taken that the length allows for a full engagement of the nut. Commercial lengths for fasteners increase by the following increments:

Standard length increments:
For fastener lengths ¼″ to 1″ = ⅛″
For fastener lengths 1″ to 4″ = ¼″

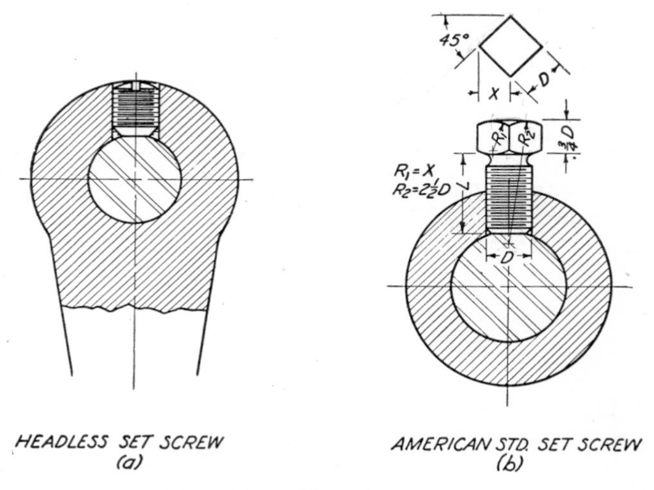

Fig. 17.30. Use of set screws.

17.23. Set screws. Set screws are used principally to prevent rotary motion between two parts, such as that which tends to occur in the case of a rotating member mounted on a shaft. A set screw is screwed through one part until the point presses firmly against the other part (Fig. 17.30).

The several forms of safety heads shown in Fig. 17.31 are available in combination with any of the points. Headless set screws comply with safety codes and should be used on all revolving parts. The many serious injuries that have been caused by the projecting heads of square-head set screws have led to legislation prohibiting their use in some states.

Set screws are specified by giving the diameter, number of threads per inch, series, class of fit, length, type of head, and type of point.

EXAMPLE: ¼-20UNC-2A × ½ SLOTTED CONE PT. SET SC.

The preferred abbreviated form gives the diameter, number of threads per inch, length, type of head, and type of point.

EXAMPLE: ¼-20 × ½ HEX. SOCKET CONE PT. SET SC.

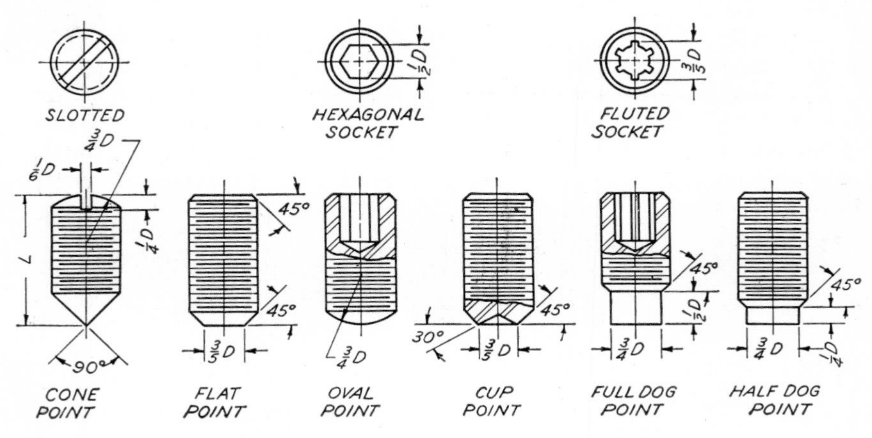

Fig. 17.31. Set screws.

17.24. Application of set screws. Fig. 17.32 illustrates the method of milling a flat surface on a shaft to provide a seat for a set screw. This practice prevents the formation of a burr on the rounded surface and creates a more resistant pressure between the set-screw point and the shaft.

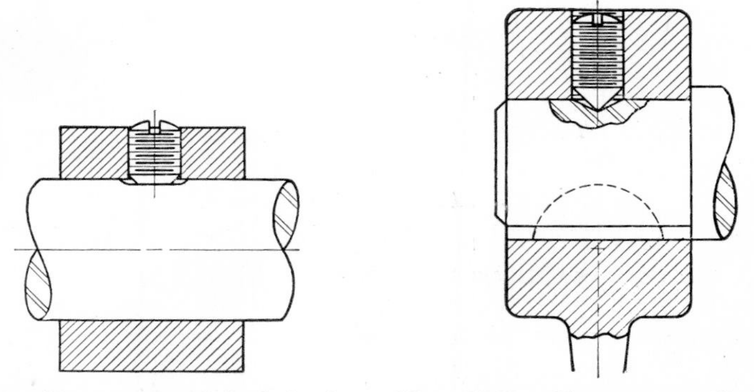

Fig. 17.32. Treatment of shaft for flat point set screw.

Fig. 17.33. Treatment of shaft for cone point set screw.

The cone point which fits into a conical spot in the shaft (Fig. 17.33) is sometimes used to prevent both rotary and longitudinal axial motion.

17.25. Keys. Keys are used in the assembling of machine parts to secure them against relative motion, generally rotary, as is the case between shafts, cranks, wheels, and so on. When the relative forces are not great, a round key, saddle key, or flat key is used (Fig. 17.34). For heavier duty, rectangular keys are more suitable.

The square key (Fig. 17.35) and the Pratt and Whitney key (Fig. 17.36) are the two keys most frequently used in machine design. A plain milling

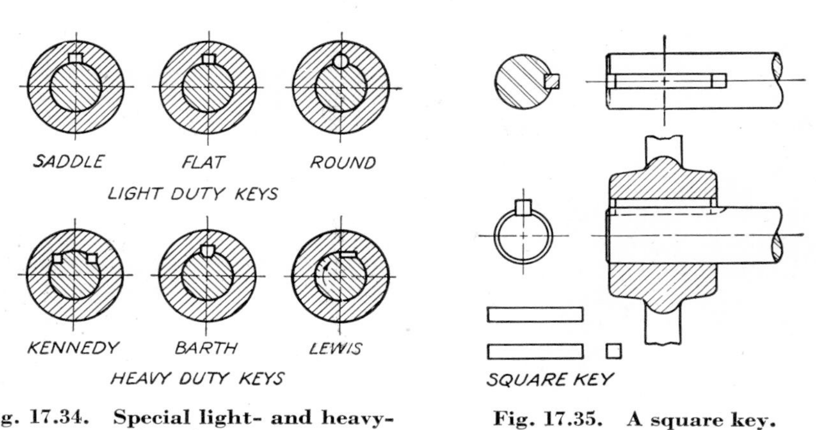

Fig. 17.34. Special light- and heavy-duty keys.

Fig. 17.35. A square key.

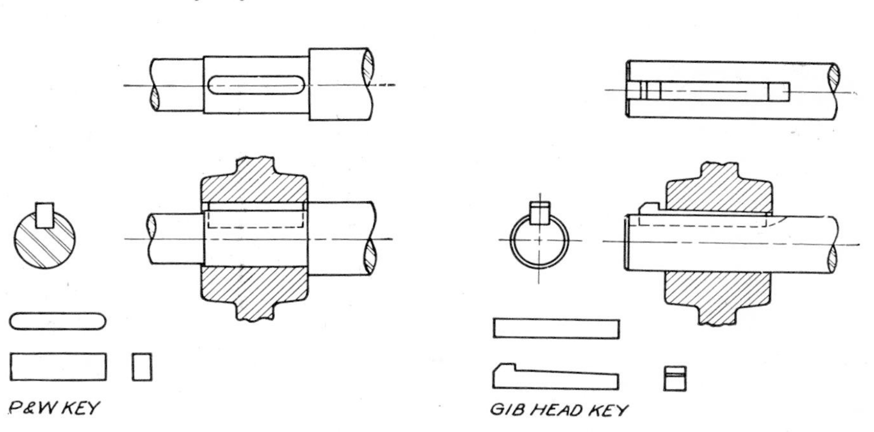

Fig. 17.36. A Pratt and Whitney key.

Fig. 17.37. A gib-head key.

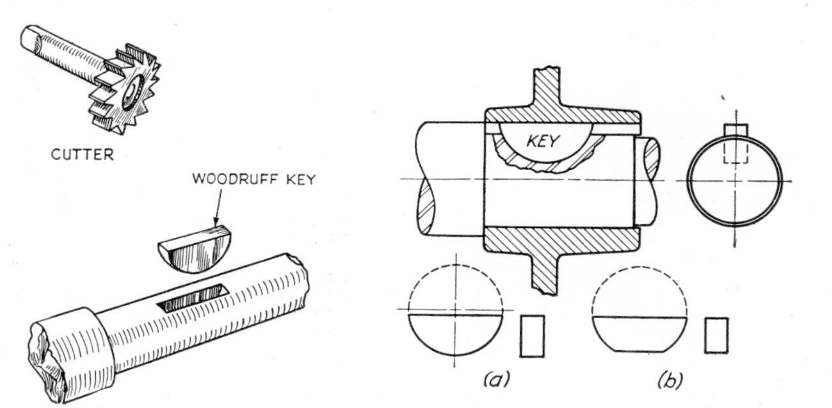

Fig. 17.38. A Woodruff key.

cutter is used to cut the keyway for the square key, while an end mill is used for the Pratt and Whitney keyway. Both keys fit tightly in the shaft and in the part mounted upon it.

The gib-head key (Fig. 17.37) is designed so that the head remains far enough from the hub to allow a drift pin to be driven to remove the key. The hub side of the key is tapered $\frac{1}{8}''$ per foot to insure a fit tight enough to prevent both axial and rotary motion. For this type of key, the keyway must be cut to one end of the shaft.

17.26. Woodruff keys. A Woodruff key is a flat segmental disc with either a flat or a round bottom (Fig. 17.38). It is always specified by a number, the last two digits of which indicate the nominal diameter in eighths of an inch, while the digits preceding the last two give the nominal width in thirty-seconds of an inch.

A practical rule for selecting a Woodruff key for a given shaft is: Choose a standard key that has a width approximately equal to one-fourth of the diameter of the shaft, and a radius nearly equal (plus or minus) to

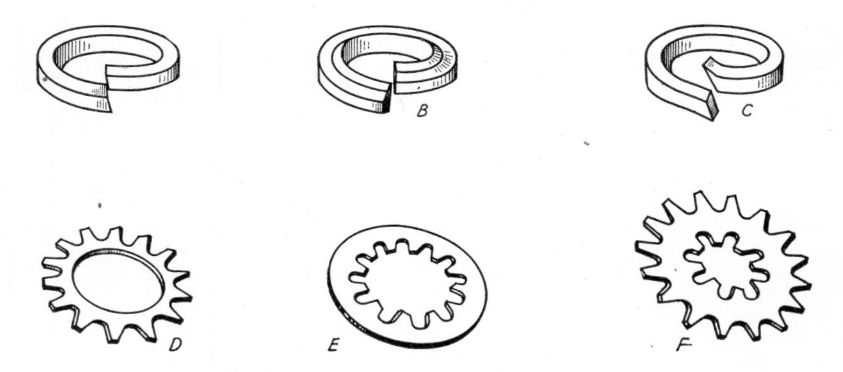

Fig. 17.39. Special lock washers.

the radius of the shaft. Table XXII in the Appendix gives the dimensions for American Standard Woodruff keys.

When Woodruff keys are drawn, it should be remembered that the center of the arc is placed above the top of the key at a distance shown in column *E* in the table.

17.27. Locking devices. A few of the many types of locking devices that prevent nuts from becoming loose under vibration are shown in Figs. 17.39–17.46.

Fig. 17.39 shows six forms of patented spring washers. The ones shown in *D*, *E*, and *F* have internal and external teeth. Although the external tooth type is used more often than the internal tooth design, the latter is desirable where a smooth outside edge is to be preferred.

A fastener and washer combination that can be purchased preassembled is shown in Fig. 17.40. The shank-locking screw (Fig. 17.41), having a slot cut in the thread, is spread to a slight "bulge" so that there will be a friction contact against the thread in the tapped hole.

Fig. 17.42 shows a bolt and nut combination along with a Palnut. The Palnut is in reality a single-thread locknut having a slotted cone-shaped thread-engaging portion. When tightened down, the outside of the nut is forced securely against the regular nut. The locking action (due to the design) is produced by a spring action upward against the thread and downward against the regular nut.

Fig. 17.40. Shakeproof preassembled fastener and washer.

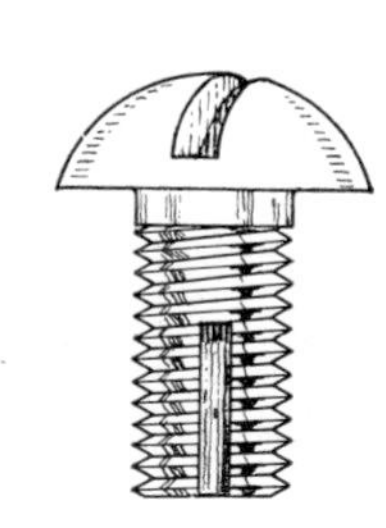

Fig. 17.41. Shank-locking screw.

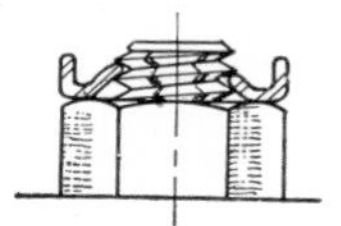

Fig. 17.42. Bolt, nut, and palnut.

Fig. 17.43 shows a preassembled nut and washer combination.

Secured in the top of the elastic stop nut shown in Fig. 17.44 is a red fiber locking collar slightly smaller than the diameter of the bolt. Because this collar is plastic in character, it forms to the bolt thread and grips securely enough to prevent the nut from coming loose under strong vibration.

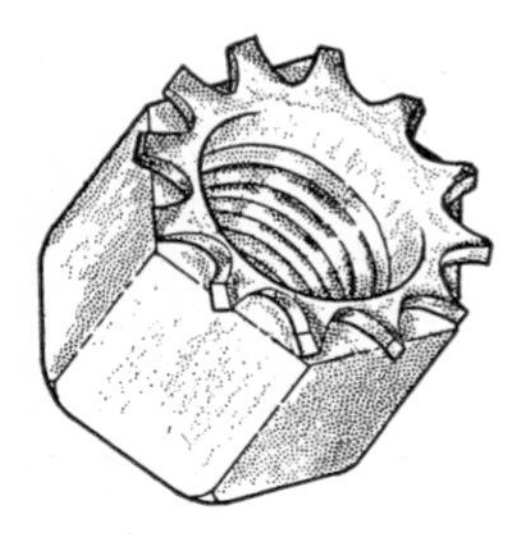

Fig. 17.43. Shakeproof preassembled nut and lock washer.

Fig. 17.44. Elastic stop nut.

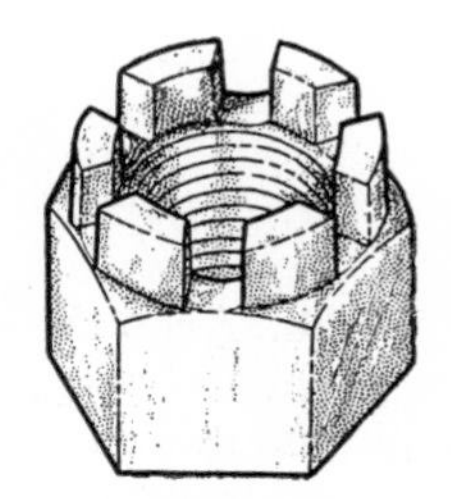

Fig. 17.45. Castellated nut.

In common use is the castellated nut (Fig. 17.46*a*) with a spring cotter pin that passes through the shaft and the slots in the top. This type is used extensively in automotive and aeronautical work.

Fig. 17.46(*b*) shows a regular nut that is prevented from loosening by an American Standard jam nut. A jam nut has the same across-flats dimension as a regular nut of the same diameter (Table VII, Appendix).

In Fig. 17.46(*c*) the use of two jam nuts is illustrated.

A regular nut with a spring-lock washer is shown in Fig. 17.46(*d*). The reaction provided by the lock washer tends to prevent the nut from turning.

A regular nut with a spring cotter pin through the shaft, to prevent the nut from backing off, is shown in Fig. 17.46(*e*).

Special devices for locking nuts are illustrated in Fig. 17.46(*f*) and (*g*). A set screw may be held in position with a jam nut as in (*h*).

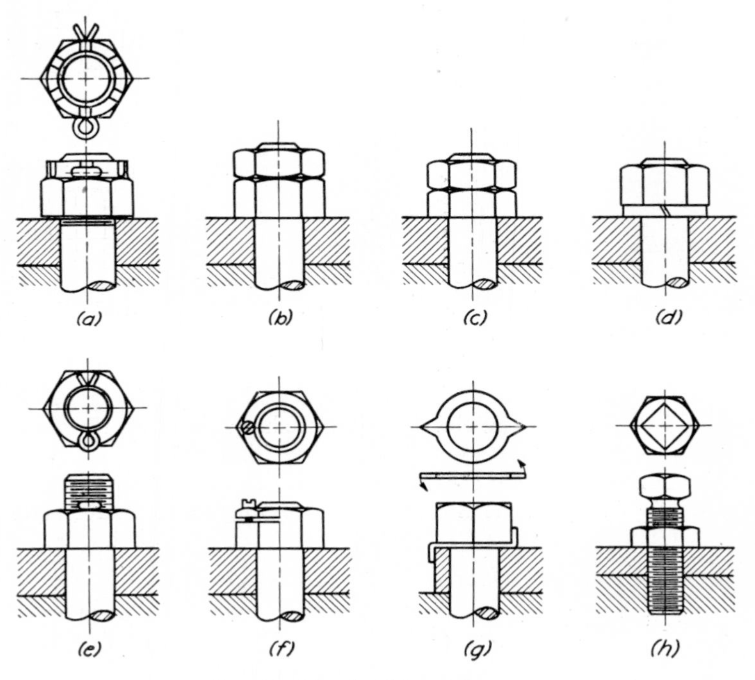

Fig. 17.46. Locking schemes.

17.28. Areo thread. The Areo-thread screw-thread system allows the use of high-strength cap screws and studs in light soft metals such as aluminum and magnesium, through the use of a phosphor bronze or stainless steel coilspring lining in the tapped hole, as shown in Fig. 17.47. This coil (screw bushing) is formed to fit a modified American Standard thread. Special inserting and extracting tools are needed for inserting the coil in the tapped hole.

17.29. Parker-Kalon self-tapping screws and nails (Fig. 17.48). Parker-Kalon self-tapping screws are unique in that they have a specially hardened thread that makes it possible for the screws to form their own internal thread as they are driven into a hole. The use of self-tapping screws eliminates costly tapping operations and the time consuming task of assembling and tightening nuts and bolts.

Type "A" fasteners, known as the original sheet metal screws, are used extensively for sheet metal work in the manufacture of signs, furnaces, automobiles, and aircraft.

Type "Z" fasteners are suitable for assembling both light and heavy sheet metal, aluminum and die castings, and parts made of plastics.

When using self-tapping fasteners and screw nails detailed information should be obtained from data sheets furnished by the Parker-Kalon Corporation.

17.30. Miscellaneous bolts, screws, and nuts. Other types of bolts and screws that have been adopted for commercial use are illustrated in Fig. 17.49.

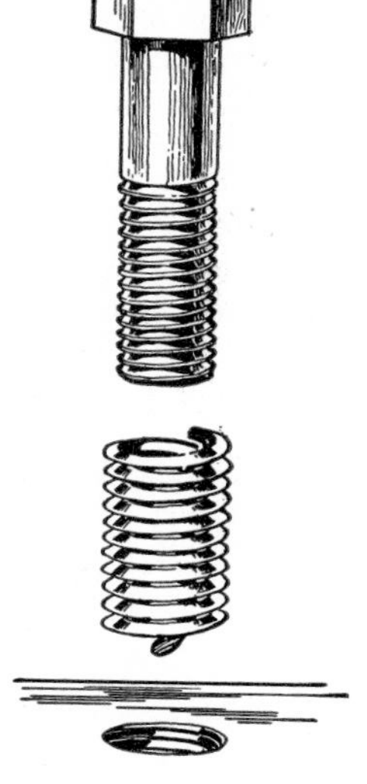

Fig. 17.47. Areo thread.

Wood screws have threads proportioned for the holding strength of wood. They are available with different forms of heads (flat, round, and oval).

The Phillips head, shown in Fig. 17.50 for a wood screw, is one of various types of recessed heads. Although special drivers are usually employed for installation, an ordinary screw driver can be used. Machine screws, capscrews, and many special types of fasteners are available with Phillips heads.

A few of the fastenings shown in Fig. 17.49 have been standardized by the American Standards Association.

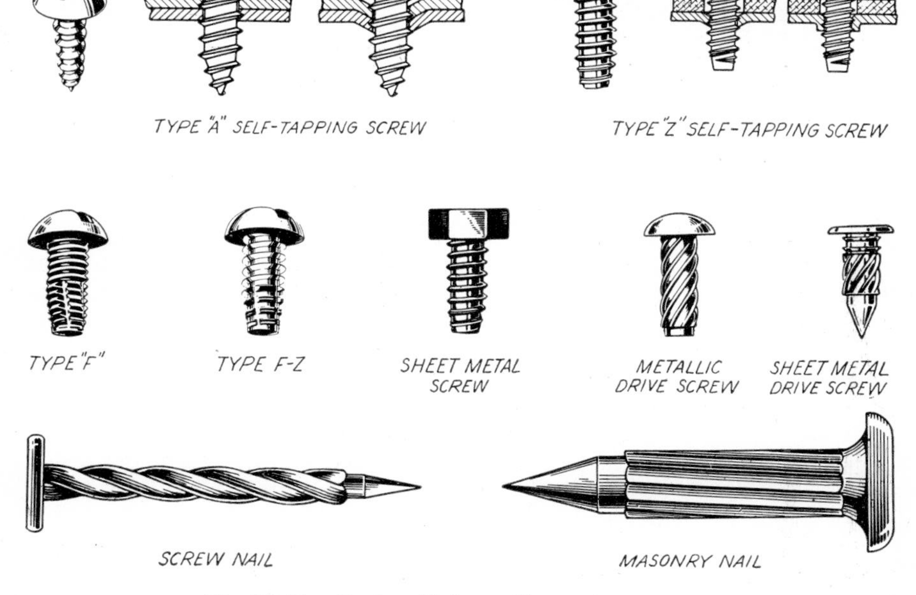

Fig. 17.48. Parker-Kalon self-tapping screws.

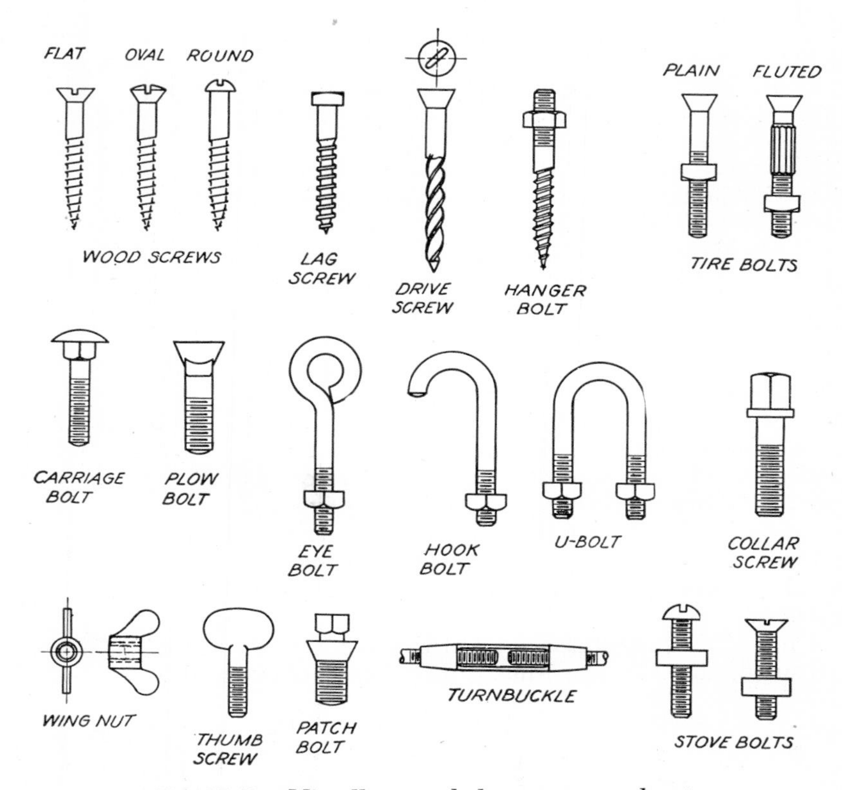

Fig. 17.49. Miscellaneous bolts, screws, and nuts.

17.31. Rivets. Rivets are permanent fasteners used chiefly for connecting members in such structures as buildings and bridges and for assembling steel sheets and plates for tanks, boilers, and ships. They are cylindrical rods of wrought iron or soft steel, with one head formed when manufactured. A head is formed on the other end after the rivet has been put in place through the drilled or punched holes of the mating parts. A hole for a rivet is generally drilled, punched, or punched and reamed $\frac{1}{16}''$ larger than the diameter of the shank of the rivet. Fig. 17.51 (*a*) illustrates a rivet in position, before heading, with enough of a shank projecting to completely fill the hole and form the head. Fig. 17.51(*b*) shows the fastening completed. Small rivets, less than $\frac{1}{2}''$ in diameter, may be driven cold, but the larger sizes are driven hot. For specialized types of engineering work, rivets are manufactured of chrome-iron, nickel, brass, copper, and so on. For-

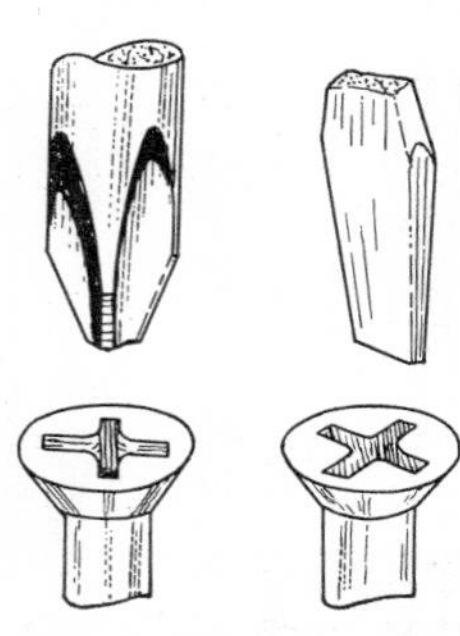

Fig. 17.50. Phillips head screw.

mula proportions for American Standard small-head rivets are shown in Fig. 17.52. (See Table XIX, Appendix.)

17.32. Riveted joints. Joints on boilers, tanks, and so on, are classified as either lap joints or butt joints (Fig. 17.53). Lap joints are generally

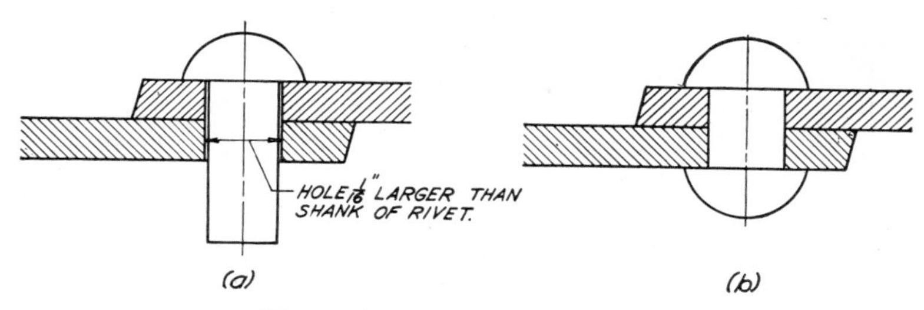

Fig. 17.51. Riveting procedure.

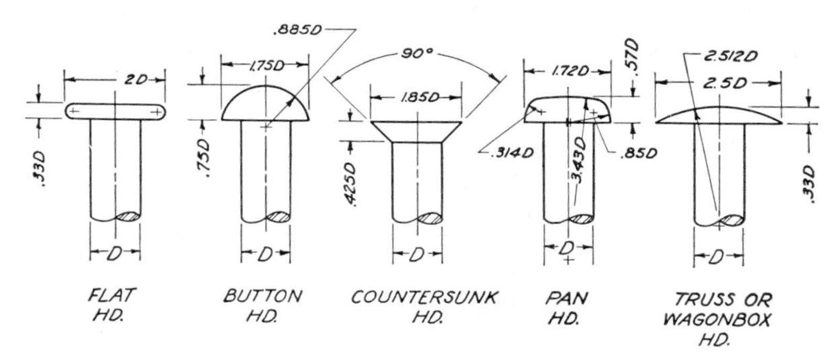

Fig. 17.52. Formula dimensions for American Standard rivets.

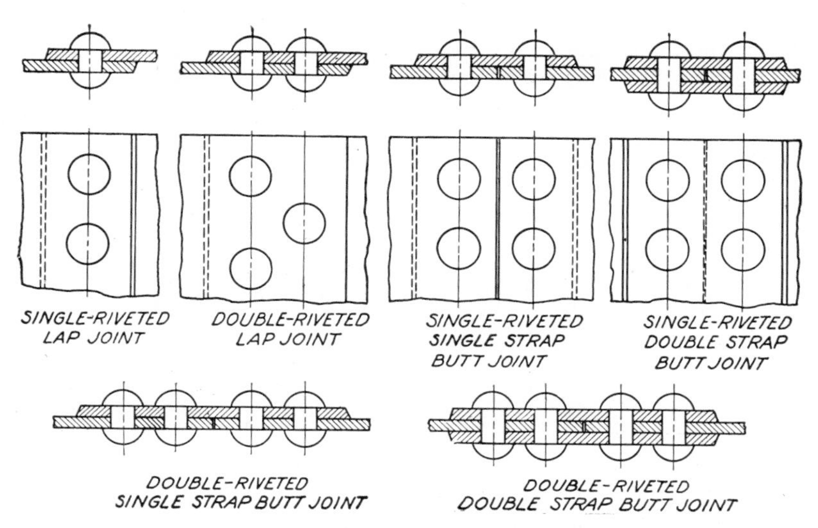

Fig. 17.53. Forms of riveted joints.

used for seams around the circumference. Butt joints are used for longitudinal seams, except on small tanks where the pressure is to be less than 100 pounds per square inch.

17.33. Springs. In production work, a spring is largely a matter of mathematical calculation rather than drawing, and it is usually purchased

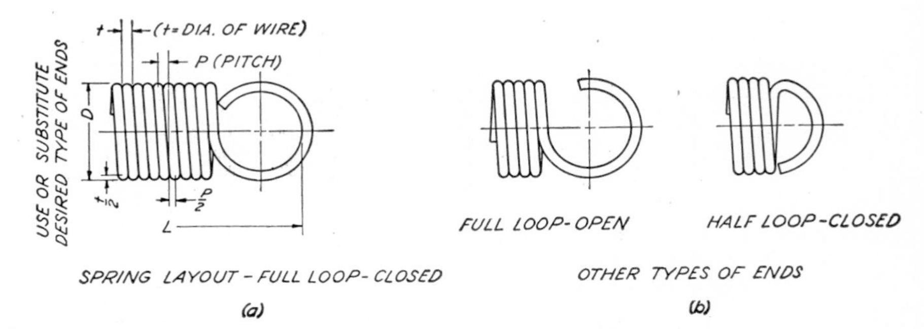

Fig. 17.54. Tension springs.

from a spring manufacturer, with the understanding that it will fulfill specified conditions. For experimental work and when only one is needed, it may be formed by winding oil-tempered spring wire or music wire around a cylindrical bar. As it is wound, the wire follows the helical path of the screw thread. For this reason the steps in the layout of the representation for a spring are similar to the screw thread as shown in Figs. 17.54 and 17.55. Pitch distances are marked off, and the coils are given a slope of one-half of the pitch. Fig. 17.54(*a*) shows a partial layout of a tension spring. Other types of ends are shown in (*b*). A compression spring layout, with various types of ends, is illustrated in Fig. 17.55.

When making a detail working drawing of a spring, it should be shown to its free length. On either an assembly or detail drawing, a fairly accurate representation, neatly drawn, will satisfy all requirements.

Single line symbols for the representation of springs are shown in Fig. 17.56.

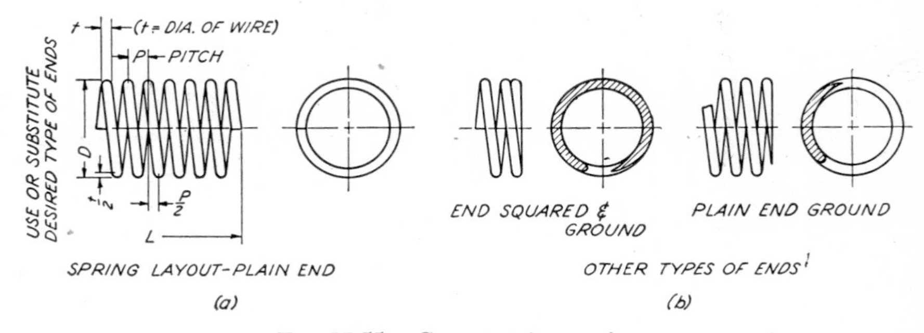

Fig. 17.55. Compression springs.

The length and controlling diameter must be given along with the size and number of turns of the wire on a detail working drawing of a spring. The type of end must always be shown even though the spring is standard and is not designed to suit some special condition.

Fig. 17.56. Single line representation of springs.*

17.34. Problems. Excellent practice in drawing threads, threaded fasteners, keys and rivets is provided through the making of some of the assembly drawings given in Chapter 19. A few of the typical situations are offered here, however, in order to familiarize the student with the approved methods of representation before he is required to use them on a working drawing.

1. Draw a semiconventional representation of a V-thread (Fig. 17.8). Make the diameter of the thread 2″, the pitch $\frac{1}{4}$″, and the length 3″.

2. Draw a semiconventional representation of a square thread. Make the diameter of the thread $2\frac{1}{4}$″, the pitch $\frac{1}{2}$″, and the length 3″.

3. Draw a semiconventional representation of an Acme thread. Make the diameter $2\frac{1}{4}$″, the pitch $\frac{1}{2}$″, and the length 3″.

4. Same as problem 3, but show a B & S worm thread.

5. Draw an American Standard hexagonal-head bolt and nut. The diameter of the bolt is to be 1″; the thread is to be UNC. The bolt is to be semifinished and have a length of 5″. Use the semiconventional representation. The length of the thread should be $1\frac{1}{2}$ D plus $\frac{1}{4}$″.

6. Using the regular symbol, as shown in Fig. 17.14, draw the following fasteners in the order given: (1) a $\frac{3}{4}$″ × 3″ hexagonal-head cap screw, (2) a $\frac{5}{8}$″ × 3″ fillister-head cap screw, (3) a $\frac{3}{4}$″ × 3″ flat-head cap screw. Balance the three drawings on an $8\frac{1}{2}$″ × 11″ or a 9″ × 12″ sheet of drawing paper.

7. Draw the threads shown in Fig. 17.57.

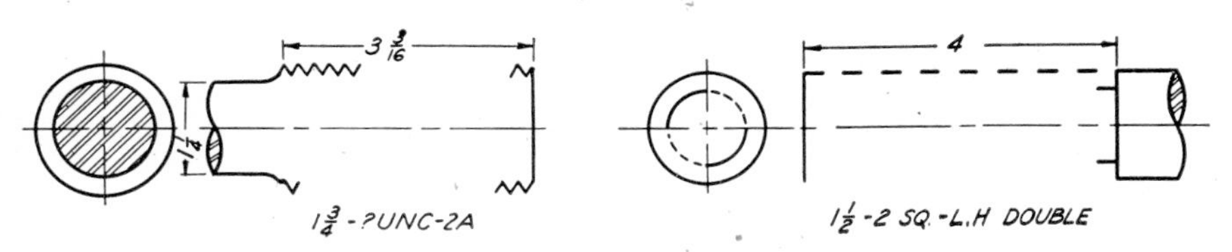

Fig. 17.57.

* ASA Z14.1–1946.

8. Draw the layout shown in Fig. 17.58, and on it show the following fasteners: (1) On center line *A-A* draw a $\frac{3}{4}''$ unfinished hexagonal-head bolt and nut. (2) On center line *B-B* draw a $\frac{7}{8}''$ square-head bolt and nut. (3) On center line *C-C* draw a $\frac{3}{4}''$ fillister-head cap screw. (4) On center line *D-D* draw a $\frac{5}{8}''$ hexagonal head cap screw. Determine the measurements for the layout by using the given scale. Make each fastener a standard length. Use the regular symbol for the representation of the threads.

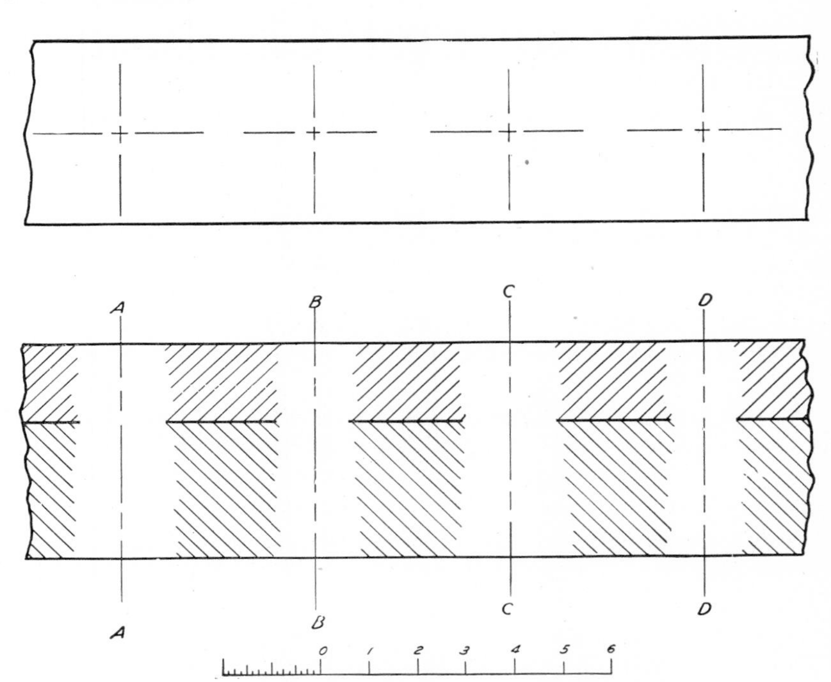

Fig. 17.58.

9. Reproduce the three layouts shown in Fig. 17.59 to full size, using the given scale to determine the measurements. On layout (1), complete the drawing to show a suitable fastener on center line *A-A*. On layout (2), show a $\frac{1}{2}''$ hexagonal-head cap screw on center line *B-B*. On layout (3), show a $\frac{3}{8}''$ button-head rivet on center line *C-C* and a No. 608 Woodruff key on center line *D-D*. Use the regular symbol for the representation of threads.

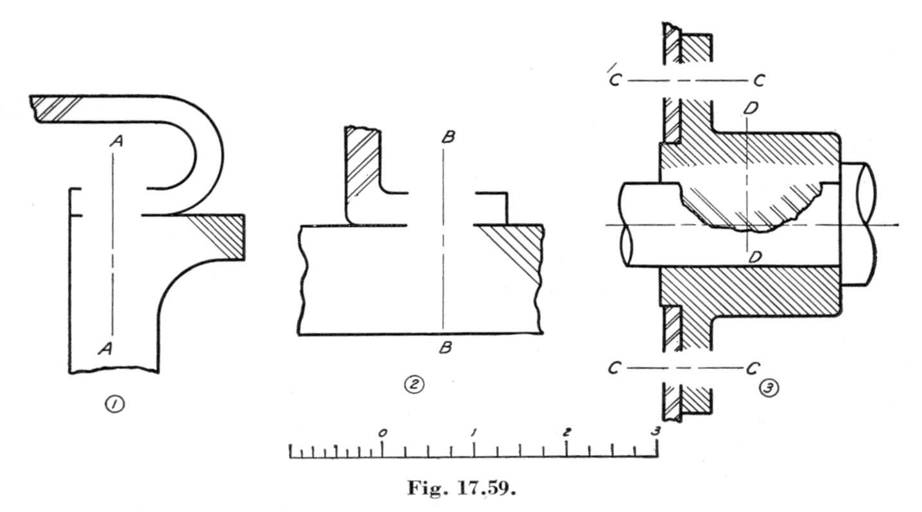

Fig. 17.59.

10. (Fig. 17.60.) Reproduce the views of the assembly of the alignment bear ing. On C. L's. A show $\frac{1}{4}''$ button-head rivets (4 required). On C. L. B show a $\frac{5}{16}'' \times \frac{1}{2}''$ Am. Std. square-head set screw. Do not dimension the views.

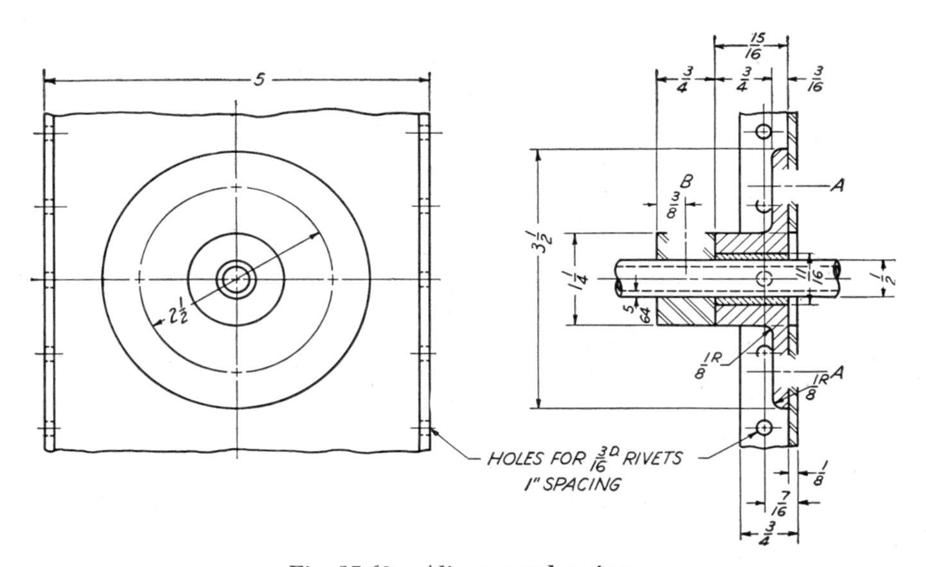

Fig. 17.60. Alignment bearing.

11. (Fig. 17.61.) Reproduce the views of the assembly of the impeller drive. On C. L's. A show $\frac{1}{4}''$-20 UNC × $\frac{1}{2}''$ round-head machine screws and regular lock washers. On C. L. B show a No. 406 Woodruff key. On C. L. C show a standard No. 2 × $1\frac{1}{2}''$ taper pin.

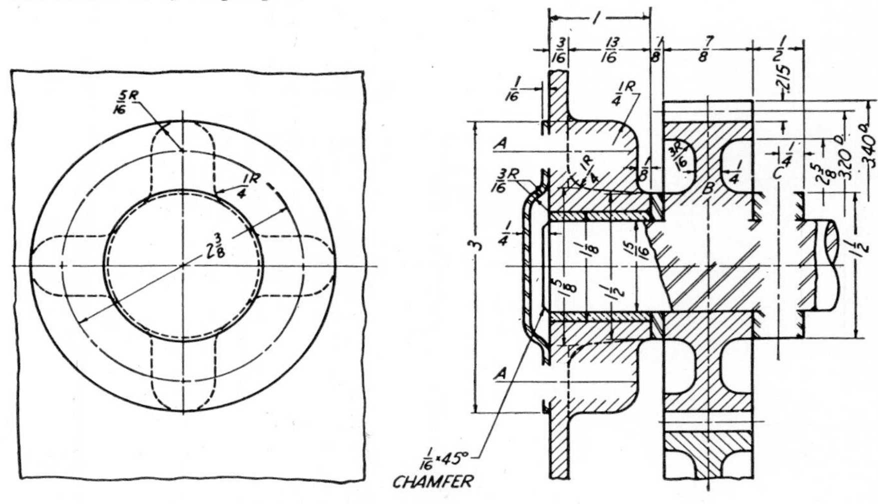

Fig. 17.61. Impeller drive.

12. (Fig. 17.62.) Reproduce the views of the assembly of the bearing head. On C. L's. A show $\frac{1}{2}''$-UNC studs with regular lock washers and regular semi-finished hexagonal nuts (4 required). On C. L's. B show $\frac{3}{8}''$-UNC × $1\frac{1}{4}''$ hexagonal-head cap screws (2 required). On C. L. C drill through and tap $\frac{1}{8}''$ pipe thread.

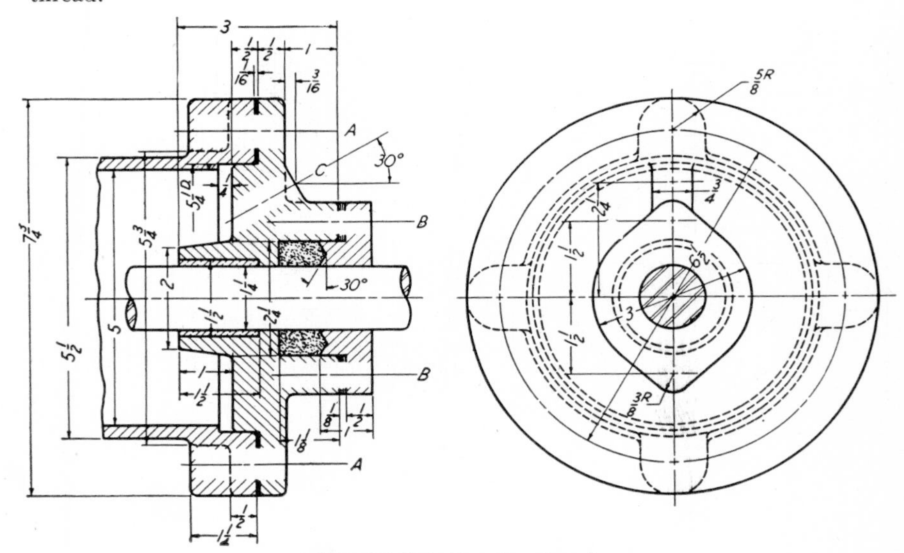

Fig. 17.62. Bearing head.

13. (Fig. 17.63.) Reproduce the views of the assembly of the air cylinder. On C. L. A-A at the left end of the shaft show a 1″-UNF semifinished hexagonal nut. At the right end show a hole tapped $\frac{3}{4}''$-UNF × $1\frac{1}{2}''$ deep. Between the piston and the (right) end plate draw a spring 3″ O.D., **5** full coils, $\frac{1}{4}''$ wire. On C. L's. B show $\frac{3}{8}''$-UNC × $1\frac{1}{4}''$ hexagonal-head cap screws. On C. L's. C draw $\frac{1}{4}$-UNC × $\frac{3}{4}''$ flat-head cap screws with heads to the left. On C. L. D show a $\frac{1}{4}''$ standard pipe thread. On C. L's. E show $\frac{1}{2}''$-UNC × $1\frac{3}{4}''$ semifinished hexagonal-head bolts. Use semifinished hexagonal nuts. Show visible fasteners on the end view.

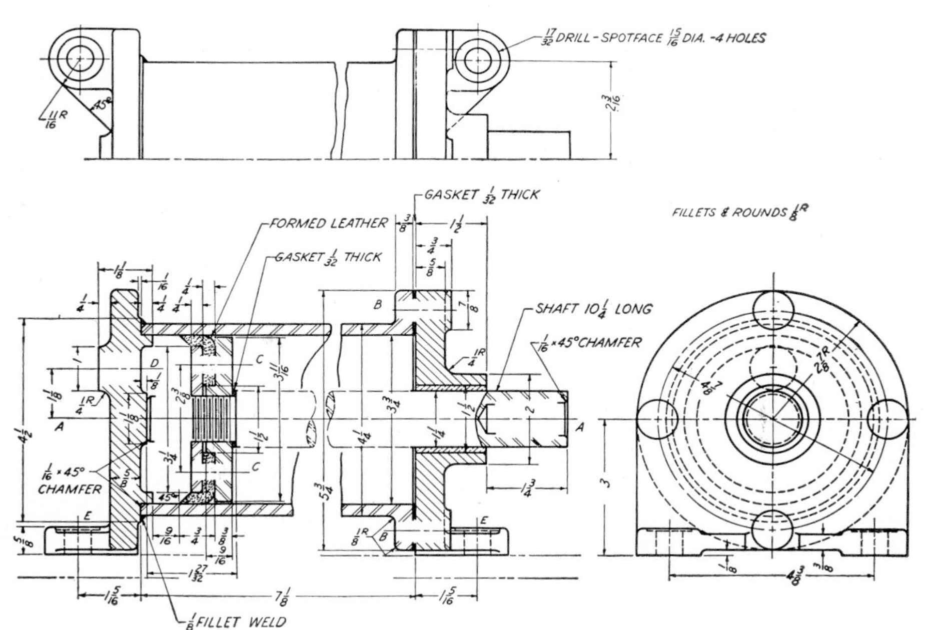

Fig. 17.63. Air cylinder.

18 PIPING DRAWINGS

18.1. Since piping is used in all types of construction for conveying fluids and gases such as oil, water, steam, and chemicals, some knowledge of it is essential not only for the draftsman making drawings but for the engineer who must select and use pipe in the design of machines, power plants, water systems, and so on. There are so many types of fittings and materials used for various purposes that only the most common can be discussed briefly in this chapter. Additional information may be obtained from publications of research associations and from the catalogs of manufacturers.

18.2. Pipe materials. The Greeks and Romans used pipes made of wood or lead, but the quick deterioration of wood and the poisoning brought about by lead made both types unsatisfactory. Not until about 1660 was iron pipe cast in a foundry; this was for the fountains at Versailles, France. Before the year 1834, when the first foundry was established at Millville, New Jersey, all cast-iron pipe used in this country was purchased in England. Pipe made of bored pine and spruce log was used in many eastern cities.* Even today water pipes composed of wood staves and steel hoops can be seen in the mountain regions of the west. For all general purposes, however, cast iron, wrought iron, and steel pipes are now used.

Cast-iron pipe is suitable for underground gas and water mains, plumbing lines, and low-pressure steam systems.

Steel pipe is used chiefly where high temperatures and high pressures are encountered. The addition of such alloys as nickel, chromium, and the like makes the steel pipe more resistant to corrosion at high temperatures.

Seamless brass pipe is the most satisfactory type for hot-water lines, condenser tubes, and so on, but it is expensive and, therefore, is used only when conditions justify the extra cost.

For lines having turns and bends in accessible locations, copper tubing is frequently used. But copper pipe, even though it is flexible and can resist the corrosive action of chemicals, is not always practical. It cannot be used in any system subject to high temperatures and repeated stress.

Lead and lead-lined pipe is widely used for chemical work, particularly where piping is subject to the action of acids.

Galvanized pipe (ordinary iron pipe that has been dipped in molten zinc to prevent rust) is suitable for lines conveying drinking water.

---

* Information from a publication of the Cast Iron Pipe Research Association.

18.3. American Standard pipe thread. The American Standard pipe taper thread, illustrated in Fig. 18.1, is similar to the ordinary American Standard thread and has the same thread angle; but it is tapered $\frac{1}{16}''$ per inch, to insure a tight joint at a fitting. The crest is flattened and the root is filled in so that the depth of the thread is $0.80P$. The number of threads per inch for any given nominal diameter can be obtained from Table XXVI in the Appendix.

The distance a pipe enters a fitting is fixed for any nominal diameter. Numerical values for this distance may be determined from Table XXVI.

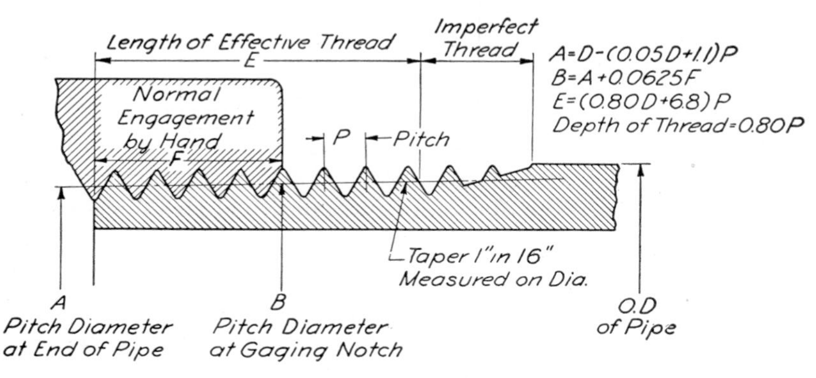

Fig. 18.1. American Standard pipe thread.

An American National straight pipe thread, having the same number of threads per inch as the taper thread, is in use for pressure-tight joints for couplings, for pressure-tight joints for grease and oil fittings, and for hose couplings and nipples. This thread may also be used for free-fitting mechanical joints. Usually a taper external thread is used with a straight internal thread, as pipe material is sufficiently ductile for an adjustment of the threads.

In specifying pipe threads, the ASA recommends that the note be formulated using symbolic letters as illustrated in Fig. 18.2. For example, the specification for a 1″ standard pipe thread should read, 1″-*NPT*. The letters *NPT*, following the nominal diameter, indicate that the thread is American National (*N*), pipe (*P*), taper (*T*) thread. Continuing with the same scheme of using letters, the specification for a 1″ straight pipe thread would read, 1″-*NPS* [National (*N*)—pipe (*P*)—straight (*S*)]. The form of note given in (*a*), reading *1″ AM. STD. PIPE THD*, is quite commonly used in practice. Identification symbols and dimensions of American National pipe threads are given in the American Standard for Pipe Threads (ASA B2.1–1945).

18.4. Drawing pipe threads. The taper on a pipe thread is so slight that it will not attract attention on a drawing unless it is exaggerated. If it is shown at all, it is usually magnified to $\frac{1}{8}''$ per inch.

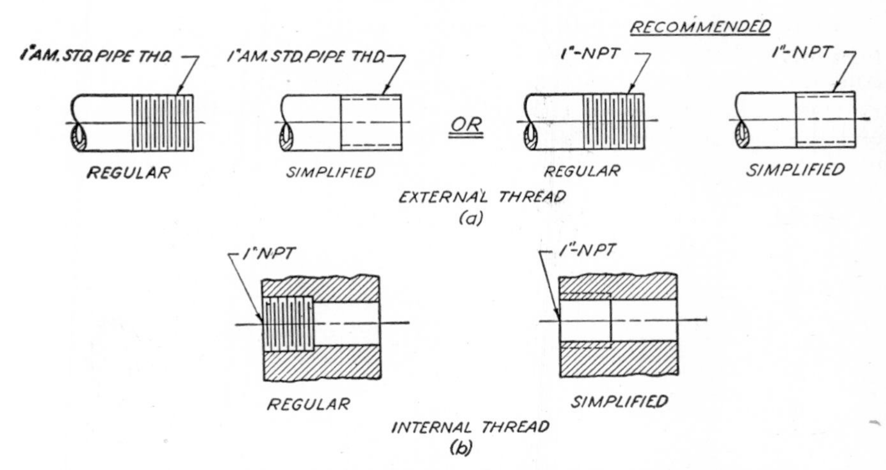

Fig. 18.2. American Standard representation of pipe threads.

Pipe threads are generally represented by the same conventional symbols used for ordinary American Standard thread. (See Fig. 18.2.)

18.5. Specification of wrought-iron and steel pipe. The standardized weights commonly used are the standard, extra strong, and double extra strong. All are specified by the nominal inside diameter.

The nominal inside diameter of standard pipe is less than the actual diameter, because early manufacturers made the wall thickness greater than necessary and, in correcting, took all of the excess from the inside to avoid altering the size of openings in fittings. Metal was added to the inside to increase wall thicknesses for the extra strong and double extra strong. As a result, all three weights of pipe for any given nominal diameter have the same outside diameter and can be used with the same fittings.

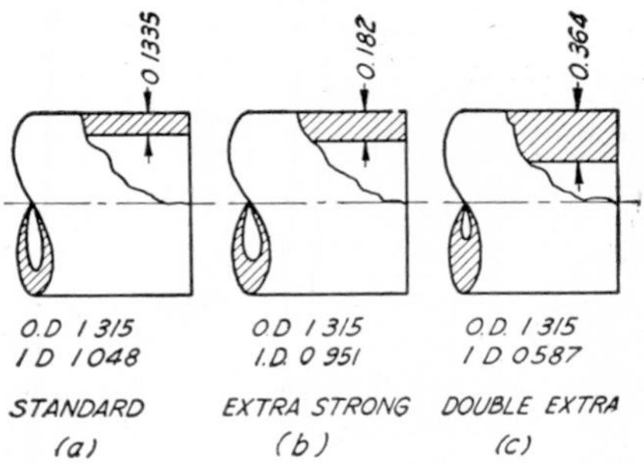

Fig. 18.3. Comparison of different weights of 1″ pipe.

Wrought-iron or steel pipe greater than 12″ in diameter is specified by giving the outside diameter and the thickness of the wall.

Fig. 18.3 illustrates the relative wall thickness of 1″ standard, extra strong, and double extra strong pipe.

18.6. Sizes of wrought-iron, steel, and cast-iron pipe. The standard-weight pipe is used for normal pressures. It may be purchased in sizes ranging from $\frac{1}{8}''$ to 12″ (nominal diameter). Pipe is received threaded on both ends with a plain coupling attached.

Extra strong pipe, designed for steam and hydraulic pressures over 125 pounds per square inch, also is manufactured in sizes $\frac{1}{8}''$ to 12″.

Double extra strong pipe, designed for extremely high pressures, is furnished in nominal diameters from ½″ to 8″ in the same lengths as the extra strong.

Cast-iron pipe, in sizes ranging up to 48″, can be used for pressures up to 350 pounds per square inch.

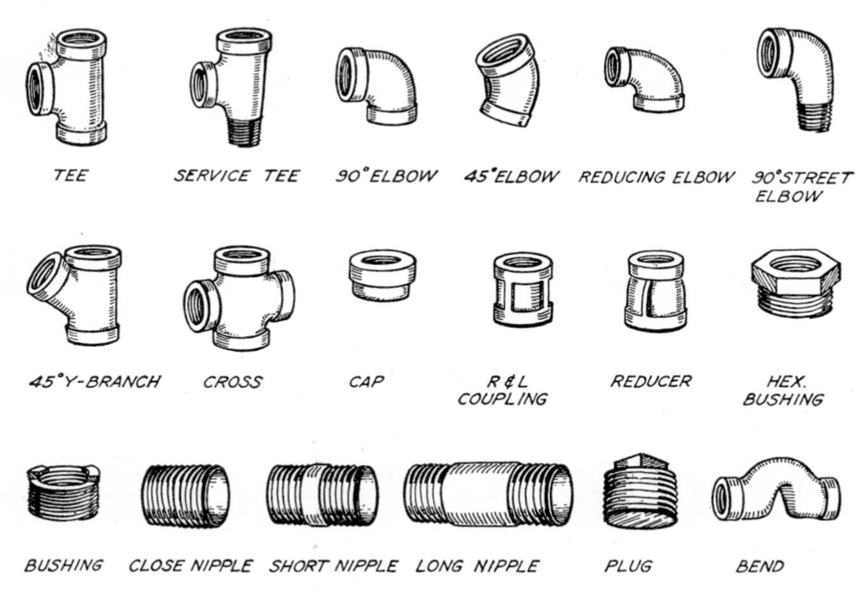

Fig. 18.4. Screwed fittings.

18.7. Pipe fittings. Fittings are parts, such as elbows, tees, crosses, couplings, nipples, flanges, and so on, which are used to make turns and connections. They fall into three general classes: screwed, welded, and flanged.

In small piping systems and for house plumbing, screwed fittings are generally used (Fig. 18.4).

Welded fittings are used where connections are to be permanent. They are manufactured of forged seamless steel, having the same thickness as the pipe. In this type of construction, the weld is depended upon to seal the joint and to carry the pipe-line stresses. Many miles of line having welded fittings are giving satisfactory service to pipe-line corporations.

Flanged fittings are used in large piping systems where pressures are high and the connection must be strong enough to carry the weight of large pipes. Table XXX in the Appendix gives the dimensions for American Standard 125-pound cast-iron flange fittings. Several types of flanges and flanged joints are shown in Figs. 18.7 and 18.8.

18.8. Screwed fittings. Straight sections of pipe are connected by a short cylindrical fitting (threaded on the inside), which is known as a *coupling*. A *right and left coupling*, which can be recognized by the ribs on the outside, is often used to close a system. A *union* is preferable, however, where pipe must be frequently disconnected.

A *cap* is screwed on the end of a pipe to close it.

A *plug* is used to close an opening in a fitting.

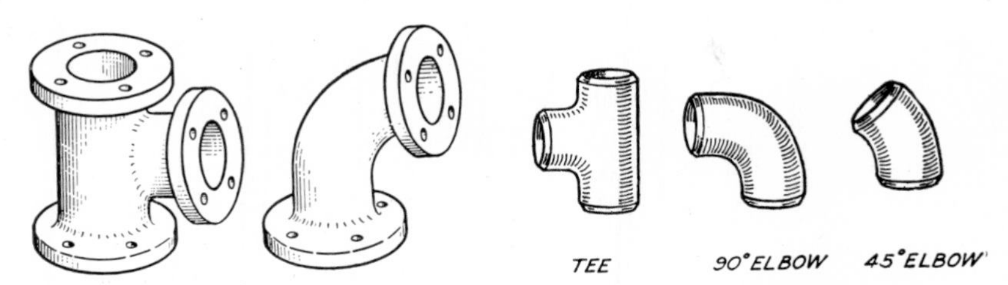

Fig. 18.5. Flanged fittings. **Fig. 18.6. Welded fittings.**

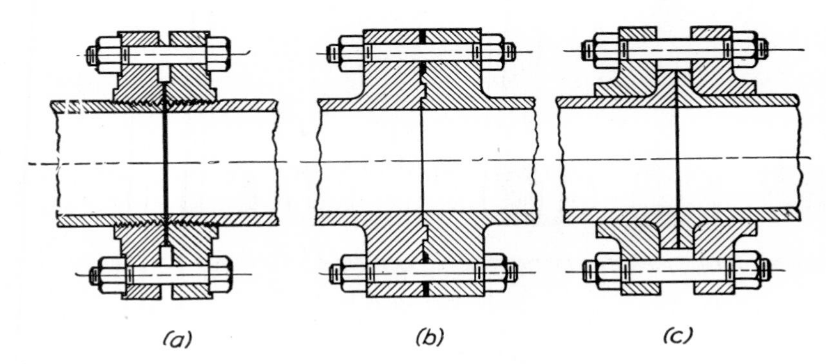

Fig. 18.7. Flanges.

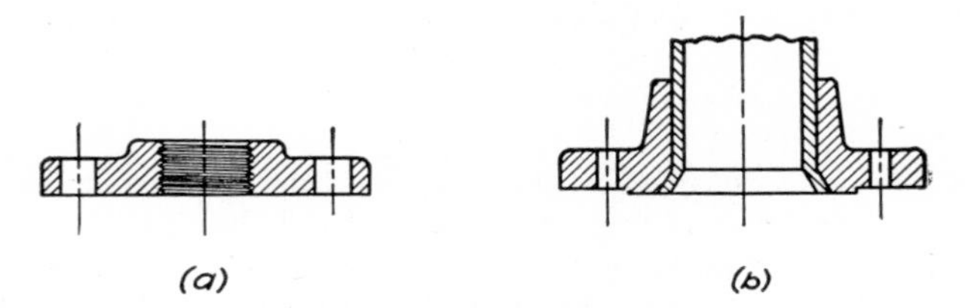

Fig. 18.8. Flanges.

A *nipple* is a short piece of pipe that has been threaded on both ends. If it is threaded the entire length, it is called a *close nipple;* if not, it is called a *short* or *long nipple*. Extra long nipples may be purchased.

A *bushing* is used to reduce the size of an opening in a fitting when it would be inconvenient to use a reducing fitting.

Tees, crosses, and *laterals* form the connections for lines and branches in a piping system.

By standardizing the screwed fittings, the American Standards Association has eliminated many difficulties that would arise if each manufacturer produced the varied sizes of elbows, tees, laterals, and so on, according to his own specifications. The adopted dimensions, now recognized by all manufacturers, will be found in Tables XXVII, XXVIII, and XXIX in the Appendix.

18.9. Specification of fittings. A fitting is specified by giving the nominal inside diameter of the pipe for which the openings are threaded,

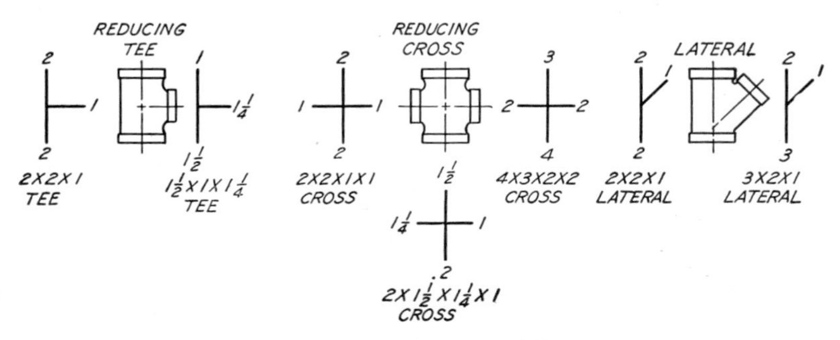

Fig. 18.9. Specification of fittings.

the type of fitting, and the material. If it connects more than one size of pipe, it is called a reducing fitting, and the largest opening of the through run is given first, followed in order by the opposite end and the outlet. Fig. 18.9 illustrates the order of specifying reducing fittings. If all of the openings are for the same size of pipe, the fitting is known as a straight tee, cross, and so on. A straight fitting is specified by the size of the openings followed by the name of the fitting (2″ tee, 4″ cross, etc.).

18.10. Unions. Screwed or flanged unions connect pipes that must be frequently disconnected for the purpose of making repairs. In many cases, screwed unions are used for making the final closing connection in a line. The union illustrated in Fig. 18.10(a) is made up of three separate

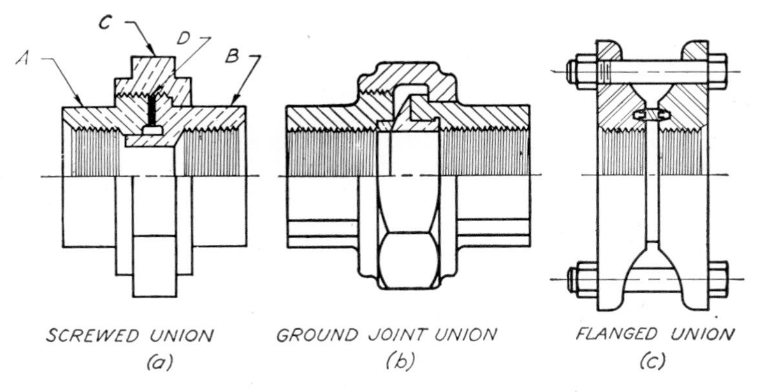

Fig. 18.10. Unions.

pieces. The mating parts, A and B, are screwed on the ends of the two pipes. The third part, the nut, draws them together so that A and B will be against the gasket, D, to insure a tight joint. In systems having pipes over 2″ in diameter, screwed unions are not generally used, because the stronger and more substantial flange unions, such as the one shown at (*c*), become desirable. A screwed union with a ground metal seat is shown at (*b*).

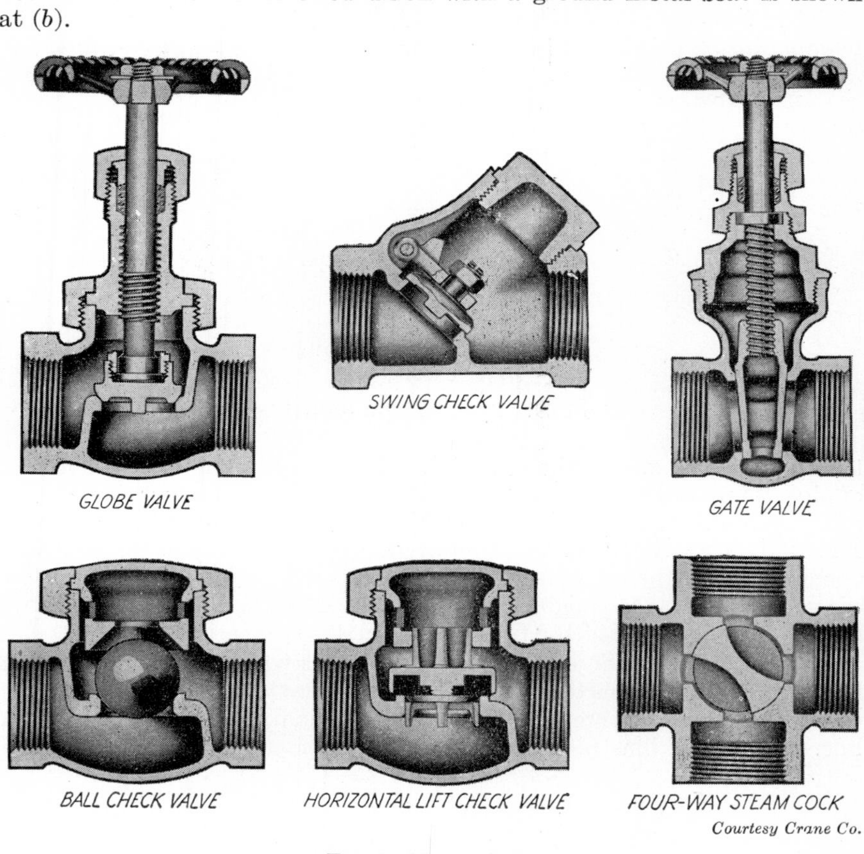

Courtesy Crane Co.

Fig. 18.11. Valves.

18.11. Valves. Valves are used in piping systems to stop or control the movement of fluids and gases. A few of the many forms are illustrated in Fig. 18.11. Of these, the globe valve and gate valve are the two types most frequently used.

Globe valves are used for throttling steam, in both high- and low-pressure steam lines, and to regulate the passage of other fluids. Their design, however, creates a slight retardation to the flow, because the fluid is forced to make a double turn and pass through the opening at 90° to the axis of the pipe. The valve disc is raised or lowered to stop or regulate the flow through a circular opening.

A gate valve allows a straight-line movement of a fluid and offers only slight resistance to the flow. Since the disc moves completely out of the passage and leaves a full opening, this type of valve is particularly suitable for water lines, oil lines, and the like.

A swing-type check valve permits movement in one direction only and prevents any back flow. It will be noted from a study of this valve that the design makes the action automatic. Such valves are used in feed-water lines to boilers. The ball-check valve is preferred for heavy liquids.

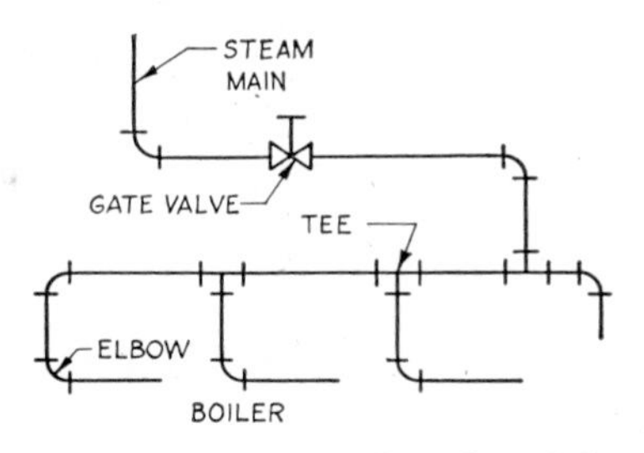

Fig. 18.12. Single-line drawing.

The dimensions of the valves given in Fig. 18.11, as well as those for many special types, may be found in the catalogs of manufacturers.

18.12. Piping drawings. Since standard pipe and fittings can be purchased for almost any purpose, a piping drawing usually shows only the arrangement of a system in some conventional form, and gives the size and location of fittings. The drawing may be a freehand sketch, single-line diagram, double-line diagram, or pictorial diagram. Occasionally, when conditions necessitate the design of special valves or the redesign of an existing type, complete working drawings are made.

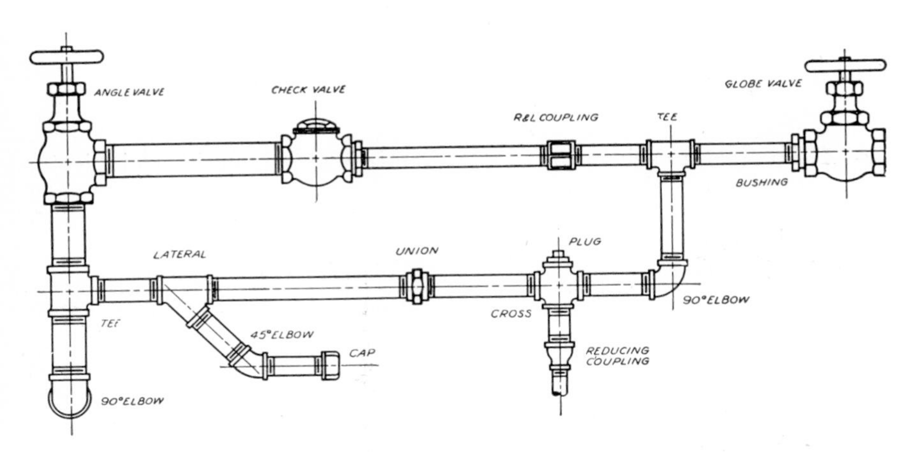

Fig. 18.13. Double-line drawing.

Single-line drawings or sketches are made in orthographic projection or are drawn as if the entire system were swung into one plane (Fig. 18.12). On these drawings, single lines represent the runs of pipe, regardless of variations in diameters; conventional symbols are used for the fittings. A developed single-line sketch is frequently used for repair work, small jobs, and for making studies and calculations. For more complicated small-scale layouts, a single-line diagram drawn in orthographic projection is more suitable.

Double-line diagrams are drawn when many similar installations are to be made at the plants of various purchasers of pumps, manufacturing equipment, heating equipment, and so on (Fig. 18.13).

A conventional pictorial diagram (Fig. 18.14), showing a piping layout in space, reveals the changes in direction and the difference in levels more clearly than does any other type of line diagram. Pictorial diagrams are often used for preliminary layouts.

18.13. Dimensions on piping drawings. The rules for dimensioning working drawings apply to piping drawings. Fittings and pipes are always located by giving center-to-center distances, because the determination of pipe lengths is generally left to the pipe fitter. Notes should be used to specify the nominal size and type of each fitting and the nominal

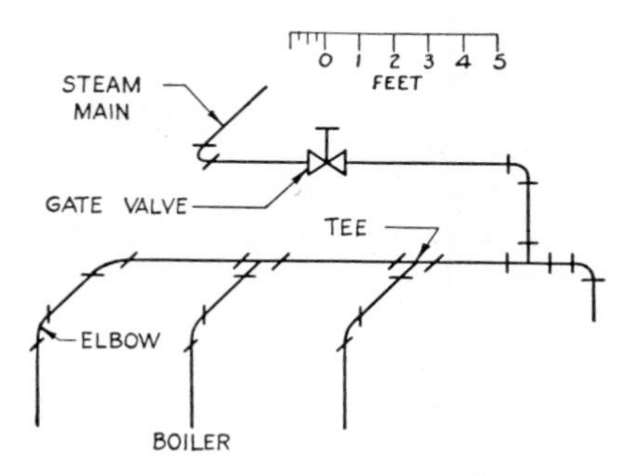

Fig. 18.14. Pictorial line diagram.

size of the pipe in each run. In addition, it is good practice to indicate, on a flanged valve, the diameter of the handwheel and its distance above the center of the fitting when wide open. It may be necessary to give over-all dimensions for other apparatus, if the maximum space to be allowed is important.

The date and a descriptive title should be given on all piping sketches and drawings.

18.14. Conventional symbols. Fig. 18.15 shows a few of the conventional symbols for fittings that have been approved by the American Standards Association.

18.15. Problems.

1. Make a freehand sketch (on $\frac{1}{8}''$ grid paper, if it is available) of a $1''$ nipple connecting, a $1''$ cast-iron elbow, and a $2'' \times 2'' \times 1''$ malleable-iron tee. The distance between centers of fittings is to be $6''$. Enter neatly, in draftsman's style, the length of the nipple to the nearest $\frac{1}{8}''$.

2. Make a freehand sketch (on $\frac{1}{8}''$ grid paper) of a $1'' \times 1'' \times 1''$ malleable-iron tee and a $1''$ cast-iron elbow joined by a length of pipe. The distance between centers of fittings is $4''$. Enter the length of the connecting pipe to the nearest $\frac{1}{8}''$.

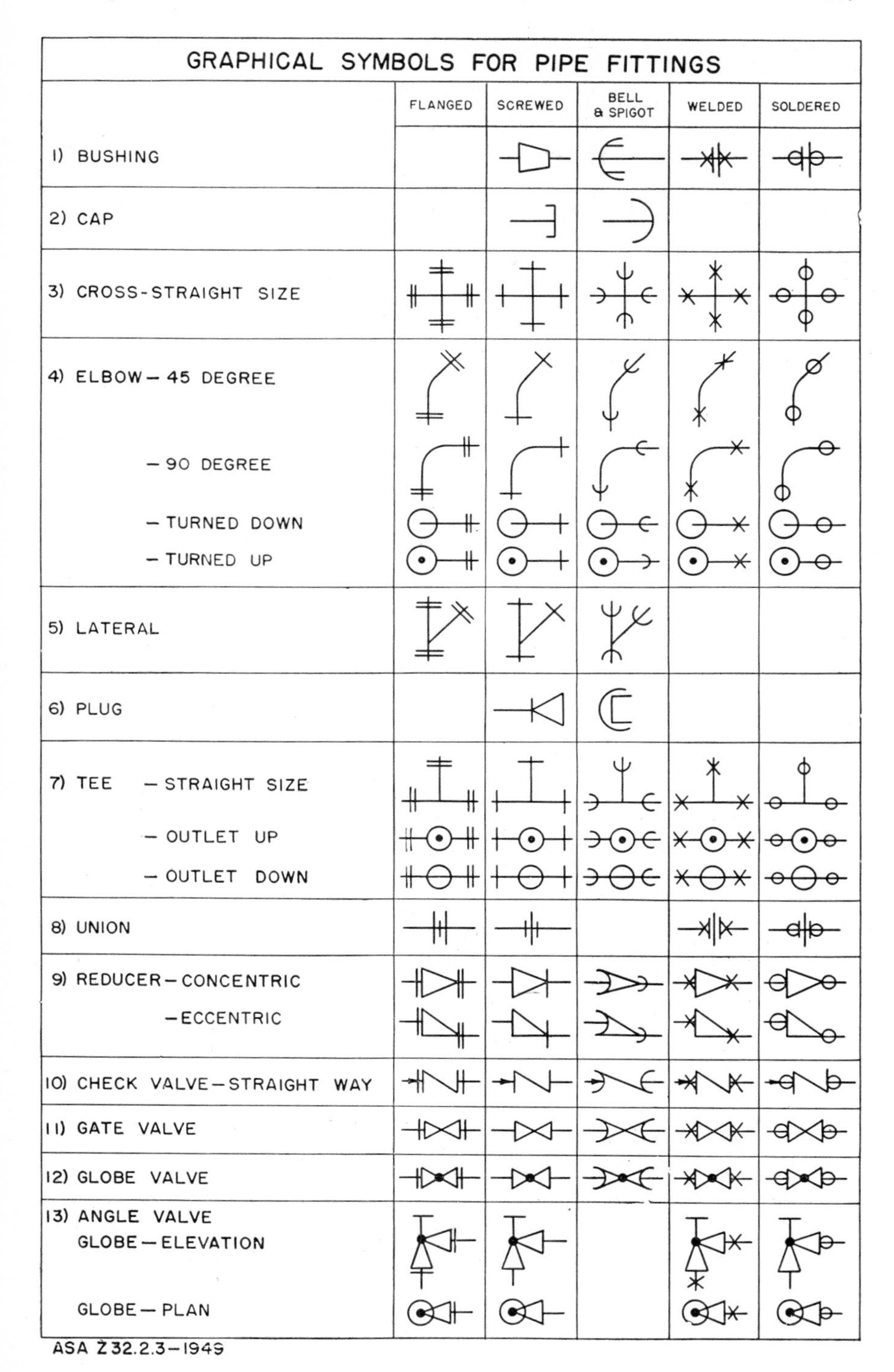

Fig. 18.15. Conventional symbols for fittings.

3. Make a single-line multiview sketch of the portion of a piping system shown in Fig. 18.14.

4. Make a double-line developed drawing of the portion of a piping system shown in Fig. 18.14. Use 2″ pipe and screwed fittings. Select a suitable scale. Determine the measurements by transferring distances from the drawing to the open-divided scale in the figure.

5. Dimension the drawing of problem 4.

19 WORKING DRAWINGS

19.1. A working drawing is prepared for the purpose of furnishing all necessary information to those persons who must manufacture and assemble the machine or structure represented. It is a technical record that must be so complete and accurate that no supplementary verbal or written explanations will be necessary. The information must be conveyed in the most understandable manner, in accordance with good drafting-room conventions and practices. Since these conventions and practices vary somewhat among different concerns, the practices presented in this text are those given in the approved standards of the American Standards Association and the Society of Automotive Engineers.*

19.2. Sketches and design drawings. The first stage in the development of an idea for a structure or machine is to prepare freehand sketches and to make the necessary calculations required to determine the feasibility of the design. From these sketches the designer prepares a layout, on which an accurate analysis of the design is worked out. It is usually drawn full size and is executed with instruments in pencil. The layout should be sufficiently complete to allow a survey of the location of parts (to avoid interference), the accessibility for maintenance, the requirements for lubrication, and the method of assembly.

Usually, only center distances and certain fixed dimensions are given. The general dimensioning, as well as the determination of material and degree of finish of individual parts, is left for the draftsman who makes the detail drawings.

Design layouts require both empirical and scientific design. Empirical design involves the use of charts, formulas, tables, and so forth, which have been derived from experimental studies and scientific computations. Scientific design, which requires a broad knowledge of the allied fields such as mechanics, metallurgy, and mathematics, is used when a new machine is designed to operate under special specified conditions for which data are not available in any handbook.

19.3. Classes of working drawings. There are two recognized classes of working drawings: detail drawings and assembly drawings.

19.4. Set of working drawings. A complete set of working drawings for a machine consists of detail sheets, giving all necessary shop information for the production of individual pieces, and an assembly drawing showing the location of each piece in the finished machine. In addition, the set

* ASA Z14.1–1946 (Now under revision)
SAE Automotive Drafting Standards—1950.

may include drawings showing a foundation plan, piping diagram, oiling diagram, and so on.

19.5. Detail drawings. A detail drawing should give complete information for the manufacture of a part, describing with adequate dimensions the part's size. Finished surfaces should be indicated and all necessary shop operations shown. The title should give the material of which the part is to be made and should state the number of the parts that are

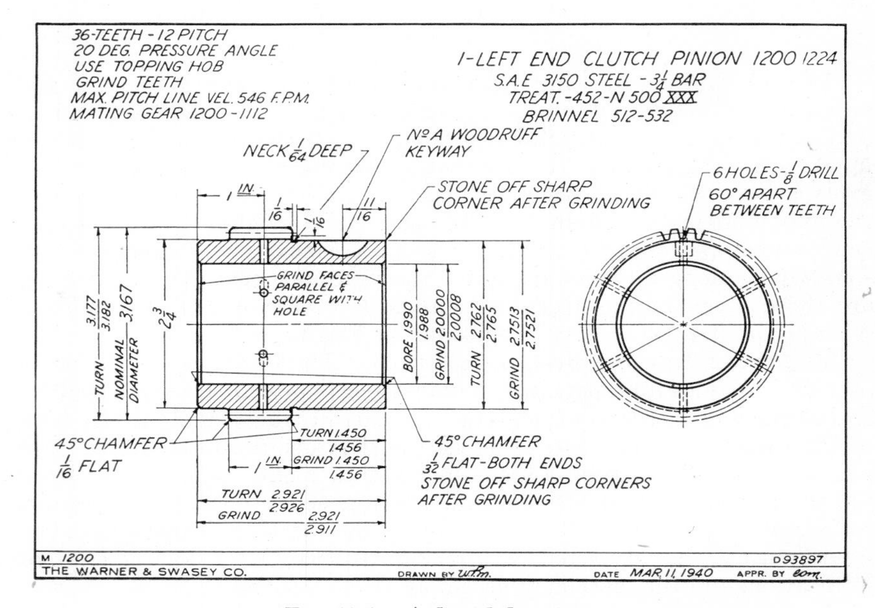

Fig. 19.1. A detail drawing.

required for the production of an assembled unit of which the part is a member. Commercial examples of detail workings are shown in Figs. 19.1 and 19.2.

Since a machinist will ordinarily make one part at a time, it is advisable to detail each piece, regardless of its size, on a separate individual sheet. In some shops, however, custom dictates that related parts be grouped on the same sheet, particularly when the parts form a unit in themselves. Other concerns sometimes group small parts of the same material together thus: castings on one sheet, forgings on another, special fasteners on still another, and so on.

19.6. Making a detail drawing. With a design layout or original sketches as a guide, the procedure for making a detail drawing is as follows:

1. Select the views, remembering that, aside from the view showing the characteristic shape of the object, there should be as many additional views as are necessary to complete the shape description. These may be sectional views that reveal a complicated interior construction, or auxiliary views of surfaces not fully described in any of the principal views.

2. Decide upon a scale that will allow, without crowding, a balanced arrangement of all necessary views and the location of dimensions and notes. Although very small parts should be drawn double size or larger, to show detail and to allow for dimensions, a full-size scale should be used

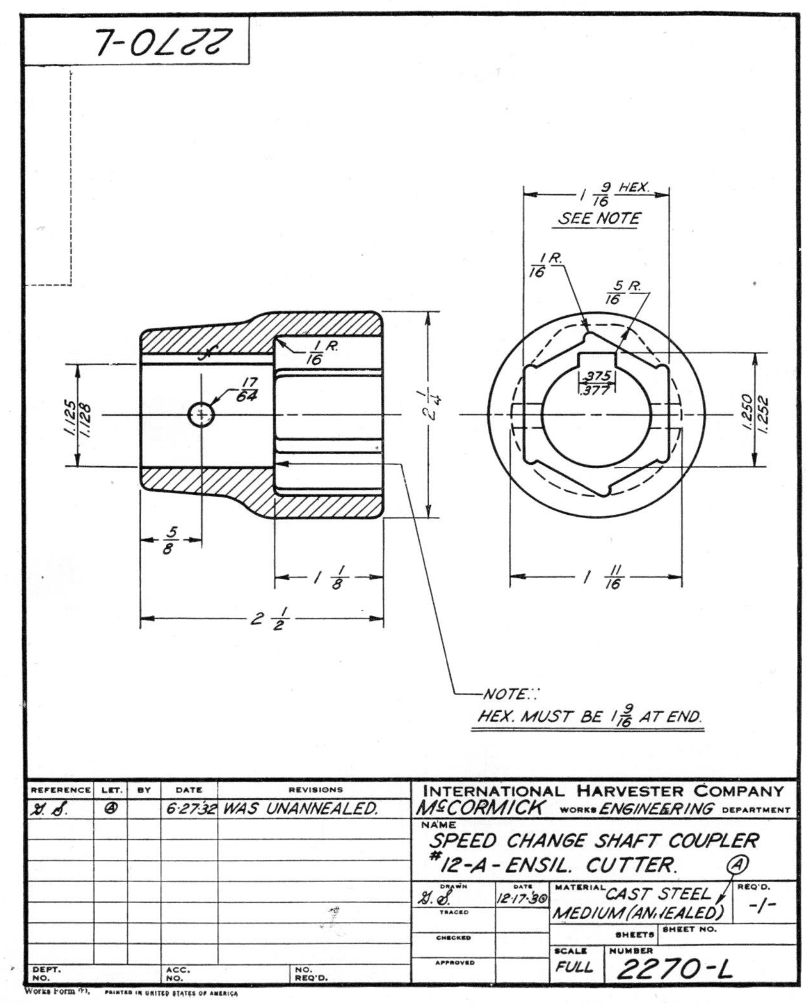

Courtesy International Harvester Co.

Fig. 19.2. A detail drawing.

when possible. In general, the same scale should be used for pieces of the same size.

3. Draw the main center lines and block in the general outline of the views with light, sharp 6*H* pencil lines.

4. Draw main circles and arcs in finished weight.

5. Starting with the characteristic view, work back and forth from view to view until the shape of the object is completed. Lines whose definite location and length are known may be drawn in their finished weight.
6. Put in fillets and rounds.
7. Complete the views by darkening the object lines.

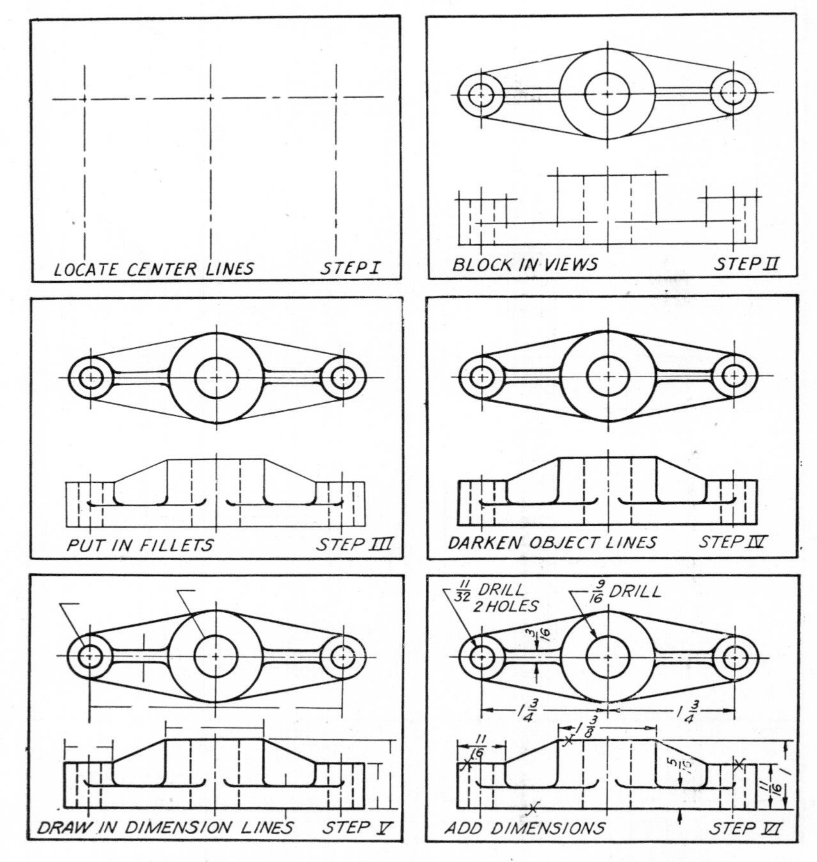

Fig. 19.3. Steps in making a detail drawing.

8. Draw extension and dimension lines.
9. Add arrowheads, dimensions, and notes.
10. Complete the title.
11. Check the entire drawing carefully.

19.7. One-view drawings. Many parts, such as shafts, bolts, studs, and washers, may require only one properly dimensioned view. In the case of each of these parts, a note can imply the complete shape of the piece without sacrificing clearness. Most engineering departments, however, deem it better practice to show two views.

19.8. Detail titles. Every detail drawing must give information not conveyed by the notes and dimensions, such as the name of the part, part number, material, number required, and so on. The method of recording and the location of this information on the drawing varies somewhat in different drafting rooms. It may be lettered either in the record strip or directly below the views. (See Figs. 19.2 and 19.4.)

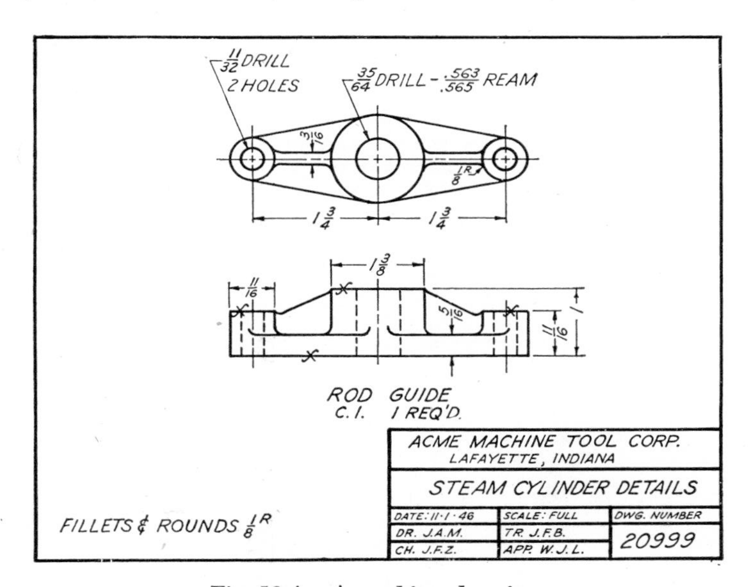

Fig. 19.4. A working drawing.

If all surfaces on a part are machined, finish marks are omitted and a title note, "Finish all over," is added to the detail title.

19.9. Title blocks and record strips. The purpose of a title or record strip is to present in an orderly manner the name of the machine, name of the manufacturer, date, scale, drawing number, and other drafting-room information.

Every commercial drafting room has developed its own standard title forms, whose features depend upon the processes of manufacture, the peculiarities of the plant organization, and the established customs of particular types of manufacturing. In large organizations, the blank form, along with the border line, is printed on standard sizes of drawing or tracing paper.

A record strip is a form of title extending almost the entire distance across the bottom of the sheet. In addition to the usual title information, it may contain a section for recording revisions, changes, and so on, with the dates on which they were adopted.

19.10. Contents of the title. The title on a machine drawing generally contains the following information:

1. Name of the part.
2. Name of the machine or structure. (This is given in the main title and is usually followed by one of two words: *details* or *assembly*.)

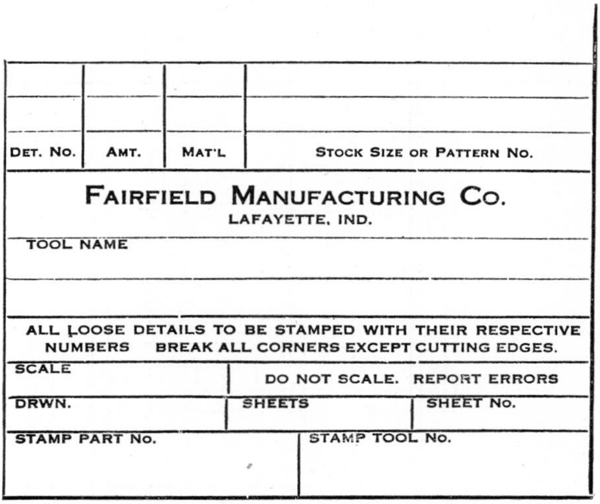

DET. NO.	AMT.	MAT'L	STOCK SIZE OR PATTERN NO.

FAIRFIELD MANUFACTURING CO.
LAFAYETTE, IND.

TOOL NAME

ALL LOOSE DETAILS TO BE STAMPED WITH THEIR RESPECTIVE NUMBERS BREAK ALL CORNERS EXCEPT CUTTING EDGES.

SCALE | DO NOT SCALE. REPORT ERRORS

DRWN. | SHEETS | SHEET NO.

STAMP PART NO. | STAMP TOOL NO.

Courtesy Fairfield Mfg. Co.

Fig. 19.5. A printed title block.

3. Name and location of the manufacturing firm.
4. Name and address of the purchasing firm, if the structure has been designed for a particular company.
5. Scale.
6. Date. (Often spaces are provided for the date of completion of each operation in the preparation of the drawing. If only one date is given, it is usually the date of completion of the tracing.)
7. Initials of the draftsman who made the pencil drawing.
8. Initials of the tracer.

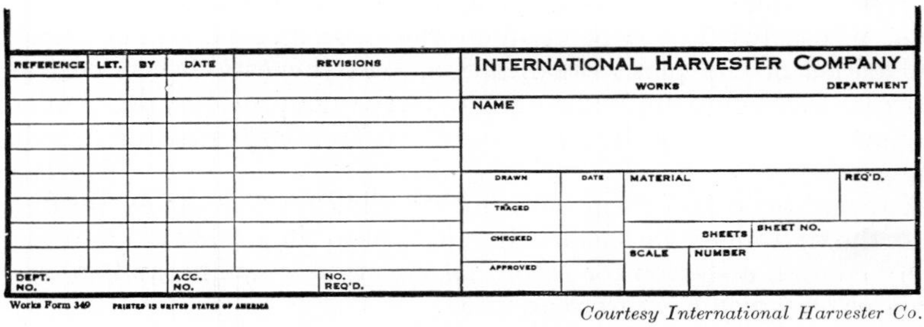

REFERENCE	LET.	BY	DATE	REVISIONS

DEPT. NO. | ACC. NO. | NO. REQ'D.

INTERNATIONAL HARVESTER COMPANY
WORKS DEPARTMENT
NAME
DRAWN | DATE | MATERIAL | REQ'D.
TRACED
CHECKED | SHEETS | SHEET NO.
APPROVED | SCALE | NUMBER

Works Form 349 PRINTED IN UNITED STATES OF AMERICA

Courtesy International Harvester Co.

Fig. 19.6. A printed record strip.

9. Initials of the checker.

10. Initials or signature of the chief draftsman, chief engineer, or another in authority who approved the drawing.

11. Drawing number. This generally serves as a filing number and may furnish information in code form. Letters and numbers may be so combined to indicate departments, plants, model, type, order number, filing number, and so on. The drawing number is sometimes repeated in

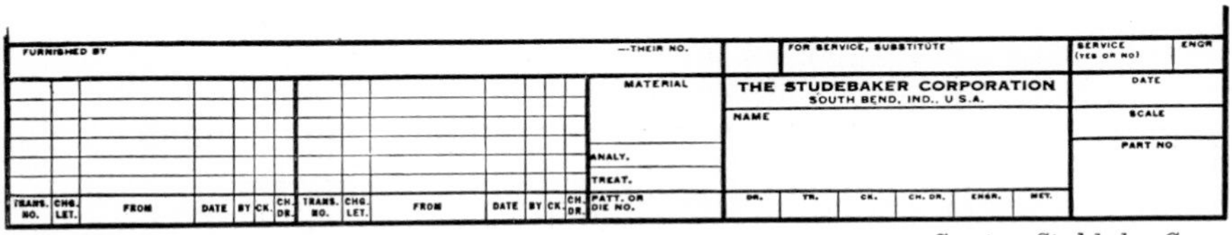

FURNISHED BY — THEIR NO. | FOR SERVICE, SUBSTITUTE | SERVICE (YES OR NO) | ENGR
MATERIAL | THE STUDEBAKER CORPORATION SOUTH BEND, IND., U.S.A. | DATE
NAME | SCALE | PART NO
ANALY. | TREAT.
TRANS. NO. | CHG. LET. | FROM | DATE | BY | CK. | CH. DR. | TRANS. NO. | CHG. LET. | FROM | DATE | BY | CK. | CH. DR. | PATT. OR DIE NO. | DR. | TR. | CK. | CH. DR. | ENGR. | MET.

Courtesy Studebaker Corp.

Fig. 19.7. A record strip.

the upper left-hand corner (in an upside-down position), so that the drawing may be quickly identified if it should become reversed in the file.

Some titles furnish information such as material, part number, pattern number, finish, treatment, estimated weight, superseded drawing number, and so on.

19.11. Corrections and alterations. Alterations on working drawings are made either by cancellation or by erasure. Cancellations are indicated by parallel inclined lines drawn through the views, lines, notes, or dimensions to be changed.

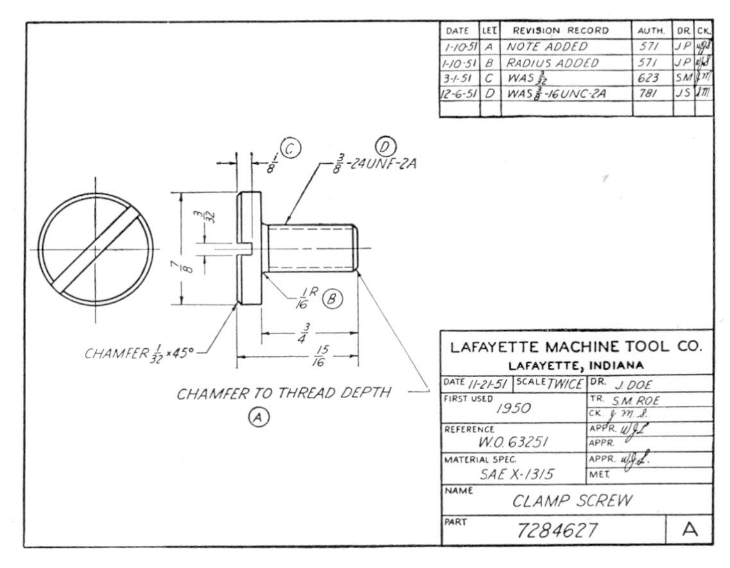

Fig. 19.8. Alterations.

Superseding dimensions should be placed above or near the original ones. If alterations are made by erasure, the changed dimensions are often underlined.

All changes on a completed or approved drawing should be recorded in a revision record that may be located either adjacent to the title block or at one corner of the drawing (Fig. 19.8). This note should contain the identification symbol, date, authorization number, character of the revision, and the initials of the draftsman and checker who made the change. The identification symbol is a letter or numeral placed in small circle near the alteration on the body of the drawing. See Fig. 19.8.

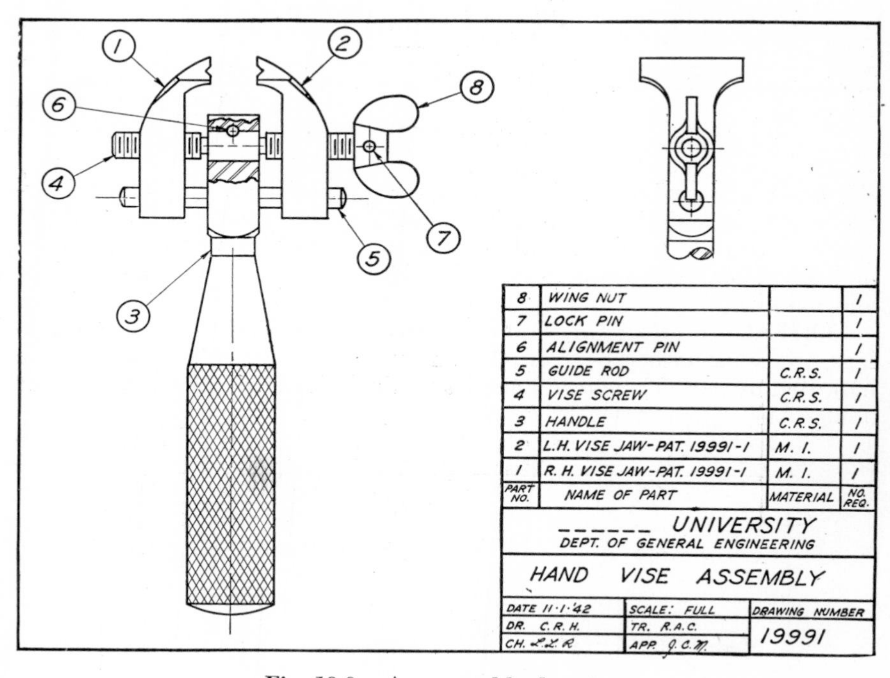

1
2
6
8
4
7
5
3
8 WING NUT 1
7 LOCK PIN 1
6 ALIGNMENT PIN 1
5 GUIDE ROD C.R.S. 1
4 VISE SCREW C.R.S. 1
3 HANDLE C.R.S. 1
2 L.H. VISE JAW-PAT. 19991-1 M. I. 1
1 R. H. VISE JAW-PAT. 19991-1 M. I. 1
PART NO. NAME OF PART MATERIAL NO. REQ.
------ UNIVERSITY
DEPT. OF GENERAL ENGINEERING
HAND VISE ASSEMBLY
DATE 11-1-'42
SCALE: FULL
DRAWING NUMBER
DR. C. R. H.
TR. R. A. C.
19991

Fig. 19.9. An assembly drawing.

If changes are made by complete erasure, record prints should be made for the file before the original is altered. Many companies make record prints whenever changes are extensive.

Since revisions on completed drawings are usually necessitated by unsatisfactory methods of production or by a customer's request, they should never be made by a draftsman unless an order has been issued with the approval of the chief engineer's office.

19.12. Pattern-shop drawings. Sometimes special pattern-shop drawings, giving information needed for making a pattern, are required for large and complicated castings. If the pattern maker receives a drawing that shows finished dimensions, he provides for the draft necessary to draw the pattern and for the extra metal for machining. He allows for shrinkage by making the pattern oversize. When, however, the draft and allowances for finish are determined by the engineering department, no finish marks appear on the drawing. The allowances are included in the dimensions.

19.13. Forge-shop drawings. If a forging is to be machined, separate detail drawings usually are made for the forge and machine shops. A forging drawing gives all the nominal dimensions required by the forge shop for a completed rough forging.

19.14. Machine-shop drawings. Rough castings and forgings are sent to the machine shop to be finished. Since the machinist is not

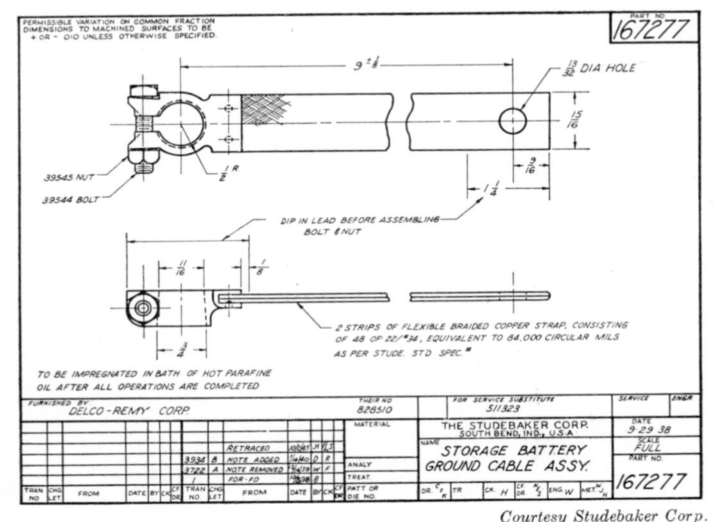

Courtesy Studebaker Corp.

Fig. 19.10. A working unit assembly drawing.

interested in the dimensions and information for the previous stages, a machine-shop drawing frequently gives only the information necessary for machining.

19.15. Assembly drawings. A drawing that shows the parts of a machine or machine unit assembled in their relative working positions is an assembly drawing. There are several types of such drawings: design assembly drawings, working assembly drawings, unit assembly drawings, installation diagrams, and so on, each of which will be described separately.

19.16. Working assembly drawings. A working assembly drawing, showing each piece completely dimensioned, is sometimes made for a simple mechanism or unit of related parts. No additional detail drawings of parts are required (Fig. 19.10).

19.17. Sub-assembly (unit) drawings. A unit assembly is an assembly drawing of a group of related parts that form a unit in a more complicated machine. Such a drawing would be made for the tail stock of a lathe, the clutch of an automobile, or the carburetor of an airplane.

A set of assembly drawings thus takes the place of a complete assembly of a complex machine (Fig. 19.11).

19.18. Installation assembly drawings. An installation drawing gives useful information for putting a machine or structure together. The names of parts, order of assembling parts, location dimensions, and special instructions for operating may also be shown.

19.19. Outline assembly drawings. Outline assembly drawings are most frequently made for illustrative purposes in catalogs. Usually they

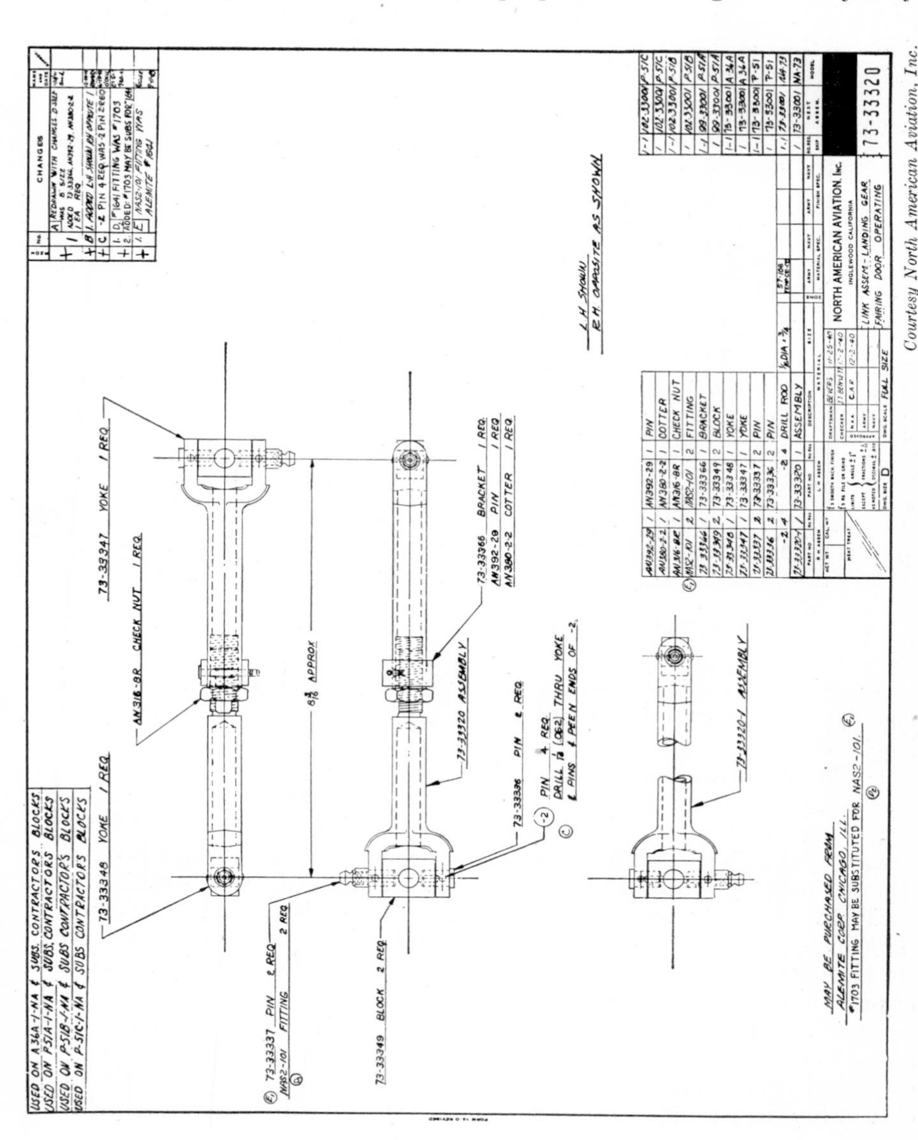

Courtesy North American Aviation, Inc.

Fig. 19.11. A unit assembly drawing.

show merely over-all and principal dimensions. (See Fig. 19.12.) Their appearance may be improved by the use of line shading.

19.20. Diagram assembly drawings. Diagram drawings may be grouped into two general classes: (1) those composed of single lines and conventional symbols, such as piping diagrams, wiring diagrams, and so on (see Fig. 19.14), and (2) those drawn in regular projection, such as an erection drawing, which may be shown in either orthographic or pictorial projection.

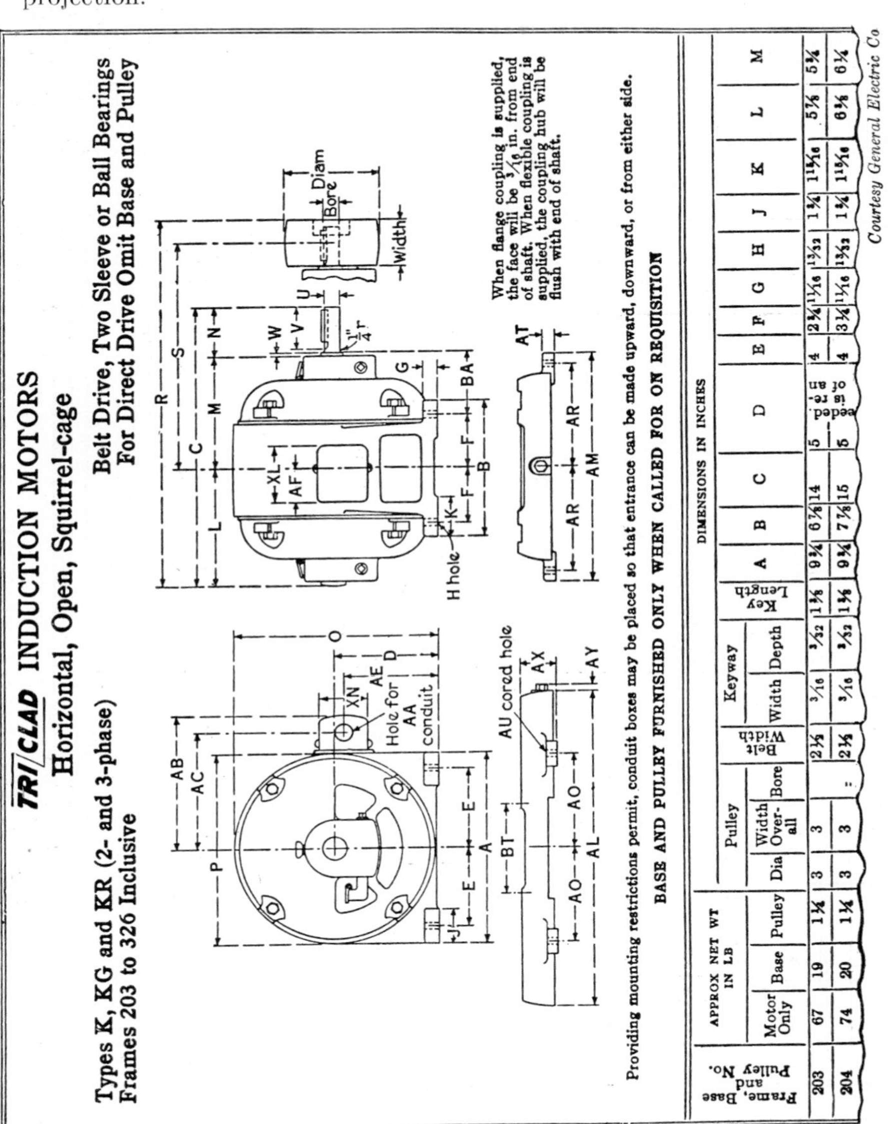

Frame, Base and Pulley No.	Approx Net Wt in Lb			Dimensions in Inches																			
				Pulley			Belt Width	Keyway		Key Length	A	B	C	D	E	F	G	H	J	K	L	M
	Motor Only	Base	Pulley	Dia	Width Over-all	Bore		Width	Depth													
203	67	19	1¼	3	3		2½	3/16	3/32	1⅜	9¾	6⅞	14	5 eeded. is re- of an	4	2¾	11/16	13/32	1¾	1 15/16	5⅞	5¾
204	74	20	1¼	3	3	"	2½	3/16	3/32	1⅜	9¾	7⅞	15	5	4	3¼	11/16	13/32	1¾	1 15/16	6⅜	6¼

Courtesy General Electric Co

Fig. 19.12. An outline assembly drawing.

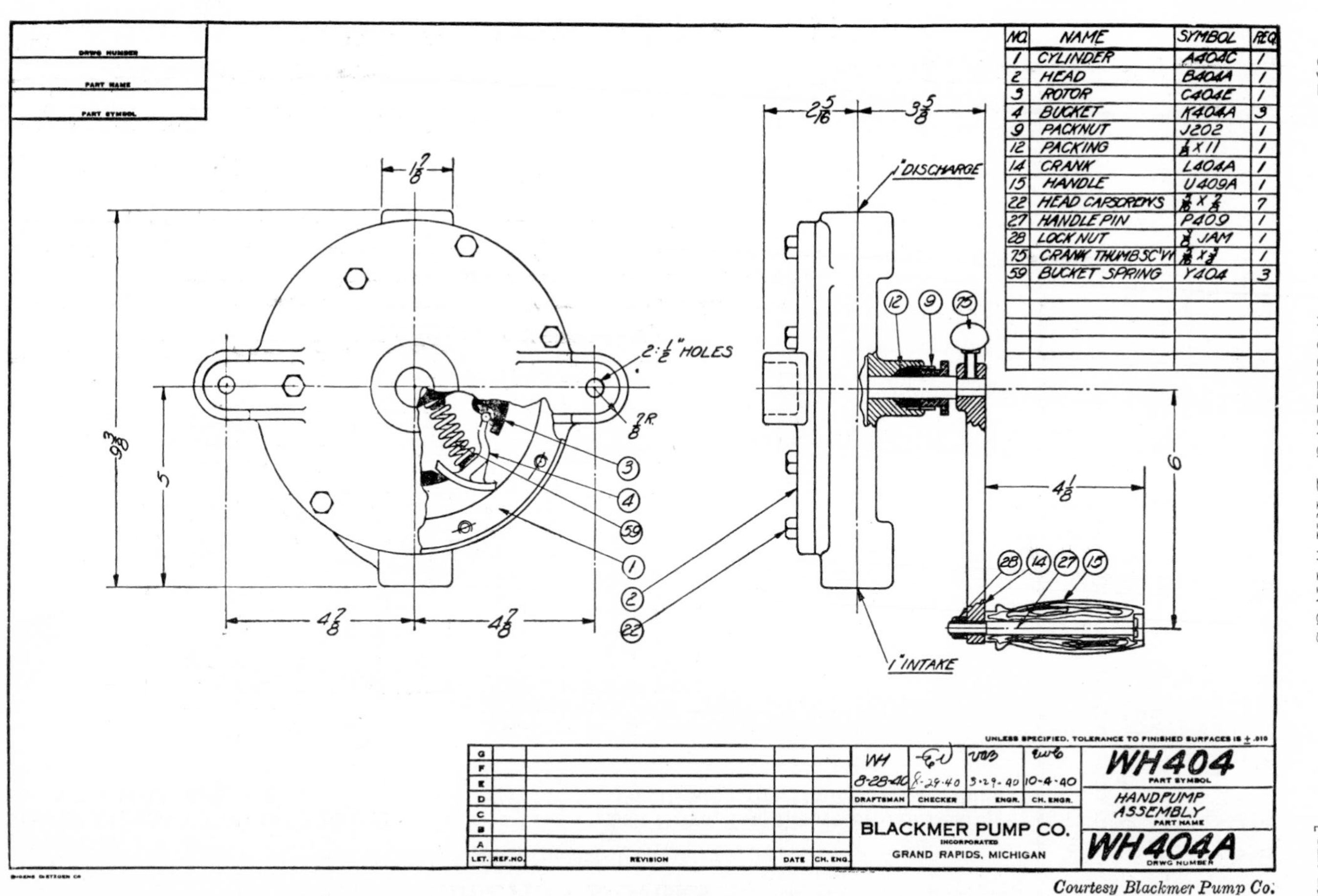

NO.	NAME	SYMBOL	REQ.
1	CYLINDER	A404C	1
2	HEAD	B404A	1
3	ROTOR	C404E	1
4	BUCKET	K404A	3
9	PACKNUT	J202	1
12	PACKING	1/8 X 11	1
14	CRANK	L404A	1
15	HANDLE	U409A	1
22	HEAD CAPSCREWS	5/16 X 5/8	7
27	HANDLE PIN	P409	1
28	LOCK NUT	1/2 JAM	1
75	CRANK THUMBSC'W	5/16 X 3/4	1
59	BUCKET SPRING	Y404	3

Courtesy Blackmer Pump Co.

Fig. 19.13. An assembly drawing.

Piping diagrams give the size of pipe, location of fittings, and so on. To draw an assembly of a piping system in true orthographic projection would add no information and merely entail needless work.

A large portion of electrical drawing is composed of diagrammatic sketches using conventional electrical symbols. Electrical engineers therefore need to know the American Standard wiring symbols given in the Appendix.*

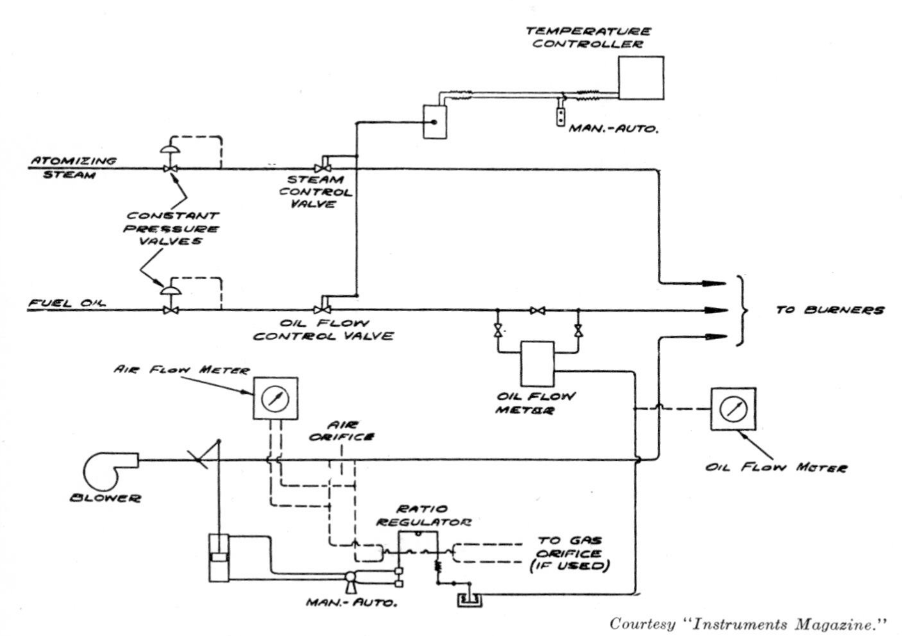

Courtesy "Instruments Magazine."

Fig. 19.14. A diagram assembly drawing.

19.21. Bill of material. A bill of material is a list of parts placed on an assembly drawing just above the title block, or, in the case of quantity production, on a separate sheet. The bill contains the part number, descriptive name, material, quantity (number) required, and so on, of each piece. Additional information, such as stock size, pattern number (castings), and so forth, is sometimes listed.

Suggested dimensions for ruling are shown in Fig. 19.15. For $\frac{1}{8}''$ letters, the lines should never be spaced closer than $\frac{5}{16}''$. Fractions are made slightly less than full height and are centered between the lines.

When listing standard parts in a bill of material, the general practice is to omit the name of the materials and to use abbreviated descriptive titles. A pattern number may be composed of the commercial job number followed

* ASA Z14.2–1935.

by the assigned number one, two, three, and so on. It is suggested that parts be listed in the following order: (*a*) castings, (*b*) forgings, (*c*) parts made from bar stock, (*d*) standard parts.

Sometimes bills of material are first typed on thin paper and then blueprinted. The form may be ruled or printed.

19.22. Title. The title strip on an assembly drawing usually is the same as that used on a detail drawing. It will be noted, when lettering in the block, that the title of the drawing is generally composed of the name of the machine followed by the word *assembly*. (See Figs. 19.9, 19.10, and 19.13.)

19.23. Making the assembly drawing. The final assembly may be traced from the design assembly drawing, but more often it is redrawn to a smaller scale on a separate sheet. Since the redrawing, being done from both the design and detail drawings, furnishes a check that frequently

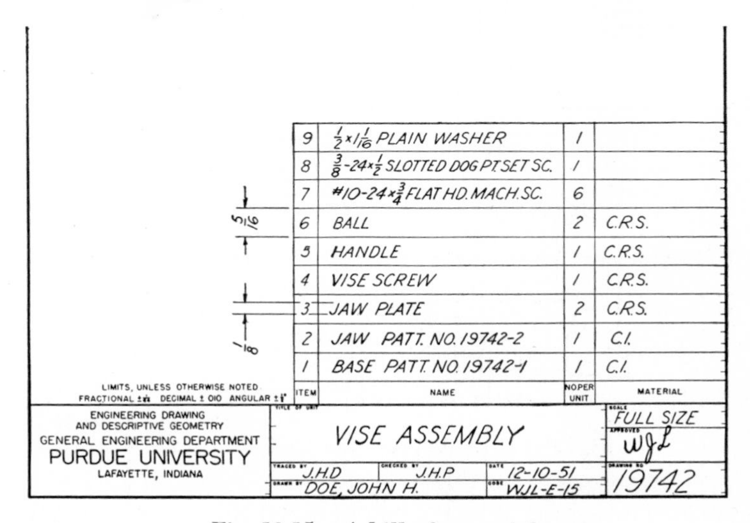

ITEM	NAME	NO. PER UNIT	MATERIAL
9	$\frac{1}{2} \times 1\frac{1}{16}$ PLAIN WASHER	1	
8	$\frac{3}{8}$-24 $\times \frac{1}{2}$ SLOTTED DOG PT. SET SC.	1	
7	#10-24 $\times \frac{3}{4}$ FLAT HD. MACH. SC.	6	
6	BALL	2	C.R.S.
5	HANDLE	1	C.R.S.
4	VISE SCREW	1	C.R.S.
3	JAW PLATE	2	C.R.S.
2	JAW PATT. NO. 19742-2	1	C.I.
1	BASE PATT. NO. 19742-1	1	C.I.

Fig. 19.15. A bill of material.

reveals errors, the assembly always should be drawn before the details are accepted as finished and the blueprints are made. The assembly of a simple machine or unit is sometimes shown on the same sheet with the details.

Accepted practices to be observed on assemblies are:

1. *Sectioning.* Parts should be sectioned using the American Standard symbols shown in Fig. 10.32. The practices of sectioning apply to assemblies.

2. *Views.* The main view, which is usually in full section, should show to the best advantage nearly all the individual parts and their locations. Additional views are shown only when they add necessary information that should be conveyed by the drawing.

3. *Hidden lines.* Hidden lines should be omitted from an assembly drawing, for they tend merely to overload it and create confusion. Complete shape description is unnecessary, since parts are either standard or are shown on detail drawings.

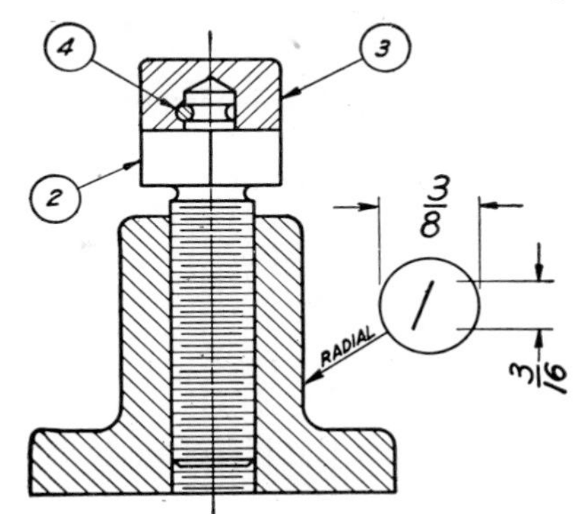

Fig. 19.16. Identification (part) numbers.

4. *Dimensions.* Over-all dimensions and center-to-center distances indicating the relationship of parts in the machine as a whole are sometimes given. Detail dimensions are omitted, except on working assembly drawings.

5. *Identification of parts.* Parts in a machine or structure are identified on the assembly drawing by numbers that are used on the details and in the bill of material. These should be made at least $\frac{3}{16}''$ high and enclosed in a $\frac{3}{8}''$ circle (Fig. 19.16). The centers of the circles are located not less than $\frac{3}{4}''$ from the nearest line of the drawing. Leaders, terminated by arrowheads touching the parts, are drawn radial with a straightedge. The numbers, in order to be centered in the circles, should be made first and the circles drawn around them. An alternate method used in commercial practice is to letter the name and descriptive information for each part and draw a leader pointing to it in the main view.

19.24. Checking drawings. Checking, the final assurance that the machine is correctly designed, should be done by a person (checker or squad foreman) who has not prepared the drawings but who is thoroughly familiar with the principles of the design. He must have a broad knowledge of shop practices and assembly methods. In commercial drafting rooms, the most experienced men are assigned to this type of work. The assembly drawing is checked against the detail drawings and corrections are indicated with either a soft or colored pencil. The checker should:

1. Survey the machine as a whole from the standpoint of operation, ease of assembly, and accessibility for repair work. He should consider the type, strength, and suitability of the materials.

2. Check each part with the parts adjacent to it, to make certain that proper clearances are maintained. (To determine whether or not all positions are free of interference, it may be necessary to lay out the extreme travel of moving parts to an enlarged scale.)

3. Study the drawing to see that each piece has been illustrated correctly and that all necessary views, types of views, treatments of views, and scales have been shown.

4. Check dimensions by scaling; calculate and check size and location dimensions that affect mating parts; determine the suitability of dimensions from the standpoint of the various departments' needs, such as pattern, forge, machine, assembly shop, and so on; examine views for proper dimensioning, and mark unnecessary, repeated, or omitted dimensions.

5. Check tolerances, making sure the computations are correct and that proper fits have been used, so that there will be no unnecessary production costs.

6. See that finishes and such operations as drilling, reaming, boring, tapping, and grinding are properly specified.

7. Check specifications for material.

8. Examine notes for correctness and location.

9. See that stock sizes have been used for standard parts such as bolts, screws, keys, and so on. (Stock sizes may be determined from catalogs.)

10. Add any additional explanatory notes that should supply necessary information.

11. Check the bill of material to see that each part is completely and correctly specified.

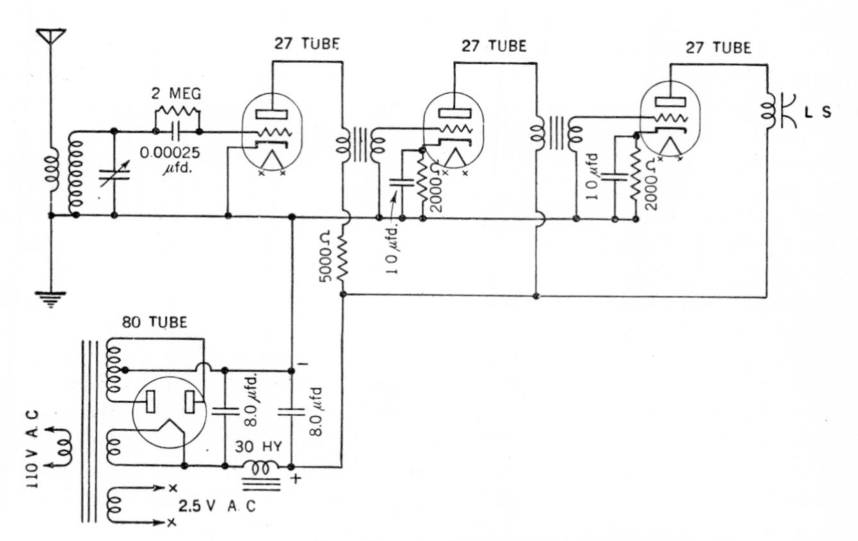

From Marcus and Horton, "Elements of Radio," Prentice-Hall, Inc.

Fig. 19.17. A schematic diagram.

12. Check items in the title block.

13. Make a final survey of the drawing in its entirety, making certain there is either a check or correction for each dimension, note, and specification.

19.25. Chemical engineering drawings. In general, the chemical engineer is concerned with plant layouts and equipment design. He must be well informed on the types of machinery used in grinding, drying, mixing, evaporation, sedimentation, and distillation, and must be able to design or select conveying machinery.

It is obvious that the determining of the sequence of operations, selecting of machinery, arranging of piping, and so on, must be done by a trained chemical engineer who can speak the basic language of the mechanical, electrical, or civil engineer with whom he must co-operate. To be able to do this, he must have a thorough knowledge of the principles of engineering drawing.

Plant layout drawings, the satisfactory development of which requires numerous preliminary sketches (layouts, scale diagram, flow sheets, and so on), show the location of machines, equipment, and the like. Often, if the machinery and apparatus are used in the manufacturing of chemicals and are of a specialized nature, a chemical engineer is called upon to do the designing. It even may be necessary for him to build experimental apparatus.

19.26. Electrical engineering drawings. Electrical engineering drawings are of two types, working drawings and diagrammatic assemblies. Working drawings, which are made for electrical machinery, involve all of the principles and conventions of the working drawings of the mechanical engineer. Diagrammatic drawings have been discussed in Sec. 19.20.

19.27. Floor-plan drawings. An engineer usually is not an architect nor is an architect usually an engineer; therefore, when a new factory is to be built or an addition is to be added to an existing one, both architect and engineer are needed and both must co-operate in the design. In this partnership, it becomes the job of the engineer to prepare the floor plans, so that the highest possible production efficiency can be obtained. He must study carefully the necessary steps of production and then decide upon the locations for the offices, supply rooms, storage rooms, shops, and finally the production machines. The design becomes a recorded study of the flow of materials and parts through the plant. Frequently, it may be necessary to show a conveyor system or a piping system on the plan. In the case of small plants, circumstances may be such that the engineer must assume full responsibility for the design of the entire building.

19.28. Problems. The four general types of problems presented in this chapter have been designed to furnish practice in the preparation of working drawings. The first type is composed of dimensioned pictorial drawings of individual pieces taken from a wide variety of mechanisms. The student should prepare complete working detail drawings of these pieces as they are assigned by his instructor. It should be recognized that dimensions are not necessarily placed the same on orthographic views as they are on pictorial drawings. In order to make it possible for the student to apply the principles presented in the previous chapters, no special effort has been made to place dimensions in accordance with the rules of good practice. Furthermore there are many cases where dimensions cannot be placed on pictorial drawings in the same locations as on the orthographic views.

The second type of problem is one that shows in pictorial all the parts of a unit mechanism. This gives the student an opportunity to prepare a complete set of working drawings of a simple unit. It is suggested that the detail drawings be prepared before the assembly is drawn.

The third and fourth types provide practice in both reading and preparing drawings, the third requiring the preparation of detail drawings from given assembly drawings, and the fourth requiring the making of assembly drawings from the details.

All the problems have been designed to fit an $8\frac{1}{2}'' \times 11''$ or an $11'' \times 17''$ sheet of drawing paper if the proper scale is selected. The scale may be either suggested by the instructor or left to the student's judgment. Although working drawings may be drawn in pencil and later traced in ink on tracing paper or cloth, it is suggested that most of the drawings be prepared in pencil on lightweight bond paper as is done extensively in industrial drawing rooms. Some drawings may be prepared as sketches.

Thread specifications containing the series identification UNC or UNF refer to the Unified Thread Standard now common to American-British-Canadian practice. Other thread specifications having a series identification of NC, NF, or N are considered to refer to either the American Standard (ASA B1.1–1949) having the Unified thread form or the American Standard with the old thread form still in use during the present changeover period. If desired, all thread specifications on a finished drawing may be given as required under the Unified Standard.

1–30. (Figs. 19.18–19.47). Make a detail drawing of an assigned machine part. Draw all necessary views. Give a detail title with suitable notes concerning material, number required, etc.

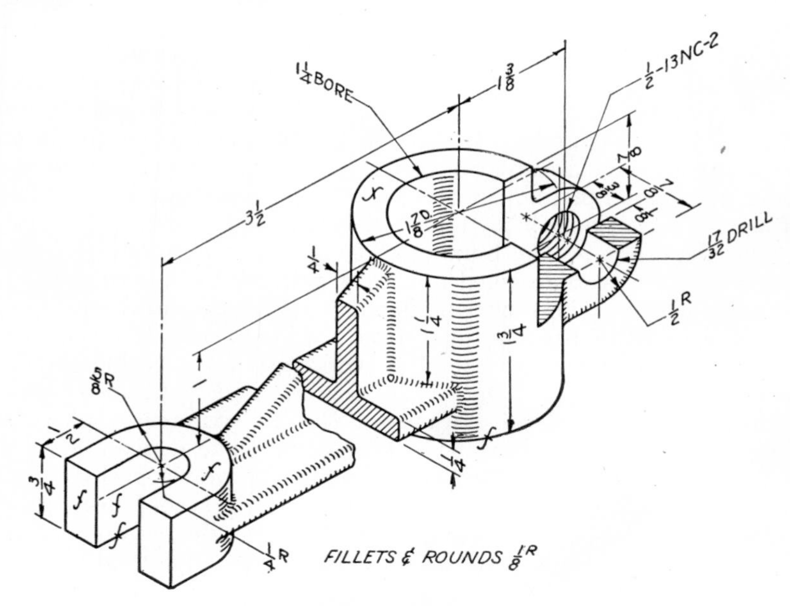

Fig. 19.18. Shifter.

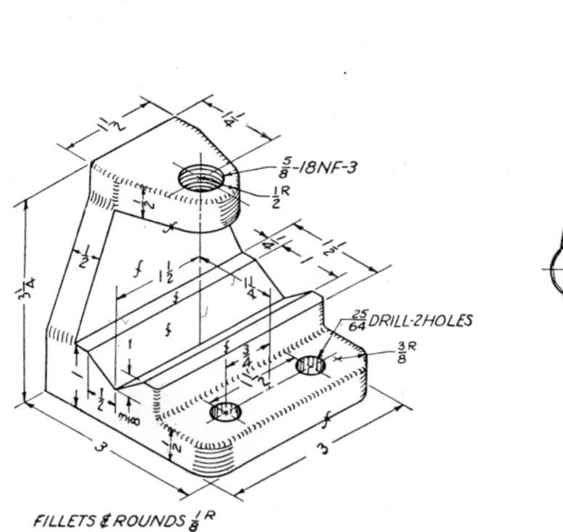

Fig. 19.19. Clamp base.

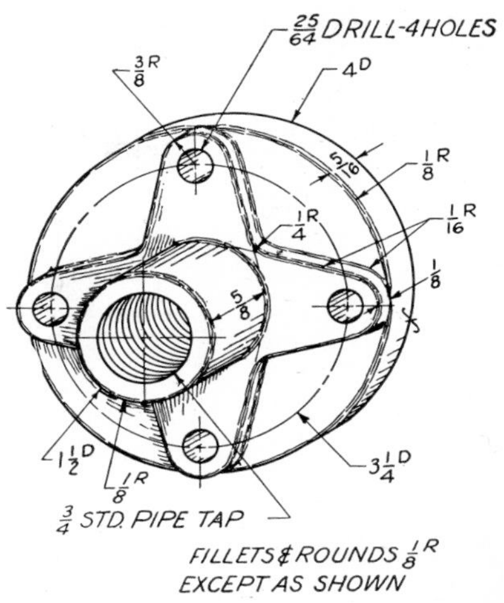

Fig. 19.20. Flange.

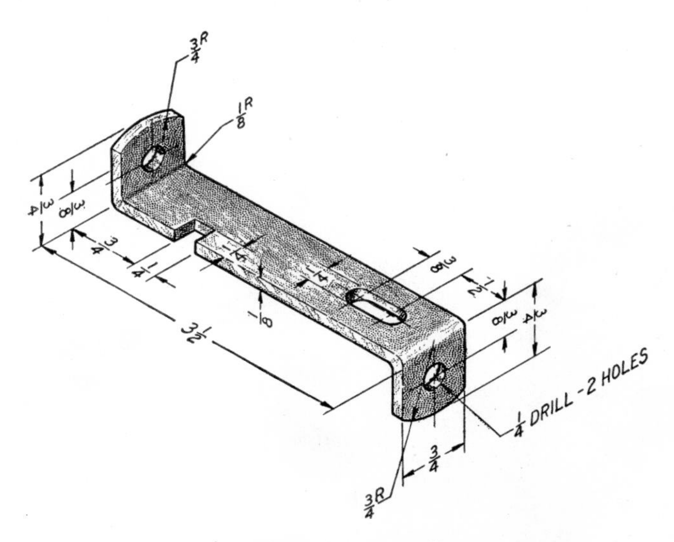

Fig. 19.21. Bent angle.

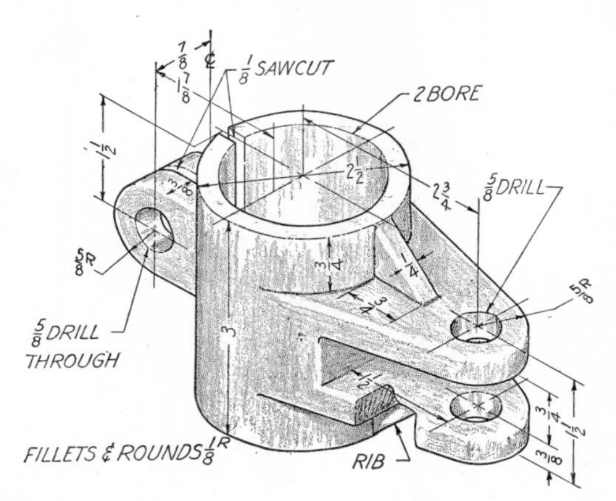

Fig. 19.22. Guide bracket.

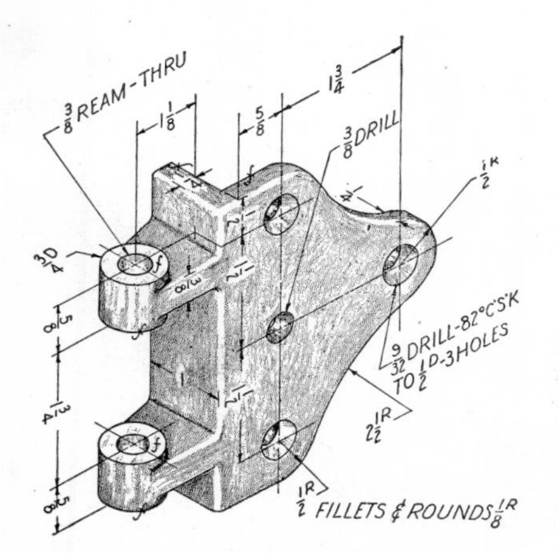

Fig. 19.23. Corner bracket.

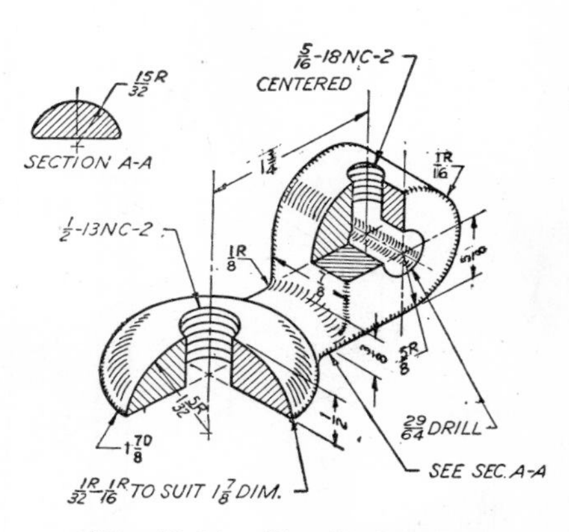

Fig. 19.24. Handle block.

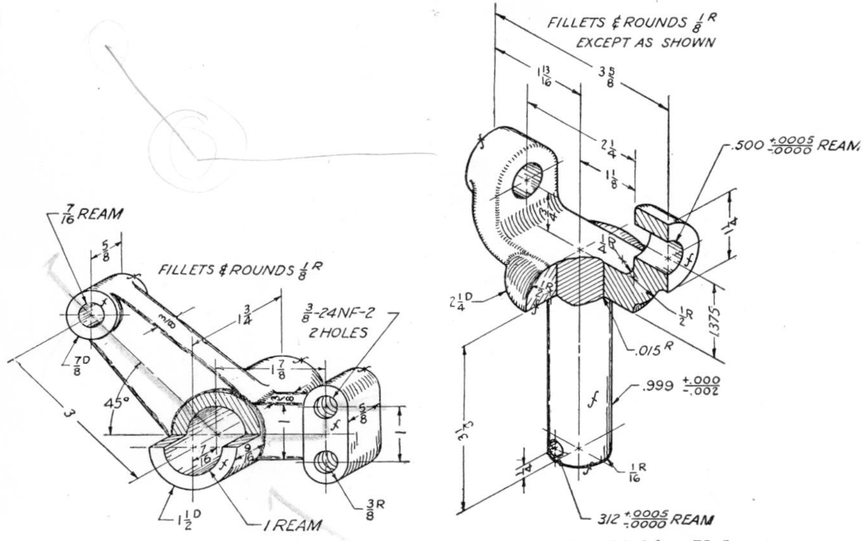

Fig. 19.25. Guide.

Fig. 19.26. Yoke.

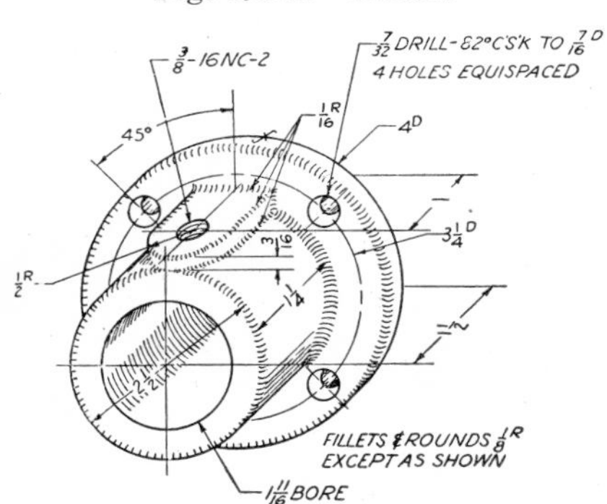

Fig. 19.27. Pipe support.

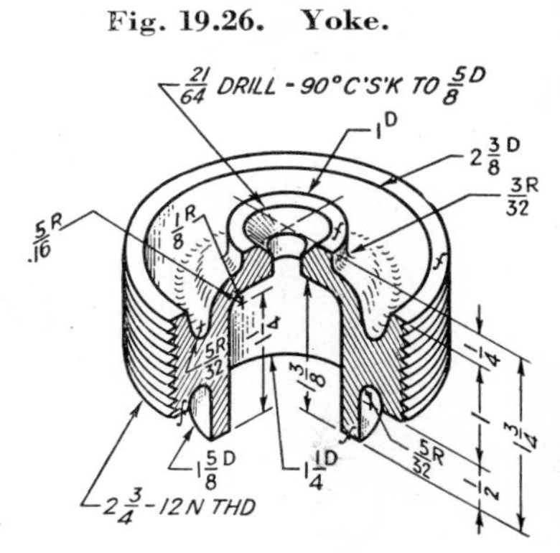

Fig. 19.28. Valve seat.

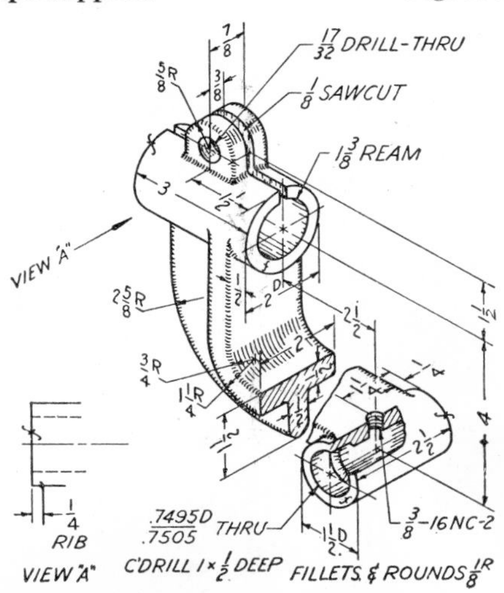

Fig. 19.29. Hanger bracket.

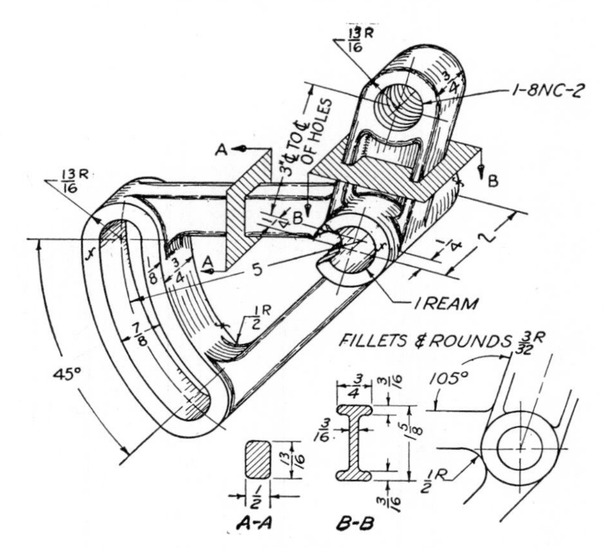

Fig. 19.30. Shifter lever.

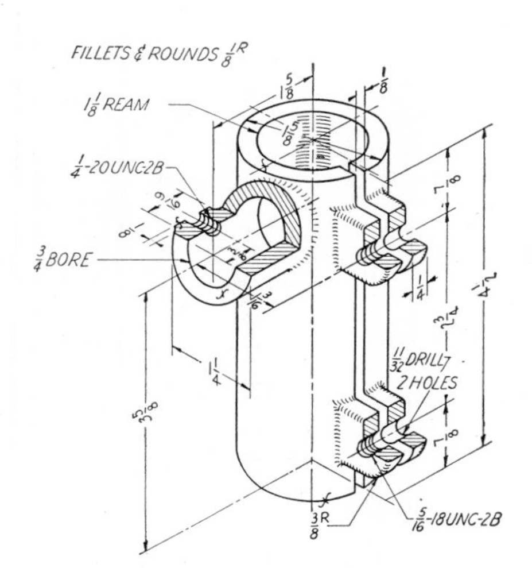

Fig. 19.31. Torch holder.

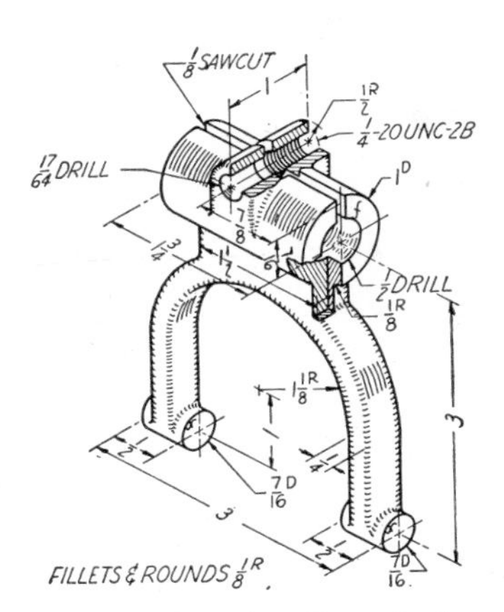

Fig. 19.32. Auxiliary fork.

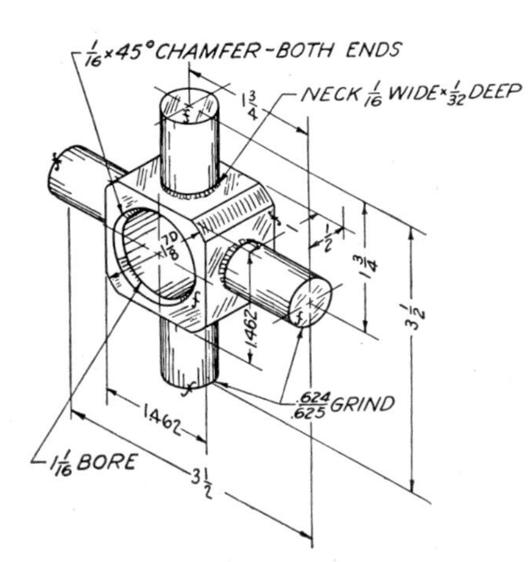

Fig. 19.33. Differential spider.

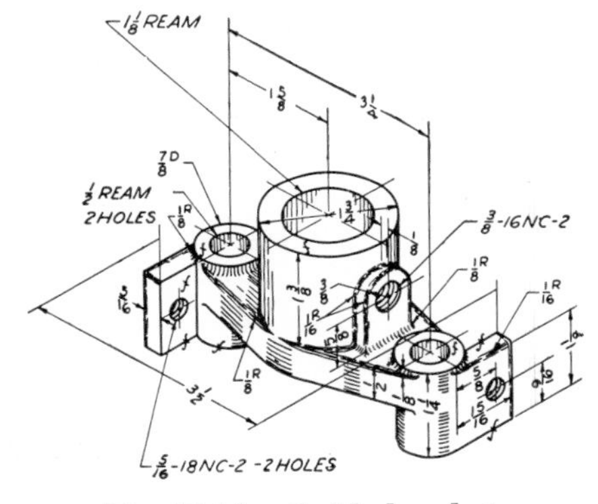

Fig. 19.34. Guide bracket.

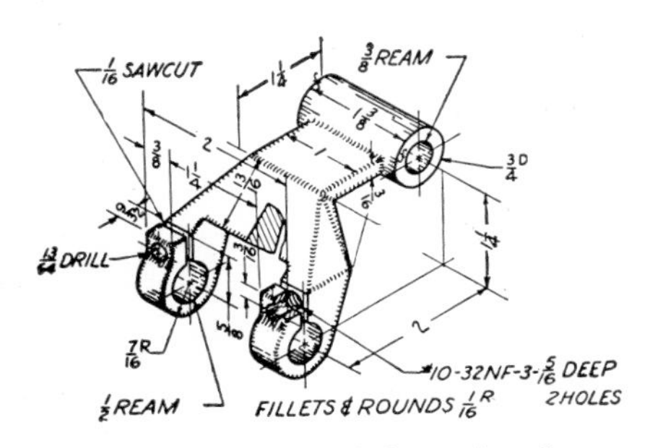

Fig. 19.35. Sound drum bracket.

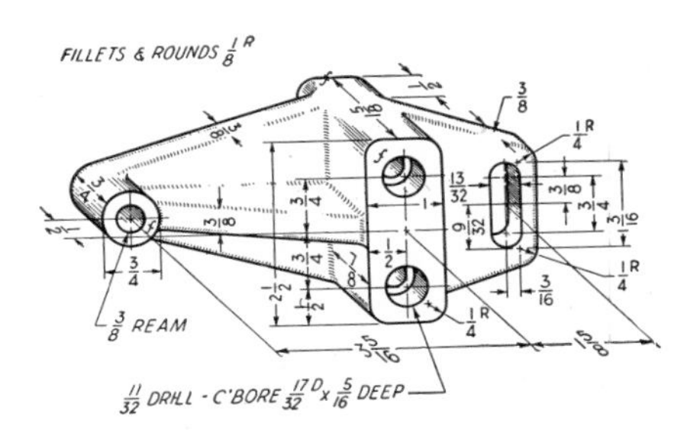

Fig. 19.36. Elevator bracket.

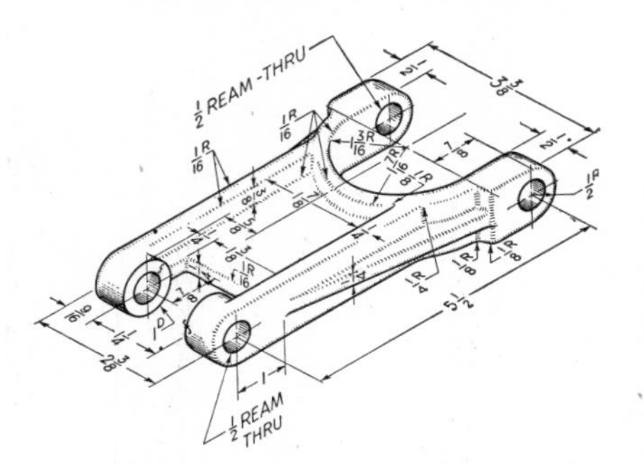

Fig. 19.37. Link.

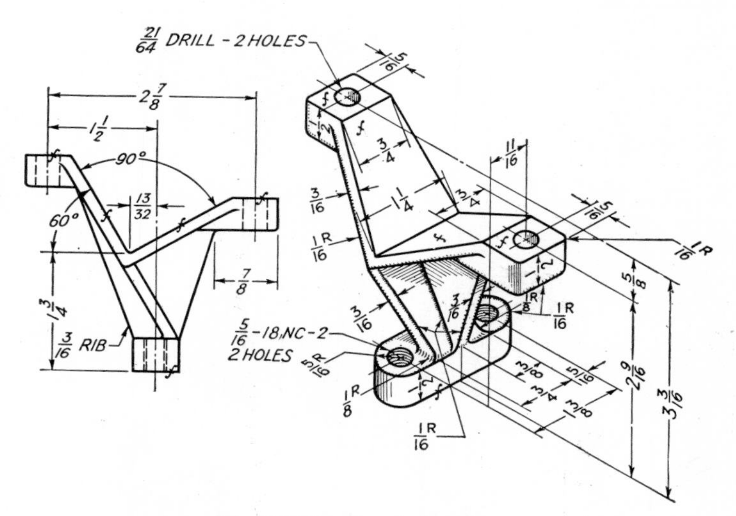

Fig. 19.38. Angle bracket.

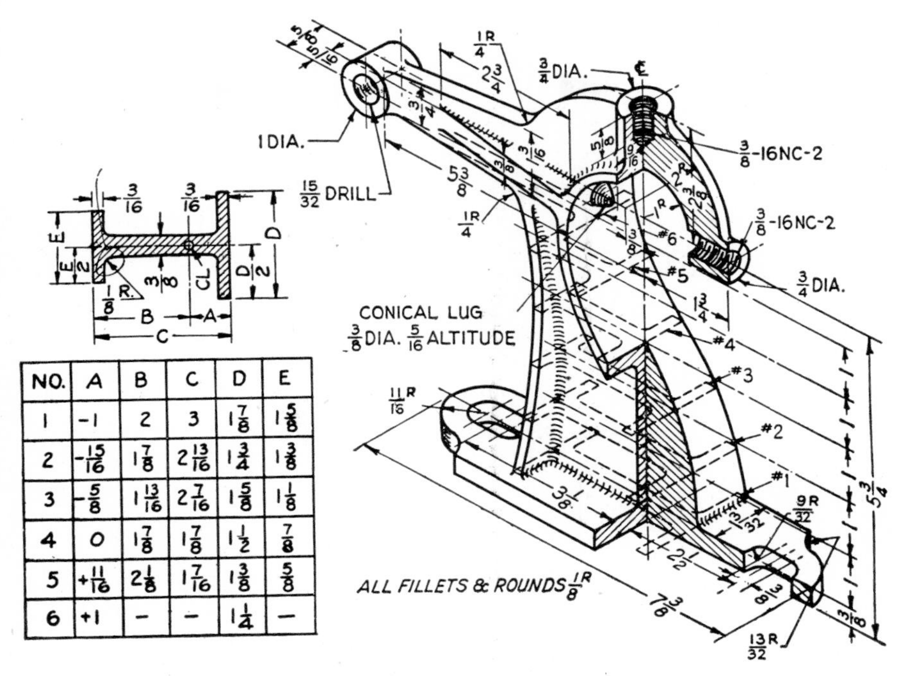

NO.	A	B	C	D	E
1	-1	2	3	1 7/8	1 5/8
2	-15/16	1 7/8	2 13/16	1 3/4	1 3/8
3	-5/8	1 13/16	2 7/16	1 5/8	1 1/8
4	0	1 7/8	1 7/8	1 1/2	7/8
5	+11/16	2 1/8	1 7/16	1 3/8	5/8
6	+1	–	–	1 1/4	–

Fig. 19.39. Shaft hanger.

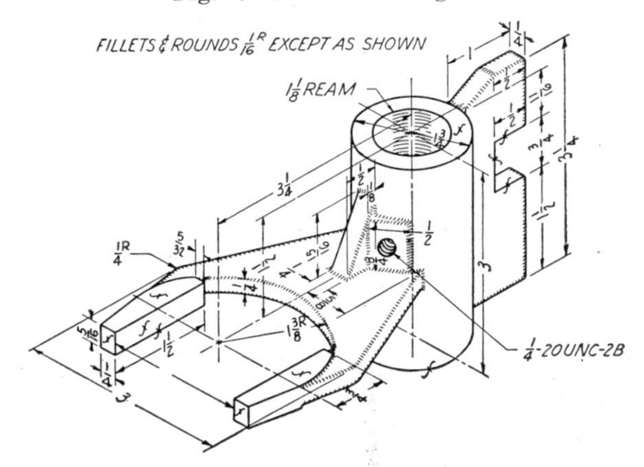

Fig. 19.40. Gear shifting fork.

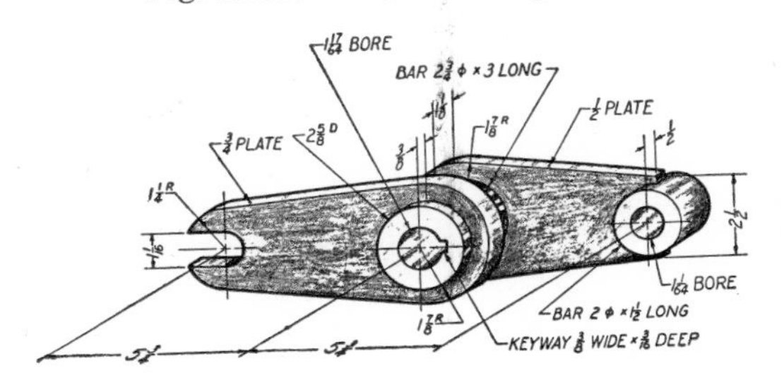

Fig. 19.41. Idler lever.

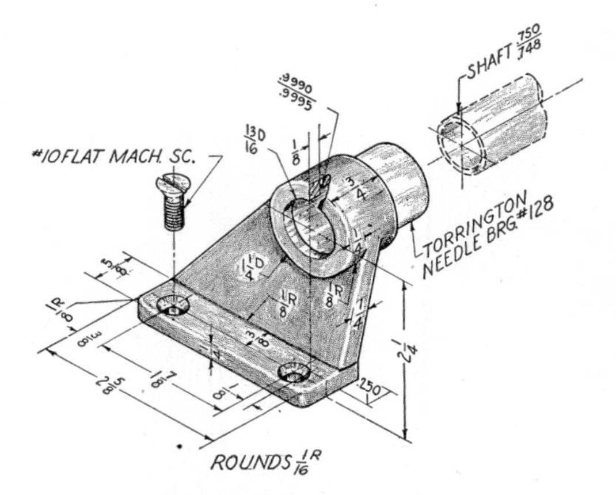

Fig. 19.42. Bearing bracket.

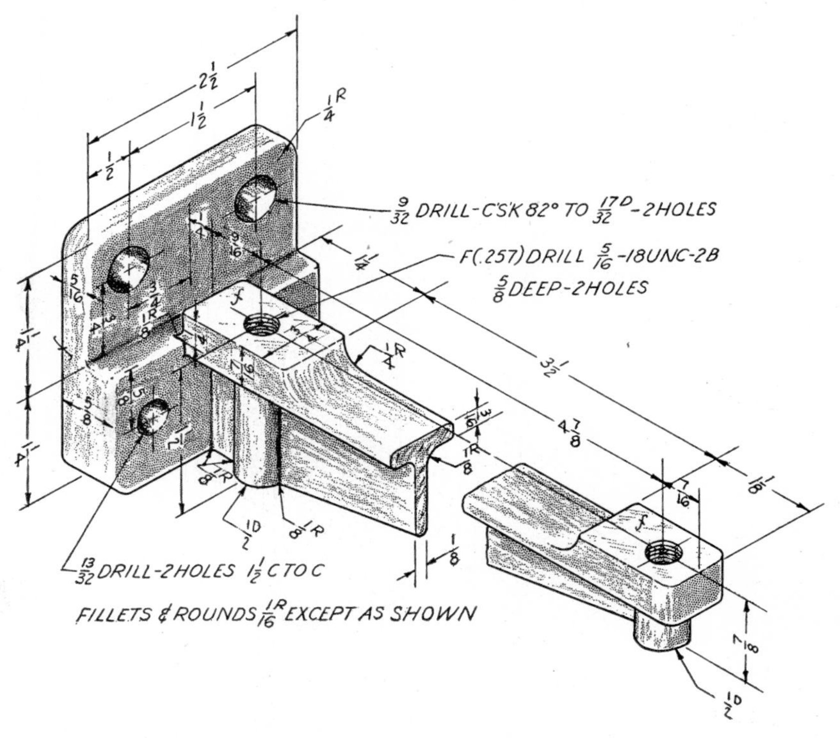

Fig. 19.43. Support bracket.

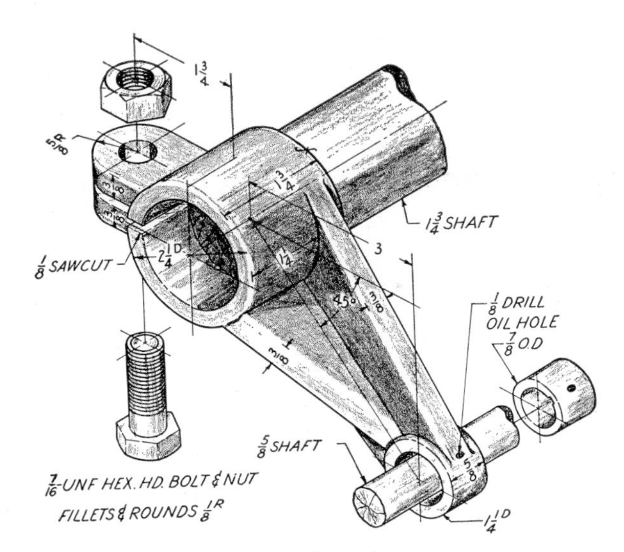

Fig. 19.44. Shaft bracket.

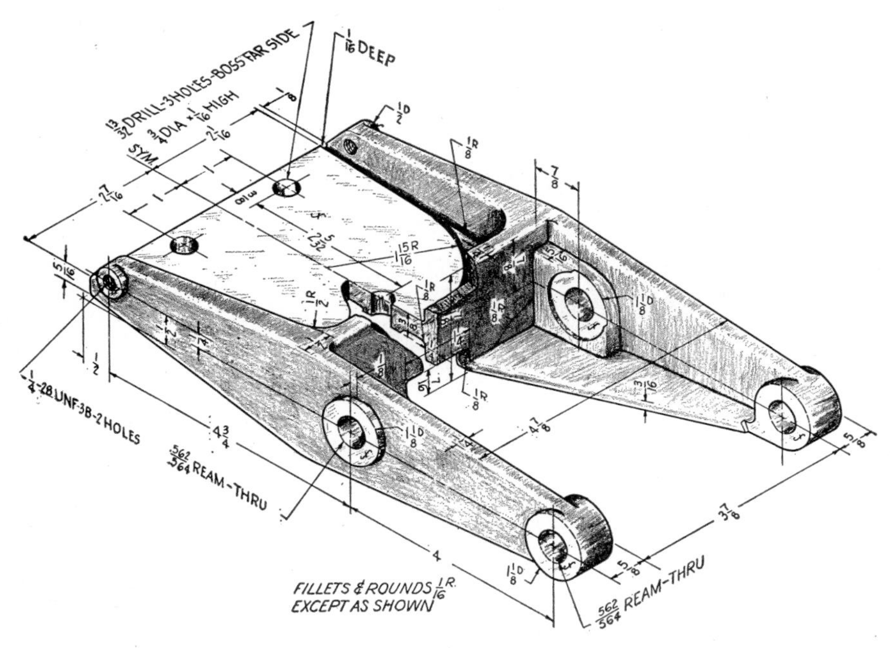

Fig. 19.45. Control pedal.

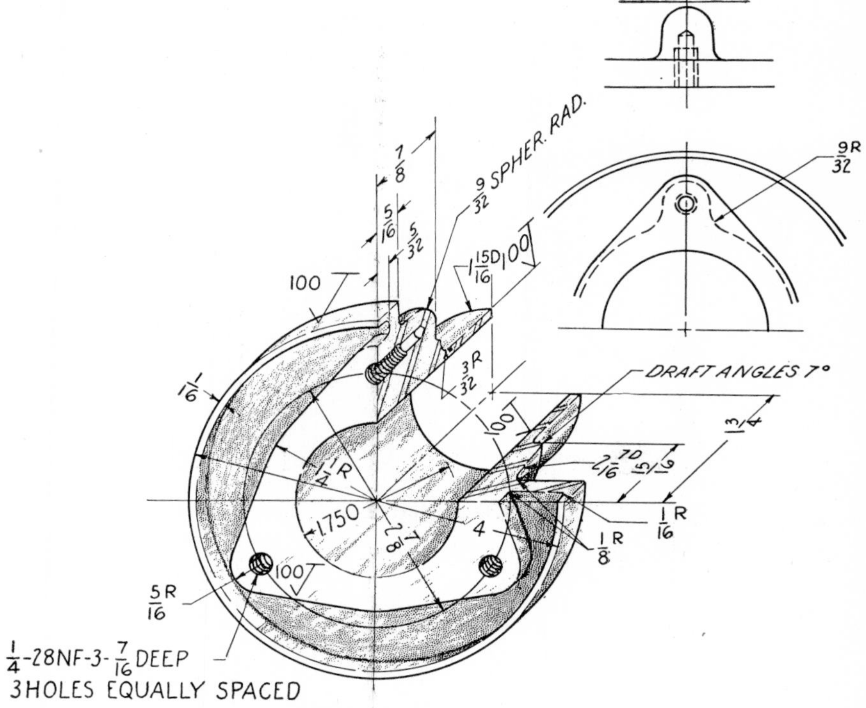

Fig. 19.46. Inlet flange.

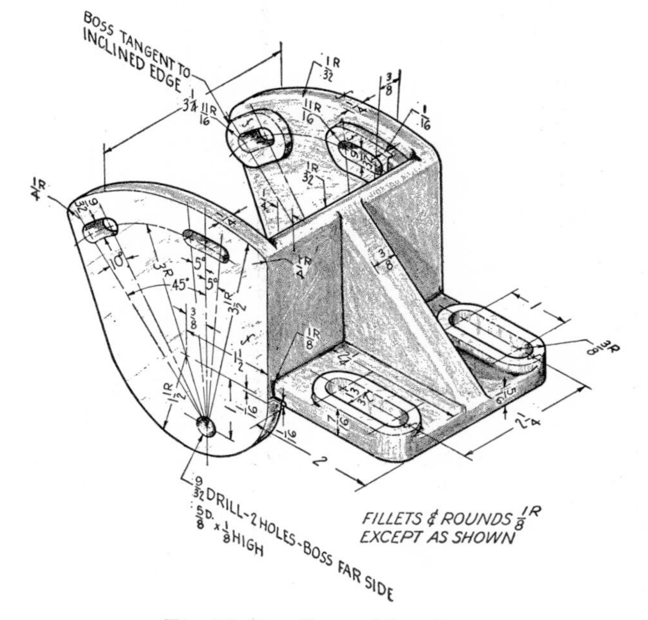

Fig. 19.47. Control bracket.

31. (Fig. 19.48.) Make a detail drawing of the cover.

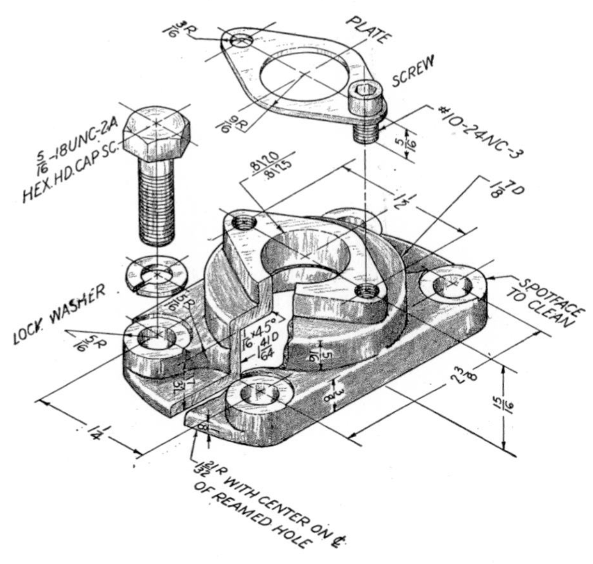

Fig. 19.48. Cover.

32. (Fig. 19.49.) Make a complete two-view orthographic drawing of the guide bracket which is shown by a pictorial sketch. The student is advised to give careful consideration to the choice of views remembering that it is the usual practice to show the circular form of each cylindrical feature on one of the selected views. Dimension the views completely while keeping in mind the fact that dimensions are often times not placed on a pictorial drawing as they should be placed on the orthographic drawing. *Supplementary information:* 1) The centerline for the main 1″ shaft is $2\frac{3}{8}$″ below the flat finished base surface. The hole for this shaft is to be reamed. 2) The length of the cylindrical portion is $1\frac{3}{4}$″ between contact faces. The O.D. is $1\frac{1}{2}$″. 3) The hole for the smaller shaft is to be reamed for a $\frac{5}{8}$″ shaft. The O.D. of the cylinder is 1″ and the distance between faces is $\frac{5}{8}$″. The $\frac{3}{8}$″ ribs should be tangent to cylindrical surfaces. 4) The flat finished base surface is $1\frac{1}{8}$″ × $2\frac{3}{4}$″. The holes which are to be drilled $\frac{1}{32}$″ over-size for $\frac{3}{8}$″ bolts are $1\frac{3}{4}$″ apart, and are centered in the direction parallel to the axes of the shafts. 5) Fillets and rounds $\frac{1}{8}$ R.

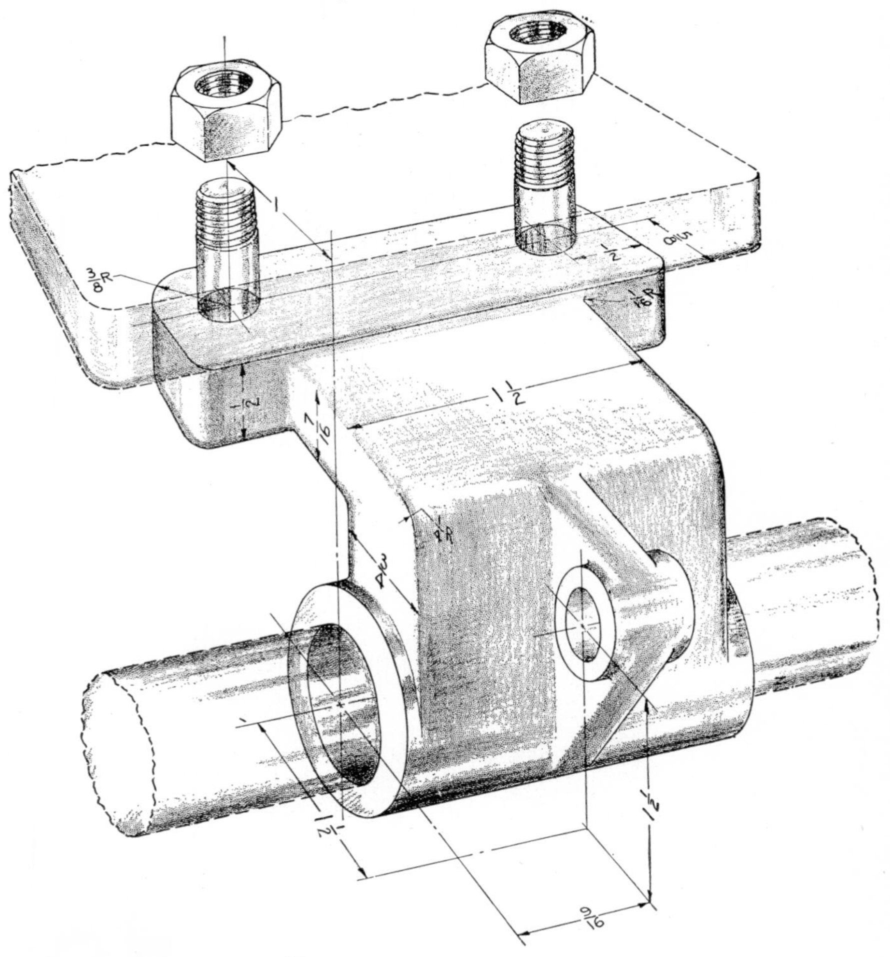

Fig. 19.49. Guide bracket.

33. (Fig. 19.50.) Make a detail working drawing of the bracket or its mating part that clamps around the $1\frac{3}{4}''$ shaft.

The given pictorial drawing shows the adjustment bracket assembly of a positioning mechanism on a cartridge type core blower. The bracket when attached to the vertical column supports a positioning clamp that may be tilted into different positions. The clamp screw keeps the positioning clamp in a desired position when it is tightened down against the clamp plate.

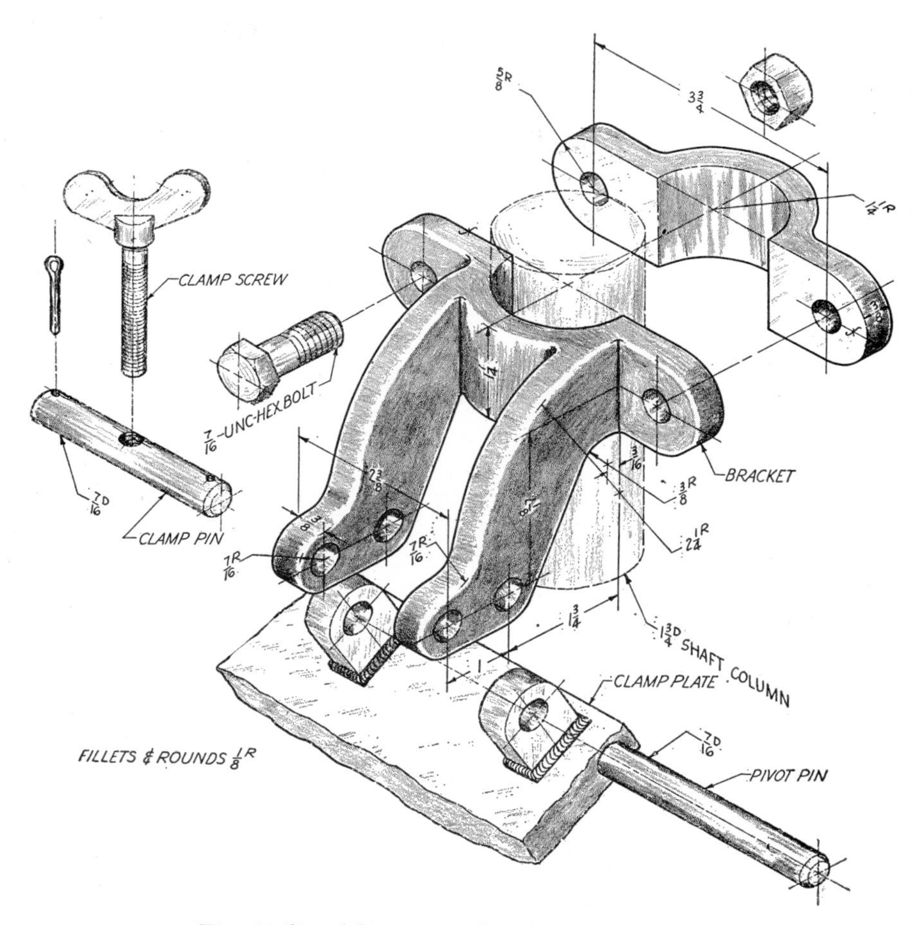

Fig. 19.50. Adjustment bracket—core blower.

34. (Fig. 19.51.) Make a detail working drawing of the bell crank. The bell crank is a part of the control mechanism of a vertical single spindle boring machine. The rod which extends downward connects with a foot-operated control. The link carries the movement to the drive unit. *Supplementary design data:* 1) The distance from the pivot center of the crank to the center of the connecting pin for the rod is $3\frac{1}{2}''$, and the distance from the center of the crank to the pin connecting the link is $2\frac{1}{2}''$. 2) The limiting position for any counter-clockwise movement of the bell crank is as shown; namely, that the line connecting the centers of the pivot and the rod-pin is horizontal. The crank is to be drawn to allow the rod a $1\frac{1}{2}''$ downward movement. The upper arm of the crank is to be located so that there will be exactly $\frac{1}{8}''$ clearance between the arm and the housing when the crank is in the extreme clockwise position. The horizontal distance from the pivot center to the left face of the housing is $1\frac{5}{8}''$. 3) The end of the rod through which the pin passes is $1\frac{1}{2}''$ in diameter, and $\frac{3}{8}''$ thick. Allow adequate clearance. 4) The crank pivots about a $1''$ diameter shoulder screw which is screwed into the bracket. Thread specification is $\frac{3}{4}$-16 UNF. 5) The crank is of cast iron. Fillets and rounds $\frac{1}{8}''$ R except as noted.

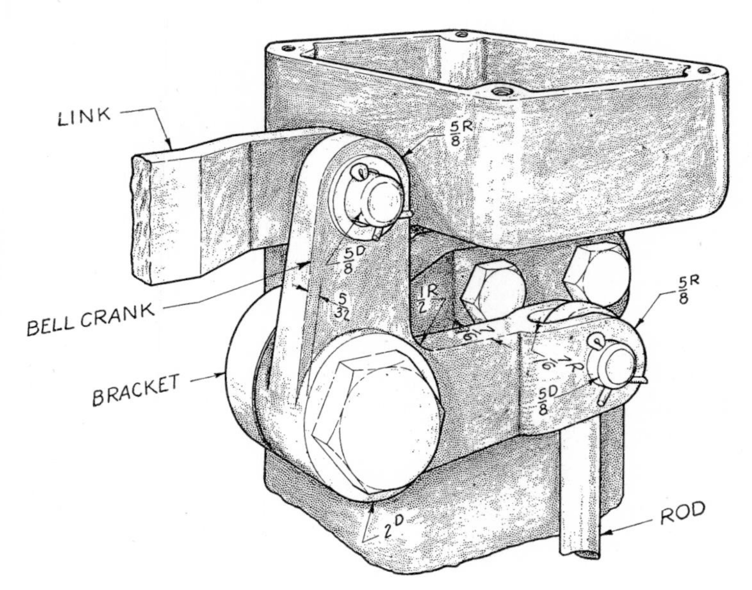

Fig. 19.51. Bell crank.

35. (Fig. 19.52.) Make a detail working drawing of a counterweight. Use an exact method for constructing the ellipse. As a matter of interest in the operation of the automatic safety control, the device stops the machine it is designed to protect if and when the speed becomes too great. As the main shaft, upon which the counterweights are attached, picks up speed, the counterweights are thrown farther and farther outward until a predetermined speed is reached. Then one or both will strike a trip causing it to move upward against a trip pin that in turn cuts off the power. *Supplementary information:* 1) The center-to-center distance between the studs is $4\frac{7}{16}''$. 2) The contact track is $\frac{3}{4}''$ wide. 3) The height of the hub is $\frac{3}{4}''$. 4) The major diameter of the ellipse is $4''$; the minor diameter is $2\frac{1}{2}''$. 5) The width of the slot for the spring is $\frac{1}{8}''$. 6) Thickness of rib $\frac{7}{16}''$. 7) Fillets and rounds $\frac{1}{8}''$ R except as shown. 8) Fillets and rounds have been purposely omitted from the pictorial drawing. They are to be shown by the student where necessary and desirable.

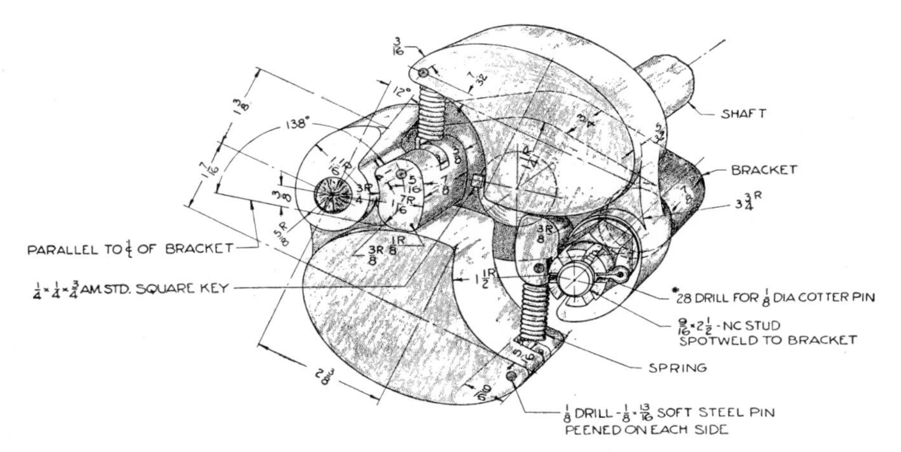

Fig. 19.52. Automatic safety control—counterweight mechanism.

36. (Fig. 19.53.) Make a detail working drawing of the rocker arm. Show a detail section taken through the ribs. *Supplementary information:* 1) The distance from the center of the shaft to the center of the hole for the pin is 4″. The distance from the shaft to the threaded hole is $4\frac{1}{2}''$. 2) The nominal diameter of the hole for the shaft is $1\frac{7}{8}''$. The hole in the rocker arm is to be reamed for a definite fit. Consult your instructor, but *do not* use a limit dimension for either the shaft or the pin. The diameter of the pin is $\frac{31}{32}''$. 3) The diameter of the threaded boss is 2″. 4) The diameter of the roller is $2\frac{1}{4}''$, and its length $1\frac{15}{32}''$. Total clearance between the roller and finished faces is to be $\frac{1}{32}''$. 5) The inside faces of the arms are to be milled in towards the hub far enough to accommodate the roller. 6) The rib is $\frac{5}{8}''$ thick. 7) The lock nut has $1\frac{1}{4}$–12 UNF thread. 8) Fillets and rounds $\frac{1}{8}''$ R except where otherwise noted.

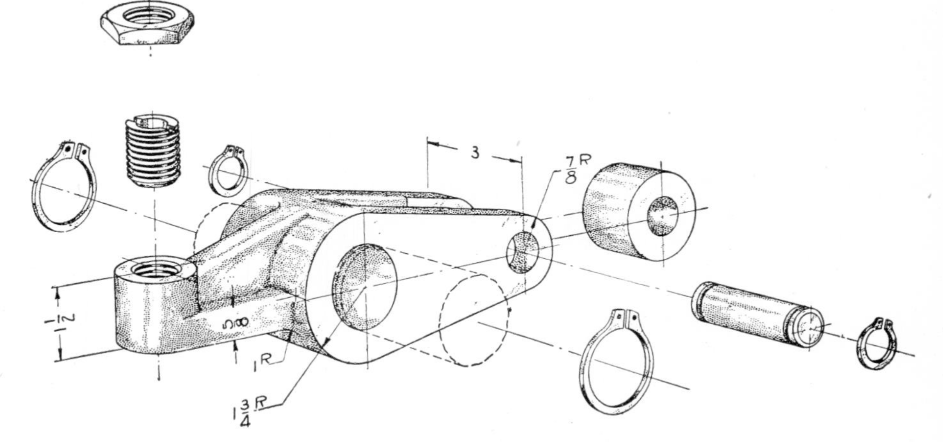

Fig. 19.53. Rocker arm.

37. (Fig. 19.54.) Make a detail working drawing of the drum. The drum rotates when it is forced along the shaft into contact with the constantly rotating driving cone. The driving cone is fixed to the rotating shaft by a Pratt and Whitney key to insure rotary motion with the shaft, and by a taper pin to prevent longitudinal axial movement. As the drum rotates it winds or unwinds a cable. The shaft is driven by a system of gears that is not shown. The partial orthographic views show the operating mechanism for sliding the drum along the shaft into contact with the driving cone. If after studying the drawings carefully you have further questions, please consult your instructor. *Supplementary information:* 1) The outside diameter of the drum is 30″. The diameter of the opening in the drum for the backing drum cone is $29\frac{1}{4}''$ and the taper is $2\frac{1}{2}''$ per ft. 2) The diameter of the cable section is 18″, and the width of opening for the cable is 10″. 3) The dimensions of the hub are: 8″ outside diameter (O.D) and $12\frac{3}{8}''$ overall length. 4) The O.D. of the bushing is $4\frac{1}{4}''$. 5) There are six $\frac{5}{8}''$ thick ribs which are equally spaced. 6) The hole in the hub for an oil fitting is tapped for a $\frac{1}{4}''$ pipe thread. The hole which is to provide access to the threaded hole is drilled $\frac{3}{4}''$ in diameter. The tapped hole is $6\frac{3}{16}''$ from the face of the hub. 7) The small hole for attaching the cable is $\frac{13}{16}''$. It is located $\frac{3}{4}''$ from the face of the flange. 8) The thickness of all sections except for the ribs is $\frac{3}{4}''$. 9) There are 124 copper rivets required to fasten the brake lining to the drum. The holes in the drum are to be drilled $\frac{1}{4}''$ in diameter and are countersunk at 90°. 10) All small radii are $\frac{3}{4}''$ R.

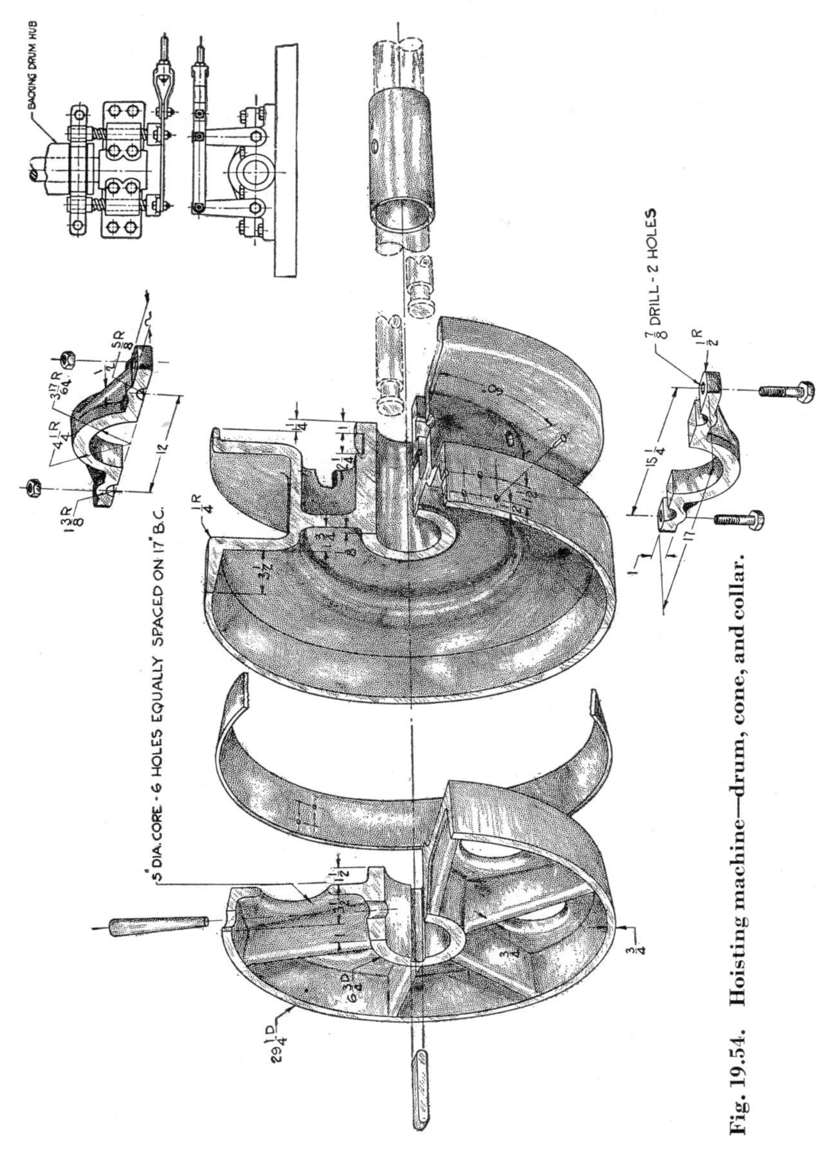

Fig. 19.54. Hoisting machine—drum, cone, and collar.

38. (Fig. 19.54.) Make a detail working drawing of the driving cone. *Supplementary information:* 1) The surface of the driving cone which contacts the lining in the drum is tapered. The taper is $2\frac{1}{2}''$ per ft. 2) The diameter of the shaft on which the driving cone is fixed is $3\frac{3}{4}''$ dia. 3) It is suggested that a No. 34 Pratt and Whitney and No. 12 Std. taper be used for the driving cone. Taper pins have a taper of $\frac{1}{4}''$ per ft. 4) The $5''$ dia. holes are to be cored in the casting

39. (Fig. 19.55.) Make a detail drawing of an assigned part of the rail wheel. Determine the dimensions by transferring them from the drawing to the accompanying scale, by means of the dividers. Compose a suitable detail title giving the name of the part, the material, the number required, etc.

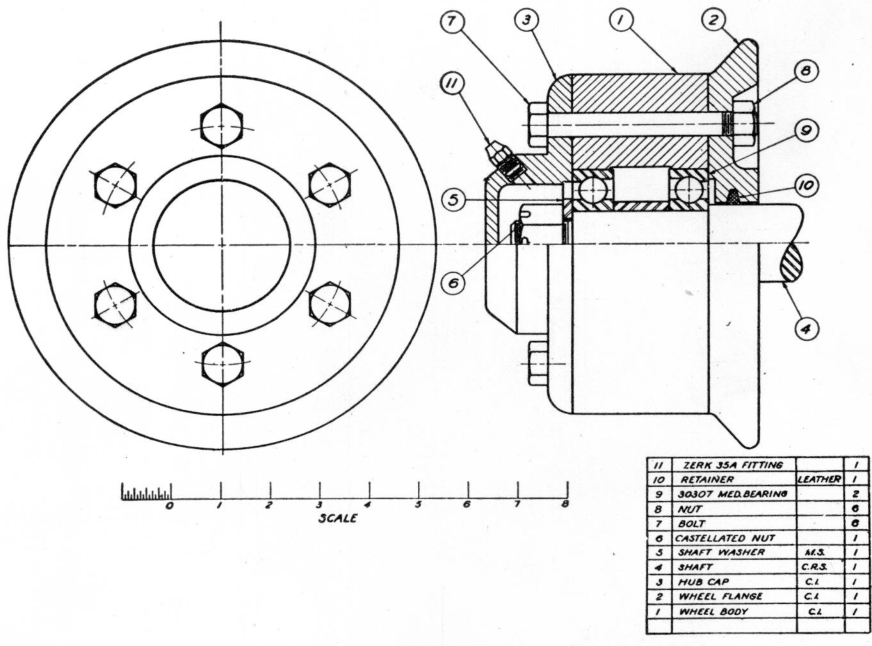

11	ZERK 35A FITTING		1
10	RETAINER	LEATHER	1
9	30307 MED. BEARING		2
8	NUT		6
7	BOLT		6
6	CASTELLATED NUT		1
5	SHAFT WASHER	M.S.	1
4	SHAFT	C.R.S.	1
3	HUB CAP	C.I.	1
2	WHEEL FLANGE	C.I.	1
1	WHEEL BODY	C.I.	1

Fig. 19.55. Rail wheel.

40. (Fig. 19.56.) Make a detail drawing of an assigned part of the thermostatic radiator trap.

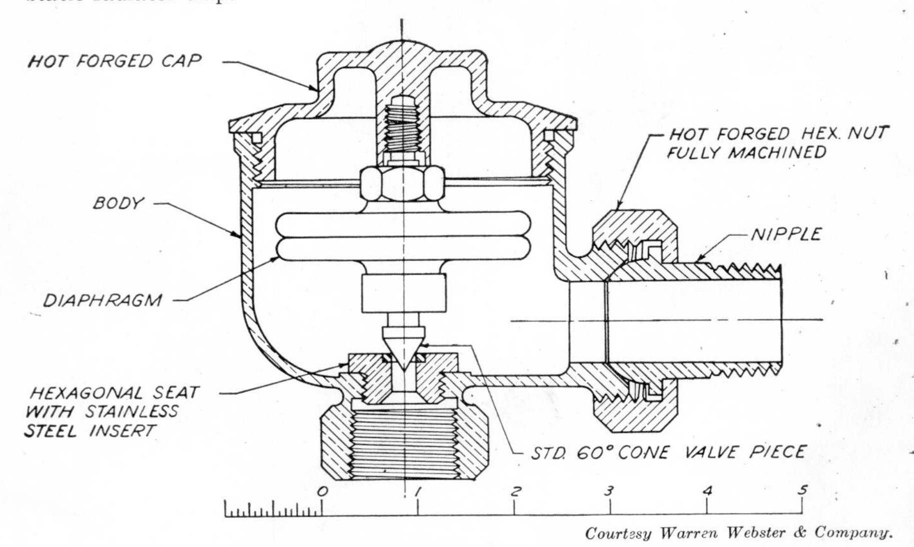

Courtesy Warren Webster & Company.

Fig. 19.56. Thermostatic radiator trap.

41. (Fig. 19.57.) Make a two-view freehand detail sketch of the fan spindle. Determine dimensions by transferring them from the drawing to the open-divided scale, by means of the dividers. The material is SAE 1045, CRS. The limits for the spindle may be found in Table XXXIII, Appendix. The last figure in the bearing number is the bearing bore number given in the tables. Use a free fit between spindle and felt retainer, spindle and felt-retaining washer, spindle and cone-clamp washer.

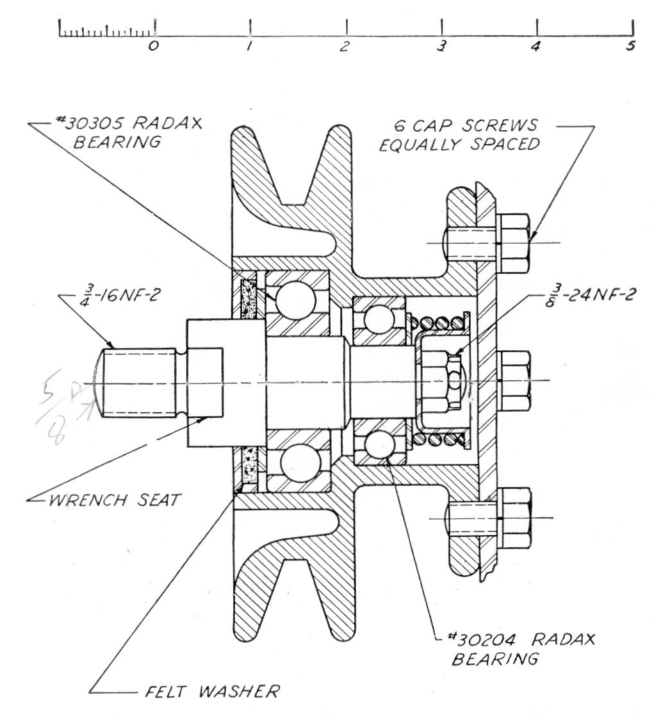

Fig. 19.57. Fan assembly.

42. (Fig. 19.57.) Make a complete two-view detail drawing of the fan pulley. It is suggested that a half-circular view and a full-sectional view be shown. Determine the dimensions as suggested in problem 41. Housing limits for the given bearings will be found in Table XXXIII, Appendix.

43. (Fig. 19.58–19.59). Make a detail drawing of an assigned part of the air cleaner. Determine the dimensions by transferring them from the drawing to the accompanying scale by means of the dividers. Compose a suitable detail title, giving the name of the part, the material, etc. Study Fig. 19.59.

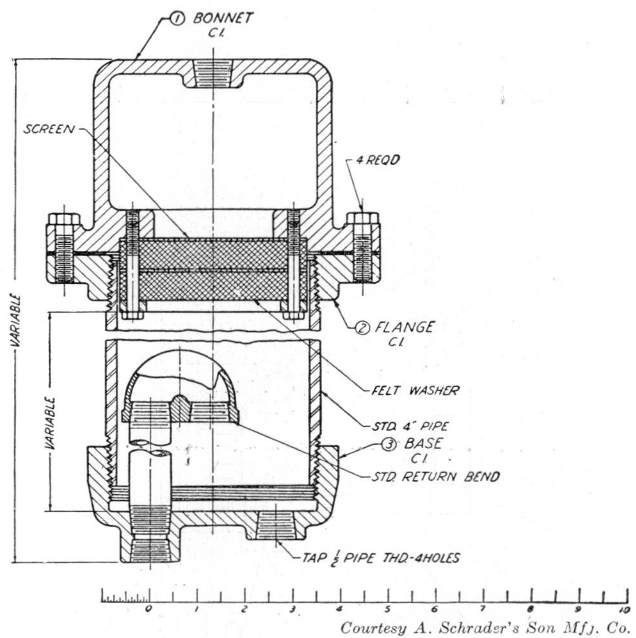

Courtesy A. Schrader's Son Mfg. Co.

Fig. 19.58. Air cleaner.

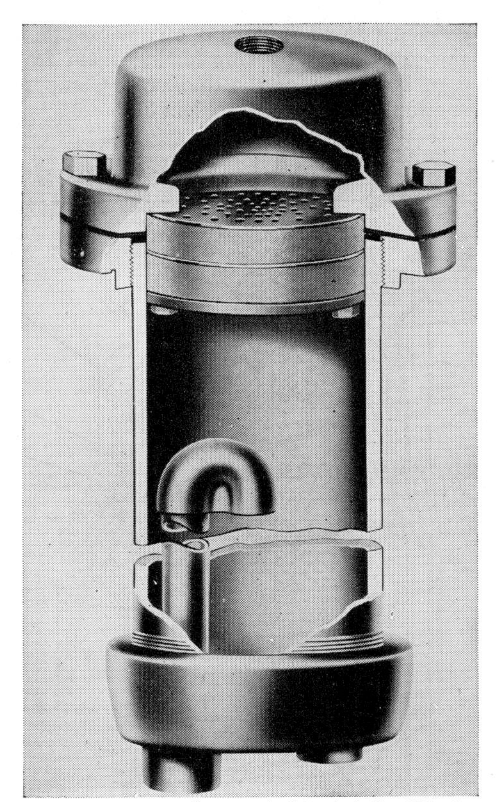

Courtesy A. Schrader's Son Mfg. Co.

Fig. 19.59. Air cleaner.

44. (Fig. 19.60.) Make a detail drawing of an assigned part of the motorcycle clutch. Determine the dimensions by transferring them from the drawing to the accompanying scale, by means of the dividers. Compose a suitable detail title, giving the information suggested in problem 39.

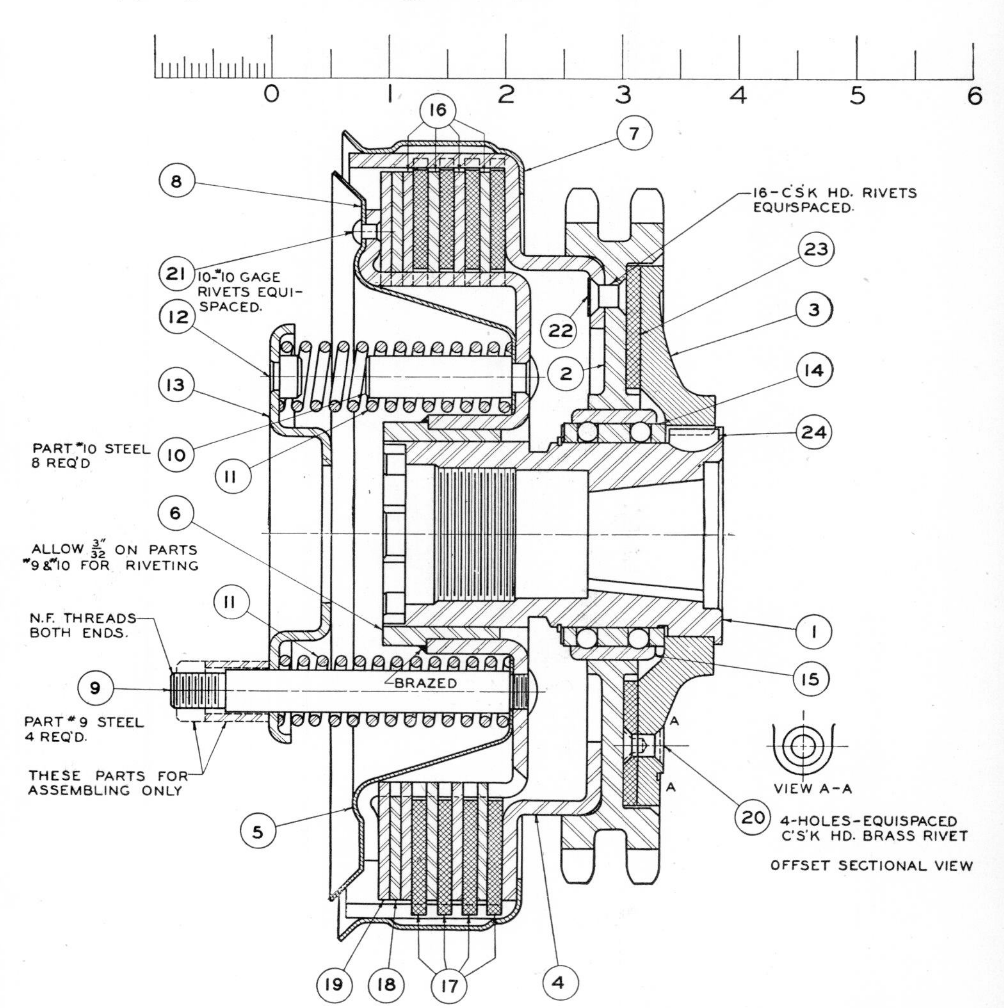

Courtesy Harley-Davidson Motor Co.

Fig. 19.60. Motorcycle clutch assembly.

45. (Fig. 19.61.) Make a detail drawing of an assigned part of the bearing bracket. Compose a suitable detail title, giving the name of the part, the material, etc.

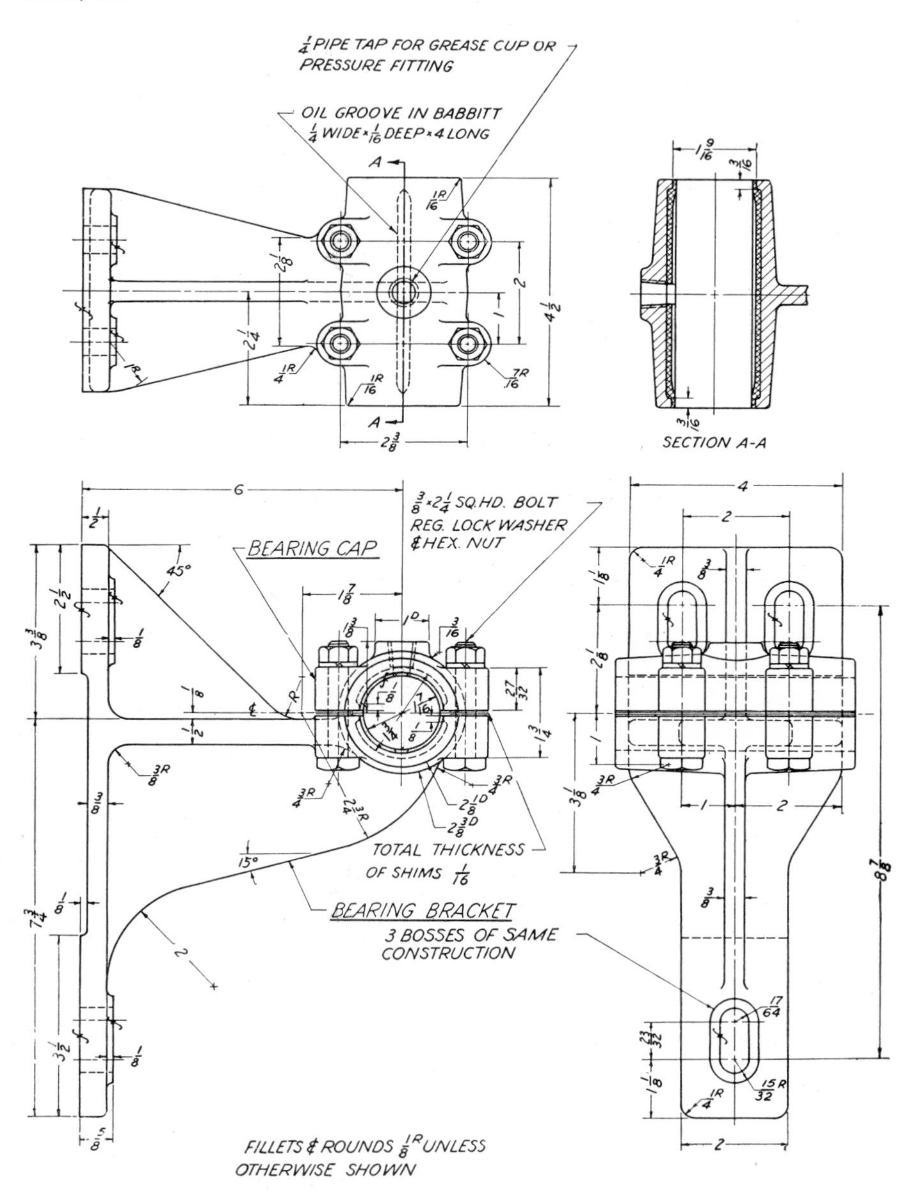

Fig. 19.61. Bearing bracket.

46. (Fig. 19.62.) Make a detail drawing of an assigned part of the pipe stand. Draw all necessary views and give all dimensions that will be required by the shop. Compose a suitable title, giving the name of the part, the material, and the number required.

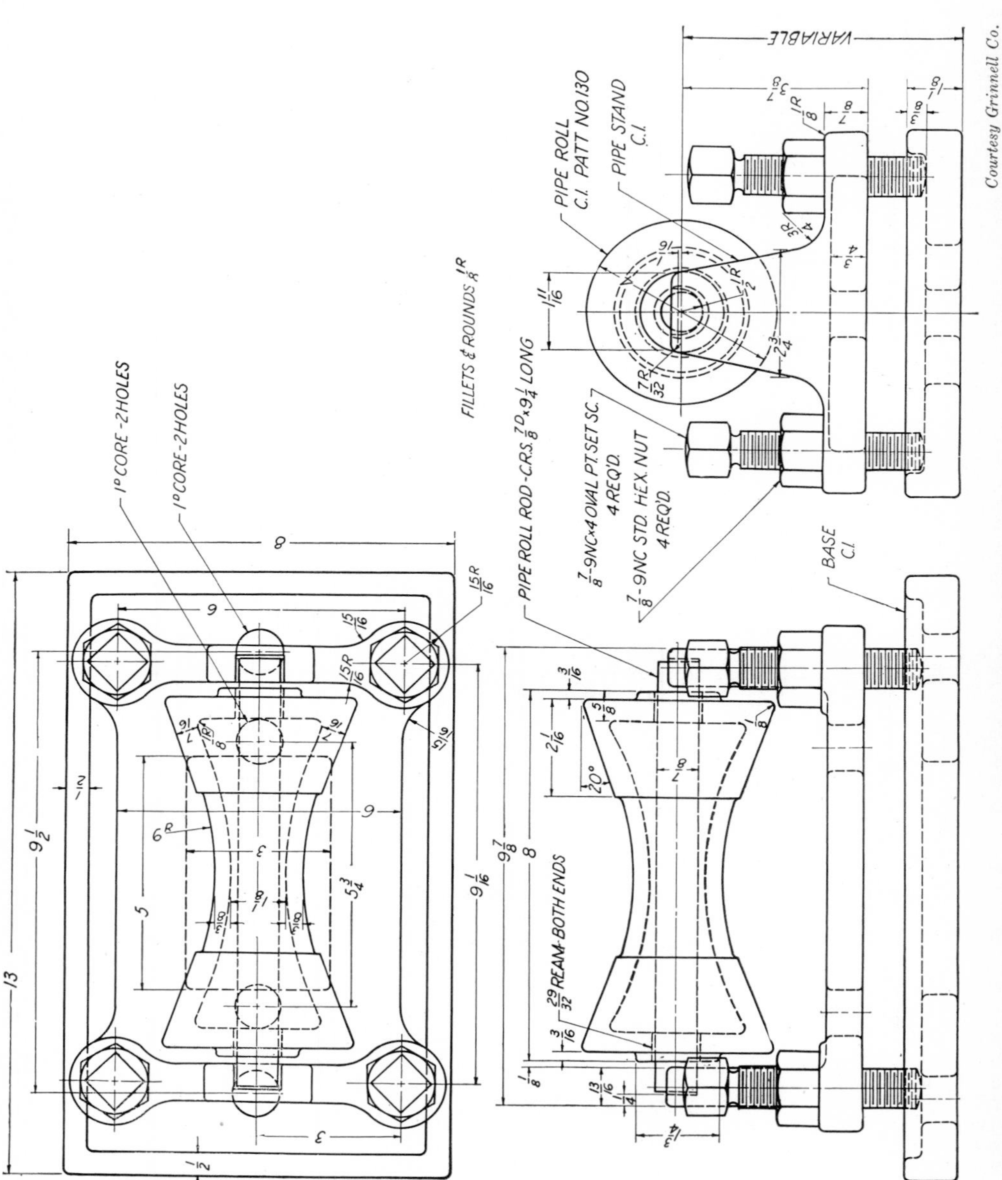

Fig. 19.62. Pipe stand

47. (Fig. 19.63.) Make a detail working drawing of an assigned part of the self-aligning shaft support. Compose a suitable title, giving the name of the part, the material, etc.

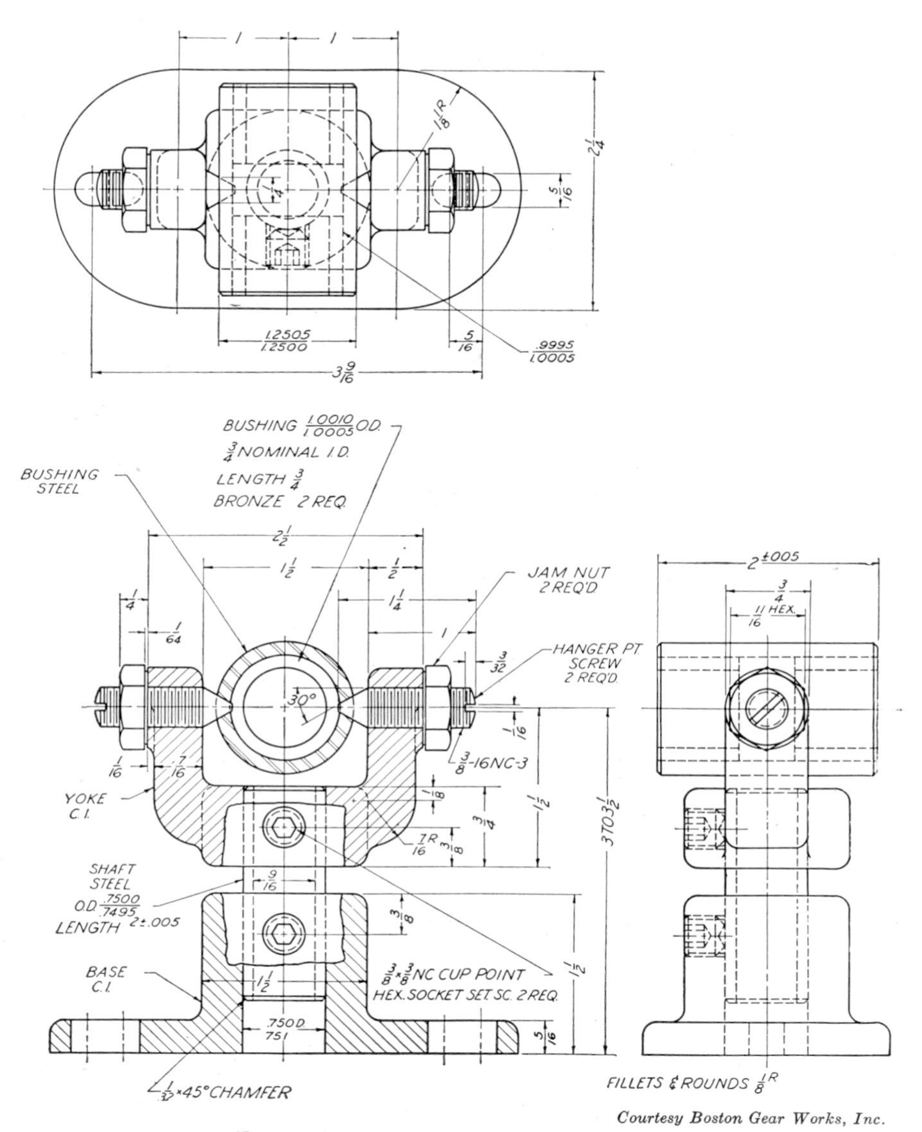

Courtesy Boston Gear Works, Inc.

Fig. 19.63. Self-aligning shaft support.

48. (Fig. 19.64.) Make a detail working drawing of an assigned part of the flexible joint. Compose a suitable title giving the name of the part, the material, etc.

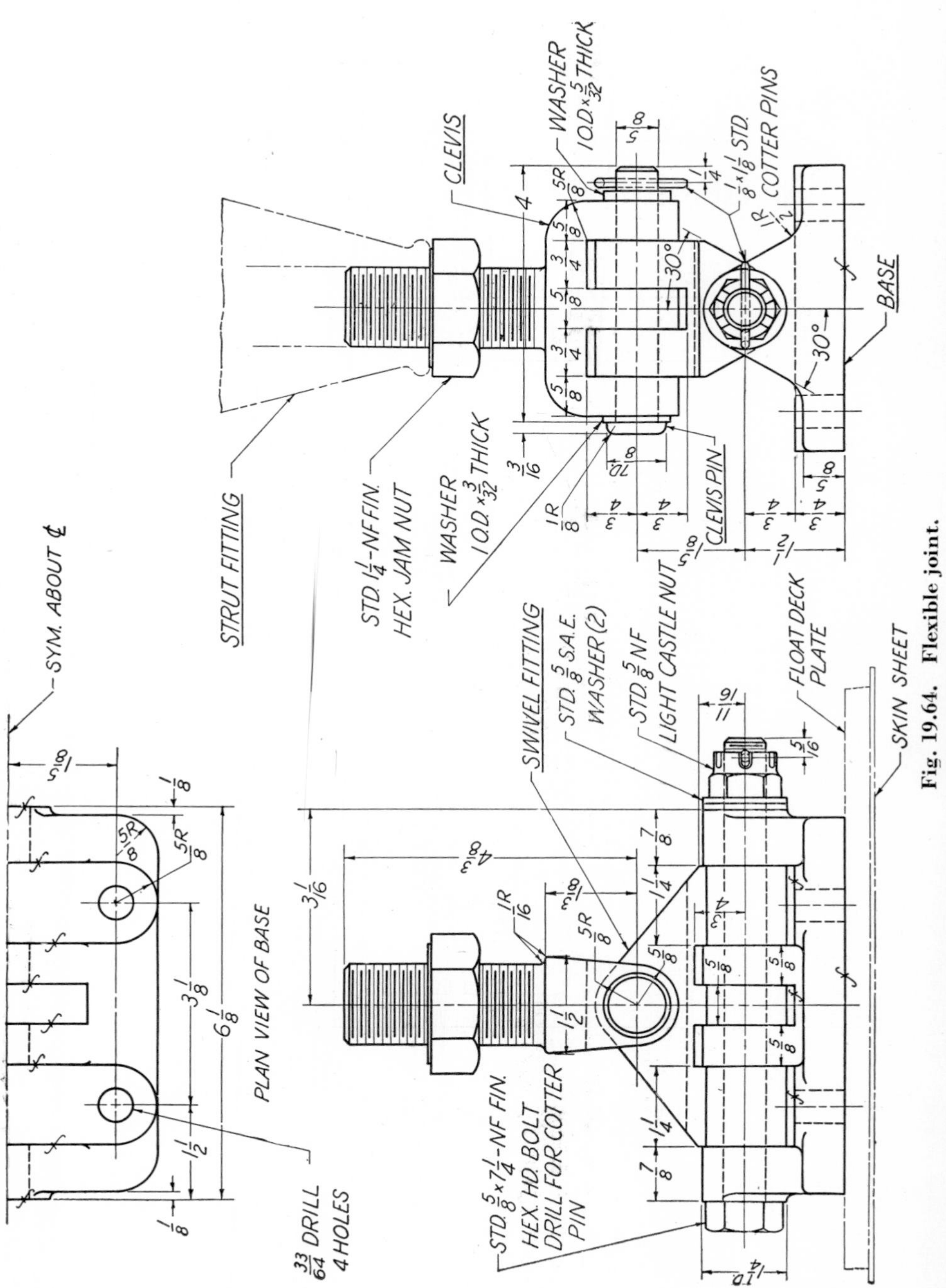

Fig. 19.64. Flexible joint.

49. (Fig. 19.65–19.66.) Make a detail drawing of an assigned part of the check valve.

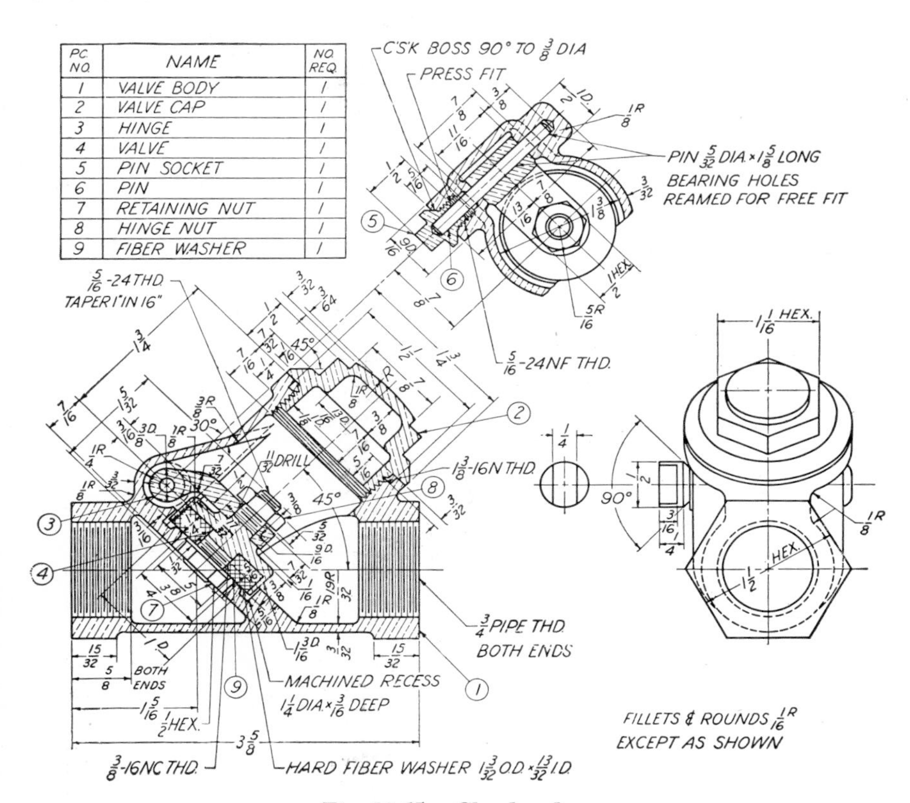

PC. NO.	NAME	NO. REQ.
1	VALVE BODY	1
2	VALVE CAP	1
3	HINGE	1
4	VALVE	1
5	PIN SOCKET	1
6	PIN	1
7	RETAINING NUT	1
8	HINGE NUT	1
9	FIBER WASHER	1

Fig. 19.65. Check valve.

Fig. 19.66. Check valve.

50. (Fig. 19.67.) Make a detail drawing of an assigned part of the handle.

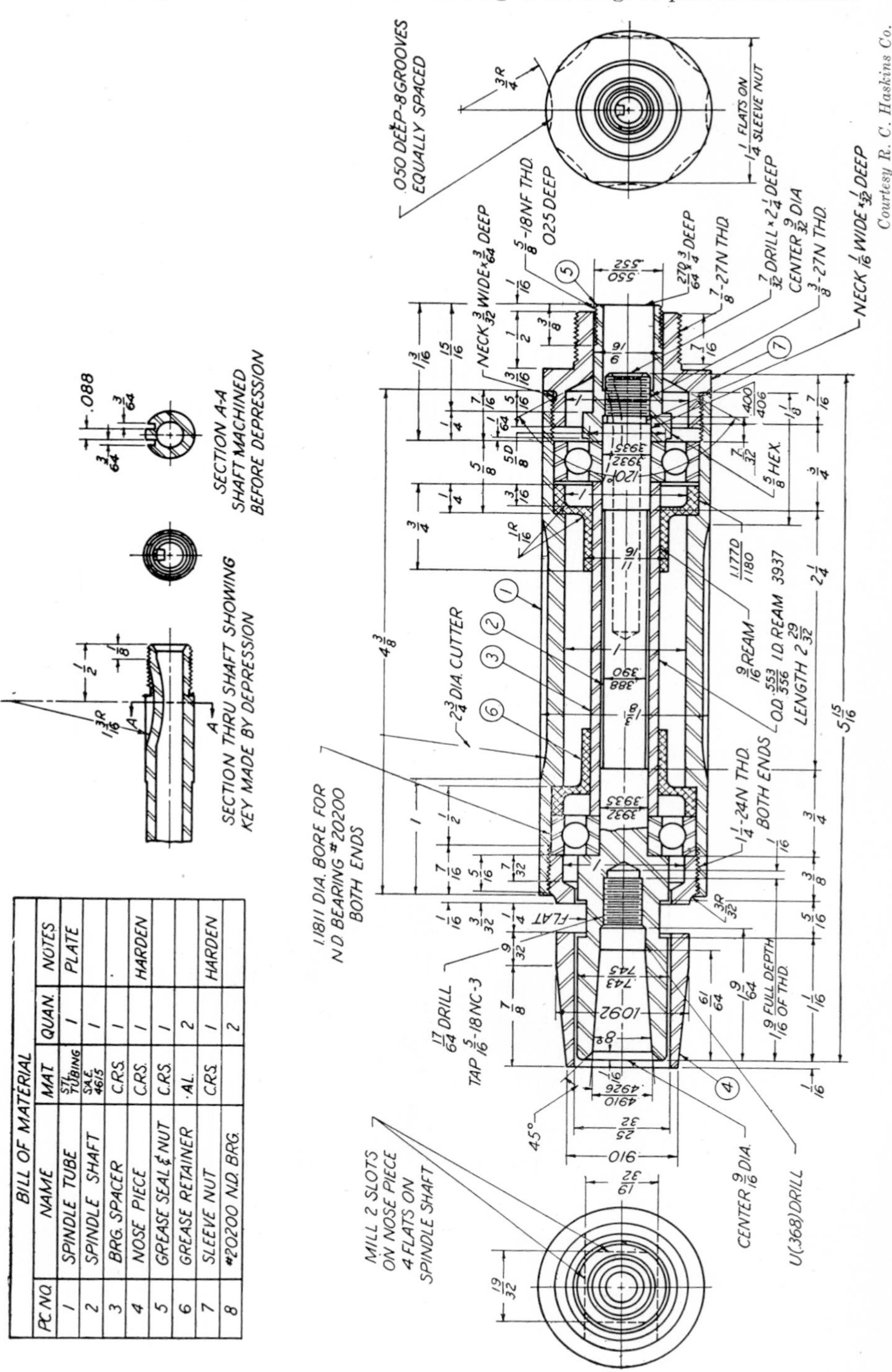

BILL OF MATERIAL

PC.NO.	NAME	MAT.	QUAN.	NOTES
1	SPINDLE TUBE	STL. TUBING	1	PLATE
2	SPINDLE SHAFT	S.A.E. 4615	1	
3	BRG. SPACER	C.R.S.	1	
4	NOSE PIECE	C.R.S.	1	HARDEN
5	GREASE SEAL & NUT	C.R.S.	1	
6	GREASE RETAINER	AL.	2	
7	SLEEVE NUT	C.R.S.	1	HARDEN
8	#20200 N.D. BRG.		2	

Fig. 19.67. Handle.

51. (Fig. 19.68.) Make a detail drawing of an assigned part of the compensating collet chuck.

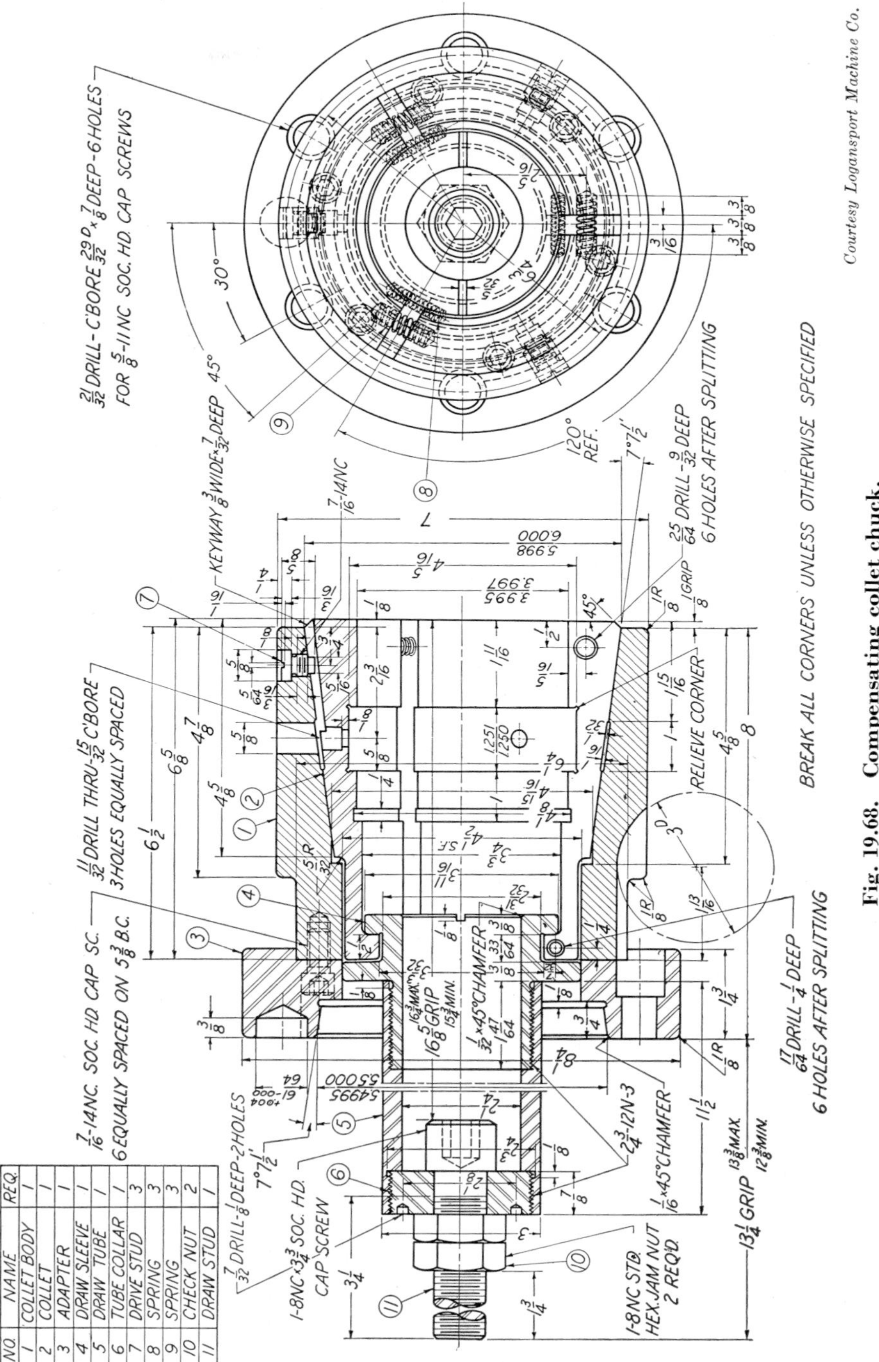

Courtesy Logansport Machine Co.

Fig. 19.68. Compensating collet chuck.

52. (Fig. 19.69.) Make a detail drawing of an assigned part of the roller-bearing stud unit.

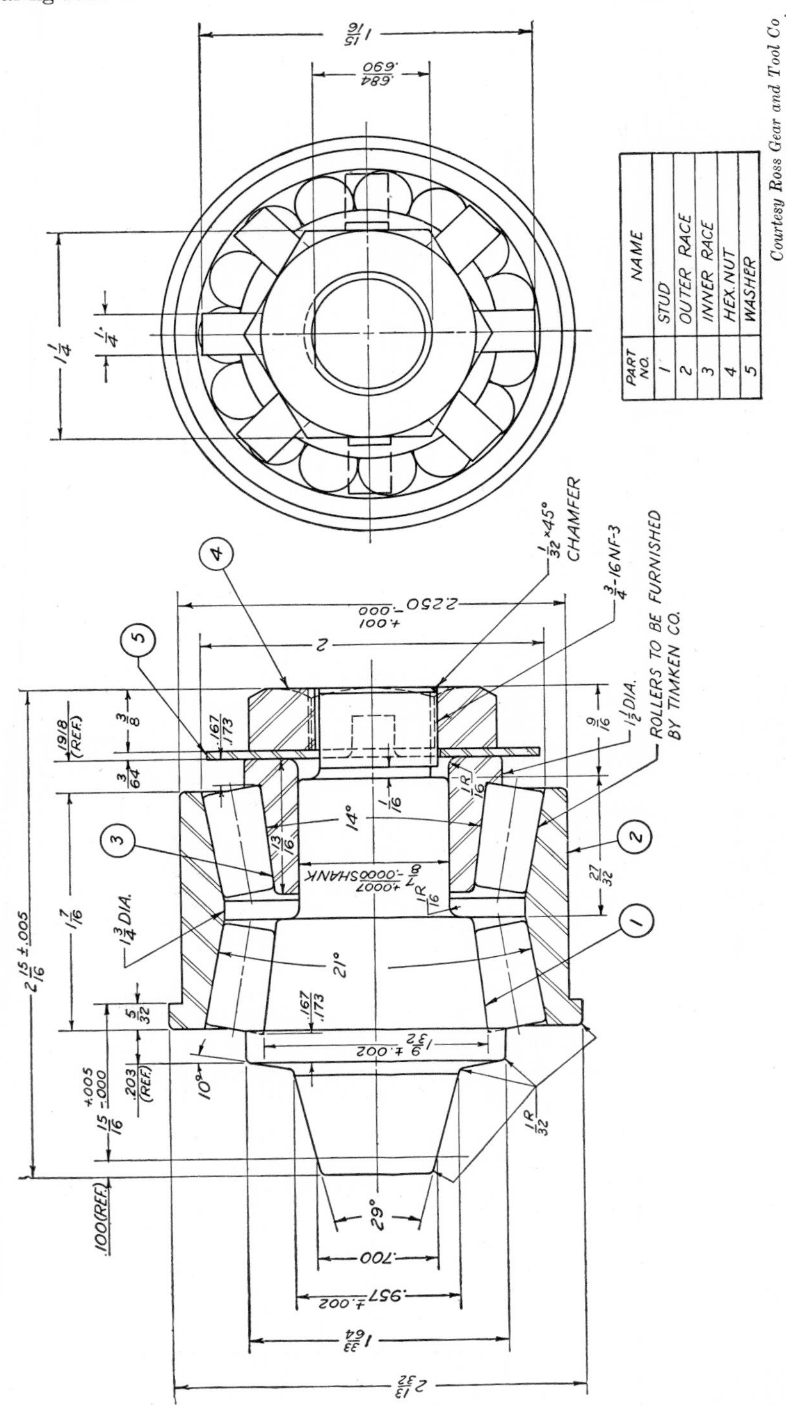

Courtesy Ross Gear and Tool Co.

Fig. 19.69. Roller-bearing stud unit.

53. (Fig. 19.70.) Make a detail drawing of an assigned part of the air cylinder.

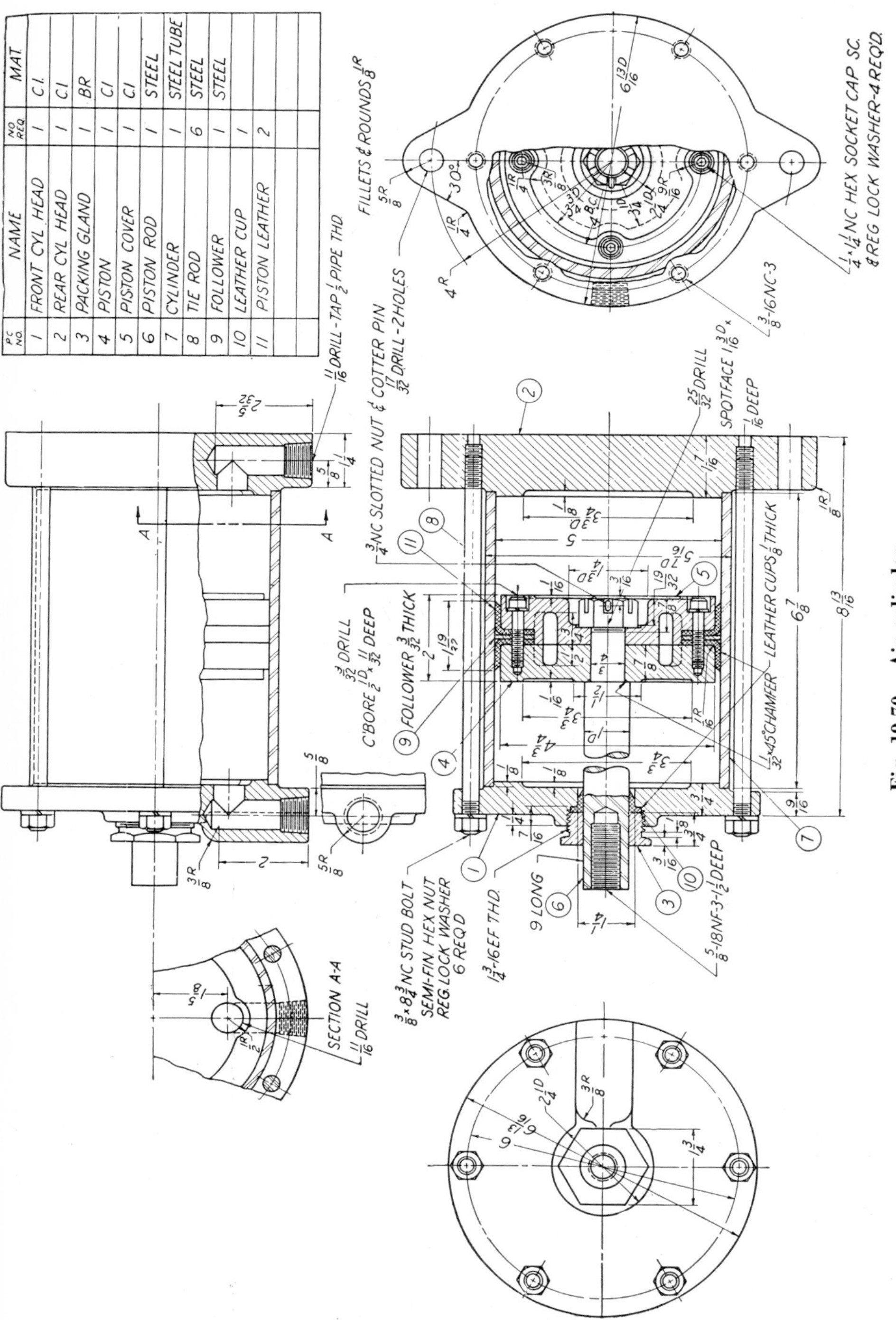

PC NO	NAME	NO REQ	MAT
1	FRONT CYL HEAD	1	C.I.
2	REAR CYL HEAD	1	C.I
3	PACKING GLAND	1	BR
4	PISTON	1	C.I
5	PISTON COVER	1	C.I
6	PISTON ROD	1	STEEL
7	CYLINDER	1	STEEL TUBE
8	TIE ROD	6	STEEL
9	FOLLOWER	1	STEEL
10	LEATHER CUP	1	
11	PISTON LEATHER	2	

Fig. 19.70. Air cylinder.

54. (Fig. 19.71.) Make a detail drawing of an assigned part of the Simplex ball bearing screw jack.

PC.NO.	NAME	QUAN.	MATERIAL	PC.NO.	NAME	QUAN.	MATERIAL
1	STANDARD	1	MALL. IRON	5	GROOVE PIN	3	$\frac{7}{32}$ D × $\frac{5}{8}$ STEEL ROD
2	SCREW	1	S.A.E. 1120 FORGING	6	LEVER BAR	1	REROLLED RAIL STK.
3	CAP	1	S.A.E. 1045 FORGING	7	$\frac{7}{8}$ DIA. BALL BEARING	1	STD.
4	THRUST WASHER	1	S.A.E. 2315				

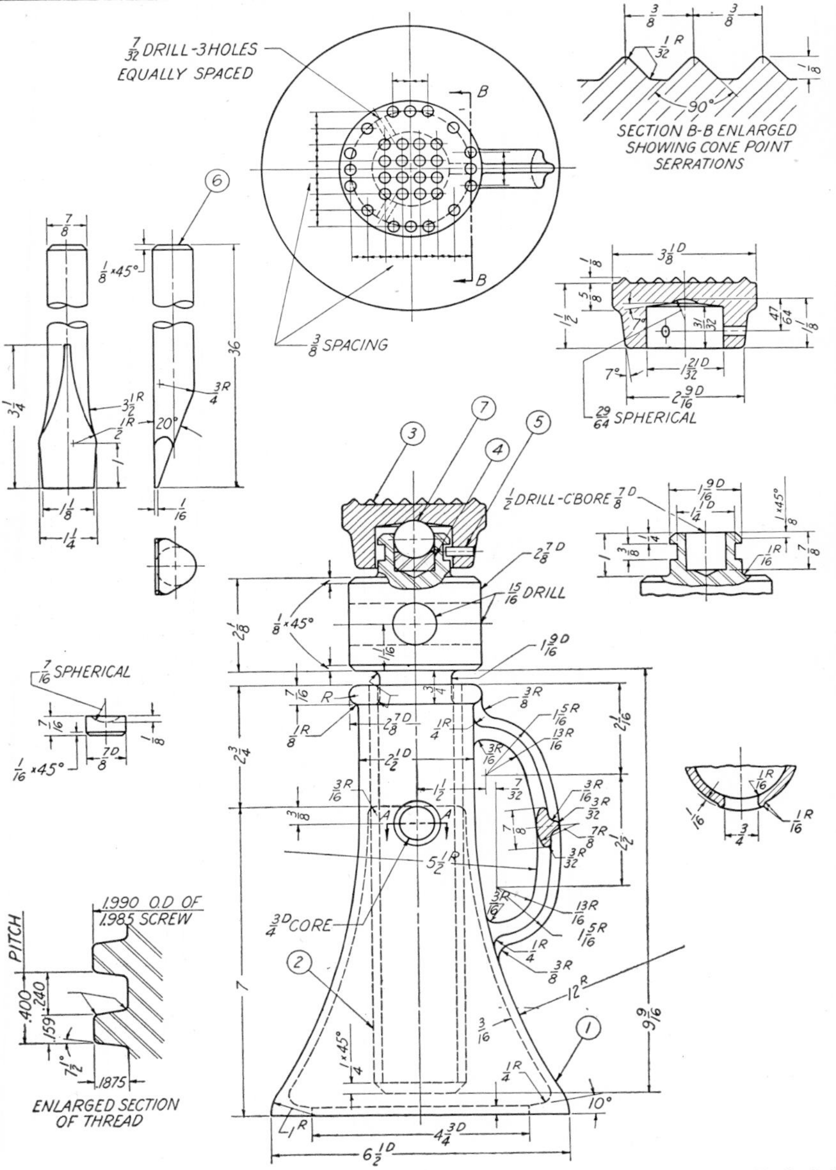

Courtesy of Templeton, Kenly & Co.

Fig. 19.71. Simplex ball bearing screw jack.

55. (Fig. 19.72.) Make a detail drawing of an assigned part of the tool holder.

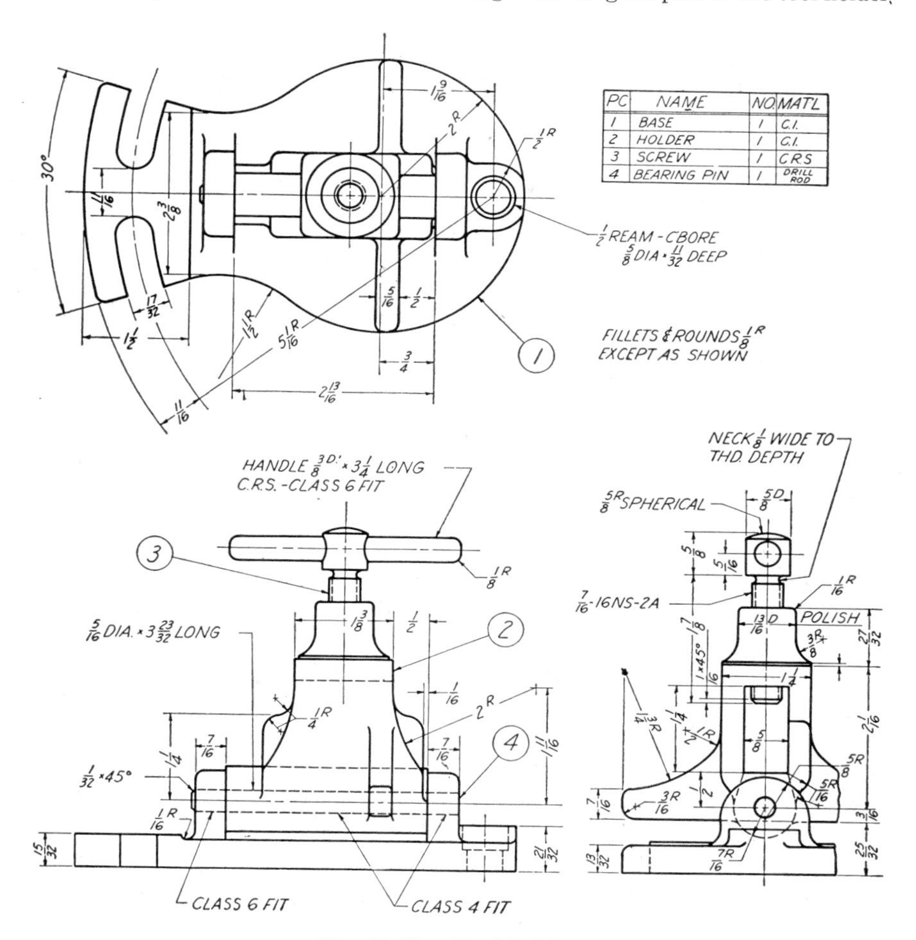

PC	NAME	NO	MATL
1	BASE	1	C.I.
2	HOLDER	1	C.I.
3	SCREW	1	C.R.S
4	BEARING PIN	1	DRILL ROD

Fig. 19.72. Tool holder.

56. (Fig. 19.73.) Make a detail drawing of an assigned part of the shaft support.

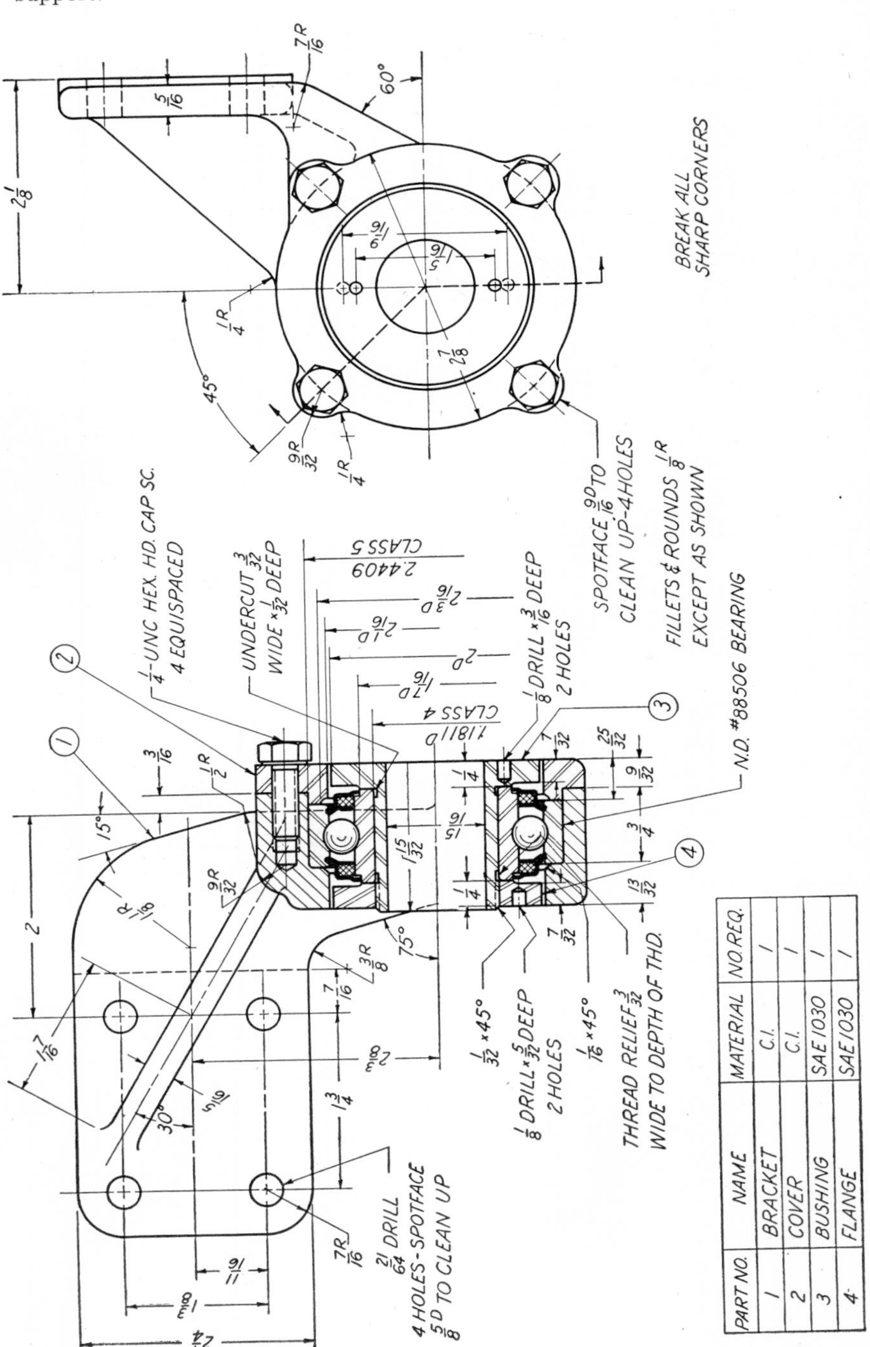

PART NO.	NAME	MATERIAL	NO. REQ.
1	BRACKET	C.I.	1
2	COVER	C.I.	1
3	BUSHING	SAE 1030	1
4	FLANGE	SAE 1030	1

Fig. 19.73. Shaft support.

57. (Fig. 19.74.) Make a detail drawing of an assigned part of the boring fixture.

PART NO.	NAME	MATERIAL	NO. REQ'D
1	HOLDER	C.R.S.	1
2	CLAMP STRAP	C.R.S.	1
3	CLAMP	C.R.S.	1
4	CLAMP SCREW	C.R.S.	1
5	PLUG	BRASS	1
6	THUMB SCREW	C.R.S.	1
7	REST BUTTON	TOOL STEEL	2
8	BUSHING	TOOL STEEL	1
9	PIN	DRILL ROD	1

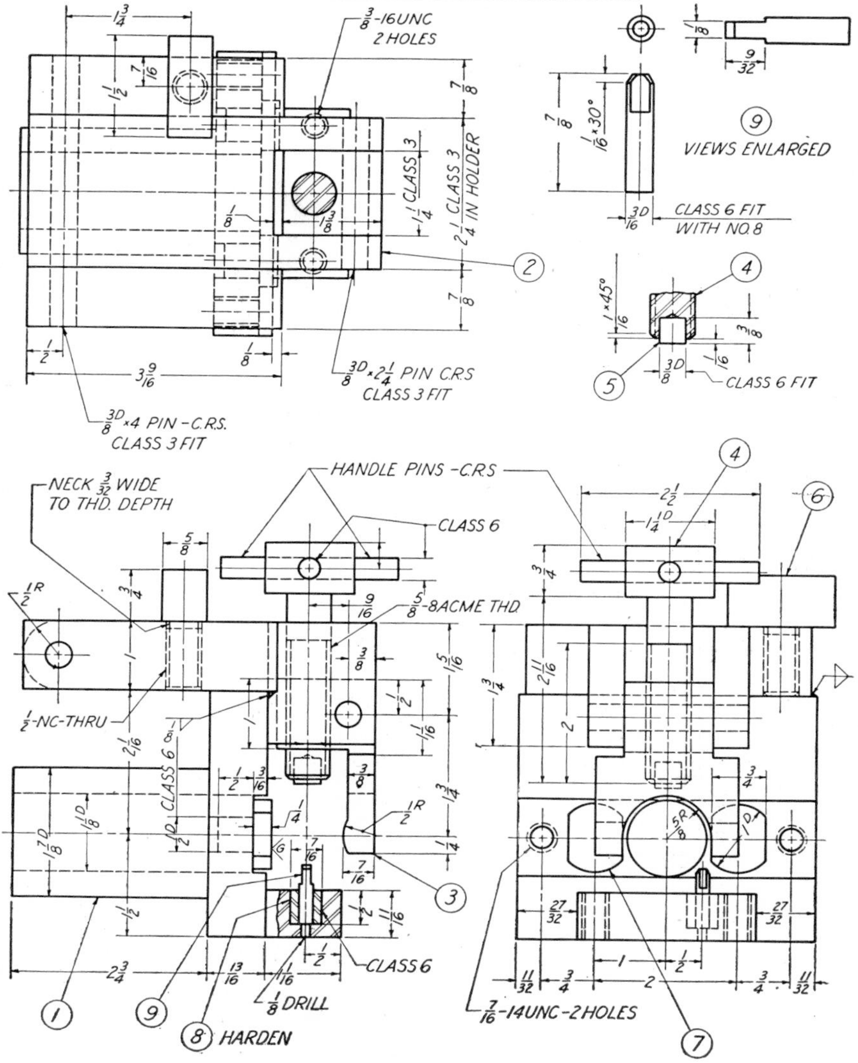

Fig. 19.74. Boring fixture.

58. (Fig. 19.75.) Make a detail drawing of an assigned part of the bench arbor press.

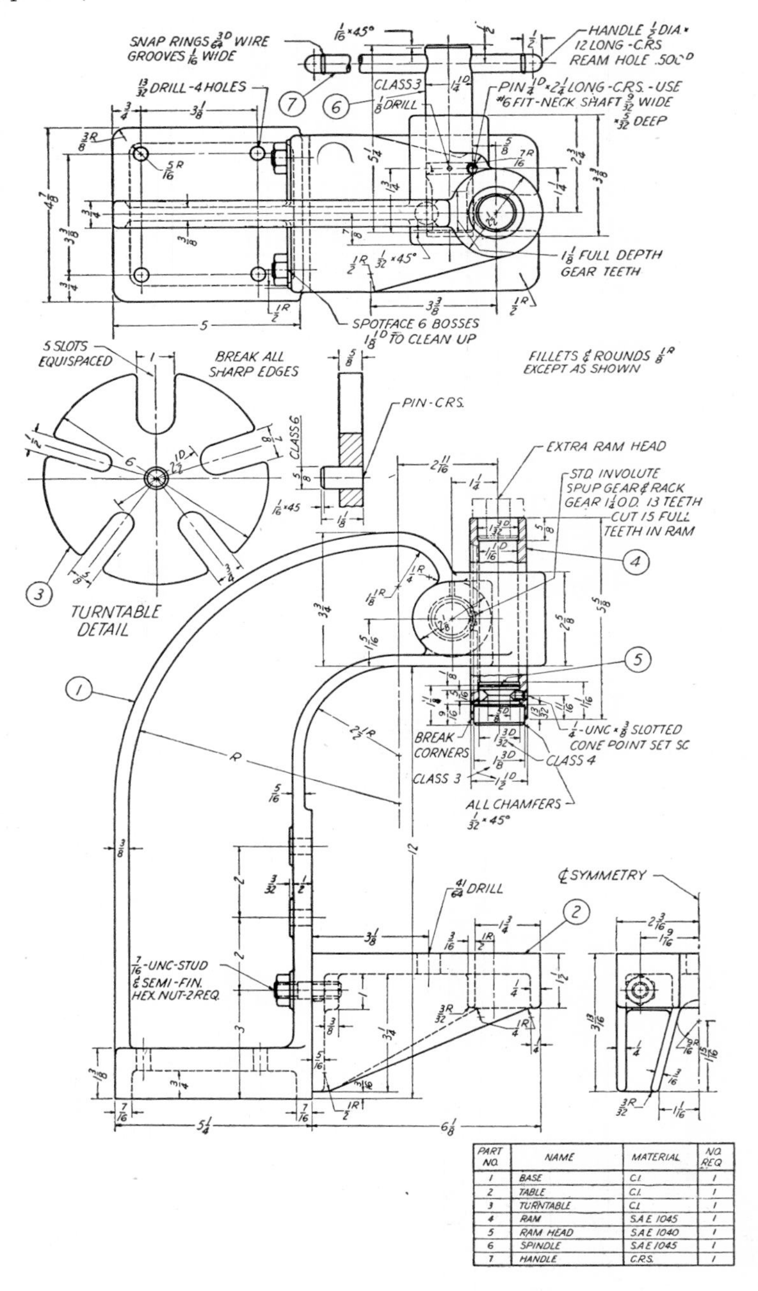

PART NO.	NAME	MATERIAL	NO. REQ.
1	BASE	C.I.	1
2	TABLE	C.I.	1
3	TURNTABLE	C.I.	1
4	RAM	S.A.E. 1045	1
5	RAM HEAD	S.A.E. 1040	1
6	SPINDLE	S.A.E. 1045	1
7	HANDLE	C.R.S.	1

Fig. 19.75. Bench arbor press.

59. (Fig. 19.76.) Make a detail drawing of an assigned part of the conveyor take-up unit.

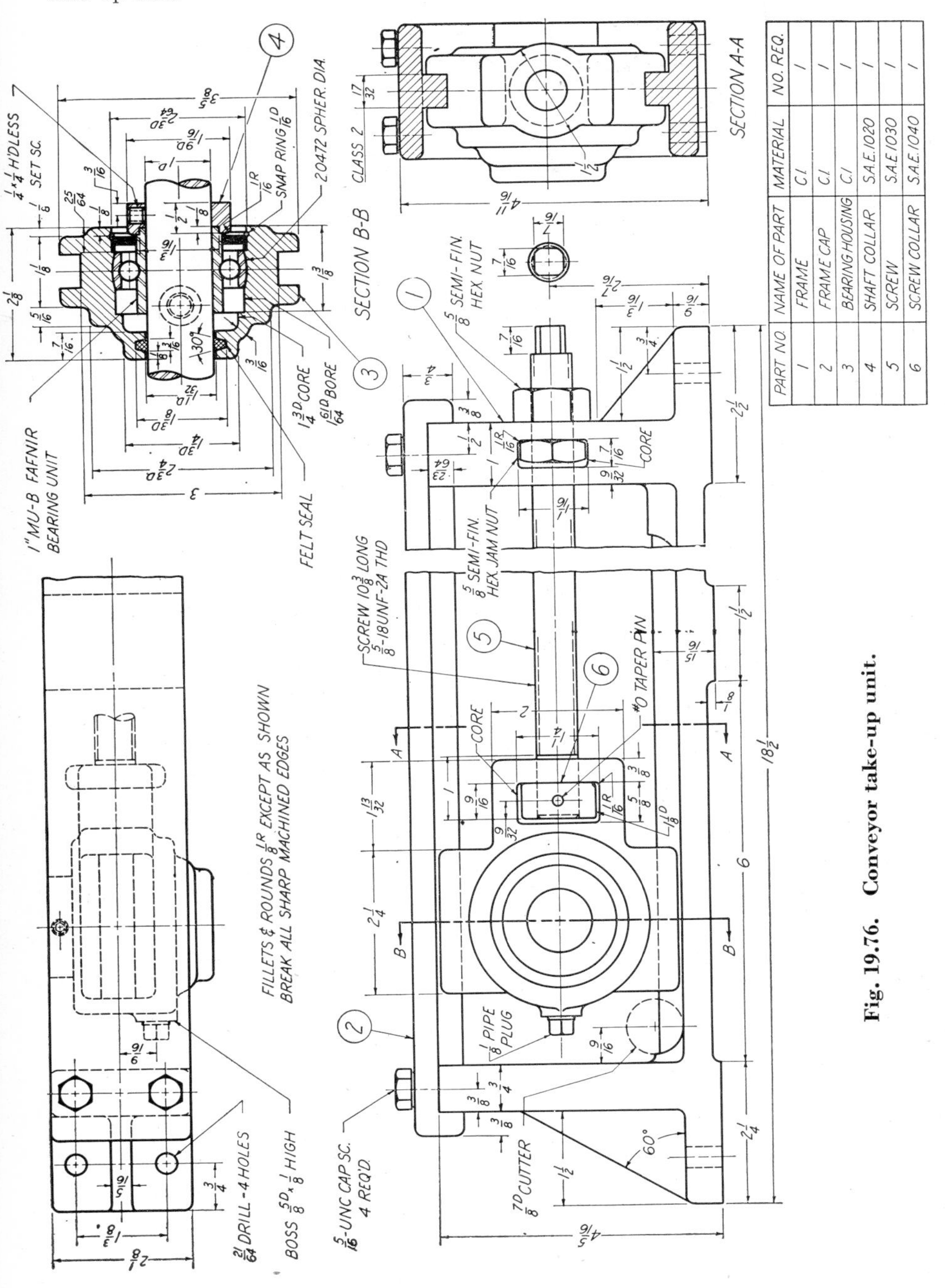

PART NO.	NAME OF PART	MATERIAL	NO. REQ.
1	FRAME	C.I	1
2	FRAME CAP	C.I	1
3	BEARING HOUSING	C.I	1
4	SHAFT COLLAR	S.A.E.1020	1
5	SCREW	S.A.E.1030	1
6	SCREW COLLAR	S.A.E.1040	1

Fig. 19.76. Conveyor take-up unit.

60. (Fig. 19.77.) Make a detail drawing of an assigned part of the gear pump.

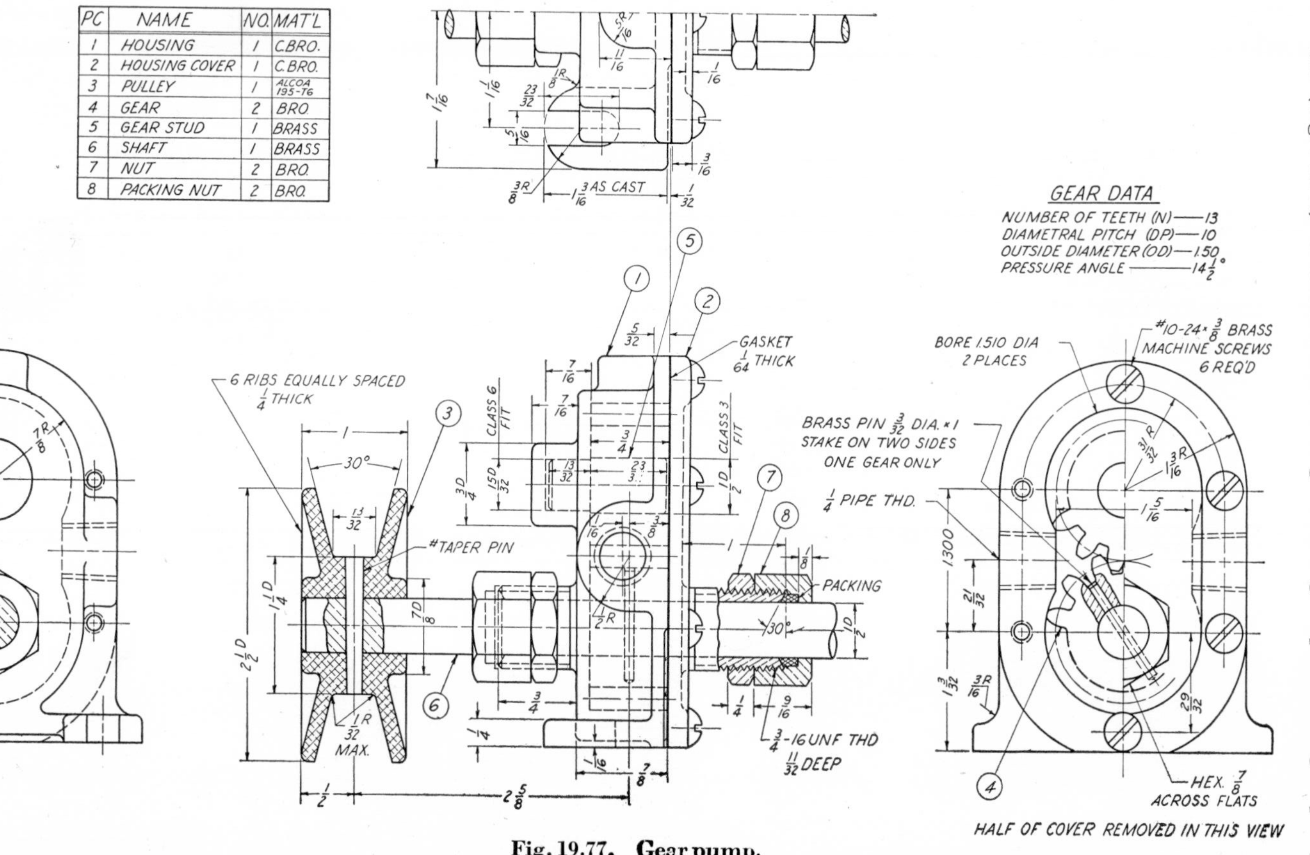

Fig. 19.77. Gear pump.

61. (Fig. 19.78.) Make a detail working drawing of an assigned part of the bench grinder.

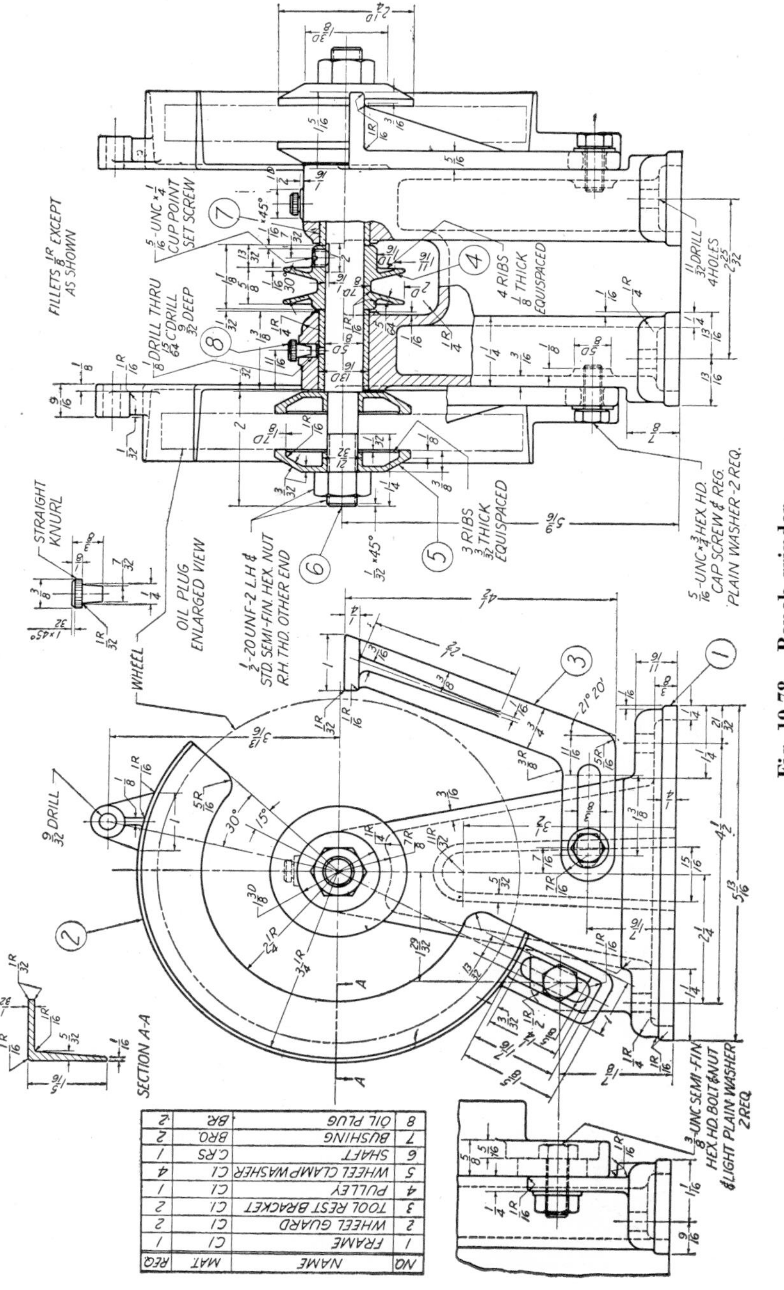

Fig. 19.78. Bench grinder.

62. (Fig. 19.79.) Make a detail drawing of an assigned part of the indexing mechanism-press dial table. Determine dimensions by transferring them from the drawing to the accompanying open-divided scale by means of the dividers. A student should consult his instructor concerning clearances and cylindrical fits.

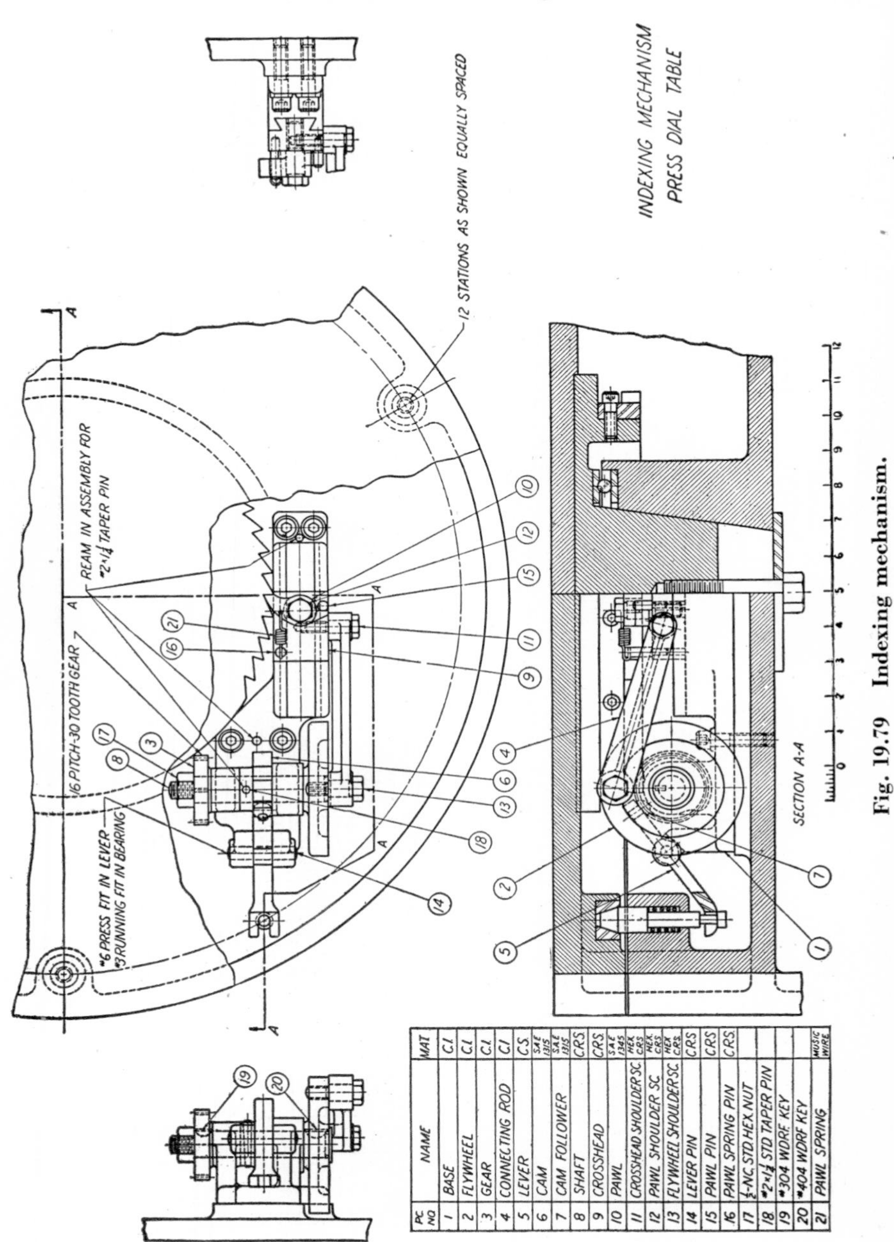

Fig. 19.79 Indexing mechanism.

63. (Fig. 19.80.) Make a complete set of working drawings of the flexible coupling. The complete set should include detail drawings of the individual parts and an assembly drawing complete with bill of material.

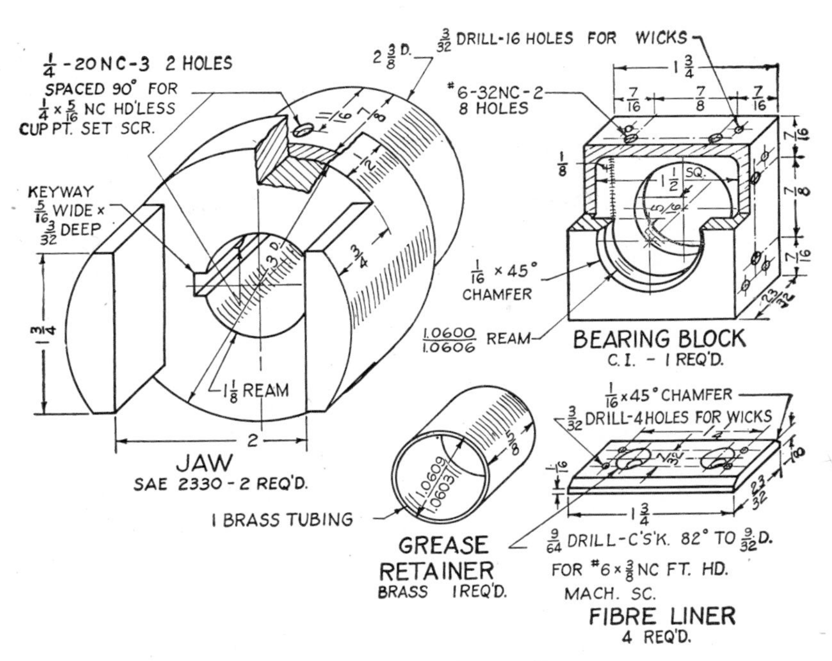

Fig. 19.80. Flexible coupling.

64. (Fig. 19.81.) Make a complete set of working drawings of the link. The complete set should consist of detail drawings of the parts and an assembly drawing.

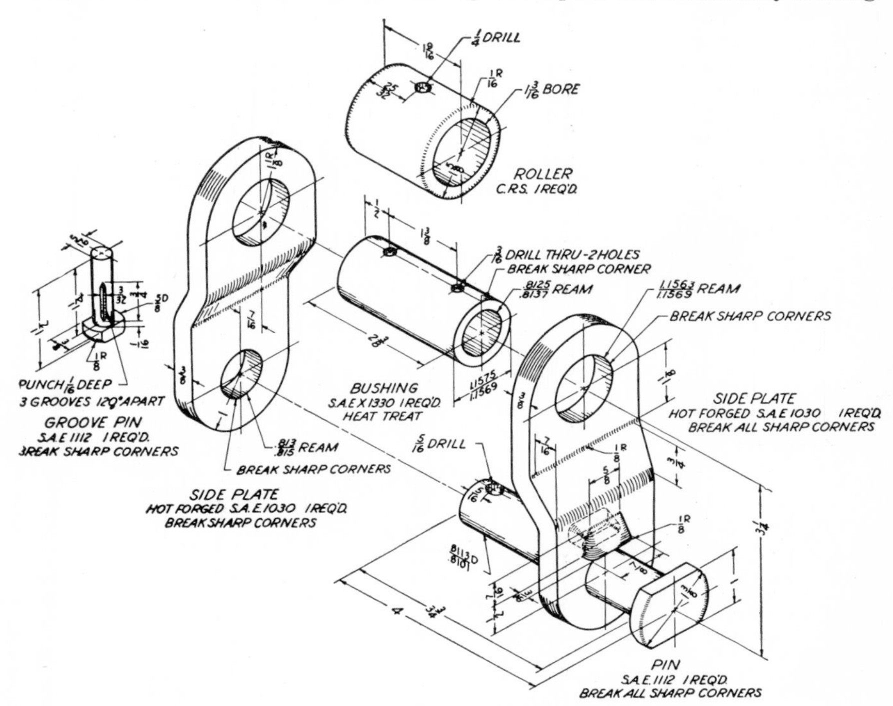

Fig. 19.81. Link.

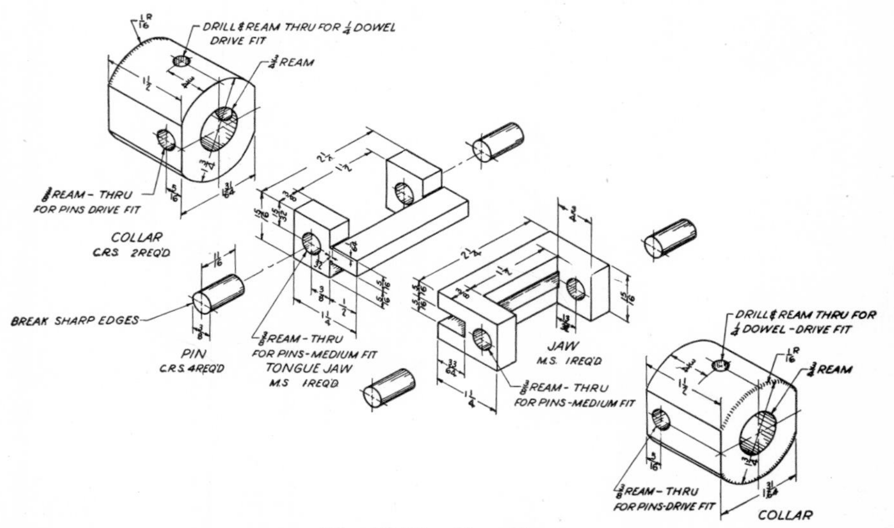

Fig. 19.82. Coupling.

65. (Fig. 19.82.) Make a complete set of working drawings of the coupling. The complete set should consist of detail drawings of the parts and an assembly drawing.

66. (Fig. 19.83.) Make a complete set of working drawings of the tool holder. The complete set should consist of detail drawings of the parts and an assembly drawing.

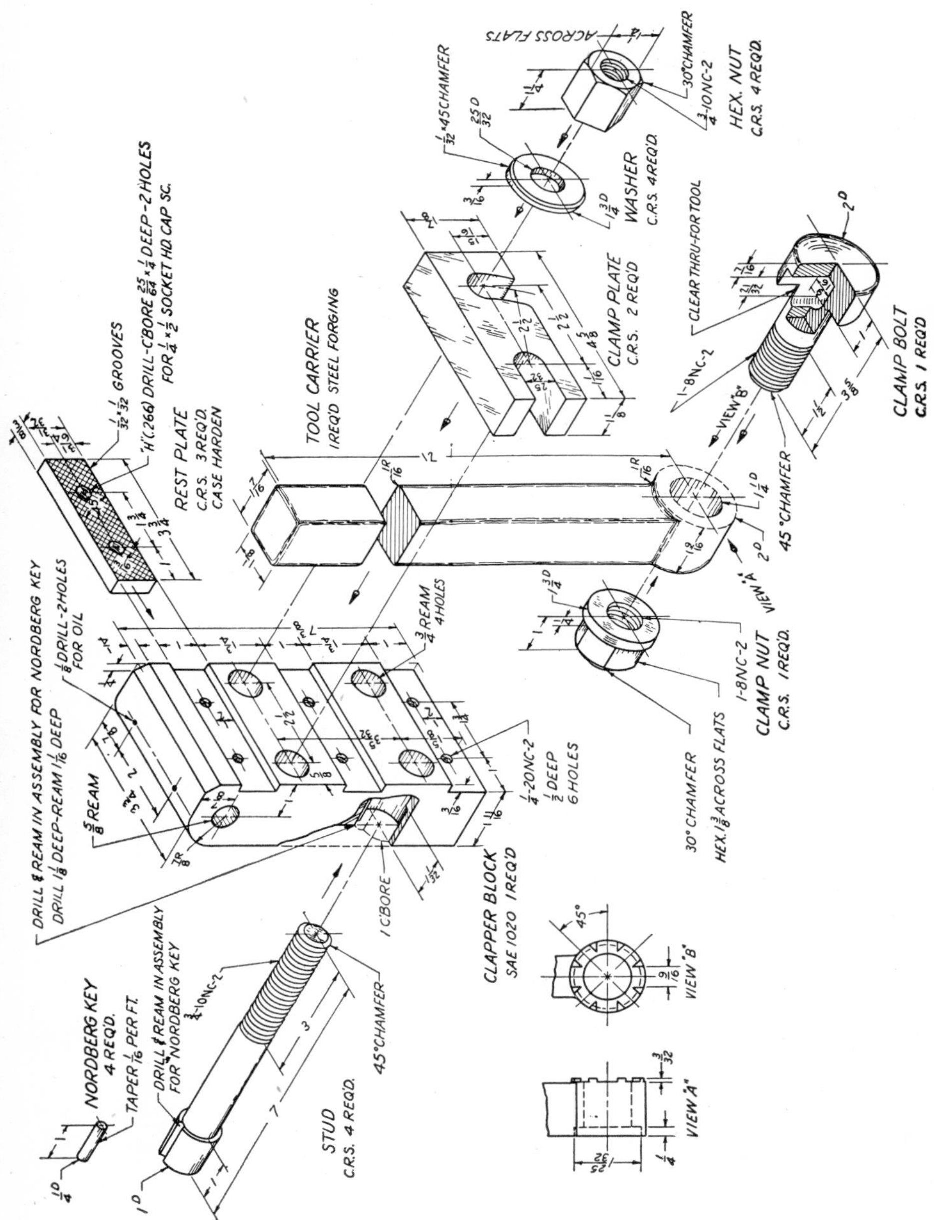

Fig. 19.83. Tool holder.

67. (Fig. 19.84.) Make a complete set of working drawings of the vise. The complete set of drawings should be composed of detail drawings of the parts (except standard parts) and an assembly drawing.

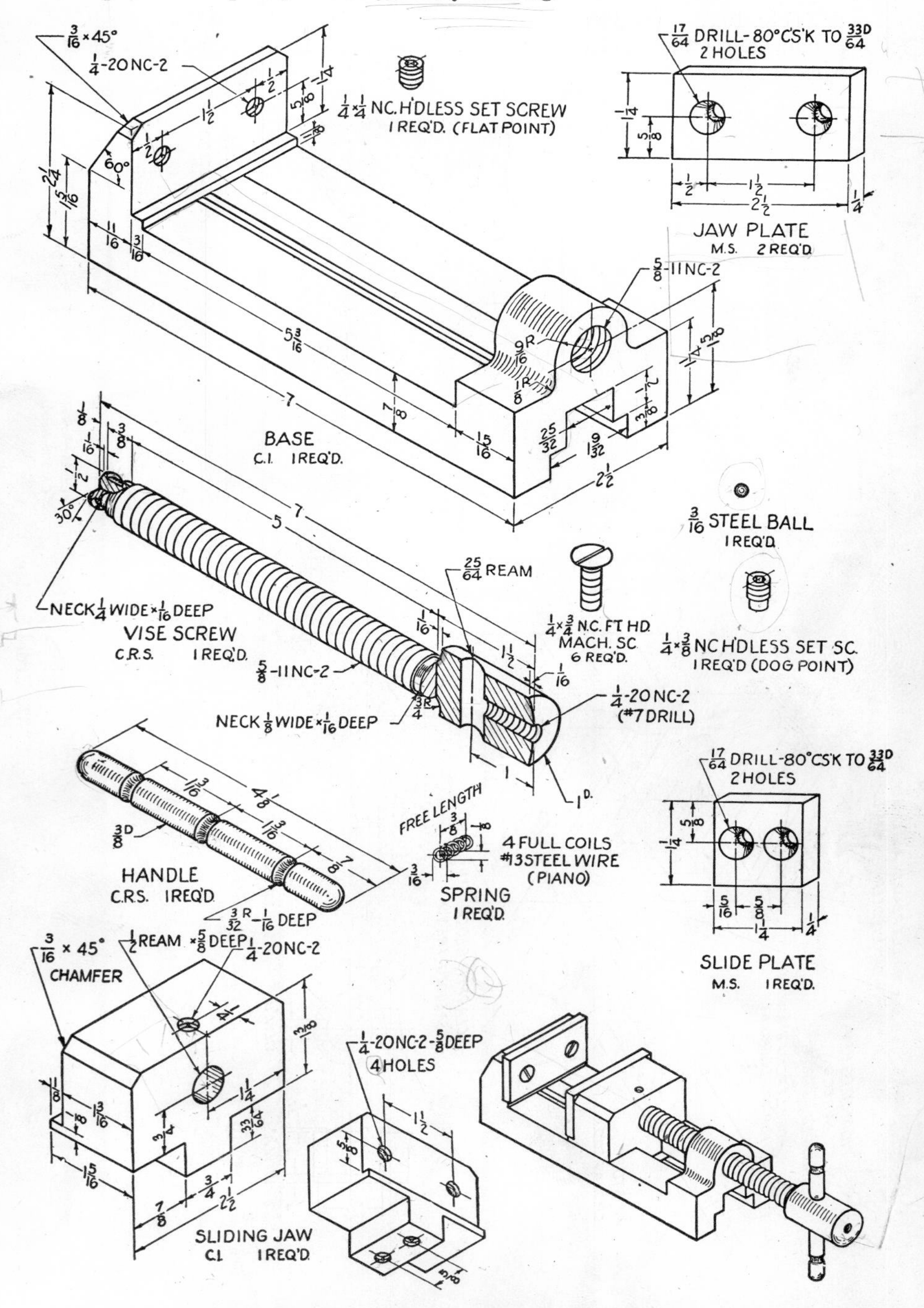

Fig. 19.84. Vise.

68. (Figs. 19.85 and 19.86.) Make detail drawings and an assembly drawing of the machine clamp.

Fig. 19.85. Machine clamp.

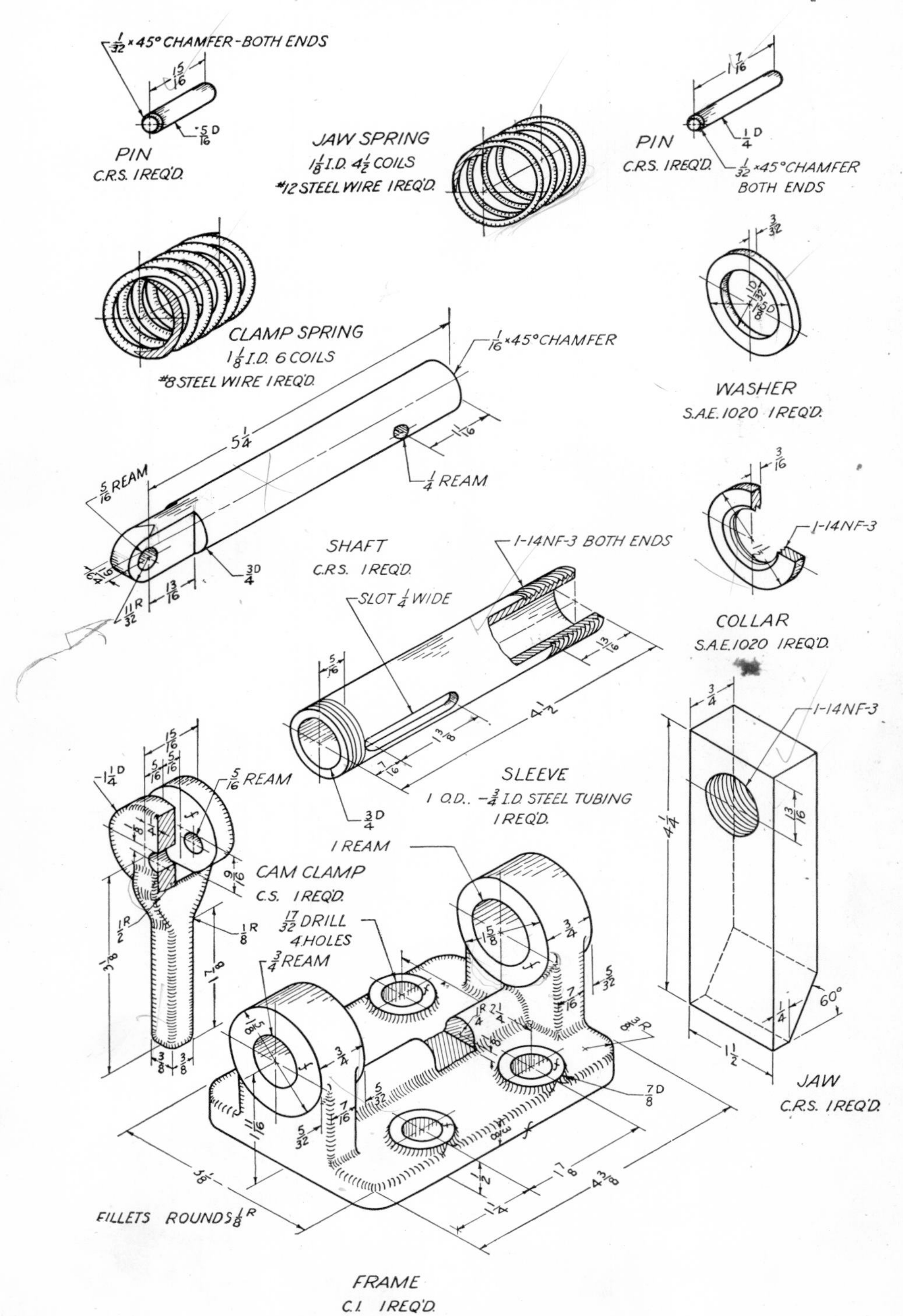

Fig. 19.86. Machine clamp.

69. (Fig. 19.87.) Make a two-view assembly drawing of the cup center of a speed reducer, using the given details. Use the regular symbol for screw threads. Study the pictorial drawing, Fig. 19.90, carefully before starting the views.

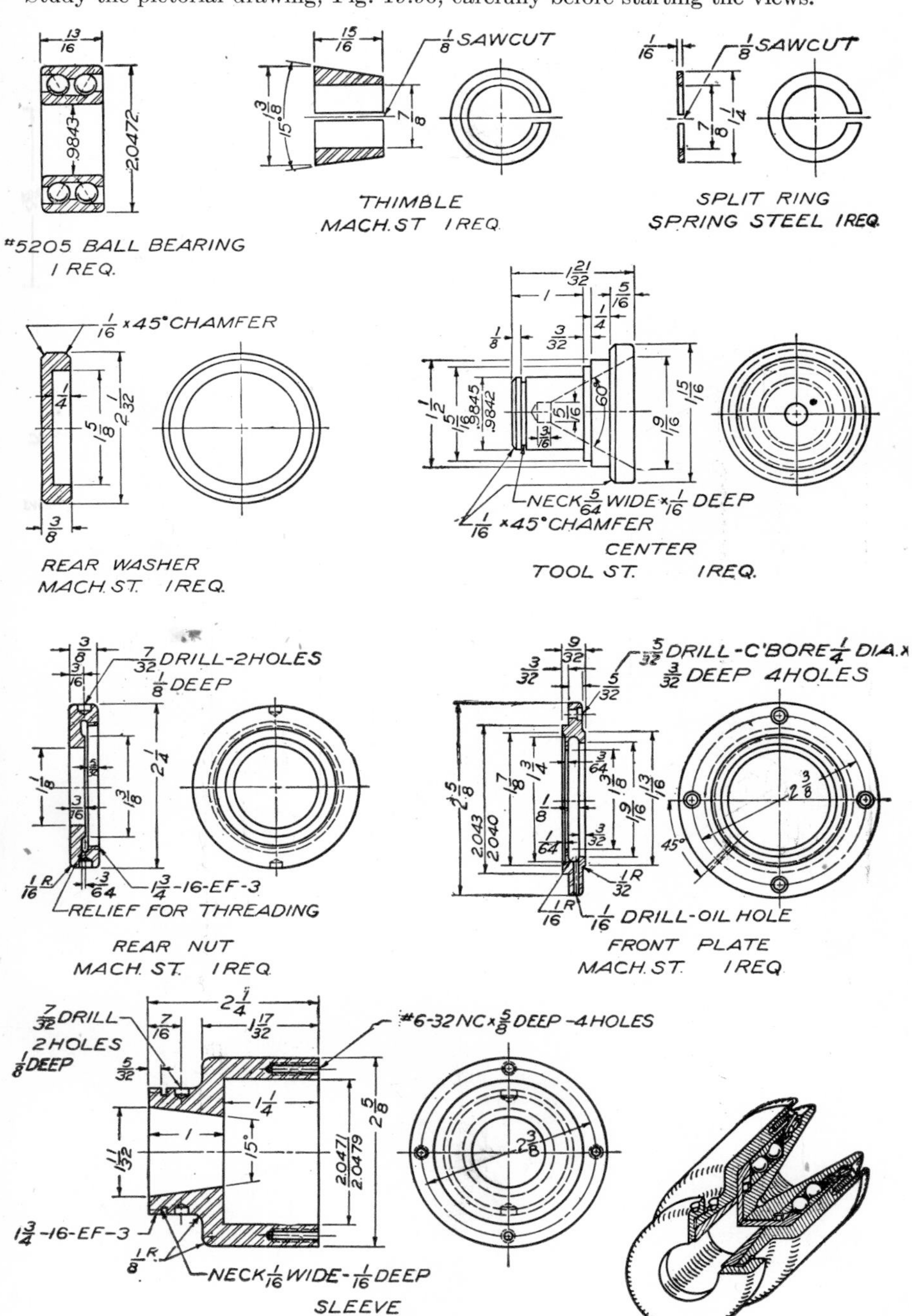

Fig. 19.87. Cup center.

70. (Figs. 19.88, 19.89, and 19.90.) Make detail drawings and an assembly drawing of the speed reducer.

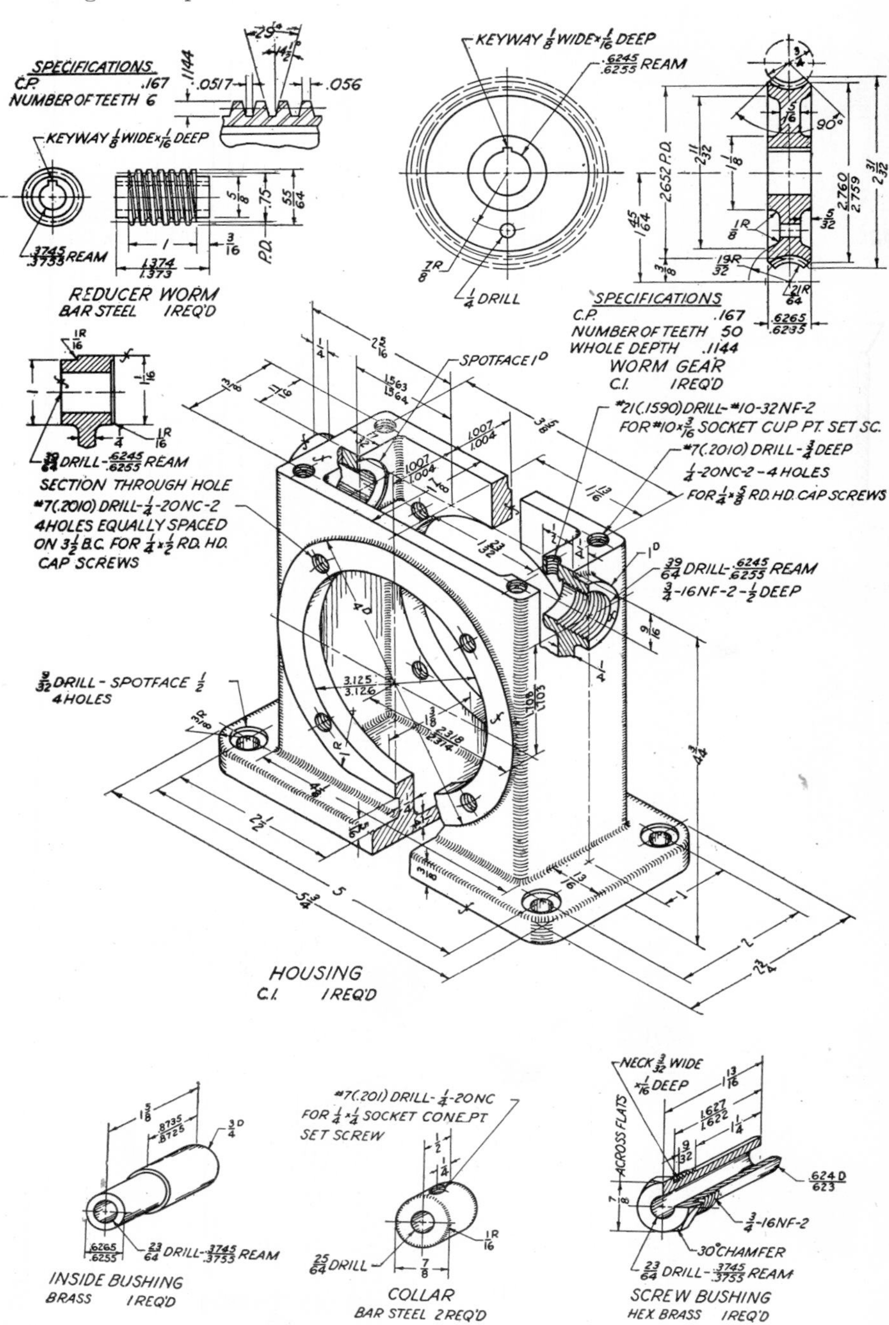

Fig. 19.88. Speed reducer.

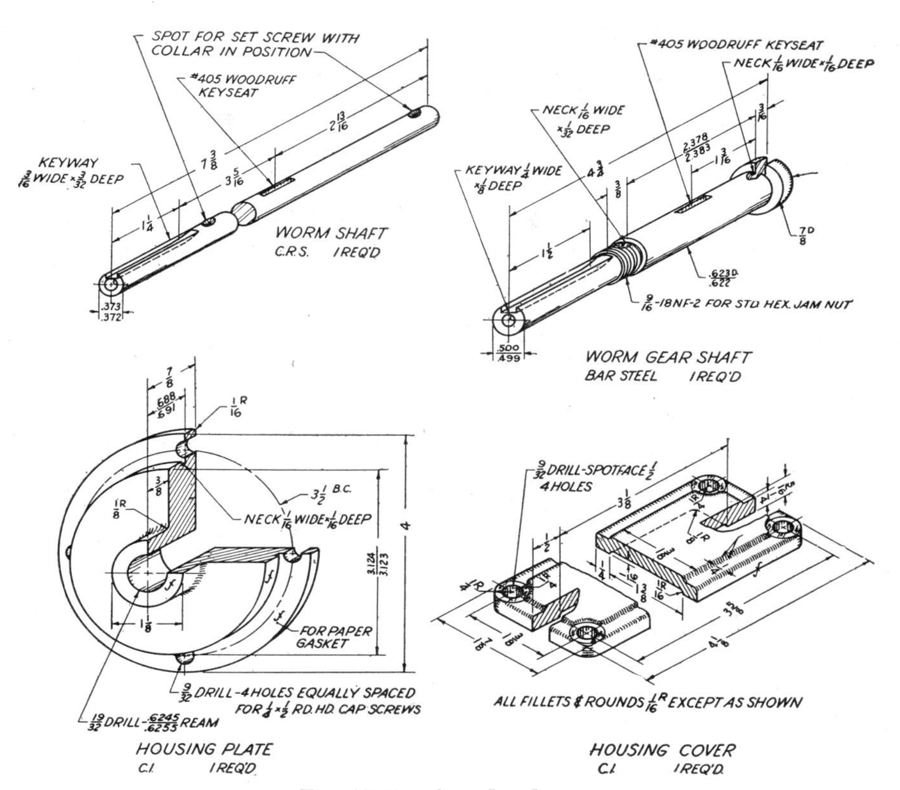

Fig. 19.89. Speed reducer.

Fig. 19.90. Speed reducer.

71. (Figs. 19.91–19.92.) Make an assembly drawing of the tumble jig, using the given details. Use the regular symbol for screw threads. The pictorial drawing should prove helpful in deciding upon the relative locations of the assembled parts.

Fig. 19.91. Tumble jig.

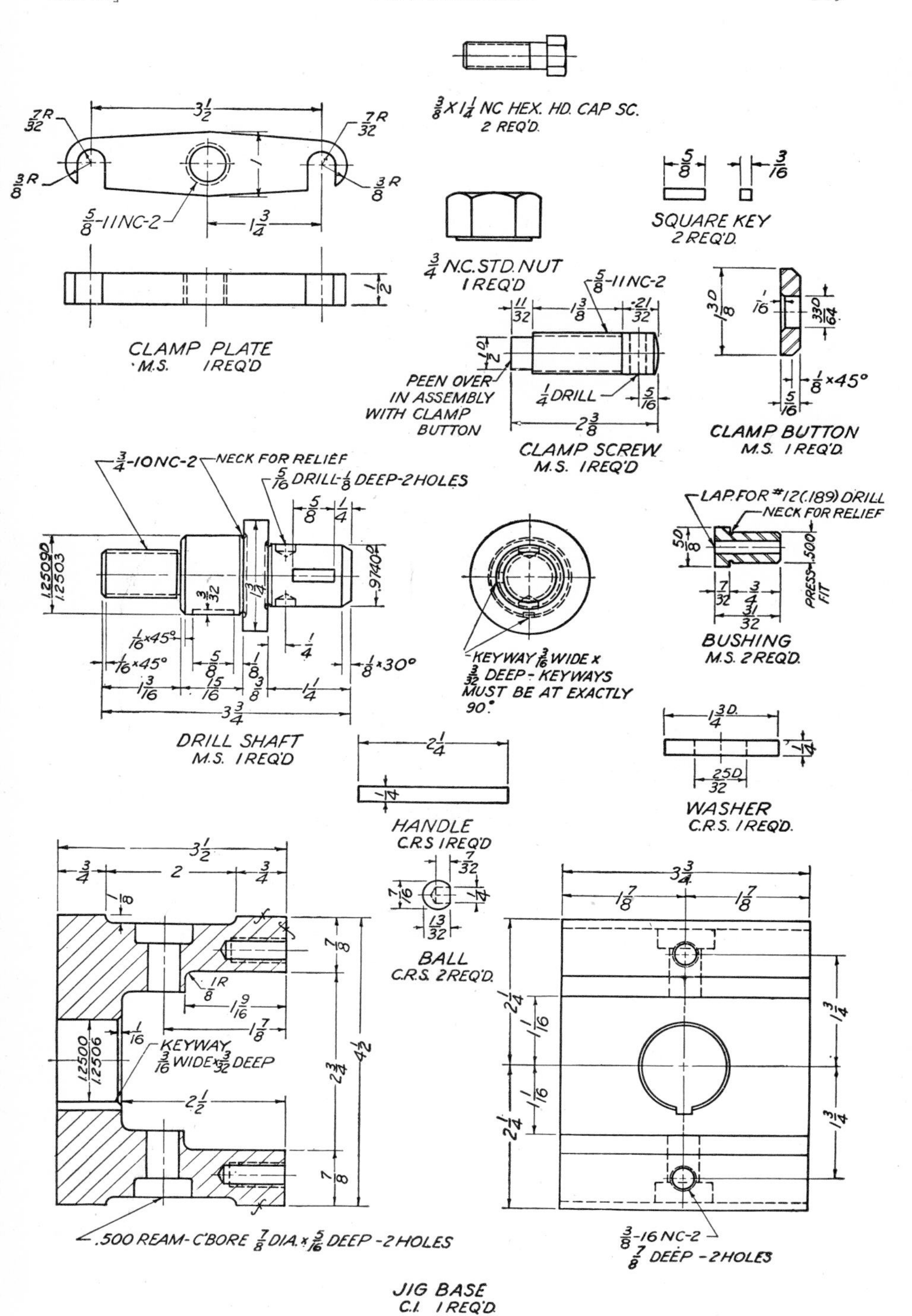

Courtesy Fairfield Mfg. Co.

Fig. 19.92. Tumble jig.

72. (Figs. 19.93, 19.94, and 19.95.) Make an assembly drawing of the pipe vise, using the given details. Use the regular symbol for screw threads.

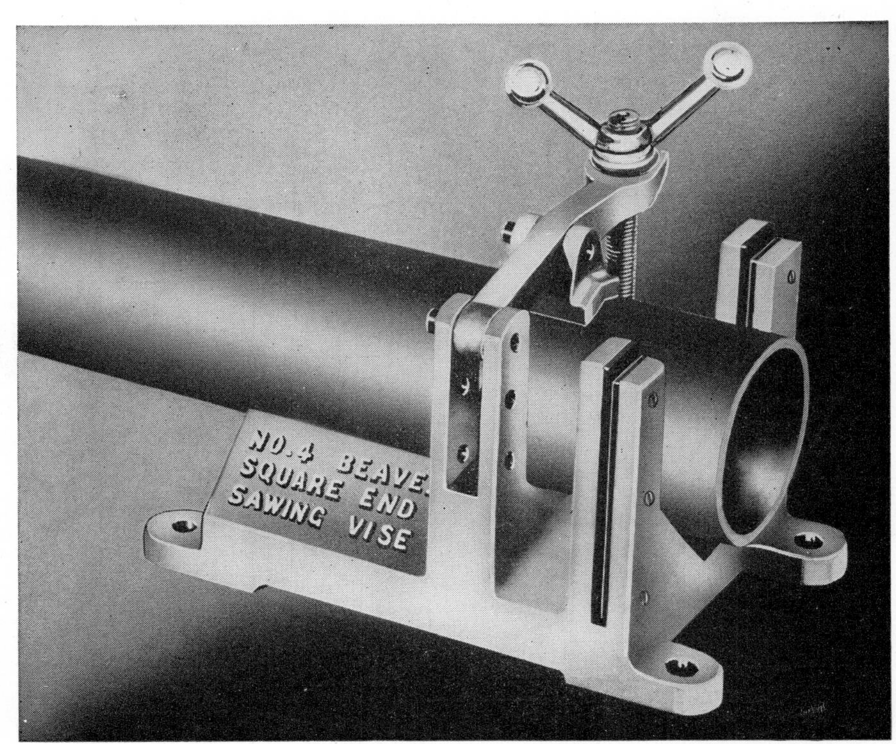

Courtesy The Borden Co.

Fig. 19.93. Pipe vise details (patented).

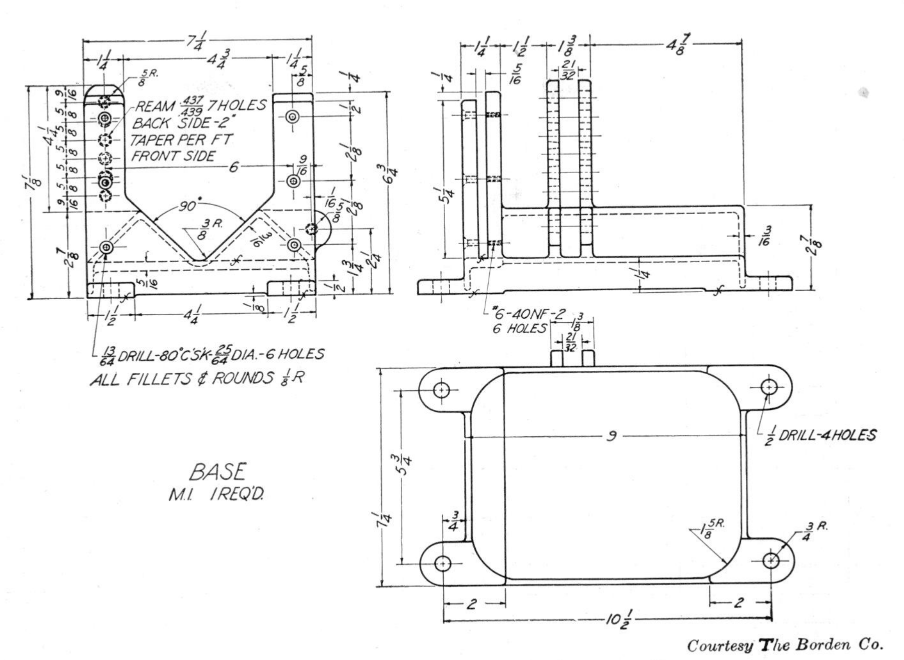

Courtesy The Borden Co.

Fig. 19.94. Pipe vise details (patented).

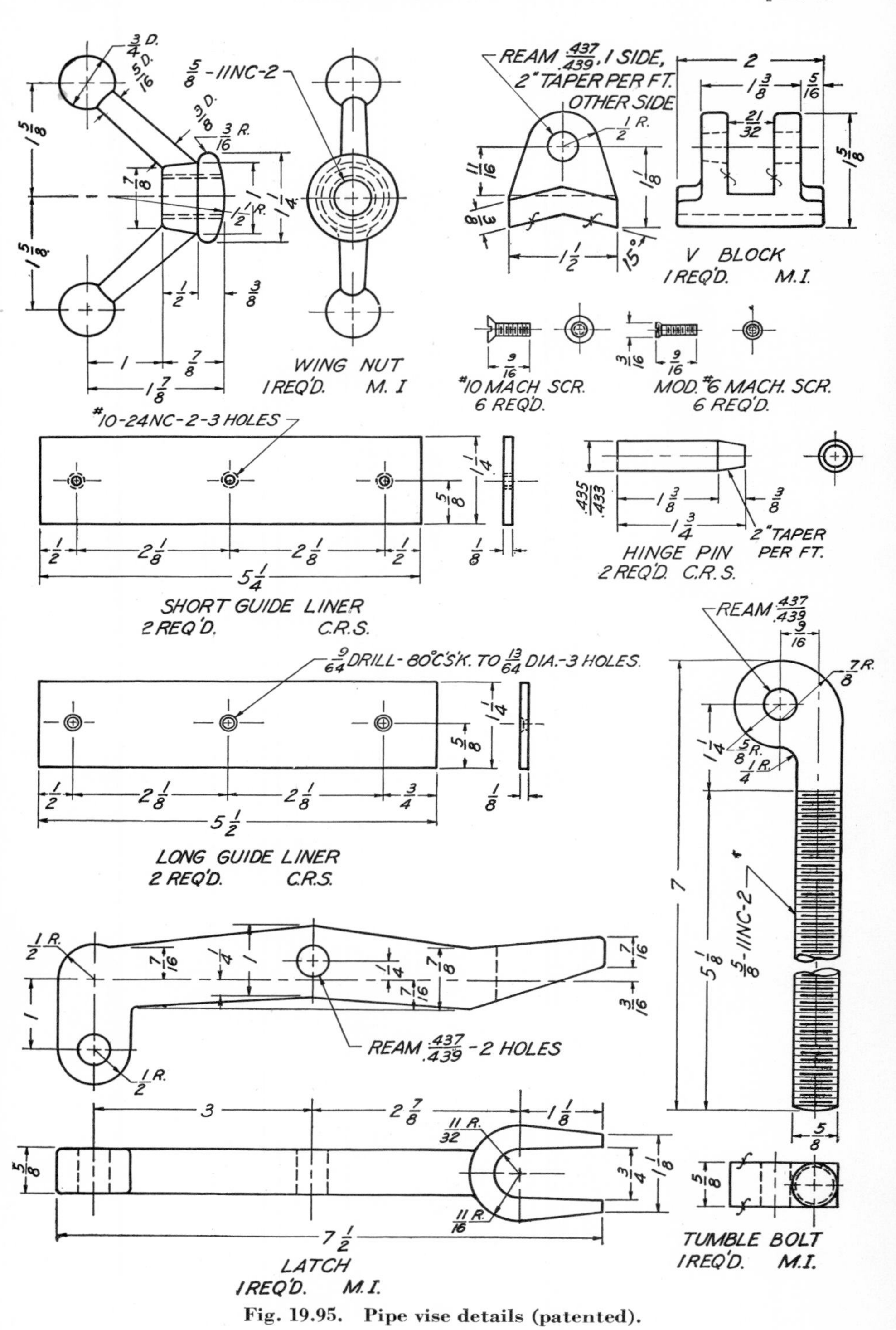

Fig. 19.95. Pipe vise details (patented).

73. (Fig. 19.96.) Make an assembly drawing of the radial engine unit, using the given details. It is suggested that one piston be shown in full section so that the relative positions of the parts will be revealed.

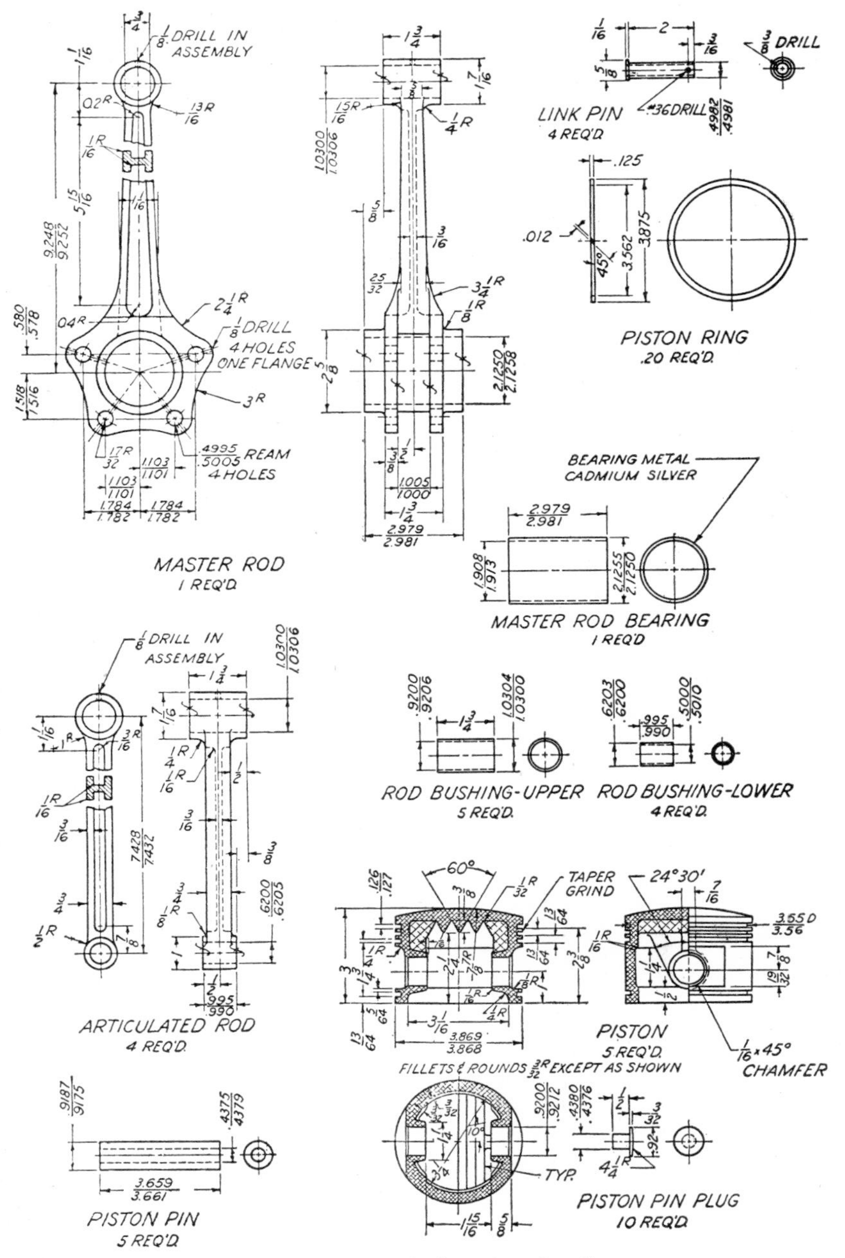

Fig. 19.96. Radial engine details.

74. (Figs. 19.97 and 19.98.) Make an assembly drawing of the idler pulley, using the given details. Use the regular symbol for screw threads.

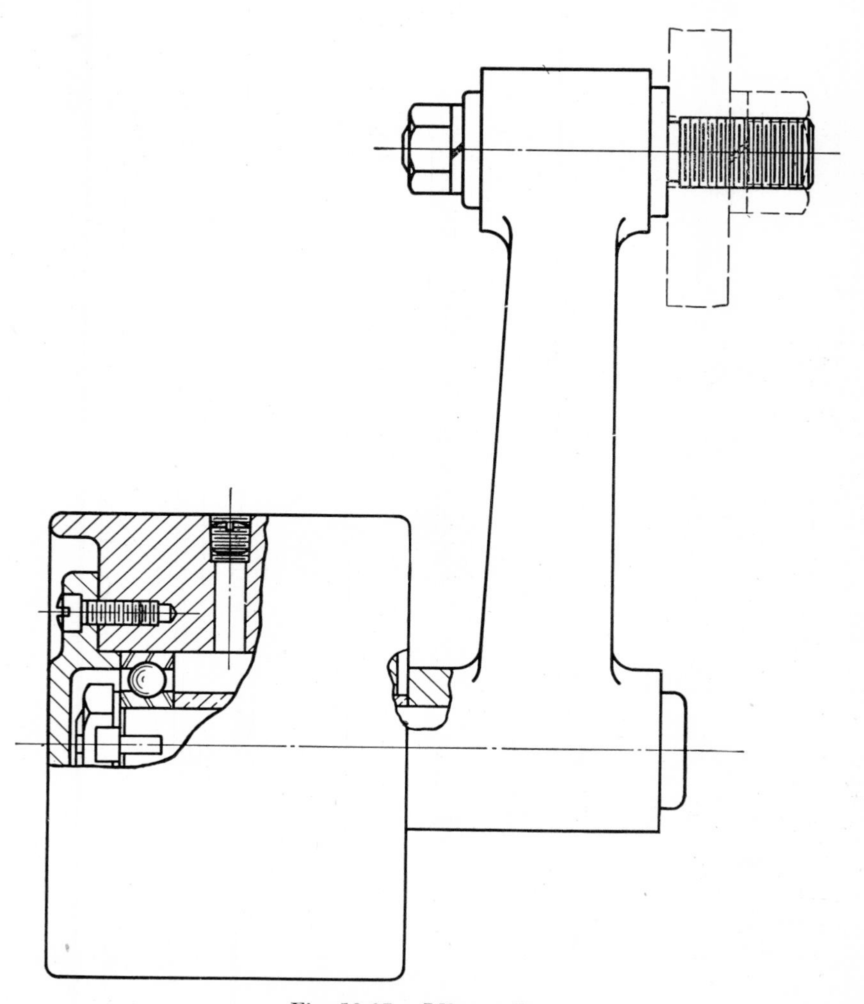

Fig. 19.97. Idler pulley.

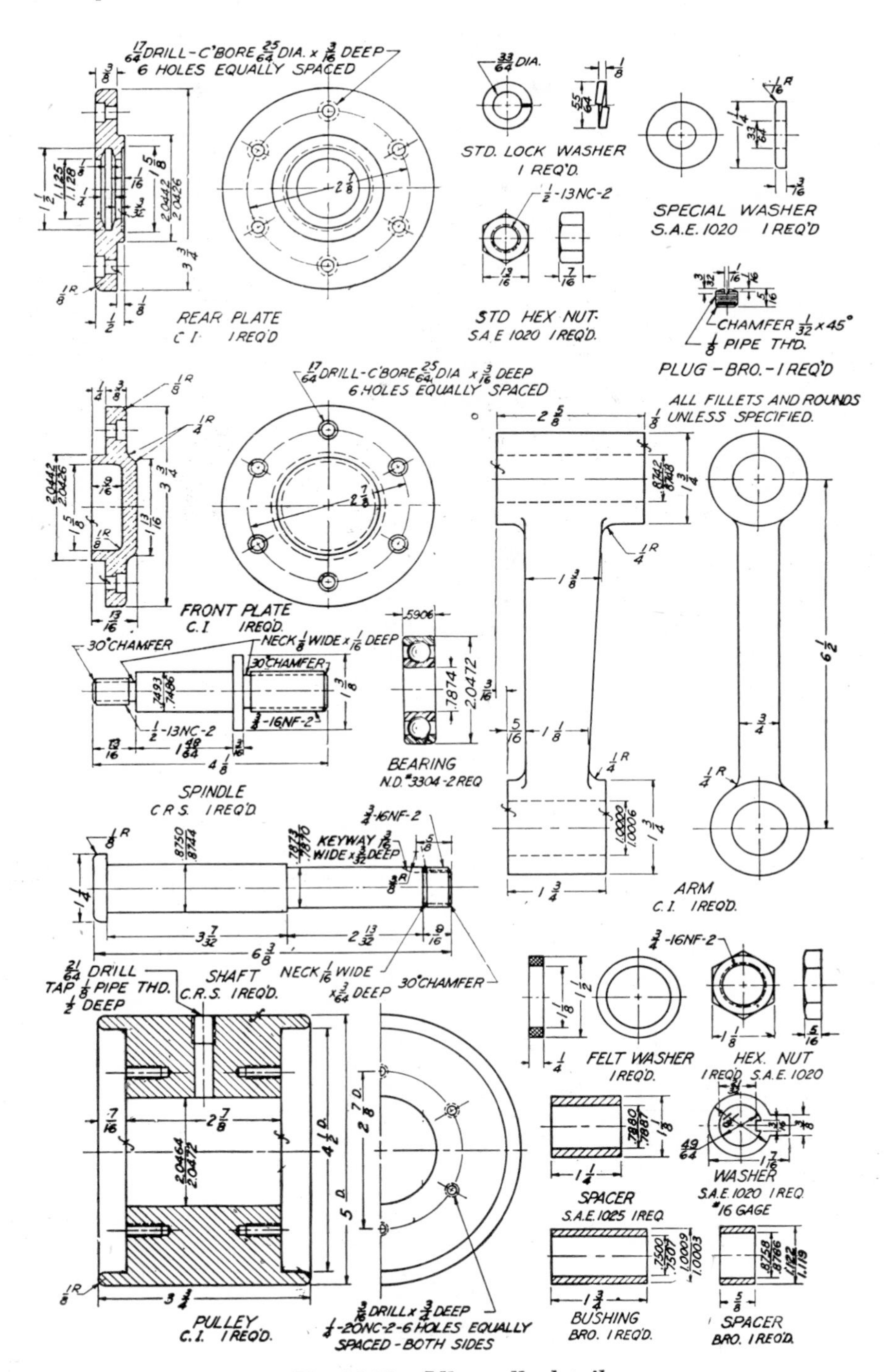

Fig. 19.98. Idler pully details.

75. (Figs. 19.99, 19.100 and 19.101.) Make an assembly drawing of the blow gun.

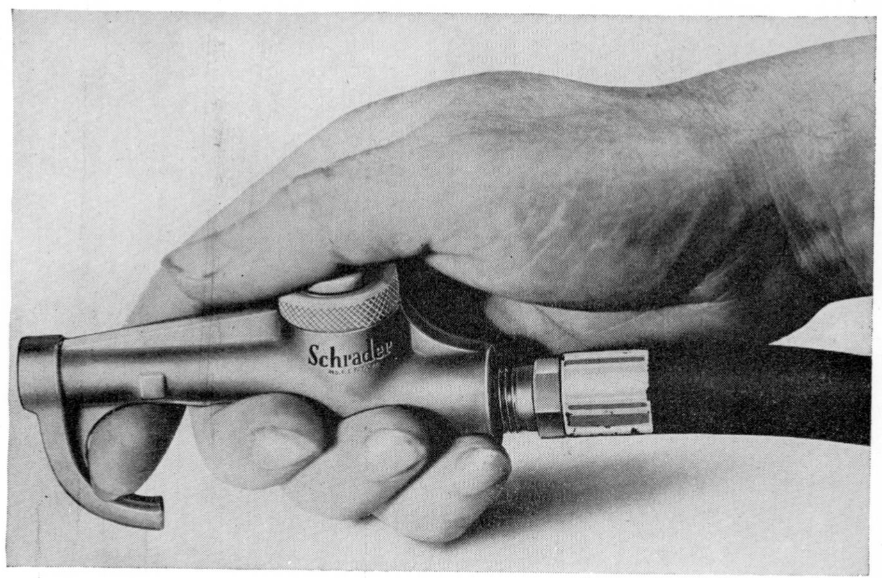

Courtesy A. Schrader's Son Mfg. Co.

Fig. 19.99. Blow gun.

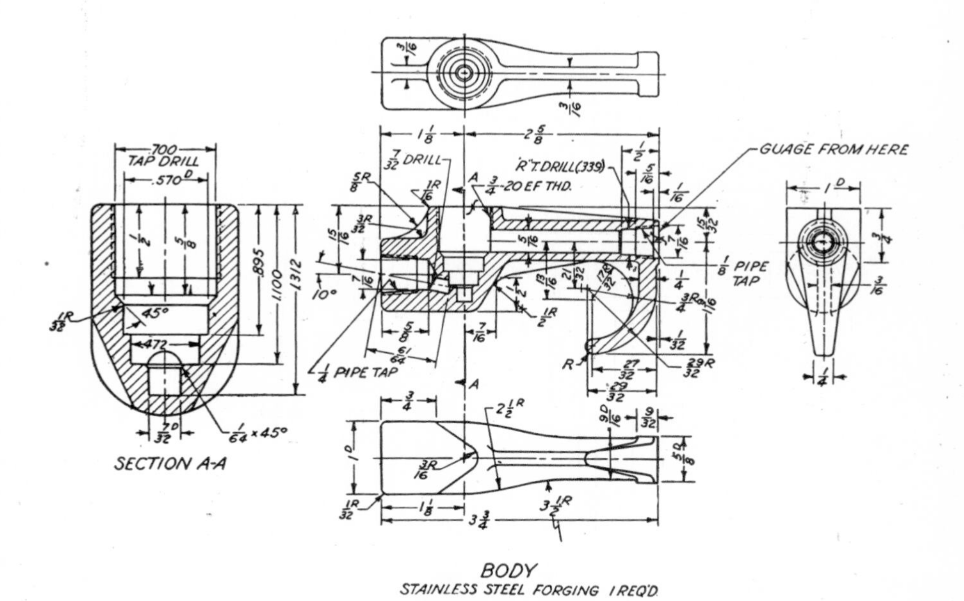

Fig. 19.100. Blow gun details.

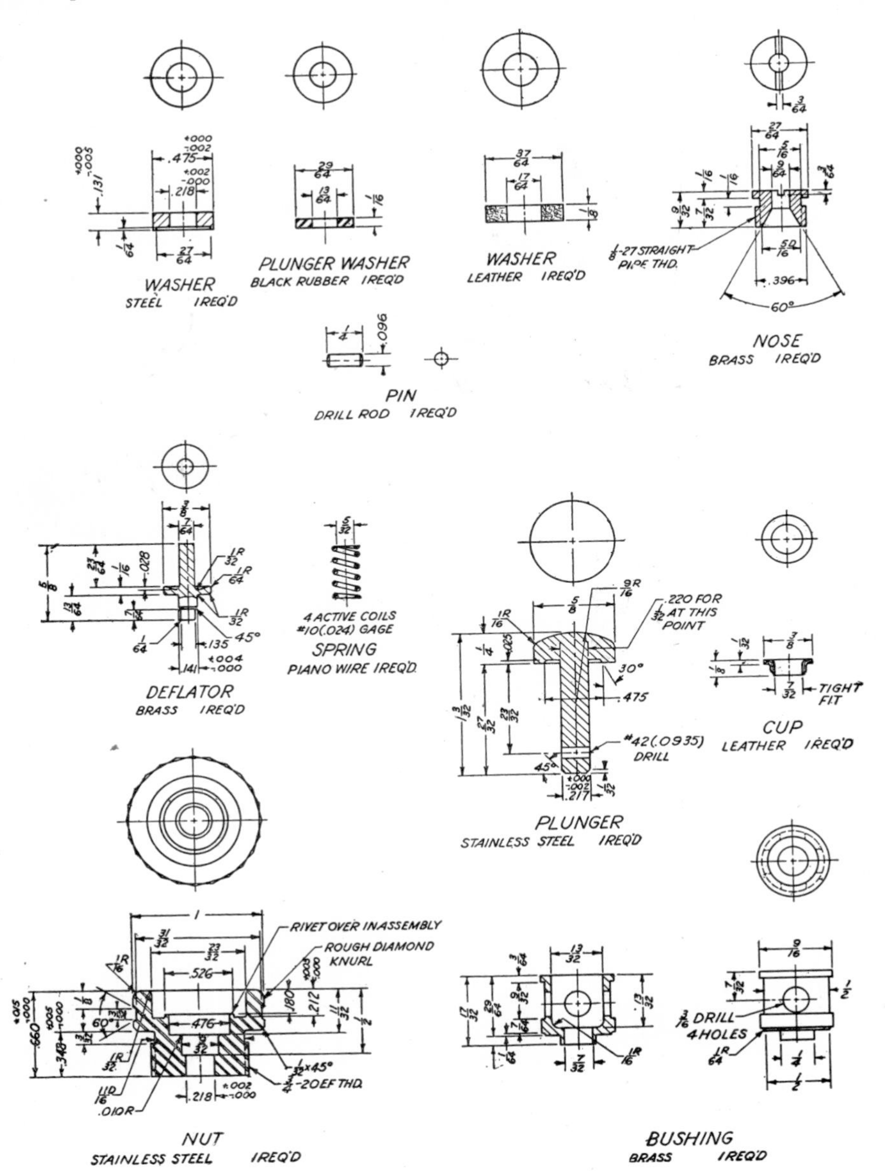

Fig. 19.101. Blow gun details.

76. (Figs. 19.102, 19.103, and 19.104.) Make an assembly drawing of the hand clamp vise, using the given details. Use the regular symbol for screw threads.

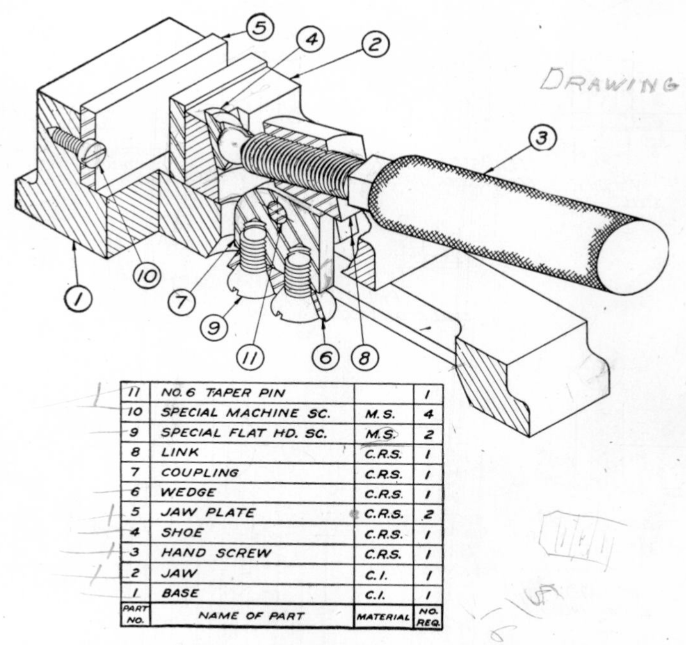

PART NO.	NAME OF PART	MATERIAL	NO. REQ.
11	NO. 6 TAPER PIN		1
10	SPECIAL MACHINE SC.	M.S.	4
9	SPECIAL FLAT HD. SC.	M.S.	2
8	LINK	C.R.S.	1
7	COUPLING	C.R.S.	1
6	WEDGE	C.R.S.	1
5	JAW PLATE	C.R.S.	2
4	SHOE	C.R.S.	1
3	HAND SCREW	C.R.S.	1
2	JAW	C.I.	1
1	BASE	C.I.	1

Fig. 19.102. Hand clamp vise.

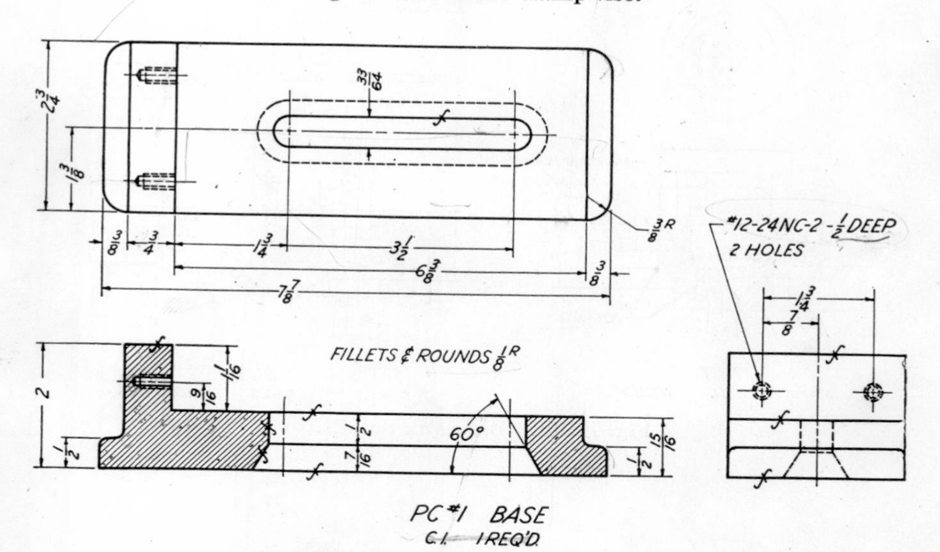

Fig. 19.103. Hand clamp vise details.

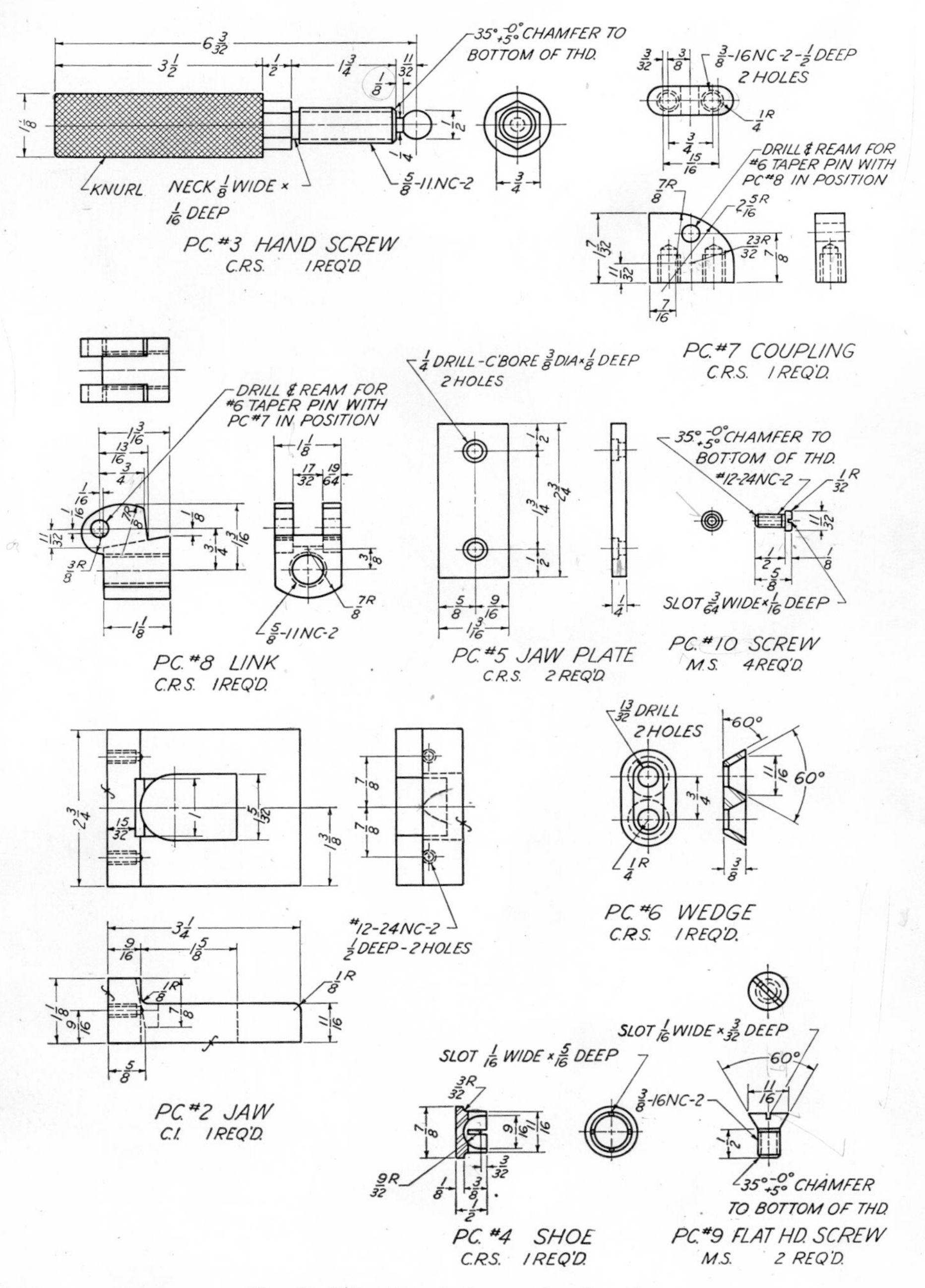

Fig. 19.104. Hand clamp vise details.

77. (Figs. 19.105, 19.106, and 19.107.) Make an assembly drawing of the hand grinder.

Fig. 19.105. Hand grinder.

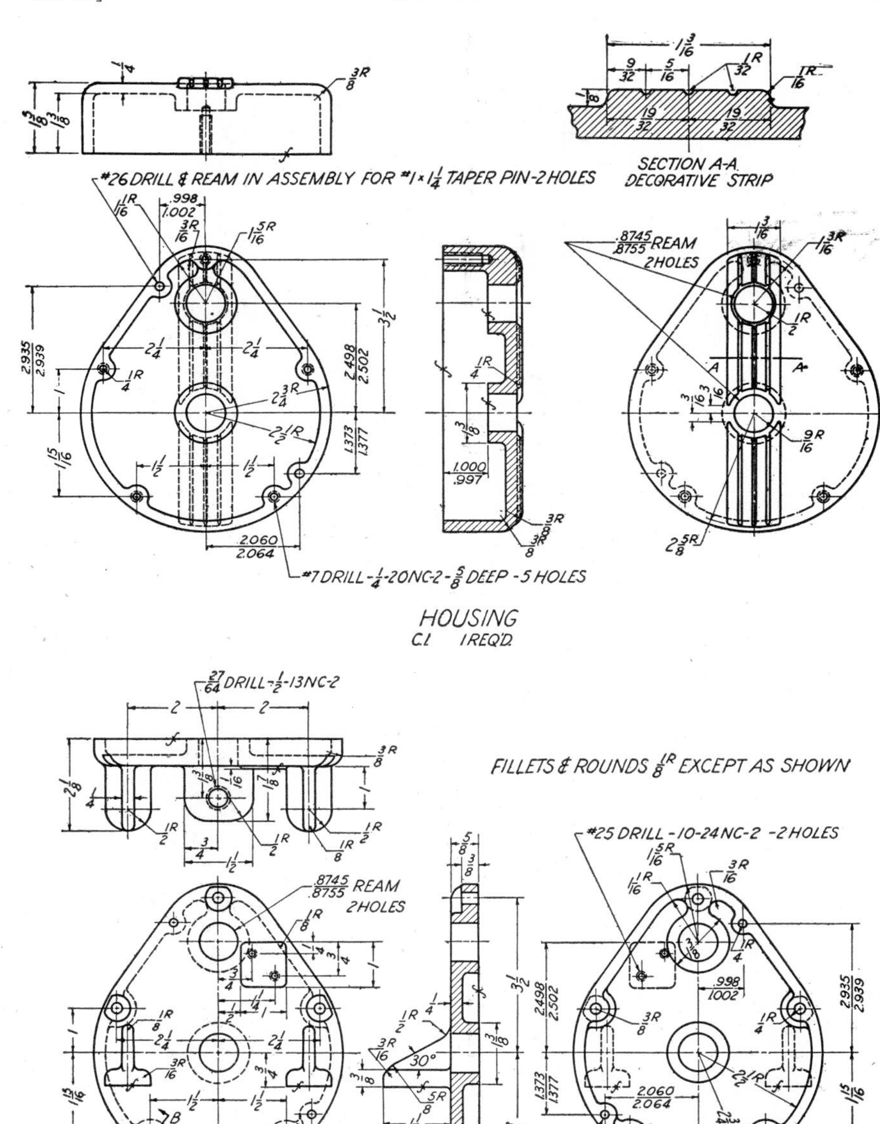

Fig. 19.106. Hand grinder details.

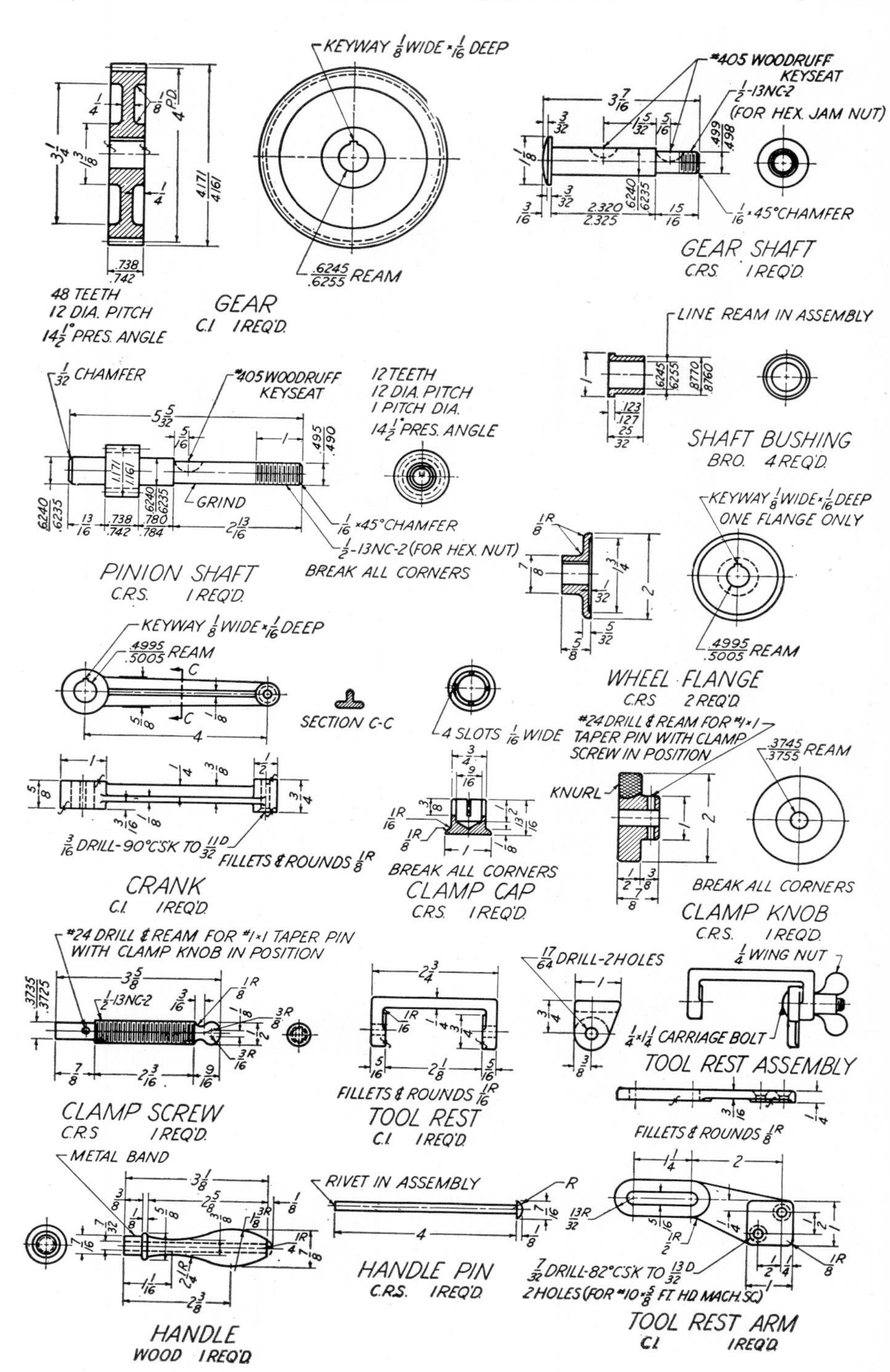

Fig. 19.107. Hand grinder details.

78. (Figs. 19.108 and 19.109.) Make an assembly drawing of the drill jig.

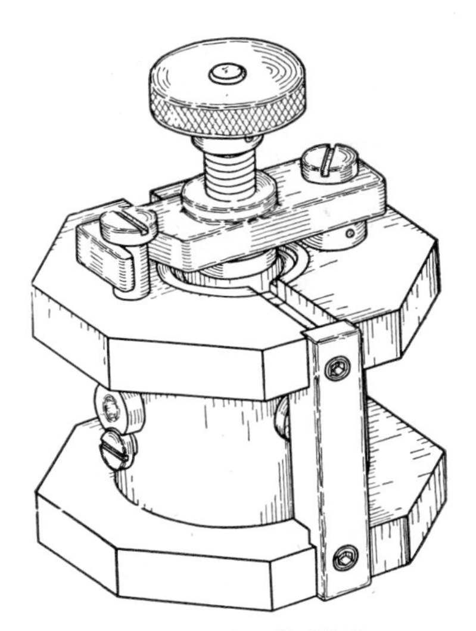

Fig. 19.108. Drill jig.

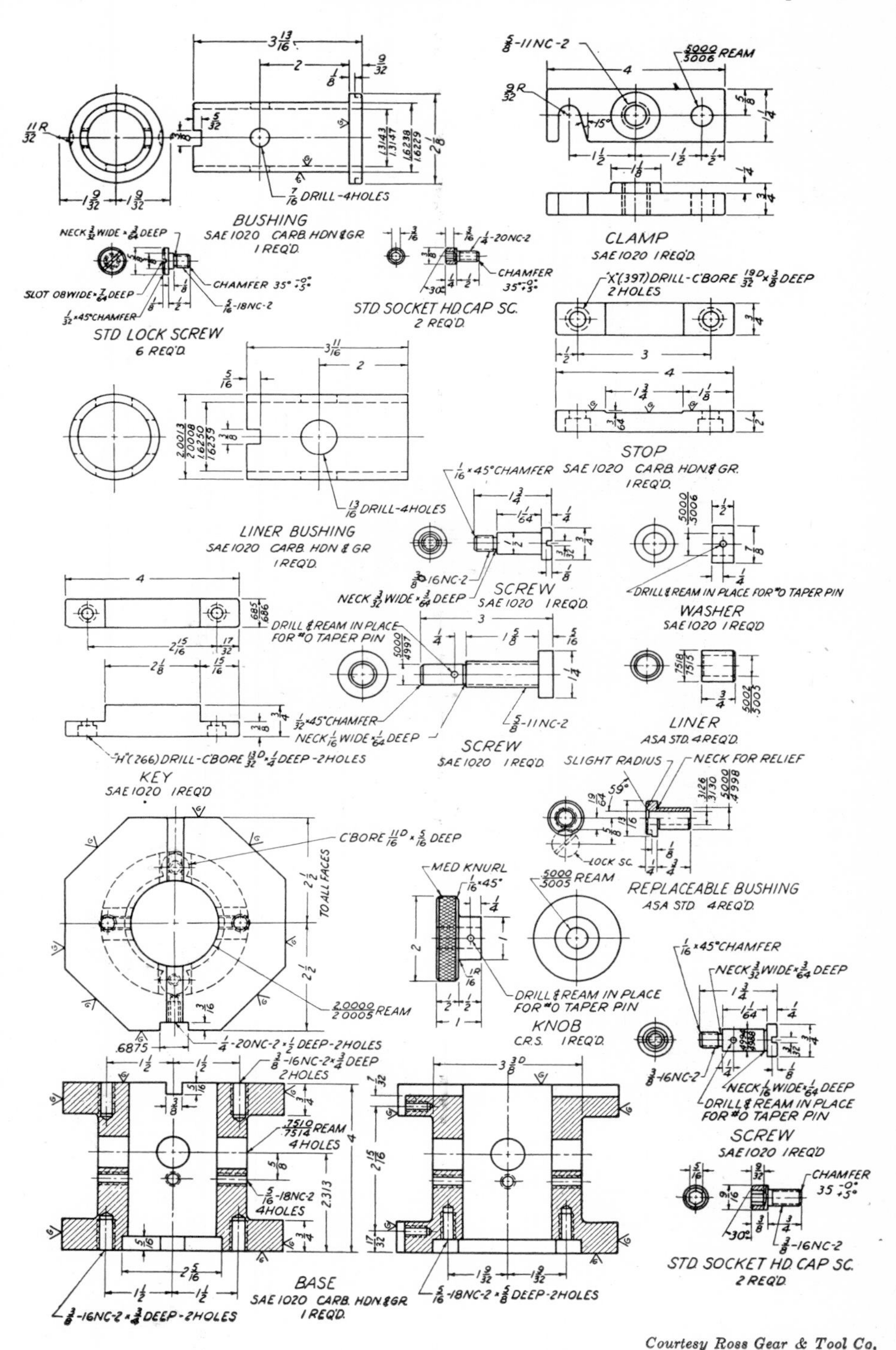

Fig. 19.109. Drill jig details.

79. (Figs. 19.110, 19.111 and 19.112.) Make an assembly drawing of the right-angle head using the given details.

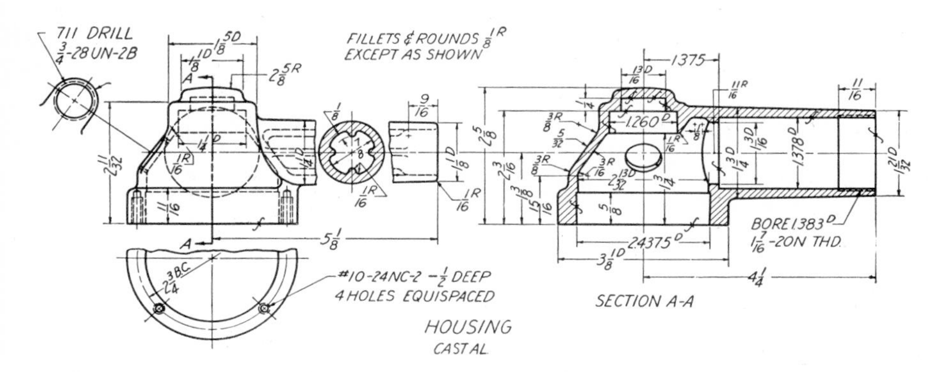

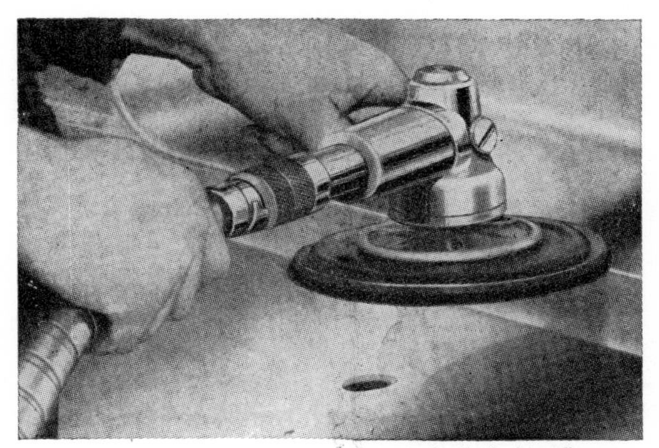

Courtesy R. C. Haskins ***Company.***

Fig. 19.110. Right-angle head details.

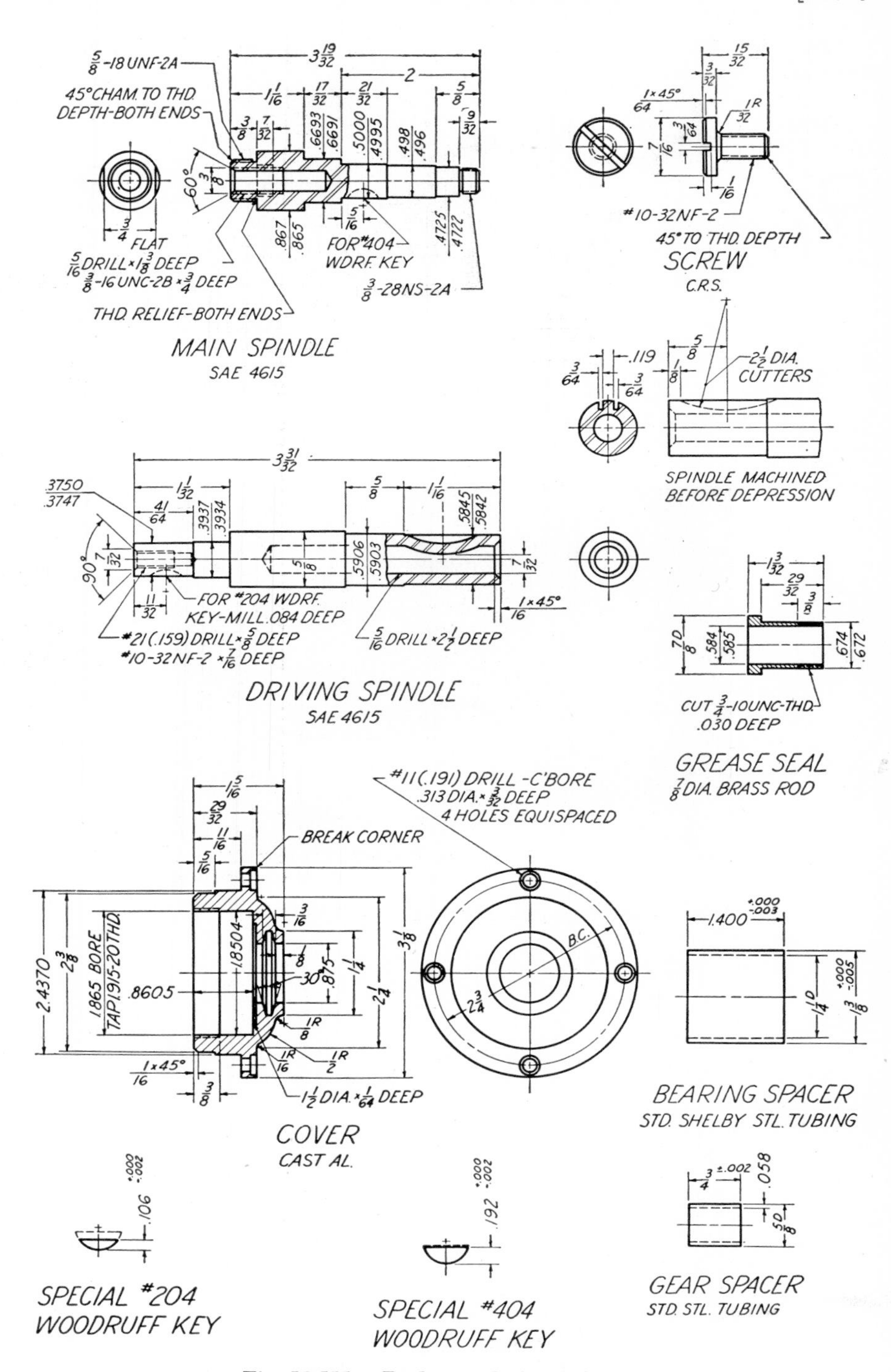

Fig. 19.111. Right-angle head details.

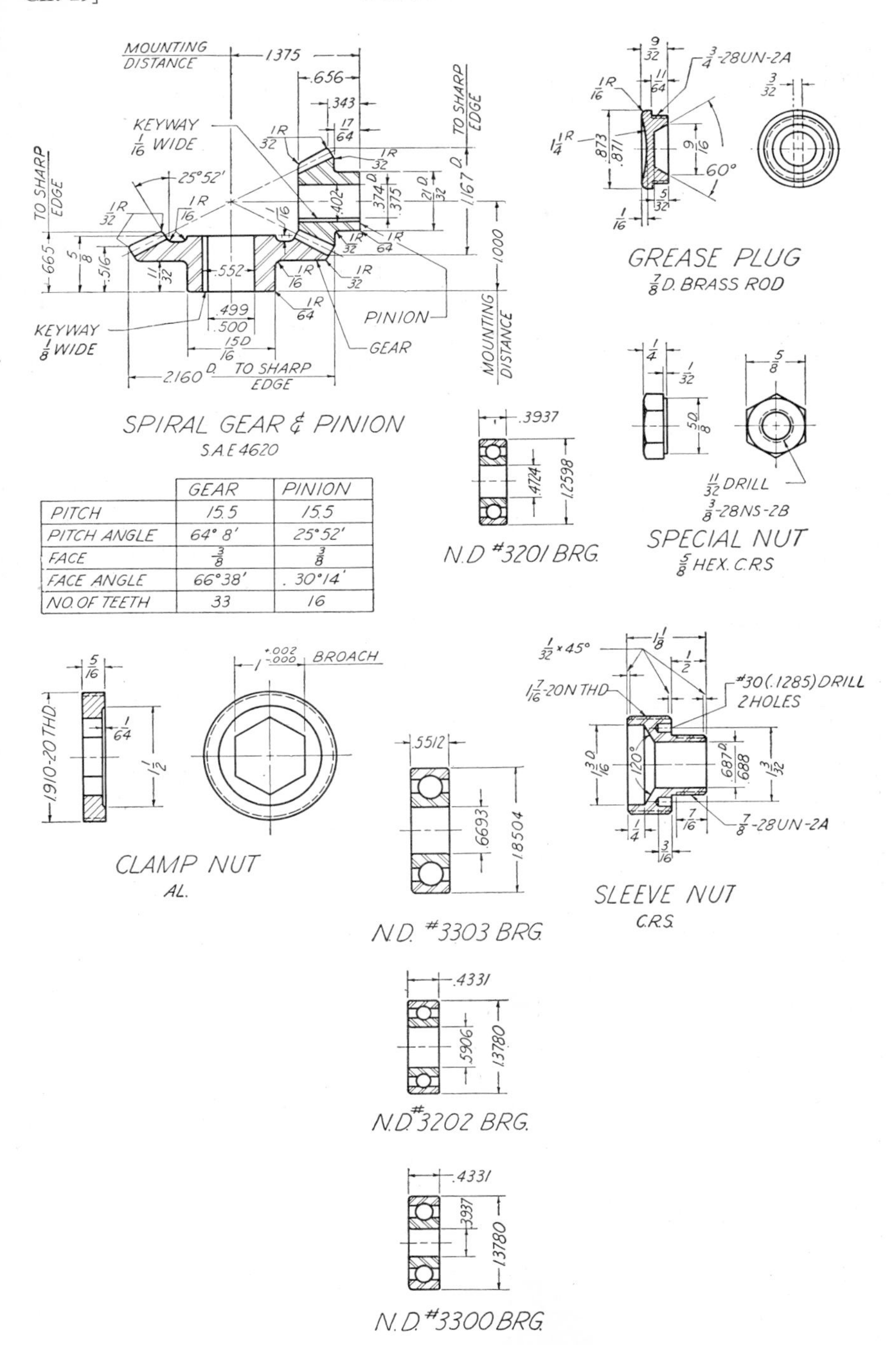

	GEAR	PINION
PITCH	15.5	15.5
PITCH ANGLE	64° 8'	25°52'
FACE	3/8	3/8
FACE ANGLE	66°38'	30°14'
NO. OF TEETH	33	16

Fig. 19.112. Right angle head details.

20 WELDING DRAWINGS

20.1. Welding processes. For convenience, the various welding processes used in commercial production may be classified into three types: pressure processes, nonpressure processes, and casting processes. The nonpressure processes are arc welding and gas welding. Metallic arc welding is the joining of two pieces of metal through the use of a sustained arc formed between the work and a metal rod held in a holder. The intense heat melts the metal of the work and at the same time heats the end of the electrode, causing small globules to form and cross the arc to the weld. In gas welding, the heat is produced by a burning mixture of two gases, which ordinarily are oxygen and acetylene. The weld is formed by melting a filler rod with the torch flame, along the line of contact, after the metal of the work has been preheated to a molten state. This method is essentially a puddling process, in that the weld is produced by a small moving molten pool that is maintained by the flame constantly directed upon it. Resistance welding is a pressure process, the fusion being made through heat and mechanical pressure. The work is heated by a strong electrical current that passes through it until fusion temperature is reached; then pressure is applied to create the weld.

The forms of resistance welding are: butt welding, seam welding, spot welding, and flash welding. In spot welding, the parts are overlapped and welds are made at successive single spots. In butt welding, the pieces are so placed that they are butted; then the weld is made by heating electrically and squeezing the parts together. A seam weld is similar to a spot weld, except that a continuous weld is produced. In projection welding, one part is embossed and welds are made at the successive projections. Thermit welding can be considered a casting process, in that molten iron is run into a mold built around the parts at the point at which they are to be connected. The liquid metal is obtained from a mixture of finely divided iron oxide and aluminum, which is ignited in a crucible. In the chemical reaction that takes place, the oxygen passes from the iron oxide to the aluminum, leaving free molten iron that flows into the mold around the preheated parts forming the joint. The metal of the members being welded fuses with the liquid metal and forms a weld when the joint is cool.

20.2. Types of joints. Fig. 20.1 illustrates in pictorial some of the various types of welded joints. Cross sectional views of the fundamental welds, which are commonly encountered, are shown in Fig. 20.2.

20.3. Working drawings of welded parts. Fig. 20.3 shows a part that is to be constructed by welding rolled shapes. It should be noted that each joint is completely specified through the use of a welding symbol. A careful study will show that the drawing, except for the absence of fillets

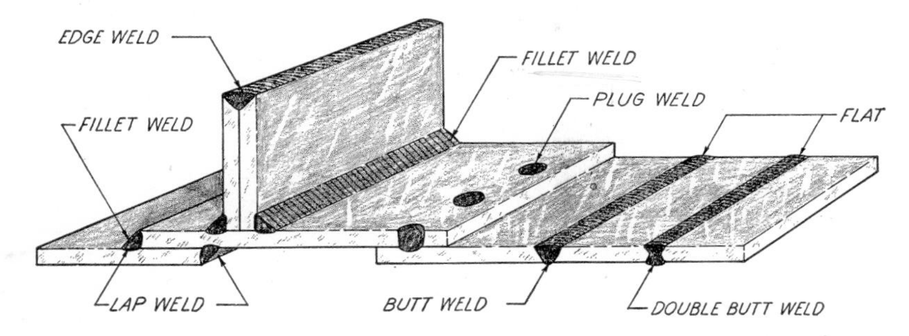

Fig. 20.1. Types of welds.

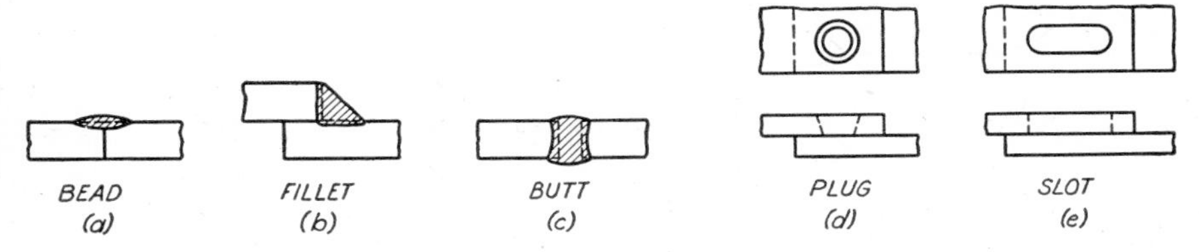

Fig. 20.2. Types of welds.

and rounds and the fact that properly composed welding symbols are directed to the necessary joints, is very much like a casting drawing.

A satisfactory welding design may be produced by a competent designer who possesses a fair amount of ingenuity, and the necessary drawing can be made by any draftsman who has a thorough understanding of the construction of the symbols created by the American Welding Society.

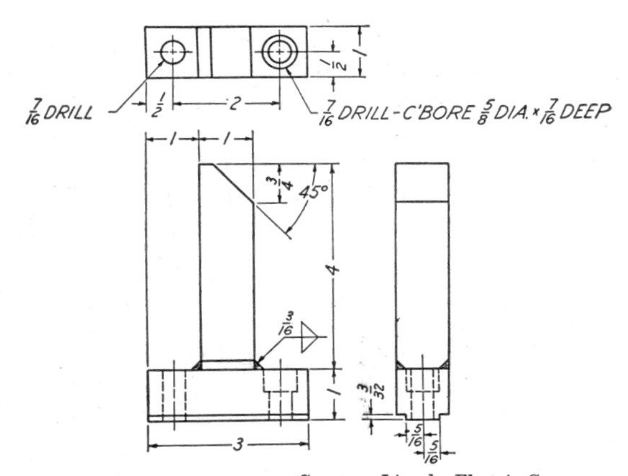

Courtesy Lincoln Electric Company.

Fig. 20.3. A welding drawing.

20.4. Near welds and far welds. In order that they may be identified on a drawing and properly specified, welds are classified as *near welds* or *far welds.* A near weld is one that is parallel to the plane of the paper and toward the observer. It is on the same side as the symbol, and the

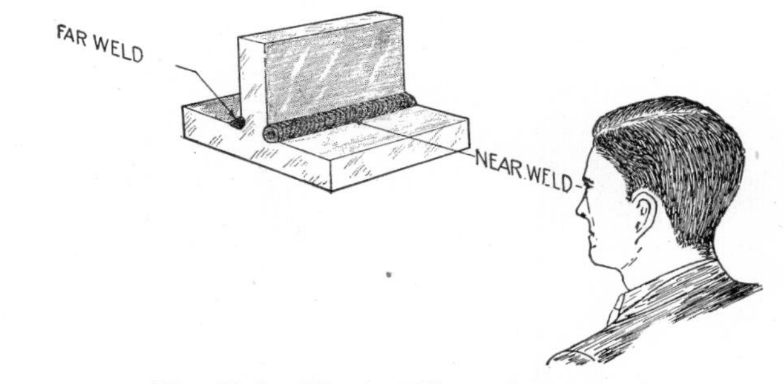

Fig. 20.4. Near welds and far welds.

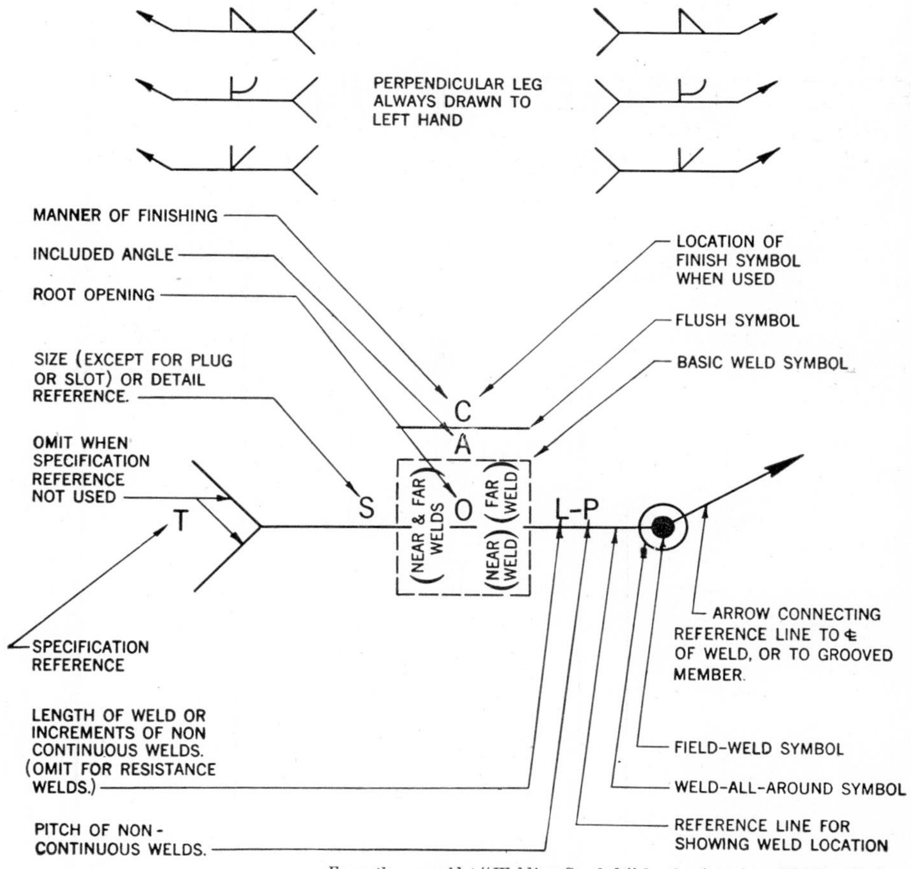

From the pamphlet "Welding Symbols" by the American Welding Society.

Fig. 20.5. The basic welding symbol.

arrow points to its face. The far weld is away from the observer, on the far side of the piece, and its face is away from the arrow. Fig. 20.4 shows the facing of welds.

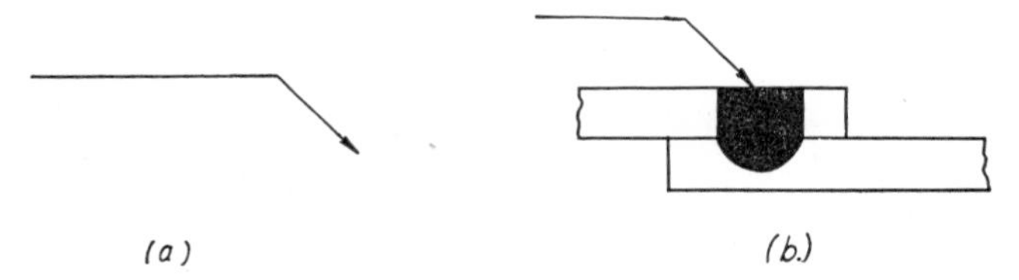

Fig. 20.6. Welding arrow.

20.5. Welding symbols. An enlarged drawing of the approved welding symbol is shown in Fig. 20.5, along with explanatory notes that indicate the proper locations of the marks and size dimensions necessary for a complete description of a weld.

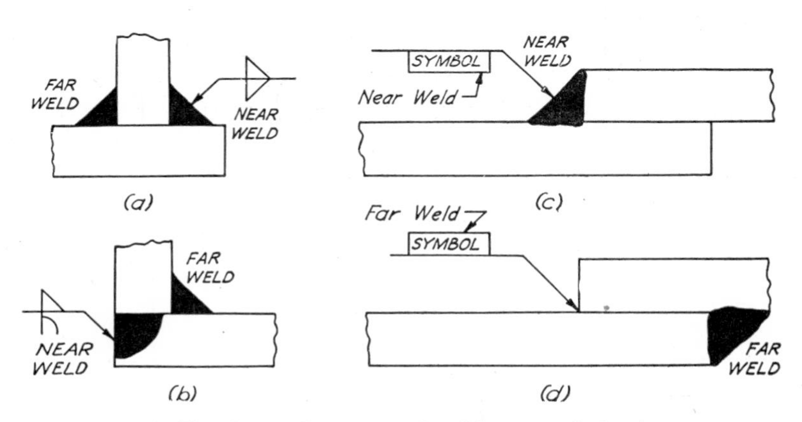

Fig. 20.7. Location of welding symbols.

The arrow is the basic portion of the symbol, as shown in Fig. 20.6(a). It points toward the joint where the required weld is to be made, as in Fig. 20.6(b).

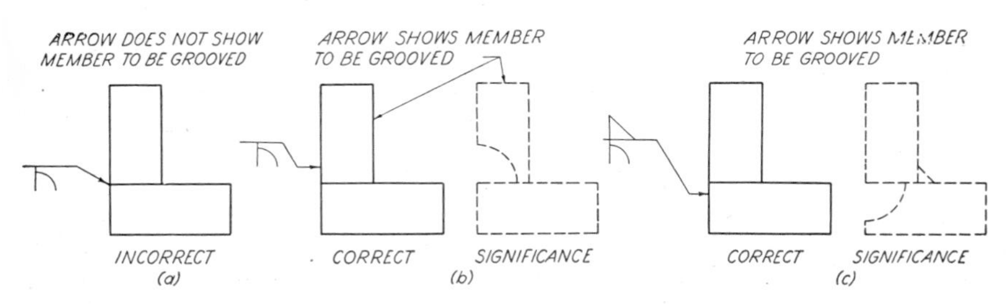

Fig. 20.8. Placement of arrow in section or end view to indicate member to be grooved.

If the weld is on the near side, toward the observer, the symbol indicating the type of weld is placed below or to the right of the base line, depending upon whether that line is horizontal or vertical (Fig. 20.7*c*). If the weld is located on the far side, the symbol should be above or to the left, as shown in (*d*).

Correct and incorrect applications of the arrow are illustrated in Fig. 20.8. When welds are not shown, it should be noted that the arrow should touch the member that is to be grooved at a point near the joint. The two views that are drawn with broken lines show the significance of the symbols used for the grooves.

To indicate that a weld is to be made all around a connection, as is necessary when a piece of tubing must be welded to a plate, a weld-all-around symbol, a circle, is placed as shown in Fig. 20.9.

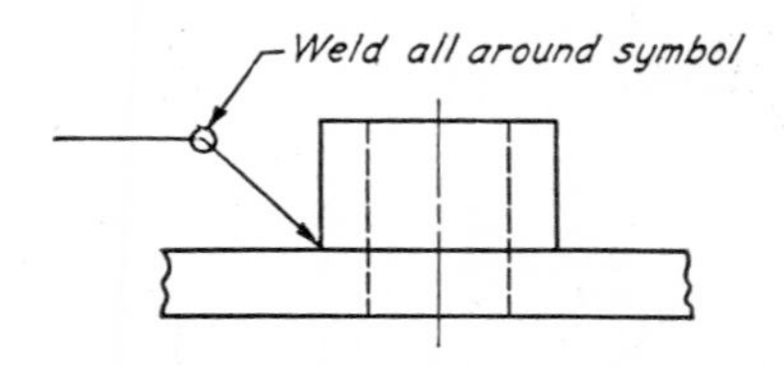

Fig. 20.9. Weld all-around symbol.

Fig. 20.10. Method of specifying the size of weld.

The size of a weld is given along the base of the arrow, at the side of the symbol, as shown in Fig. 20.10. If the welds on the near side and the far side of a lap joint are the same size, only one dimension should be given (Fig. 20.11). If they are not the same size, each dimension should be placed beside its associated symbol (Fig. 20.12).

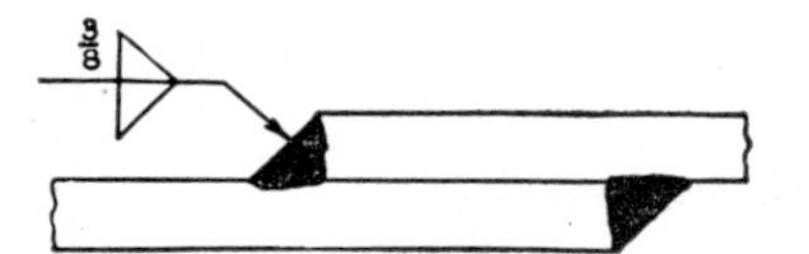

Fig. 20.11. Dimensioning a weld.

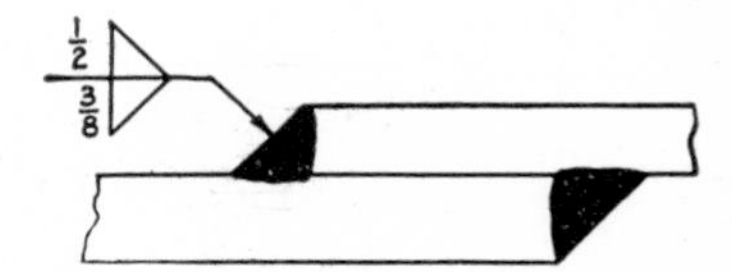

Fig. 20.12. Dimensioning a weld.

The welding terms associated with the specification of the size of welds are illustrated in Fig. 20.13.

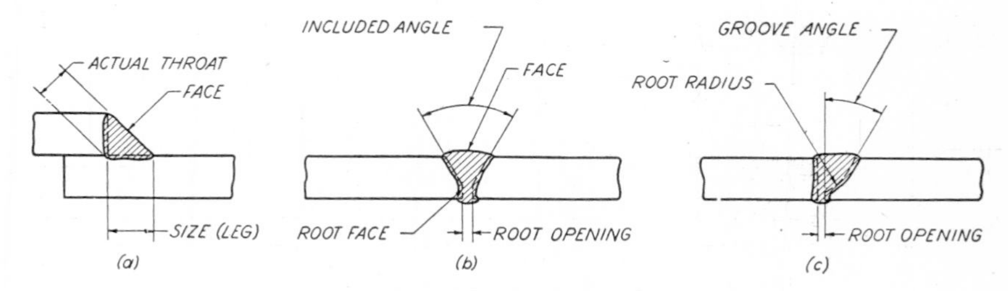

Fig. 20.13. Welding terms.

Fig. 20.14 shows the common types of single-groove welds and the related symbol for each. The symbols for double-groove welds are illustrated in Fig. 20.15.

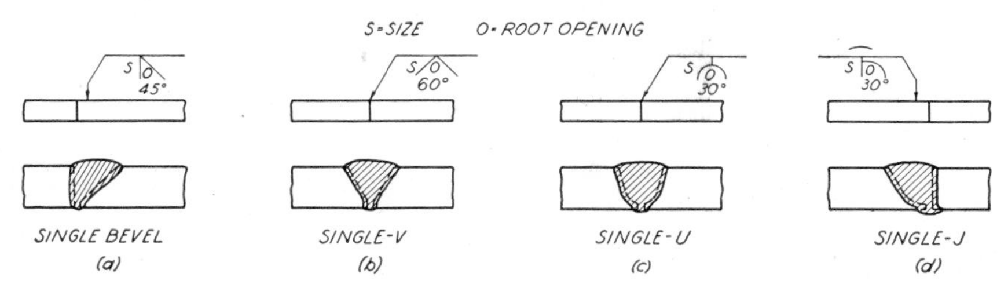

Fig. 20.14. Single-groove welds and symbols.

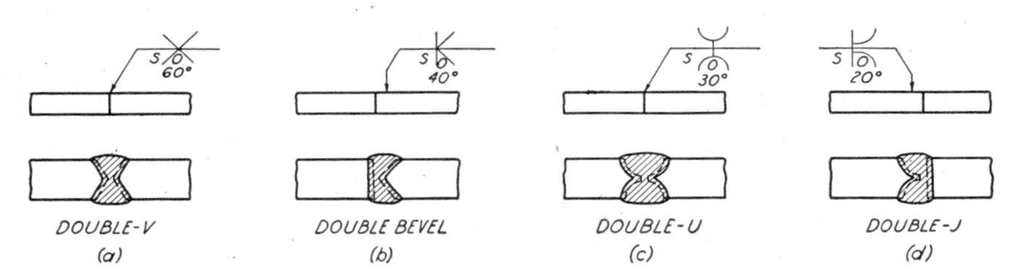

Fig. 20.15. Double-groove welds and symbols.

20.6. Classification of welded joints. Welded joints are classified in accordance with the method of assembly of the parts at a joint. See Fig. 20.16.

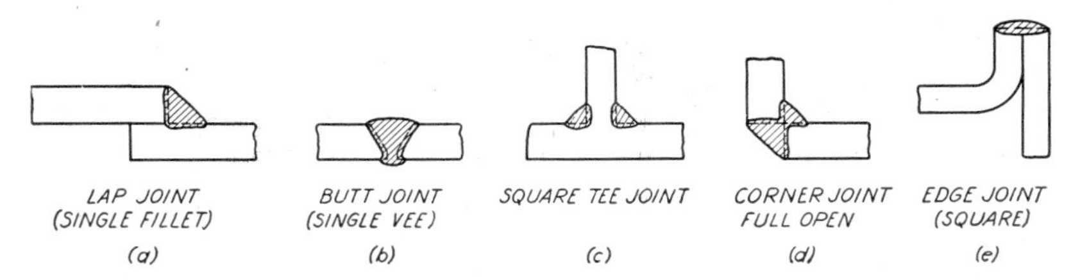

Fig. 20.16. Types of welded joints.

20.7. Gas and arc welding symbols. In order to satisfy the need for a standard group of symbols that could be understood in all manufacturing plants, the American Welding Society recommended in 1940 a set of conventional symbols so designed that each symbol resembled in a general way the type of weld it represented. Fig. 20.17 shows a condensed table of symbols. The few examples given here show the proper construction of welding specifications.

20.8. Resistance welding. Fig. 20.18 shows the symbols for the four principal types of resistance welding. The method of specifying resist-

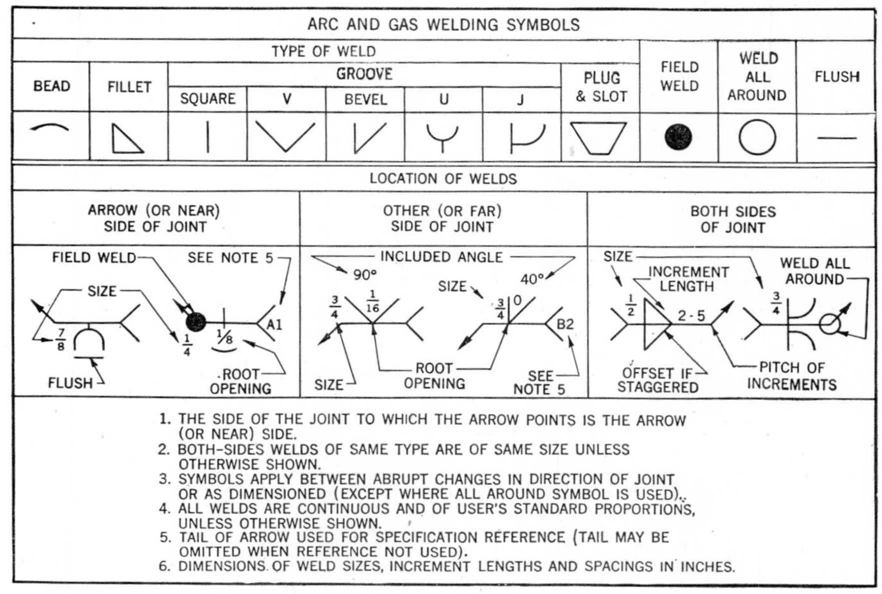

From the pamphlet "Welding Symbols" by the American Welding Society.

Fig. 20.17. Arc and gas welding symbols.

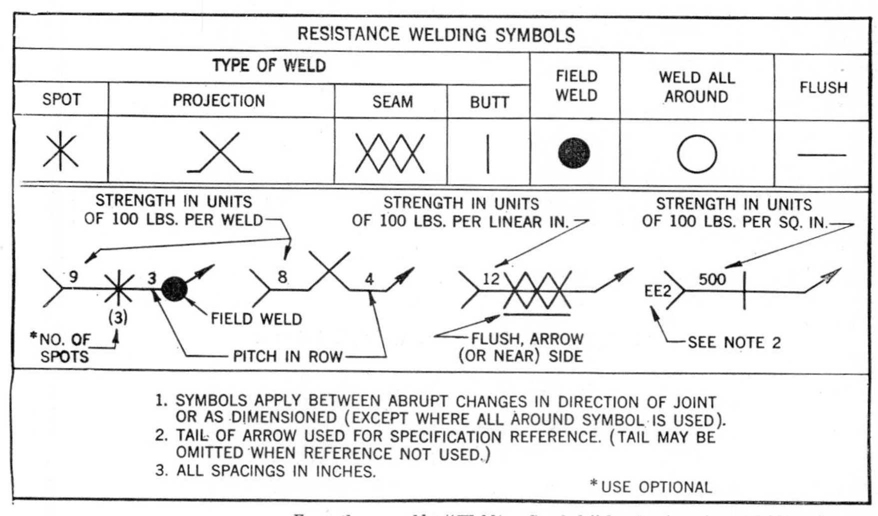

From the pamphlet "Welding Symbols" by the American Welding Society.

Fig. 20.18. Resistance welding symbols.

ance welds differs from the methods used for arc and gas welds. In the former, the strength of a weld is given in units instead of size, and the symbols do not show the form of the weld. In the table, the strength of spot and projection welds is given in units of 100 pounds per weld. The

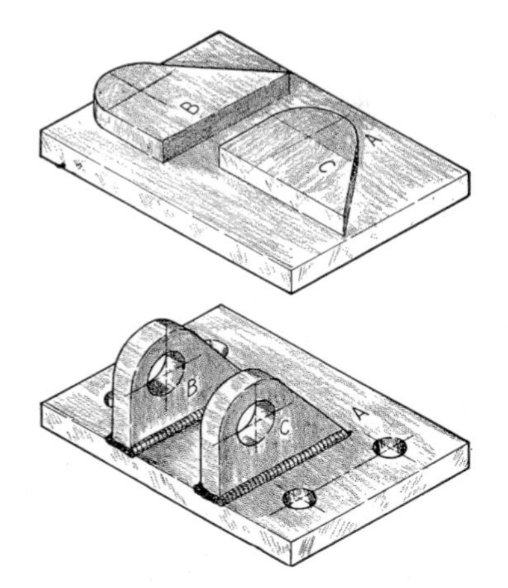

Fig. 20.19. Bracket-welded design.

strength for seam welds is given in units of 100 pounds per linear inch, while for a butt weld the same units are applied to the square inch of weld.

20.9. Welded machine parts. Many machine parts often can be constructed of welded rolled shapes at a much lower cost than if they were cast. This is due to the fact that the cost of the preparation of patterns is completely eliminated, less material is required, and labor costs are lower. A welded part is sometimes more desirable for a particular mechanism,

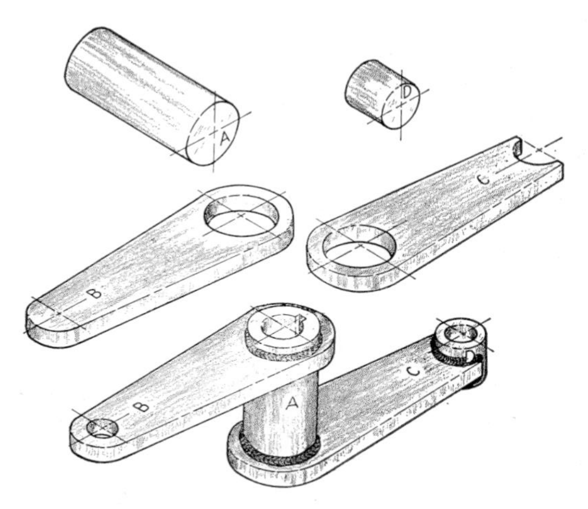

Fig. 20.20. Link-welded design.

because steel is stiffer, stronger in tension, and more resistant to fatigue stresses and sudden impact. Also, aside from the production of new parts, welding can be used to make a machine part to replace a broken cast part when it is necessary to place a machine back in operation in the shortest possible time. Fig. 20.19 shows a part that is constructed of plates. Fig. 20.20 shows the construction of a link using plates and round bar stock.

As previously stated, a designer is limited only by his own ingenuity. Parts of all shapes and sizes may be produced of readily available rolled forms. Simple bearings, levers, cranks, clevises, gear arms, and even cams can be quickly and easily made.

20.10. Instructions for use of welding symbols.*

I. *General:*

(*a*) Do not use the word "weld" as a symbol on drawings.
(*b*) Symbols may or may not be made freehand as desired.
(*c*) Inch, degree, and pound marks may or may not be used as desired.
(*d*) The symbol may be used without specification references or tails to designate the most commonly used specification when the following note appears on the drawing: "Unless otherwise designated, all welds to be made in accordance with welding specification No —."
(*e*) When specification references are used, place in tail, thus:

Fig. 20.21.

(*f*) Symbols apply between abrupt changes in direction of joint or to extent of hatching or dimension lines (except where all-around symbol is used).
(*g*) Faces of welds assumed to have user's standard contours unless otherwise indicated.
(*h*) Faces of welds assumed not to be finished other than cleaned unless otherwise indicated.
(*i*) All except plug, spot, and projection welds assumed continuous unless otherwise indicated.

II. *Arc and Gas Welds:*

1. General:

(*a*) Do not put symbol directly on lines of drawing; place symbol on reference line and connect latter to joint with arrow, thus:

Fig. 20.22.

* From the pamphlet, *Welding Symbols and Instructions for Their Use* (1942), by the American Welding Society.

(*b*) For welds on arrow (or near) side of joint show symbol on near side of reference lines, face toward reader, thus:

Fig. 20.23.

(*c*) For welds on other (or far) side show symbol on far side of reference line, face away from reader, thus:

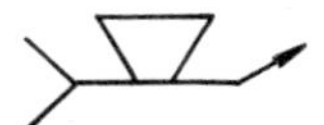

Fig. 20.24.

(*d*) For welds on both sides of joint show symbols on both sides of reference line, faces toward and away from reader, thus:

Fig. 20.25.

(*e*) Where the part shown is but one of a series of practically identical parts, the applicability of the symbols to the concealed parts shall be in accordance with the user's standard drawing practices with regard to the dimensioning and part-numbering such parts.
(*f*) Where one member only is to be grooved, show arrow pointing unmistakably to that member.
(*g*) Read symbols from bottom and right-hand side of drawing in the usual manner and place numerical data on vertical reference lines so that reader will be properly oriented.
(*h*) Show symbol for each weld in joints composed of more than one weld, thus:

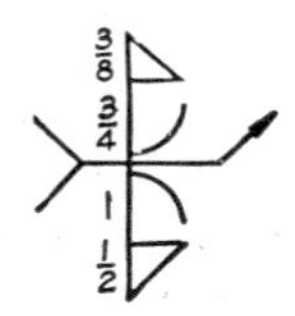

Fig. 20.26.

(Give numerical data in proper location with regard to each symbol.)
(*i*) In complicated joints requiring large compound symbols two separate sets of symbols may be used if desired.

(*j*) Show dimensions of weld on same side of reference line as symbol, thus:

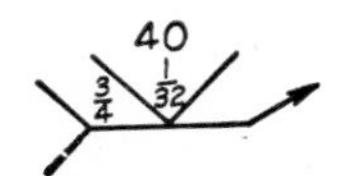

Fig. 20.27.

(*k*) Show dimensions of one weld only when welds on both sides of the joint are of the same type and size, thus:

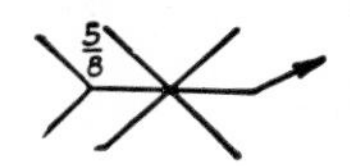

Fig. 20.28.

(If size of undimensioned fillets is governed by a note on the drawing, all weld sizes different from that covered in the note must be given.)

(*l*) Show dimensions for welds on both sides of the joint, when the arrow-side and other-side welds are different, thus:

Fig. 20.29.

(*m*) Indicate specific lengths of welds in conjunction with dimension lines, thus:

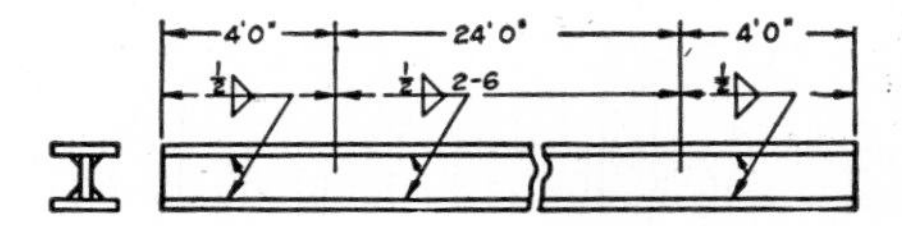

Fig. 20.30.

(*n*) Show the welding between abrupt changes in the direction of the weld thus (except when all-around symbol is used):

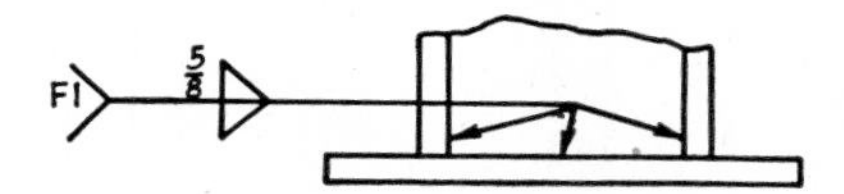

Fig. 20.31.

(*o*) When it is desired to show extent of welds by hatching, use one type of hatching with definite end lines, thus:

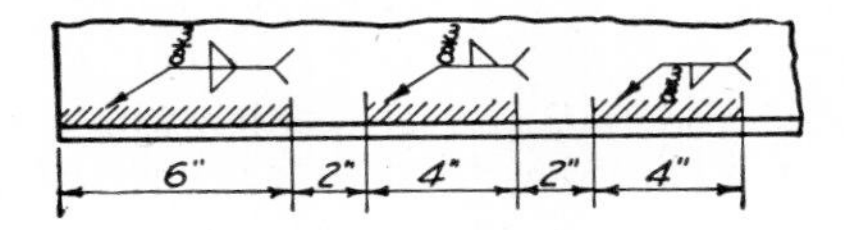

Fig. 20.32.

(*p*) If actual outlines of welds are drawn in section or end elevation, basic symbol is not necessary to show type and location; size or other numerical details only need to be given, thus:

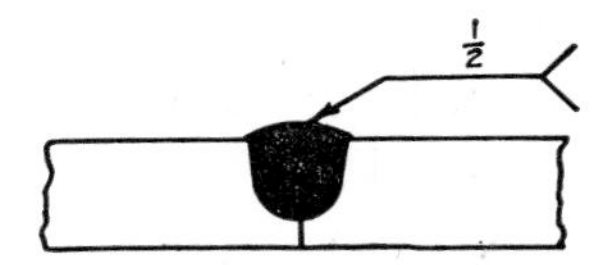

Fig. 20.33.

(*q*) Show fillet, bevel- and J-groove weld symbols with perpendicular leg always to the left hand, thus:

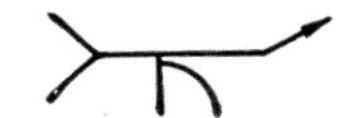

Fig. 20.34.

2. Bead Welds:
   (*a*) Show bead welds used in building up surfaces (size is minimum height of pad) thus:

Fig. 20.35.

   (*b*) When a small but no specific minimum height of pad is desired, show thus:

Fig. 20.36.

3. Fillet Welds:
   (*a*) Show size of fillet weld to the left of the perpendicular leg. (See Fig. 20.10.)
   (*b*) Show specific length of fillet weld or increment after size so that data read from left to right, thus:

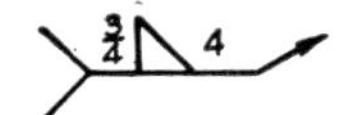

Fig. 20.37.

   (*c*) Show center-to-center pitch of increments of intermittent fillet welds after increment length so that data read from left to right, thus:

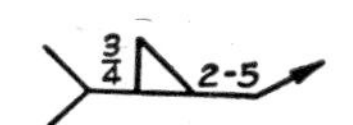

Fig. 20.38.

(*d*) Use separate symbol for each weld when intermittent and continuous fillet welds are used in combination.

(*e*) Show two intermittent fillet welds with increments opposite each other (chain) thus:

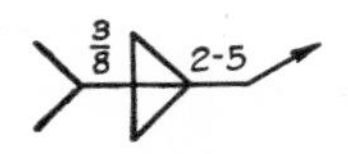

Fig. 20.39.

(*f*) Show two intermittent fillet welds with increments not opposite each other (staggered) thus:

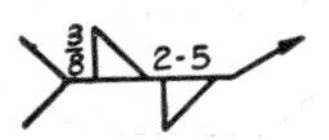

Fig. 20.40.

(*g*) Measure pitch of intermittent fillet welds between centers of increments on one side of member.

(*h*) Increments and not spaces assumed to be at ends of all intermittent welds and overall length dimensions govern to ends of those increments, thus:

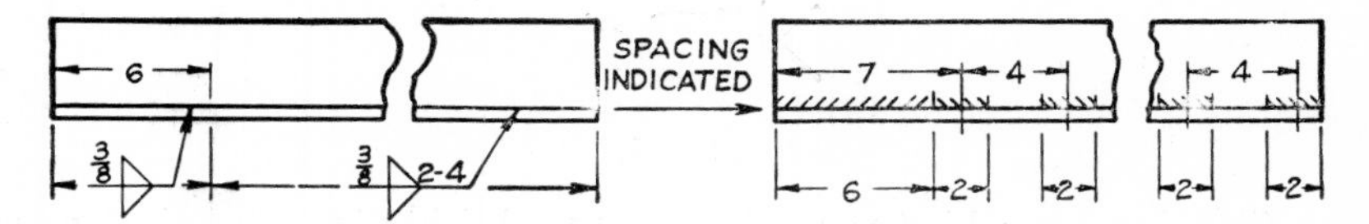

Fig. 20.41.

(*i*) Faces of fillet welds assumed to be at 45° from legs unless otherwise indicated.

(*j*) When the face of a fillet weld is to be at any other angle than 45°, two dimensions are necessary to fully designate the size of the weld. Place these dimensions in parentheses so that the two dimensional size data will be a single entity and will not be confused with length of increment and spacing data. Show on drawings positions of legs relative to members.

Fig. 20.42.

4. Groove Welds:

(*a*) Show side from which square-groove weld is made by bead or flush symbols, thus:

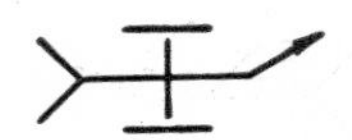

Fig. 20.43.

(*b*) Total penetration of square-groove welds assumed to be complete unless otherwise indicated.

(*c*) Show size of square-groove welds (depth of penetration) when penetration is less than complete, thus:

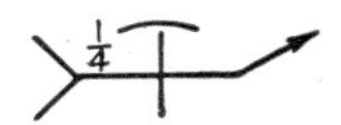

Fig. 20.44.

(*d*) Show root opening of open, square-groove welds inside symbol, thus:

Fig. 20.45.

(*e*) Total depth of V- and bevel-grooves before welding assumed to be equal to thickness of member unless otherwise indicated.

(*f*) Show size of V- and bevel-groove welds (depth of single groove before welding) when grooving is less than complete, thus:

Fig. 20.46.

(*g*) Total depth of penetration of V- and bevel-groove welds assumed complete, unless with usual welding processes, depth of grooving is such that complete penetration is not possible, when depth of penetration is assumed to be depth of groove plus normal penetration. When using welding processes giving abnormal penetration, give information on latter by detail or note.

(*h*) Root opening of V- and bevel-groove welds assumed to be user's standard unless otherwise indicated.

(*i*) Show root openings of V- and bevel-groove welds when not user's standard, inside symbol, thus:

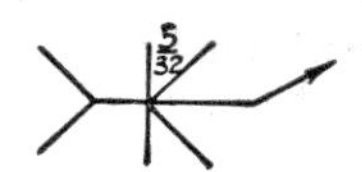

Fig. 20.47.

(*j*) Included angle of V- and bevel-groove welds assumed to be user's standard unless otherwise indicated.

(*k*) Show included angle of V- and bevel-groove welds when not user's standard inside symbol, thus:

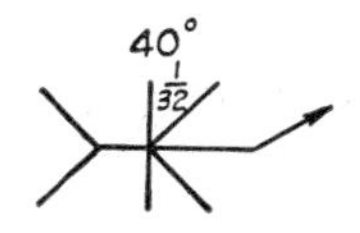

Fig. 20.48.

(*l*) Proportions of U- and J-groove welds assumed to be user's standard unless otherwise indicated.

(*m*) Show size of U- and J-groove welds (depth of single groove before welding) having user's standard proportions but incomplete penetration, thus:

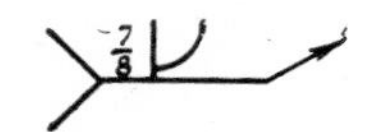

Fig. 20.49.

(*n*) When proportions of U- and J-groove welds are not user's standard, show weld by detail or reference drawing and use reference symbol, thus:

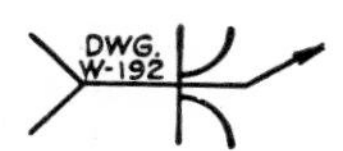

Fig. 20.50.

(*o*) Show welding done from root side of single-groove welds with bead weld symbol, thus:

Fig. 20.51.

5. Plug and Slot Welds:

(*a*) Show size of plug and slot welds (root opening and root length), thus: (Root opening equals root length for plug welds.)

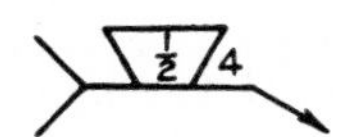

Fig. 20.52.

(*b*) Included angle of bevel of plug and slot welds assumed to be user's standard unless otherwise indicated.

(*c*) Show included angle of bevel of plug and slot welds when not user's standard, thus:

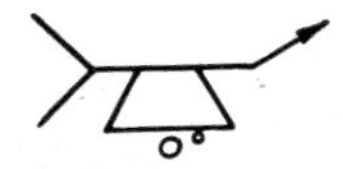

Fig. 20.53.

(*d*) Show pitch of plug and slot welds in row, thus:

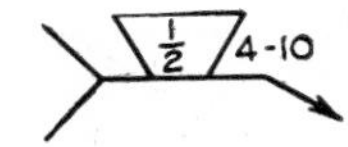

Fig. 20.54.

(*e*) Show fillet welded holes and slots with proper fillet weld symbols and not with plug weld symbols.

III. *Resistance Welds:*

1. General:

(*a*) Center resistance welding symbols for spot and seam welds on reference line because these symbols have no arrow side or other side (near and far side) significance; but do not center projection welding symbols because the latter have such significance.

(*b*) Designate resistance welds by strength rather than size (because of impracticability of determining latter).

(*c*) Spot and seam weld symbols may be used directly on drawings, thus (but projection weld symbols should not):

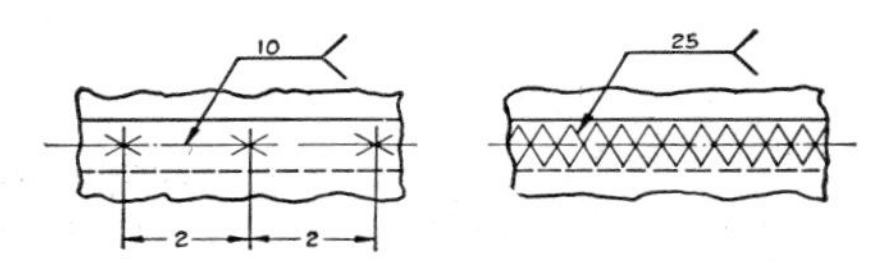

Fig. 20.55.

(*d*) When not used on lines of drawing, connect reference line to center line of weld or rows of welds with arrow, thus:

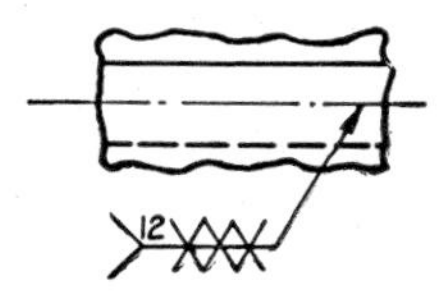

Fig. 20.56.

(*e*) Show welds of extent less than between abrupt changes in direction of joint, thus:

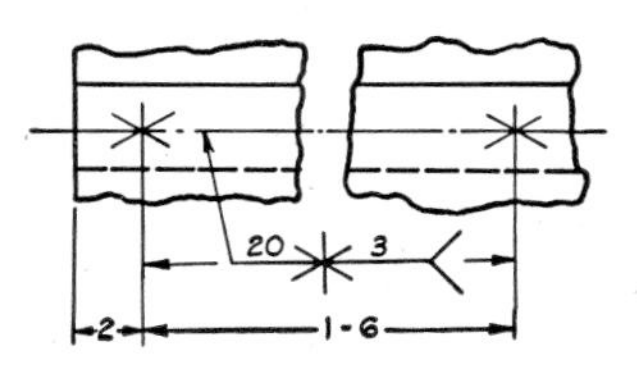

Fig. 20.57.

(*f*) When tension, impact, fatigue or other properties are required, use reference symbol, thus:

Fig. 20.58.

2. Spot and Projection Welds:
   (a) Show strength of spot and projection welds in single shear in units of 100 pounds per weld, thus:

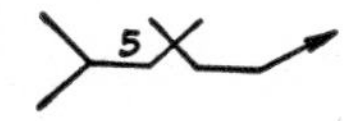

Fig. 20.59.

   (b) Show strength and center-to-center spacing of spot and projection welds in row, thus:

Fig. 20.60.

   (c) When a definite number of spot or projection welds is desired in a certain joint or connection, show that number by a number in parentheses below the symbol, thus:

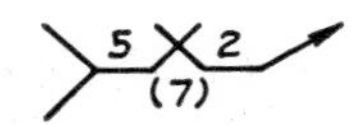

Fig. 20.61.

   (d) Proportions of projections assumed given on drawing.
   (e) In a projection-welded joint parallel, or nearly so, to the plane of the paper, show whether the arrow (or near) side or other (or far) side member is to be embossed by placing the projection weld symbol on the arrow (or near) or the other (or far) side of the reference line, thus:

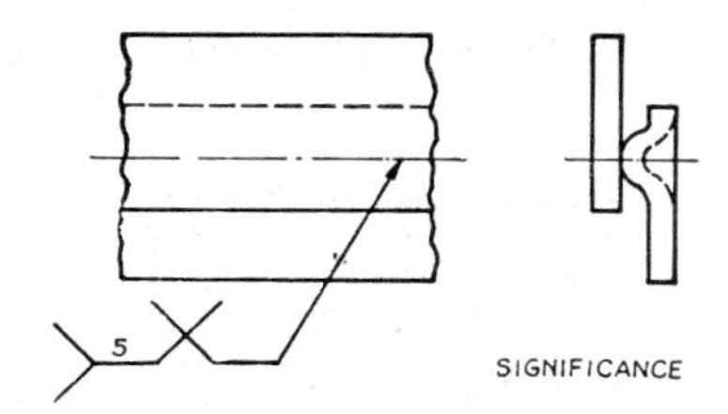

Fig. 20.62.

   (f) In a projection-welded joint shown in section or end view, show which member is to be embossed by pointing arrow to that member, thus:

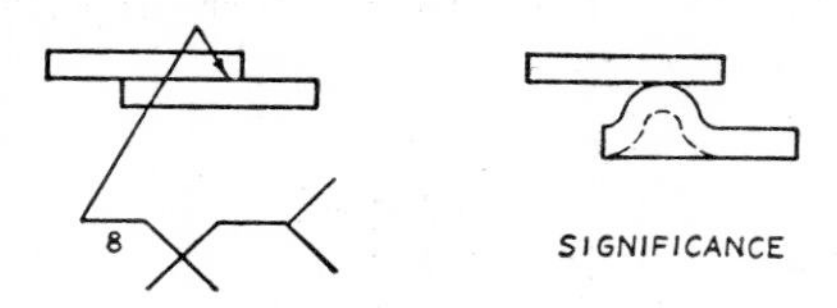

Fig. 20.63.

3. Seam Welds:
   (*a*) Seam welds assumed to be of overlapping or tangent spots. If any spacing exists between spots, welds considered a series of spot welds, and spot symbol should be used.
   (*b*) Show shear strength of seam welds in units of 100 pounds per linear inch, thus:

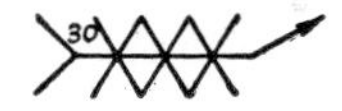

Fig. 20.64.

4. Butt Welds:
   (*a*) Show resistance butt welds without bead weld symbol signifying that weld is not made from any side, but all at once, thus:

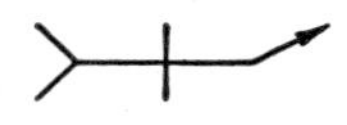

Fig. 20.65.

   (*b*) Resistance butt welds assumed to be equal to strength of base metal in tension unless otherwise indicated.
   (*c*) When a different strength is desired, show strength of butt welds in tension in units of 100 pounds per square inch, thus:

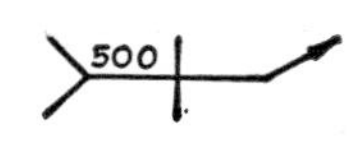

Fig. 20.66.

IV. *Supplementary Symbols:*
   (*a*) Show "field" welds (any weld not made in shop), thus:

Fig. 20.67.

   (*b*) Show "all-around" welds, weld encircling joint (or joints) in so far as is possible, thus:

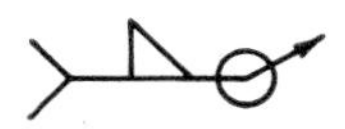

Fig. 20.68.

   (*c*) When the weld encircles the joint but there is no abrupt change in the direction of the joint or parts of the joint (changes in the direction of rolled structural sections are considered abrupt even though there are fillets in the corners), the all-around symbol may or may not be used as desired, thus:

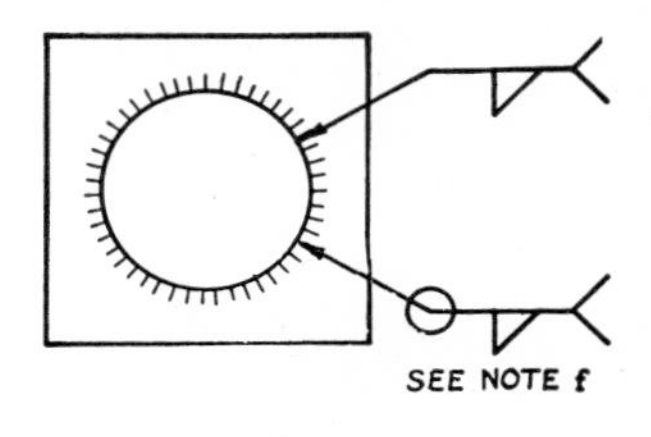

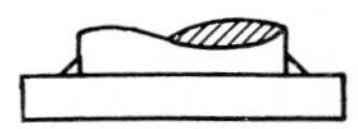

Fig. 20.69.

(*d*) The all-around symbol extends control of the welding symbol beyond abrupt changes in the direction of one joint, or parts of one joint, to encirclement of the complete joint in so far as is possible, thus:

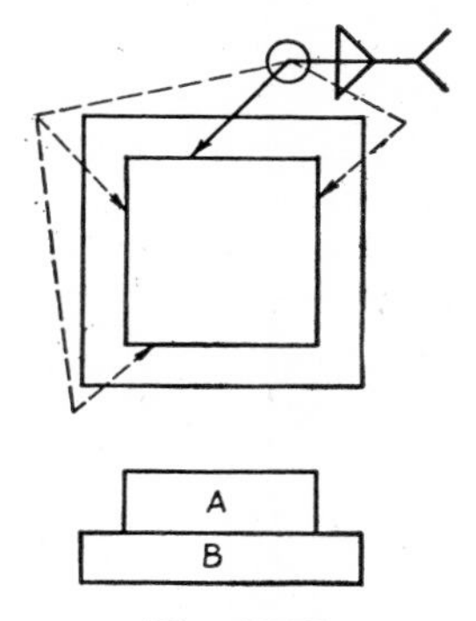

Fig. 20.70.

(*e*) The all-around symbol extends the control of the welding symbol not only beyond abrupt changes in the direction of one joint, but to two or more joints to the encirclement of the joints in so far as is possible, thus:

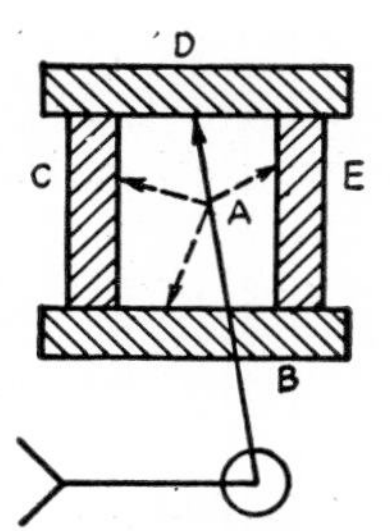

FOUR JOINTS AB AC, AD, AND AE BETWEEN 5 MEMBERS A,B,C,D, AND E.

Fig. 20.71.

(*f*) When the use of an arrow-side or other-side symbol, together with an all-around symbol, results in a weld on both sides of the joint as a whole, it is advisable to use the both-sides symbol, thus, even though a one-side symbol may be strictly correct:

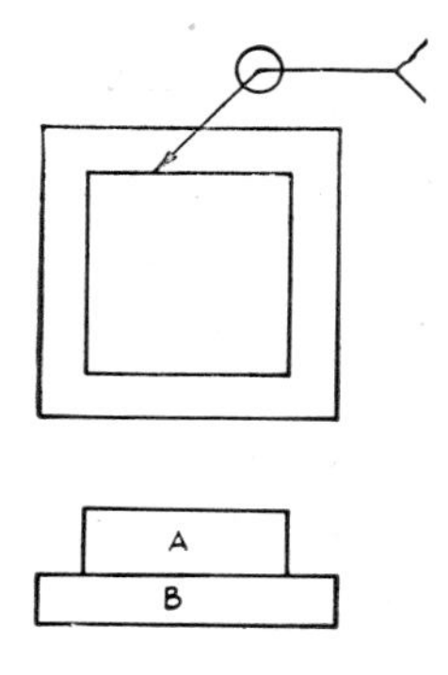

Fig. 20.72.

(*g*) When the member involved is hollow or annular and there is more than one encircling weld, and there is likelihood of confusion existing whether or not a both-sides symbol would refer to a part of the joint or to the joint as a whole, show each encircling weld with a separate arrow, thus:

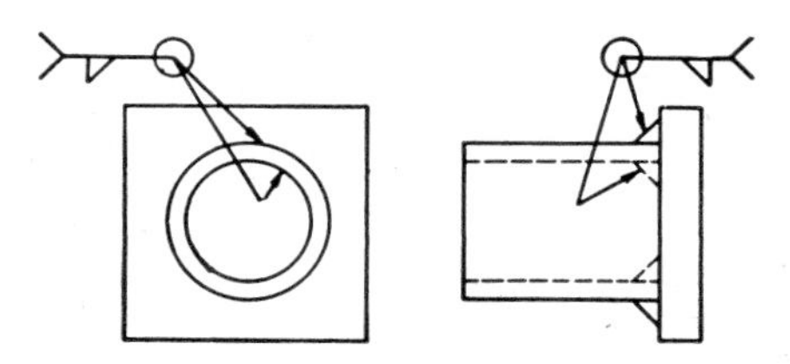

Fig. 20.73.

(*h*) The locations of the flush and finish symbols have the usual arrow and other (near and far) side significance and govern only the sides on which they are shown.

(*i*) Finish marks govern faces of welds only and not base metal either before or after welding.

(*j*) Show arc and gas welds made flush without recourse to any kind of finishing, thus:

Fig. 20.74.

(*k*) Show arc and gas welds made flush by mechanical means with both flush and user's standard finish symbols, thus:

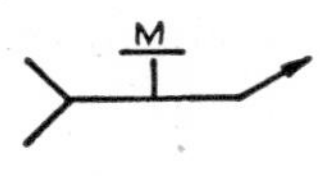

Fig. 20.75.

The following letters are suggested for indicating finishing processes:

C—Chip G—Grind M—Machine

(*l*) Show finishing on face of arc and gas welds, which need not be flush, with user's standard finish symbols on bead symbol, thus:

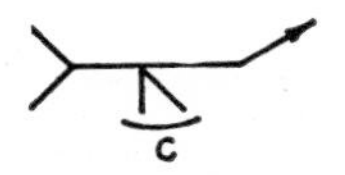

Fig. 20.76.

(*m*) Show spot, seam, or projection welds made practically flush (with minimum indentation), thus:

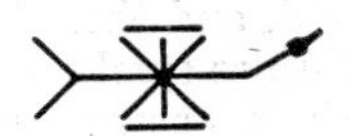

Fig. 20.77.

(*n*) Show resistance butt welds, finished by mechanical means, without flush symbol.

(*o*) Show special welds not covered by any of the above symbols by a detailed section or reference drawing, or give any supplementary information by means of a note and refer weld to section, drawing, or note by a reference symbol. Reference symbol has usual location significance, thus:

Fig. 20.78.

20.11. Problems. Two problems offering experience in the preparation of welding drawings are given in Figs. 20.79 and 20.80. Others may be had by redesigning many of the cast parts, given at the end of the chapter on multiview drawing and in some of the other chapters, in such a way that they may be made of welded steel shapes. The student will find in these problems an opportunity to exercise some of his own ingenuity.

1. Prepare a welding drawing of the bracket shown in Fig. 20.79.

2. Prepare a welding drawing of the caster bracket shown in Fig. 20.80. The length of the tubing is $2\frac{11}{16}''$.

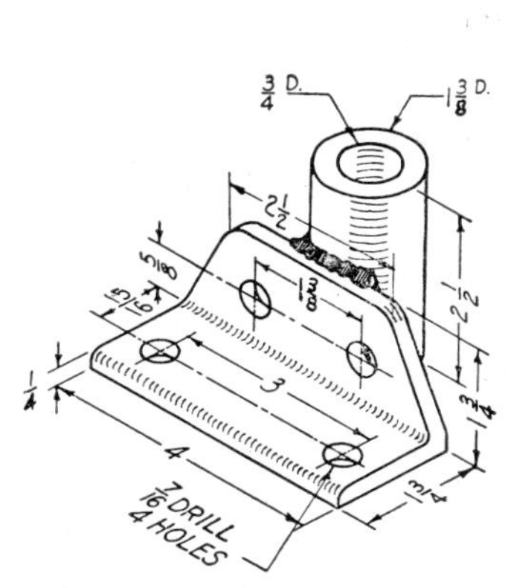

Fig. 20.79. Bracket.

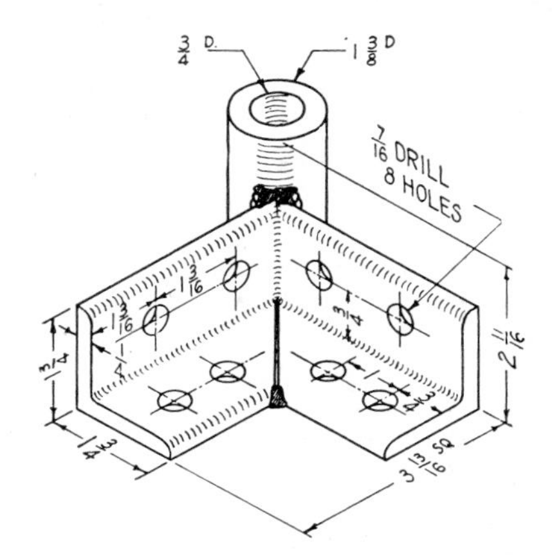

Fig. 20.80. Caster bracket.

3. Make a two-view orthographic drawing of the object shown in Fig. 20.1. The dimensions are to be assumed. The plates are $\frac{3}{8}''$ thick. Show the correct specification for each type of weld.

4. Make a three-view detail drawing of the bracket shown in Fig. 20.19. The dimensions are to be assumed. Show the correct specification for the welds.

5. Make a two-view detail drawing of the link shown in Fig. 20.20. The dimensions are to be assumed. Show correct specifications for the welds.

21 MACHINE ELEMENTS

21.1. Gears. The draftsman frequently is called upon to make representations of gears and gear teeth. It is therefore important for him to know the general proportions and nomenclature pertaining to gearing. In Fig. 21.1 the nomenclature for bevel gears is shown. It will be noted that, in general, the definitions pertaining to gear-tooth parts can be represented in a right section of the gear.

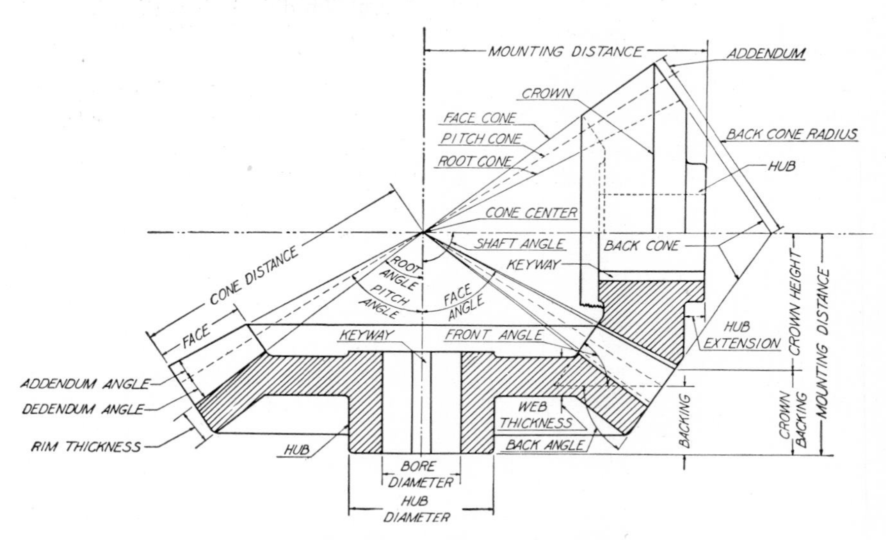

Fig. 21.1. Bevel-gear nomenclature.

The theory of gears is a part of the study of mechanism. In working drawings of gears and toothed wheels it is necessary to draw at least one tooth of each gear. Some of the terms used in defining gear teeth are shown in Fig. 21.2.

Two systems of generating tooth curves are in general use, the involute system and the cycloidal system. The curve most commonly used for gear-tooth profiles is the involute of a circle.

An involute is the curve generated by a point on a straight-edge as the straight-edge is rolled on a cylinder. It also may be defined as the curve generated by a point in a taut string as the string is unwrapped from a cylinder. The circle from which the involute is developed is called the *base circle.*

A method of constructing an involute curve is shown in Fig. 21.3. Starting with point 0, on the base circle, divide the base circle into a convenient number of equal arcs of length 0–1, 1–2, 2–3, and so forth. (Where the lengths of the divisions on the base circle are not too great, the chord can be taken as the length of the arc.) Draw a tangent to the base circle,

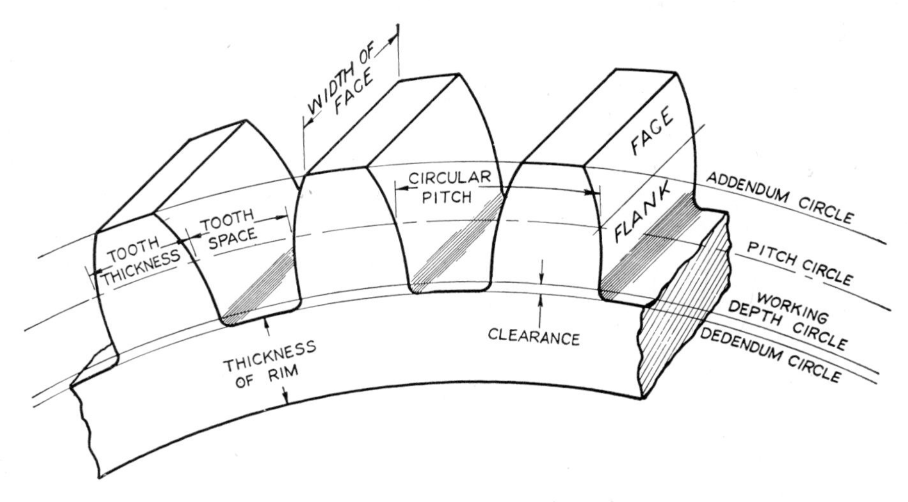

Fig. 21.2. Spur-gear nomenclature.

at point 0, and divide this line to the left of 0 into equal parts of the same lengths as the arcs. Next, draw tangents to the circle from points 1, 2, 3, and so on. With the center of the base circle "0" as a pivot, draw concentric arcs from 1′, 2′, 3′, and so forth, until they intersect the tangent lines drawn from 1, 2, 3, and so forth. The intersection of the arcs and the tangents are points on the required involute curve, such as 1″, 2″, 3″, and so forth. The illustration at the right in Fig. 21.3 shows the portion XY of the tooth outline as part of the involute curve.

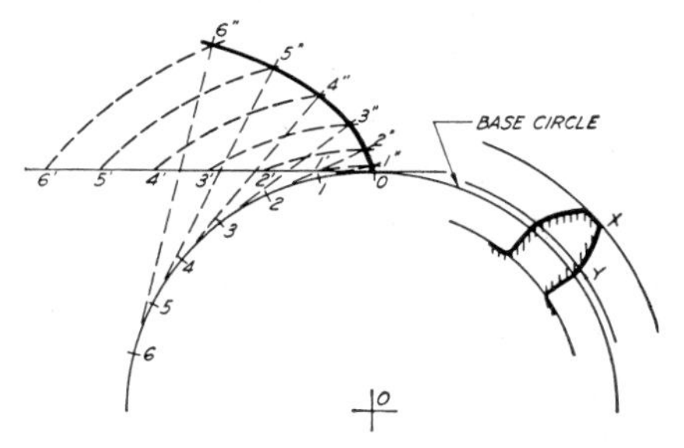

Fig. 21.3. Involute tooth.

The cycloidal system, as the name implies, has tooth curves of cycloidal form. A cycloid is the curve generated by a point on the circumference of a circle as the circle rolls on a straight line. If the circle rolls on the outside of another circle, the curve generated is called an epicycloid; if it rolls on the inside of another circle, the curve generated is called a hypocycloid. In Fig. 21.4, let R be the radius of the fixed circle and r be the radius of the rolling circle. Draw through a a circle arc, AB, concentric with the fixed circle. Lay off on the rolling circle a convenient number of divisions, such as 0-1, 1-2, 2-3 and so forth; then divide the fixed-circle circumference into divisions of the same length, such as 0-1′, 1′-2′, 2′-3′, and so on. Through these points on the fixed circle, draw radii and extend them to intersect the arc AB, thus producing points a_1, a_2, a_3, and so on. These points will be the centers of the successive positions of the rolling circle. Draw the positions of the rolling circle, using the centers a_1, a_2, a_3, and so forth. Next draw, on the rolling circle with the center "0" of the fixed circle as the pivot point, concentric arcs through

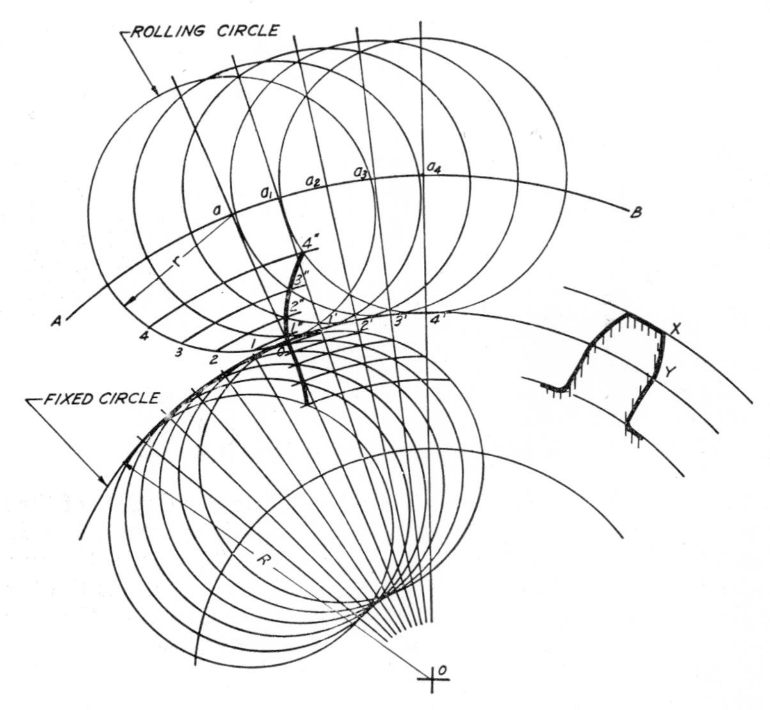

Fig. 21.4.

points 1, 2, 3, and so forth. The intersection of these arcs with the rolling circles about a_1, a_2, a_3, and so forth, determine points, such as 1″, 2″, 3″, and so forth, on the epicyclic curve. The illustration at the right in Fig. 21.4 shows XY of the tooth outline as part of the epicyclic curve.

The hypocyclic curve construction is the same as that for the epicyclic curve. In the construction of the hypocyclic curve, if the rolling circle has a diameter equal to one-half of the diameter of the fixed circle, the hypocyclic curve thus generated will be a radial line of the fixed circle.

GEAR TERMS

1. The addendum circle is drawn with its center at the center of the gear and bounds the ends of the teeth. (See Fig. 21.2.)
2. The dedendum circle, or root circle, is drawn with its center at the center of the gear and bounds the bottoms of the teeth. (See Fig. 21.2.)
3. The pitch circle is a right section of the equivalent cylinder the toothed gear may be considered to replace.
4. Pitch diameter is the diameter of the pitch circle.
5. The addendum is the radial distance from the pitch circle to the outer end of the tooth.
6. The dedendum is the radial distance from the pitch circle to the bottom of the tooth.
7. The clearance is the difference between the dedendum of one gear and the addendum of the mating gear.
8. The face of a tooth is that portion of the tooth surface lying outside the pitch circle.
9. The flank of a tooth is that portion of the tooth surface lying inside the pitch circle.
10. The thickness of a tooth is measured on the arc of the pitch circle. It is the length of an arc and not the length of a straight line.
11. The tooth space is the space between the teeth measured on the pitch circle.
12. Backlash is the difference between the tooth thickness of one gear and the tooth space on the mating gear, measured on the pitch circles.
13. The circular pitch of a gear is the distance between a point on one tooth and the corresponding point on the adjacent tooth, measured along the arc of the pitch circle. The circular pitches of two gears in mesh are equal.
14. The diametral pitch is the number of teeth per inch of pitch diameter. It is obtained by dividing the number of teeth by the pitch diameter.
15. The face of a gear is the width of its rim measured parallel to the axis. It should not be confused with the face of a tooth, for the two are entirely different.
16. The pitch point is on the line joining the centers of the two gears where the pitch circles touch.
17. The common tangent is the line tangent to the pitch circles at the pitch point.
18. The pressure angle is the angle between the line of action and the common tangent.
19. The line of action is a line drawn through the pitch point at an angle (equal to the pressure angle) to the common tangent.
20. The base circle is used in involute gearing to generate the involutes that form the tooth outlines. It is drawn from the center of each pair of mating gears tangent to the line of action.
21. When two gears mesh with each other, the larger is called the *gear* and the smaller the *pinion*.

It should be noted that *circular pitch* is a linear dimension expressed in inches, whereas *diametral pitch* is a ratio. There must be a whole number of teeth on the circumference of a gear. Thus it is necessary that the circumference of the pitch circle, divided by the circular pitch, be a whole number.

For circular pitch, let P' = circular pitch in inches, D = pitch diameter, and T = number of teeth. Then

$$TP' = \pi D, \qquad T = \frac{\pi D}{P'}, \qquad P' = \frac{\pi D}{T}, \qquad \text{and} \qquad D = \frac{TP'}{\pi}.$$

For diametral pitch, let P = diametral pitch, D = pitch diameter, and T = number of teeth. Then

$$T = PD, \qquad D = \frac{T}{P}, \qquad \text{and} \qquad P = \frac{T}{D}.$$

The Brown and Sharpe $14\frac{1}{2}$-degree involute system has been adopted as one of the American standards and is commonly known as the $14\frac{1}{2}$-Degree Composite System. The tooth proportions of this system are given in terms of the diametral pitch P and circular pitch P'.

Pressure angle = $14\frac{1}{2}°$.

Addendum (inches) $= \dfrac{1}{\text{diametral pitch}} = \dfrac{1}{P}$.

Dedendum (inches) = addendum plus clearance $= \dfrac{1}{P} + 0.05P'$.

Clearance = 0.05 × circular pitch = $0.05P'$.

Whole depth of tooth = 2 × addendum + clearance $= 2 \times \dfrac{1}{P} + 0.05P'$.

Working depth of tooth = 2 × addendum $= 2 \times \dfrac{1}{P}$.

Thickness of tooth $= \dfrac{\text{circular pitch}}{2} = \dfrac{P'}{2}$.

Width of tooth space $= \dfrac{\text{circular pitch}}{2} = \dfrac{P'}{2}$.

Minimum radius of fillet = clearance = $0.05P'$.

In the above calculations the backlash is zero. Actually, however, it is common practice to provide backlash, and this is accomplished by using standard cutters and cutting the teeth slightly deeper than for standard teeth.

21.2. To lay out a pair of standard involute spur gears. The following facts are known regarding the laying out of a pair of standard spur gears: (1) number of teeth on each gear—large gear 24, small gear 16, (2) diametral pitch = 2, (3) pressure angle = $14\frac{1}{2}°$.

To draw a pair of spur gears, determine the pitch diameters, thus:

$$D = \frac{T}{P} = \frac{24}{2} = 12'' \text{ for large gear.}$$

$$D = \frac{T}{P} = \frac{16}{2} = 8'' \text{ for small gear.}$$

In Fig. 21.5, with radii O_1P and O_2P equal to 6″ and 4″ respectively; draw the pitch circles and, through P, draw the common tangent. Draw the line of action XY at an angle of $14\frac{1}{2}°$ to the common tangent. Drop perpendiculars from the centers O_1 and O_2, cutting the line of action at A and B, respectively. O_1A and O_2B are the radii of the base circles that can now be drawn.

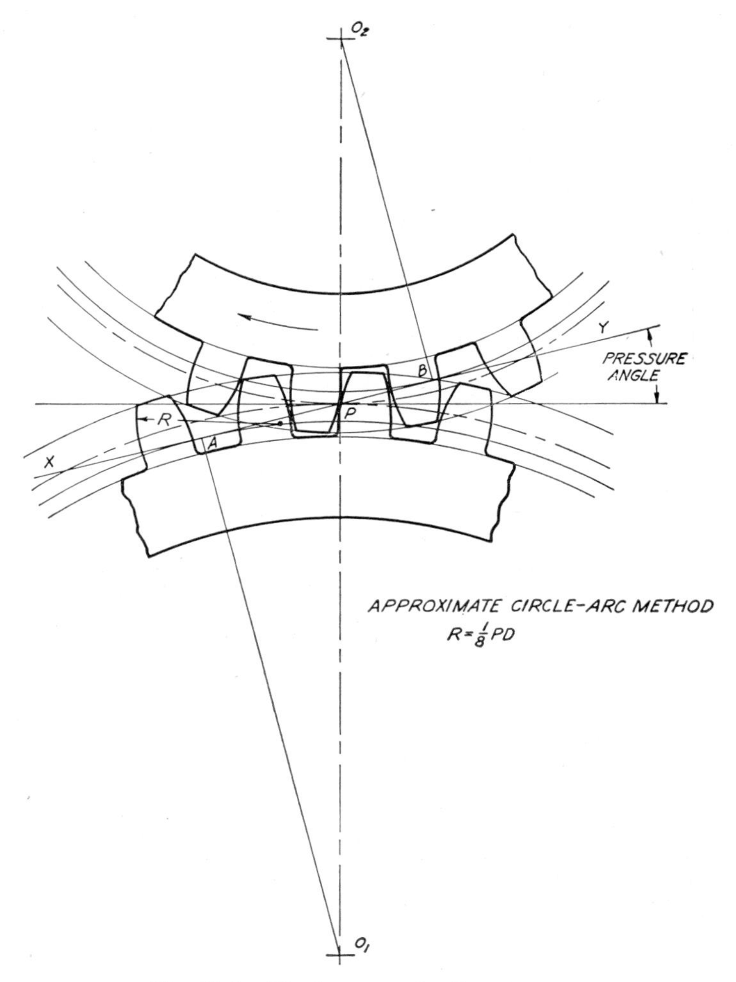

Fig. 21.5. To draw a pair of spur gears.

From Sec. 21.1, determine the addendum and dedendum of the teeth, and draw in the respective addendum and dedendum circles.

Divide the pitch circle of the smaller gear into 16 equal parts and the pitch circle of the larger gear into 24 equal parts, which will give the circular pitch. Assuming that no allowance is made for backlash, bisect the circular pitch on each of the gears, which will give 32 equal divisions on the small gear and 48 equal divisions on the large gear.

At any point on the base circle of each gear, develop an involute (see Fig. 21.3) and draw in the curves between the base and addendum circles through alternate points on the pitch circles. This produces one side of all the teeth in each gear. The curve for the other side of the tooth is the reverse of the side just drawn. The part of the tooth between the base

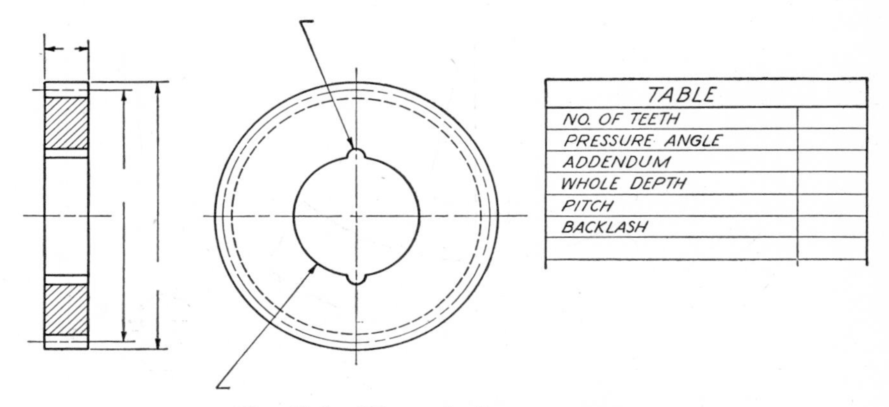

TABLE
NO. OF TEETH
PRESSURE ANGLE
ADDENDUM
WHOLE DEPTH
PITCH
BACKLASH

Fig. 21.6. Dimensioning a spur gear.

and dedendum circles is part of a radial line drawn from the base circles to the centers of the gears. The tooth is finished by putting in a small fillet between the working depth and dedendum circles.

21.3. Dimensioning gears. On a detail drawing, a gear may be represented by a one-view section, except for the larger sizes, where it is necessary to show spokes, and for the small sizes, when a full description of some feature would not be given. A second view was drawn in Fig.

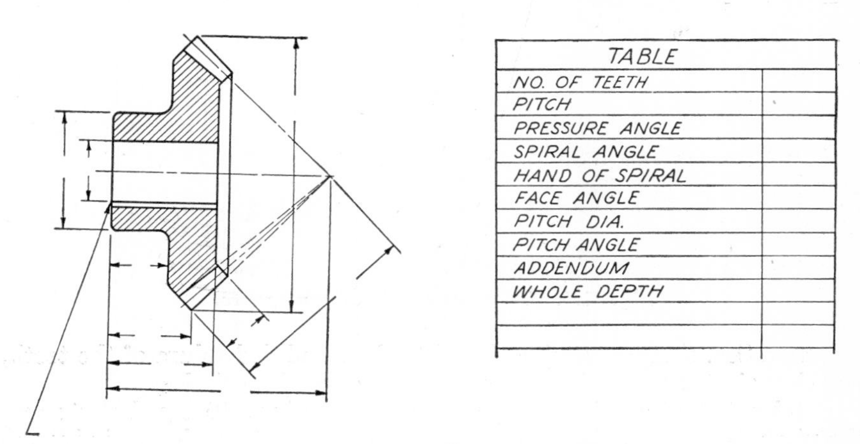

TABLE
NO. OF TEETH
PITCH
PRESSURE ANGLE
SPIRAL ANGLE
HAND OF SPIRAL
FACE ANGLE
PITCH DIA.
PITCH ANGLE
ADDENDUM
WHOLE DEPTH

Fig. 21.7. Dimensioning a bevel gear.

21.6 to reveal the shape of the keyway. In dimensioning, it is recommended that the dimensions be given on the view or views as shown in Figs. 21.6 and 21.7 and that the cutting data be incorporated in an accompanying table.

21.4. Working drawings of gears. Fig. 21.8 shows a working drawing of a helical gear. In practice it is customary to show one view in section and just enough of the circular view to supply needed information for the shop. Individual teeth are never shown on the circular view unless the drawing is to be used for display purposes. In some drafting rooms where practice requires a full circular view, the addendum circle is represented by a fine solid line, the pitch circle is given as a center line, and the root circle is shown by a dashed line (Fig. 21.6).

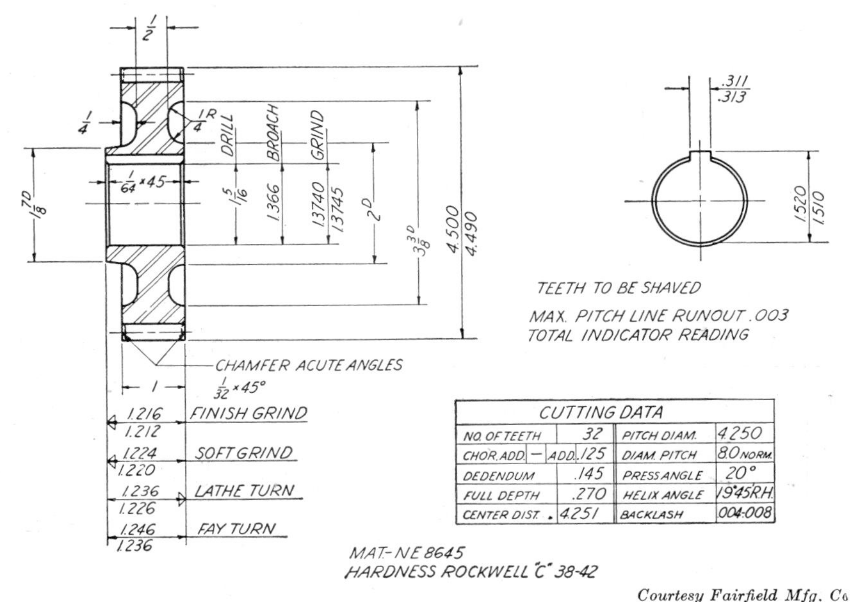

CUTTING DATA			
NO. OF TEETH	32	PITCH DIAM.	4.250
CHOR. ADD. — ADD.	.125	DIAM. PITCH	8.0 NORM.
DEDENDUM	.145	PRESS ANGLE	20°
FULL DEPTH	.270	HELIX ANGLE	19°45' R.H.
CENTER DIST.	4.251	BACKLASH	.004-.008

Courtesy Fairfield Mfg. Co.

Fig. 21.8. Detail drawing of a helical gear.

It should be noted that the dimensions for the gear blank are given on the sectioned view while the necessary data for cutting the teeth are given in a table. This is in accordance with the practice recommended in Sec. 21.3.

A working drawing of a spiral bevel gear is shown in Fig. 21.9. The same practices apply as for spur gears. Before starting to prepare a working drawing of a bevel gear one should study Fig. 21.1, which illustrates bevel-gear nomenclature.

Fig. 21.10 shows a working drawing of a worm.

21.5. Cams. A cam is a plate, cylinder, or any solid having a curved outline or curved groove that, by its oscillating or rotating motion, gives a predetermined motion to another piece, called the follower, in contact

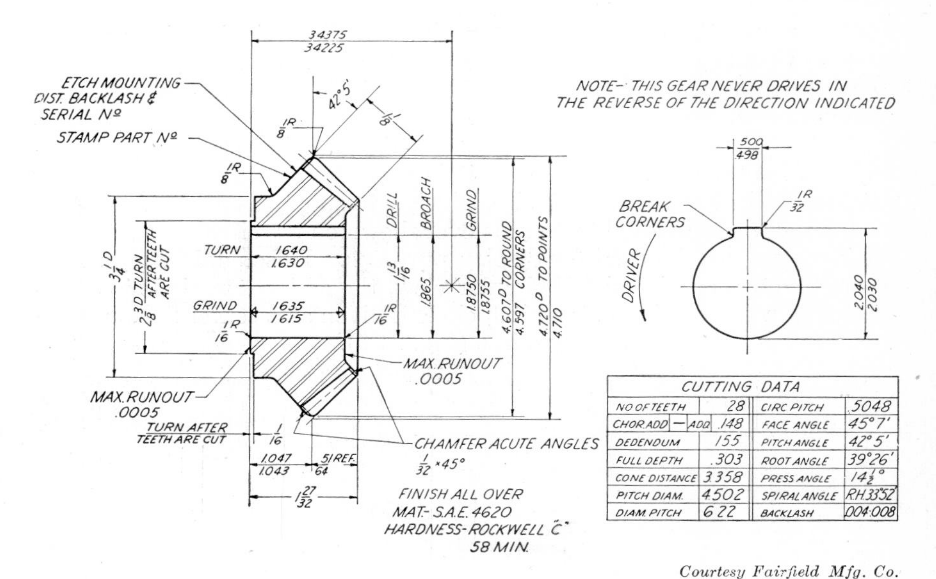

CUTTING DATA			
NO OF TEETH	28	CIRC PITCH	.5048
CHOR. ADD — ADD	.148	FACE ANGLE	45°7′
DEDENDUM	.155	PITCH ANGLE	42°5′
FULL DEPTH	.303	ROOT ANGLE	39°26′
CONE DISTANCE	3.358	PRESS ANGLE	$14\frac{1}{2}°$
PITCH DIAM.	4.502	SPIRAL ANGLE	R.H. 33°52′
DIAM. PITCH	6.22	BACKLASH	.004-.008

Courtesy Fairfield Mfg. Co.

Fig. 21.9. Detail drawing of a spiral bevel gear.

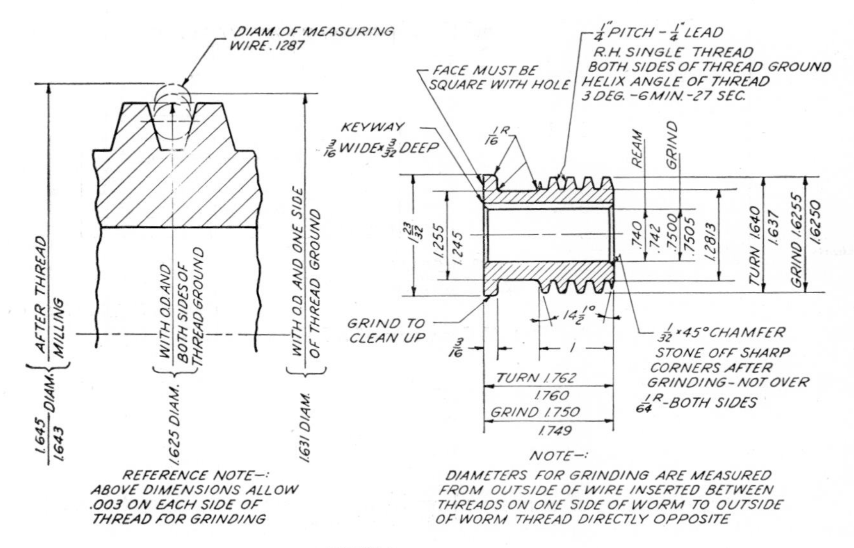

WORM
S.A.E. X1315 STEEL (COLD FINISHED) - $1\frac{3}{4}$ BAR
TREAT. - B75 - 40Z - 400 XXX
ROCKWELL - C55 - 62

Courtesy of The Warner & Swasey Co.

Fig. 21.10. Detail drawing of a worm.

with it. The cam plays a very important part in the operation of many classes of machines. Cam mechanisms are commonly used to operate valves in automobiles and stationary and marine internal combustion engines. They also are used in automatic screw machines, clocks, locks, printing machinery, and in nearly all kinds of machinery that we generally regard as "automatic machines." The applications of cams are practically unlimited, and their shapes or outlines are found in wide variety.

All cam mechanisms consist of at least three parts: (1) the cam, which has a contact surface either curved or straight; (2) the follower, whose motion is produced by contact with the cam surface; and (3) the frame, which supports the cam and guides the follower.

The most common type of cam is the disc or plate cam. Here the cam takes the form of a revolving disc or plate, the circumference of the disc or plate forming the profile with which the follower makes contact. In Figs. 21.11 and 21.12, two simple examples of a disc cam and follower are shown. In Fig. 21.11, the cam is given a motion of rotation, thus causing the follower to rise and then return again to its initial position. In cams of this type it is necessary to use some external force, such as the spring, to keep the follower in contact with the cam at all times. Contact between the follower and the cam is made through a roller, which serves to reduce friction. It is sometimes necessary to use a flat-faced follower, instead of the roller type, an example of which is shown in Fig. 21.12. The follower face that comes in contact with the cam is usually provided with a hardened surface, to prevent excessive wear.

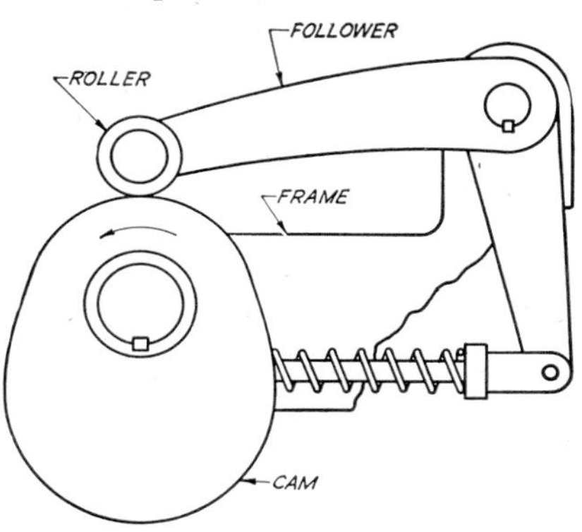

Fig. 21.11.

Another type of cam is one in which the follower is constrained to move in a definite path without the application of external forces. (See Fig. 21.13.) In this type, two contact surfaces of the follower bear on the cam at the same time, thus controlling the motion of the follower in two directions.

21.6. Design of a cam. The design of a cam outline is governed by the requirements with respect to the motion of the follower. In the layout of a cam, the initial position, displacement, and character of the motion of the follower are generally known. It is convenient to make first a graphical representation of the follower movement, a procedure which is called *making a displacement diagram.* This is a linear curve in which the length of the diagram represents the time for one revolution of the cam. The height of the diagram represents the total displacement of the follower; the length is made to any convenient length and is divided into equal time intervals, the total representing one rotation of the cam.

In Fig. 21.14 is shown a displacement diagram in which the follower rises 2″ during 180° of rotation of the cam, then rests for 30° and returns to its initial position for the remainder of the cam revolution. Cam outlines should be designed to avoid sudden changes of motion at the begin-

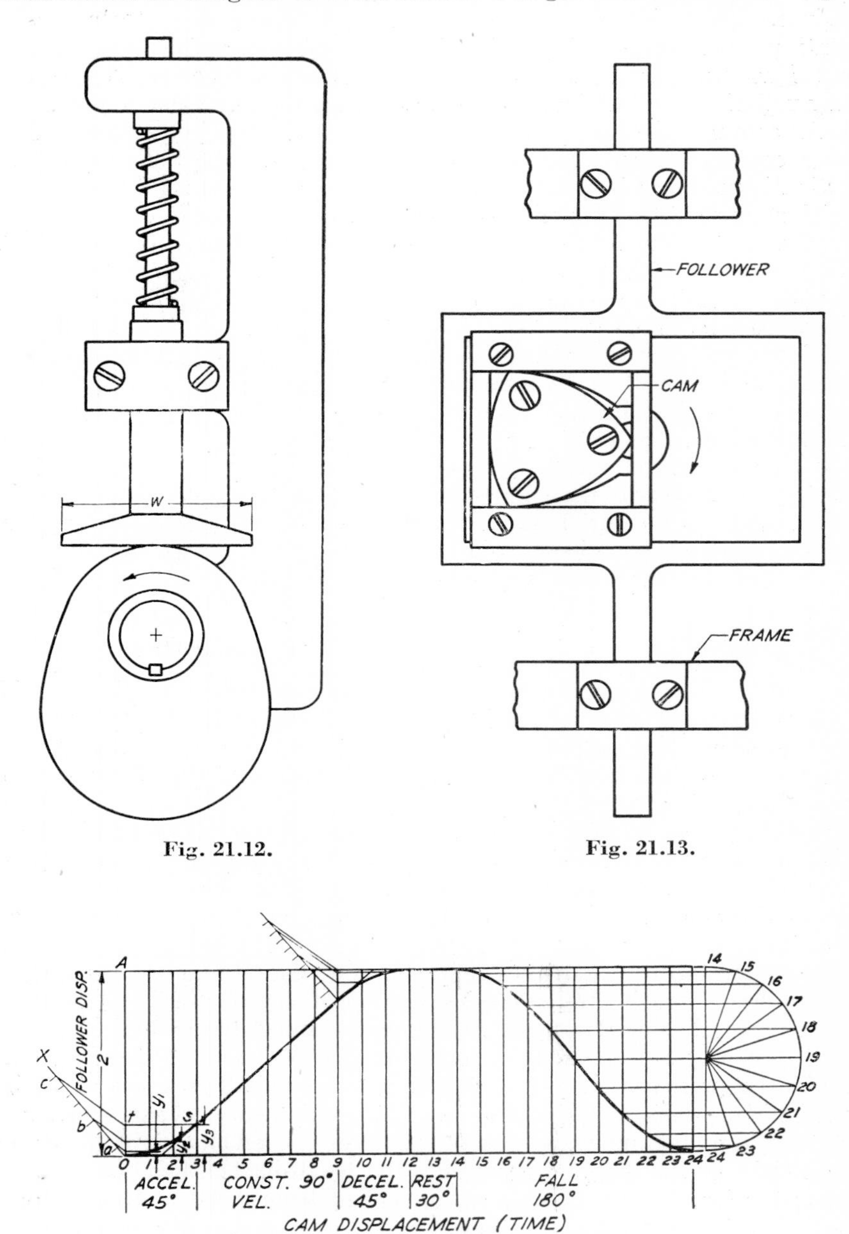

Fig. 21.12.

Fig. 21.13.

Fig. 21.14. A displacement diagram.

ning and end of the follower stroke. This can be accomplished by having a uniformly accelerated and decelerated motion at the beginning and end of the constant-velocity curve. The construction for uniformly accelerated motion is shown in Fig. 21.14. On a line, OX, making any convenient angle with OA, mark off any unit of length in this figure equal to Oa. The next point, b, is found by marking off, from O, 4 units of length. Point c is found by marking off 9 units of length. Next, project the inter-

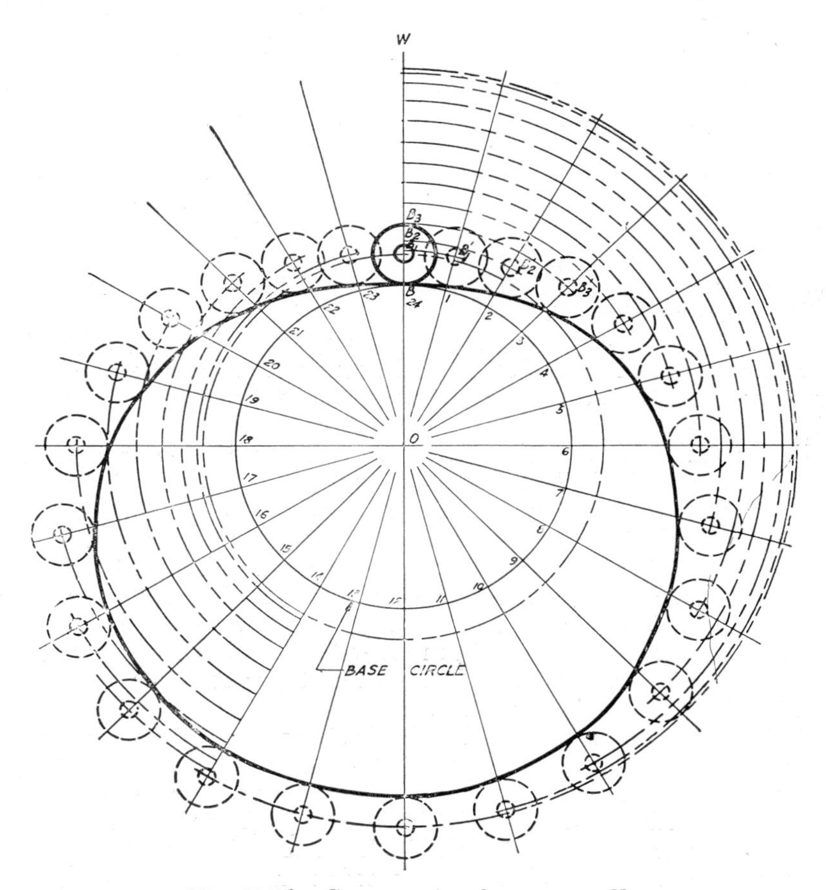

Fig. 21.15. Construction for cam profile.

section (point s) of time unit 3 and the constant-velocity line over to the line OA, thus locating point t. Connect points c and t with a straight line and draw parallel lines from a and b intersecting the line OA. From these intersections draw lines parallel to ts, intersecting the time-unit lines 1 and 2, respectively. These intersections are points on the displacement curve. With uniformly decelerated motion, the series of points are laid off in the reverse order, such as 9-4-1. It will be noted that the units are laid off according to the square of the time unit. Thus, if there were four time units, the acceleration curve would be laid off according to the ratio of 1, 4, 9, 16, and the deceleration, 16, 9, 4, 1.

The construction for the displacement diagram for simple harmonic motion is shown in the same figure. A semicircle is drawn as shown, the follower displacement being used as a diameter, and is then divided into a convenient number of parts equal to the number of cam displacement units. Horizontal projection lines are drawn from the semicircle, and the intersections of these lines with the cam displacement lines are points on the displacement curve. Thus, the projection of point 15 on the semicircle to time unit line 15 locates one point on the displacement curve for simple harmonic motion.

The next step is that of finding the cam profile necessary to produce these movements. The construction is shown in Fig. 21.15. Select a base circle of convenient size, and on it lay off radial lines according to the number of time units of cam displacement. Draw line OB extended to W, and on it lay off the distances Y_1, Y_2, Y_3, and so forth, obtained from the displacement diagram, from the center of the roller shown in the starting position, thus locating points B_1, B_2, B_3, and so forth. With O as a center, draw arcs B_1-B_1', B_2-B_2', B_3-B_3', and so forth, and at B_1', B_2', B_3', and so forth draw in the circles representing the diameter of the roller. To complete the cam outline, draw a smooth curve tangent to the positions of the roller.

21.7. Bearings. A draftsman ordinarily is never called upon to make a detail drawing of a ball or roller bearing, because bearings of these two types are precision-made units that are purchased from reliable manufacturers. All draftsmen working on machine drawings, however, should be familiar with the various types commonly used, and should be able to represent them correctly on an assembly drawing. An engineer will find it necessary to determine shaft-mounting fits and housing-mounting fits from a manufacturers' handbook, in order to place the correct limits on shafts and housings. Fig. 21.16 shows two types of ball bearings. A roller bearing is shown in Fig. 21.17.

Ball bearings may be designed for loads either perpendicular or parallel to the shaft. In the former, they are known as radial bearings, in the latter, as thrust bearings. Other types, designated by various names, are made to take both radial and thrust loads, either light or heavy. In most designs, bearings are forced to take both radial and thrust loads. Ball bearings are designated by a letter and code number, the last number of which represents the bearing bore. They may be extra light, light, medium, or heavy, and still have the same bore number. That is, bearings of different capacities and different outer diameters can fit shafts having the same nominal size. Tables XXXII and XXXIII, in the Appendix, give all the necessary information concerning the bearings used in the problems of this text. Fig. 21.18 shows typical mountings in a single mechanism.

Roller bearings are designed for both radial and thrust loads. The Timken bearing consists of tapered rollers that roll between an inner and

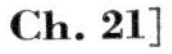

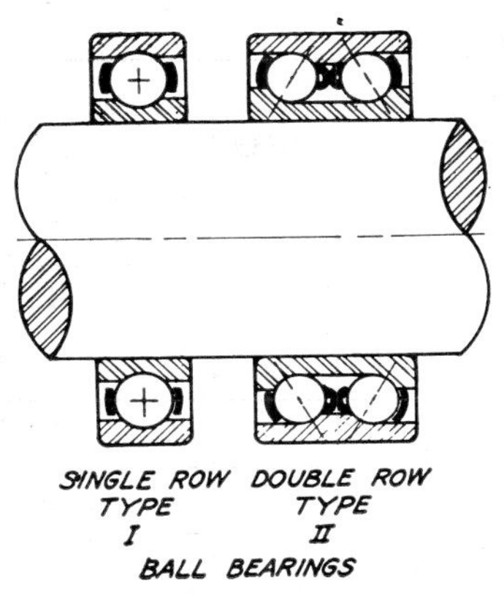

Fig. 21.16. New Departure ball bearings.

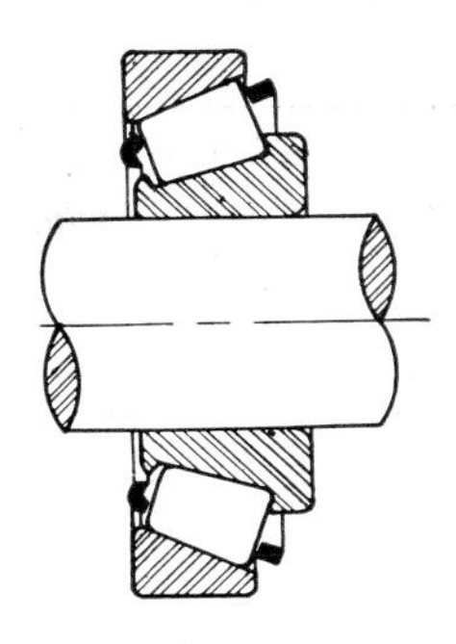

ROLLER BEARINGS

Fig. 21.17. Timken roller bearing.

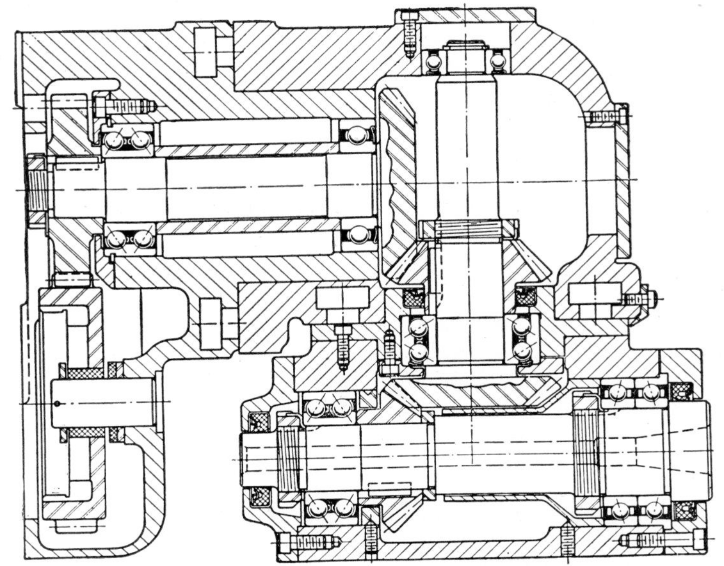

Courtesy New Departure Bearing Co., division of General Motors.

Fig. 21.18. Ball bearings.

an outer race. The rollers are enclosed in a retainer (cage) that keeps them properly spaced.

21.8. Problems. Gears and cams.

Gear Problems

1–6. Following the method shown in Sec. 21.2, lay out a pair of standard involute spur gears as assigned from the table below. The pinion is the driver

	Gear				Pinion				
Prob. No.	*Circular Pitch*	*Diametral Pitch*	*Pitch Dia.*	*No. of Teeth*	*Circular Pitch*	*Diametral Pitch*	*Pitch Dia.*	*No. of Teeth*	*Pressure Angle*
1	1.31″			24	1.31″			16	$14\frac{1}{2}°$
2		2		20		2		14	$14\frac{1}{2}°$
3		2.5	10			2.5	8		$14\frac{1}{2}°$
4	1.0			30	1.0			20	$14\frac{1}{2}°$
5	2.0			18	2.0			12	$14\frac{1}{2}°$
6		3	8			3	6		$14\frac{1}{2}°$

Cam Problems

Cam Data:

Diameter of Cam Shaft . . . . $1\frac{1}{4}''$
Diameter of Cam Hub . . . . $2\frac{1}{4}''$
Diameter of Roller . . . . 1″
Keyway . . . . $\frac{1}{4}'' \times \frac{1}{8}''$
Diameter of Base Circle . . . . $2\frac{3}{4}''$
Follower Displacement . . . . 2″
Scale: Full size
Cam rotation: As noted

Determine points on the cam profiles at intervals of 15°.

7. Using the above data, design a plate cam to satisfy the following conditions: (*a*) a rise of 2″ in 180°, with constant velocity, except for uniform acceleration for the first 30° and uniform deceleration for the last 45°; (*b*) rest 30°; (*c*) return with simple harmonic motion. Use clockwise cam rotation.

8. Same as problem 7, except that the follower is of the flat-face type and is $2\frac{1}{2}''$ wide.

9. Using the data for problem 7, design a plate cam to satisfy the following conditions: (*a*) rise of 2″ during 180°, the first 45° of which is uniformly accelerated motion, the next 60° being constant velocity, and the last 75° of rise being uniformly decelerated motion; (*b*) rest 15°; (*c*) return to starting position with simple harmonic motion. Use counterclockwise cam rotation.

10. Same as problem 9, except that the follower is of the flat-face type and is $2\frac{1}{2}''$ wide.

11. Using the data for problem 7, design a plate cam to satisfy the following conditions: (*a*) rise of 2″ during 150°, by simple harmonic motion; (*b*) rest 30°; (*c*) return to starting position during remainder of the revolution, with uniformly accelerated and decelerated motion, the value of the deceleration being two times that of the acceleration. Use clockwise cam rotation.

12. Using the data for problem 7, except that the follower is to be of the flat-face type, $2\frac{1}{2}''$ wide, design a plate cam to satisfy the following conditions: (*a*) rise of $2''$, with simple harmonic motion, in 120°; (*b*) rest 30°; (*c*) return in 150°, with constant velocity, except for uniform acceleration for the first 45° and uniform deceleration for the last 30° of fall; (*d*) rest the balance of the revolution. Use counterclockwise cam rotation.

22 DEVELOPMENTS AND INTERSECTIONS

22.1. A comprehensive study of intersections and developments is logically a part of the subject of Descriptive Geometry. A few of the many practical applications that can be handled without advanced study in projection, however, are presented in this chapter. Desired lines of intersection between geometrical surfaces may be obtained by applying the principles of orthographic projection with which the student is already familiar. Although developments are laid out and are not drawn by actual projection in the manner of exterior views, their construction nevertheless requires the application of orthographic projection in finding the true lengths of elements and edges.

22.2. Geometric surfaces. A geometric surface is generated by the motion of a geometric line, either straight or curved. Surfaces that are generated by a moving straight line are known as *ruled surfaces*, and those generated by a curved line are known as *double curved surfaces.* Any position of the generating line, known as a generatrix, is called an *element of the surface.*

Ruled surfaces include planes, single curved surfaces, and warped surfaces.

A *plane* is generated by a straight line moving in such a manner that one point touches another straight line as it moves parallel to its original position.

A *single curved surface* is generated by a straight line moving so that in any two of its near positions it is in the same plane.

A *warped surface* is generated by a straight line moving so that it does not lie in the same plane in any two near positions.

Double curved surfaces include surfaces that are generated by a curved line moving in accordance with some mathematical law.

22.3. Geometric objects. Geometric solids are bounded by geometric surfaces. They may be classified as follows:

1. Solids bounded by plane surfaces:
   Tetrahedron, cube, prism, pyramid, and others.
2. Solids bounded by single curved surfaces:
   Cone and cylinder (generated by a moving straight line).
3. Solids bounded by warped surfaces:
   Conoid, cylindroid, hyperboloid of one nappe, and warped cone.
4. Solids bounded by double curved surfaces:
   Sphere, spheroid, torus, paraboloid, hyperboloid, and so on (surfaces of revolution generated by curved lines).

DEVELOPMENTS

22.4. A layout of the complete surface of an object is called a development or pattern. The development of an object bounded by plane surfaces may be thought of as being obtained by turning the object, as illustrated in Figs. 22.1 and 22.2, so as to unroll the imaginary enclosing surface upon a plane. Practically, the drawing operation consists of

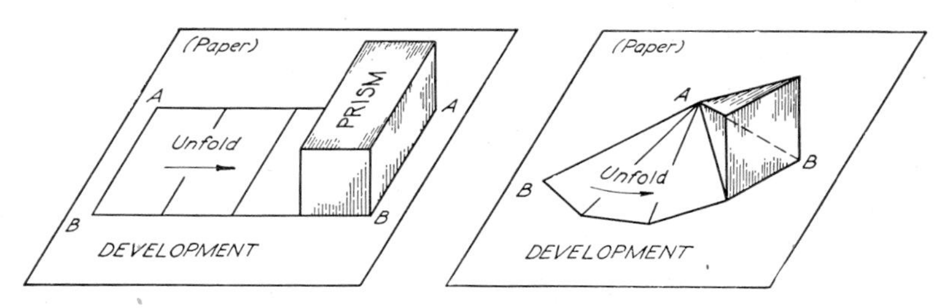

Fig. 22.1. The development of a prism.

Fig. 22.2. The development of a pyramid.

drawing the successive surfaces in their true size with their common edges joined.

The surfaces of cones and cylinders also may be unrolled upon a plane. The development of a right cylinder (Fig. 22.3) is a rectangle having a width equal to the altitude of the cylinder and a length equal to the cylinder's computed circumference (πd). The development of a right

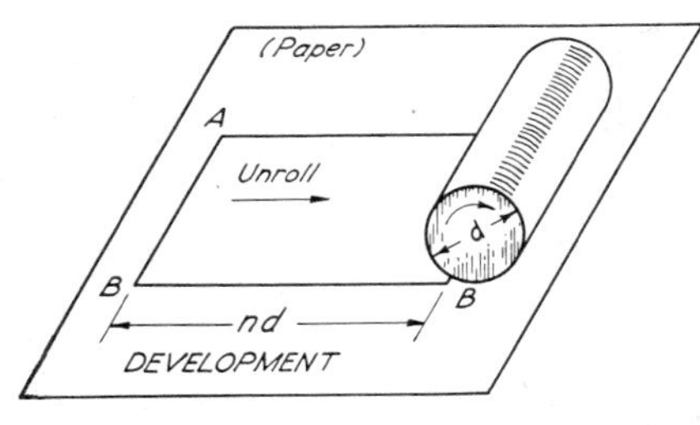

Fig. 22.3. The development of a cylinder.

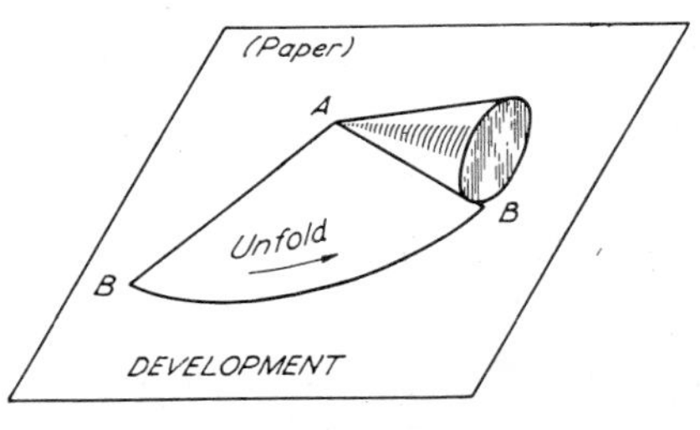

Fig. 22.4. The development of a cone.

circular cone (Fig. 22.4) is a sector of a circle having a radius equal to the slant height of the cone and an arc length equal to the circumference of its base.

Warped and double curved surfaces cannot be developed accurately, but they may be developed by some approximate method. Ordinarily, an approximate pattern will prove to be sufficiently accurate for practical purposes if the material of which the piece is to be made is somewhat flexible.

Plane and single curved surfaces (prisms, pyramids, cylinders, and cones), which can be accurately developed, are said to be developable. Warped and double curved surfaces, which can be only approximately developed, are said to be nondevelopable.

22.5. Practical developments. On many industrial drawings, a development must be shown to furnish the necessary information for making a pattern to facilitate the cutting of a desired shape from sheet metal. Present-day draftsmen must have a broad knowledge of the methods of constructing varied types of developments, because of the rapid advance of the art of manufacturing an ever-increasing number of pieces by fold-

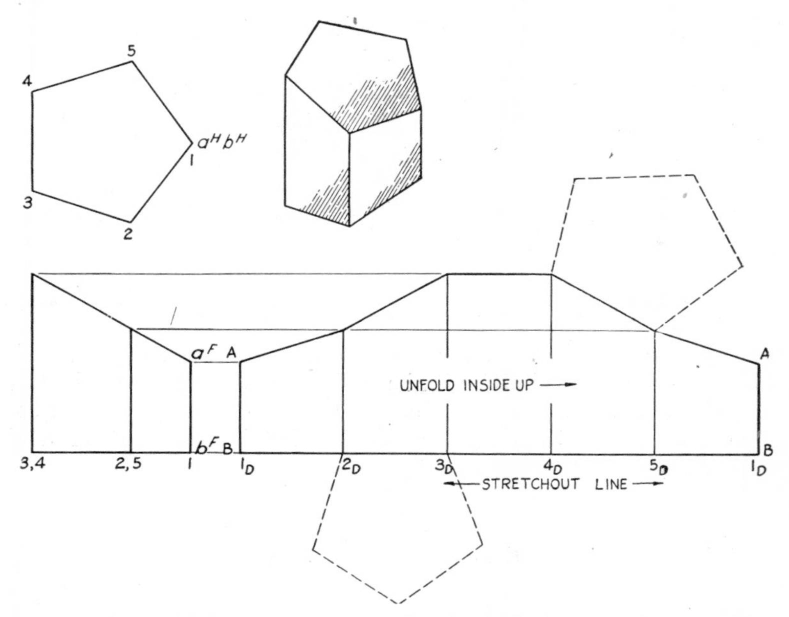

Fig. 22.5. The standard method of developing the lateral surface of a right prism.

ing, rolling, or pressing cut sheet-metal shapes. Patterns also are used in stone cutting as guides for shaping irregular faces.

A development of a surface should be drawn with the inside face up, as it theoretically would be if the surface were unrolled or unfolded as illustrated in Figs. 22.1–22.4. In commercial drafting, this practice is further justified by the fact that sheet-metal workers must make the necessary punch marks for folding on the inside surface.

Although in actual sheet-metal work extra metal must be allowed for lap at seams, no allowance will be shown on the developments in this chapter. Many other practical considerations have been purposely ignored, as well, in order to avoid confusing the beginner.

22.6. To develop a right truncated prism. Before the development of the lateral surface of a prism can be drawn, the true lengths of the edges and the true size of a right section must be determined. In the right truncated prism, shown in Fig. 22.5, the true lengths of the prism edges are shown in the front view and the true size of the right section is shown in the top view.

The lateral surface is "unfolded" by first drawing a "stretch-out line" and marking off the widths of the faces (distances 1-2, 2-3, 3-4, and so on, from the top view) along it in succession. Through these points light construction lines are then drawn perpendicular to the line 1_D-1_D, and the length of the respective edge is set off on each by projecting from the front view. When projecting edge lengths to the development, the points

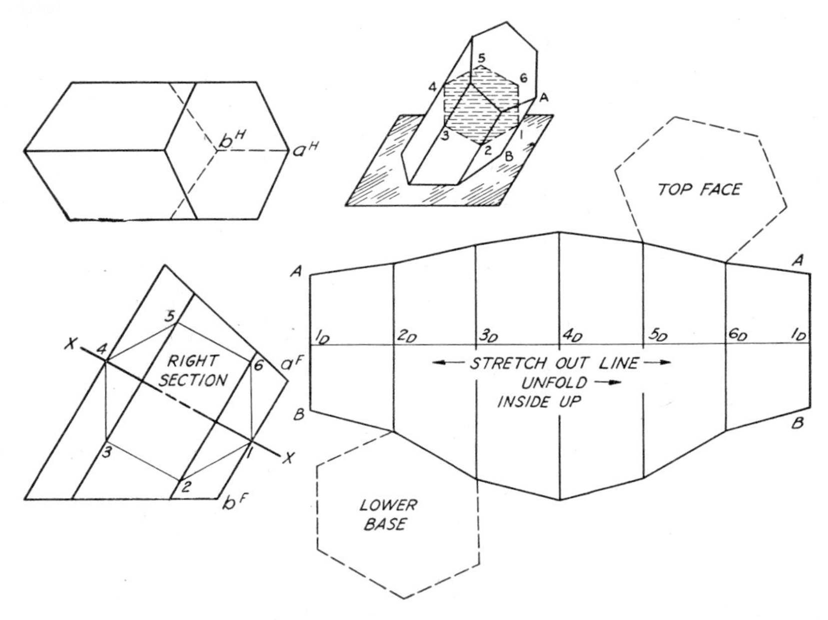

Fig. 22.6. The development of an oblique prism.

should be taken in a clockwise order around the perimeter as indicated by the order of the figures in the top view. The outline of the development is completed by joining these points. Thus far, nothing has been said about the lower base or the inclined upper face. These may be joined to the development of the lateral surface, if so desired.

In sheet-metal work, it is the usual practice to make the seam on the shortest element in order to save time and conserve solder or rivets.

22.7. To develop an oblique prism. The lateral surface of an oblique prism, such as the one shown in Fig. 22.6, is developed by the same general method used for a right prism. Similarly, the true lengths of the edges are shown in the front view, but it is necessary to find the true size of the right section by auxiliary plane construction. The width of the faces, as taken from the auxiliary right section, are set off along the stretch-out line, and perpendicular construction lines representing the edges are drawn through the division points. The lengths of the portions of each respective edge, above and below plane X-X, are transferred to the corresponding line in development. Distances above plane X-X are laid off above the stretch-out line, and distances below X-X are laid off below it. The development of the lateral surface is then completed by joining the end points of the edges by straight lines. Since an actual fold will be made at each edge line when the prism is formed, it is the usual practice to heavy these edge (fold) lines on the development.

The stretch-out line might well have been drawn in a position perpendicular to the edges of the front view (see Fig. 22.7), so that the length

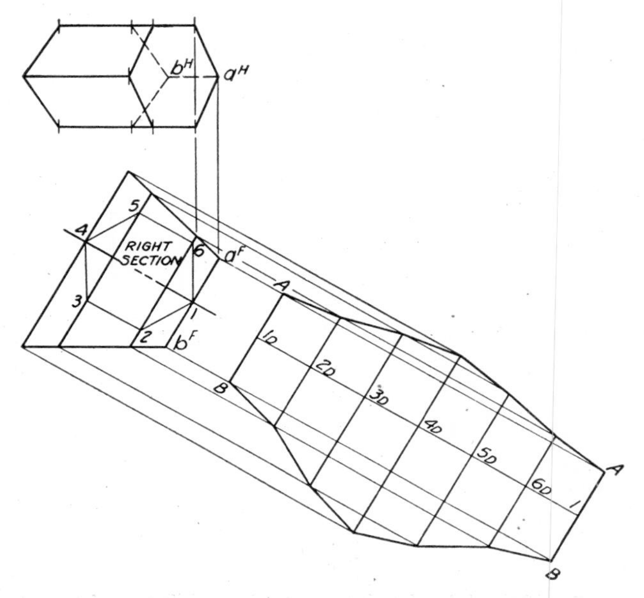

Fig. 22.7. Development of an oblique prism.

of each edge might be projected to the development (as in the case of the right prism). Much better balance of the views usually is obtained, however, when the stretch-out line is drawn in a horizontal position.

22.8. To develop a right cylinder. When the lateral surface of a right cylinder is rolled out upon a plane, the base develops into a straight line (Fig. 22.8). The length of this line, which is equal to the circumference of a right section ($\pi \times$ dia.), may be calculated and laid off as the stretch-out line 1_D-1_D.

Since the cylinder can be thought of as being a many-sided prism, the development may be constructed in a manner similar to the method illustrated in Fig. 22.5. The elements drawn on the surface of the cylinder serve as edges of the many-sided prism. Twelve or twenty-four of these elements ordinarily are used, the number depending upon the size of the cylinder. Usually they are spaced by dividing the circumference of the base, as shown by the circle in the top view, into an equal number of parts. The stretch-out line is divided into the same number of equal parts, and perpendicular elements are drawn through each division point. Then the true length of each element is projected to its respective representation on the development, and the development is completed by joining the points with a smooth curve. In joining the points, it is advisable to sketch the curve in lightly, freehand, before using the French curve. Since the surface of the finished cylindrical piece forms a continuous curve, the elements on the development are not heavied. When the development is symmetrical, as in this case, only one-half need be drawn.

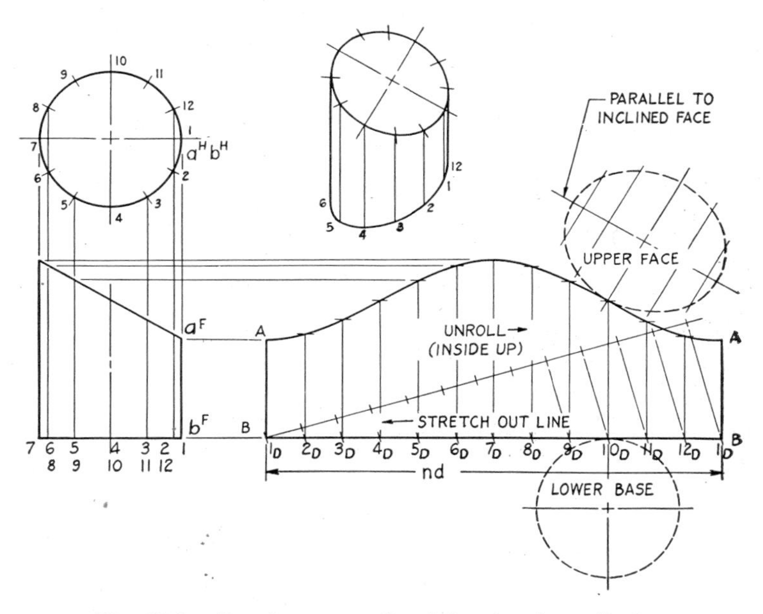

Fig. 22.8. Development of a right circular cylinder.

A piece of this type might form a part of a two-piece, three-piece, or four-piece elbow. The pieces are usually developed as illustrated in Fig. 22.9. The stretch-out line of each section is equal in length to the computed perimeter of a right section.

22.9. To develop an oblique cylinder. Since an oblique cylinder theoretically may be thought of as enclosing a regular oblique prism having an infinite number of sides, the development of the lateral surface of the cylinder shown in Fig. 22.10 may be constructed by using a method similar to the method illustrated in Fig. 22.6. The circumference of the right section becomes stretch-out line 1_D-1_D for the development.

22.10. To determine the true length of a line. In order to construct the development of the lateral surface of some objects, it frequently is necessary to determine the true lengths of oblique lines that represent the edges. The general method for determining the true lengths of lines inclined to all of the co-ordinate planes of projection has been explained in detail in Sec. 9.8. This article should be reviewed before reading the discussion that follows.

If a line is oblique to each of the three planes of projection, none of its principal projections will show its true length. Note in Fig. 22.11 that the

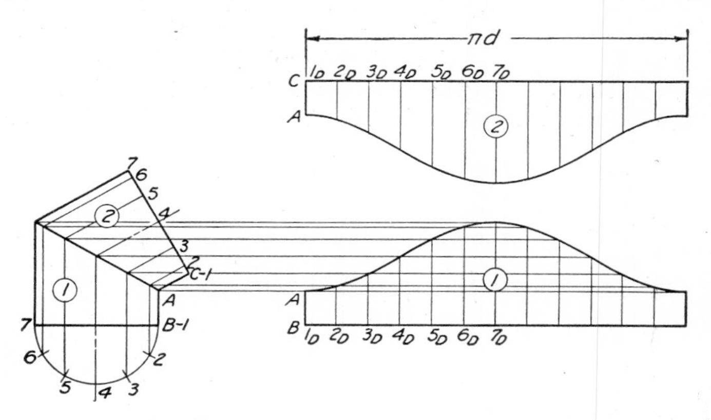

Fig. 22.9. Two-piece elbow.

three principal projections of the edge AB are inclined. To determine the true length of AB, it may be revolved into a position parallel to either the H, F, or P co-ordinate planes, as shown in Figs. 22.11, 22.12, and 22.13. In Fig. 22.11, AB has been revolved into a position parallel to the F

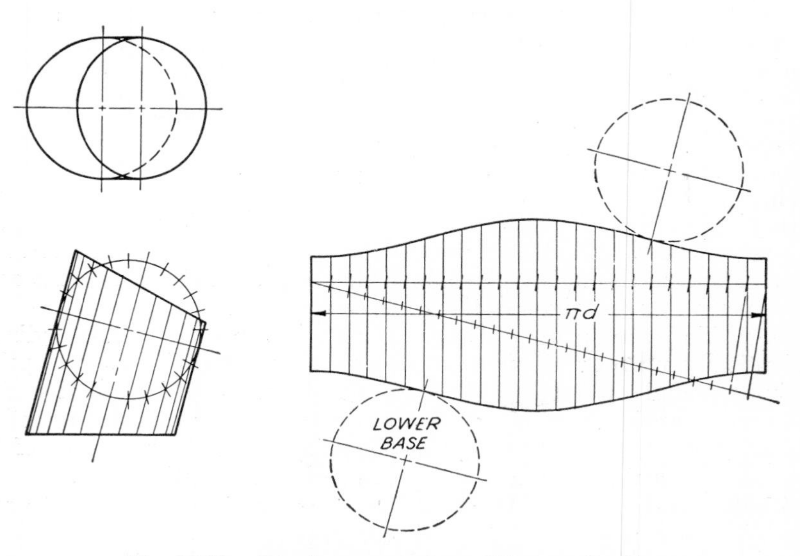

Fig. 22.10. Development of an oblique cylinder.

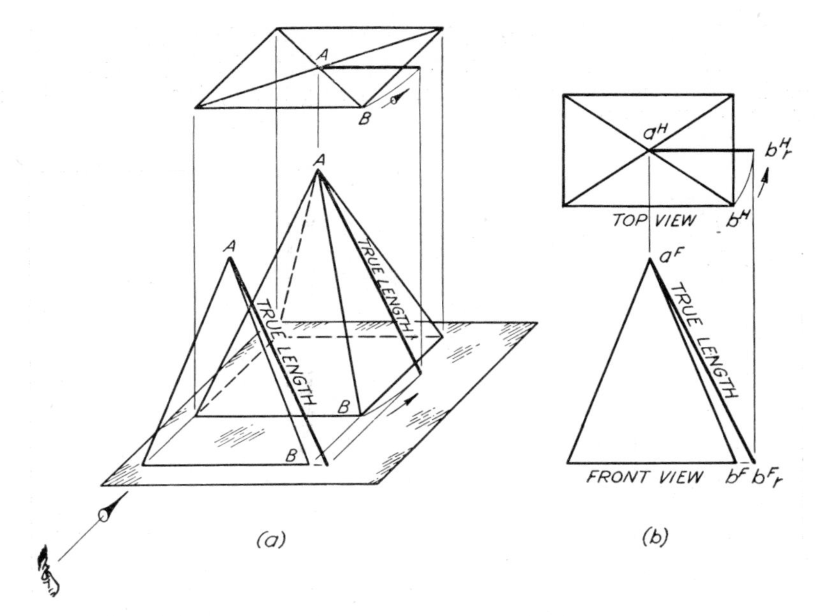

Fig. 22.11. Revolution to position parallel to front plane.

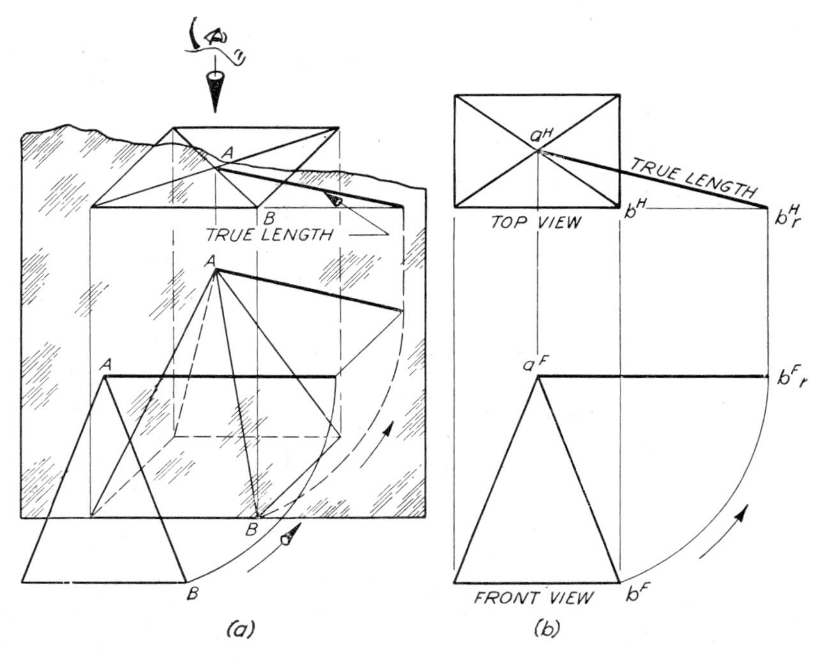

Fig. 22.12. Revolution to position parallel to top plane.

(frontal) plane. AB (revolved), in (*a*), and $a^F b^F r$, in (*b*), show the true length. In Fig. 22.12, AB was revolved parallel to the H (top) plane, and $a^H b^H r$ in (*b*) shows the true length. In Fig. 22.13, the edge is shown revolved parallel to the P (profile) co-ordinate plane.

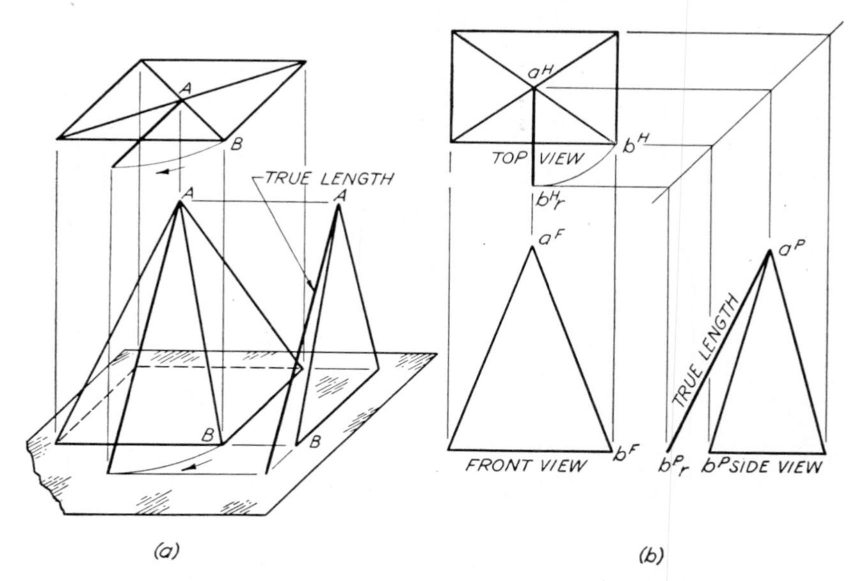

Fig. 22.13. Revolution to position parallel to side plane.

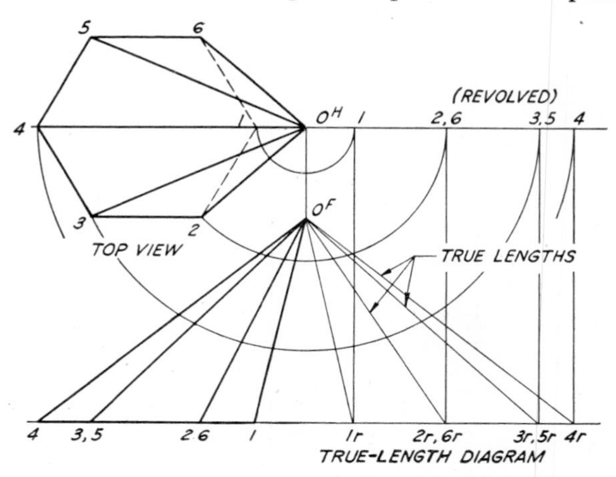

Fig. 22.14. A true-length diagram (the revolution method).

22.11. True-length diagrams. When it is necessary, in developing a surface, to find the true lengths of a number of edges or elements, some confusion may be avoided by constructing a true-length diagram adjacent to the orthographic view as shown in Fig. 22.14. The elements were revolved into a position parallel to the F (frontal) plane so that their true lengths show in the diagram. This practice prevents the front view in the illustration from being cluttered with lines, some of which would represent elements and others their true lengths.

Fig. 22.15 shows a diagram that gives the true lengths of the edges of the pyramid. Each line representing the true length of an edge is the hypotenuse of a right triangle whose altitude is the altitude of the edge in the front view and whose base is equal to the length of the projection of the edge in the top view. The lengths of the top projections of the edges of the pyramid are laid off horizontally from the vertical line $o^F X$, which could have been drawn at any distance from the front view. Since all the edges have the same altitude, this line is a common vertical leg for all the right triangles in the diagram. For example, $o^F X1'$ is a true-

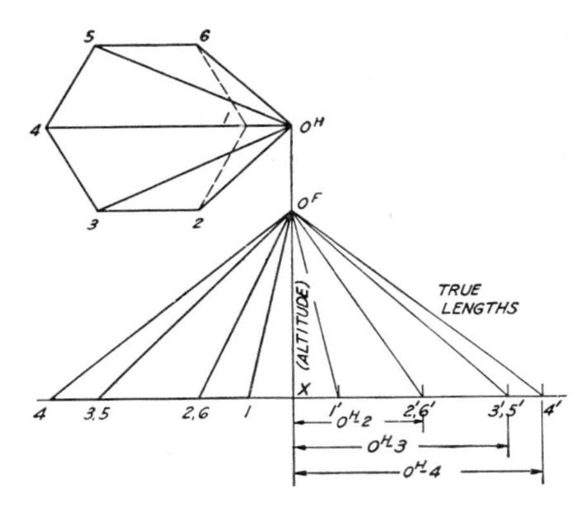

Fig. 22.15. True-length diagram (right triangle method).

length triangle having the line $o^F X$ as a vertical leg and $X1'$, which is equal in length to $o^H 1$ in the top view, as a base. Other triangles are $o^F X2'$, $o^F X3'$, $o^F X4'$, and so on. The true-length diagram shown in Fig. 22.14 could very well have been constructed by this method.

22.12. To develop a right pyramid. To develop (unfold) the lateral surface of a right pyramid, it is first necessary to determine the true lengths of the edges and the true size of the base. With this information, the development can be constructed by laying out the faces in successive order with their common edges joined. If the surface is imagined to be unfolded by turning the pyramid, as shown in Fig. 22.2, each triangular face is revolved into the plane of the paper about the edge that is common to it and the preceding face.

Since the edges of the pyramid shown in Fig. 22.16 are all equal in length, it is necessary only to find the length of the one edge $A1$ by revolving it into the position $a^F 1r$. The edges of the base, 1-2, 2-3, and so on, are parallel to the horizontal plane of projection and consequently show in their true length in the top view. With this information, the development is easily completed by constructing the four triangular surfaces.

In practice, this construction can be simplified by adhering to the following procedure. First, draw an arc of radius a^F1r with some convenient point A_D as a center. Second, step off the perimeter of the base along the arc. Third, join the end points of the edges of the base (1_D, 2_D, 3_D, and 4_D) with the vertex A_D to complete the development. The base may be attached to the development, if so desired.

22.13. To develop the surface of a frustum of a pyramid. To develop the lateral surface of the frustum of a pyramid (Fig. 22.17), it is necessary to determine the true lengths of edges of the complete pyramid as well as the true lengths of edges of the frustum. The desired develop-

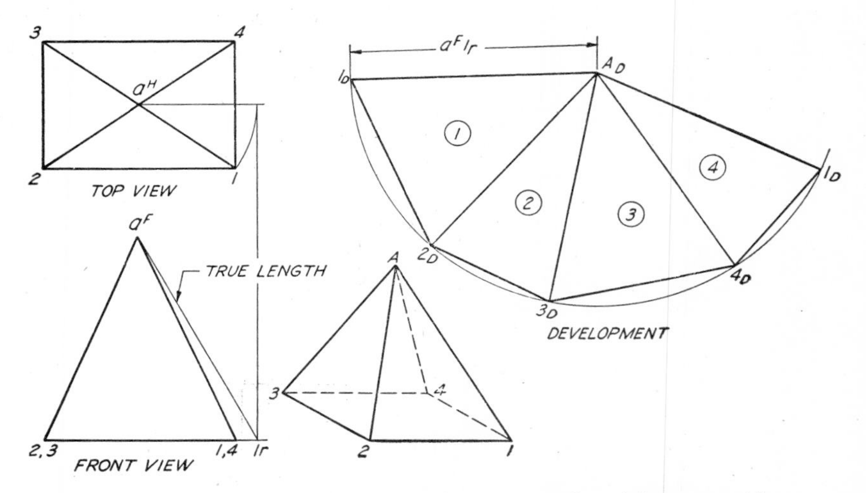

Fig. 22.16. The development of a rectangular right pyramid.

ment is obtained by first constructing the development of the complete pyramid and then laying off the true lengths of the edges of the frustum on the corresponding lines of the development.

It may be noted with interest that the true length of the edge $B3$ is equal to the length $b'3'$ on the true-length line a^F3', and that the location of point b' can be established by the short-cut method of projecting horizontally from point b^F. Point b' on a^F3' is the true revolved position of point B, because the path of point B is in a horizontal plane that projects as a line in the front view.

22.14. To develop a right cone. As previously explained in Sec. 22.4, the development of a regular right circular cone is a sector of a circle. The development will have a radius equal to the slant height of the cone and an included angle at the center equal to $\frac{r}{s} \times 360°$ (Fig. 22.18). In this equation, r is the radius of the base and s is the slant height.

22.15. To develop a right truncated cone. The development of a right truncated cone must be constructed by a modified method of triangulation, in order to develop the outline of the elliptical inclined surface. This commonly used method is based upon the theoretical assumption that a cone is a pyramid having an infinite number of sides. The development of the incomplete right cone shown in Fig. 22.19 is constructed upon a layout of the whole cone by a method similar to the standard method illustrated for the frustum of a pyramid in Fig. 22.17.

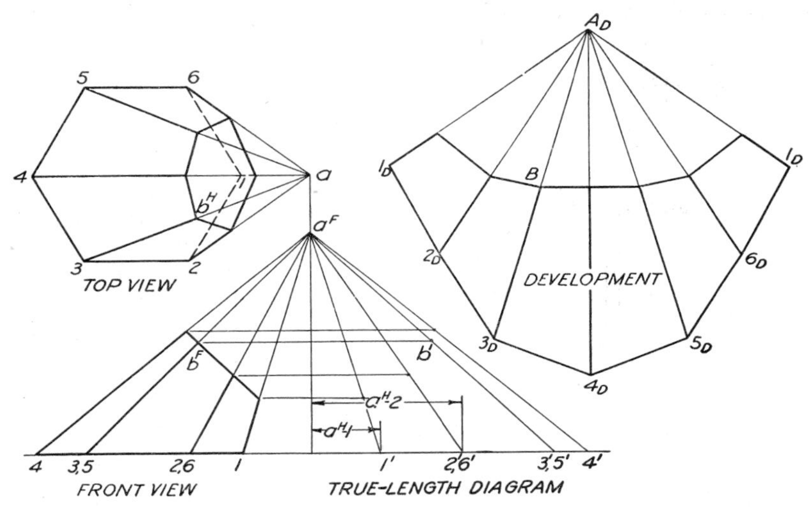

Fig. 22.17. Development of the frustum of a pyramid.

Elements are drawn on the surface of the cone to serve as edges of the many-sided pyramid. Either twelve or twenty-four are used, depending upon the size of the cone. Their location is established upon the developed sector by dividing the arc representing the unrolled base into the same

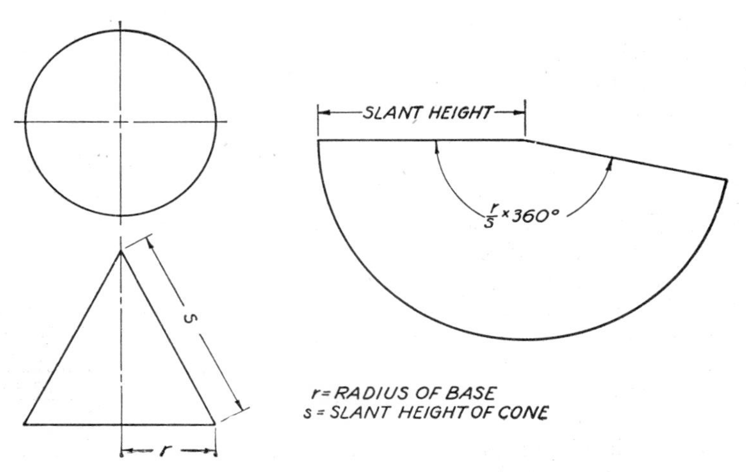

Fig. 22.18. Development of a right cone.

number of equal divisions, into which the top view of the base has been divided. At this point in the procedure, it is necessary to determine the true lengths of the elements of the frustum in the same manner that the true lengths of the edges of the frustum of a pyramid were obtained in Fig. 22.17. With this information, the desired development can be completed by setting off the true lengths on the corresponding lines of the development and joining the points thus obtained with a smooth curve.

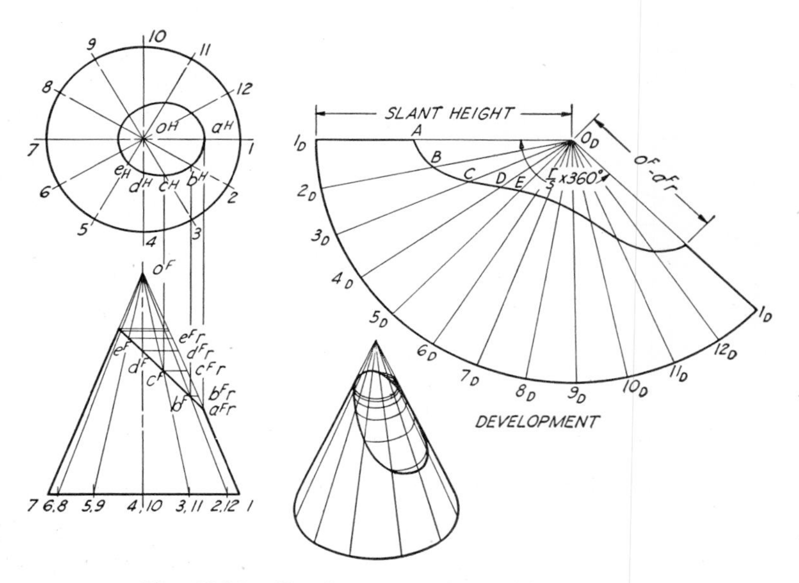

Fig. 22.19. Development of a truncated cone.

22.16. The triangulation method of developing approximately developable surfaces. A nondevelopable surface may be developed approximately if the surface is assumed to be composed of a number of small developable surfaces (Fig. 22.21). The particular method ordinarily used for warped surfaces and the surfaces of oblique cones is known as the triangulation method. The procedure consists of completely covering the lateral surface with numerous small triangles that will lie approximately on the surface (Fig. 22.20). These triangles, when laid out in their true size with their common edges joined, produce an approximate development that is accurate enough for most practical purposes.

Although this method of triangulation is sometimes used to develop the lateral surface of a right circular cone, it is not recommended for such purpose. The resulting development is not as accurate as it would be if constructed by one of the standard methods (see Secs. 22.14 and 22.15).

22.17. To develop an oblique cone using the triangulation method. A development of the lateral surface of an oblique cone is constructed by a method similar to that used for an oblique pyramid. The surface is divided into a number of unequal triangles having sides that are elements on the cone and bases that are the chords of short arcs of the base.

The first step in developing an oblique cone (Fig. 22.22) is to divide the circle representing the base into a convenient number of equal parts

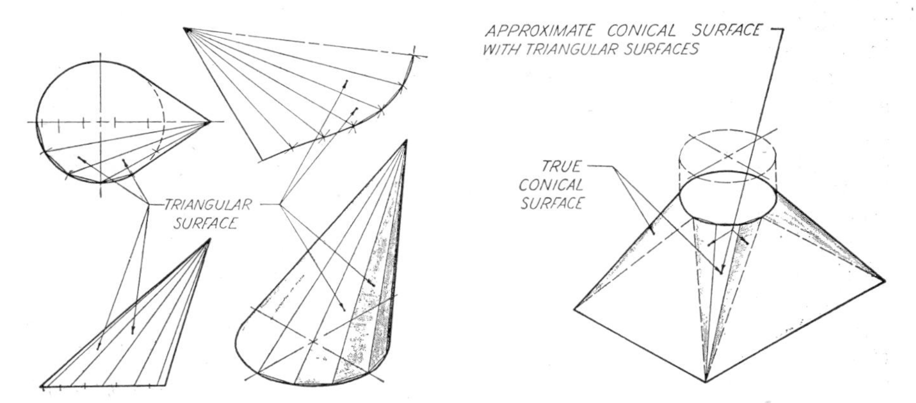

Fig. 22.20. Triangulation of an oblique cone. **Fig. 22.21. Triangulation of a surface.**

and draw elements on the surface of the cone through the division points (1, 2, 3, 4, 5, and so on). To construct the triangles forming the development, it is necessary to know the true lengths of the elements (sides of the triangles) and chords. In the illustration, all the chords are equal. Their true lengths are shown in the top view. The true lengths of the

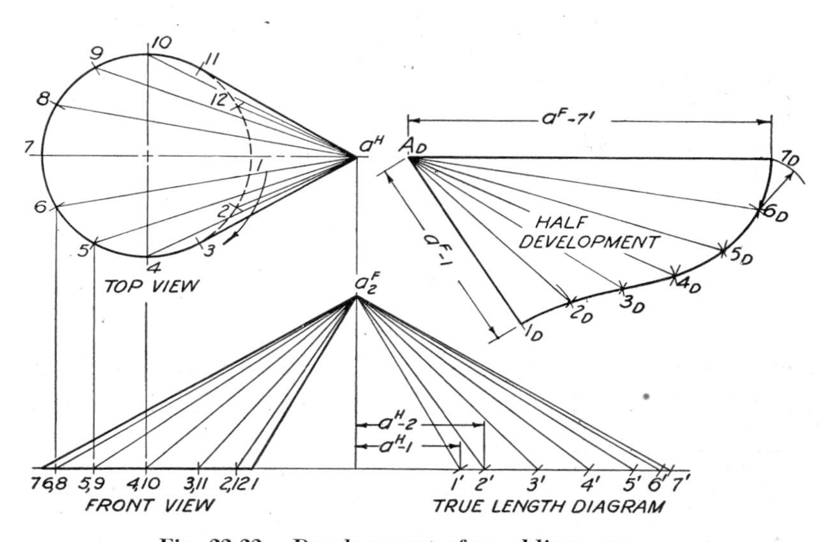

Fig. 22.22. Development of an oblique cone.

oblique elements may be determined by one of the standard methods explained in Sec. 22.11.

Since the seam should be made along the shortest element, $A1$ will lie on the selected starting line for the development and $A7$ will be on the center line. To obtain the development, the triangles are constructed in order, starting with the triangle A-1-2 and proceeding around the cone in a clockwise direction (as shown by the arrow in the top view). The first step in constructing triangle A-1-2 is to set off the true length a^F1' along the starting line. With point A_D of the development as a center, and with a radius equal to a^F2', strike an arc; then, with point 1_D as a center, and with a radius equal to the chord 1-2, strike an arc across the first arc to locate point 2_D. The triangle $A_D2_D3_D$ and the remaining triangles are formed in exactly the same manner. When all the triangles have been laid out, the development of the whole conical surface is completed by drawing a smooth curve through the end points of the elements.

After the beginner has constructed a few such developments, he will find that much time can be saved by drawing all the long arcs before striking off any of the short ones. To offset any errors in judgment about their approximate correct location, the long arcs may be made fairly long.

22.18. Transition pieces. A few of the many types of transition pieces used for connecting pipes and openings of different shapes and sizes

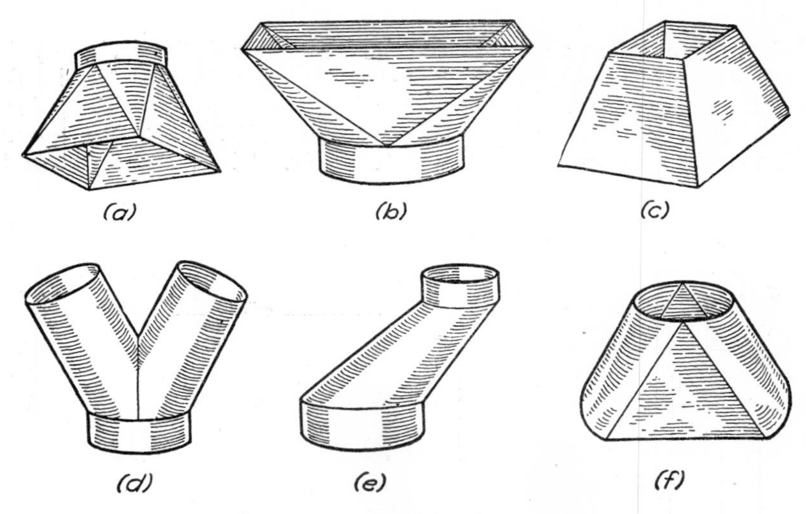

Fig. 22.23. Transition pieces.

are illustrated pictorially in Fig. 22.23. The transition at (*a*), which is composed of triangular and conical surfaces, connects a square opening with a round one. The transition at (*b*) serves similarly. At (*c*), the transition piece is the frustum of a pyramid. The transition shown at (*d*) is formed of cylinders. The ones at (*e*) and (*f*) are special types that are not frequently encountered.

22.19. To develop a transition piece connecting rectangular

pipes. The transition piece shown in Fig. 22.24 is designed to connect two rectangular pipes of different sizes on different axes. Since the piece is a frustum of a pyramid, it can be accurately developed by the method explained in Sec. 22.13.

22.20. To develop a transition piece connecting two circular pipes. The transition piece shown in Fig. 22.25 connects two circular pipes on different axes. Since the piece is a frustum of an oblique cone, the surface must be triangulated, as explained in Sec. 22.17, and the development must be constructed by laying out the triangles in their true

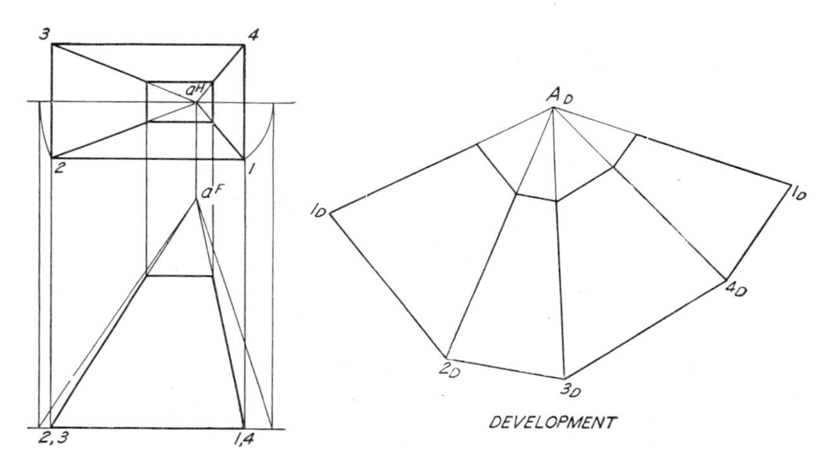

Fig. 22.24. Transition piece.

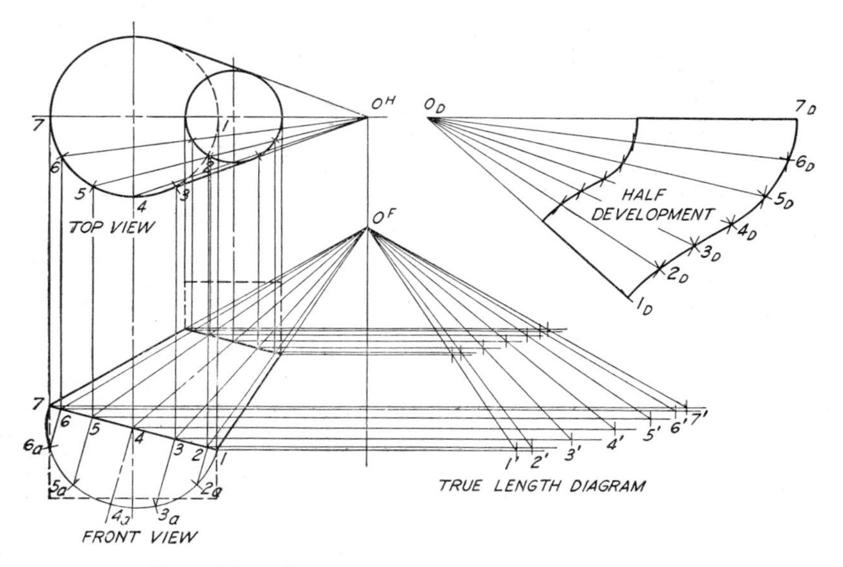

Fig. 22.25. Transition piece connecting two pipes.

size in regular order. The general procedure is the same as that illustrated in Fig. 22.22. In this case, however, since the true size of the base is not shown in the top view, it is necessary to construct a partial auxiliary view to find the true lengths of chords between the end points of the elements.

22.21. To develop a transition piece connecting a circular and a square pipe. A detailed analysis of the transition piece shown in Fig. 22.26 reveals the fact that it is composed of four isosceles triangles whose bases form the square base of the piece and four conical surfaces that are parts of oblique cones. It is not difficult to develop this type of

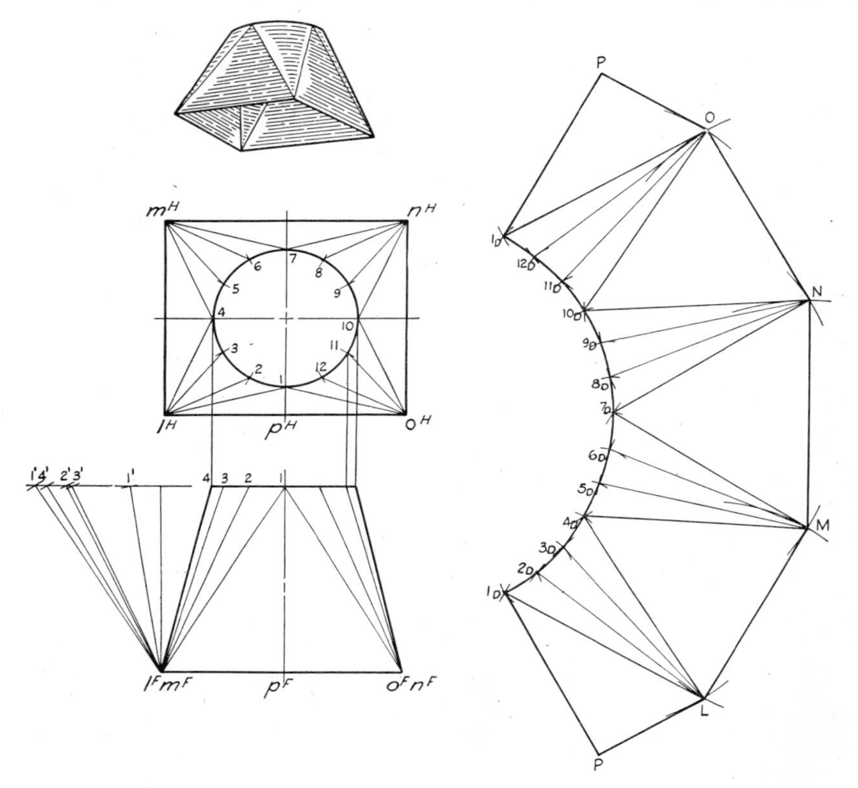

Fig. 22.26. Transition piece connecting a circular and square pipe.

transition piece, because, since the whole surface may be "broken up" into component surfaces, the development may be constructed by developing the first and then each succeeding component surface separately (Fig. 22.21). The surfaces are developed around the piece, in a clockwise direction, in such a manner that each successive surface is joined to the preceding surface at their common element. In the illustration, the triangles 1*LO*, 4*LM*, 7*MN*, and 10*NO* are clearly shown in top view. Two of these, 1*LO* and 10*NO*, are visible on the pictorial drawing. The apexes of the conical surfaces are located at the corners of the base.

Before starting the development, it is necessary to determine the true lengths of the elements by constructing a true-length diagram as explained in Sec. 22.11. The true lengths of the edges of the lower base (LM, MN, NO, and OL) and the true lengths of the chords (1-2, 2-3, 3-4, and so on) of the short arcs of the upper base are shown in the top view. The development is constructed in the following manner: First, the triangle 1_DPL is constructed, using the length p^Hl^H, taken from the top view, and true lengths from the diagram. Next, using the method explained in Sec. 22.17, the conical surface whose apex is at L is developed in an attached position. Triangle 4_DLM is then added, and so on, until all component surfaces have been drawn.

22.22. To develop a transition piece having an approximately developable surface by the triangulation method. Fig. 22.27 shows a half development of a transition piece that has a warped surface instead

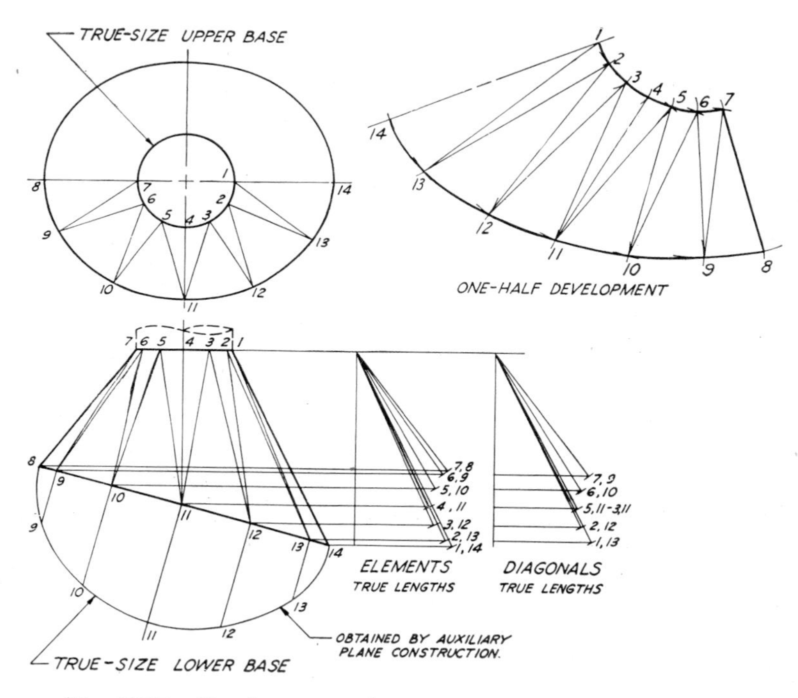

Fig. 22.27. Development of transition piece by triangulation.

of a partially conical one like that discussed in Sec. 22.21. The method of constructing the development is somewhat similar, however, in that it is formed by laying out, in true size, a number of small triangles that approximate the surface. The true size of the circular intersection is shown in the top view, and the true size of the elliptical intersection is shown in the auxiliary view, which was constructed for that purpose.

The front half of the circle in the top view should be divided into the same number of equal parts as the half-auxiliary view. By joining the division points, the lateral surface may be initially divided into narrow quadrilaterals. These in turn may be subdivided into triangles, by drawing diagonals which, though theoretically they are curved lines, are assumed to be straight. The true lengths of the elements and the diagonals are found by constructing two separate true-length diagrams by the method illustrated in Fig. 22.15.

22.23. To develop a sphere. The surface of a sphere is a double curved surface that can be developed only by some approximate method. The standard methods commonly used are illustrated in Fig. 22.28.

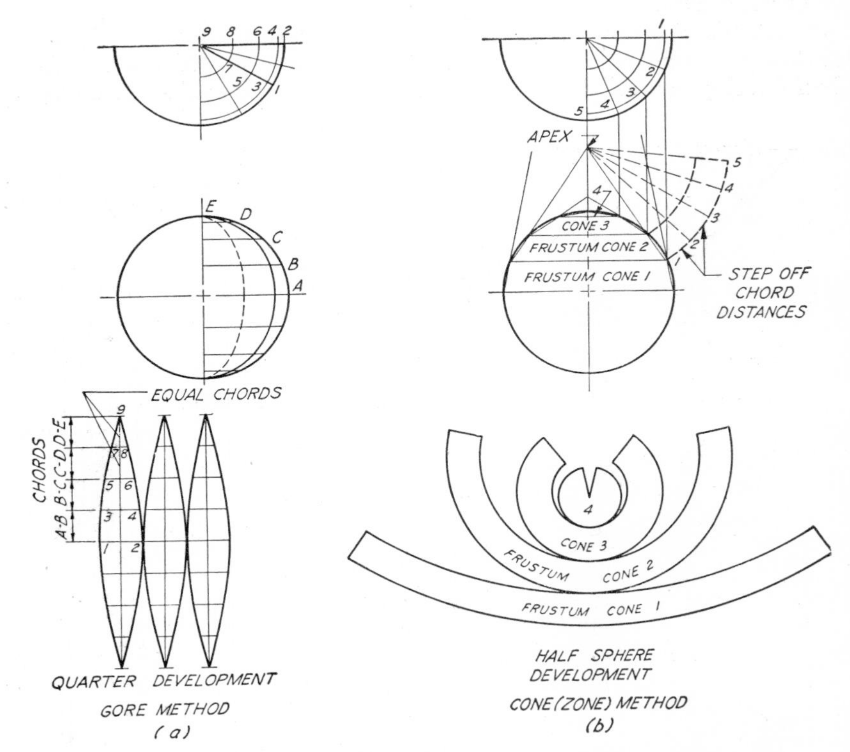

Fig. 22.28. The approximate development of a sphere.

In (*a*) the surface is divided into a number of equal meridian sections of cylinders. The developed surfaces of these form an approximate development of the sphere. In drawing the development, it is necessary to develop the surface of only one section, for this can be used as a pattern for the developed surface of each of the others.

In (*b*) the sphere is cut by parallel planes which divide it into a number of horizontal sections, the surfaces of which approximate the surface of the sphere. Each of these sections may be considered the frustum of a right cone whose apex is located at the intersection of the chords extended.

INTERSECTIONS

22.24. Lines of intersection of geometric surfaces. The line of intersection of two surfaces is a line that is common to both. It may be considered the line that would contain the points in which the elements of one surface would pierce the other. Almost every line on a practical orthographic representation is a line of intersection; therefore, the following discussion may be deemed an extended study of the same subject. The methods presented in this chapter are the recognized easy procedures for finding the more complicated lines of intersection created by intersecting geometric surfaces.

Commercial draftsmen, in order to complete a view of a working drawing or a view necessary for developing the surfaces of intersecting geometric shapes, frequently must find the line of intersection between surfaces. On an ordinary working drawing, the line of intersection may be "faked in" through a few critical points. On a sheet-metal drawing, however, a sufficient number of points must be located to obtain an accurate line of intersection and an ultimately accurate development.

The line of intersection of two surfaces is found by determining a number of points common to both surfaces and drawing a line or lines through these points in correct order. The resulting line of intersection may be straight, curved, or straight and curved. The problem of finding such a line may be solved by one of two general methods, depending upon the type of surfaces involved.

For the purpose of simplifying this discussion of intersections, it should be assumed that all problems are divided into these two general groups:

Group I. Problems involving two surfaces, both of which are composed of plane surfaces.

Group II. Problems involving two surfaces which are either single curved or double curved.

For instance, the procedure for finding the line of intersection of two prisms is the same as that for finding the line of intersection of a prism and a pyramid; hence, both problems belong in the same group (Group I). Since the problem of finding the line of intersection of two cylinders and the problem of finding the line of intersection of a cylinder and a cone both involve single curved surfaces, these two also belong in the same group (Group II).

Problems of the first group are solved by locating the points through which the edges of each of two geometrical shapes pierce the other. These points are vertices of the line of intersection. Whenever one of two intersecting plane surfaces appears as a line in one view, the points through which the lines of the other surfaces penetrate it usually may be found by inspecting that view.

Problems of the second group may be solved by drawing elements on the lateral surface of one geometrical shape in the region of the line of intersection. The points at which these elements intersect the surface of the other geometrical shape are points that are common to both surfaces and consequently lie on their line of intersection. A curve, traced through these points with the aid of a French curve, will be a representation of the required intersection. To obtain accurate results, some of the elements must be drawn through certain critical points at which the curve changes sharply in direction. These points usually are located on contour elements. Hence, the usual practice is to space the elements equally around the surface, starting with a contour element.

A thorough knowledge of descriptive geometry is necessary to solve the more difficult problems of this second group, but, since these do not logically form a part of the subject of engineering drawing, the following discussions will concern only problems of a type that can be solved by means of elements cut by imaginary planes that would be perpendicular to at least one of the co-ordinate planes of projection.

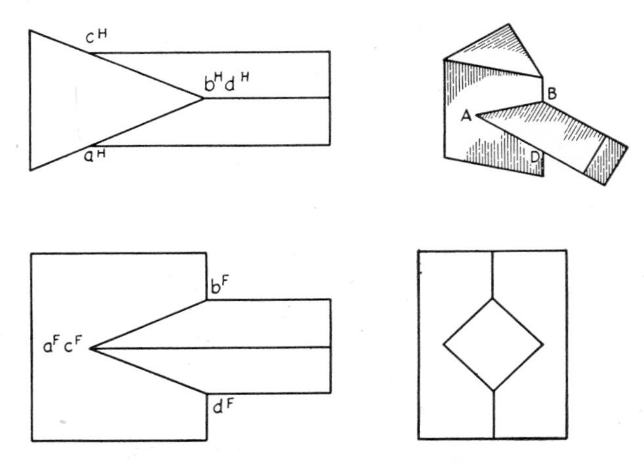

Fig. 22.29. Intersecting prisms.

22.25. To find the intersection of two prisms. In Fig. 22.29 (see pictorial), points A, B, C, and D, through which the edges of the horizontal prism pierce the faces of the triangular prism, are the critical points or vertices of the closed intersection. The location of these piercing points may be found in the top view by inspection. Then they may be projected to the front view, to establish their location there. For example, the top view shows that the front edge of the horizontal prism pierces the near face of the vertical triangular prism at point a^H. Point a^H, projected downward to the line representing that edge in the front view, locates point a^F in the front view. After the piercing points B, C, and D have been found and projected to the front view in a similar manner, the intersection is completed by joining, in order, the projected points a^F, b^F, c^F, and d^F with straight lines.

22.26. To establish the location of the piercing point of an edge intersecting an inclined surface. In Fig. 22.30, points A, C, and D, through which the edges of the horizontal prism pierce the vertical prism, are first found in the top view and are then projected downward to the corresponding edges in the front view. Point B, through which the edge of the vertical prism pierces the near face of the triangular prism, cannot be found in this manner because the side view from which it could be projected to the front view is not shown. Its location, however, can be established in the front view without even drawing a partial side view, if some scheme like the one illustrated in the pictorial drawing is used. In this scheme, the intersection line AB, whose direction is shown in the top view as line $a^H b^H$, is extended on the triangular face to point X on the top edge. Point x^H is projected to the corresponding edge in the front view and a light construction line is drawn between the points a^F and x^F.

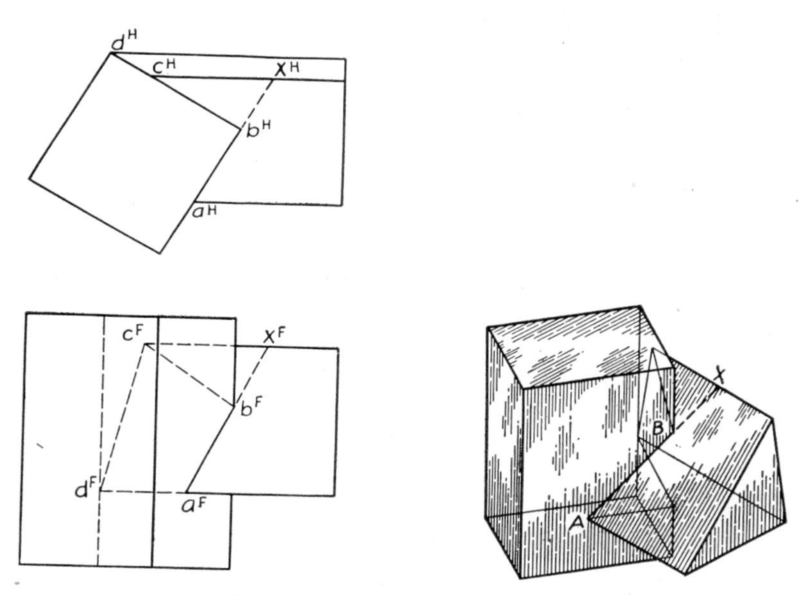

Fig. 22.30. Intersecting prisms

Since point B is located on line AX (see pictorial) at the point where the edge of the prism pierces the line, its location in the front view is at point b^F where the edge cuts the line $a^F x^F$.

22.27. To find the intersection of a pyramid and a prism. The intersection of a right pyramid and a prism (see Fig. 22.31) may be found by the same general method used for finding the intersection of two prisms (see Sec. 22.25).

22.28. To find the intersection of two cylinders. If a series of elements are drawn on the surface of the small horizontal cylinder, as in Fig. 22.32, the points A, B, C, and D in which they intersect the vertical cylinder will be points on the line of intersection (see pictorial). These points, which are shown as a^H, b^H, c^H, and d^H in the top view, may be located in the front view by projecting them downward to the corresponding elements in the front view where they are shown as points a^F, b^F, c^F,

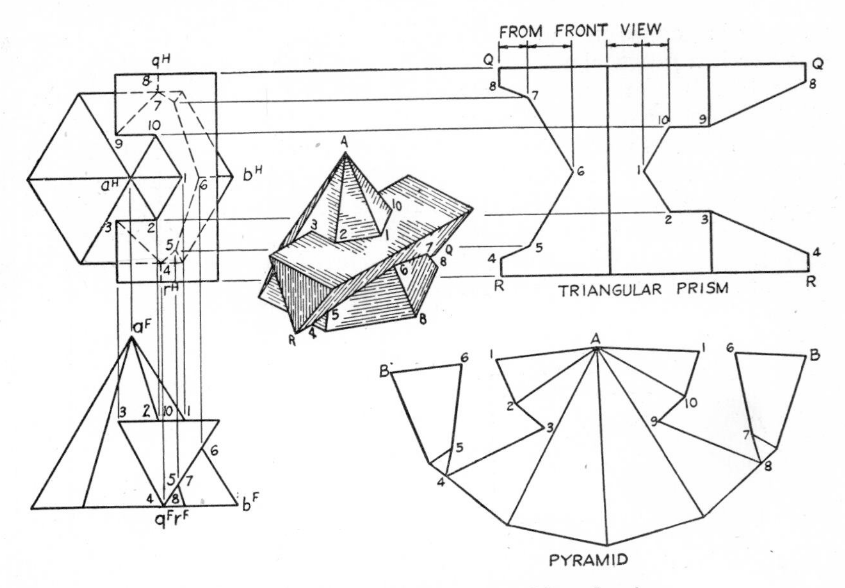

Fig. 22.31. Intersecting pyramid and prism.

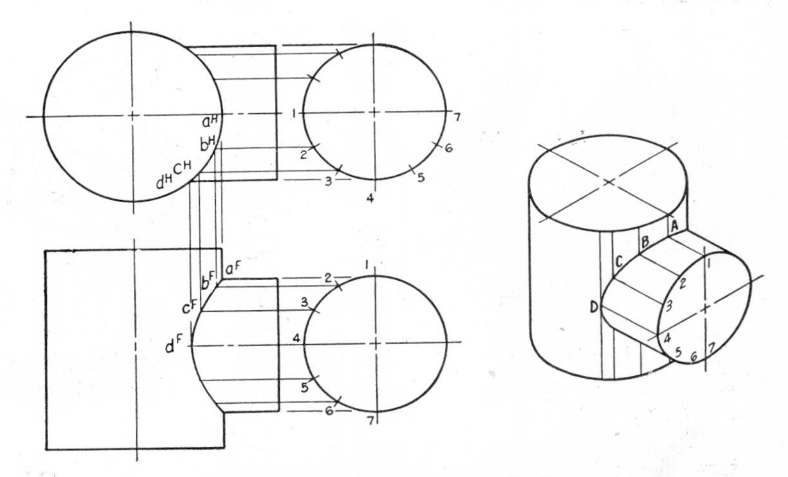

Fig. 22.32. Intersecting cylinders.

and d^F. The desired intersection is represented by a smooth curve drawn through these points.

22.29. To find the intersection of two cylinders oblique to each other. The first step in finding the line of intersection of two cylinders that are oblique to each other (see Fig. 22.33) is to draw a revolved right section of the oblique cylinder directly on the front view of that cylinder. If the circumference of the right section then is divided into a number of

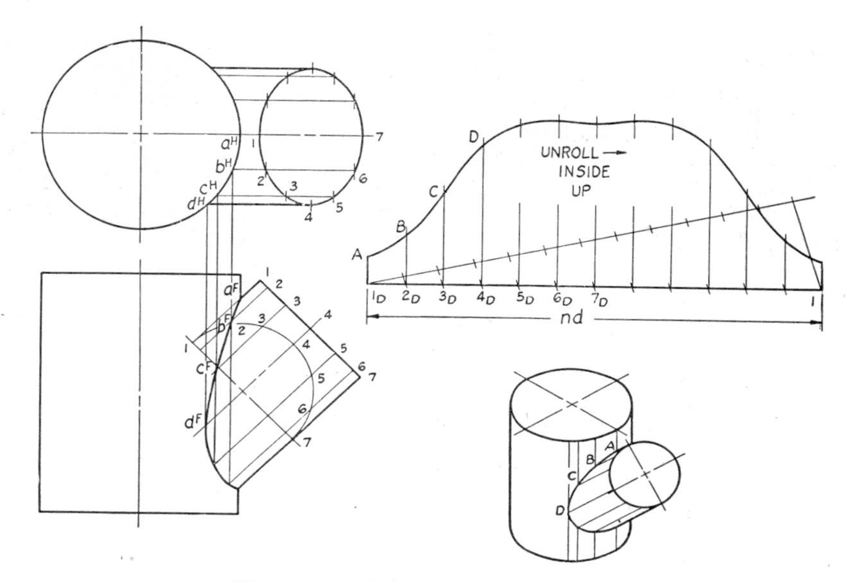

Fig. 22.33. Intersecting cylinders.

equal divisions (say six) and elements are drawn through the division points, the points *A*, *B*, *C*, and *D* in which the elements intersect the surface of the vertical cylinder will be points on the line of intersection (see pictorial). In the case of the above illustration, these points are

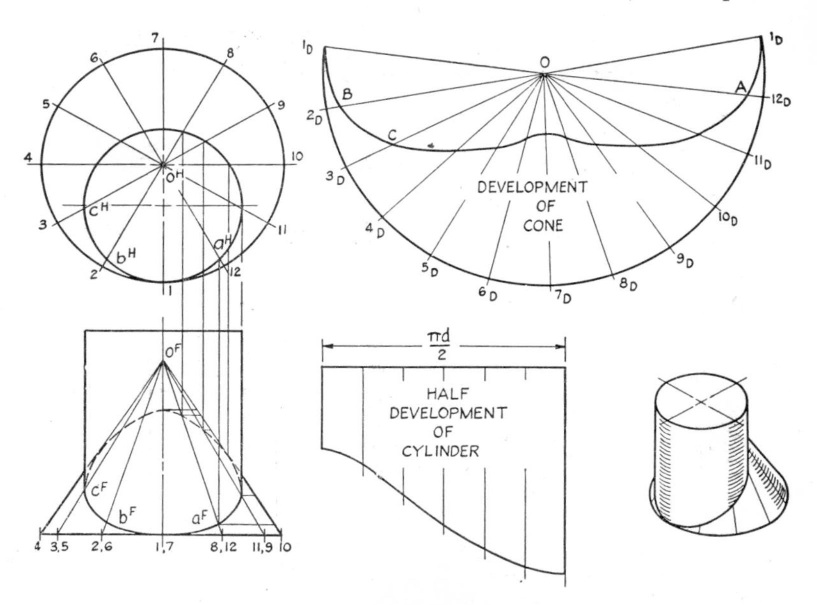

Fig. 22.34. Intersecting cylinder and cone.

found first in the top view and then are projected downward to the corresponding elements in the front view. The line of intersection in the front view is represented by a smooth curve drawn through these points.

22.30. To find the intersection of a cylinder and a cone. The intersection of a cylinder and a cone may be found by assuming a number of elements upon the surface of the cone. The points at which these elements cut the cylinder are on the line of intersection (see pictorial drawings in Figs. 22.34 and 22.35). In selecting the elements, it is the usual prac-

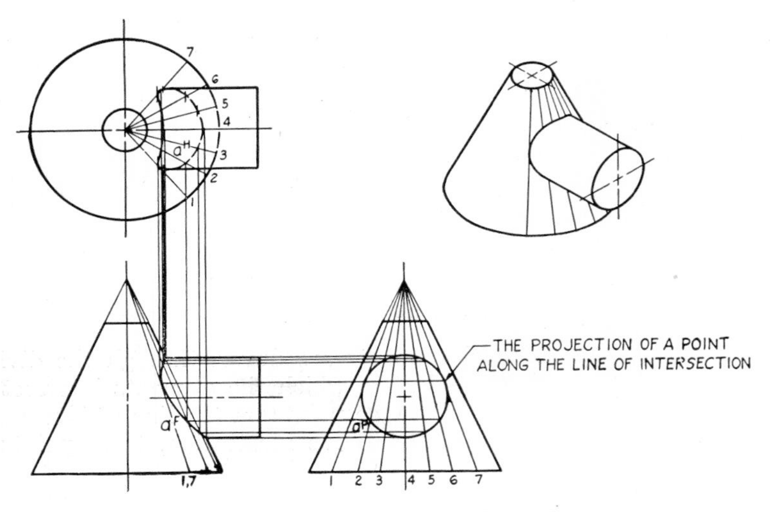

Fig. 22.35. Intersecting cylinder and cone.

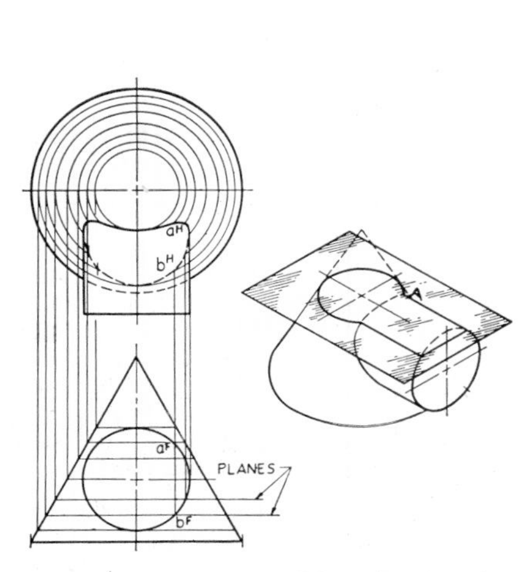

Fig. 22.36. Intersecting cylinder and cone.

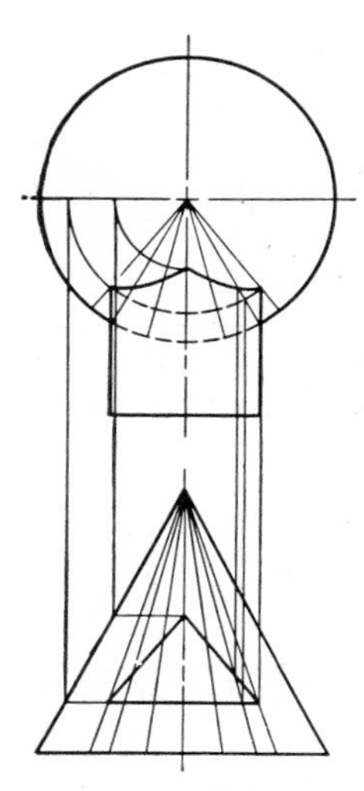

Fig. 22.37. Intersecting cone and prism.

tice to divide the circumference of the base into a number of equal parts and draw elements through the division points. To obtain needed points at locations where the intersection line will change suddenly in curvature, however, there should be additional elements.

In Fig. 22.34, the points at which the elements pierce the cylinder are first found in the top view and are then projected to the corresponding elements in the front view. A smooth curve through these points forms the figure of the intersection.

In Fig. 22.35, the intersection points are first found in the side view.

An alternate method for finding the line of intersection of a cylinder and a right cone is illustrated in Fig. 22.36. Here horizontal cutting planes are passed through both geometrical shapes in the region of their line of intersection. In each cutting plane, the circle cut on the surface of the cone will intersect elements cut on the cylinder at two points common to both surfaces (see pictorial). A curved line traced through a number of such points in different planes is a line common to both surfaces and is therefore the line of intersection.

22.31. To find the intersection of a prism and a cone. The complete line of intersection may be found by drawing elements on the surface of the cone (see Fig. 22.37) to locate points on the intersection as explained in Sec. 22.30. To obtain an accurate curve, however, some thought must be given to the placing of these elements. For instance, although most of the elements may be equally spaced on the cone to facilitate the construction of its development, additional ones should be drawn through the critical points and in regions where the line of intersection changes sharply in curvature. The elements are drawn on the view that will reveal points on the intersection; then, the determined points are projected to the corresponding elements in the other view or views. In this particular illustration a part of the line of intersection in the top view is a portion of the arc of a circle that would be cut by a horizontal plane containing the bottom surface of the prism.

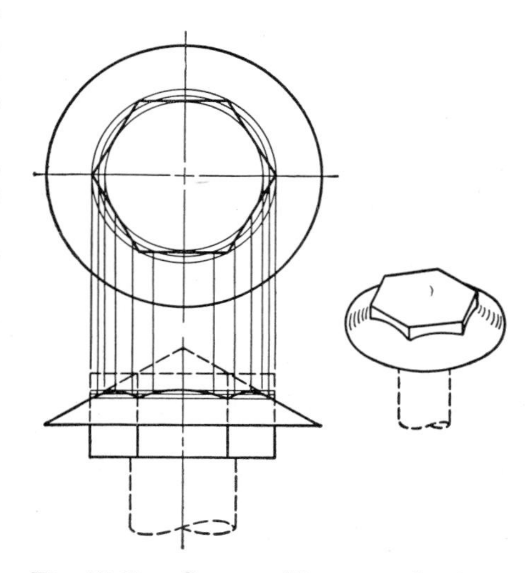

Fig. 22.38. Cone and hexagonal prism.

If the surfaces of the prism are parallel to the axis of the cone, as in Fig. 22.38, the line of intersection will be made up of the tips of a series of hyperbolas. The intersection may be found by passing planes that will cut circles on the surface of the cone. The points at which these cutting circles pierce the faces of the prism are points common to the lateral surfaces of both shapes and are therefore points on the required line of intersection. It should be noted that the resulting solution represents a chamfered bolthead.

22.32. Problems. The problems of this chapter have been designed to offer an opportunity to apply the principles of intersections and developments and to provide further drill in projection.

1. (Fig. 22.39.) Develop the lateral surface of one or more of the prisms as assigned.

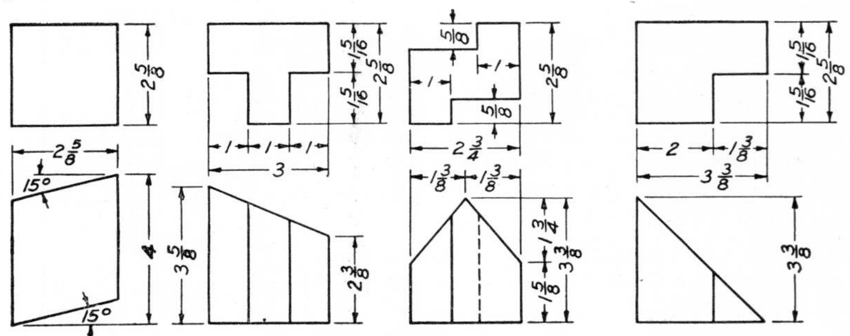

Fig. 22.39. Prisms.

2. (Fig. 22.40.) Develop the lateral surface of one or more of the prisms as assigned.

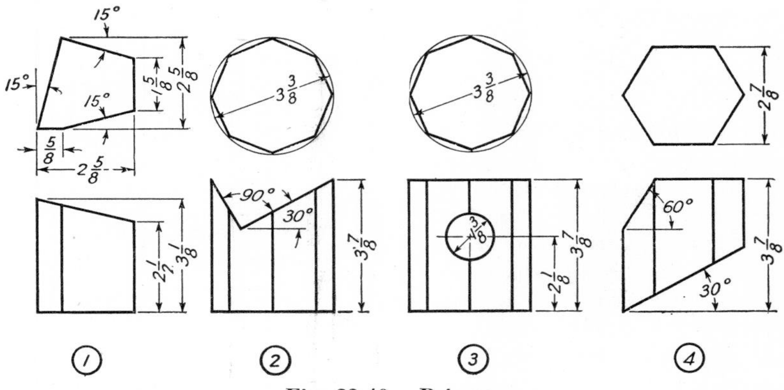

Fig. 22.40. Prisms.

3. (Fig. 22.41.) Develop the lateral surface of one or more of the pyramids as assigned. Make construction lines light. Show construction for finding the true lengths of the lines.

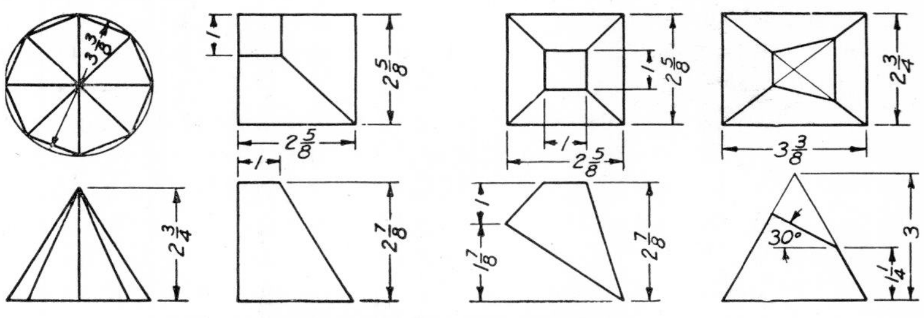

Fig. 22.41. Pyramids.

4. (Fig. 22.42.) Develop the lateral surface of one or more of the pyramids as assigned. With a hard pencil, show the construction for finding the true lengths of the lines.

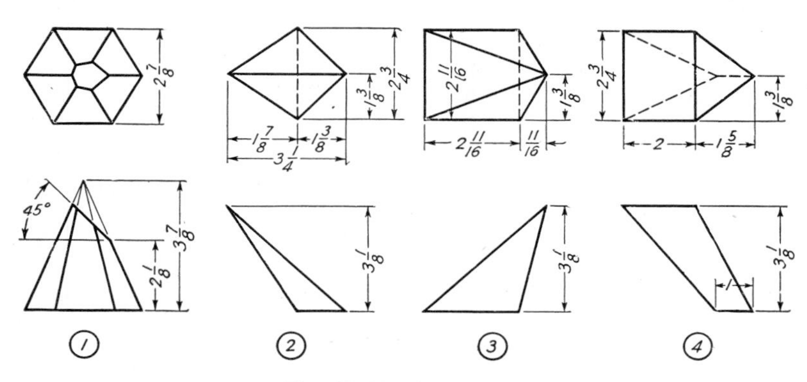

Fig. 22.42. Pyramids.

5. (Fig. 22.43.) Develop the lateral surface of one or more of the cylinders as assigned. Use a hard pencil for construction lines and make them light.

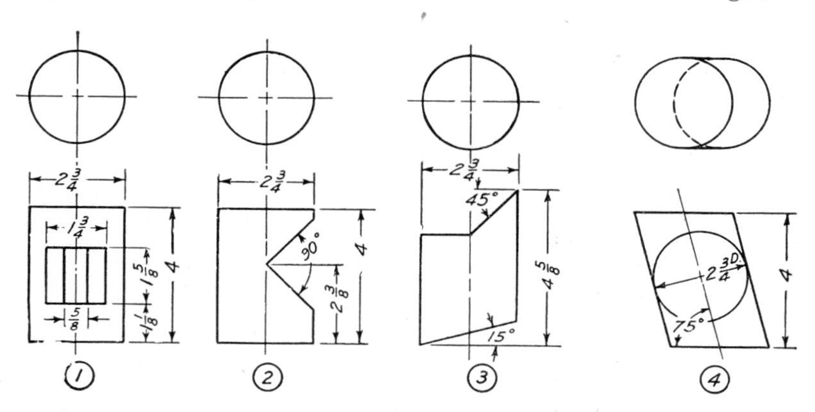

Fig. 22.43. Cylinders.

6. (Fig. 22.44.) Develop the lateral surface of one or more of the cones as assigned. Show all construction. Use a hard pencil for construction lines and make them light. In each case start with the shortest element and unroll, inside up. It is suggested that 12 elements be used, in order to secure a reasonably accurate development.

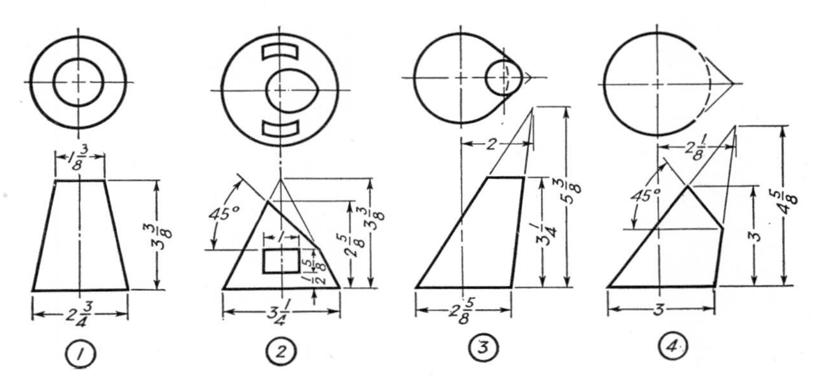

Fig. 22.44. Cones.

7. (Fig. 22.45.) Develop the lateral surface of one or more of the transition pieces as assigned. Show all construction lines in light sharp pencil lines. Use a sufficient number of elements on the curved surfaces to assure an accurate development.

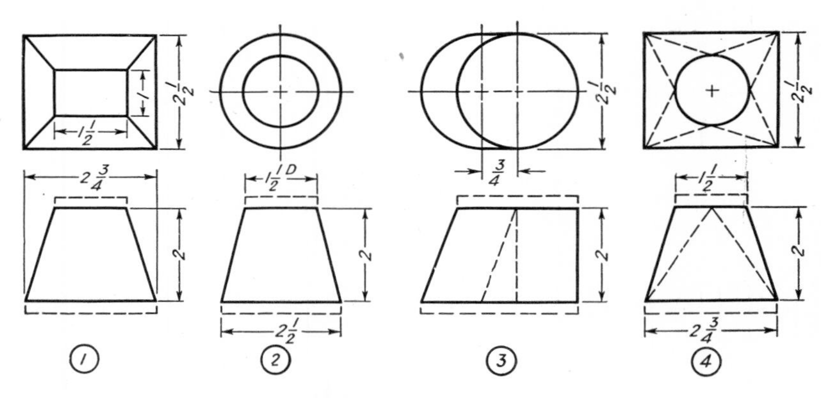

Fig. 22.45. Transition pieces.

8. (Fig. 22.46.) Develop the sheet-metal connections. On pieces 3 and 4, use a sufficient number of elements to obtain a smooth curve and an accurate development.

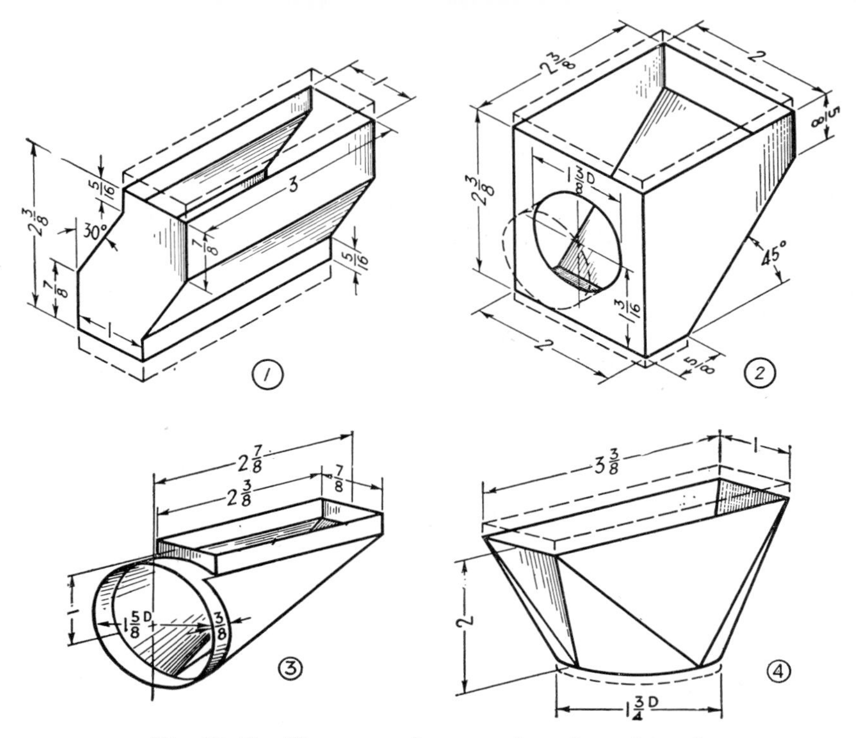

Fig. 22.46. Sheet-metal connections (transitions).

9. (Fig. 22.47.) Draw the line of intersection of the intersecting geometrical shapes as assigned. Show the invisible portions of the lines of intersection as well as the visible. Consider that the interior is open.

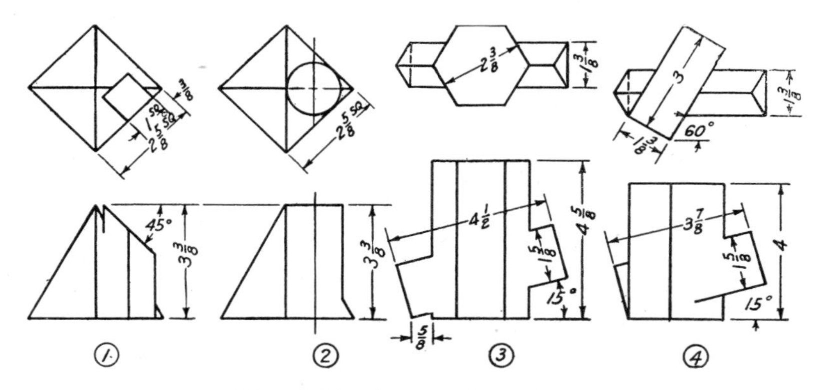

Fig. 22.47. Intersecting prisms.

10–11. (Figs. 22.48 and 22.49.) Draw the line of intersection of the intersecting geometrical shapes as assigned. It is suggested that the elements that are used to find points along the intersection be spaced 15° apart. Do not erase the construction lines. One shape does not pass through the other.

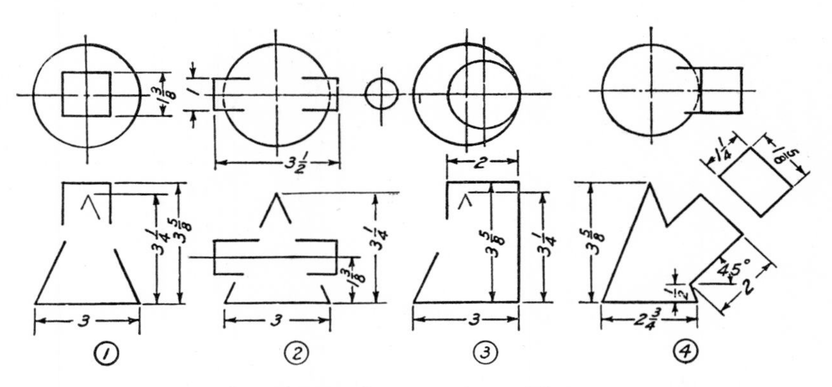

Fig. 22.48. Intersecting surfaces.

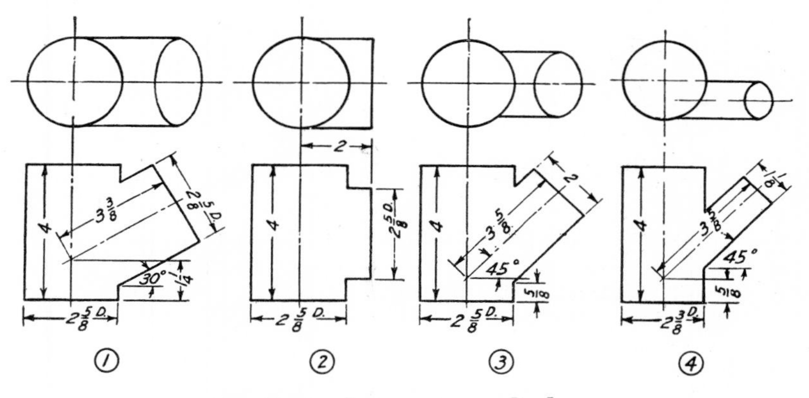

Fig. 22.49. Intersecting cylinders.

12–13. (Figs. 22.50 and 22.51.) Draw the line of interesection of the intersecting geometrical shapes as assigned. Show the invisible portions of the line of intersection as well as the visible. Show construction with light sharp lines drawn with a hard pencil. The interior of the combination is hollow. One shape does not pass through the other.

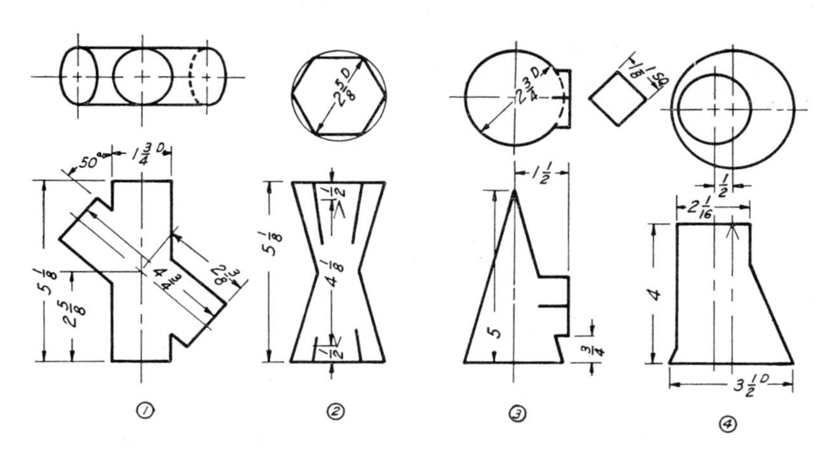

Fig. 22.50. Intersecting surfaces.

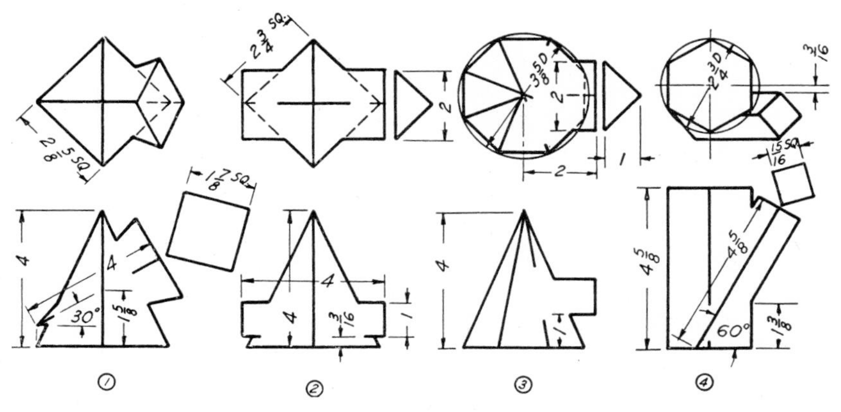

Fig. 22.51. Intersecting surfaces.

23 ARCHITECTURAL DRAWING

23.1. Introduction. The principles of architectural drafting are the same as those for other technical drawing work, except that the application of these principles requires special methods, symbols, and conventions. Architectural drawings of a building include floor plans, elevations, sections, and details sufficiently descriptive to permit the construction of the building according to the architect's ideas.

Although the architect and the architectural draftsman work hand-in-hand in the preparation of a set of plans for a structure, there is a wide gap between the experience and knowledge that each possesses. The architect may be his own draftsman, but the draftsman cannot be his own architect. The draftsman's function, therefore, is to assist in the execution of the architect's ideas. The architect must know not only how to prepare accurate working drawings, but also, he must understand the best uses of buildings from the economic and social points of view; he must know business administration so that he may understand the financial and legal transactions incident to modern building construction; he must develop a sense of proportion and a knowledge of pleasing form and color through the study of the history of Architecture; he must be familiar with the mechanical trades such as plumbing, heating, electricity, and other engineering features that have such an important bearing on the safety and durability of a structure.

23.2. Preliminary studies. Before the architect or draftsman is required to draw the plans and elevations or the working drawings of the house, the owner and architect should have reached certain conclusions about the general design or style of the house, the kind of material to be used, the size, and the approximate cost of the proposed structure. While it is impossible to give an accurate schedule of costs at this point, the following is an indication of the relative percentage of the cost of materials, labor, and land involved in building the average home.

Cost of Materials	45.40%
Construction Labor	29.80%
Overhead and Profit	12.20%
Cost of Land	12.60%
	100.00%

Following is an outline that the architect may prepare for further development by himself or his draftsman after consulting with the owner.

DESIGN FOR TWO LEVEL STONE MASONRY AND FRAME HOUSE

ROOMS—MAIN FLOOR
1. Living room with fireplace
2. Dining room
3. Kitchen
4. Storage and heater room

SECOND FLOOR
5. Two bedrooms with closets
6. Bathroom
7. Terrace or sun deck

TYPE OF CONSTRUCTION
8. Concrete footings; masonry wall construction for first floor; frame walls for second floor; red wood siding.
9. Double hung frame windows; 6 lights for each frame
10. Flat canvas deck roofs, insulated
11. Heating: one-pipe hot water; recessed convectors
12. Sewage disposal: septic tank and leaching pool.
13. Provide for future breeze-way and one-car garage

23.3. Preliminary sketches. In many instances the architect will prepare for himself or submit to the draftsman a freehand sketch of the

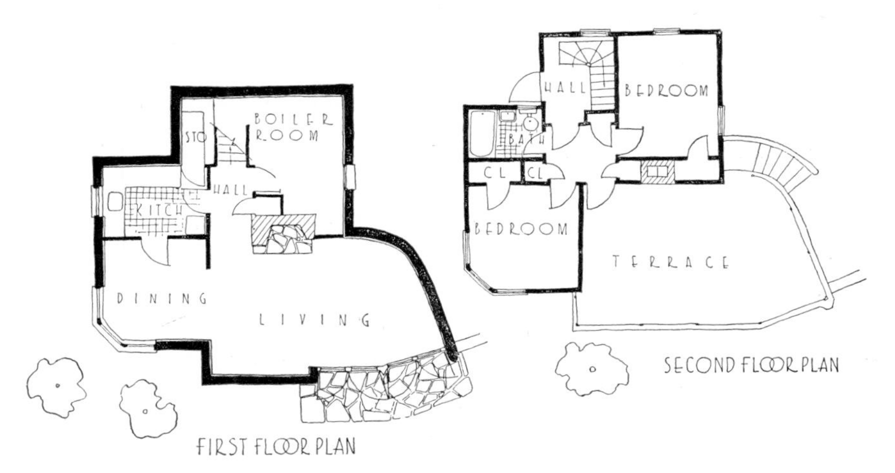

Fig. 23.1. Preliminary sketches.

plan showing the arrangement of rooms and indicating the approximate size of each room, Fig. 23.1. From this sketch the draftsman will prepare a preliminary drawing to a scale of $\frac{1}{8}'' = 1'\text{-}0''$. Of course, certain considerations and adjustments must be made as far as the arrangement and general dimensions of rooms are concerned, because the scale drawing will never quite work out in exact accordance with the preliminary rough sketch. When good circulation and a suitable arrangement of rooms are obtained, the draftsman will then layout the $\frac{1}{4}$-in. scale drawing of the main floor plan.

23.4. Presentation drawings. The primary purpose of presentation drawings is to give the owner a general, realistic picture of the proposed structure. Presentation drawings may be made in several ways. One method is to prepare a perspective view of the exterior of the building, rendered in pencil, ink, or color. Walks, shrubbery, or trees that may surround the building are included. With the rendered perspective it is customary to show the main-floor plan giving the names and sizes of rooms in order that the client may study the room arrangement. A rendered perspective drawing is shown in Fig. 23.2(*a* and *b*).

In place of the rendered perspective, actual scale models of the proposed building are finding favor with many architects. Models are made in the drafting room, using drawing paper and cardboard, cut to size and glued together forming an exact replica of the proposed building. The effect of shrubbery, trees, hedges, and grass can be attained by colored sponges, sawdust, and sand. Such models are of great value to both architect and client because they can be viewed from all angles and their proportions can be studied more accurately.

23.5. Working drawings. A set of working drawings consists of all of the drawings that are necessary for the contractor to erect the building. The set is composed of the plans, elevations, sections, details, and the lettered notes that assist in the interpretation of the drawings. In addition to the working drawings, the contractor also receives written instructions called *the specifications.* These specifications cover all the features that are not shown on the blueprints, such as the quality and quantity of the materials, and the methods to be used in the construction, or the manner in which the work is to be conducted. Like the plans, the specifications are indispensable to the builder. They are typed and accompany a set of working drawings.

23.6. The plans. When a set of working drawings is prepared, the main-floor plan is generally drawn first, as in Fig. 23.3. This plan is a horizontal cut taken through the building at a level half-way up the windows. Its purpose is to show the builder the location of both outside and inside walls, their thicknesses, lengths, and the materials of which they are constructed. The location of windows and doors, stairs and fireplace, and other data pertaining to electrical outlets, fixtures, floor finishes, and the direction and sizes of overhead floor joists are indicated.

From the main- or first-floor plan the outlines of other floor plans are traced, such as the basement or foundation plan, the second-floor plan (Fig. 23.4), or the roof plan. Since many drawings are needed in the erection of a building, it is quite common to use a separate sheet for each plan. Special details that apply to the particular drawing are included.

23.7. The elevations. The primary purpose of the elevation drawings, Fig. 23.5 and 23.6, is to give the builder the height dimensions of doors, windows, floor-to-floor heights, ridge heights, chimney height, and the finished grade level in relation to the finished floor level. On the elevations are also indicated the type of outside wall finishes, roof finishes, and the style of doors and windows. In many cases two elevation drawings, front and side, are sufficient to give the necessary information, but it is advisable to draw the four elevations of the building when each elevation has a distinct feature that could not be clearly shown on other drawings.

23.8. The plot plan. One of the functions of a plot plan is to locate the house on the lot so that the builder knows where to begin. When

Fig. 23.2(a). Presentation drawing.

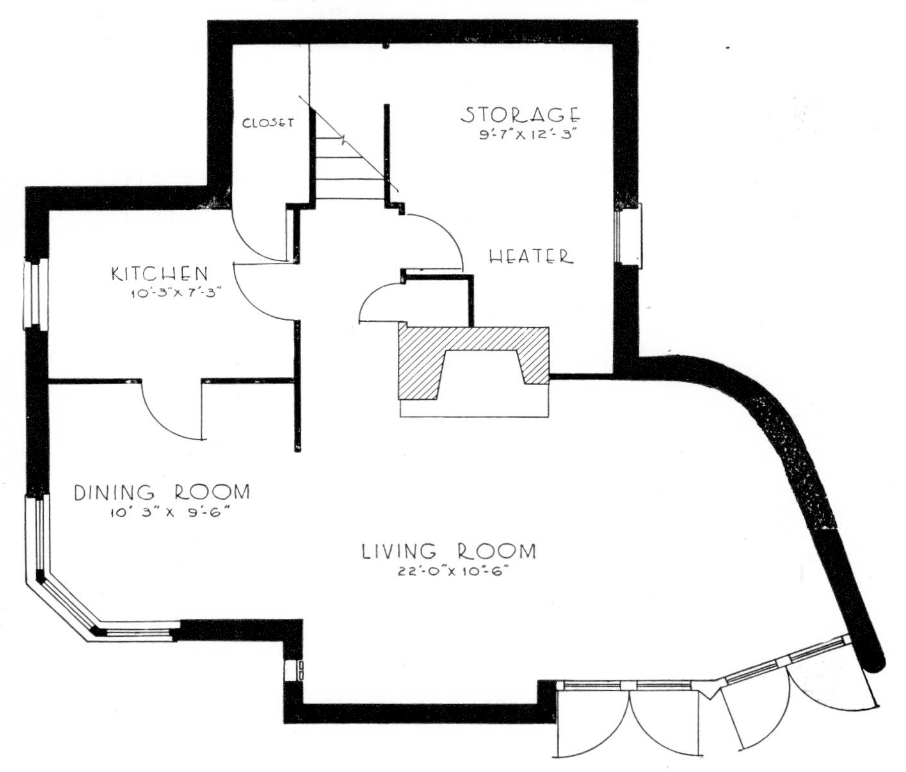

Fig. 23.2(b).

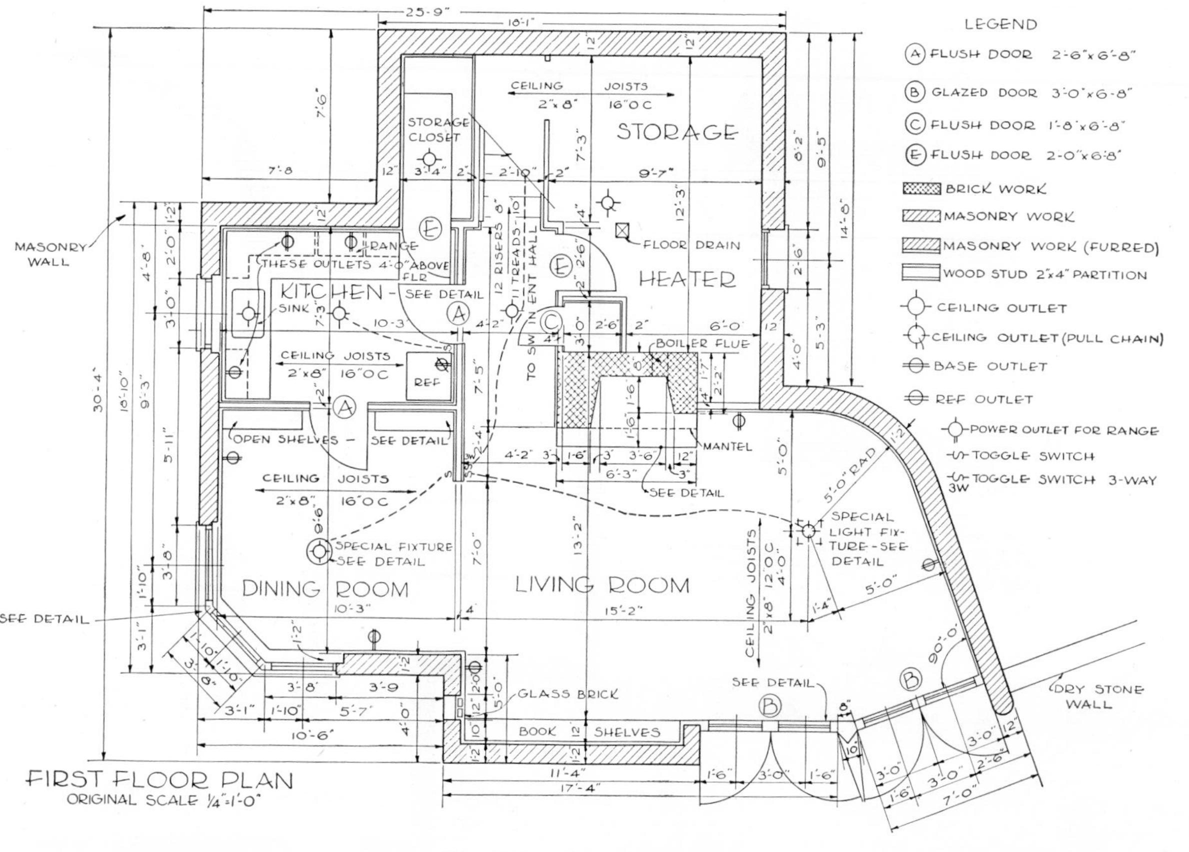

Fig. 23.3. First-floor plan.

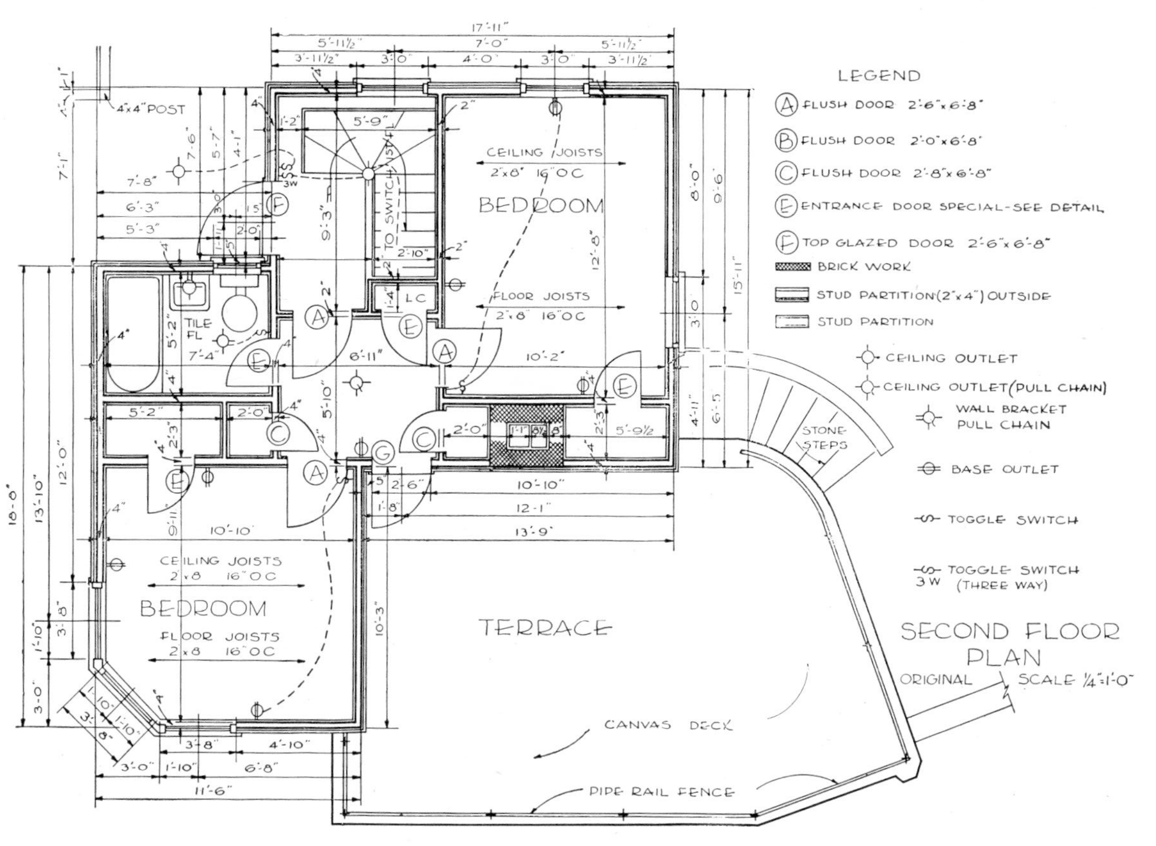

Fig. 23.4. Second-floor plan.

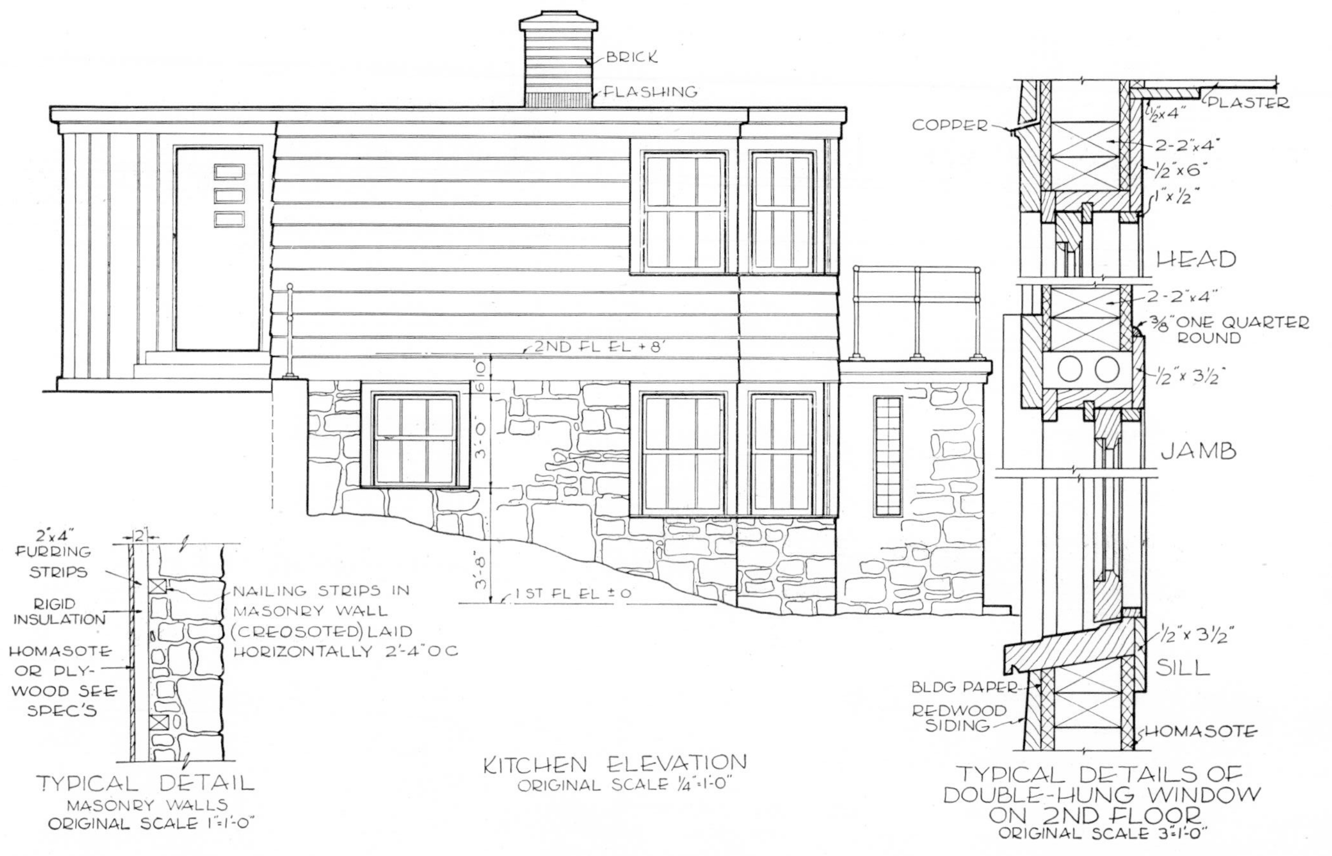
BRICK
FLASHING
2ND FL EL + 8'
6'10"
3'-0"
3'-8"
1 ST FL EL ± 0
2"x4" FURRING STRIPS
RIGID INSULATION
HOMASOTE OR PLY-WOOD SEE SPEC'S
2"
NAILING STRIPS IN MASONRY WALL (CREOSOTED) LAID HORIZONTALLY 2'-4" O C
TYPICAL DETAIL
MASONRY WALLS
ORIGINAL SCALE 1"=1'-0"
KITCHEN ELEVATION
ORIGINAL SCALE ¼"=1'-0"
COPPER
PLASTER
½"x4"
2-2"x4"
½"x6"
1"x½"
HEAD
2-2"x4"
3/8" ONE QUARTER ROUND
½"x 3½"
JAMB
½"x 3½"
SILL
BLDG PAPER
REDWOOD SIDING
HOMASOTE
TYPICAL DETAILS OF DOUBLE-HUNG WINDOW ON 2ND FLOOR
ORIGINAL SCALE 3"=1'-0"

Fig. 23.5. Elevation.

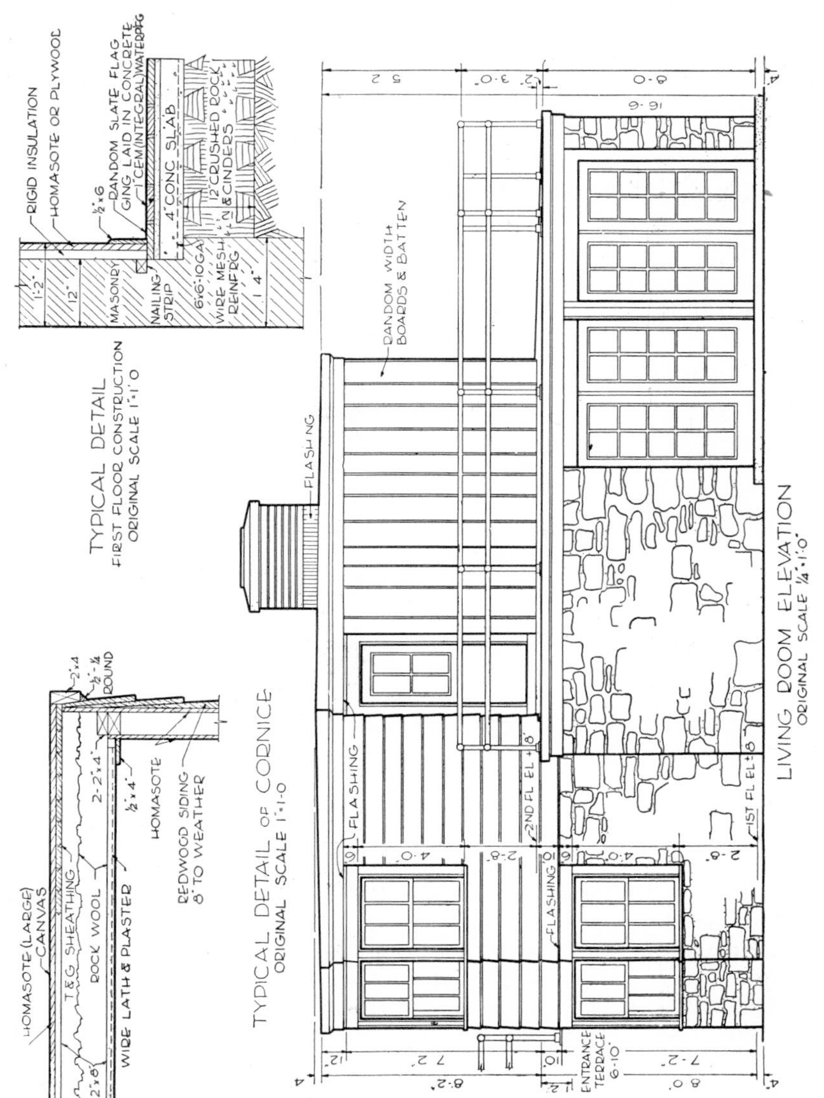

Fig. 23.6. Elevation.

a tract of land is intended for a home development site it is generally the practice to lay in public utilities, such as sewerage disposal systems, water, gas, and electricity. This necessitates a pattern of streets and avenues with sidewalks forming blocks. A block is generally understood to mean an area of land rectangular in form bounded by streets and avenues. Each block, in turn, is subdivided into lots of the same or varying sizes, Fig. 23.7. Local building regulations frequently call for certain restrictions on the "frontage" or the distance that must be maintained between the street and the location of the house on the lot. In such cases the plot plan must show the exact location of the house on the lot. In unrestricted areas a land owner may build his house without defining

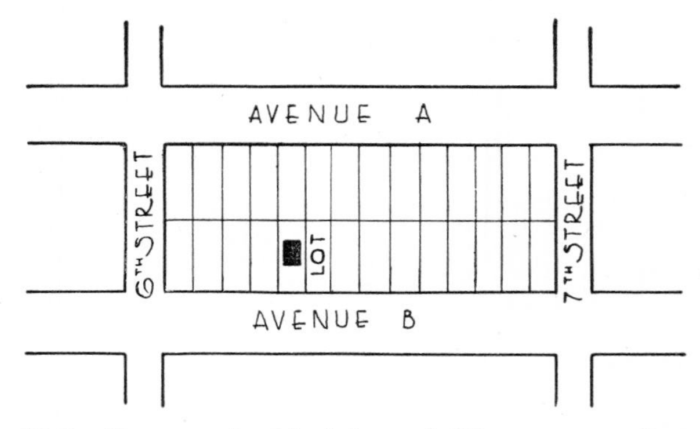

Fig. 23.7. Rectangular block bounded by streets and avenues subdivided into lots.

the location of the house on the land, as shown in Fig. 23.8. Plot plans also show where sewer lines, water, gas, and drainage lines are located. If driveways and walks are to be built, they must also be shown. Shrubbery, existing trees, and the points of the compass are included on a finished-plot plan.

23.9. Sections. In addition to the plans and elevations, "part sections" are often used to clarify the drawings further. These "part sections," Fig. 23.9, are often shown on the same drawing with the elevations, but generally are of larger scale. The longitudinal or cross section is intended to show the interior construction and architectural treatment. It is a cut taken on a vertical plane through the center of the building. This cutting plane need not be continuous, but may be staggered to include as much information as possible. Longitudinal or cross sections, as shown in Fig. 23.10, are of definite value to the builder. They show him the construction of the building from the footings to the roof rafters. This type of outside-wall construction is represented by its symbols; floor and ceiling joists are clearly shown and their sizes given; partition walls, stairs, fireplace, and interior wall finishes can be indicated. Important height dimensions given from finished floor to finished ceiling are a definite aid in understanding the construction. On longitudinal sections cellar floor con-

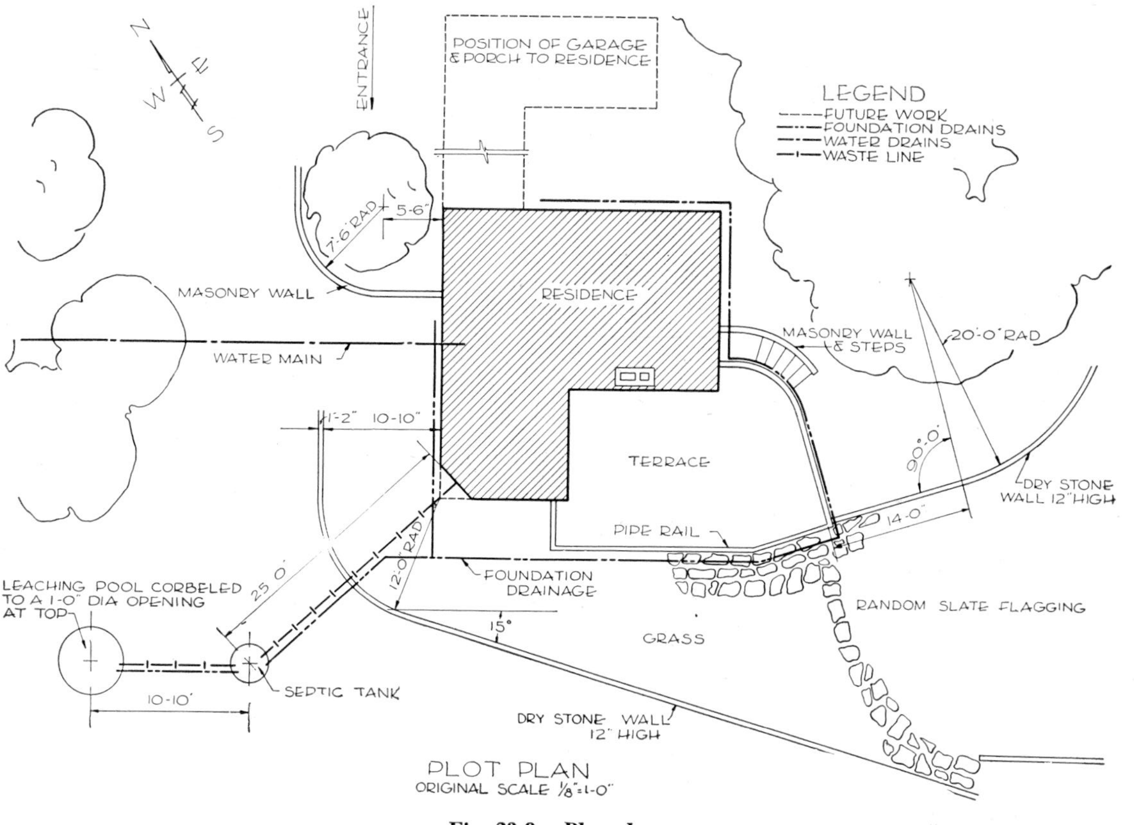

Fig. 23.8. Plot plan.

structions can also be indicated with dimensions and specifications so that in many instances larger details are not required.

23.10. Wall sections. On smaller construction it is often desirable to draw a "wall section" in place of the longitudinal or cross section so that all the necessary height dimensions and the construction can be shown. Wall sections are drawn to scales of $\frac{1}{2}''$, $\frac{3}{4}''$, or $1'' = 1'\text{-}0''$. A wall section such as that shown in Fig. 23.11 gives the depth of the footing below grade and the dimensions of the footing and the foundation wall. The 4″ concrete floor on 6″ cinder fill, on earth, is understood to be typical throughout. The section includes a window located by dimension above the finished floor level, and the height and type is shown. The method of spanning the window opening by a precast reinforced concrete lintel is

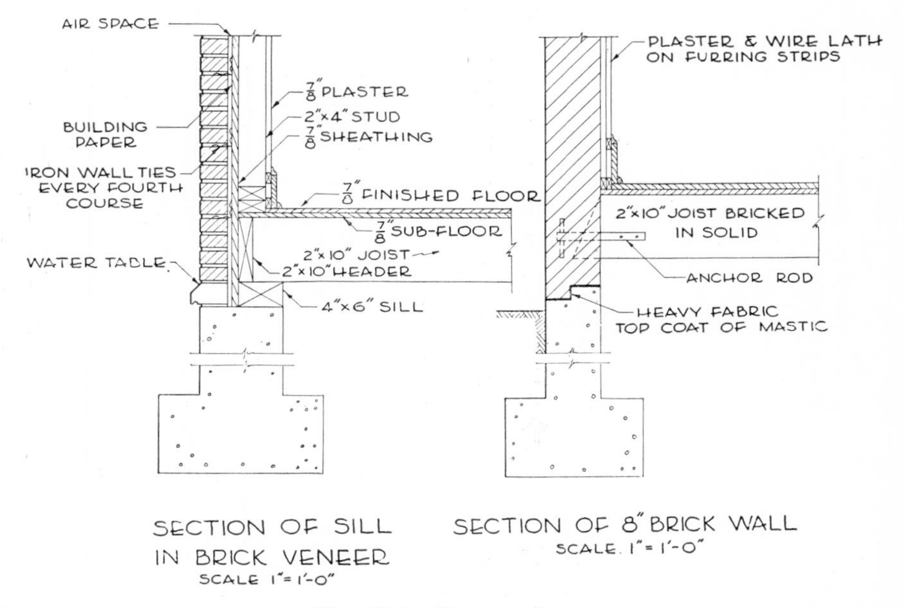

Fig. 23.9. Part sections.

indicated. The section further shows a built-up roof properly flashed to the wall. The exterior and interior wall finish can be represented by symbols and notes.

23.11. Details. A set of working drawings is never quite complete without the large-scale detail drawings. Large-scale details are made when other drawings cannot describe the construction clearly. They are drawn to a scale of full size, half size, $3'' = 1'\text{-}0''$, $1\frac{1}{2}'' = 1'\text{-}0''$, $1'' = 1'\text{-}0''$, $\frac{1}{2}'' = 1'\text{-}0''$, $\frac{3}{4}'' = 1'\text{-}0''$. Typical details, such as that shown for the small house, Fig. 23.12, include the elevation of the fireplace wall in the living room, special lighting fixtures, entrance door details, and other details that can be clearly described but could not be shown on other drawings at smaller scales. For larger buildings many additional detail drawings must

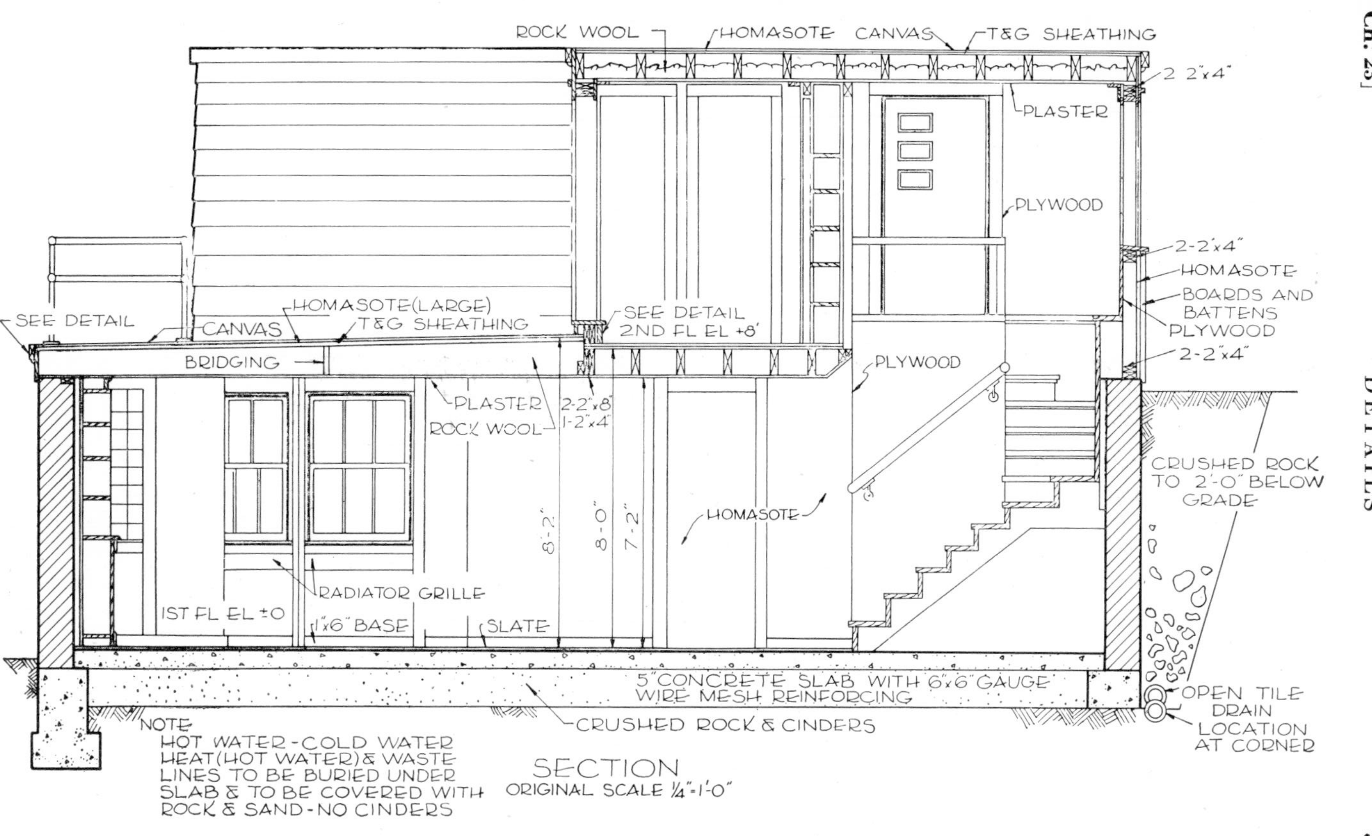

Fig. 23.10. Longitudinal section.

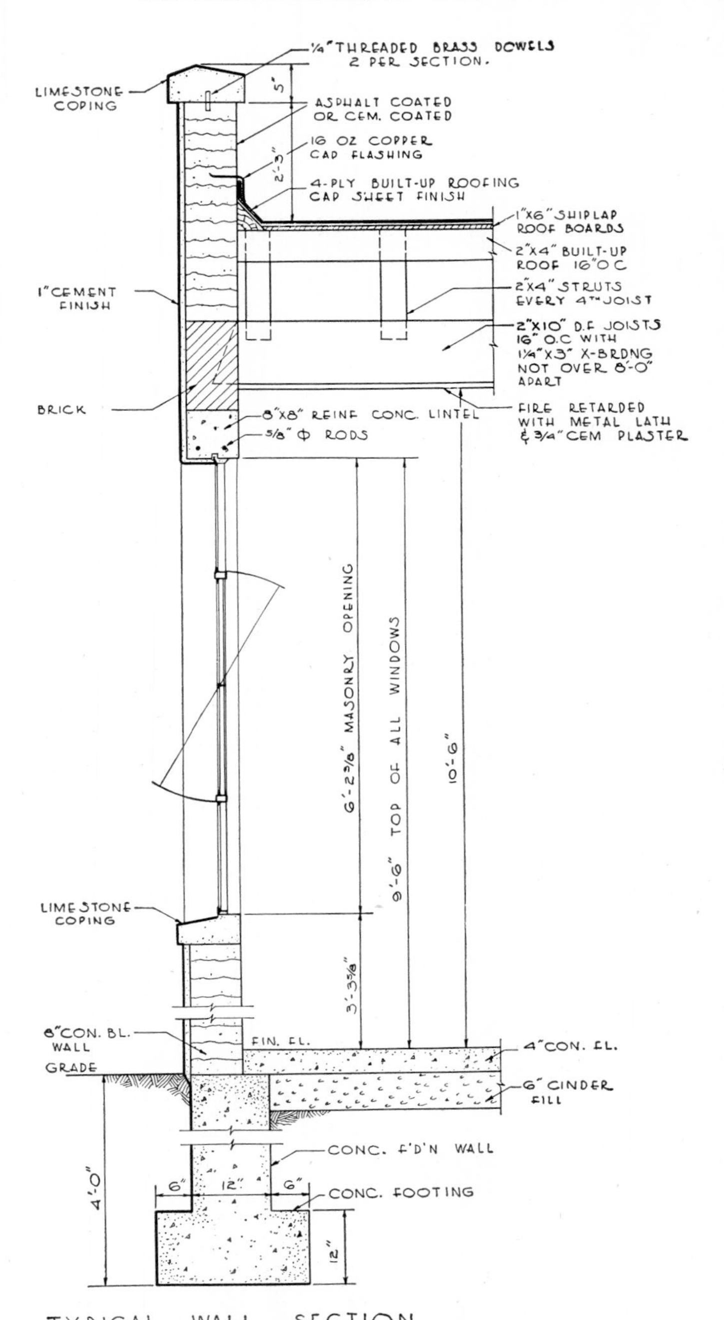

Fig. 23.11. Wall section.

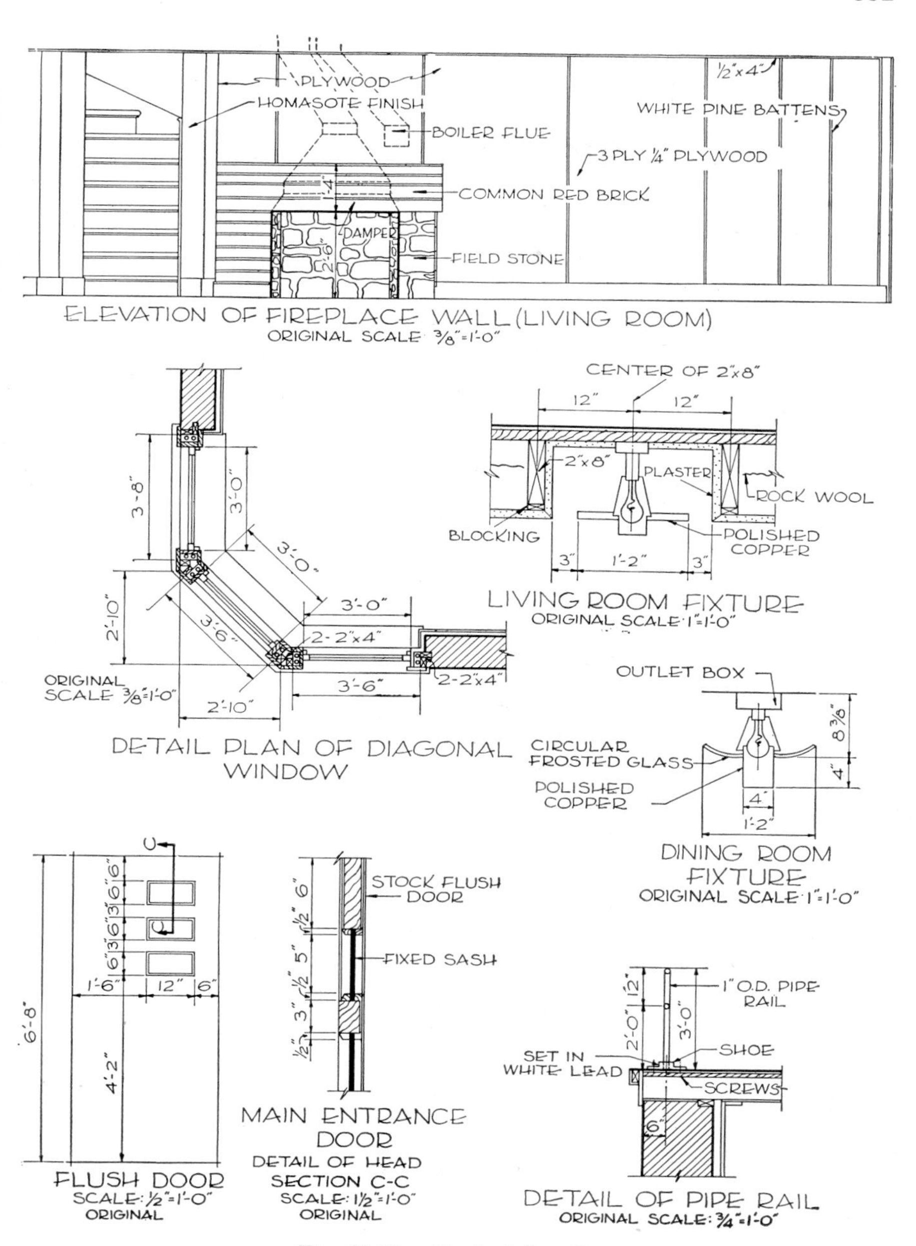

Fig. 23.12. Typical details.

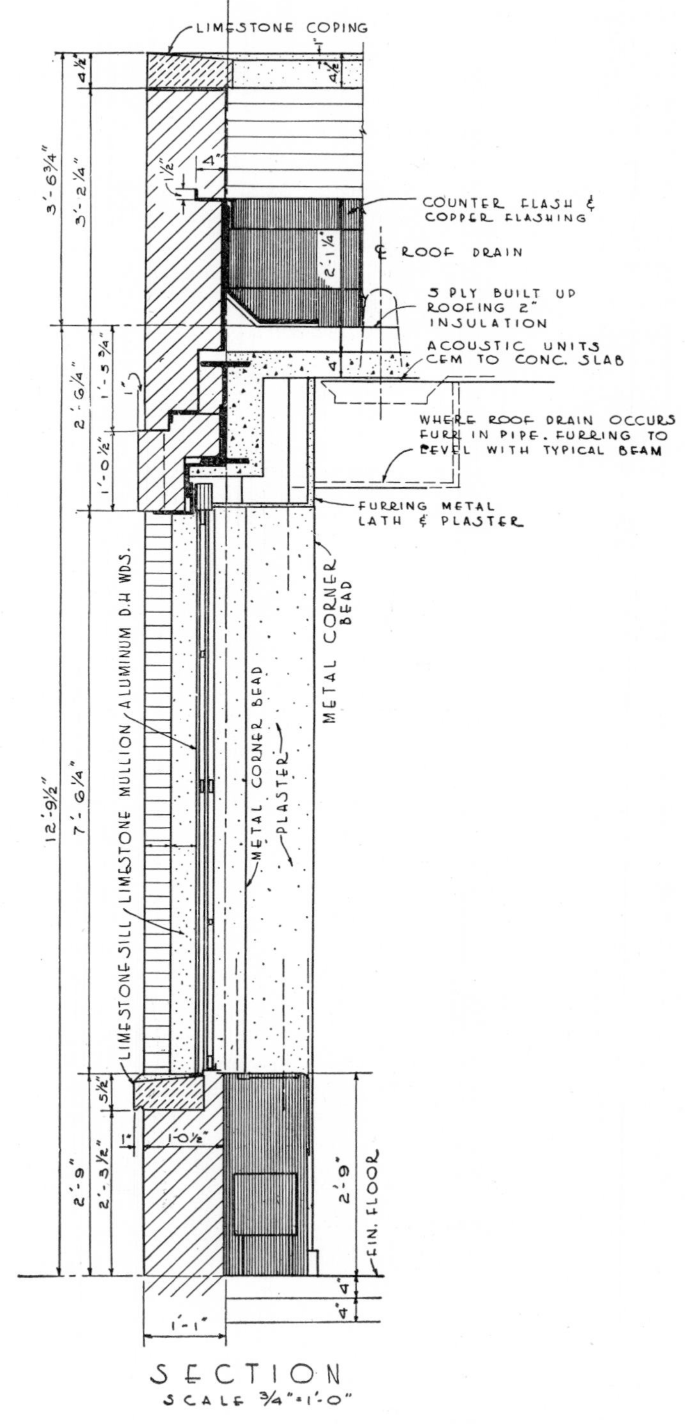
LIMESTONE COPING
COUNTER FLASH & COPPER FLASHING
℄ ROOF DRAIN
5 PLY BUILT UP ROOFING 2" INSULATION
ACOUSTIC UNITS CEM TO CONC. SLAB
WHERE ROOF DRAIN OCCURS FURR IN PIPE. FURRING TO LEVEL WITH TYPICAL BEAM
FURRING METAL LATH & PLASTER
METAL CORNER BEAD
METAL CORNER BEAD
PLASTER
ALUMINUM D.H WDS.
LIMESTONE MULLION
LIMESTONE SILL
FIN. FLOOR
3'-6¾"
3'-2¼"
4½"
2'-6¼"
1'-5¾"
1'-0½"
12'-9½"
7'-6¼"
2'-9"
2'-3½"
5½"
1'-0½"
1'-1"
2'-9"
2'-1¼"
SECTION
SCALE ¾"=1'-0"

Fig. 23.13. Window detail.

be prepared, as illustrated in the window detail in Fig. 23.13. To be able to prepare good detail drawings the draftsman needs much experience in the use of trade literature, catalogs, and books dealing with the principles of construction. It might be well to mention here that in order to draw complex details the draftsman is largely dependent upon manufacturer's information and previous similar drawings.

23.12. Special features. In present-day building construction, many parts that are used are manufactured by firms specializing in one particular item. As an example, wood sash details vary with different manufacturers. The architect gets scale details from the makers and draws his building to conform. Fig. 23.14 shows a detail of a double-hung window and a table of cellar window and picture window sizes as supplied by the manufacturer. Other items such as stair parts, doors, railings, fans, radiators, heating equipment, and many other special features are always planned from drawings supplied by the manufacturers.

23.13. Symbols. The working drawings for a structure are composed largely of symbols and conventions representing manufactured items and materials. For example, in a plan a foundation wall made up of concrete block has a symbol of cross lines and dots. This symbol is universally understood to mean concrete blocks. The symbol for concrete is represented by small triangles, circles, and dots representing crushed stone or gravel, sand, and cement. All architects, draftsmen, and builders understand these symbols that form a language of lines and correlate thought in the trade. Many symbols for materials have been standardized by the American Standards Association to facilitate understanding. Some of the new materials that have been added to the building industry in recent years have not as yet been standardized. When such materials are used on drawings a key to the materials must be included with the work. Fig. 23.15 shows materials and conventions that have been standardized.

23.14. Dimensioning. Dimensioning of the working plans and elevations is governed primarily by knowledge of building construction. Dimensions must be so placed that they are most convenient for the workman. On plans it is desirable to show dimensions around the outside of the plan whenever possible. Inside dimensions are generally those locating partitions, columns, beams, doors, or other openings. Dimensions on frame plans are given from the outside faces of studs on exterior walls to the center line of the window or door opening. Stud partitions may be located to the center of the partition or to the stud face. On masonry, outside walls dimensions are given from the outer face of the wall to the opening of the window or door, then across the opening. Masonry wall openings, such as doors and windows, may also be dimensioned to the center line of the opening. The elevations or cross sections must give the height or vertical dimensions of floors, windows, beams, roofs, and chimney. The plans in Figs. 23.3 and 23.4 and the elevations and cross section in Figs. 23.5, 23.6, and 23.10 should be carefully studied by the student before he attempts to place dimensions on a drawing.

23.15. Special notes. In addition to the written specifications furnished the contractor, special notes are lettered on the drawings to clarify

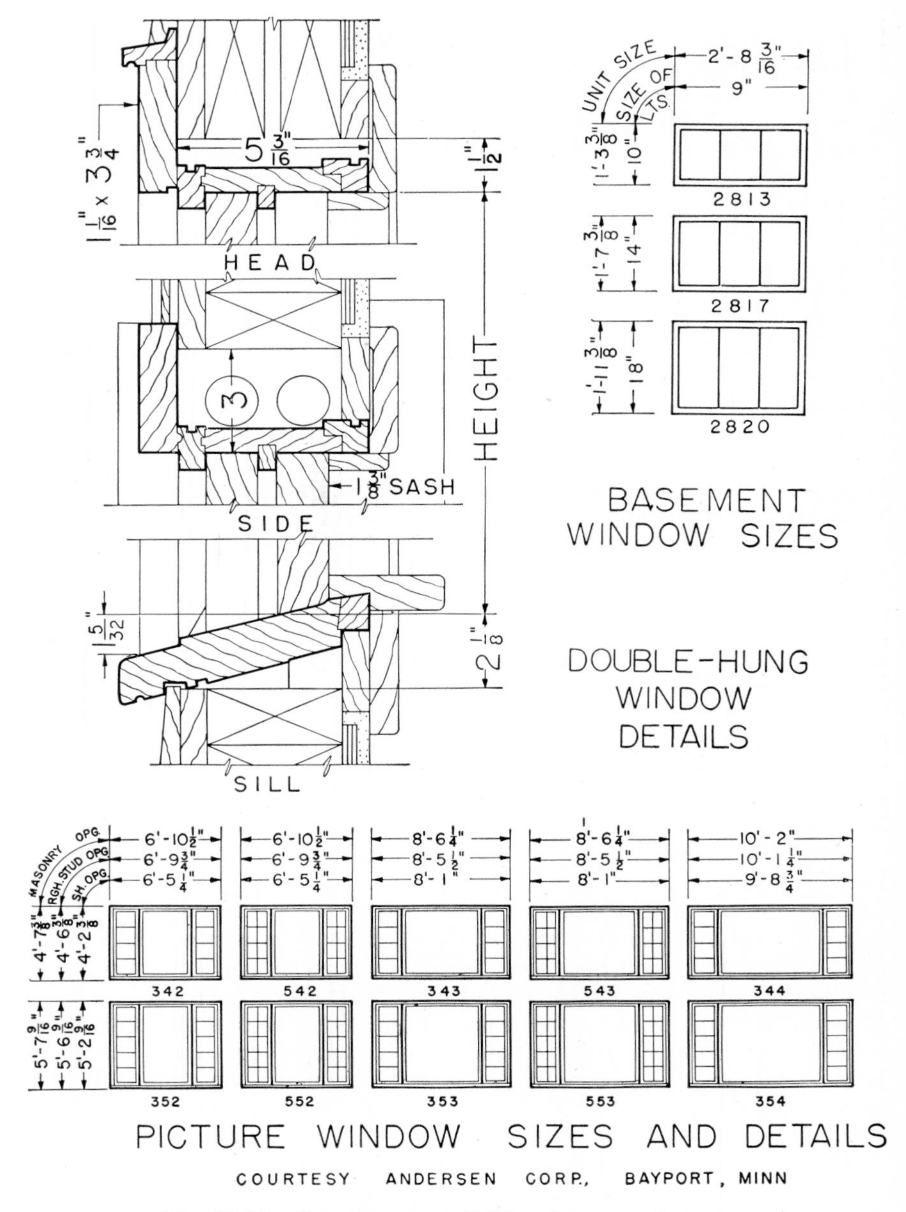

Fig. 23.14. Drawings supplied by the manufacturer.

the work. Builders are apt to overlook a point mentioned only in the specifications, but because they are using the drawings constantly they will be sure to see a reference or note on the drawing of the part in question. It is also common practice to use "schedules"—notes laid out in tabular

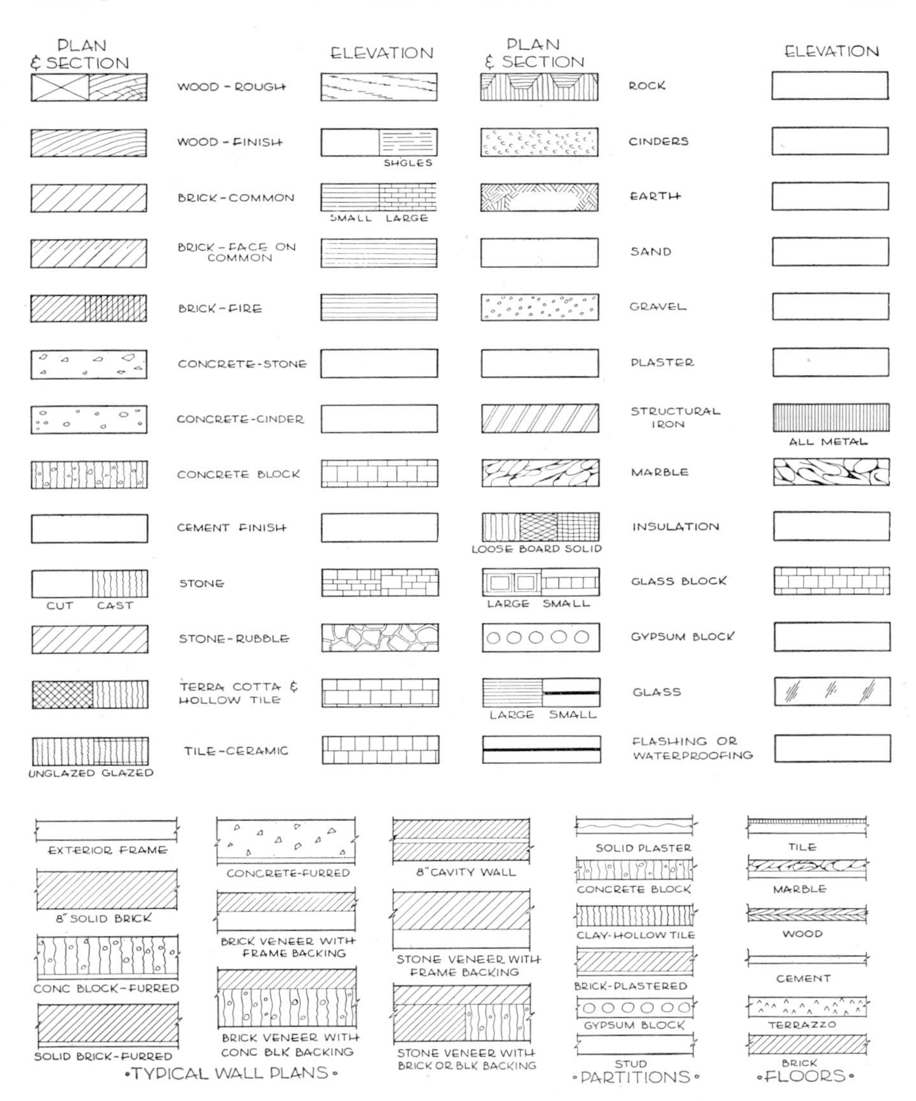

Fig. 23.15. Symbols and conventions.

form. The finish schedule shown in Fig. 23.16 gives finish treatments of rooms, floors, and ceilings. Door schedules and window schedules are also commonly used on drawings so that the work will be better understood by the tradesmen.

23.16. Lettering. The lettering on drawings is as important as the plans of the building, because without lettered explanatory notes, titles, and dimensions, the plans could hardly be understood. The single stroke architectural letter shown in Fig. 23.17 is typical of that used by the architect. The style is closely related to the old Roman form. It is becoming increasingly evident that single stroke upper-case architectural letters are gaining favor over the lower-case form and the trend is towards letters that resemble more closely the mechanical style of letter used in previous chapters of this text. In large architectural firms where many

FINISH SCHEDULE						
ROOM	FLOOR	BASE	WAINSCOT	WALLS	CEILING	TRIM
SALES	CONCRETE	WOOD PAINTED	PLASTER PAINTED		PLASTER PAINTED	WOOD PAINTED
TOILETS	CERAMIC TILE	CERAMIC TILE	CERAMIC TILE	PLASTER PAINTED	PLASTER PAINTED	WOOD PAINTED
STORAGE	CONCRETE	NONE	MASONRY CLEANED UN PAINTED		CEMENT PLASTER UN PAINTED	WOOD PAINTED
SERVICE ROOMS	CONCRETE	NONE	MASONRY PAINTED		CEMENT PLASTER PAINTED	WOOD PAINTED
NOTE: FOR COLOR OF PAINT AND NUMBER OF COATS SEE SPECIFICATIONS						

Fig. 23.16. Finish schedule.

ABCDEFGHIJKLMN
OPQRSTUVWXYZ&

1234567890

COMPRESSED FORM *for* LIMITED SPACE

INCISED

Fig. 23.17. Architectural lettering.

draftsmen are employed, mechanical guides are used for lettering in order to minimize individuality of style of the draftsman and to make the drawings more consistent in character. Another type of lettering the architect is called upon to execute is the *incised* or the old Roman style that is used when letters are cut into stone, bronze, or other material used in connection with design (Fig. 23.17).

23.17. Problems. The following problems permit the student to prepare the necessary working drawings for building construction and introduce him to the study of Architectural Design. The problems may be modified or amplified by the teacher to the particular student needs.

1. Draw the first-floor plan of a small house similar to the one represented in Fig. 23.3. The student may modify the plan or create one of his own design. It is advisable first to prepare rough, freehand thumbnail sketches of the plan to study room arrangements, window locations, and space for furniture. Have instructor check preliminary sketches and then proceed to draw a $\frac{1}{8}''$ scale plan. After studying the plan again, proceed with the final $\frac{1}{4}'' = 1'\text{-}0''$ scale plan and dimension it completely. Check Fig. 23.12 for conventional representations of windows, doors, fireplace, stairs, fixtures, and material symbols.

2. Draw the foundation plan of the house to a scale of $\frac{1}{4}'' = 1'\text{-}0''$. Indicate concrete footings, foundation walls, footing for chimney, lally columns, if any, and windows. Completely letter and dimension the plan.

3. Draw the remaining two elevations of the house shown in Figs. 23.5 and 23.6. Refer to the plans in Figs. 23.3 and 23.4. Use scale of $\frac{1}{4}'' = 1'\text{-}0''$. Particular attention should be given to the conventional representations of windows on the elevation, and the important height dimensions.

4. Draw the detail of a window used in the plan of your own design showing the head section, jamb, and sill, to a scale of either $1\frac{1}{2}'' = 1'\text{-}0''$, or $3'' = 1'\text{-}0''$. Refer to window detail Fig. 23.13 or 23.14. Indicate the rough openings and sash openings. These dimensions can be secured from manufacturers' catalogs.

5. Draw the front elevation to the plan drawn in Problem 1, to a scale of $\frac{1}{4}'' = 1'\text{-}0''$. Make preliminary sketches of the elevation and have them checked by the instructor before proceeding with the scale drawing. Check Figs. 23.5 and 23.6 for correct window conventions in elevation and symbols for exterior treatment. Place the necessary height dimensions on your drawing.

6. Draw a side elevation for the plan drawn in Problem 1, to a scale of $\frac{1}{4}'' = 1'\text{-}0''$. Heights, such as floor, grade, ceiling, and roof may be projected from the front elevation. Make use of the plans for location of windows and doors.

7. Make the framing plans of the house of your design. Trace the outline of the foundation plan in Problem 2, and select joist sizes from standard tables on "Joist Spans and Sizes." Double the floor joists where partitions run parallel to the joists. Study the framing around stairwell and chimney openings.

8. Draw a longitudinal cross section through the house of your design. Use scale of $\frac{1}{4}'' = 1'\text{–}0''$. Refer to plans and elevations for lengths and heights. Take section through stair and fireplace if possible. Use Fig. 23.10 for reference. Indicate all material by proper symbol and dimension section completely.

9. To a scale of $1\frac{1}{2}'' = 1'\text{-}0''$, draw a wall section showing the footing, foundation wall, sill construction, window-in-wall section, and cornice construction. Show all necessary dimensions. Refer to Fig. 23.11 for methods of dimensioning.

10. Draw any details necessary to clarify fully the working drawings completed. For suggestions as to the type of details, refer to Fig. 23.12.

24 STRUCTURAL DRAWING

24.1. Although structural drawings are prepared in accordance with the general principles of projection, they differ somewhat from machine drawings in certain practices. These differences, which have gradually developed due to the type of raw material used and methods of fabrication, have become established drawing room customs that are recognized universally throughout the industry and must be understood and adhered to by every prospective structural engineer.

Steel structures vary widely and include almost everything fabricated from rolled shapes and plates.

Fabrication consists in shearing, flame cutting, punching, bending, forging, and machining, then fitting and aligning the parts, and finally permanently fastening the assembly by bolting, riveting, or welding. Although small roof trusses and girder bridges may be assembled as complete units in the shop, the size of most structures makes necessary the fabrication of sub-assemblies and shipment in knock-down form.

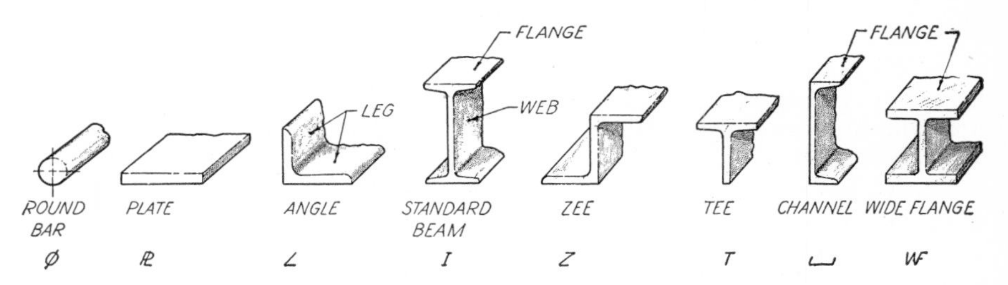

Fig. 24.1. Structural shapes.

Sections of the principal shapes (angles, I-beams, channels, wide flange sections, and plates) are shown in Fig. 24.1.

The dimensions of the various standard shapes and other available information required by a structural detailer are given in structural steel handbooks published by different manufacturers and by the American Institute of Steel Construction.

24.2. Equipment of a structural draftsman. The equipment needed by a structural draftsman is the same as for any other line of industrial drafting with a few additions. Smaley's tables of trigonometric functions and logarithms, and Smaley's tables of slopes and rises are a

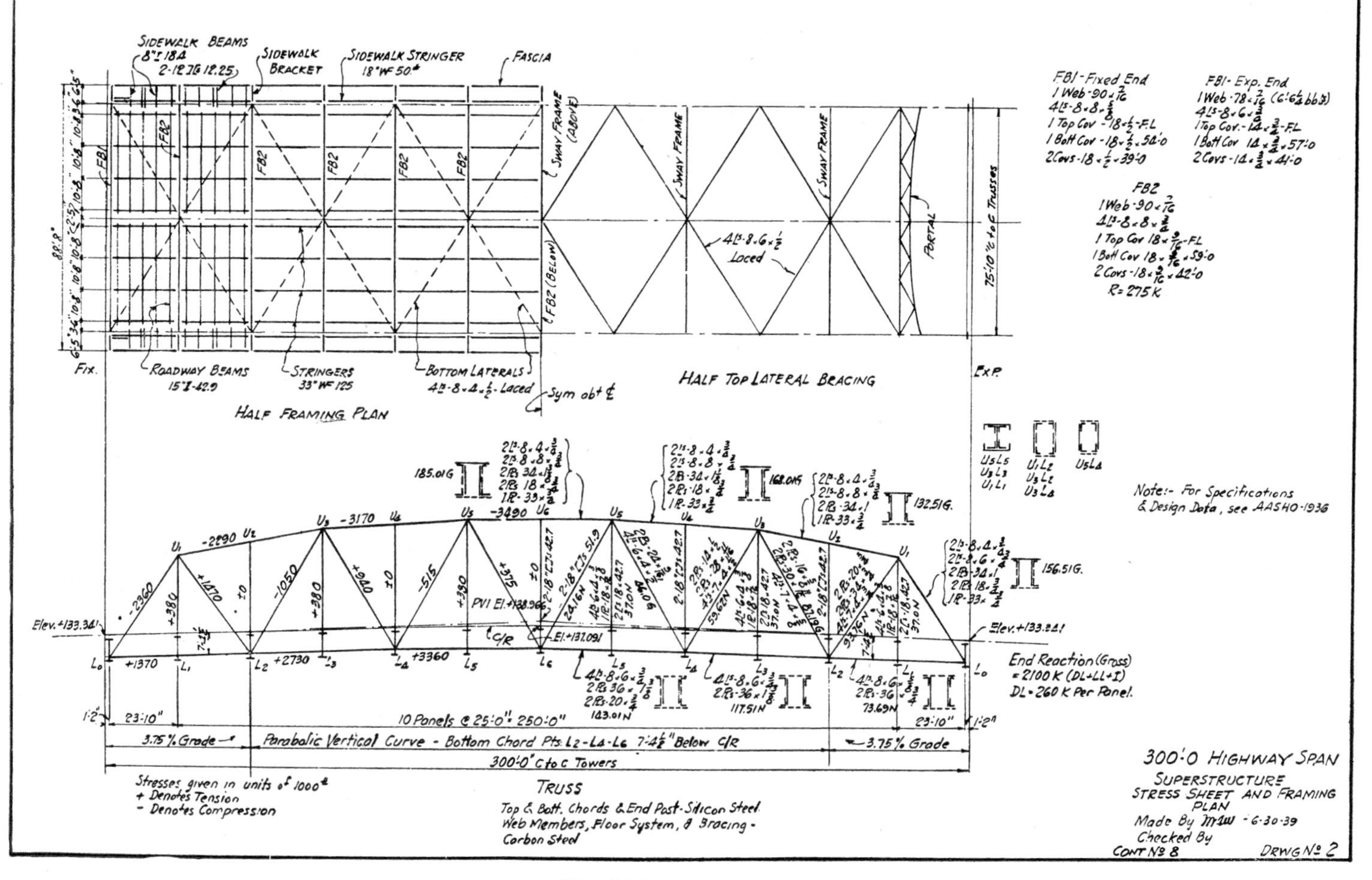

Fig. 24.2. Stress sheet.

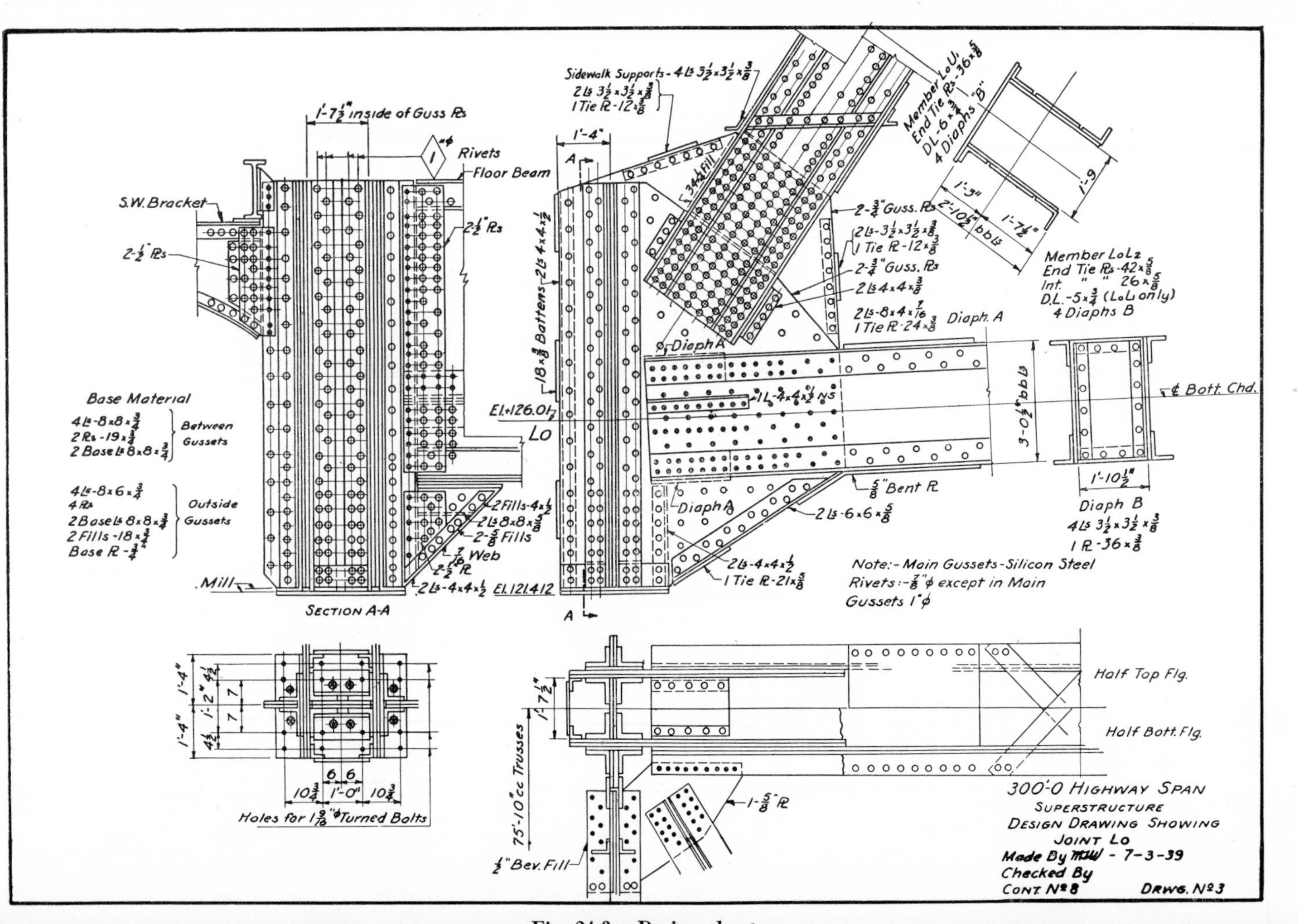
Sidewalk Supports - 4 Ls 3 1/2 x 3 1/2 x 3/8
2 Ls 3 1/2 x 3 1/2 x 3/8
1 Tie Pl - 12 x 3/8
1'-7 1/2" inside of Guss Pls
1" φ Rivets
Floor Beam
S.W. Bracket
2-1/2" Pls
2-1/2" Pls
Base Material
4 Ls - 8 x 8 x 3/4
2 Pls - 19 x 3/4
2 Base Ls 8 x 8 x 3/4
Between Gussets
4 Ls - 8 x 6 x 3/4
4 Pls
2 Base Ls 8 x 8 x 3/4
2 Fills - 18 x 3/4
Base Pl - 3/4
Outside Gussets
Mill
Section A-A
18 x 3/8 Battens - 2 Ls 4 x 4 x 1/2
El. +126.01
Lo
2 Fills - 4 x 1/2
2 Ls 8 x 8 x 3/8
2 - 5/8 Fills
7/16 Web
2 - 1/2 Pl
2 Ls - 4 x 4 x 1/2
El. 121.412
1'-4"
A
Member LoU1
End Tie Pls - 36 x 5/8
DL - 6 x 3/8
4 Diaphs "B"
1'-3"
2'-10 1/2" bbls
1'-7 1/2"
1'-9
2 - 3/4" Guss. Pls
2 Ls - 3 1/2 x 3 1/2 x 3/8
1 Tie Pl - 12 x 3/8
2 - 3/4" Guss. Pls
2 Ls 4 x 4 x 3/8
2 Ls - 8 x 4 x 7/16
1 Tie Pl - 24 x 3/8
Diaph. A
Member LoL2
End Tie Pls - 42 x 5/8
Int. " " 26 x 5/8
D.L. - 5 x 3/4 (LoL1 only)
4 Diaphs B
Diaph A
1 L - 4 x 4 x 3/8 NS
3'-0 1/4" bbls
Bott. Chd.
1'-10 1/2"
Diaph B
4 Ls 3 1/2 x 3 1/2 x 3/8
1 Pl - 36 x 3/8
5/8" Bent Pl
Diaph A
2 Ls - 6 x 6 x 5/8
2 Ls - 4 x 4 x 1/2
1 Tie Pl - 21 x 5/8
Note:- Main Gussets - Silicon Steel
Rivets: - 7/8" φ except in Main
Gussets 1" φ
1'-4"
1'-4"
1'-2"
4 1/2
4 1/2
7
7
6 6
10 3/4
1'-0"
10 3/4
Holes for 1 9/16" φ Turned Bolts
1'-7 1/2"
75'-10" cc Trusses
1/2" Bev. Fill
1 - 5/8" Pl
Half Top Flg.
Half Bott. Flg.
300'-0 Highway Span
Superstructure
Design Drawing Showing
Joint Lo
Made By MW - 7-3-39
Checked By
Cont. No 8
Drwg. No 3

necessity. A copy of the structural handbook published by the American Institute of Steel Construction must be readily available for constant use.

Some companies furnish each draftsman with a book that gives drawing room standards. Included are typical drawings illustrating the arrangement of views, approved dimensioning practices, and notes for various types of structures. Some information also may be given about plant equipment.

24.3. Classes of structural drawings. Most of the large steel fabricators maintain a design office and a detailing office. The former prepares design drawings and estimates costs in the preparation of bids and frequently serves in a consulting capacity on designs furnished by a customer. The detailing office, which is usually located at the fabricating plant, orders material and prepares shop and erection plans from the design sheets.

Design drawings usually are line diagrams showing the shape of a structure, the principal dimensions, structural sections, and in some cases the stresses to be used in detailing the connections. Fig. 24.2 is an example of a design drawing.

For the use of the layout man a set of design drawings may contain elaborate design details, showing the type of connections, thickness of gusset plates, and the number of rivets. Fig. 24.3 is the design detail for joint L_O of the truss shown in Fig. 24.2. Design drawings of this type, however, are furnished only for important or complicated structures. Quite often the design of connections becomes a detailers task.

A set of specifications covering special conditions, unit stresses, materials to be used, and so forth, is considered as part of the design information.

Shop detail drawings show all of the information necessary for shop fabrication.

Erection plans, which are prepared primarily for use in the field, consist of line diagrams giving dimensions, shipping marks, and notes in sufficient detail to guide the erector in assembling the parts to complete the finished structure.

24.4 Layouts. The first step in the development of structural steel detail drawings is the drawing of the layout sheets. These are intermediate drawings that are used only in the drafting room of the fabricating shop. Layouts are used for ordering material, obtaining early approval of details, and co-ordinating the work of the several draftsmen who may be employed on the project. As a general rule, layouts are made only when the complexity of the work demands a carefully scaled picture. For example, layouts would be necessary for all types of skewed work, and for truss joints. Layouts may be drawn to any appropriate scale, but usually the detail drawing and layout scales are the same. They usually are made on bond paper that is thin enough to permit blue-printing. Layouts are not completely dimensioned, but the layout man may indicate any dimensions he wishes to be used.

Fig. 24.4 is a layout of the cross frame of a deck-girder bridge. The detailer takes a layout of this kind, in addition to the design drawings for

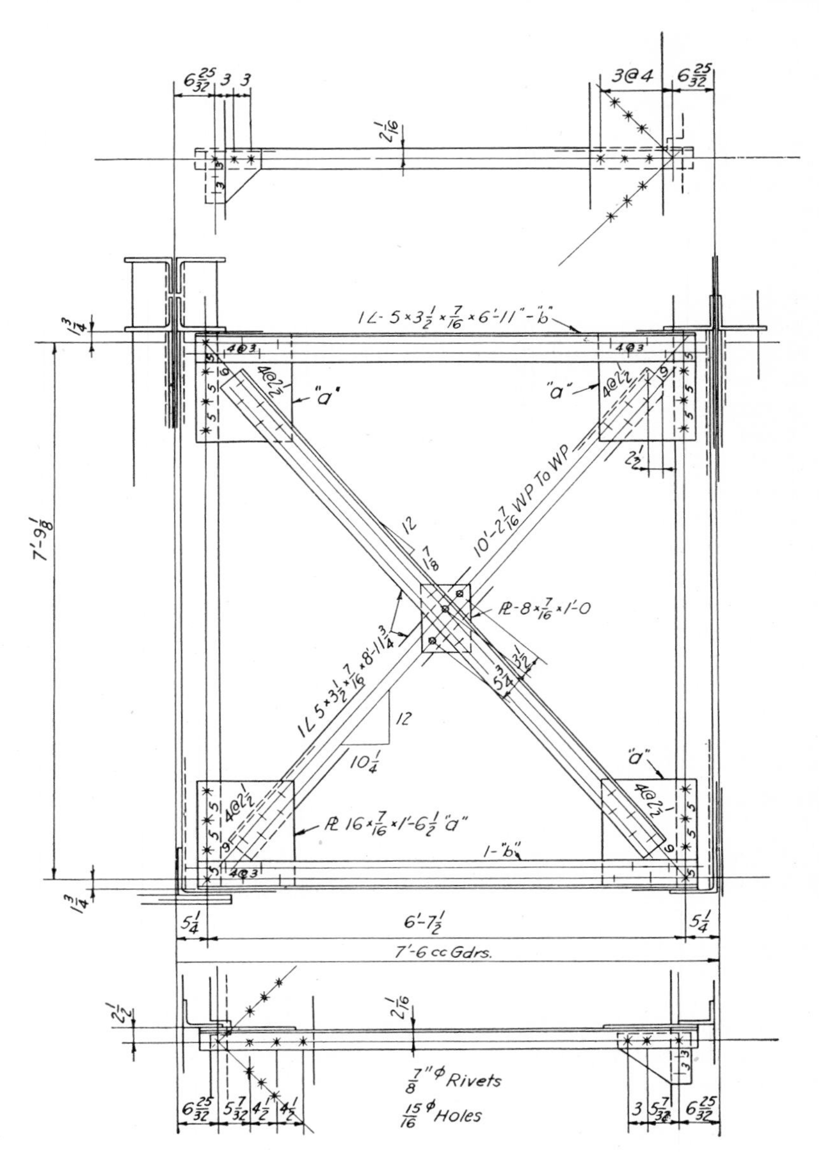

Fig. 24.4. Layout for internal cross frame.

the project, and completely details the structure so that it may be used in the shop for fabricating.

24.5. Detail drawings. The making of the detail drawing is the final step in the process of creating structural steel working drawings. These drawings must be clear and concise, to enable men in the shop to do their portion of the work efficiently. To insure accuracy, a thorough check of all arrangements and dimensions is made in the drafting room by a checker.

Parts to be riveted together in the shop are detailed in their assembled positions in the structure, instead of being detailed individually, as is the practice for machine work. Fig. 24.5 is a detail drawing of a cross frame. It describes each plate and main member and shows the relations of the various elements of the structure to one another. When the structure is too large to be completely assembled in the shop and shipped in one piece, an assembly or erection diagram becomes necessary.

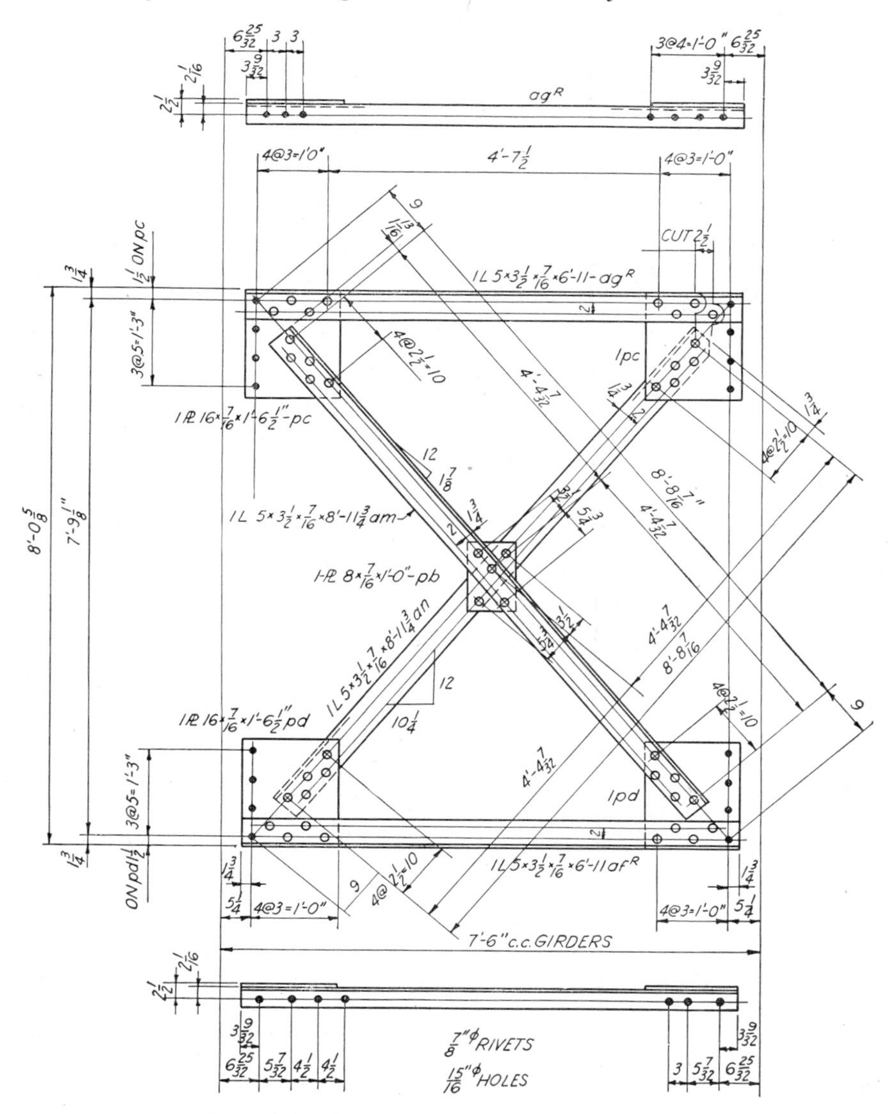

Fig. 24.5. Detail drawing of a cross frame.

The scales in general use are not large enough to permit direct scaling of dimensions. One of the scales most commonly used in structural work is: $\frac{3}{4}'' = 1'$. Often structural members are too long to be drawn to scale and yet be contained on the sheet of drawing paper. In this event, the transverse dimensions and the details are drawn to one scale and the longitudinal dimensions are shortened or drawn to a smaller scale.

Structural steel drawings incorporate a few practices of projection which differ from other types of work. In all structural work the view of the structure which corresponds to the front view in a machine drawing is termed the *elevation* of the structure. The view that corresponds to the top view in a machine drawing is called the *plan view* of the structure. The view below the cross frame in Fig. 24.5 is a plan view of the lower-chord member and is not a bottom view. Likewise, the two views at the bottom of the sheet in Fig. 24.3 are not bottom views of the joint but are sectional views looking downward. The left view shows the location of the anchor bolts and the right view shows both the top and the bottom of the member L_O-L_I where it frames into the joint. Shop men prefer the use of bottom sections because the elevation of a piece, while being fitted, corresponds to the elevation on the drawings. Any fitting or inspection of the bottom is more easily accomplished by looking down than by crawling under and looking upward.

Angular dimensions on structural drawings are shown as slopes that are expressed in inches per foot. A slope triangle is a right triangle constructed with its hypotenuse on the gage or working line whose slope is to be shown. The longer of the two legs is always given as 12″, and the length of the shorter leg determines the slope. These slope triangles are not drawn to scale but are constructed any convenient size (Fig. 24.5).

Structural drawings are currently made in pencil on translucent bond paper. Pencil work requires particular care on the part of the draftsman to make his lines black enough to blueprint clearly. The outlines of the structural members should be wider than the gage lines and dimension lines because the contrast makes the blueprints easier to read.

Pencil tracings on special cloth or ink tracings on cloth are required by certain customers.

24.6. Structural definitions and notations.

′ = foot or feet	∠ = angle
″ = inch or inches	I = I-beam
ϕ = diameter	⊔ = channel
# = pound or pounds	WF = wide flange section

Anchor bolt. A bolt used to fasten steel girders, columns, trusses, and so on, to masonry.

Beam. A horizontal structural member (usually an I-beam or WF beam).

Bearing plate. A plate used under the end of a truss, beam, or girder, to increase the bearing area.

Chip. To chip off projecting parts with a chisel (pneumatic chisel).

Clearance. A general term applying to an opening or space between two adjacent pieces, without which interference would result (Fig. 24.10).

Column. A general term for a vertical member supporting beams or trusses.

Countersink. The operation of chamfering the edges of a hole to receive the conical head of a bolt, rivet, or screw.

Detail. To prepare a working structural drawing. (Working drawings are called details.) (Fig. 24.5.)

Driving clearance. The distance from the center of a rivet to the nearest obstruction that would interfere with the driving of the rivet.

Edge distance. The distance from the center of a rivet or hole to the edge of the member (Fig. 24.10).

Erection diagram. An assembly diagram drawn to aid the erector in placing members of the structure in their proper position.

Fabrication. The shop work of converting rolled shapes into complete structural members.

Field clearance. Minimum distance between unfinished edges that abut when erected at the site. Usually $\frac{1}{2}''$ to $\frac{3}{4}''$.

Field rivet. A rivet driven in the structure at the site of construction.

Filler. A plate or washer used to fill up space between two surfaces.

Flame cut. To cut by hand or by a machine-guided oxyacetylene torch.

Flange. A general term for the outstanding part of a member (Fig. 24.1).

Gage. The distance from the back of an angle or channel to the center line of a row of rivets, or the distance between the center lines of two rows of rivets (Fig. 24.13).

Gage line. The center line of a row of rivets (Fig. 24.13).

Girder. A horizontal member built up of plates and angles.

Grip. The combined thickness of members connected by a rivet.

Gusset plate. A connection plate used to connect several members of a truss (Fig. 24.10).

Layout. A preliminary scale drawing made in the detailing department prior to detailing, for the purpose of ordering material and co-ordinating the work of the several detailers (Fig. 24.4).

Leg. The name for either of the two flanges of an angle (Fig. 24.1).

Line diagram. A drawing in which each member is represented by a single line (Fig. 24.2).

Pitch. The center-to-center longitudinal distance between adjacent rivets (Fig. 24.13).

Plate. A flat piece of structural steel having a rectangular cross section (Fig. 24.1).

Punch. To make a hole by forcing a nonrotating tool through the material.

Ream. To enlarge and finish a punched hole, using a rotating fluted cutter.

Rivet. A cylindrical rod of steel that is used to fasten together members of a steel structure. It has one head formed when manufactured, the other is formed after the rivet is in position.

Shape. The structural term for rolled steel having any cross section (except a steel plate). (See Fig. 24.1.)

Shop clearance. Minimum distance between unfinished abutting edges of members assembled in the shop. Usually $\frac{1}{4}''$.

Shop drawing. A working drawing made for the shop. Commonly called a *detail* drawing. (Fig. 24.5.)

Slope. The inclination of a line designated by a slope triangle expressed in inches of rise to a base of 12″ (Fig. 24.5).

Span. The center-to-center distance between the supports of a beam, girder, or truss.

Staggered rivets. Rivets spaced alternately in parallel rows (Fig. 24.13).

Stitch rivets. Rivets spaced at intervals along a built-up member to cause the component parts to act as a unit.

Stress sheet. A drawing having a line diagram on which are recorded the stresses in the main members of a structure (Fig. 24.2).

Truss. A rigid framed structure, in the form of a series of triangles, which acts as a beam (Fig. 24.14).

Web. The thin portion between the flanges of a member. (See Fig. 24.1.)

Weldment. Any welded assembly or sub-assembly.

Working point. The point of intersection of working lines (usually gage lines) (Fig. 24.14).

24.7. Sizes of standard members. The following structural specifications and abbreviations are those adopted by the American Institute of Steel Construction.

Plates. Width (in inches) × thickness × length. (*Pl* $15 \times \frac{3}{8} \times 1'\text{-}10''$.) If it is a connection plate on a truss, cross frame, and so on, which is fabricated in the shop, the specification will be followed by the letters *pa*, *pb*, *pc*, or *pd*, and so on, which indicate the location of the plate. (*Pl* $15'' \times \frac{3}{8} \times 1'\text{-}10''$ *pa.*)

Angles—Equal legs. Size of leg × size of leg × thickness × length. ($\angle 3\frac{1}{2} \times 3\frac{1}{2} \times \frac{3}{8} \times 7'\text{-}6''$.)

Angles—Unequal legs. Size of leg shown × size of outstanding leg × thickness × length. ($\angle 4 \times 3 \times \frac{5}{16} \times 24'\text{-}7''$.)

I-Beams. Depth of *I*-weight per ft. × length. (12″ *I* 31.8# × 15′-4″.)

Channels. Depth of ⊔-weight per ft. × length. (10″ ⊔ 15.3# × 15′-10″.)

Wide flange sections. Depth of WF-weight per ft. × length. (24″ WF 74# × 12′-6″.)

24.8. Detailing information. The type of rivets and their treatment are indicated on structural drawings by the American Standard conventional symbols shown in Fig. 24.6.

The holes for field rivets are indicated in solid black on a drawing, while shop rivets are shown by open circles having the same diameter as the rivet head (Fig. 24.11). Rivets should be drawn with either a drop pen or a bow pencil. In practice, the circles representing rivets are often drawn freehand on pencil drawings.

24.9. Location of dimension lines. Since shopmen are never permitted to scale a drawing, all dimensions must be placed in such a manner that they will be easily understood. Principal dimensions are generally obtained from the design sheets; other dimensions necessary for detailing are found in tables or are determined by the detailer.

Dimensions for rivet spacing, minor location and size dimensions, and so on, are placed close to the view, while the longer dimensions such as over-all lengths are placed farther away so that extension lines will not cross dimension lines (Figs. 24.7, 24.8, and 24.9).

SHOP RIVETS															FIELD RIVETS			
BUTTON HEADS		COUNTERSUNK AND CHIPPED			COUNTERSUNK NOT CHIPPED			FLATTENED TO $\frac{1}{4}$ HIGH FOR $\frac{1}{2}''$ AND $\frac{5}{8}''$ RIVETS			FLATTENED TO $\frac{3}{8}$ HIGH FOR $\frac{3}{4}''$ TO $1''$ RIVETS			FULL HEADS	COUNTERSUNK AND CHIPPED		
BOTH SIDES	BOTH SIDES	NEAR SIDE	FAR SIDE	BOTH SIDES	NEAR SIDE	FAR SIDE	BOTH SIDES	NEAR SIDE	FAR SIDE	BOTH SIDES	NEAR SIDE	FAR SIDE	BOTH SIDES	BOTH SIDES	NEAR SIDE	FAR SIDE	BOTH SIDES

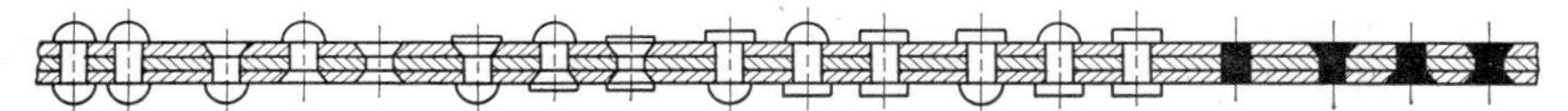

Fig. 24.6. Conventional symbols for rivets.

Dimension figures are generally placed above continuous (unbroken) dimension lines, which are made narrow and black. These lines usually should be placed off the view, but oftentimes added clearness may be obtained by putting a few dimensions in an open area on the view itself. Dimension lines ordinarily should not be placed less than $\frac{3}{8}''$ apart or closer to the view than $\frac{1}{2}''$. All of the above rules for the location of dimension lines may be modified to suit the available space (Fig. 24.8).

24.10. Dimensions and notes in structural detailing.

1. Figures may be compressed without reducing their height in order to place them in a limited space between arrowheads.

2. Figures can be placed to one side, with a leader to the dimension line, if the available space is very small.

3. Figures and notes must read from the bottom and the right side of the sheet because shopmen are accustomed to reading from these positions (Fig. 24.7).

4. For dimensions less than one foot, the inch marks ($''$) may be omitted (Fig. 24.9).

5. With the exception of widths of plates and depths of sections, all dimensions of one foot or more are expressed in feet and inches (Fig. 24.7).

Correct	*Incorrect*
$\frac{1}{4}$	$0\frac{1}{4}$
9	$0'$-$9''$
10	$10''$
$1'$-$0''$	$12''$
$2'$-$3\frac{1}{4}''$	$2'$-$03\frac{1}{4}''$
$4'$-$0\frac{1}{4}''$	$4'\frac{1}{4}''$

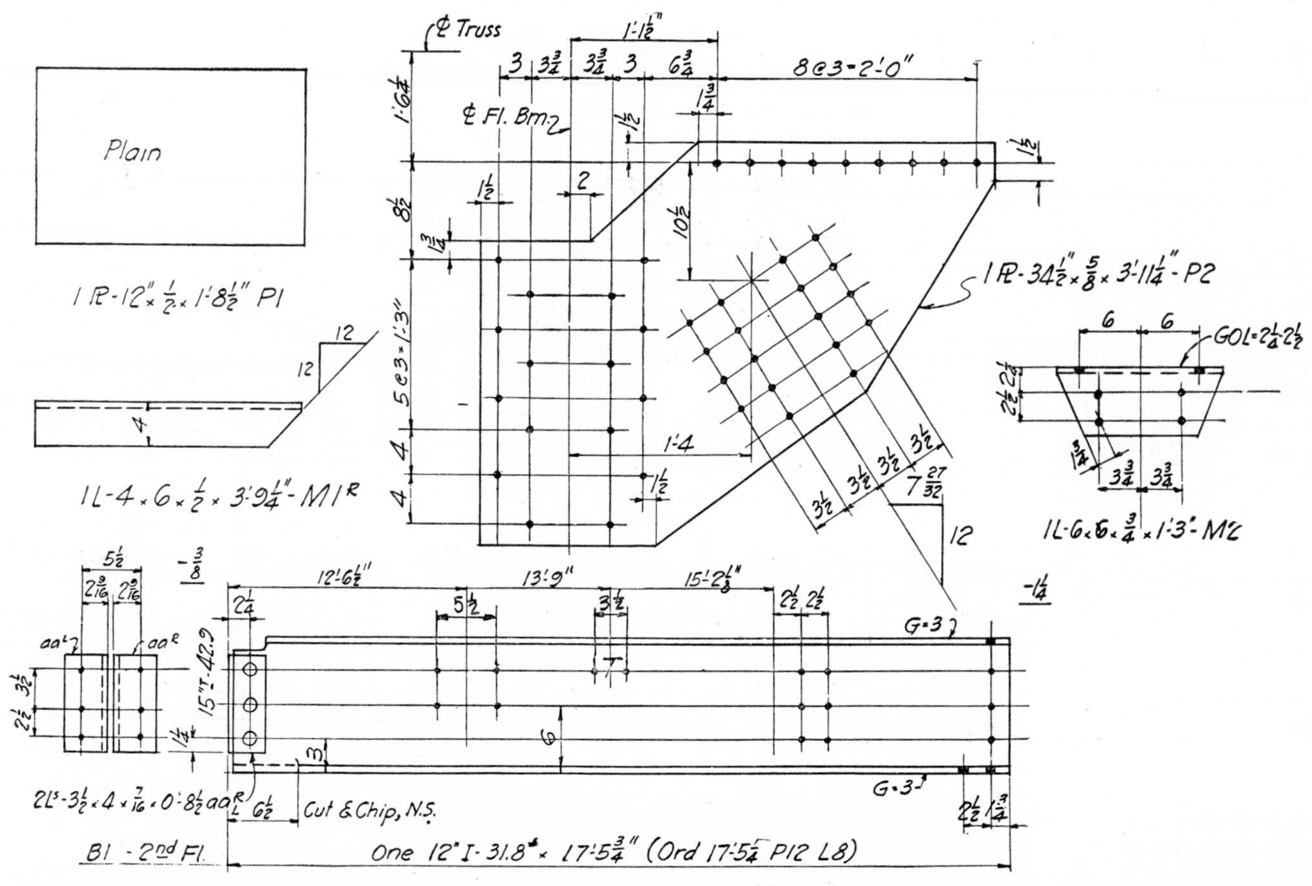

Fig. 24.7. Structural dimensioning.

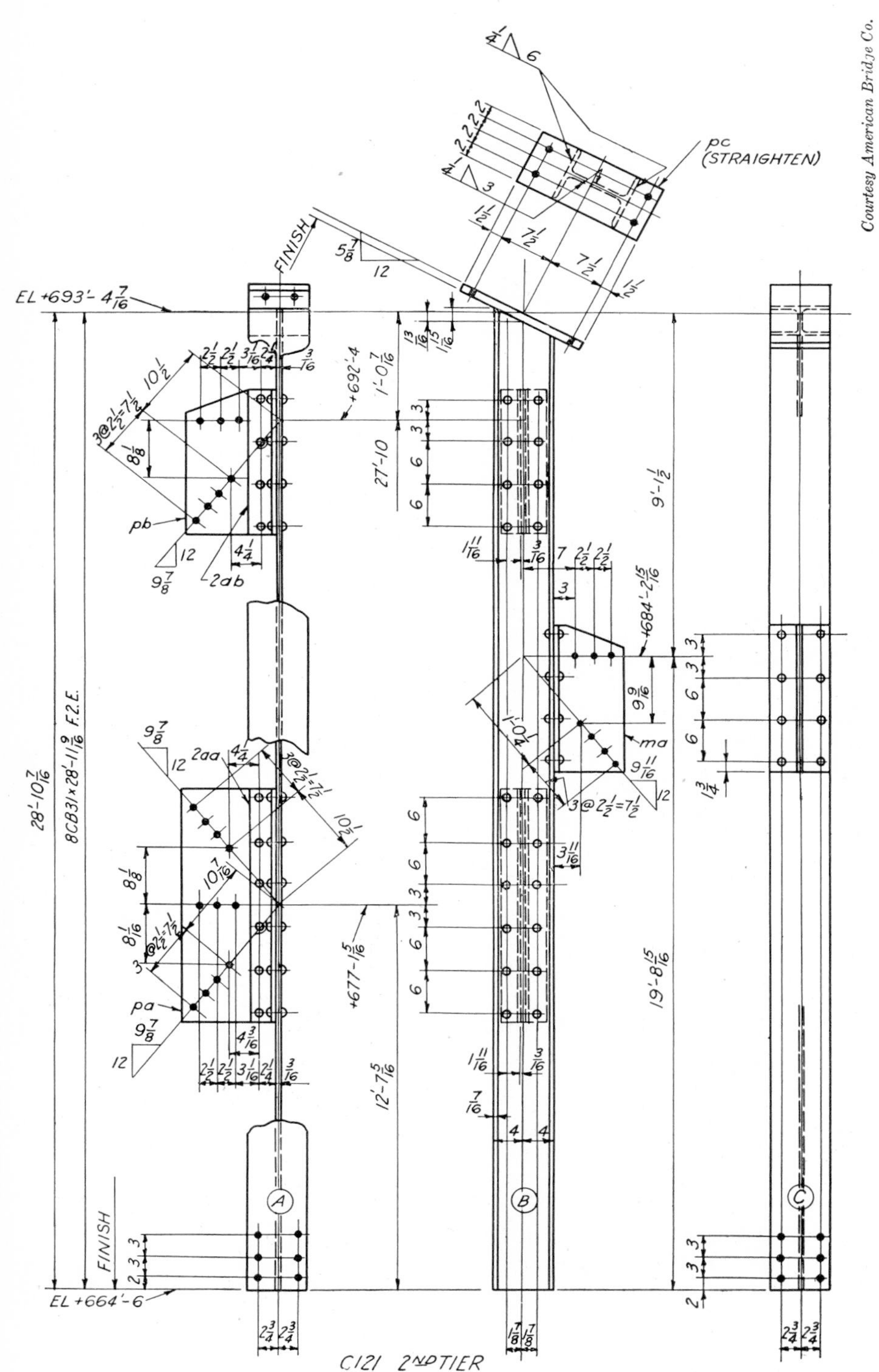

Courtesy American Bridge Co.

Fig. 24.8. Dimensioning a column.

6. Usually, dimensions for rivet spacing are given in multiples of $\frac{1}{8}''$ or, preferably, $\frac{1}{4}''$. It is not desirable to use multiples of $\frac{1}{16}''$ or $\frac{1}{32}''$, except in rare cases.

7. Decimals found in tables should be converted into fractions to the nearest $\frac{1}{16}''$ (except for machine shop drawings for gears, shafts, and so forth).

8. To avoid complications that arise when corrections are made, dimensions shown on one view should not be repeated on another.

9. Rivets and holes are located by dimensions from center to center (Fig. 24.7).

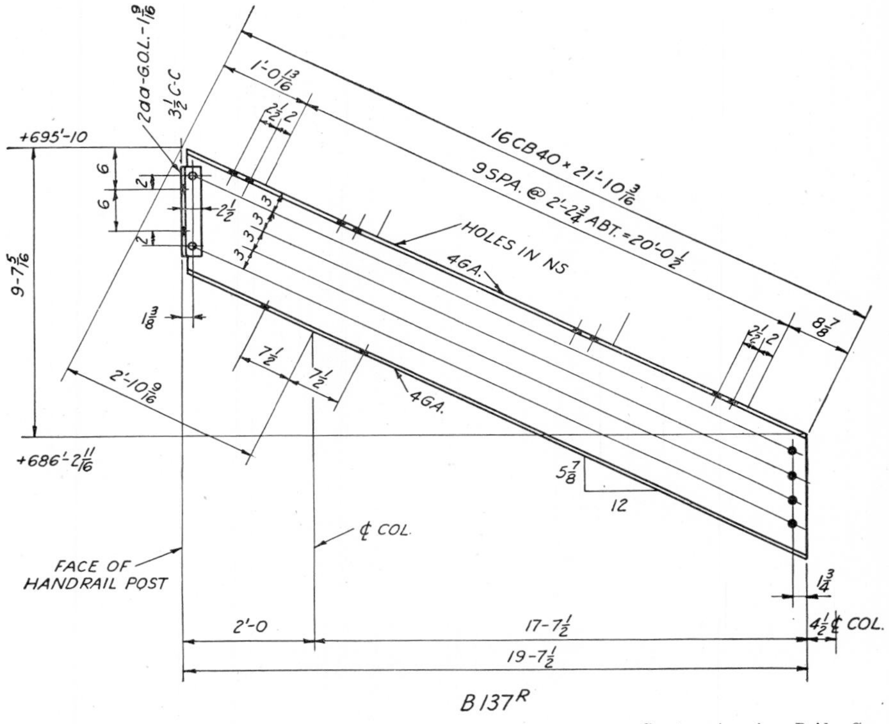

Courtesy American Bridge Co.

Fig. 24.9. Structural dimensioning.

10. Edge distances are frequently omitted, unless they are necessary to insure clearances with connecting parts. (The shopmen understand that the distances on opposite edges are to be made equal.)

11. Dimensions *always* should be given to the center lines of I-beams and to the backs of angles and channels. (See Sec. 24.6, "gage.")

12. When three or more rivet spaces for a line of rivets are equal, they should be dimensioned as a group (4 @ 3″ = 1′-0″). Staggered rivets are dimensioned as if they were on one gage line (Fig. 24.7).

13. Since a workman must use a rule or tape to lay off angles, a slope

triangle should be shown to give the inclination of a working line (Fig. 24.9).

14. A man in the shop never should be compelled to add or subtract to obtain a necessary dimension.

15. A general note is usually placed on a detail drawing giving painting instructions, size of rivets, size of open holes, reaming instructions, and so on.

16. Members that are shipped separately for field erection are given a shipping mark of a letter and number that appears on the detail drawing and on the erection plan (Fig. 24.7).

17. The size of a member is indicated by a specification (in the form of a note) parallel to it (Fig. 24.7).

18. The width of a plate is always given in inches (Fig. 24.7).

24.11. Procedure for making a layout of a gusset plate. The general procedure for making the layout of a gusset plate that connects two members of a roof truss to the bottom chord member is given in Fig. 24.10. Each member is composed of two angles.

Step 1. Calculate the slopes of the diagonal members and draw in the working lines [Fig. 24.10(1)]. Use a scale of $1\frac{1}{2}'' = 1'$ or $3'' = 1'$. (Ordinarily the working lines will be gage lines.)

Step 2. Determine the correct dimensions and gages (Fig. 24.13) and draw in the lines representing the outstanding and perpendicular legs of the angles on the proper sides of the working lines. Draw in the clear-

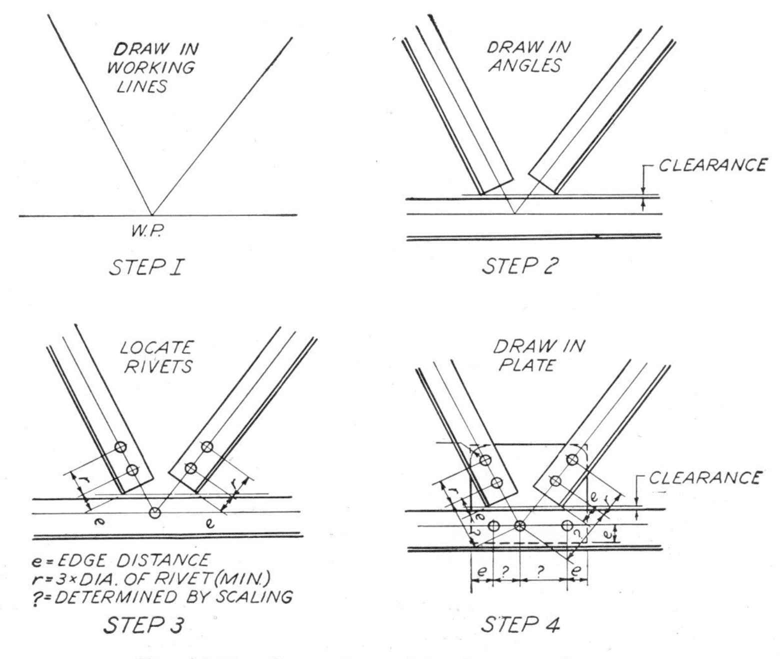

Fig. 24.10. Steps for making layout of gusset.

ance line at a preferred distance above the bottom chord angle and cut the diagonal angles perpendicular to their axes so that the corners fall on the clearance line.

Step 3. Locate an initial rivet in each diagonal at the desired edge distance from the sheared edge of the member. Since it is customary in structural drawing to give the distance from the working point to the first rivet, to the nearest $\frac{1}{4}''$, it usually will be found necessary to change either the edge distance or the clearance to meet this requirement. Locate the remaining rivets in each diagonal, using minimum spacing ($3 \times$ diameter of rivet), so that the plate will not be larger than is absolutely necessary.

Step 4. Draw in the edges of the gusset plate, after giving some consideration to the factors involved in an economical treatment of the design. The points to be observed are: (*a*) allow not less than minimum

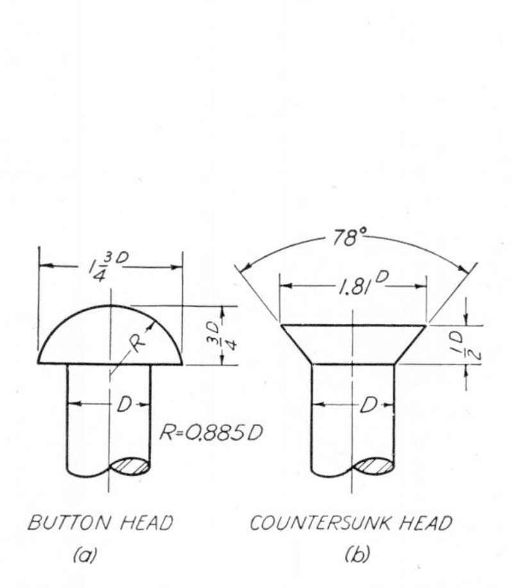

Fig. 24.11. **Dimensions of rivet heads.**

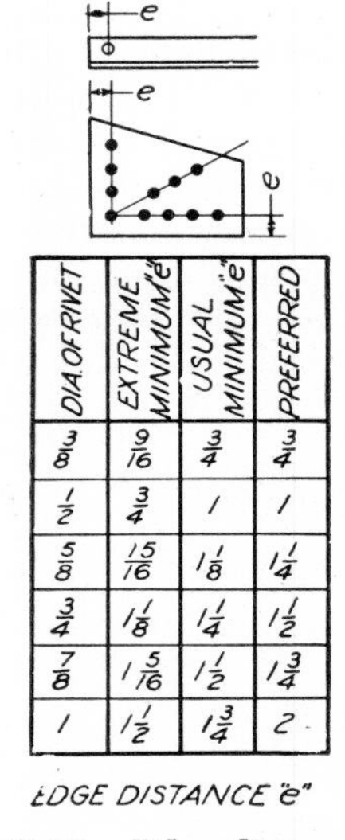

DIA OF RIVET	EXTREME MINIMUM "e"	USUAL MINIMUM "e"	PREFERRED
3/8	9/16	3/4	3/4
1/2	3/4	1	1
5/8	15/16	1 1/8	1 1/4
3/4	1 1/8	1 1/4	1 1/2
7/8	1 5/16	1 1/2	1 3/4
1	1 1/2	1 3/4	2

EDGE DISTANCE "e"

Fig. 24.12. **Edge distance "e."**

edge distance *e* from the center of each rivet to the nearest edge of the plate (Fig. 24.12); (*b*) allow no corners of the plate to project beyond the angle; (*c*) design the plate so that there will be a minimum number of cuts, for each cut increases the labor cost; (*d*) make at least two edges parallel at a distance apart equal to a standard plate width, so that unnecessary cuts and material waste may be avoided.

The shorter dimension usually is considered to be the width, and the longer dimension, the length. If the longer dimension is across the plate between parallel sides, however, it should be given as the width, because the plate may be cut from a long plate of that width. The length dimension usually is given to the nearest $\frac{1}{4}''$. The dimensions of a plate are always those of a rectangle from which the plate may be cut.

24.12. Machine shop work. The structural detailer will occasionally be called upon to prepare detail drawings for castings for bridge shoes and roadway expansion joints and at times drawings for complicated gearing and shafting for movable bridges. Regular machine drawing practices apply, the principal difference being that bridge machinery in general is ponderous with single castings often weighing ten or fifteen tons.

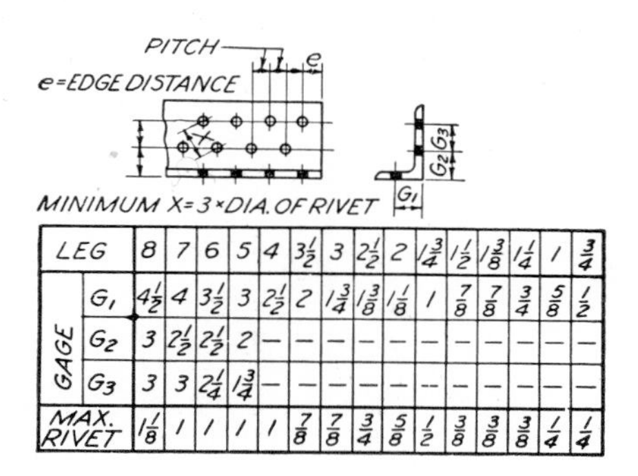

LEG		8	7	6	5	4	$3\frac{1}{2}$	3	$2\frac{1}{2}$	2	$1\frac{3}{4}$	$1\frac{1}{2}$	$1\frac{3}{8}$	$1\frac{1}{4}$	1	$\frac{3}{4}$
GAGE	G_1	$4\frac{1}{2}$	4	$3\frac{1}{2}$	3	$2\frac{1}{2}$	2	$1\frac{3}{4}$	$1\frac{3}{8}$	$1\frac{1}{8}$	1	$\frac{7}{8}$	$\frac{7}{8}$	$\frac{3}{4}$	$\frac{5}{8}$	$\frac{1}{2}$
	G_2	3	$2\frac{1}{2}$	$2\frac{1}{2}$	2	—	—	—	—	—	—	—	—	—	—	—
	G_3	3	3	$2\frac{1}{4}$	$1\frac{3}{4}$	—	—	—	—	—	—	—	—	—	—	—
MAX. RIVET		$1\frac{1}{8}$	1	1	1	1	$\frac{7}{8}$	$\frac{7}{8}$	$\frac{3}{4}$	$\frac{5}{8}$	$\frac{1}{2}$	$\frac{3}{8}$	$\frac{3}{8}$	$\frac{3}{8}$	$\frac{1}{4}$	$\frac{1}{4}$

Fig. 24.13. Gage distances.

24.13. Structural welding. Since a large portion of structural work is either partially or completely welded, a working knowledge of the use of welding symbols (see Chap. 20) is a requirement for a structural draftsman.

Sizes and location of welds are usually given on the design drawing, but very often connections and minor details are left to the detailer.

24.14. Problems. The following problems are intended to furnish experience in the preparation of layouts and to emphasize the principles of structural drawing.

1. Make a pencil layout, plan, and elevation, of joint *A*, Fig. 24.14. Follow carefully the steps outlined in Sec. 24.11 for making a layout of a gusset plate. The following requirements must be observed.

Use $\frac{3}{4}''$ ϕ rivets.

Make the minimum allowable clearance between members = $\frac{1}{4}''$.

Use minimum rivet spacing = 3 × diameter of rivets.

Use the preferred edge distance given in the table in Fig. 24.12.

Use standard gage distances as given in the table in Fig. 24.13.

Make the width of the plate equal to the width of a standard plate. The variation of plate widths is by inches.

The bearing plate is a $9'' \times \frac{3}{4}'' \times 1'\text{-}0''$ steel plate. The rivet pitch in the plan view should be equal to the pitch of the rivets in the vertical leg, and they must be so located that the distances *c*, *f*, and *k* are equal to or exceed the minimum values for these distances for a $\frac{3}{4}''$ rivet as given in structural handbooks. The minimum value of *f* for a $\frac{3}{4}''$ rivet is $1\frac{1}{4}''$; the minimum value of *k* is $1\frac{3}{4}''$; and, the minimum value of *c* is $1\frac{1}{4}''$. These three values represent minimum driving clearance for a $\frac{3}{4}''$ rivet.

The holes for the anchor bolts are $\frac{13}{16}''$ in diameter. Letter the correct specifications for the gusset plate.

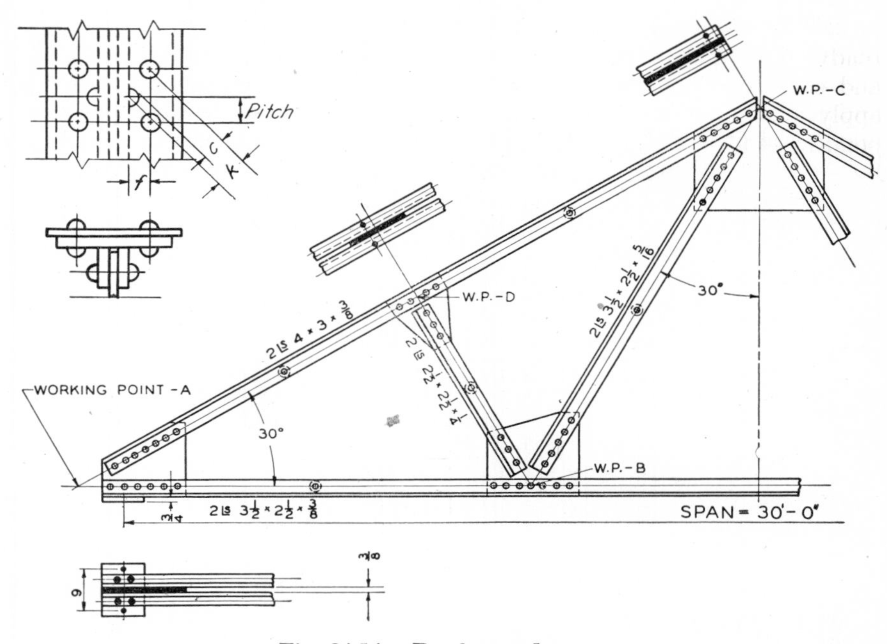

Fig. 24.14. Roof truss layout.

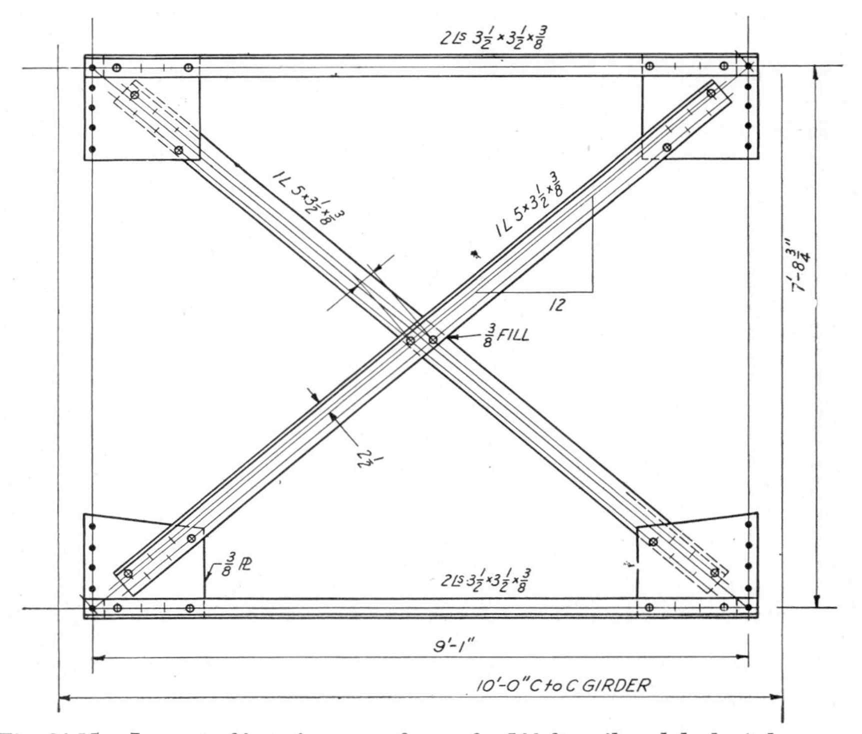

Fig. 24.15. Layout of interior cross-frame for 100 ft. railroad deck girder span.

2. Make a pencil drawing of the cross frame shown in Fig. 24.15. The following requirements must be observed:

Use $\frac{7}{8}''$ rivets.

Use a minimum rivet pitch of $2\frac{1}{2}''$.

The elevation of the cross frame is the only view that is required.

Use standard gage and preferred edge distances as shown in Figs. 24.12 and 24.13.

Use Fig. 24.5 as a model for the placing of complete dimensions.

The open holes are spaced at $3\frac{1}{2}''$ pitch.

25 TOPOGRAPHIC AND ENGINEERING MAP DRAWING

25.1. Map drawing. A map is a drawing that represents a portion of the earth's surface area. Since it usually represents a relatively small part, and the third dimension (the height) is not shown except in some cases by contour lines, a map may be thought of as a one-view orthographic projection (Fig. 25.1). Various forms of maps have been devised

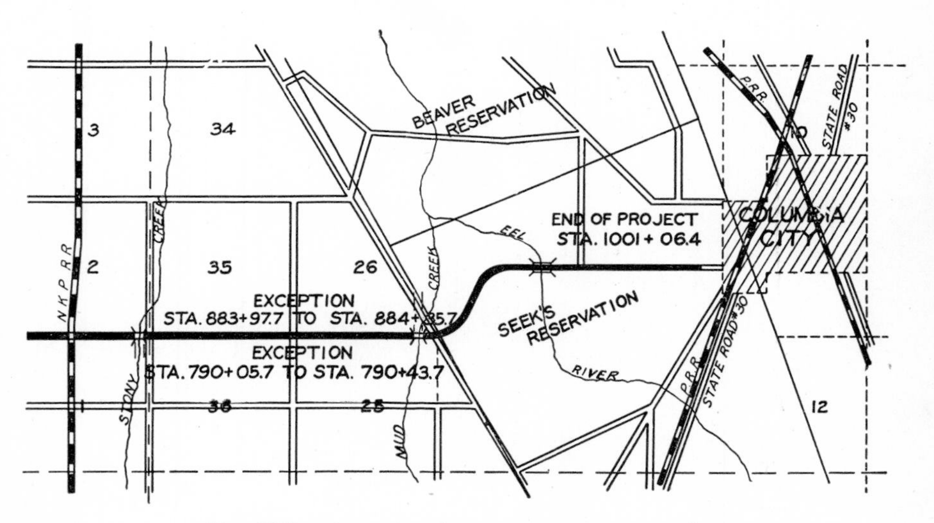

Fig. 25.1. A section from an engineering map.

to satisfy different requirements. Land maps, plats, and so on, which fulfill their purpose by revealing only the natural and man-made features along with imaginary division lines and geometrical measurements, show only two dimensions. Others, such as topographical maps, show three dimensions, by representing height by means of contours.

25.2. Classification of maps. Maps of interest to the engineer may be grouped for study into four general classes, in accordance with their purpose and method of preparation. The recognized classes are: (1) topographical, (2) cadastral, (3) engineering, and (4) aerial photographic.

25.3. Topographic maps. Topographic maps, although they are drawn to a relatively small scale, contain much detail. All natural

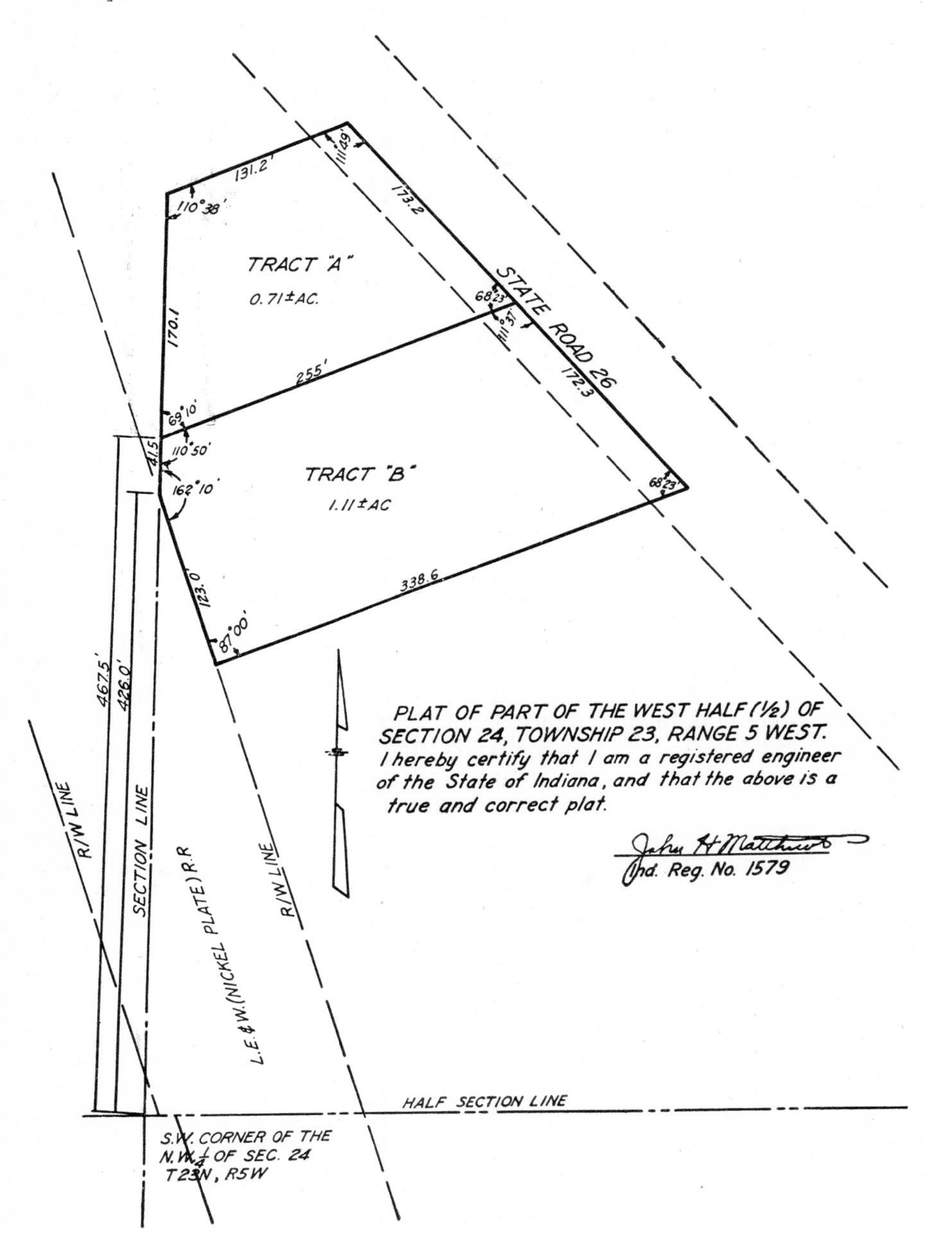

Fig. 25.2. A plat of a land survey.

features, such as lakes, streams, forests, fields, mines, and so on, and important permanent man-made creations, such as buildings, bridges, and houses, may be represented if necessary to fulfill the purpose of a map. Topographic maps, prepared by the United States Geological survey to a scale of approximately one inch to a mile $\left(\frac{1}{62,500}\right)$, naturally do not contain very much detail. The form of the surface of the ground is represented by contour lines. Any one contour line passes through points of the same elevation and closes either on the map or beyond its limits. Closed contour lines represent either a hill or a depression. Fig. 25.5 shows a topographic map.

25.4. Cadastral maps. The major portion of this group consists of city plats, city development maps, town maps, county maps, and maps prepared to show ownership (particularly for the purpose of governmental control and for taxation). These maps, although they show practically no detail, must be accurate and for this reason are drawn to a large scale. Property lines, political boundaries, and a few important features, such as streams, roads, and towns, may be given on township and county maps, to enable a reader to identify particular locations.

25.5. Engineering maps. Working maps prepared for engineering projects are known as engineering maps. They may be drawn for either reconnaissance or construction purposes. They usually are made to a large scale, and accurately show the location of all property lines and important features. On maps of a topographic nature, practically all natural and man-made features along a right-of-way or on a site are shown, and the form of the surface of the ground is indicated by means of contours.

25.6. Plats of land surveys. A plat of a tract of land should contain a complete description of the land surveyed. It should show the lengths and bearings of the bounding sides and division lines, the included acreages, the locations of the monuments, and the names of the owners of the adjoining properties. Fig. 25.2 shows a plat of a typical land survey. Note that a clear, concise title is lettered in the large open area. A certification of the survey is generally required by law. In most states, a plat must bear the seal of a licensed surveyor.

25.7. Subdivision plats. A plat of a real-estate development should show the measurements and angles of the survey of the whole tract of land, the size of the included lots, the widths of the streets and drives, and the location of all monuments. Plats of subdivisions must be complete and accurate, since they are filed as a public record in the county recorder's office. Sufficient information must be given to enable a surveyor to locate the corners of any lot with precision when making a resurvey at a later date. Fig. 25.3 is a plat of a city subdivision.

25.8. Plats and partial city maps. Plats made from subdivision plats or city maps are prepared by the engineering departments of cities and public utilities. The purpose of these partial maps is to record special information concerning such things as proposed improvement projects, the location of lines of transportation, and the location of existing and

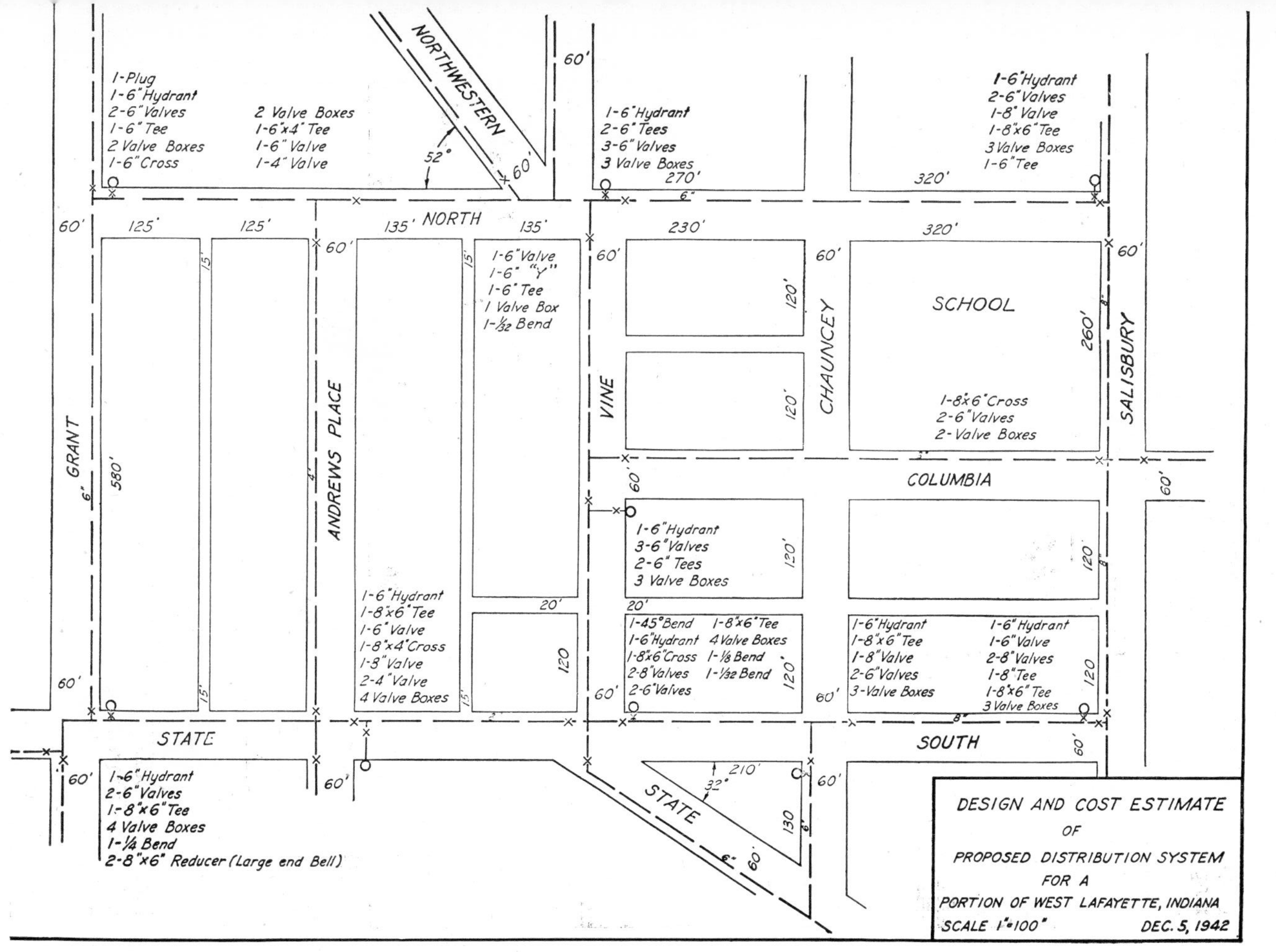

Fig. 25.4. A plat or partial city map showing the proposed location of water mains and fire hydrants.

proposed water mains, sewers, and so on. It is not necessary for such a map to contain all the information given on the subdivision plat from which it is made. The location of monuments and angles generally is not shown. The widths of streets and the sizes of lots may or may not be shown, depending upon the usefulness of such information. A few

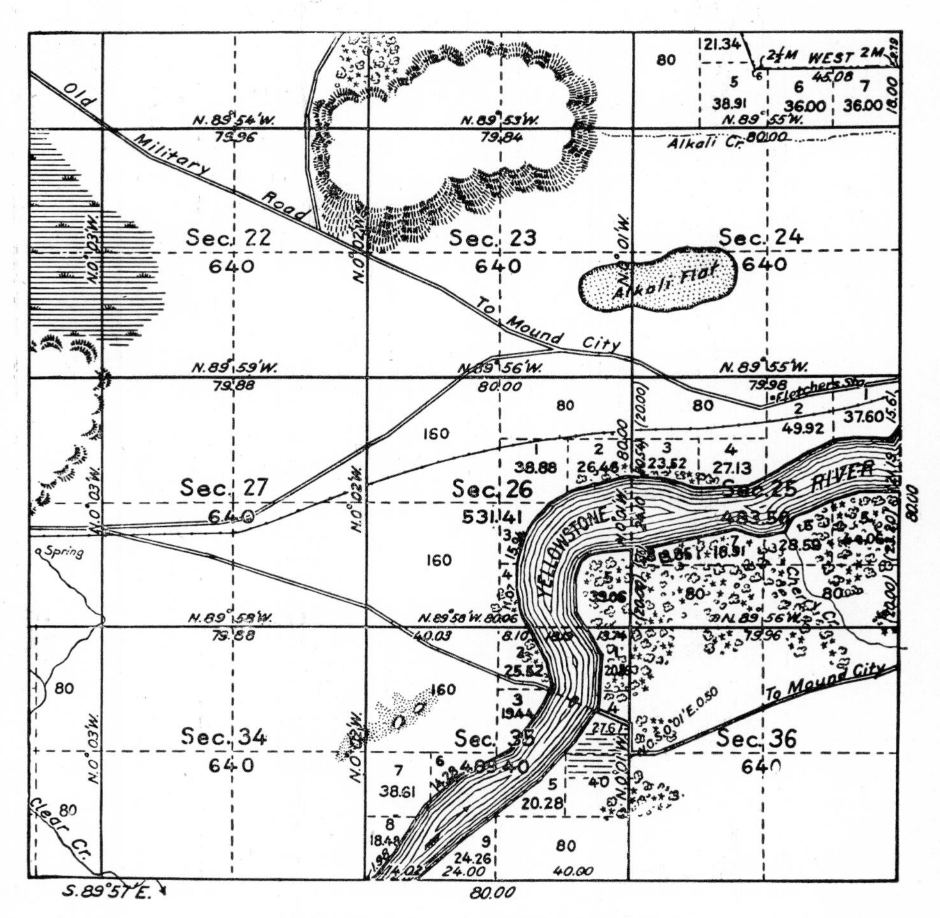

Fig. 25.5. A topographic map.*

important buildings may be indicated for the sake of aiding the reader in orienting himself. Fig. 25.4 shows the proposed location of water mains and fire hydrants in a portion of a city.

25.9. Topographic drawing. As previously stated, a topographic map is a reproduction, to scale, of a small area. On a complete topo-

* A portion of a topographic map taken from a manual prepared by the U. S. Department of the Interior—1930.

graphic map, the natural and artificial features are represented by recognized conventional symbols and the form of the ground is shown by contours. Excessive detail should be avoided, and only necessary surface features should be shown. All names and required notes should be lettered in a position where they can be easily read; a complete title should be lettered in the lower right-hand corner. Ordinarily, single-stroke Reinhardt lettering is preferable on topographic maps prepared solely for construction projects, while vertical modern Roman is more desirable on finished maps where effect and pleasing appearance are important. Fig. 25.5 shows a topographic map.

The scale to be used for a topographic map depends upon the size of the area and the amount of the detail that must be shown. Scales range from 1 inch = 100 feet to 1 inch = 4 miles. Maps prepared by the United States Geological Survey are usually drawn to 1:62,500, which is almost one inch to a mile.

25.10. Standard topographic symbols (U.S.G.S.). Recognized signs and symbols are used to represent the natural and artificial features on a topographic map. Many of these symbols have been designed to bear some pictorial resemblance to the feature or object represented and, for convenience, may be grouped as follows: (1) physical features (buildings, highways, railroads, and so on); (2) ground formations (elevations and depressions); (3) water-surface features (rivers, lakes, and streams); and (4) vegetation growths (grass, trees, and cultivated crops).

Conventional symbols used by the United States Geological Survey for representing the works and structures of man are shown in Fig. 25.6. Symbols for natural land formations, water features, and vegetation growths, both natural and cultivated, are shown in Figs. 25.7 to 25.9.

25.11. The drawing of symbols. Topographic symbols are drawn either freehand or mechanically, depending upon the character of the features to be represented. For example, the symbols representing natural features are drawn freehand, while those representing artificial works are drawn mechanically. (See Figs. 25.6 to 25.9.) On topographic maps prepared for engineering projects, the symbols are drawn in India ink. When colors are used, as in finished maps, the artificial features (buildings, bridges, railroads, and so on) are drawn in black, the contours in brown, the water features in blue, and vegetation growths in green

Although the size of symbols may vary somewhat with the size of the map, they are never to scale but are always exaggerations. The usual mistake of the beginner is to draw symbols too large or too close together. Either fault produces a disagreeable appearance and tends to attract the reader's attention away from more important features. The symbols representing prominent features are made to stand out from those of lesser importance by being drawn slightly larger and with heavier lines.

The beginner should study carefully the symbols as given in the various illustrations, so as not to miss some of the essential points in their construction. For instance, he should note that the symbol for a tree (Fig. 25.9) is composed of separate lines, irregularly located, and not of

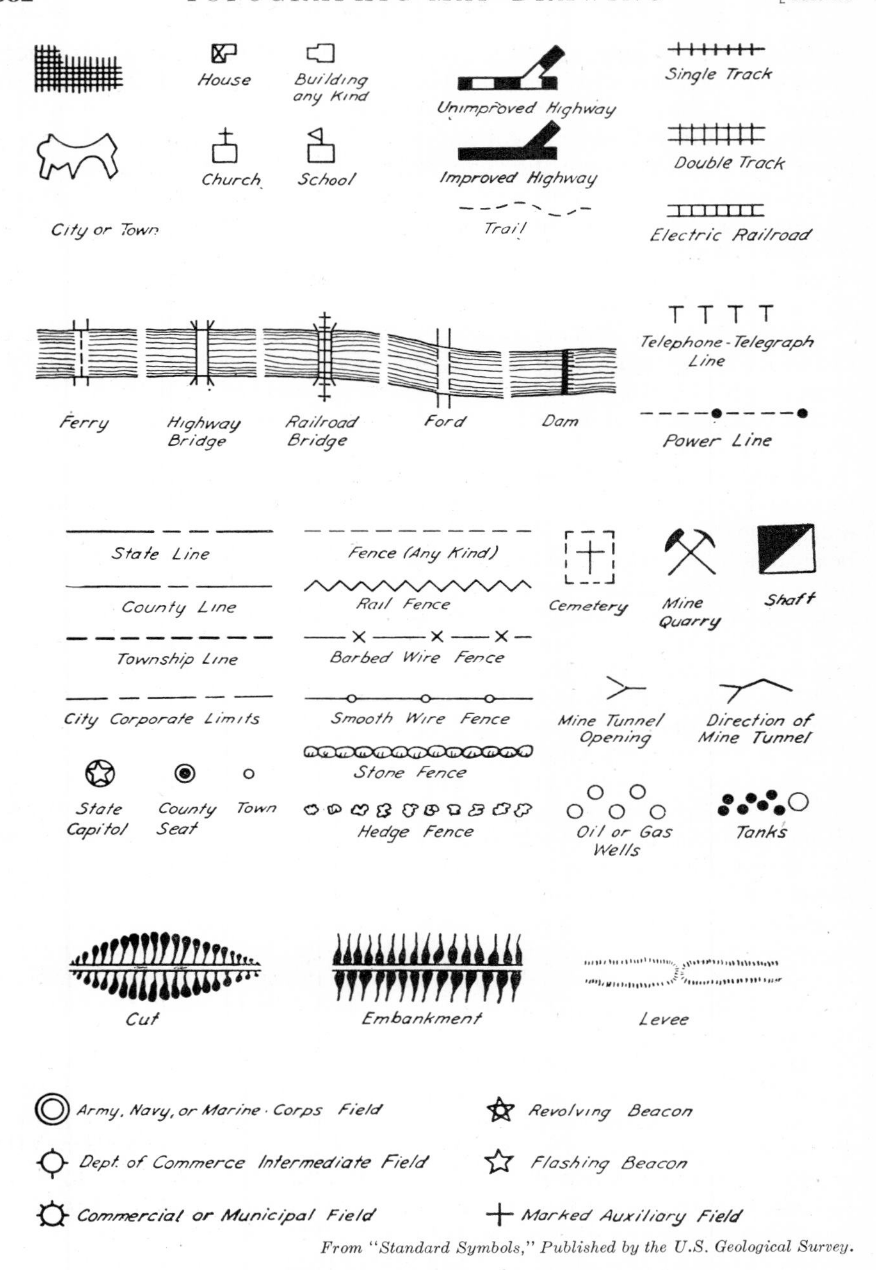

From "Standard Symbols," Published by the U.S. Geological Survey.

Fig. 25.6. Standard symbols for works and structures.

one closed line drawn without lifting the pen. The symbols for grass, corn, and other vegetation should be placed with the bases of the tufts and stocks parallel to the lower border line.

25.12. The drawing of water lines. Water lining, used to indicate water surfaces, is done entirely freehand with an ordinary lettering pen.

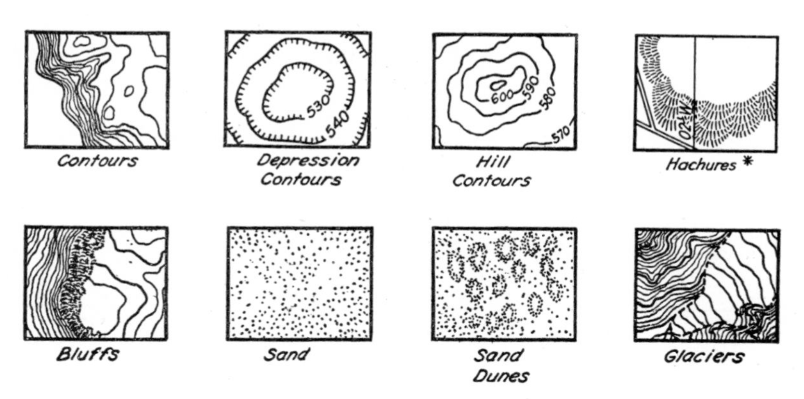

Fig. 25.7. Relief (natural land formations).

The starting line (shore line) should be fairly heavy, and each successive line should decrease in width until the center of the body of water is reached. (See Fig. 25.8.) The line next to the shore line should be drawn parallel to it throughout its entire length, and the space between should be equal to the width of the shore line. The spacing between succeeding lines should increase gradually to the center, but the change should be so slight that no marked increase will be noticeable. Each added line should show fewer of the small irregularities of the shore line, the last few following only the prominent ones.

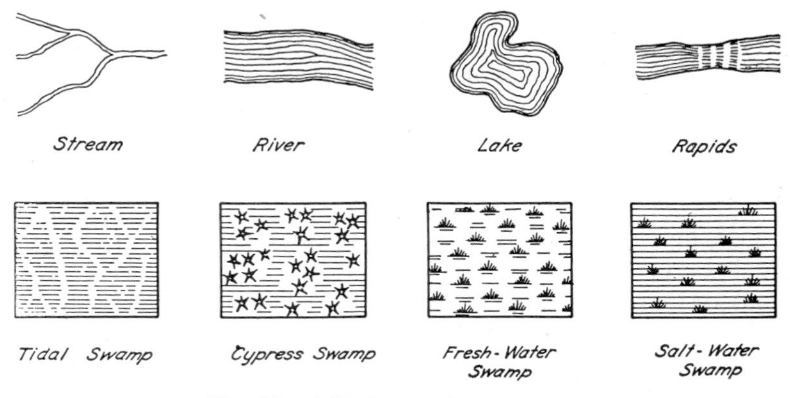

Fig. 25.8. Hydrographic symbols.

* From topographic map shown in Fig. 25.5.

If several bodies of water are to be indicated on the same map, a good way to obtain uniformity is to draw all the shore lines first, then all the lines next to the shore lines, and so on, working back and forth from one body of water to another until the representations are completed. Excessive waviness gives these lines an unnatural appearance and should be avoided.

25.13. Contour lines. A contour line is a line through points of the same elevation on the surface of the ground. Theoretically, the contour lines on a map may be thought of as the lines of intersection of a series of horizontal planes and the ground surface. In practice, the imaginary planes are equally spaced vertically so that the contour intervals will be

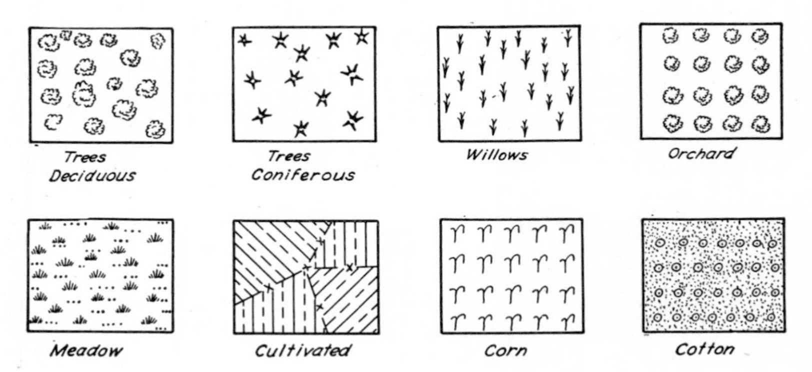

Fig. 25.9. Vegetation symbols.

equal and the horizontal distances between contours on a map will indicate the steepness of the rise or descent of the surface. The closer they are together, the greater the slope, and conversely, the farther they are apart, the less the slope. An arrangement of contour lines that close indicates either a hill or a depression. The case, whatever it is, usually can be determined by reading the values of the elevations of the contours. Usually, each fifth contour is drawn heavier than the others and has a break in it where its elevation above a datum plane is recorded. If a U.S.G.S. bench mark is used, the datum plane will be at mean sea level.

The selection of the contour interval (vertical distance between contour planes) for a topographic survey is determined by the nature of the ground forms and the purpose for which the map will be prepared. For instance, if the area is relatively level, a one- or two-foot interval probably would be desirable while, if the area is rugged, an interval of fifty feet or even one hundred feet might be used.

Contour lines are plotted from survey notes made in the field. In the case of small areas, the usual method for locating contours is to divide the area into squares and take level readings at every intersection and at intermediate points where a pronounced change in slope takes place (Fig. 25.10). On the assumption that the slope of the ground is uniform between two points, the contours are sketched in by interpolating between the readings to establish the points at which the contours cross the survey lines. The interpolation may be done by eye or by calculation.

Frequently, contours are determined from level readings taken along known lines or from stadia survey notes. When extreme accuracy is necessary and the land is fairly level, contours are established by finding and locating points directly on each contour.

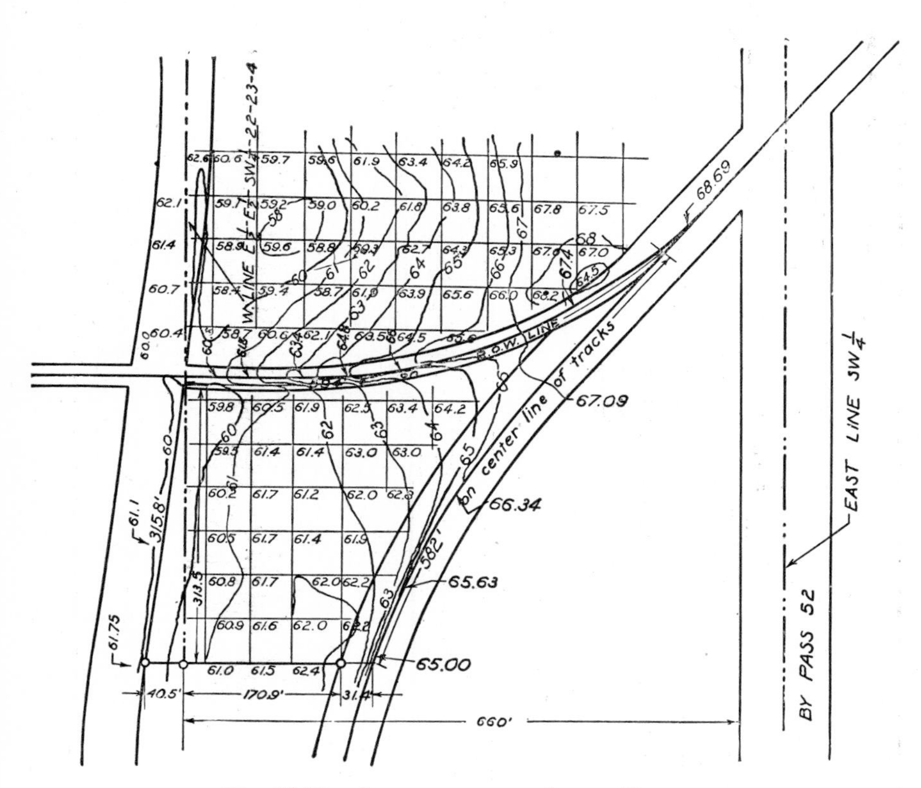

Fig. 25.10. A contour map of a small area.

25.14. Profiles. The profile of a line is prepared to show the relative elevation of every point on the line. Theoretically, it may be thought of as a view showing the line of intersection of a vertical plane through the line and the ground surface. Fig. 25.11 shows a plan view and a profile of a section of a proposed highway project. Profiles are plotted to an exaggerated vertical scale, in order to magnify the relative differences in elevations of points along the line. When the plan and profile are on the same sheet, as in the illustration, the horizontal scale for the profile should be the same as the scale for the plan view (1″ = 100′) and the vertical scale should be 10 or 20 feet to the inch, depending upon the amount of vertical exaggeration needed to emphasize surface irregularities. In deciding upon the vertical scale to be used, a draftsman should deter-

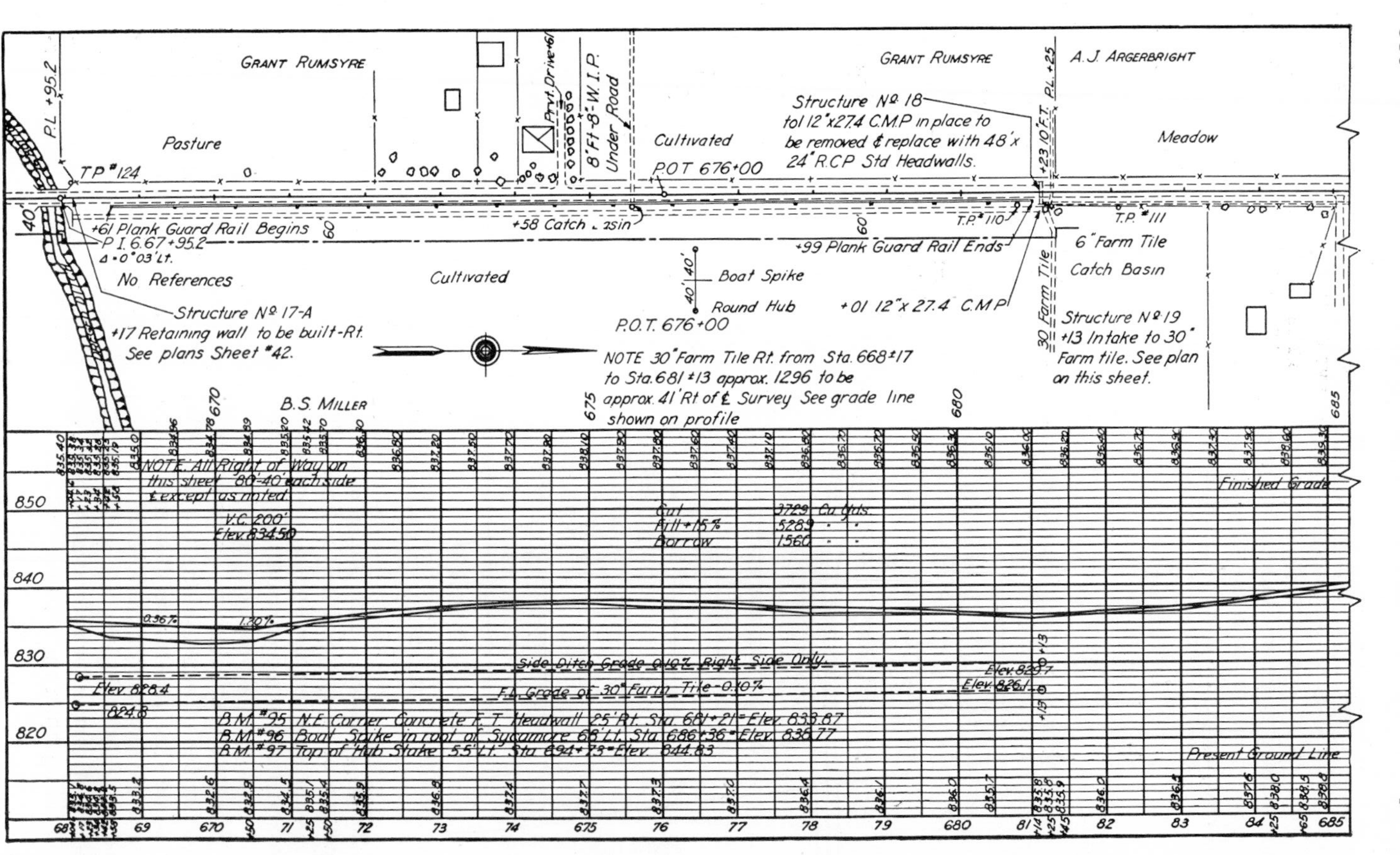

Fig. 25.11. A sheet showing a plan and profile of a proposed highway project.

mine the range of elevations and then should make his selection so that the heavy horizontal lines represent full feet at regular intervals such as 650, 655, 660, and so on. In cases where it is impossible to plot a profile within the range of the grid, it is permissible to break the profile at a heavy vertical line and start again at a lower level. When the line is broken in this way, however, it is necessary to indicate the changed range of elevations by lettering in the new values for the heavy horizontal lines to the right of the "break line."

Profiles are drawn by plotting elevations computed from level readings taken at regular intervals on the ground and at points where the ground changes in slope. Since the slope between adjacent points is assumed to be uniform, a profile consists of a series of straight lines joining successive points.

26 SHADE LINING AND SURFACE SHADING

26.1. Shade lines. In the preparation of certain types of drawings, such as Patent Office drawings, display drawings for advertising literature, and so forth, draftsmen convey the impression of solidity by using the effect of illumination. This is done conventionally, by making the object lines that separate dark surfaces from light surfaces considerably heavier than the other lines (Fig. 26.1). The scheme is known as *shade lining*, and the heavy lines are called *shade lines*.

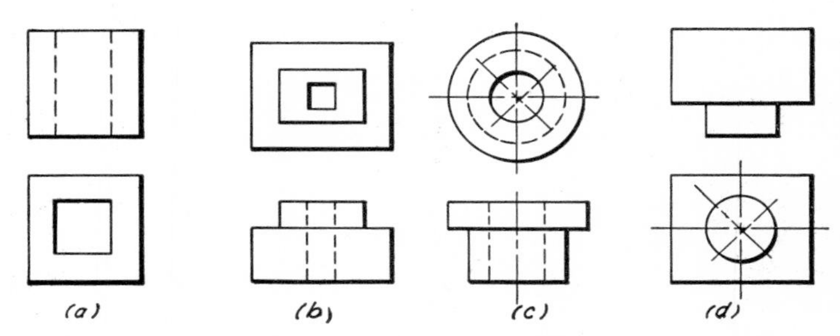

Fig. 26.1. The effect of shade lines.

Shade lines are seldom used on ordinary working drawings. Any small advantage that might be gained in the form of increased legibility is not worth the extra labor involved. On Patent Office drawings, however, they are required. On drawings prepared for advertising literature or technical publications, they may or may not be used, depending upon the importance of the idea of shape.

26.2. The conventional method for drawing shade lines. In accordance with the accepted system of shade lining, an object is considered to be illuminated from a source an infinite distance away. Theoretically, the light rays are assumed to be parallel and to come downward from the left, at an angle of 45°, in the direction of a body diagonal of a cube. In the cube shown in Fig. 26.2(*a*), the illuminated faces would be the left, front, and top. The shaded edges would be the back and right-hand edges in the top view and the lower and right-hand edges in the front view. In practice, however, it is customary to ignore theory and arbitrarily to shade the lower and right-hand edges of all views, as illustrated in Fig. 26.2(*b*). In other words, the conventional practice is to treat all views as front views. Shade lines should be about three times as wide as the other visible object lines. The extra thickness should be added on the outside surface of solids and on the inside surface of openings. Hidden object lines are never shaded.

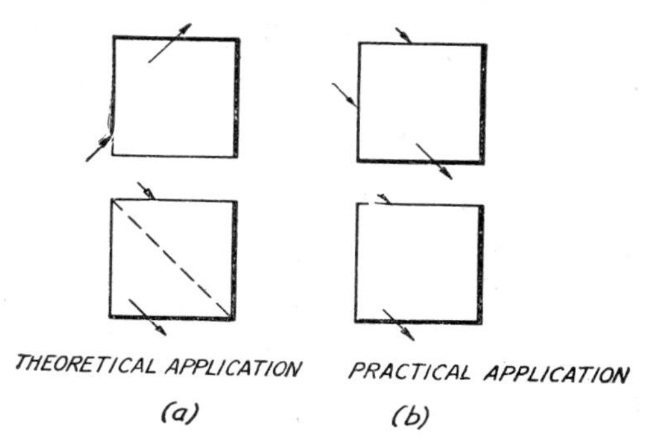

Fig. 26.2. Shade lines.

Circles and circular arcs are shaded in accordance with the same scheme. In shading a circle representing a cylinder (Fig. 26.3*a*), the center is shifted downward to the right, along a 45° line, by an amount equal to the width of the shade line; then a semicircle is drawn. The semicircle starts and stops at the 45° tangent points. It has the same radius as the full circle. When the cylinder has a circular hole (Fig. 26.3*b*), the same center is used for shading both circles.

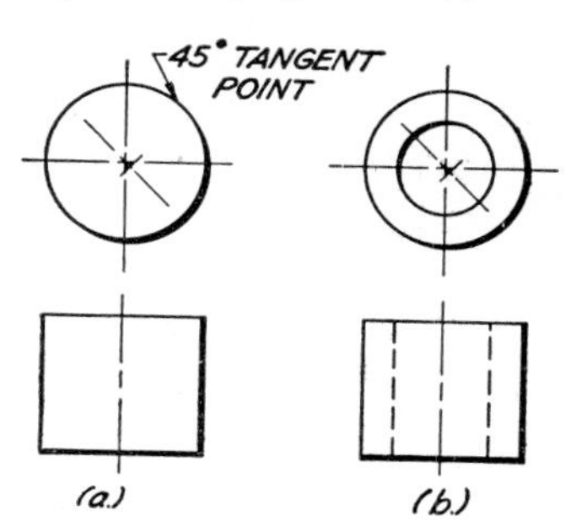

Fig. 26.3. Cylinders.

In general, although shade lines may make a pictorial view more attractive, they have little value from a practical standpoint. They neither improve the pictorial effect nor make the drawing easier to read. When a pictorial drawing of a cube is treated conventionally, the shade lines appear as shown in Fig. 26.4. Some draftsmen, however, shade the edges intersecting at the nearest corners instead. (See Fig. 26.5.)

In dimensioning shaded views, each extension line limiting a dimension

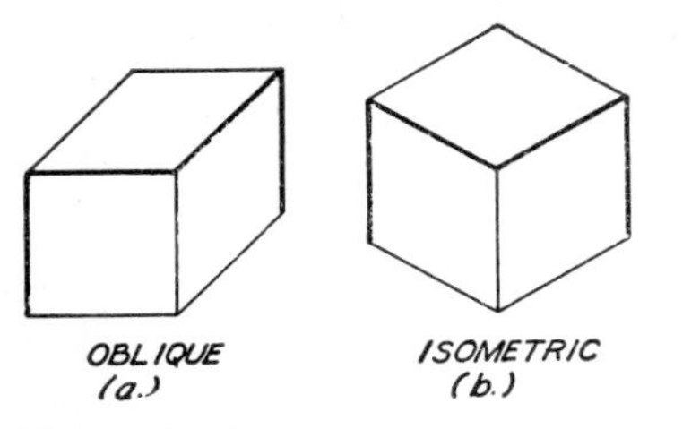

Fig. 26.4. Shaded pictorial drawings.

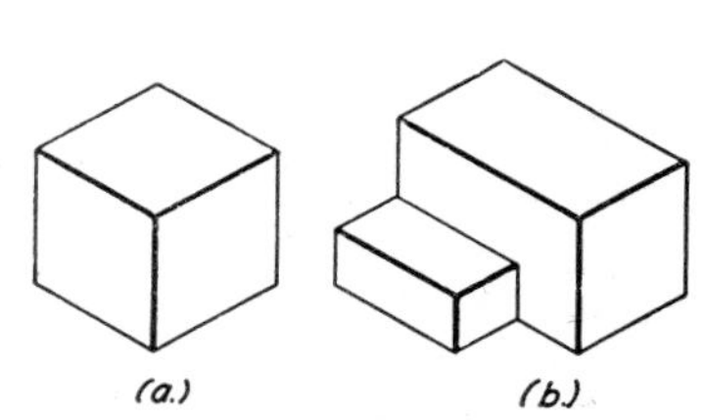

Fig. 26.5. Conventional shading.

to a shaded edge should form an extension of the original line representing the edge before it was shaded (Fig. 26.6).

26.3. Surface shading by means of lines. Line shading is a conventional method of representing, by ruled lines, the varying degrees of illumination on the surfaces of an object. It is a means of giving clearer definition to the shapes of objects and a finished appearance to certain types of drawings. In practice, line shading is used on Patent Office drawings, display drawings, and on some illustrations prepared for publications. It is never used on ordinary drawings, and for this reason few draftsmen ever gain the experience necessary to enable them to employ it effectively.

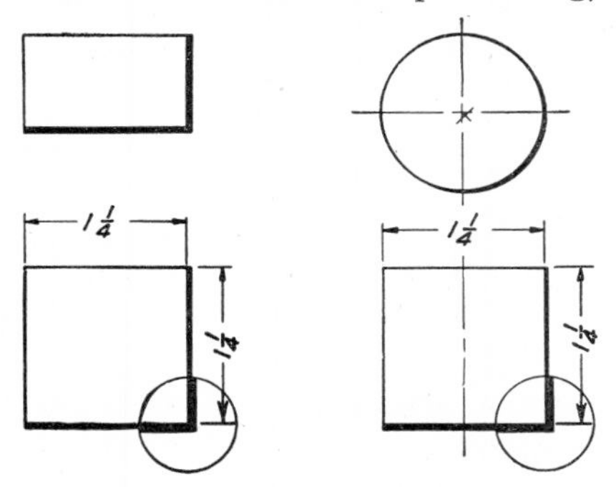

Fig. 26.6. Dimensions on shaded views.

In shading surfaces, the bright areas are left white and the dark areas are represented by parallel shade lines (Fig. 26.7). Varying degrees of shade may be represented in one of the following ways (Fig. 26.8):

1. By varying the weight of the lines while keeping the spacing uniform, as in (*a*).
2. By using uniform straight lines and varying the spacing, as in (*b*).
3. By varying both the weight of the lines and the spacing, as in (*c*).

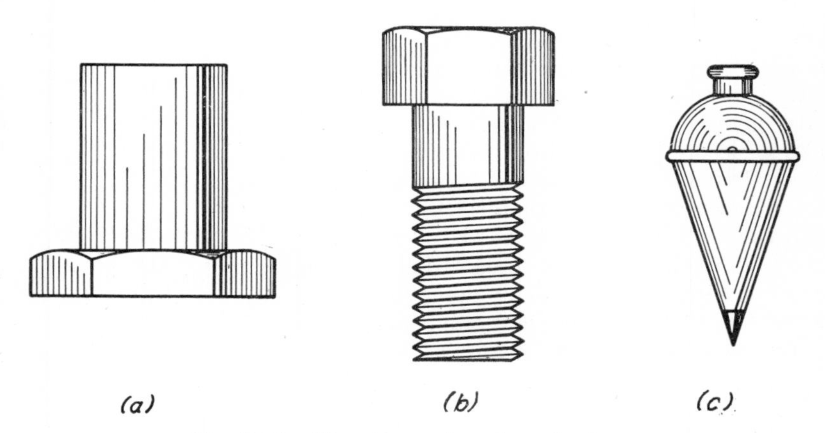

Fig. 26.7. The effect of surface shading.

As in the case of shade lines, the rays of light are assumed to be parallel and coming from the left, over the shoulder of the draftsman (Fig. 26.9). In accordance with this, two of the visible faces of the hexagonal prism, shown in Fig. 26.9, would be illuminated, while the remaining visible inclined face would be dark. It should be noted that the general principle of shading is modified in the case of flat inclined surfaces, which, theoretically, would be uniformly lighted. Such surfaces are shaded in accordance with a conventional scheme, the governing rule of which may be stated as follows: *The portion of an illuminated inclined surface nearest the eye is the lightest, while the portion of a shaded inclined surface nearest the eye is the*

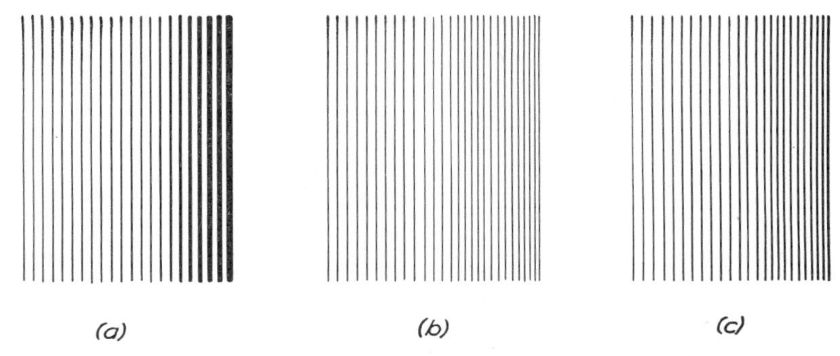

Fig. 26.8. Conventional methods of surface shading.

darkest. In the application of this rule, the shading on an inclined illuminated face will increase in density as the face recedes, while on an unilluminated inclined surface it will decrease in density as the face recedes, as shown in Fig. 26.9.

A cylinder would be shaded as shown in Fig. 26.10. The lightest area on the surface is at the *brilliant line,* where light strikes it and is reflected

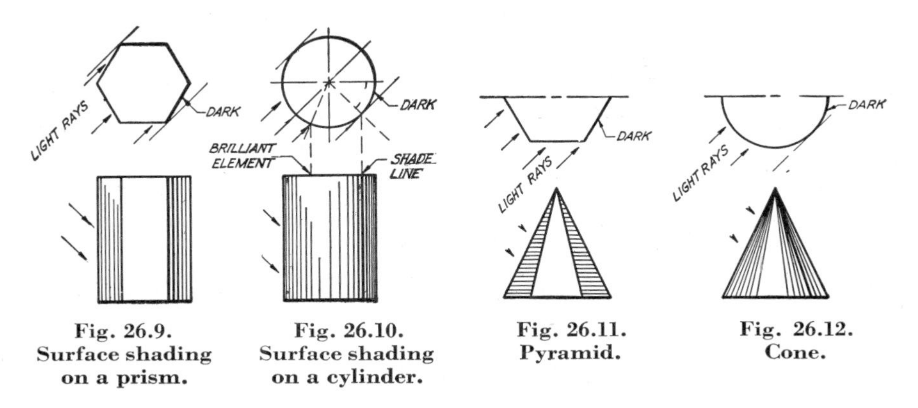

Fig. 26.9. Surface shading on a prism.

Fig. 26.10. Surface shading on a cylinder.

Fig. 26.11. Pyramid.

Fig. 26.12. Cone.

directly to the eye; the darkest is along the *shade line,* where the light rays are tangent to the surface. The brilliant line passes through the point at which the bisector for the angle formed by a light ray to the center and the visual ray from the center line to the eye would pierce the external surface. In shading a cylinder, the density of the shading is increased in both directions, from the bright area long the brilliant line to the contour element on the left and the shade line on the right. The density of the shading is slightly decreased on the shaded portion beyond the shade line. Since one would expect this area to be even darker, some draftsmen extend the dark portion to the contour element. On very small cylinders, the bright side (left side) usually is not shaded.

A sphere is shaded by drawing concentric circles having either the geometric center of the view or the "brilliant point" as a center (Fig. 26.13). The darkest portion of the surface is along the shade line, where

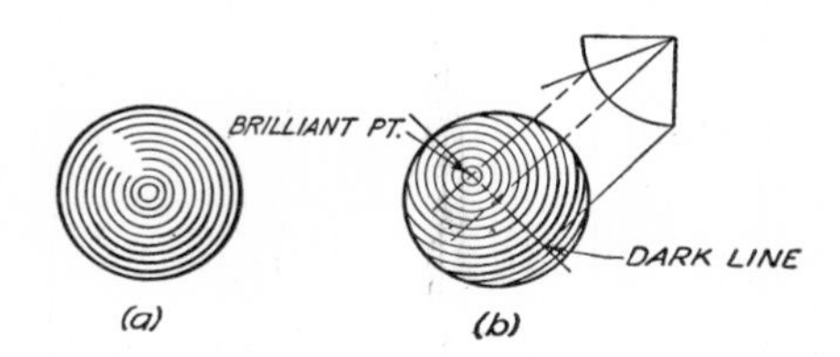

Fig. 26.13. Surface shading on a sphere.

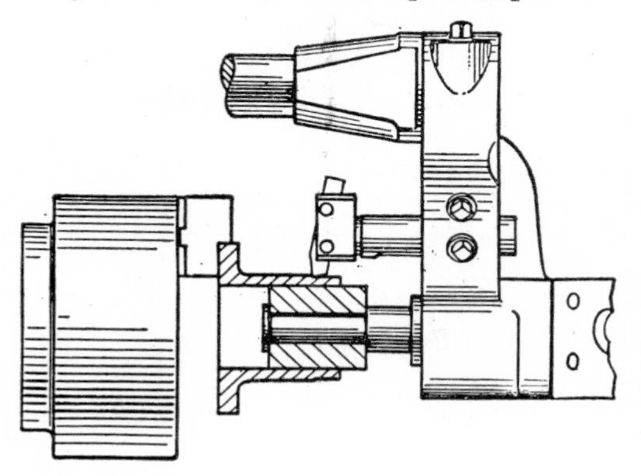

Fig. 26.14. A line-shaded drawing.

Courtesy Socony-Vacuum Oil Co

Fig. 26.15. A line-shaded pictorial drawing.

the parallel rays of light are tangent to the sphere and the lightest portion is around the *brilliant point*. The *brilliant point* is where the bisector of the angle between a light ray to the center and the visual ray from the center to the eye pierces the external surface. The construction necessary to determine the dark line and the brilliant point is shown in Fig. 26.13(*b*).

Although good line shading requires much practice and some artistic

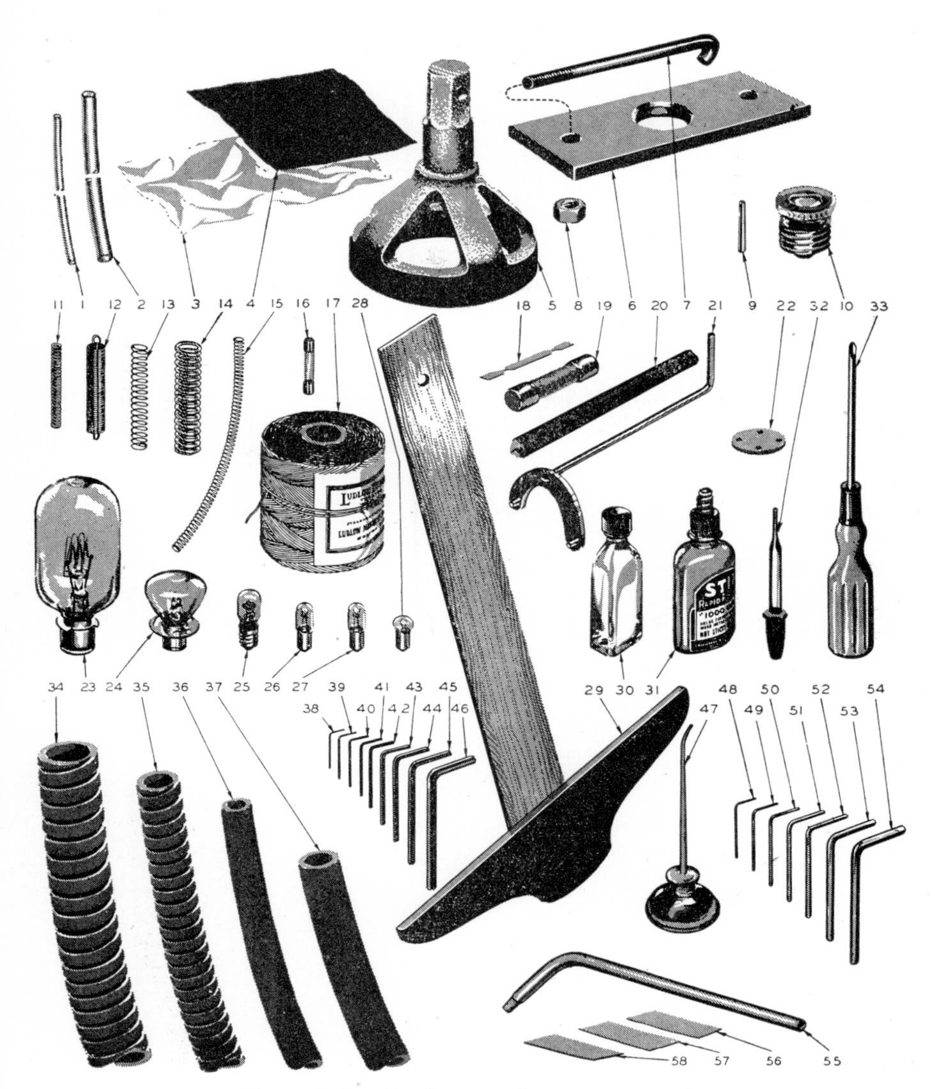

Fig. 26.16. Shading on Craftint paper.*

---

* Reproduction of drawings made on Craftint Doubletone by Link Aviation Devices, Inc., Binghamton, N. Y.

sense, a skillful draftsman should not avoid shading the surfaces of an object simply because he never before has attempted to do so. After careful study, he should be able to produce fairly satisfactory results. Often the shading of a view makes it possible to eliminate another view that otherwise would be necessary.

Figs. 26.14 and 26.15 show applications of line shading on technical illustrations.

26.4. Craftint papers. Craftint papers are used extensively by illustrators in making industrial and catalogue drawings. Fig. 26.16 shows how various objects might be shaded using one of the two available types of Craftint papers. An illustrator has a choice between a single-tone and a double-tone paper.

In using these papers, the drawing is "inked-in" on the Craftint paper in black waterproof ink. Then, the shading is added by brushing on special developers over the areas to be shaded. A single-tone paper requires the use of only one developer and gives a single pattern. On a double-tone paper, it is necessary to use two types of developing fluids and two patterns are obtained. Both developers may be used over the same area to obtain a dark shading. Various patterns are available for both types of papers.

Another form of paper that is popular with illustrators is known to the trade as Ross-board. This special board, one type of which was used for the shaded illustrations in this text, is available with several surface textures formed on a plaster base with a heavy paper back. Ross-board is suitable for both ink and pencil, but the shading must be done with a very soft jet black pencil. It will be found difficult to draw fine ink lines on Ross-board because the ruling pen becomes clogged with plaster from the surface and the indentations of the pattern discourages the beginner who attempts some lettering.

27 PATENT OFFICE DRAWINGS

27.1. A person who has invented a new machine or device, or an improvement for an existing machine, and who applies for a patent, is required by law to submit a drawing showing every important feature of his invention. When the invention is an improvement, the drawing must contain one or more views of the invention, alone, and a separate view showing it attached to the portion of the machine for which it is intended.

Patent drawings must be carefully prepared in accordance with the strict rules of the Patent Office. These rules are published in a pamphlet entitled "Rules of Practice in the United States Patent Office," which may be obtained, without charge, by writing to the Commissioner of Patents, Washington, D. C.

In the case of a machine or mechanical device, the complete application for a patent will consist of a petition, a "specification" (written description), and a drawing. An applicant should employ a patent attorney, preferably one who is connected with or regularly employs competent draftsmen capable of producing well-executed drawings that conform with all of the rules. Ordinary draftsmen lack the skill and experience necessary to produce such drawings.

An excellent patent drawing is reproduced in Fig. 27.1.

27.2. Rules. The following rules (49–55) are quoted verbatim from the pamphlet, "Rules of Practice in the United States Patent Office":

49. The applicant for a patent is required by law to furnish a drawing of his invention whenever the nature of the case admits of it.

50. The drawing may be signed by the inventor or one of the persons indicated in rule 25, or the name of the applicant may be signed on the drawing by his attorney in fact. The drawing must show every feature of the invention covered by the claims, and the figures should be consecutively numbered, if possible. When the invention consists of an improvement on an old machine, the drawing must exhibit, in one or more views, the invention itself, disconnected from the old structure, and also in another view, so much only of the old structure as will suffice to show the connection of the invention therewith.

51. Two editions of patent drawings are printed and published—one for office use, certified copies, etc., of the size and character of those attached to patents, the work being about 6 by $9\frac{1}{2}$ inches; and one reduction of a selected portion of each drawing for the Official Gazette.

52. This work is done by the photolithographic process, and therefore the character of each original drawing must be brought as nearly as possible to a uniform standard of excellence, suited to the requirements of the process, to give the best results, in the interests of inventors, of the office, and of the public. The

G. S. MEIKLE.
RECTIFIER.
APPLICATION FILED MAY 7, 1915.

1,182,291. Patented May 9, 1916.

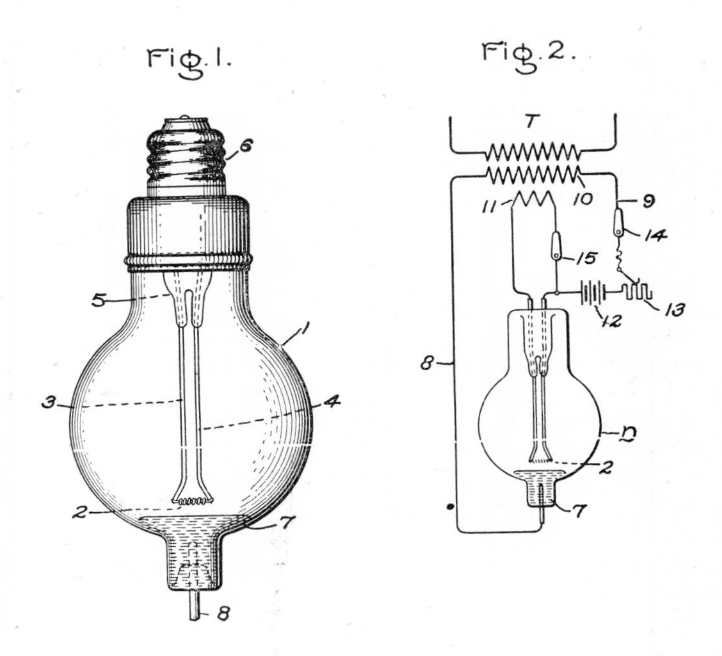

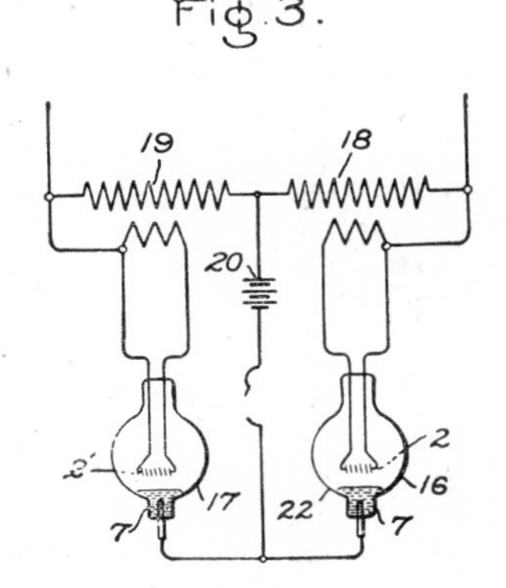

Inventor:
George S. Meikle,
by Albert G. Davis
His Attorney.

Courtesy G. S. Meikie

Fig. 27.1. A patent drawing.

following rules will therefore be rigidly enforced, and any departure from them will be certain to cause delay in the examination of an application for letters patent:

(*a*) Drawings must be made upon pure white paper of a thickness corresponding to two-sheet or three-sheet Bristol board. The surface of the paper must be calendered and smooth. India ink alone must be used, to secure perfectly black and solid lines.

(*b*) The size of a sheet on which a drawing is made must be exactly 10 by 15 inches. One inch from its edges a single marginal line is to be drawn, leaving the "sight" precisely 8 by 13 inches. Within this margin all work and signatures must be included. One of the shorter sides of the sheet is regarded as its top, and measuring downwardly from the marginal line, a space of not less than $1\frac{1}{4}$ inches is to be left blank for the heading of title, name, number, and date.

(*c*) All drawings must be made with the pen only. Every line and letter (signatures included) must be absolutely black. This direction applies to all lines, however fine, to shading, and to lines representing cut surfaces in sectional views. All lines must be clean, sharp, and solid, and they must not be too fine or crowded. Surface shading, when used, should be open. Sectional shading should be made by oblique parallel lines, which may be about one-twentieth of an inch apart. Solid black should not be used for sectional or surface shading. Free-hand work should be avoided wherever it is possible to do so.

(*d*) Drawings should be made with the fewest lines possible consistent with clearness. By the observance of this rule the effectiveness of the work after reduction will be much increased. Shading (except on sectional views) should be used only on convex and concave surfaces, where it should be used sparingly, and may even there be dispensed with if the drawing be otherwise well executed. The plane upon which a sectional view is taken should be indicated on the general view by a broken or dotted line, which should be designated by numerals corresponding to the number of the sectional view. Heavy lines on the shade sides of objects should be used, except where they tend to thicken the work and obscure letters of reference. The light is always supposed to come from the upper left-hand corner at an angle of 45°.

(*e*) The scale to which a drawing is made ought to be large enough to show the mechanism without crowding, and two or more sheets should be used if one does not give sufficient room to accomplish this end; but the number of sheets must never be more than is absolutely necessary.

(*f*) The different views should be consecutively numbered. Letters and figures of reference must be carefully formed. They should, if possible, measure at least one-eighth of an inch in height, so that they may bear reduction to one twenty-fourth of an inch; and they may be much larger when there is sufficient room. They must be so placed in the close and complex parts of drawings as not to interfere with a thorough comprehension of the same, and therefore should rarely cross or mingle with the lines. When necessarily grouped around a certain part they should be placed at a little distance, where there is available space, and connected by lines with the parts to which they refer. They should not be placed upon shaded surfaces, but when it is difficult to avoid this, a blank space must be left in the shading where the letter occurs, so that it shall appear perfectly distinct and separate from the work. If the same part of an invention appear in more than one view of the drawing, it must always be represented by the same character, and the same character must never be used to designate different parts.

(*g*) The signature of the applicant should be placed at the lower right-hand corner of each sheet, and the signatures of the witnesses, if any, at the lower left-hand corner, all within the marginal line, but in no instance should they trespass upon the drawings. The title should be written with pencil on the back of the sheet. The permanent names and title constituting the heading will be applied subsequently by the office in uniform style.

(*h*) All views on the same sheet must stand in the same direction and must, if possible, stand so that they can be read with the sheet held in an upright position. If views longer than the width of the sheet are necessary for the proper illustration of the invention, the sheet may be turned on its side. The space for heading must then be reserved at the right and the signatures placed at the left, occupying the same space and position as in the upright views and being horizontal when the sheet is held in an upright position. One figure must not be placed upon another or within the outline of another.

(*i*) As a rule, one view only of each invention can be shown in the Gazette illustrations. The selection of that portion of a drawing best calculated to explain the nature of the specific improvement would be facilitated and the final result improved by the judicious execution of a figure with express reference to the Gazette, but which must at the same time serve as one of the figures referred to in the specification. For this purpose the figure may be a plan, elevation, section, or perspective view, according to the judgment of the draftsman. All its parts should be especially open and distinct, with very little or no shading, and it must illustrate the invention claimed only, to the exclusion of all other details. (See specimen drawing.) When well executed it will be used without curtailment or change, but any excessive fineness or crowding or unnecessary elaborateness of detail will necessitate its exclusion from the Gazette.

(*j*) Drawings transmitted to the office should be sent flat, protected by a sheet of heavy binder's board; or should be rolled for transmission in a suitable mailing tube, but should never be folded.

(*k*) An agent's or attorney's stamp, or advertisement, or written address will not be permitted upon the face of a drawing, within or without the marginal line.

53. In reissue applications the drawings upon which the original patent was issued may be used upon the filing of suitable permanent photographic copies thereof, if no changes are to be made in the drawings.

54. The foregoing rules relating to drawings will be rigidly enforced. A drawing not executed in conformity thereto may be admitted for purposes of examination if it sufficiently illustrate the invention, but in such case the drawing must be corrected or a new one furnished before the application will be allowed. The necessary corrections will be made by the office, upon applicant's request and at his expense.

55. Applicants are advised to employ competent draftsmen to make their drawings.

The office will furnish the drawings at cost, as promptly as its draftsmen can make them, for applicants who cannot otherwise conveniently procure them.

28 REPRODUCTION AND DUPLICATION OF ENGINEERING DRAWINGS

28.1. Usually it is necessary to duplicate a set of drawings of a machine or structure, one or more copies being made for the office and extra copies for interested persons connected with the home organization or an outside co-operating firm. Sometimes many sets are required. Under modern production methods, the various parts of a machine or structure may be produced in numerous departments and plants that are located miles apart. Each of these departments must have exact copies of the original drawings. To satisfy this demand, several economical processes have been devised.

The various processes may be grouped in accordance with the general similarity in methods. The mechanical processes form a group that includes mimeographing, hectographing, and printing; the photochemical processes, using reflected light, include photography and photocopying; the photochemical processes, requiring transmitted light, include blueprinting, Ozalid printing, Van Dyke printing, and so on. A few processes, such as photolithography, are combinations of methods.

28.2. Blueprints. At present the blueprint process is more widely used than any other method of reproduction, despite the fact that some of the others offer more advantages. The method for making blueprints was first introduced in the United States about 1876.

A blueprint may be considered a photographic copy of an original drawing in that the process is similar to that of photography. A piece of sensitized paper is exposed to light transmitted through a negative (tracing) and then is developed in water to bring out the image. The negative is a transparent sheet of paper or transparentized cloth upon which the image of the original drawing has been traced with opaque lines. The printing paper is a white paper that has been coated with a solution of ammonia citrate of iron and ferrocyanide of potassium. When the paper is exposed through the tracing, a chemical action takes place wherever the light is able to reach the sensitized surface. In the first bath of clear water, the coating is washed away from the parts of the surface protected by these lines, exposing the original surface of the paper against a developed blue background. The contrast between the blue background and white lines may be intensified by dipping the print in an oxidizing solution of potassium bichromate in water, after which the print must be rinsed thoroughly in clean water to avoid stain marks.

The best results are always obtained with new blueprint paper which, when new, has a pale yellowish-green printing surface. The age of the paper is an important factor, for it greatly affects the printing time. When not being used, it should be kept well wrapped and should be stored in a metal can or a cool dark room.

Notations and changes can be made on a blueprint by lettering and drawing with an alkaline solution strong enough to bleach out the blue compound. Although a solution of sodium hydroxide (caustic soda) is best for this purpose, ordinary sodium bicarbonate (baking soda) in water, may be used.

Blueprints may be made in a sun frame, if only a few prints are desired (Fig. 28.1). This is done by first placing the tracing in the frame with

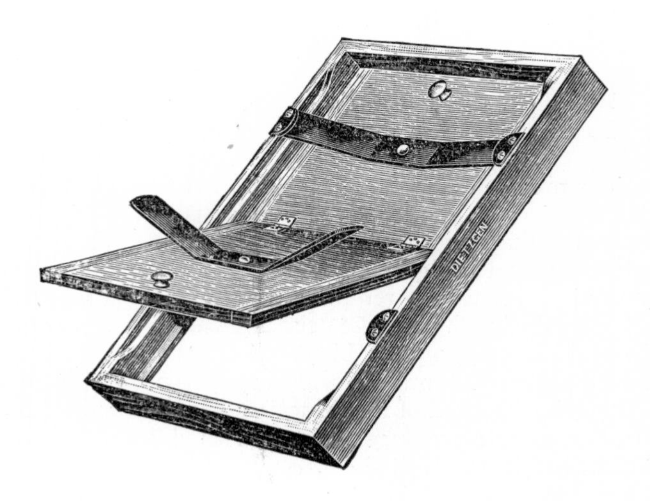

Fig. 28.1. Sun frame.

the inked side next to the glass and then laying the blueprint paper over it with the sensitized surface toward the tracing. Care should be taken, when locking the back of the frame, to see that no corners of the tracing or the paper are folded under. With the tracing and the printing paper thus held in contact with each other, the next step is to expose the printing surface to the direct sunlight. The length of time for the exposure varies with the intensity of the light and the speed of the paper. In direct sunlight, the correct exposure may vary from thirty seconds (for fast paper) to as much as several minutes (for slow paper). Since a good print with clear white lines against a uniform brilliant blue background can be obtained only by proper timing of the exposure, it is well to make one or two trial (part) prints on small scraps of blueprint paper before making the final print. If the background is a pale blue, the trial print was underexposed and the time of exposure should be increased; if the trial print has a scorched appearance with indistinct lines against a very dark blue background, the print was overexposed and the time of exposure should be decreased.

28.3. Typed material. In preparing a typewritten original for printing, a "soft record" ribbon should be used and the sheet should be "backed" with a piece of carbon paper so that the typed characters will be on two sides. Troublesome smearing can be somewhat reduced by spraying the sheet (both sides) with "fixative."

28.4. Blueprint machines. Because the intensity of the sunlight is subject to constant change, all large industrial firms and commercial blueprint concerns now use printing machines having some form of an electric exposing lamp. There are two types of such machines: the vertical type and the continuous type (Fig. 28.2). The vertical machine has an electric arc lamp that descends at a uniform rate of speed. The speed can be

Courtesy C. F. Pease Company.

Fig. 28.2. Continuous electric printing machine.

adjusted to suit the type of paper being used. The tracing and the printing paper are held against the cylindrical glass surface by a fabric curtain, which is rolled aside to allow the tracing and paper to be placed in position, then unrolled to hold both in contact for printing.

When a large quantity of prints must be made daily, some form of continuous machine is desirable. On such a machine the paper unwinds continuously from a roll, as the tracings are "fed in" with the inked sides up. The exposure is made as the tracing passes upward in contact with a glass cylinder containing a bank of arc lights. Some machines are equipped with a washer and drier, thus allowing the prints to be made in one operation (Fig. 28.3), but these are so expensive that only firms making a great number of prints daily find them a worth-while investment. Small firms have found it much cheaper to have their prints made by commercial printing concerns, of which there are at least one or two in every fairly large industrial city.

28.5. Brown prints. A negative brown print is made on so-called Van Dyke paper, a thin printing paper with a yellowish-green sensitized surface that turns to a light bronze on exposure and a deep brown when washed in water. In order to intensify a developed brown print and make it permanent, it is "fixed" in a solution of sodium hyposulphite and again washed in water. If the print is to be used for making positive prints, it

Courtesy C. F. Pease Company.

Fig. 28.3. Continuous printing machine with washer and drier.

should be made by exposing with the tracing reversed so that the inked lines are toward the Van Dyke paper. A reversed negative will print faster and will produce sharper lines if it has been transparentized by rubbing the back with a specially prepared oil (white Vaseline in benzine).

A positive brown print, having brown lines on white background, is made on brown print paper by using a brown print negative as a substitute for the original tracing. Prints showing a change may be made without altering the original tracing if the part to be changed is "blocked out" on the negative print and drawn in on the positive print.

28.6. Blue-line prints. A positive blue-line print, having blue lines on a white background, may be made on regular blueprint paper by exposing with a brown print negative in the place of the original tracing. Such prints also may be made from an original tracing, if a paper coated with a solution of gum arabic, ammonia citrate of iron, and chloride of iron is used. When the print is developed in solution of ferrocyanide of potassium, the coated surface turns blue where it has been protected from light and remains white where it has been exposed. The print must be washed thoroughly in water when it is taken from the developer.

An advantage offered by blue-line prints is that alterations may be more easily indicated and read on a white background. Furthermore, if

Courtesy General Analine and Film Corp.

Fig. 28.4. Ozalid printing machine.

the prints are made on blueprint paper using a negative print, the original tracing is protected against wear.

28.7. Ozalid prints. Ozalid prints, depending upon the type of Ozalid paper used, show black, blue, or maroon lines on a white background. The prints are exposed in the same manner as for other contact processes. They are developed in controlled dry ammonia vapor and, since no liquid solution is used with this process, a finished print will be an undistorted exact-scale reproduction of the original tracing.

Until recently the Ozalid process was not used to any great extent by industrial concerns, because there were no satisfactory developing machines available. Simple tube developers could be purchased, but they were unsuitable for the rapid production of a number of prints. The modern combined printing and developing machines were introduced only a few years ago, and since then the Ozalid process has received wide acceptance. Ozalid printer-developer units, such as the one shown in Fig. 28.4, produce finished prints in two simple steps without any auxiliary apparatus. No washing, fixing, rinsing, or drying is required.

Courtesy Charles Bruning Company, Inc.

Fig. 28.5. B & W continuous printing and developing machine.

An Ozalid duplicate tracing, which is known as an intermediate, may be made on either Ozalid sepia-line papers (single and double coated), Ozalid sepia-line cloth, or Ozalid foil. Since each of these types of intermediate materials is translucent, an intermediate on any one type may be used in place of the original tracing to produce drawing room and shop prints. The use of intermediates make it possible to file away the original drawing where it will not be damaged or smudged and will be safe from fire. The intermediate can be used for all reference work and may be altered when design changes become necessary. Changes may be made and obsolete detail removed with a corrector fluid and the new lines, dimensions, and notes may then be added. A second intermediate may then be made from the first one. The use of changed intermediates makes retracing unnecessary when rather extensive alterations in design become desirable. Also, the valuable original can remain untouched in the file for record purposes. As a matter of interest an intermediate will often make a much better print than an original tracing.

28.8. Black and white prints (*BW*). Positive black-line prints may be made direct from an original tracing by using a specially prepared black-print paper. When developed, the sensitized surface turns black where it has been protected and remains white where exposed. Only two steps are required to obtain a fully developed print: exposure and development. This method of printing is similar to that used for making blueprints, except that the print is developed by a solution in a special developing unit on top of the printer (Fig. 28.5). Black and white prints are more desirable than blueprints, because of their greater legibility and the fact that they can be made in only two steps where blueprints require five. This is one of the few methods that eventually should replace the blueprint method.

28.9. Duplicate tracings. A duplicate tracing may be produced on a special waterproof reproduction cloth. A negative brown print is used, and the cloth is exposed in a regular blueprint machine. The sensitized surface of this waterproof cloth turns black where exposed to light and remains transparent where protected. A few industrial firms produce "dupe" tracings, of original pencil drawings. This is done by photographing a drawing and using the negative in exposing the cloth. To obtain a satisfactory negative, careful consideration must be given to the weight of the pencil lines. Full directions for making duplicate tracings may be secured from almost any large commercial distributor of drawing supplies. In view of the fact that "dupe" tracings from original pencil drawings eliminate all possible errors that might result from ink tracing, and cost only a fraction of the price of the latter to produce, this method eventually should become widely adopted.

28.10. Photocopies. Photocopies (photostat prints) are direct photographic reproductions made from original drawings or printed matter with an automatic machine equipped with a large camera that focuses an image directly upon a sensitized paper. After being properly exposed, the print is washed and dried within the machine. Copies may be made to any scale of reduction or enlargement.

Although photocopies made from original drawings are brown prints with white lines on a dark background, positive prints having dark lines on a white background may be made by rephotographing brown-print photocopies. Since photocopy paper is orthochromatic, black and white copies can be made from colored originals by copying through a color filter.

This method is used extensively for preparing drawings for engineering reports and, occasionally, for changing the scales of related drawings so that they may be combined.

A photostat machine is shown in Fig. 28.6.

28.11. Lithoprinting. The planograph or photo-offset process (a form of photolithography) is used to produce a considerable number of copies of a drawing at a very low cost.

In this process a positive image is produced upon a flexible zinc or aluminum plate by the use of a photographic negative and a sensitizing emulsion. For satisfactory results, the plate must have a grained surface that will absorb water. In the press, the plate passes under a moistened felt roller that wets the background, so that when it next passes an ink roller only image will be inked (the ink will not stick to the wet surface).

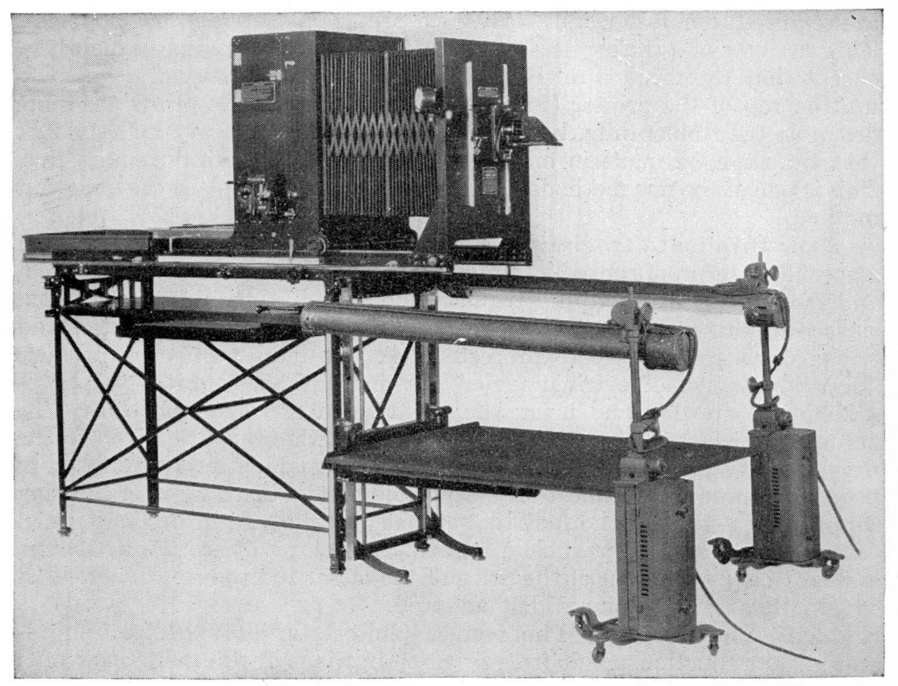

Courtesy Photostat Corporation.

Fig. 28.6. A photostat machine.

The plate finally passes a rubber roller where the inked image imparts a negative imprint that is transferred by this roller to the printing paper as a positive image.

28.12. The mechanical copying methods. Small line drawings and sketches may be reproduced by either the mimeograph process or the hectograph process.

In the former, a direct image is made on sheets of mimeograph copying paper by the use of a stencil and an inked pad. The stencil is a thin sheet having a prepared surface upon which the material to be copied is drawn, lettered, or typed. When the stencil has been cut and is ready to produce copies, it is stretched over a perforated metal cylinder that has a fixed inked pad. As the paper is fed through the mimeograph machine by rotating the cylinder, the ink from the pad passes through the stencil where the lines and letters have been cut and forms an image on the paper. By a photochemical method, the A. B. Dick Company is able to produce stencils of drawings to a reduced scale and to copy material that would be too complicated to be drawn satisfactorily by hand. For this purpose, the company uses a special stencil upon which it is impossible to type or draw.

In the hectograph process, copies are made by direct contact with a gelatin pad that has received an imprint from an original typed or drawn in aniline materials. Although, to obtain a transferred image having sharp rich-colored lines, a special type of paper should be used, copies

Fig. 28.7. BW Copyflex machine.

frequently are made on various weights of paper, from the very thin to heavy card stock. In size, the copies range from small tags to large 22″ × 34″ sheets. "Master" copies must be made with a special reproducing ink, pencil, carbon paper, or typewriter ribbon. Copies made with ink may have as many as eight colors.

Various machines on the market employ the hectograph principle. A few run off copies at the rate of eighty per minute and produce as many as five or six hundred from an original "master." Some machines do not employ a gelatin pad but depend instead upon a special liquid that moistens the master copy so that the print may be taken directly from the master.

28.13. Copyflex positive prints. The BW Copyflex machine, shown in Fig. 28.7 copies any size of original matter up to $11\frac{1}{2}$ inches wide by any length. The Copyflex makes exact contact prints of letters, records reports, or line drawings within itself. No stencil or negative is required. The BW Diazo process is employed and the machine needs no inks and does not give off any annoying fumes. The paper is coated with an aniline dye that during processing is bleached by actinic light rays except where the line-drawing or record has markings.

If the original is on opaque stock the machine quickly copies it onto reflex film and the film is then used to make the desired copies.

28.14. Industrial practice in automobile body design. In automobile body design, full-sized drawings of each year's models are made on the painted surface of a large sheet of aluminum. The drawings are carefully laid out with instruments directly on the painted surfaces; then the lines are scratched in. A detail drawing, such as one showing the details of a doorpost on a particular model, is made by tracing directly from the aluminum sheet. Aluminum is used because a body-design drawing for a model must be prepared two or three years in advance of the production date and the medium on which it is prepared must be strong enough to withstand constant wear and rough treatment. Furthermore, a drawing on an aluminum sheet is not affected by weather changes.

29 ENGINEERING GRAPHS AND CHARTS GRAPHICAL CALCULUS

29.1. A properly designed graphical representation will convey correlated data and facts to an average individual more rapidly and effectively than a verbal, written, or tabulated description, because a visual impression is easily comprehended and requires less mental effort than would be necessary to ascertain the facts from complex tables and reports (Fig. 29.1). It is because of this that diverse kinds of graphs and charts have been developed to present scientific, statistical, and technical information. Note how quickly the relationship presented by the line graph in Fig. 29.2 can be interpreted.

Engineers, even though they are concerned mainly with technical graphs, should be familiar also with the popular forms, for every industrial

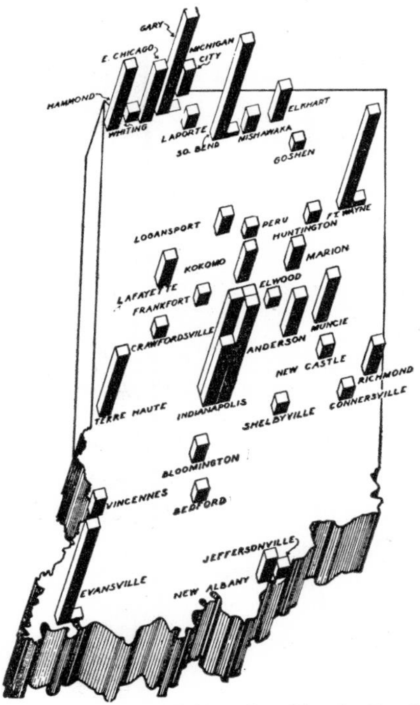

Courtesy Indiana State Planning Board.

Fig. 29.1. Population chart.

concern frequently must prepare popular types of graphs in order to strengthen their relationship with the public.

It is impossible to treat exhaustively the subject of graphical representation in a single chapter. Only a few of the most common forms used to analyze economic, scientific, and technical data can be discussed in detail. Many of the principles followed in the construction of engineering graphs, however, apply to the other types.

As much drafting skill is required in the execution of a graph as in making any other type of technical drawing. Good appearance is important and can be achieved only with the help of good lettering and smooth, uniform, and properly contrasted lines.

29.2. Classification of charts, graphs, and diagrams. Graphs, charts, and diagrams may be divided into two classes in accordance with their use, and then further subdivided according to type. When classified according to use, the two divisions are, first, those used for strictly scientific

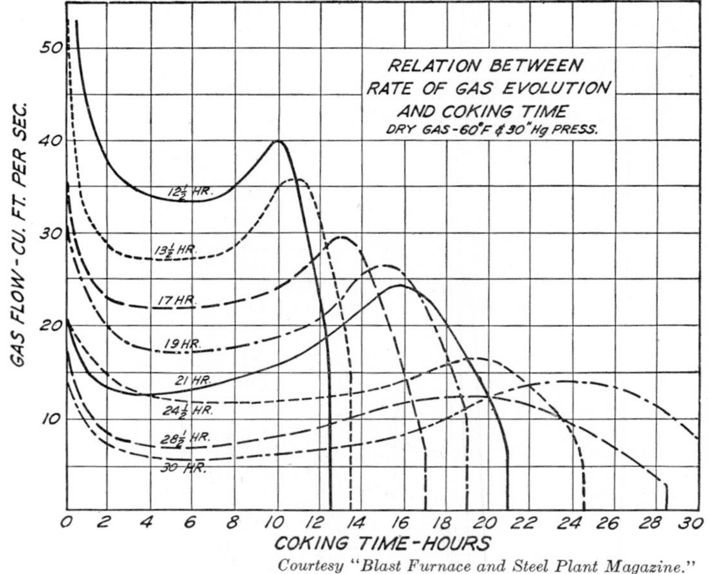

Courtesy "Blast Furnace and Steel Plant Magazine."

Fig. 29.2. An engineering graph prepared for publication.

and technical purposes and, second, those used for the purpose of popular appeal. The classification according to type is as follows:

1. Rectilinear charts
2. Semilogarithmic charts
3. Logarithmic charts
4. Barographs, area, and volume charts
5. Percentage charts
6. Trilinear charts
7. Polar charts
8. Alignment charts (nomographs)
9. Pictorial charts

29.3. Quantitative and qualitative charts and graphs. In general, charts and diagrams are used for one of two purposes, either to read values or to present a comparative picture relationship between variables. If a chart or graph is prepared for reading values, it is called a *quantitative* graph; if prepared for presenting a comparative relationship, it is called *qualitative*. Obviously, some charts serve both purposes and cannot be classified strictly as either type. One of these purposes, however, must be predominant. Since a number of features in the preparation depend upon the predominant purpose, such purpose must be determined before attempting to construct a graph.

29.4. Ordinary rectangular co-ordinate graphs. Most engineering graphs, prepared for laboratory and office use, are drawn on ruled rectangular graph paper and are plotted in the first quadrant (upper right-hand), with the intersection of the X (horizontal) axis and Y (vertical) axis at the lower left used as the zero point or origin of co-ordinates. The paper is ruled with equispaced horizontal and vertical lines, forming small rectangles. The type most commonly used for chart work in experimental engineering is $8\frac{1}{2}'' \times 11''$ and is ruled

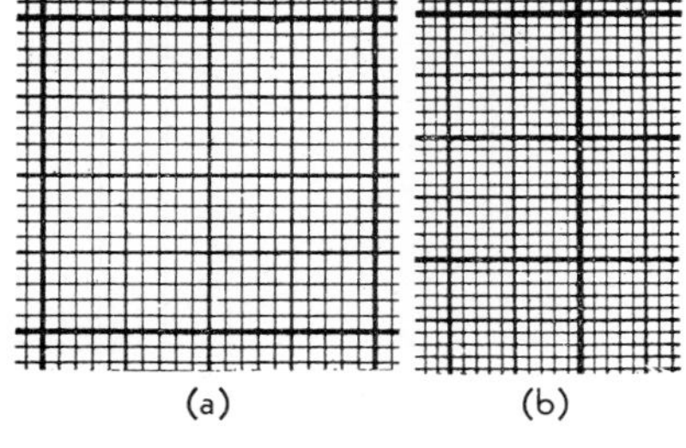

Fig. 29.3. Types of graph paper.

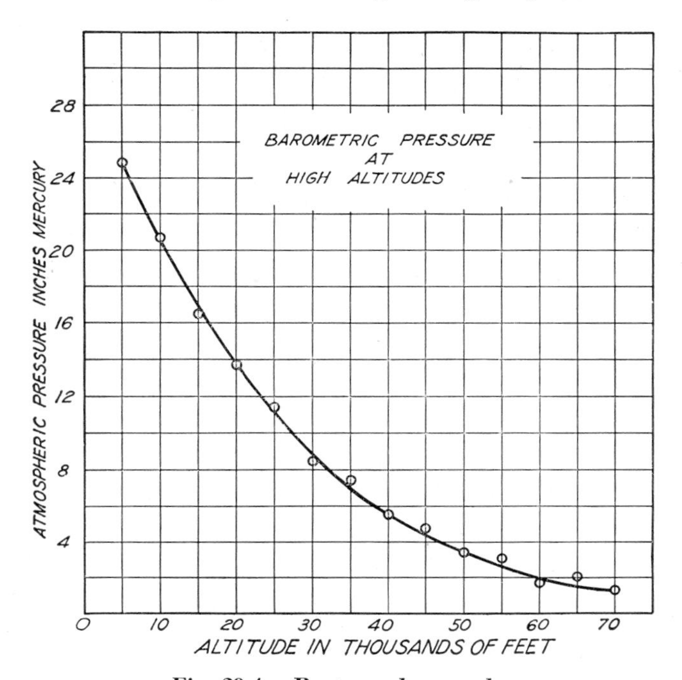

Fig. 29.4. Rectangular graph.

to form one-twentieth-inch squares (Fig. 29.3*a*), every fifth line being heavy. Another type of paper frequently used, which is suitable for most laboratory reports in technical schools, has rulings that form one-millimeter and one-centimeter squares (Fig. 29.3*b*). Other rulings run $\frac{1}{10}''$, $\frac{1}{8}''$, or $\frac{1}{4}''$ apart. Ordinarily the ruled lines are spaced well apart on charts prepared for reproduction in popular and technical literature (Fig. 29.2). The principal advantage of having greater spacing between the lines is that large squares or rectangles tend to make the graph easier to read. Ready printed graph papers are available with various rulings in several colors.

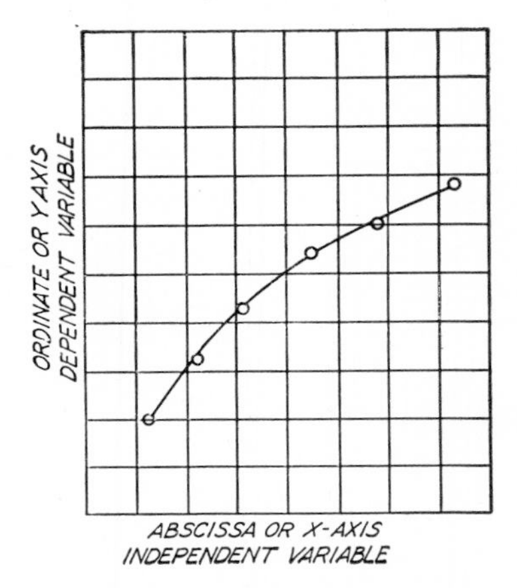

Fig. 29.5. Independent and dependent variables.

Ordinary co-ordinate line graphs are used extensively because they are easily constructed and easily read. The known relationship between the variables is expressed by one or more continuous lines, which may be straight, broken, or curved.

The graph in Fig. 29.4 shows the approximate barometric pressure at different heights above sea level.

A graphical representation may be drawn easily and correctly if, after the required data have been assembled, careful consideration is given to the principles of curve drawing discussed in the following articles.

29.5. The determination of the variables for ordinate and abscissa. The independent variable, the quantity arbitrarily varied during

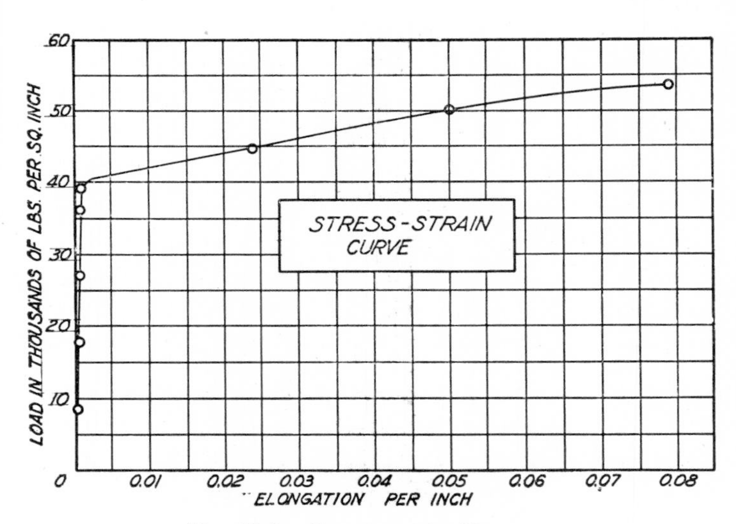

Fig. 29.6. Stress-strain diagram.

the experiment, usually is chosen for the abscissa (Fig. 29.5). Certain kinds of experimental data, however, such as a stress-strain diagram (Fig. 29.6), are plotted with the independent variable along the ordinate.

29.6. The selection of suitable scales.* The American Society of Mechanical Engineers in a standard for engineering and scientific graphs recommends:

(*a*) Very careful consideration should be given to the choice of scales since this has a controlling influence on the slope of the curve. The slope of the curve, as a whole and also at intermediate points, provides a visual impression of the degree of change in the dependent variable for a given increment in the independent variable. Creating the right impression of the relationship to be shown by a line graph is, therefore, probably controlled more critically by the relative stretching of the vertical and horizontal scales than by any other feature involved in the design of the graph.

(*b*) The range of scales should be chosen to insure effective and efficient use of the co-ordinate area in attaining the objective of the chart.

(*c*) The zero line should be included, if visual comparison of plotted magnitudes is desired.

(If the chart is quantitative, the intersection of the axes need not be at the origin of co-ordinates. If it is qualitative, however, both the ordinate and abscissa generally should have zero value at the intersection of the axes, as in Fig. 29.2.)

(*d*) For arithmetic scales, the scale numbers shown on the graph and space between co-ordinate rulings should preferably correspond to 1, 2, or 5 units of measurement, multiplied or divided by 1, 10, 100, etc.

(Other units could be used except for the fact that they create situations where it becomes difficult to interpolate values. For example, one square should equal one of the following.)

0.01	0.1	1	10	100	etc.
0.02	0.2	2	20	200	etc.
0.04	0.4	4	40	400	etc.
0.05	0.5	5	50	500	etc.
etc.	etc.	etc.	etc.	etc.	etc.

(*e*) The horizontal (independent variable) scale values should usually increase from left to right and the vertical (dependent variable) from bottom to top.

29.7. Locating the axes and marking the values of the variables. On graphs prepared for laboratory reports and not for publication, the axes should be located 1″ or more inside the border of the co-ordinate ruling. (See Fig. 29.7.) When selecting the scale units and locating the axes, it should be remembered that the abscissa may be taken either the long way or short way of the co-ordinate paper, depending upon the range of the scales.

Concerning the numbers, the ASME standard recommends:

* These statements were abstracted from the American Standard for Engineering and Scientific Graphs for Publication (ASA Z15.3–1943). Copies may be obtained from the American Society of Mechanical Engineers, 29 W. 39th St., New York, N. Y.

The use of many digits in scale numbers should be avoided. This can usually be accomplished by a suitable designation in the scale caption.

EXAMPLE: PRESSURE, MM. OF HG. $\times 10^{-5}$; RESISTANCE, THOUSANDS OF OHMS.

The numbers should read from the bottom when possible (Fig. 29.7). For the sake of good appearance, they never should be crowded. Always place a cipher to the left of the decimal point when the quantity is less than one.

Usually, only the heavy co-ordinate lines are marked to indicate their values or distance from the origin, and, even then, the values may be

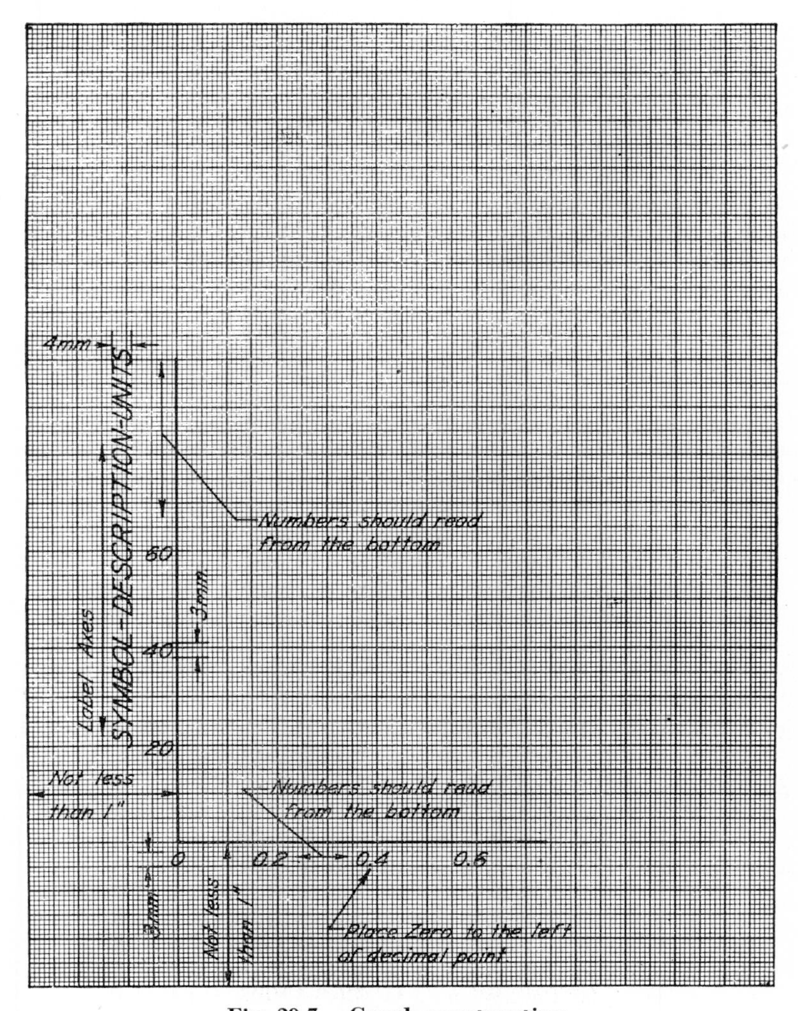

Fig. 29.7. Graph construction.

shown only at a regular selected interval. (See Fig. 29.7.) These numbers should be placed to the left of the Y-axis and just below the X-axis.

When several curves representing different variables are to appear on the same graph, a separate axis generally is required for each variable. (See Fig. 29.8.) In this case, a corresponding description should be given

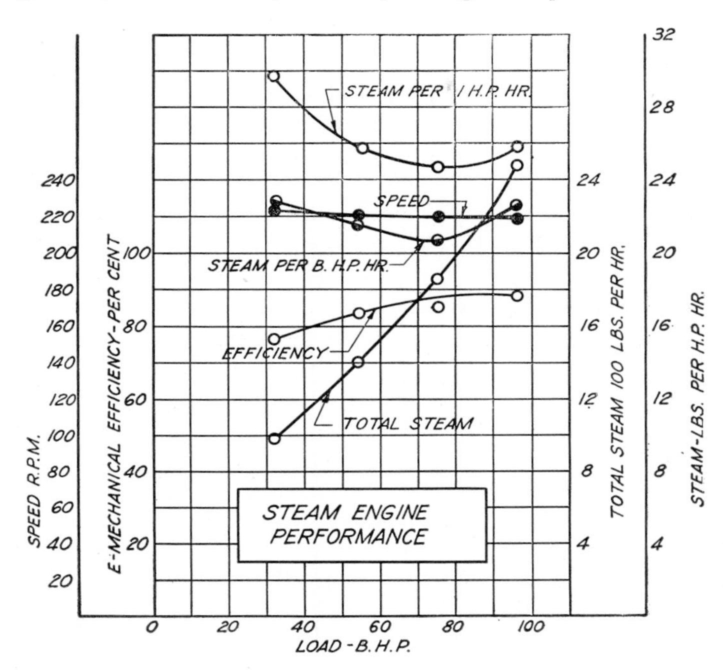

Fig. 29.8. Representation of several curves on a graph.

along each axis. The axes should be grouped at the left or at the bottom of the graph, unless it is desirable to place some at the right or along the top.

29.8. Indicating plotted points representing the data. If the data represent a set of experimental observations, the plotted points of a single-curve graph should be marked by small circles approximately 0.1″ in diameter (see Fig. 29.9). The following practice is recommended: open circles, filled-in circles, and partially filled-in circles (○ ● ◒) rather than crosses, squares, and triangles should be used to differentiate observed points of several curves on a graph. Filled-in symbols may be made smaller than those not filled in.

Mathematical curves are frequently drawn without distinguishing marks at computed positions.

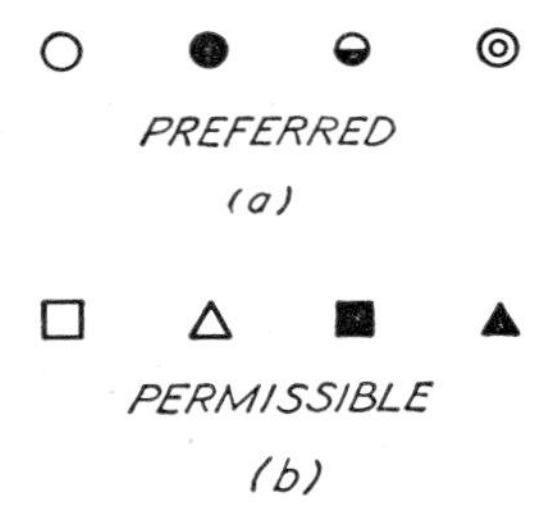

Fig. 29.9. Identification symbols.

29.9. Drawing a curve. Since most physical phenomena are continuous, curves on engineering graphs usually represent an average of plotted points. (See Fig. 29.10.) Discontinuous data should be plotted with a broken line, as shown in Fig. 29.11.

It is preferable to represent curves by solid lines. If more than one curve appears on a graph, differentiation may be secured by varied types of lines; but the most important curve should be represented by a solid one. A very fine line should be used for a quantitative curve, if values are to be read accurately. A heavy line ($\frac{1}{40}''$ width) is recommended for a qualitative curve. It should be observed in Figs. 29.10 and 29.11 that the curve line does not pass through open circles.

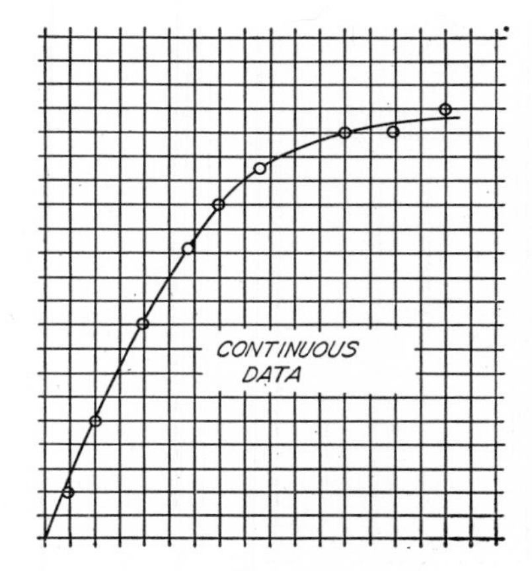

Fig. 29.10. Continuous curve.

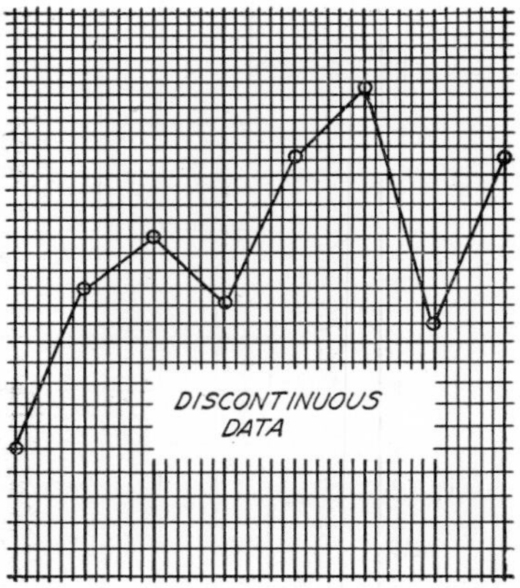

Fig. 29.11. Discontinuous data.

For ordinary qualitative graphs, the ASME standard proposes:

(*a*) When more than one curve is presented on a graph, relative emphasis or differentiation of the curves may be secured by using different types of line, i.e., solid, dashed, dotted, etc. A solid line is recommended for the most important curve.

(*b*) When more than one curve is presented on a graph, each should bear a suitable designation.

(*c*) Curves should, if practicable, be designated by brief labels placed close to the curves (horizontally or along the curves) rather than by letters, numbers or other devices requiring a key. [See Fig. 29.8.]

29.10. The labeling of the scales. Each scale caption should give a description of the variable represented and the unit of measurement. The captions on engineering graphs frequently contain an added identifying symbol such as "N-EFFICIENCY-PER CENT" or "P-OUTPUT-H.P."

All lettering should be readable from the bottom and right side of the graph (not the left side). When space is limited, standard abbreviations should be used, particularly for designating the unit of measurement.

To avoid confusing the reader, the draftsman should use only recognized word contractions.

29.11. Titles, legends, notes, and so on. The title of a graph should be clear, concise, complete, and symmetrical. It should give the name of the curve, the source of the data, the date, and other important information (Fig. 29.12). It should be so placed that it gives a balanced effect to the completed drawing. (See Fig. 29.2.) In addition to the title, a wiring diagram, pictorial diagram, formula, or explanatory note is often necessary to give a clear picture of the nature of the experiment. For example, if there is any great irregularity in the plotted points or a condition that may have affected the values as shown by the data, a note of explanation should be given. A legend or key is sometimes included to explain a set of curves in greater detail.

STRESS - STRAIN DIAGRAM
FOR
COMPRESSION
IN
CAST IRON

Fig. 29.12. A title.

In commercial practice, alcohol is often used to clear a rectangular area of co-ordinate lines in order that the title may be printed in an open space.

29.12. Procedure for making a graphical representation in ink.

1. Select the type of co-ordinate paper.
2. Determine the variables for ordinate and abscissa.
3. Determine the scale units.
4. Locate the axes and mark the scale values in pencil.
5. Plot the points representing the data. [Many draftsmen ink the symbol (○ ◒) indicating the points at this stage.]
6. Draw the curve. If the curve is to strike an average among the plotted points, a trial curve should be drawn in pencil. If the curve consists of a broken line, as is the case with discontinuous data, the curve need not be drawn until the graph is traced in ink.
7. Label the axes directly in ink.
8. Letter the title, notes, and so on. The title should be lettered on a trial sheet that can be used as a guide for lettering directly in ink on the graph.
9. Check the work and complete the diagram by tracing the curve in ink.

29.13. Logarithmic graphs. Logarithmic co-ordinate graphs are constructed on prepared paper on which the parallel horizontal and parallel vertical rulings are spaced proportional to the logarithms of numbers (Fig. 29.13). This type of graph has two principal advantages over the ordinary co-ordinate type. First, the error in plotting or reading values is a constant percentage, and, second, an algebraic equation of the form $y = ax^b$ appears as a straight line if x has a value other than 0. The exponent b may be either plus or minus.

The equation for a falling body, $D = \frac{1}{2}gt^2$, is represented in Figs. 29.13 and 29.14. A practical application of interest to engineers is in the design of drop hammers. In this equation, based on uniform accelerated motion,

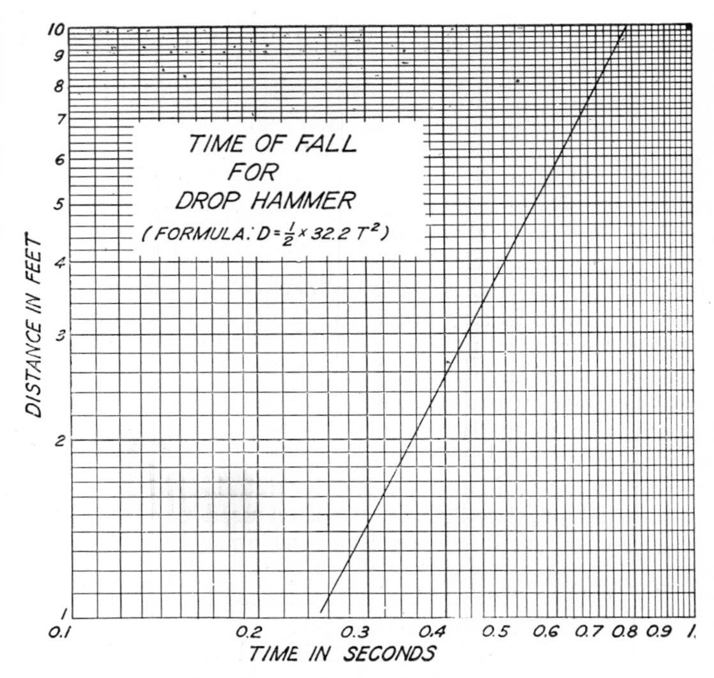

Fig. 29.13. Logarithmic graph.

t represents time in seconds and d the distance traveled in t seconds by a freely falling body with no initial velocity. Observe that the plotted points form a parabolic curve on ordinary co-ordinate graph paper, and a

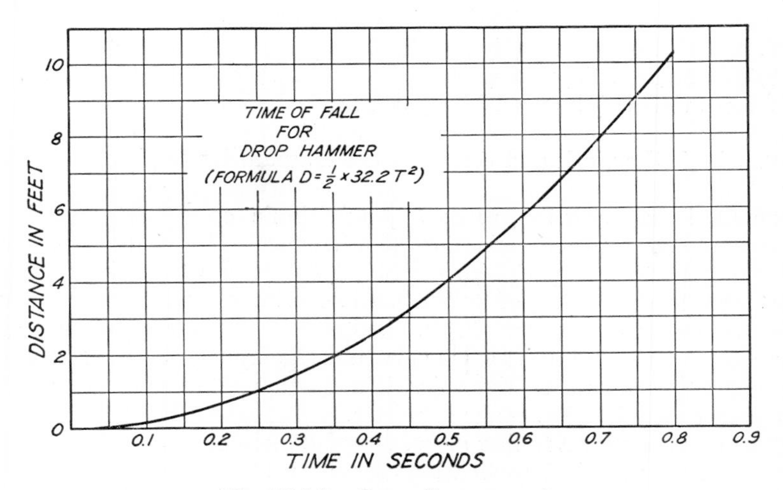

Fig. 29.14. Co-ordinate graph.

straight line on logarithmic paper. To draw the line on the graph in Fig. 29.13, it is necessary to calculate and locate only two points, while in Fig. 29.14 several points must be plotted to establish the location of the corresponding curved-line representation. The line on Fig. 29.13 has a slope of 2 to 1, because the exponent of t is 2. Therefore, the line could be drawn by utilizing one point and the slope, instead of plotting two points and joining them with a straight line.

Log paper is available with rulings in one or more cycles for any range of values to be plotted. Part-cycle and split-cycle papers may also be purchased.

29.14. Semilogarithmic graphs. Semilogarithmic paper has ruled lines that are spaced to a uniform scale in one direction and to a logarithmic scale in the other direction (Fig. 29.15). Charts drawn on this form of paper are used extensively in scientific studies, because functions having values in the form of geometric progressions are represented by straight lines. In any case, the main reason for the use of semilogarithmic paper is that the slope of the resulting curve indicates rate of change rather than amount of change, the opposite being true in the case of curves on ordinary co-ordinate graph paper. If those who are interested desire, they may determine the rate of increase or decrease at any point by measuring the slope. A straight line indicates a constant rate of change. In commercial work this form of paper is generally called "ratio paper," and the charts are known as "rate-of-change charts."

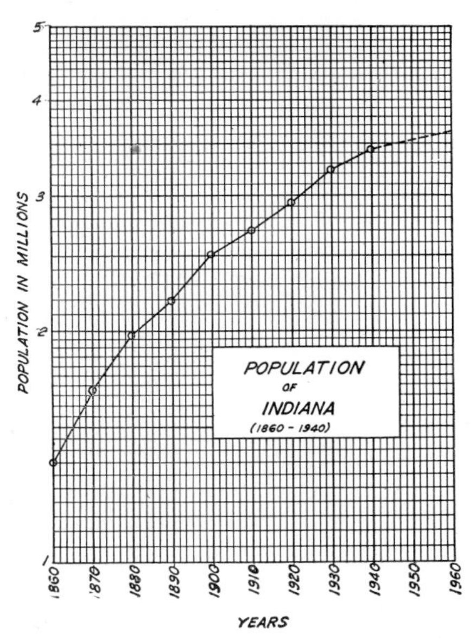

Fig. 29.15. Semilogarithmic chart.

As previously stated, the choice of a type of graph paper depends upon the information to be revealed. Curves drawn on uniform co-ordinate graph paper to illustrate the percentage of expansion or contraction of sales, and so on, present a misleading picture. The same data plotted on semilogarithmic paper would reveal the true rate of change to the business management. For this reason, semilogarithmic paper should be used whenever percentage of change rather than quantity change is to be shown. In scientific work, when the value of one variable increases in a geometric progression and the other in an arithmetic progression, this form is valuable.

29.15. Bar charts. Bar charts or barographs are used principally in popular literature covering economic and industrial surveys. They are a simple diagrammatic form giving a pictorial summary of statistical data and can be easily understood by the average person. Logarithmic and uniform co-ordinate graphs are less suited for this purpose, because few people know the procedure for reading curves or understand their picture qualities.

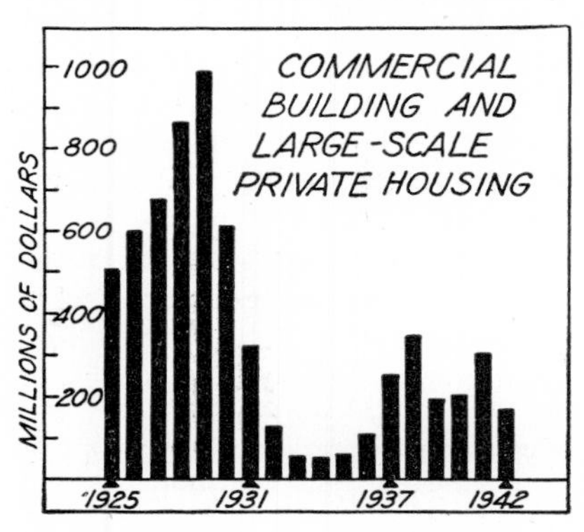

Fig. 29.16. A bar chart.

Whenever values or quantities are illustrated, as in Fig. 29.16, by consecutive heavy bars whose lengths are proportional to the amounts they represent, the resulting representation is called a *bar chart.*

The bars on this type of diagram may be drawn either horizontally or vertically, but all should start at the same zero line. Their lengths should be to some fixed scale, the division values of which may be given in the margin along the bottom or left side of the graph. When it is necessary to give the exact values represented, the figures should be placed along

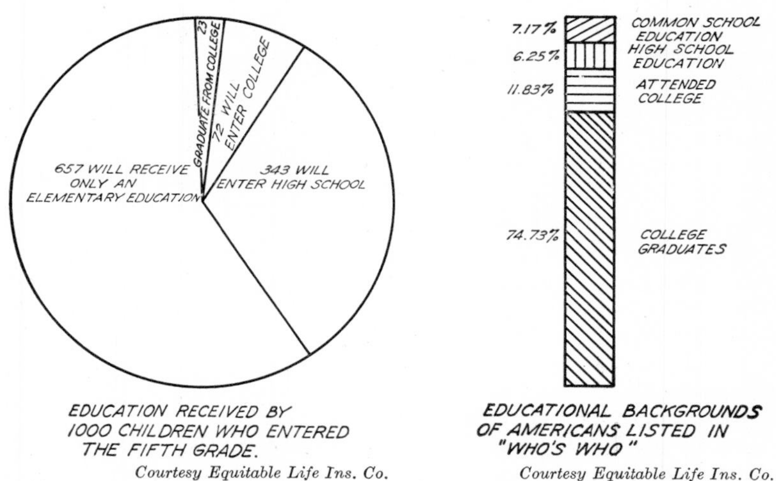

Courtesy Equitable Life Ins. Co.

Fig. 29.17. Pie chart.

Courtesy Equitable Life Ins. Co.

Fig. 29.18. Percentage bar chart.

each bar in a direction parallel to it. To place the values at the end gives the illusion of increasing the length of the bars. Usually, the names of the items are lettered to the left of the vertical starting line on a horizontal chart and below the starting line on a vertical chart.

29.16. Area (percentage) charts. An area diagram can be used profitably when it is desirable to present pictorially a comparison of related quantities in percentage. This form of representation illustrates the relative magnitudes of the component divisions of a total of the distribution of income, the composition of the population, and so on. Two common types of the various forms of area diagrams used in advertising literature are illustrated in Figs. 29.17 and 29.18. Percentages, when represented by sectors of a circle or subdivisions of a bar, are easy to interpolate.

The pie chart (Fig. 29.17) is the most popular form of area diagram, as well as the easiest to construct. The area of the circle represents 100 per cent and the sectors represent percentages of the total. In order to make the chart effective, a description of each quantity and its corresponding percentage should be lettered in its individual sector. All lettering should be completed before the areas are crosshatched or colored. The percentage bar chart shown in Fig. 29.18 fulfills the same purpose as

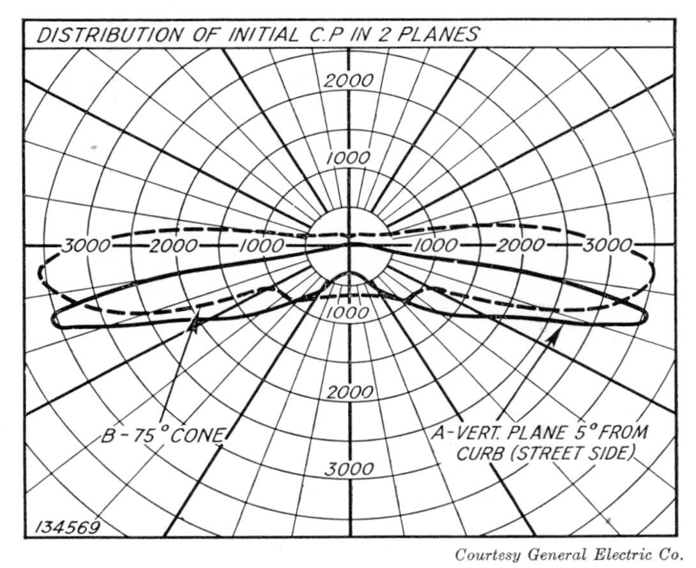

Courtesy General Electric Co.

Fig. 29.19. Polar chart.

the pie chart. The all-over area of the bar represents 100 per cent. Note that each percentage division is crosshatched in a different direction. The descriptions may be placed on either side of the bar; the percentages should be on the bar or at the side.

29.17. Polar charts. Certain types of technical data can be more easily plotted and better represented on polar co-ordinate paper. Polar charts drawn by self-recording instruments, polar diagrams, and plotted polar curves representing various kinds of scientific data are very common. Polar curves are used to represent the intensity of diffused light, intensity of heat, and so on. The polar chart in Fig. 29.19 gives, in terms of candle power, the intensity of light in two planes.

29.18. Trilinear charts. Trilinear charts are used principally in the study of the properties of chemical compounds, mixtures, solutions, and alloys (Fig. 29.20). Basically this is a 100 per cent chart the use of which, owing to its geometrical form, is limited to the investigation of that which is composed of three constituents or variables. Its use depends upon the geometrical principle that the sum of the three perpendiculars from any point is equal to the altitude. If the altitude represents 100 per cent, the perpendiculars will represent the percentages of the three variables composing the whole.

The ruling can be accomplished conveniently by dividing any two sides of the triangle into the number of equal percentage divisions desired and drawing through these points lines parallel to the sides of the triangle.

29.19. Chemical engineering charts. Fig. 29.21 shows a type of flow chart that must be prepared frequently by chemical engineers in industrial practice.

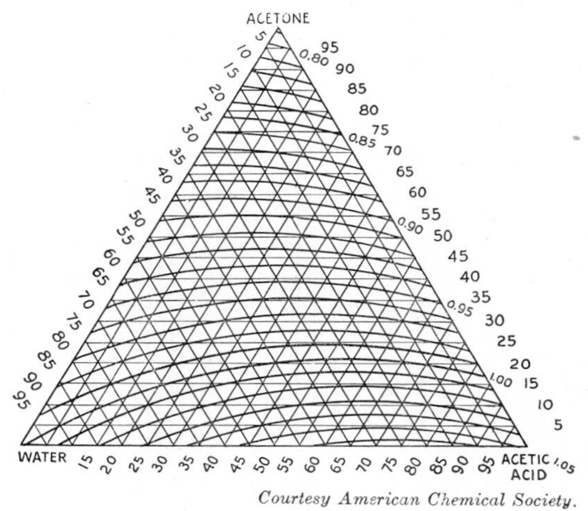

Courtesy American Chemical Society.

Fig. 29.20. Trilinear chart.

29.20. Alignment charts (nomographs). The purpose of alignment charts is to eliminate many of the laborious calculations necessary to solve formulae containing three or more variables. Such a chart is often complicated and difficult to construct, but if it can be used repeatedly the labor involved in making it will be justified. In the commercial field, these charts appear in varied forms, which may be very simple or very complicated. Fig. 29.22 illustrates an alignment chart consisting of three graduated parallel lines.

Briefly stated, the simplest form of alignment chart consists of a set of three or more inclined or vertical scales so spaced and graduated as to represent graphically the variables in a formula. The scales may be divided into logarithmic units or some other types of functions, depending upon the form of equation. As illustrated in Fig. 29.22, the unknown value may be found by aligning the working edge of a triangle to the points representing known values on two of the scales. With the triangle so placed, the numerical value representing the solution of the equation can be read on the third scale at the point of intersection.

Although alignment charts are being used more and more by engineers, it is impossible in this brief treatment of charts and graphs to explain fully the mathematics involved in their construction. The purpose here is merely to arouse the student's interest in this form of graphical representation. To satisfy the growing demand for training in nomographic drawing, many technical schools have added special courses dealing with alignment charts, special slide rules, and so on. Several reliable books on

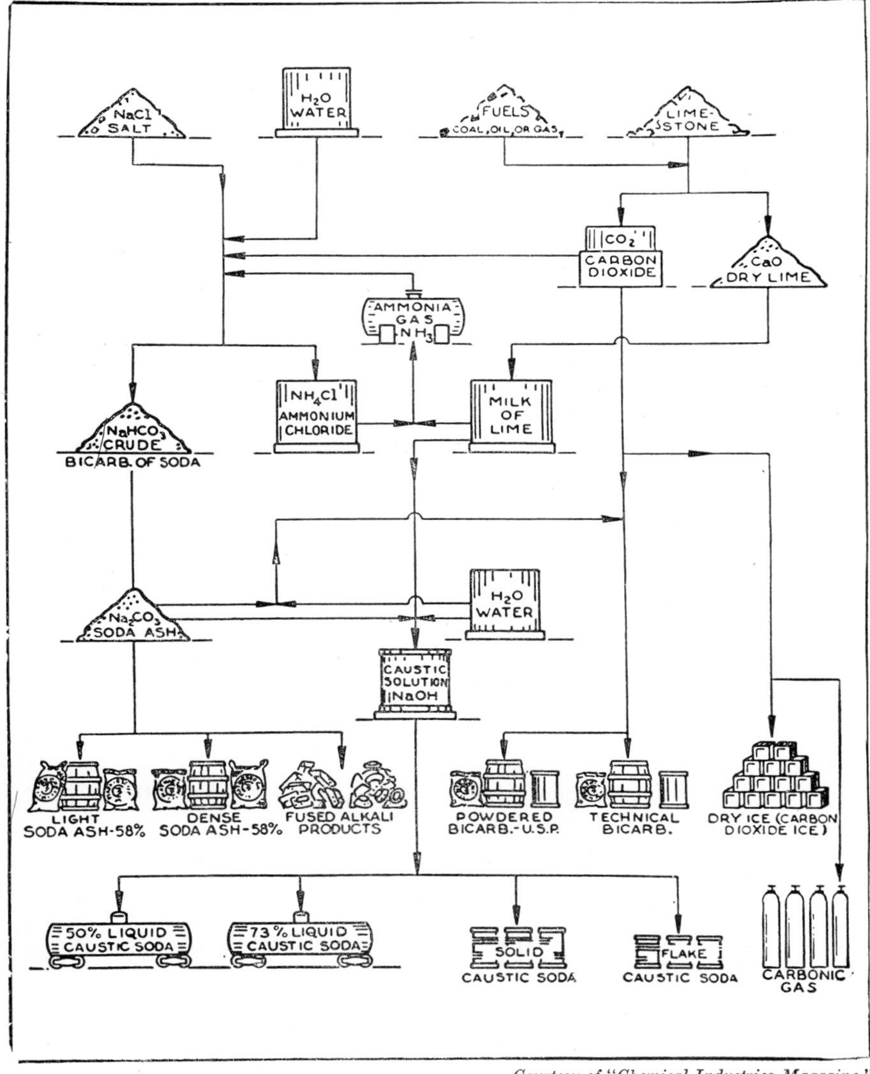

Courtesy of "Chemical Industries Magazine."

Fig. 29.21. Flow chart of ammonia-soda operations.

the subject are available. (See "Bibliography of Engineering Drawing and Allied Subjects" in the Appendix.)

29.21. Graphical calculus. In solving engineering problems it is frequently desirable and often necessary to present a graphical analysis of empirical data. Even though it is often possible to make an evaluation through the use of analytical calculus, a graphical representation is more meaningful because it is pictorial in character. Graphical integration and

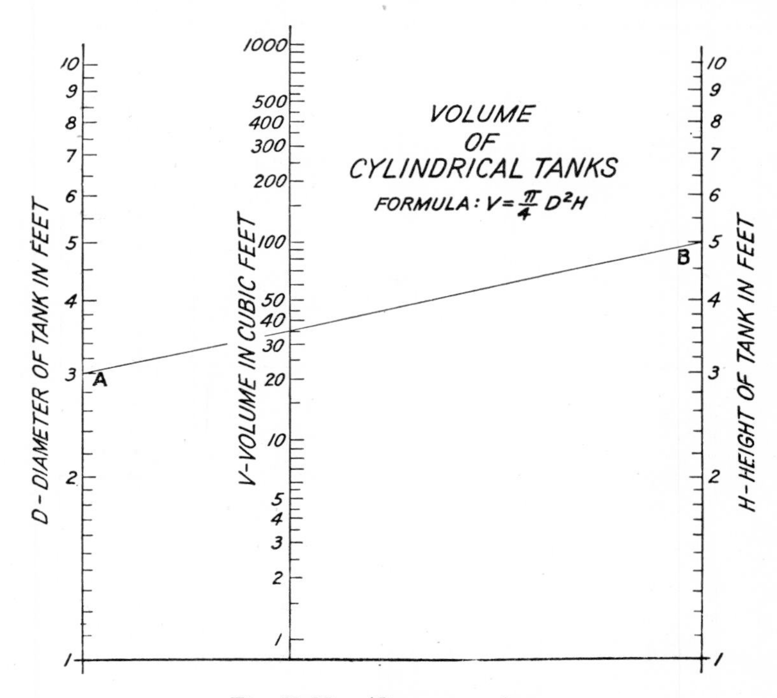

Fig. 29.22. Alignment chart.

differentiation are particularly desirable for problems for which only a set of values are known, or for curves that have been produced mechanically as in the case of steam engine indicator diagrams, or if the results cannot be determined by the analytical methods of calculus.

The following sections are devoted to the graphical rules and methods for determining derived curves. Discussion of the interpretation of results has been intentionally omitted since interpretation is not usually graphical and, therefore, not within the scope of this text.

29.22. Graphical integration. In deriving curves of a higher order the principle is applied that the area bounded by two successive ordinates, the curve, and the axis is equal to the difference in magnitude of the corresponding ordinates of the integral curve. Fig. 29.23 illustrates this principle of graphical integration. In (*a*) an increment of a curve is shown enlarged. The area under the curve will be approximately equal to the area of the shaded rectangle $ABCD$ when the line AB is drawn so that the area AM1 above the curve is approximately equal to the area MB2 below the curve. With a little practice one will find it easy to establish a line such as AB quite accurately by eye if a strip of celluloid or a triangle is used through which the curve can be seen.

By applying the principle of graphical integration to a series of increments, an integral curve may be drawn as shown in Fig. 29.24. At this point, it should be recognized that since the difference between successive ordinates represents increase in area, the difference between the final ordinate and the initial ordinate represents the total area between these ordinates that is bounded by the curve and the X-axis.

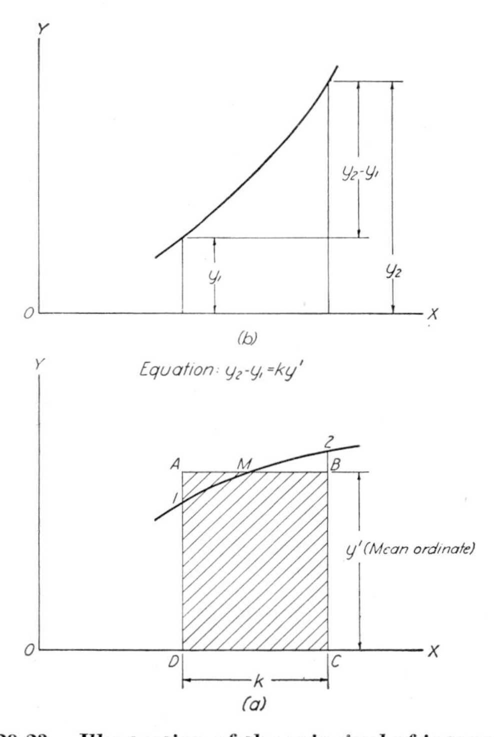

Fig. 29.23. Illustration of the principal of integration.

The scale selected for the Y axis of the integral curve need not be the same as the scale for the given curve.

Portions of a lower-order curve that are above the X-axis are considered to be positive while areas below with negative ordinates are recognized as negative. See Fig. 29.25(a). Since the negative area between any two ordinates on the lower-order curve represents only the difference in the length of the corresponding ordinates on the integral curve, the length of y_7 is less than the length of y_6 by an amount equal to the negative area. Also, because areas represent only differences in length of successive ordinates of the integral curve, the initial point on the integral curve might have any value and still fulfill its purpose. For example, either integral curve shown in Fig. 29.25(*b*) is a satisfactory solution for the curve in (*a*).

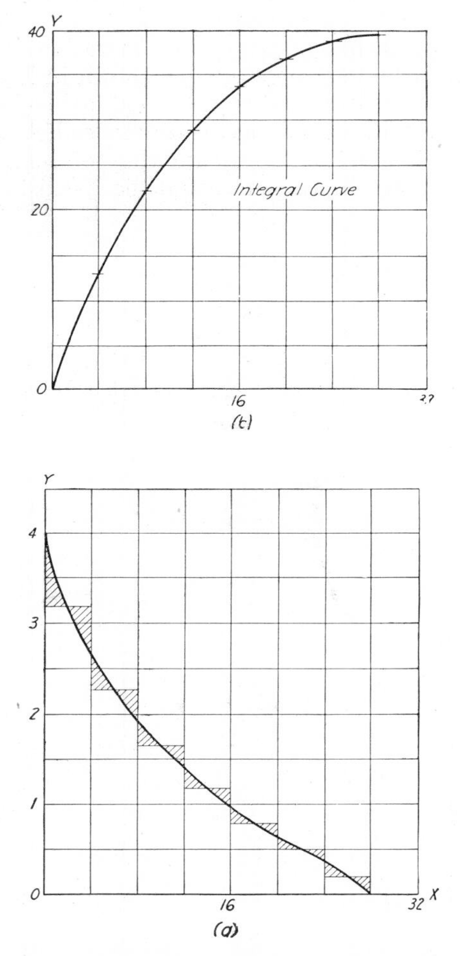

Fig. 29.24. The integration of a curve.

Fig. 29.26 shows the derived curves for a falling drop hammer. It is common practice, when drawing related curves, to place them in descending order as shown, that is, the lower-order curve is placed below.

In (*a*) the straight line represents a uniform acceleration of 32.2 feet per second per second, which is the acceleration for a freely falling body. The initial velocity is *O*. The units along the *X*-axis represent time in seconds and the units along the *Y*-axis represent acceleration in feet per second per second.

Since the acceleration is uniform, the velocity curve will be a straight line of constant slope, (*b*). The length of the last ordinate is equal to the total area under the acceleration curve, namely 25.76 feet per second (fps).

The distance curve, which is obtained by integrating the velocity time curve, is shown in (*c*). The length of the ordinate at any interval point is equal to the total area below the velocity curve between the origin and the point $[D = A = \frac{1}{2}(32.2T)T]$. See Figs. 29.23, 29.24, and 29.25.

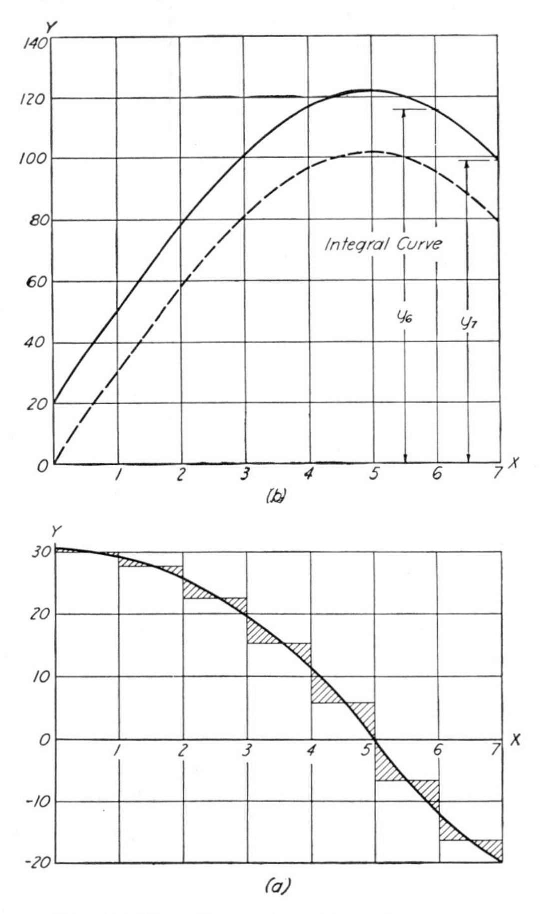

Fig. 29.25. The integration of a curve.

29.23. To integrate a curve by the ray polygon method. An integral curve may be drawn by a purely graphical process known as the ray polygon method.

This method of integrating the area under a curve is illustrated in Fig. 29.27.

Divide the *X*-axis into intervals and draw ordinates at the division points. Then, select the pole point *P* at some convenient location that

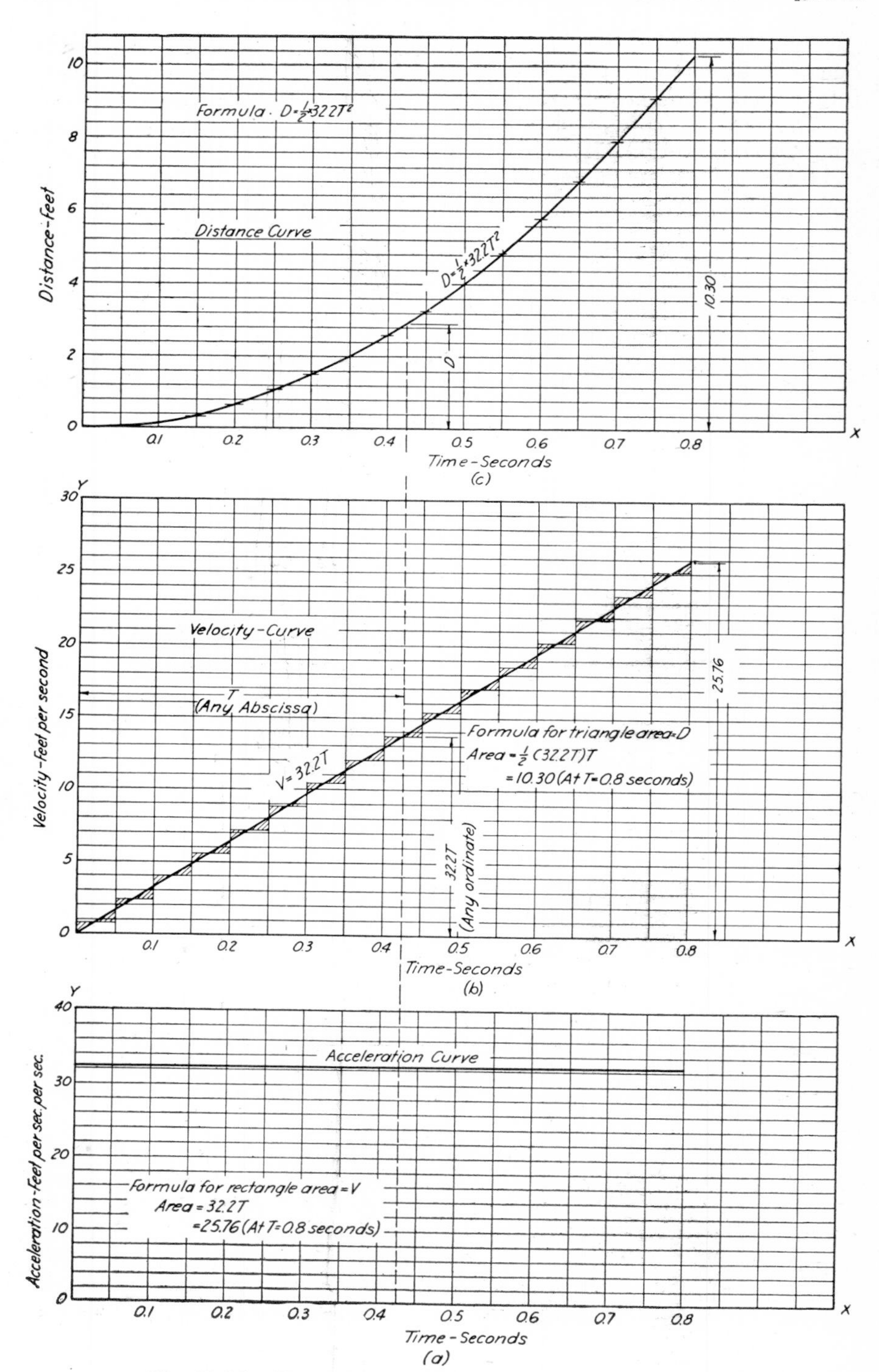

Fig. 29.26. Derived curves for a falling drop hammer.

will make the distance d equal to any number of the full units assigned to the X-axis. The selection of the number of units for the distance d determines the length of the scale along a Y-axis for the integral curve. To establish relationship between y_1 and y_0 the following equation based on similar right triangles can be written.

$$y_1 : k = y_0 : d$$

$$y_1 \cdot d = k \cdot y_0$$

$$y_1 = \frac{k \cdot y_0}{d} = \frac{k}{d} \cdot y_0$$

Determine the mean ordinate for each strip and transfer its height to the Y-axis as length OA, OB, OC, and so forth. Draw rays from P to points A, B, C, D, E, and F.

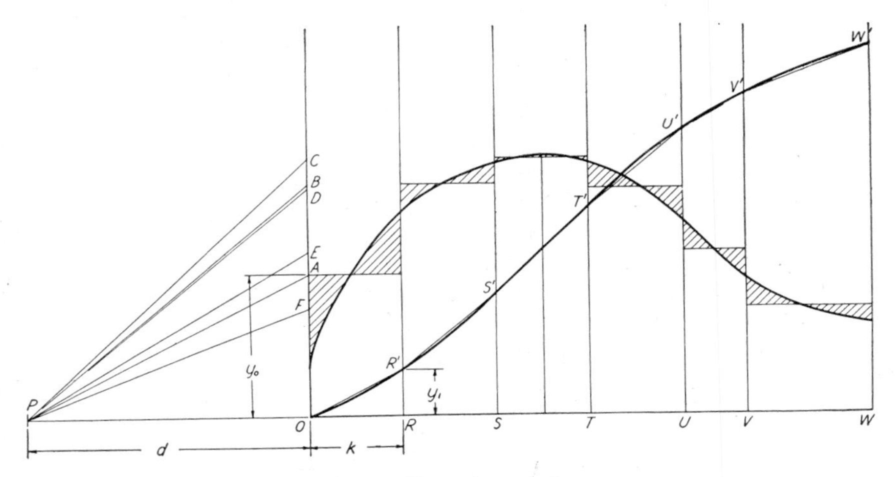

Fig. 29.27. Use of ray polygon.

To construct the integral curve, start at O and draw a line parallel to PA cutting the first vertical through R at R'. Through R' draw a line parallel to PB until it cuts the second vertical through S at S'. Repeat this procedure to obtain points T', U', and so on. Points R', S', T', U', V', and W' are points on the required integral curve. In Fig. 29.27 the integral curve is constructed on the same coordinate axes as the lower-order curve.

29.24. Graphical differentiation. Curves of a lower order are derived through the application of the principle that the ordinate at any point on the derived curve is equal to the slope of a tangent line at the corresponding point on the given curve. The slope of a curve at a point is the tangent of the angle with the X-axis formed by the tangent to the curve at the point. For all practical purposes, when constructing a derivative curve, the slope may be taken as the rise of the tangent line parallel to the Y-axis in one unit of distance along the X-axis, or the slope of the tangent equals $\frac{y_1}{k}$ as shown in Fig. 29.28.

Fig. 29.28 illustrates the application of this principle of graphical differentiation. The length of the ordinate y_1' at point A' on the derived curve is equal to the slope $\frac{y_1}{k}$ at point A on the given curve as shown in (a). When the slope is zero as at point C, the length of the ordinate is zero and point C' lies on the X-axis for the derived curve. When the slope is negative, as shown at D, the ordinate is negative and lies below the X-axis.

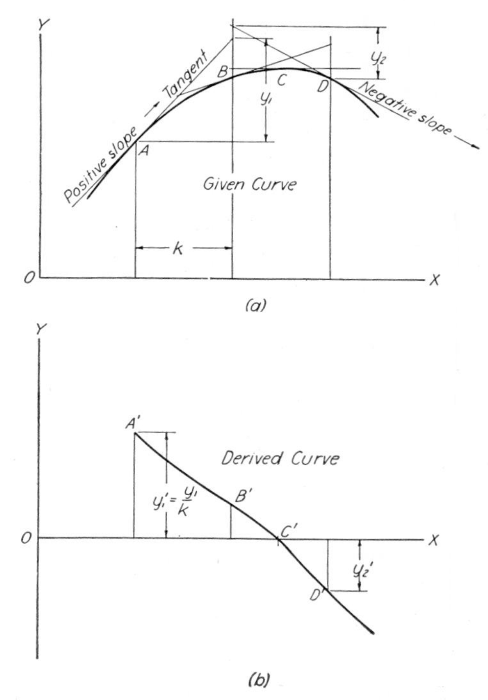

Fig. 29.28. Illustration of the principle of differentiation.

The graph shown in Fig. 29.29 is composed of segments of straight lines. Since the slope is constant for the interval *0–1*, the derivative curve in the interval is a horizontal line. In the interval *1–2*, the slope is also constant but of a lesser magnitude. Thus, the derivative curve is composed of straight line segments as shown in (b).

At this point in the discussion of graphical calculus it becomes possible to determine the relationship between the principles of integration and differentiation and to show that one is derived from the other.

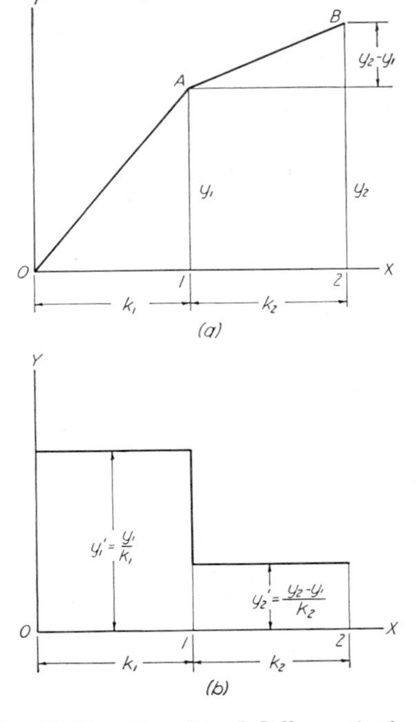

Fig. 29.29. Graphical differentiation.

From inspection of the graphs shown in Fig. 29.29 equations may be formulated as follows:

By the principle of differentiation

$$y_2' = \frac{y_2 - y_1}{k_2}$$

in the interval 1–2 where

$$\frac{y_2 - y_1}{k_2}$$

represents the slope of AB. The area under the curve in (b) in the interval 1–2 is equal to

$$y_2' \cdot k_2 = \frac{y_2 - y_1}{k_2} \cdot k_2 = y_2 - y_1 \quad \text{(integral curve)}$$

and

$$y_2' = \frac{y_2 - y_1}{k_2} \quad \text{(differential curve)}$$

In constructing a derivative curve the determination of the tangent lines is often difficult because the direction of a tangent at a particular point is usually not well defined by the curvature of the graph. Two related schemes that may be used for constructing tangents are shown in

Fig. 29.30(*a*) and (*b*). In (*a*) the tangent is drawn parallel to a chord of the curve, the arc of which is assumed to approximate the arc of a parabola. A sufficiently accurate location for the point of tangency T_1 may be determined by drawing a line from the mid-point of the chord to the arc, parallel to an assumed direction for the diameter of the parabola. When working with small segments of the curve one may assume the diameter to be either horizontal or vertical.

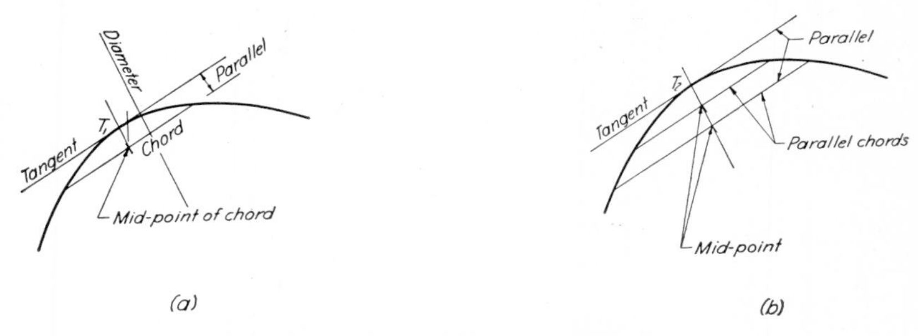

Fig. 29.30. Construction of a tangent line.

A more accurate construction is shown in (*b*) where the tangent is drawn parallel to two parallel chords. The point of tangency T_2 is determined by connecting the mid-points of the chords and extending this line to the curve. This line determines the direction of the diameter.

The construction in (*b*) using two chords to establish a tangent is

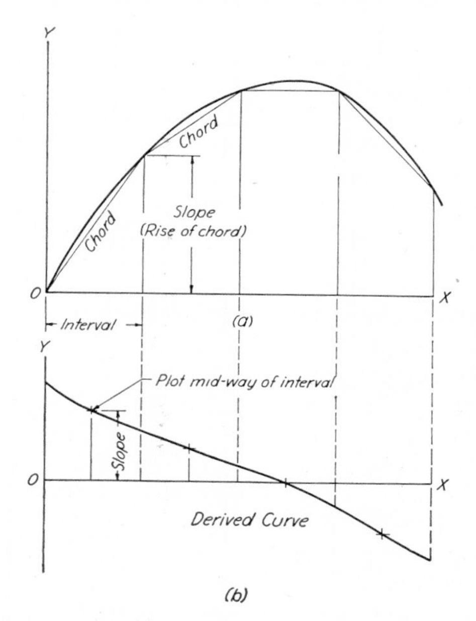

Fig. 29.31. Use of chords in the place of tangents.

applicable to any curve that may be approximated by a portion of a circle, ellipse, parabola, or hyperbola.

Since a tangent is assumed to be parallel to a chord, it is common practice to use chords instead of tangents for constructing a derivative curve, as shown in Fig. 29.31(*a*). The slope is plotted on an ordinate located midway in the corresponding interval of the derived curve.

A derivative curve can also be drawn using the ray polygon method as explained in Sec. 29.23 in reverse. See Fig. 29.32. The lines *PA*, *PB*,

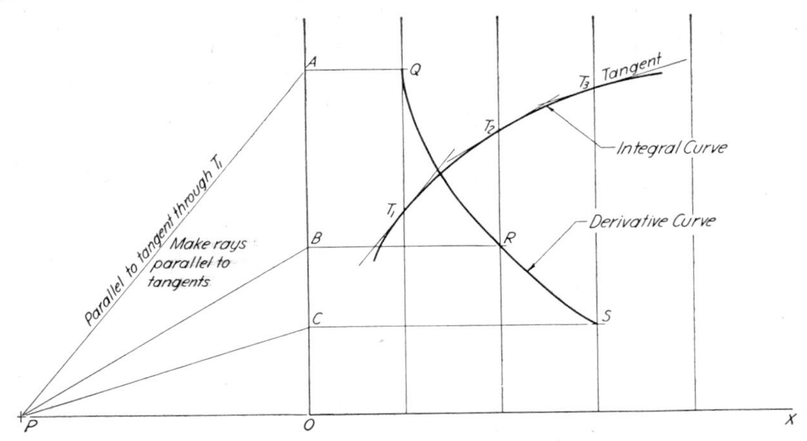

Fig. 29.32. Ray polygon method.

and *PC* of the ray polygon are drawn parallel to the tangents at points T_1, T_2, and T_3. Point *Q* is found by drawing a line horizontally from point *A* to the ordinate through the point of contact of the tangent parallel to *PA*. Points *R* and *S* are found similarly.

Fig. 29.33 shows the differentiation of a curve using chords instead of tangents. The given distance-time curve was plotted from data obtained for a passenger train leaving a small station near a large city. The velocity and acceleration curves reveal that the train moves with a constant acceleration for approximately 100 seconds until it reaches a velocity of fifty-five miles per hour. From this point it travels with a constant velocity towards its destination.

29.25. Problems. The following problems have been designed to emphasize the fundamental principles underlying the preparation and use of scientific and technical graphs.

1. Determine the values for the following equations, as assigned, and plot the curve in each case for quantitative purposes.

Parabola	$Y = 4x^2$, x from 0 to 5
Ellipse	$Y^2 = 100 - 2x^2$
Sines	$Y = \sin x$, x from 0° to 360°
Cosines	$Y = \cos x$, x from 0° to 360°
Logarithms	$Y = \log\ x$, x from 1 to 10
Reciprocals	$Y = \frac{1}{x}$, x from 1 to 10

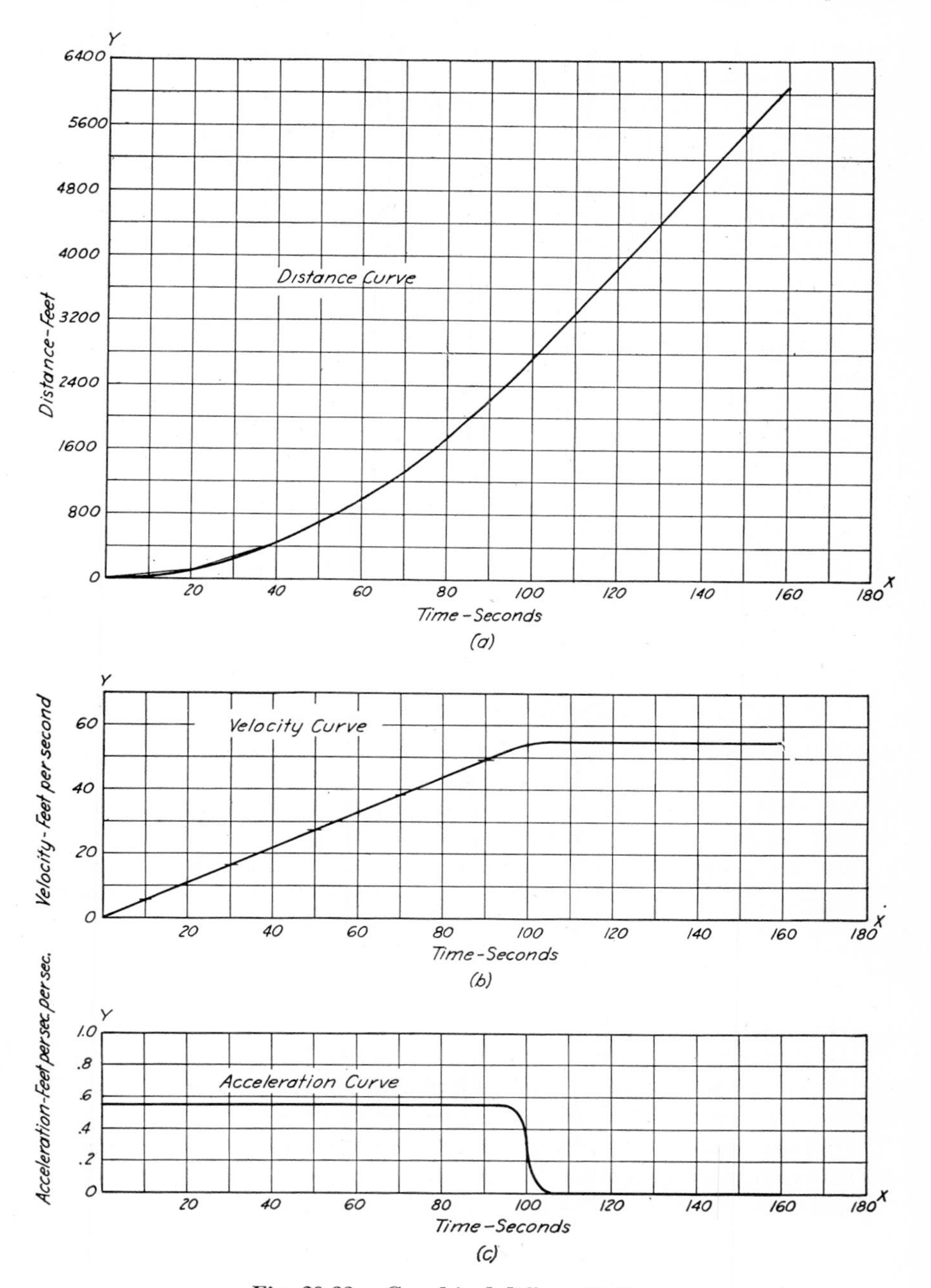

Fig. 29.33. Graphical differentiation.

2. The freezing temperature for two common antifreeze solutions for various compositions are given below.

Prestone		Denatured Alcohol	
% by Vol.	*Temp. °F.*	*% by Vol.*	*Temp. °F.*
10	25	10	25
20	16.5	20	17.5
25	11	25	14
30	5	30	5
35	−3	35	−1
40	−12	40	−11
45	−25	45	−18
50	−38	50	−25
55	−47	55	−32
		65	−45

Prepare a chart for these data, mainly quantitative in character, from which the required per cent volume can be read for any desired freezing temperature. Use India ink and the type of paper shown in Fig. 29.3(*b*).

3. Approximate barometric pressures at different heights above sea level are given below. Prepare a qualitative chart for the given data, using India ink on rectangular co-ordinate paper.

Note that the curve would be straight on semilogarithmic paper.

H—Altitude in miles										
0	1	2	3	4	5	6	7	8	9	10
29.92	24.5	20.0	16.2	13.45	11.0	8.9	7.28	5.95	4.87	4.0
B—Barometric pressure, in. of Hg.										

4. Data on rate of growth are frequently plotted on semilogarithmic paper, because the slope of the curve then represents the rate of growth. On semilogarithmic paper, plot the data for the enrollment in a university.

Year	*Enrollment*	*Year*	*Enrollment*	*Year*	*Enrollment*	*Year*	*Enrollment*
1900	1012	1910	1915	1920	3199	1930	5745
1901	1181	1911	1981	1921	3331	1931	5273
1902	1336	1912	2091	1922	3360	1932	4564
1903	1434	1913	2422	1923	3414	1933	4278
1904	1524	1914	2542	1924	3660	1934	4534
1905	1963	1915	2487	1925	4010	1935	5364
1906	2047	1916	2438	1926	4239	1936	6332
1907	2090	1917	1844	1927	4573	1937	7125
1908	1936	1918	2605	1928	4960	1938	7613
1909	1882	1919	2955	1929	5364	1939	7923

Place the vertical axis 1 unit in from the left edge and the horizontal axis at the extreme bottom of the page ruling. Letter in an appropriate title.

Draw also the curve of the general trend and enter on the chart, just below the title, what the enrollment would be in 1942 if the same rate of growth is maintained.

5. In a hydraulics laboratory, the construction of a quantitative curve that would give the weight of water contained in tubes of various diameters and lengths was desired. This was accomplished by filling tubes of known diameters with water to a depth of one foot and observing the weight of water thus added. The water was kept at a temperature for maximum density and the following data were obtained:

D = Diam. of Tube in Inches	*W = Weight of 1 Ft. Col. of Water*	*D = Diam. of Tube in Inches*	*W = Weight of 1 Ft. Col. of Water*
2	1.362	5	8.512
$2\frac{1}{2}$	2.128	$5\frac{1}{2}$	10.299
3	3.064	6	12.257
$3\frac{1}{2}$	4.171	$6\frac{1}{2}$	14.385
4	5.448	7	16.683
$4\frac{1}{2}$	6.895	$7\frac{1}{2}$	19.152
		8	21.790

On a sheet of graph paper (Fig. 29.3*b*), plot the above data. Place the axes 3 centimeters in from the edges. Letter the title in any convenient open space.

6. Owing to uncontrollable factors, such as lack of absolute uniformity of material or test procedure, repeated tests of samples of material do not give identical results. Also, it has been observed in many practical situations that:

1. Large departures from the average seldom occur.
2. Small variations from average occur quite often.
3. The variations are equally likely to be above average and below average.

The foregoing statements are borne out by the accompanying data showing the results of 4,000 measurements of tensile strength of malleable iron.

On a sheet of co-ordinate graph paper (Fig. 29.3(*a*) or (*b*)) prepare a graph showing frequency of occurrence of various strength values as ordinates, and tensile strength as abscissa. Draw a smooth symmetrical curve approximating the given data.

Range of Tensile Strength Values in Lb. per Sq. In.	*No. of Observations*
Under 45,000	0
45,000–45,999	1
46,000–46,999	2
47,000–47,999	3
48,000–48,999	6
49,000–49,999	20
50,000–50,999	232
51,000–51,999	376
52,000–52,999	590
53,000–53,999	740
54,000–54,999	771
55,000–55,999	604

Range of Tensile Strength Values in Lb. per Sq. In.	*No. of Observations*
56,000–56,999	383
57,000–57,999	184
58,000–58,999	60
59,000–59,999	20
Over 60,000	8
	4,000

7. On a sheet of paper, of the type shown in Fig. 29.3(*b*), using India ink, plot a curve to represent the data given below. *Note:* For *stress-strain diagrams,* although the load is the independent variable, it is plotted as ordinate, contrary to the general rule as given in Sec. 29.5. Fig. 29.6 shows a similar chart. In performing tests of this nature, some load is imposed before any readings of elongation are taken.

It is suggested that the label along the abscissa be marked "Strain, 0.00001 in. per in.," then fewer figures will be required along the axis.

Stress, lb. per sq. in.	*Strain, in. per in.*	*Stress, lb. per sq. in.*	*Strain, in. per in.*
3,000	0.0001	25,000	0.00090
5,000	0.0002	30,000	0.00106
10,000	0.00035	32,000	0.00112
15,000	0.00054	33,000	0.00130
20,000	0.00070	34,000	0.00140

8. Make a vertical multiple bar chart showing the enrollment at ____________ University from 1900 to 1939. Obtain data from problem 4.

9. Make a semilogarithmic graph showing the enrollment of your school for the last twenty years.

10. A beam 10 ft. long is uniformly loaded at 20# per ft. as shown in the accompanying diagram. Plot distance in feet along the X-axis. Draw (1) the integral curve to show the shearing force, and (2) the second integral curve to show the bending moment.

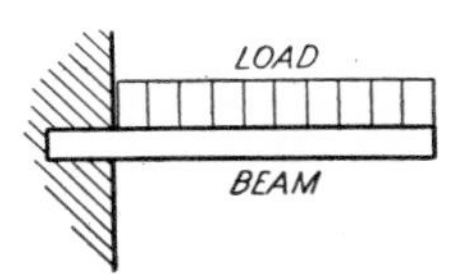

Fig. 29.34.

11. A beam 15 ft. long and supported at both ends is loaded uniformly at 18# per foot as shown in the accompanying diagram. Plot distance in feet along the X-axis and load along the Y-axis. Draw (1) the integral curve to show the shearing force, and (2) the second integral curve to show the bending moment.

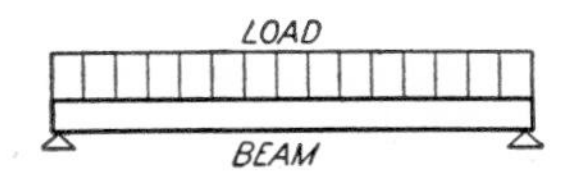

Fig. 29.35.

12. Plot the points given in the table and draw a smooth curve. Construct the derivative curve. Write the equation of the derivative curve

x	0	1	2	3	4	5	6	7	8	9	10
y	10	10.5	12	14.5	18	22.5	28	34.5	42	50.5	60

Equation of given curve $y = \frac{1}{2}x^2 + 10$.

13. Construct the distance-time, velocity-time, and acceleration-time curves for an automobile moving as follows: time = 10 seconds, acceleration = 5 feet per second per second throughout the interval, initial velocity = 0.

14. The passenger train for which derived curves are shown in Fig. 29.33 is brought to a stop with a constant negative acceleration of 1.0 feet per second per second. Before applying the brakes the train was traveling with a constant velocity of 55 feet per second. Construct the curves showing acceleration-time, velocity-time, and distance-time relationships.

APPENDIX

CONTENTS

ELECTRIC POWER AND WIRING[1]

	One Line	Complete[2]
A-C Generator or Motor—Basic Symbol[3]	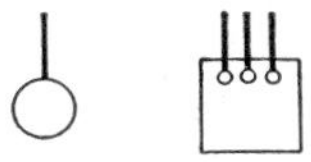	
D-C Generator or Motor—Basic Symbol	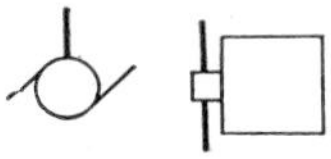	
Induction Motor[3]	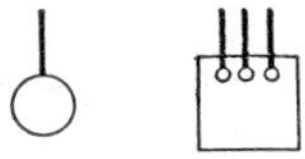	
Synchronous Converter[3]	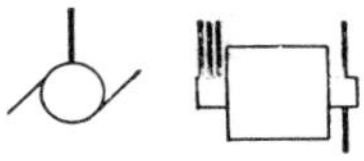	
Direct Connected Units—Basic Symbols[3]	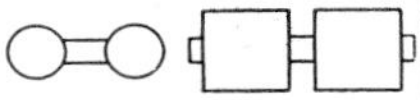	
Single-Phase Two-Winding Transformer—Basic Symbols[3, 4]	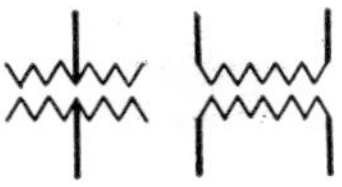	
Disconnecting Switch Basic Symbol		
Knife Switch, Single-Throw	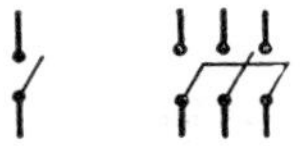	
Double-Throw Switch	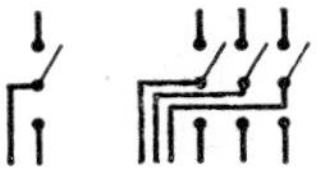	
Oil Circuit Breaker, Single-Throw	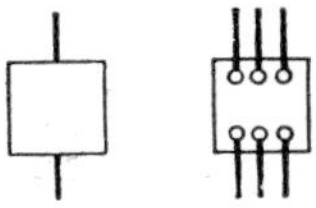	

	One Line	Complete[2]
Air Circuit Breaker	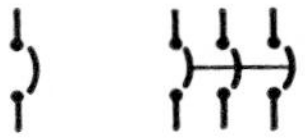	
Fuse		
Resistor		
Rheostat		
Reactor		
Capacitor[4]	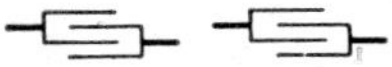	
Lightning Arrestor Basic Symbol[4]	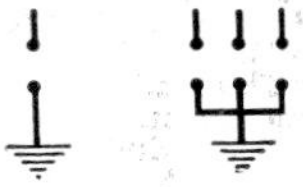	
Indicating Instrument—Basic Symbol[3]		(6)
Graphic Instrument Basic Symbol	 GRAPH	(6)
Ampere-Hour Meter		(6)
Ammeter		(6)
Frequency Meter		(6)
Watthour Meter		(6)

ELECTRIC POWER AND WIRING[1] (Continued)

	One Line	Complete[2]		One Line	Complete[2]
Wattmeter	(W)	(6)	Conductors, Crossing but not Connected		
Voltmeter	(V)	(6)	Conductors, Crossing and Electrically Connected		
Instrument Shunt			Conductors (with Branches)		
Conductors			Bus (with Branches)		
			Ground Connection		

[1] These Symbols for Electric Power and Wiring were extracted from American Standard for Graphical Symbols ASA Z14.2-1935.

[2] The "complete" symbol is intended to illustrate the method of treatment for any desired polyphase combination rather than to show the exact symbol required.

[3] Use symbol (-\/\/\/\/\/-) for windings of apparatus as required, and connect to suit particular case. It is recognized that no symbol list can show symbols for complete diagrams for all possible methods of connection.

[4] This symbol has not been approved as American Standard because there is still a major difference of opinion concerning the representation of this piece of equipment.

[5] Letter within circle indicates type of instrument if but one is used. If more than one instrument is used, "I" appears within the circle with abbreviation alongside.

(6) For complete symbol show outline approximating that of rear view of actual device and indicate terminals in actual relative location, current terminals by open circles, and potential terminals by solid circles. Scale range and type number may be marked adjacent to symbol, if desired.

TABLE I

Standard Conversion Table

4ths	*8ths*	*16ths*	*32nds*	*64ths*	*To 4 Places*	*To 3 Places*	*To 2 Places*
				1/64	.0156	.016	.02
			1/32		.0312	.031	.03
				3/64	.0469	.047	.05
		1/16			.0625	.062	.06
				5/64	.0781	.078	.08
			3/32		.0938	.094	.09
				7/64	.1094	.109	.11
	1/8				.1250	.125	.12
				9/64	.1406	.141	.14
			5/32		.1562	.156	.16
				11/64	.1719	.172	.17
		3/16			.1875	.188	.19
				13/64	.2031	.203	.20
			7/32		.2188	.219	.22
				15/64	.2344	.234	.23
1/4					.2500	.250	.25
				17/64	.2656	.266	.27
			9/32		.2812	.281	.28
				19/64	.2969	.297	.30
		5/16			.3125	.312	.31
				21/64	.3281	.328	.33
			11/32		.3438	.344	.34
				23/64	.3594	.359	.36
	3/8				.3750	.375	.38
				25/64	.3906	.391	.39
			13/32		.4062	.406	.41
				27/64	.4219	.422	.42
		7/16			.4375	.438	.44
				29/64	.4531	.453	.45
			15/32		.4688	.469	.47
				31/64	.4844	.484	.48
					.5000	.500	.50
				33/64	.5156	.516	.52
			17/32		.5312	.531	.53
				35/64	.5469	.547	.55
		9/16			.5625	.562	.56
				37/64	.5781	.578	.58
			19/32		.5938	.594	.59
				39/64	.6094	.609	.61
	5/8				.6250	.625	.62
				41/64	.6406	.641	.64
			21/32		.6562	.656	.66
				43/64	.6719	.672	.67
		11/16			.6875	.688	.69
				45/64	.7031	.703	.70
			23/32		.7188	.719	.72
				47/64	.7344	.734	.73
3/4					.7500	.750	.75
				49/64	.7656	.766	.77
			25/32		.7812	.781	.78
				51/64	.7969	.797	.80
		13/16			.8125	.812	.81
				53/64	.8281	.828	.83
			27/32		.8438	.844	.84
				55/64	.8594	.859	.86
	7/8				.8750	.875	.88
				57/64	.8906	.891	.89
			29/32		.9062	.906	.91
				59/64	.9219	.922	.92
		15/16			.9375	.938	.94
				61/64	.9531	.953	.95
			31/32		.9688	.969	.97
				63/64	.9844	.984	.98
					1.0000	1.000	1.00

TABLE II

Screw Threads

Nominal Diameter	Unified and American Thread Series*					
	Coarse (NC) (UNC)		*Fine (NF) (UNF)*		*Extra Fine (NEF) (UNEF)*	
	Threads per Inch	*Tap Drill†*	*Threads per Inch*	*Tap Drill†*	*Threads per Inch*	*Tap Drill†*
0	—	—	80	$\frac{3}{64}$	—	—
1	64	No. 53	72	No. 53	—	—
2	56	No. 50	64	No. 50	—	—
3	48	No. 47	56	No. 45	—	—
4	**40**	No. 43	48	No. 42	—	—
5	40	No. 38	44	No. 37	—	—
6	**32**	No. 36	40	No. 33	—	—
8	**32**	No. 29	36	No. 29	—	—
10	**24**	No. 25	**32**	No. 21	—	—
12	24	No. 16	28	No. 14	32	—
1/4	**20**	No. 7	**28**	No. 3	32	No. 2
5/16	**18**	*F*	**24**	*I*	32	*K*
3/8	**16**	$\frac{5}{16}$	**24**	*Q*	32	*S*
7/16	**14**	*U*	**20**	$\frac{25}{64}$	**28**	*Y*
1/2	**13**	$\frac{27}{64}$	**20**	$\frac{29}{64}$	**28**	$\frac{15}{32}$
9/16	**12**	$\frac{31}{64}$	**18**	$\frac{33}{64}$	24	$\frac{17}{32}$
5/8	**11**	$\frac{17}{32}$	**18**	$\frac{37}{64}$	24	$\frac{19}{32}$
3/4	**10**	$\frac{21}{32}$	**16**	$\frac{11}{16}$	**20**	$\frac{45}{64}$
7/8	**9**	$\frac{49}{64}$	**14**	$\frac{13}{16}$	**20**	$\frac{53}{64}$
1	**8**	$\frac{7}{8}$	**12**	$\frac{59}{64}$	**20**	$\frac{61}{64}$
1 1/8	**7**	$\frac{63}{64}$	**12**	$1\frac{3}{64}$	18	$1\frac{5}{64}$
1 1/4	**7**	$1\frac{7}{64}$	**12**	$1\frac{11}{64}$	18	$1\frac{13}{64}$
1 3/8	**6**	$1\frac{13}{64}$	**12**	$1\frac{19}{64}$	18	—
1 1/2	**6**	$1\frac{21}{64}$	**12**	$1\frac{27}{64}$	18	$1\frac{29}{64}$
1 3/4	**5**	$1\frac{35}{64}$	—	—	**16**	$1\frac{11}{16}$
2	**4 1/2**	$1\frac{25}{32}$	—	—	**16**	$1\frac{15}{16}$
2 1/4	**4 1/2**	$2\frac{1}{32}$	—	—	—	—
2 1/2	**4**	$2\frac{1}{4}$	—	—	—	—
2 3/4	**4**	$2\frac{1}{2}$	—	—	—	—
3	**4**	$2\frac{3}{4}$	—	—	—	—
3 1/4	**4**	3	—	—	—	—
3 1/2	**4**	$3\frac{1}{4}$	—	—	—	—
3 3/4	**4**	$3\frac{1}{2}$	—	—	—	—
4	**4**	$3\frac{3}{4}$	—	—	—	—

* ASA B1.1–1949 (third printing).
Bold type indicates Unified threads. To be designated UNC or UNF for sizes above $\frac{1}{4}''$.
Unified Standard—Classes 1A, 2A, 3A, 1B, 2B, 3B.
For recommended hole size limits before threading see Table 41, ASA B1.1–1949.
† Tap drill for a 75 per cent thread (not Unified—American Standard).
Bold type sizes smaller than $\frac{1}{4}''$ accepted for limited applications by the British, but the symbols NC or NF, as applicable, are retained.

TABLE III

UNIFIED-AMERICAN SPECIAL THREADS*
(8 PITCH, 12 PITCH, AND 16 PITCH SERIES)

Dia.	*Threads per Inch*			*Dia.*	*Threads per Inch*		
1/2	—	**12**	—	2 3/16	—	—	16
9/16	—	**12**	—	**2 1/4**	**8**	**12**	**16**
5/8	—	12	—	2 5/16	—	—	16
11/16	—	12	—	2 3/8	—	12	16
3/4	—	12	**16**	2 7/16	—	—	16
13/16	—	12	**16**	**2 1/2**	**8**	**12**	**16**
7/8	—	12	**16**	2 5/8	—	12	16
15/16	—	**12**	**16**	**2 3/4**	**8**	**12**	**16**
1	8	12	**16**	2 7/8	—	12	16
1 1/16	—	**12**	**16**	**3**	**8**	**12**	**16**
1 1/8	8	**12**	**16**	3 1/8	—	12	16
1 3/16	—	**12**	**16**	**3 1/4**	**8**	**12**	**16**
1 1/4	8	**12**	**16**	3 3/8	—	12	16
1 5/16	—	**12**	**16**	**3 1/2**	**8**	**12**	**16**
1 3/8	8	**12**	**16**	3 5/8	—	12	16
1 7/16	—	**12**	**16**	**3 3/4**	**8**	**12**	**16**
1 1/2	8	**12**	**16**	3 7/8	—	12	16
1 9/16	—	—	16	**4**	**8**	**12**	**16**
1 5/8	8	12	16	**4 1/4**	**8**	**12**	**16**
1 11/16	—	—	16	**4 1/2**	**8**	**12**	**16**
1 3/4	**8**	**12**	**16**	**4 3/4**	**8**	**12**	**16**
1 13/16	—	—	16	**5**	**8**	**12**	**16**
1 7/8	8	12	16	**5 1/4**	**8**	**12**	**16**
1 15/16	—	—	16	**5 1/2**	**8**	**12**	**16**
2	**8**	**12**	**16**	**5 3/4**	**8**	**12**	**16**
2 1/16	—	—	16	6	**8**	**12**	**16**
2 1/8	8	12	16				

ASA B1.1–1949.
For recommended hole size limits before threading see Table 41, ASA B1.1–1949.
Bold type indicates Unified threads (UN).

TABLE IV

Screw Threads

Nominal Diameter	American Thread Series* (Class 2–Class 3 External and Internal Threads)			
	Coarse (NC)		*Fine (NF)*	
	Threads per Inch	*Tap Drill*†	*Threads per Inch*	*Tap Drill*†
0	—	—	80	$\frac{3}{64}$
1	64	No. 53	72	No. 53
2	56	No. 50	64	No. 50
3	48	No. 47	56	No. 45
4	40	No. 43	48	No. 42
5	40	No. 38	44	No. 37
6	32	No. 36	40	No. 33
8	32	No. 29	36	No. 29
10	24	No. 25	32	No. 21
12	24	No. 16	28	No. 14
$\frac{1}{4}$	20	No. 7	28	No. 3
$\frac{5}{16}$	18	*F*	24	*I*
$\frac{3}{8}$	16	$\frac{5}{16}$	24	*Q*
$\frac{7}{16}$	14	*U*	20	$\frac{25}{64}$
$\frac{1}{2}$	13	$\frac{27}{64}$	20	$\frac{29}{64}$
$\frac{9}{16}$	12	$\frac{31}{64}$	18	$\frac{33}{64}$
$\frac{5}{8}$	11	$\frac{17}{32}$	18	$\frac{37}{64}$
$\frac{3}{4}$	10	$\frac{21}{32}$	16	$\frac{11}{16}$
$\frac{7}{8}$	9	$\frac{49}{64}$	14	$\frac{13}{16}$
1	8	$\frac{7}{8}$	14	$\frac{59}{64}$
$1\frac{1}{8}$	7	$\frac{63}{64}$	12	$1\frac{3}{64}$
$1\frac{1}{4}$	7	$1\frac{7}{64}$	12	$1\frac{11}{64}$
$1\frac{3}{8}$	6	$1\frac{13}{64}$	12	$1\frac{19}{64}$
$1\frac{1}{2}$	6	$1\frac{21}{64}$	12	$1\frac{27}{64}$
$1\frac{3}{4}$	5	$1\frac{35}{64}$	—	—
2	$4\frac{1}{2}$	$1\frac{25}{32}$	—	—
$2\frac{1}{4}$	$4\frac{1}{2}$	$2\frac{1}{32}$	—	—
$2\frac{1}{2}$	4	$2\frac{1}{4}$	—	—
$2\frac{3}{4}$	4	$2\frac{1}{2}$	—	—
3	4	$2\frac{3}{4}$	—	—
$3\frac{1}{4}$	4	3	—	—
$3\frac{1}{2}$	4	$3\frac{1}{4}$	—	—
$3\frac{3}{4}$	4	$3\frac{1}{2}$	—	—
4	4	$3\frac{3}{4}$	—	—

* ASA B1.1–1949.
American Standard—Classes 2 and 3.
† Tap drill for a 75 per cent thread (not American Standard).

TABLE V

Acme Threads			
Nom. Dia.	*Thds. per In.*	*Nom. Dia.*	*Thds. per In.*
$\frac{1}{4}$	16	$1\frac{1}{2}$	4
$\frac{5}{16}$	14	$1\frac{3}{4}$	4
$\frac{3}{8}$	12	2	4
$\frac{7}{16}$	12	$2\frac{1}{4}$	3
$\frac{1}{2}$	10	$2\frac{1}{2}$	3
$\frac{5}{8}$	8	$2\frac{3}{4}$	3
$\frac{3}{4}$	6	3	2
$\frac{7}{8}$	6	$3\frac{1}{2}$	2
1	5	4	2
$1\frac{1}{8}$	5	$4\frac{1}{2}$	2
$1\frac{1}{4}$	5	5	2
$1\frac{3}{8}$	4		

ASA B1.3–1941.

TABLE VI

Standard Bolts

RECOMMENDED MINIMUM THREAD LENGTHS FOR BOLTS†

Bolt* Length	Nominal Diameter of Bolt														
	No. 10, 1/4	5/16, 3/8	7/16, 1/2	9/16, 5/8	3/4	7/8	1	1 1/8, 1 1/4	1 3/8, 1 1/2	1 5/8, 1 3/4	1 7/8, 2	2 1/4	2 1/2	2 3/4	3
	Minimum Thread Length														
3/4	1/2	1/2	..	...	..	...	..	..	..	..	..	..	..	..	..
1	3/4	3/4	3/4	3/4	..	...	..	..	..	..	..	..	..	..	..
1 1/4	3/4	3/4	1	1	1	...	..	..	..	..	..	..	..	..	..
1 1/2	3/4	7/8	1	1 1/8	1 1/8	1 1/8	..	..	..	..	..	..	..	..	..
1 3/4	3/4	7/8	1	1 3/16	1 3/8	1 3/8	1 3/8	..	..	..	..	..	..	..	..
2	3/4	1	1 1/4	1 1/4	1 3/8	1 9/16	1 5/8	1 5/8	..	..	..	..	..	..	..
2 1/2	3/4	1	1 1/4	1 1/2	1 1/2	1 9/16	1 3/4	2	2	..	..	..	..	..	..
3	7/8	1	1 1/4	1 1/2	1 3/4	1 3/4	1 3/4	2 1/8	2 1/2	2 1/2	..	..	..	..	..
4	7/8	1	1 1/4	1 1/2	1 3/4	2	2 1/4	2 1/4	2 1/2	2 7/8	3 1/4	3 1/4	3 1/4	..	..
5	7/8	1 3/16	1 1/4	1 1/2	1 3/4	2	2 1/4	2 3/4	2 3/4	2 7/8	3 1/4	3 5/8	4	4 1/8	4 1/4
6	7/8	1 3/16	1 1/2	1 1/2	1 3/4	2	2 1/4	2 3/4	3 1/4	3 1/4	3 1/4	3 5/8	4	4 1/8	4 3/4
8	7/8	1 3/16	1 1/2	1 13/16	2	2	2 1/4	2 3/4	3 1/4	3 3/4	4	4	4	4 1/8	4 3/4
10	7/8	1 3/16	1 1/2	1 13/16	2 1/8	2 7/16	2 1/2	2 3/4	3 1/4	3 3/4	4 1/4	4 3/4	4 3/4	4 3/4	4 3/4
12	7/8	1 3/16	1 1/2	1 13/16	2 1/8	2 7/16	2 3/4	2 3/4	3 1/4	3 3/4	4 1/4	4 3/4	5 1/4	5 3/4	6 1/4
16	1	1 3/16	1 1/2	1 13/16	2 1/8	2 7/16	2 3/4	3 1/4	3 1/4	3 3/4	4 1/4	4 3/4	5 1/4	5 3/4	6 1/4
20	1	1 3/8	1 1/2	1 13/16	2 1/8	2 7/16	2 3/4	3 3/8	4	4 5/8	4 3/4	4 3/4	5 1/4	5 3/4	6 1/4
30	...	...	1 3/4	1 13/16	2 1/8	2 7/16	2 3/4	3 3/8	4	4 5/8	5 1/4	5 7/8	6 1/2	6 1/2	6 1/2

† Recommended by the ASA but does not comprise a part of the standard ASA B18.2-1941 Appendix.

* For intermediate bolt lengths, the minimum thread length shall be the same as that specified in the table for the next shorter length of bolt of the same diameter

All dimensions given in inches.

Minimum thread length is measured from the end of the bolt to the last complete thread.

TABLE VII

Standard Wrench-head Bolts and Nuts—Regular Series*

Bolt Dia.	Bolt Heads			Nuts				
	Width across Flats	*Height of Head*		*Width across Flats*	*Thickness*			
					Regular		*Jam*	
	Unfinished and Semi-finished Square and Hexagonal	*Unfinished Square and Hexagonal*	*Semi-finished Hexagonal Only*	*Regular and Jam*	*Unfinished Square and Hexagonal*	*Semi-finished Hexagonal Only*	*Unfinished Square and Hexagonal*	*Semi-finished Hexagonal Only*
$\frac{1}{4}$	$\frac{3}{8}$	$\frac{11}{64}$	$\frac{5}{32}$	$\frac{7}{16}$	$\frac{7}{32}$	$\frac{13}{64}$	$\frac{5}{32}$	$\frac{9}{64}$
$\frac{5}{16}$	$\frac{1}{2}$	$\frac{13}{64}$	$\frac{3}{16}$	$\frac{9}{16}$	$\frac{17}{64}$	$\frac{1}{4}$	$\frac{3}{16}$	$\frac{11}{64}$
$\frac{3}{8}$	$\frac{9}{16}$	$\frac{1}{4}$	$\frac{15}{64}$	$\frac{5}{8}$	$\frac{21}{64}$	$\frac{5}{16}$	$\frac{7}{32}$	$\frac{13}{64}$
$\frac{7}{16}$	$\frac{5}{8}$	$\frac{19}{64}$	$\frac{9}{32}$	$\frac{3}{4}$	$\frac{3}{8}$	$\frac{23}{64}$	$\frac{1}{4}$	$\frac{15}{64}$
$\frac{1}{2}$	$\frac{3}{4}$	$\frac{21}{64}$	$\frac{19}{64}$	$\frac{13}{16}$	$\frac{7}{16}$	$\frac{27}{64}$	$\frac{5}{16}$	$\frac{19}{64}$
$\frac{9}{16}$	$\frac{7}{8}$	$\frac{3}{8}$	$\frac{11}{32}$	$\frac{7}{8}$	$\frac{1}{2}$	$\frac{31}{64}$	$\frac{11}{32}$	$\frac{21}{64}$
$\frac{5}{8}$	$\frac{15}{16}$	$\frac{27}{64}$	$\frac{25}{64}$	1	$\frac{35}{64}$	$\frac{17}{32}$	$\frac{3}{8}$	$\frac{23}{64}$
$\frac{3}{4}$	$1\frac{1}{8}$	$\frac{1}{2}$	$\frac{15}{32}$	$1\frac{1}{8}$	$\frac{21}{32}$	$\frac{41}{64}$	$\frac{7}{16}$	$\frac{27}{64}$
$\frac{7}{8}$	$1\frac{5}{16}$	$\frac{19}{32}$	$\frac{9}{16}$	$1\frac{5}{16}$	$\frac{49}{64}$	$\frac{3}{4}$	$\frac{1}{2}$	$\frac{31}{64}$
1	$1\frac{1}{2}$	$\frac{21}{32}$	$\frac{19}{32}$	$1\frac{1}{2}$	$\frac{7}{8}$	$\frac{55}{64}$	$\frac{9}{16}$	$\frac{35}{64}$
$1\frac{1}{8}$	$1\frac{11}{16}$	$\frac{3}{4}$	$\frac{11}{16}$	$1\frac{11}{16}$	1	$\frac{31}{32}$	$\frac{5}{8}$	$\frac{39}{64}$
$1\frac{1}{4}$	$1\frac{7}{8}$	$\frac{27}{32}$	$\frac{25}{32}$	$1\frac{7}{8}$	$1\frac{3}{32}$	$1\frac{1}{16}$	$\frac{3}{4}$	$\frac{23}{32}$
$1\frac{3}{8}$	$2\frac{1}{16}$	$\frac{29}{32}$	$\frac{27}{32}$	$2\frac{1}{16}$	$1\frac{13}{64}$	$1\frac{11}{64}$	$\frac{13}{16}$	$\frac{25}{32}$
$1\frac{1}{2}$	$2\frac{1}{4}$	1	$\frac{15}{16}$	$2\frac{1}{4}$	$1\frac{5}{16}$	$1\frac{9}{32}$	$\frac{7}{8}$	$\frac{27}{32}$
$1\frac{5}{8}$	$2\frac{7}{16}$	$1\frac{3}{32}$	$1\frac{1}{32}$	$2\frac{7}{16}$	$1\frac{27}{64}$	$1\frac{25}{64}$	$\frac{15}{16}$	$\frac{29}{32}$
$1\frac{3}{4}$	$2\frac{5}{8}$	$1\frac{5}{32}$	$1\frac{3}{32}$	$2\frac{5}{8}$	$1\frac{17}{32}$	$1\frac{1}{2}$	1	$\frac{31}{32}$
$1\frac{7}{8}$	$2\frac{13}{16}$	$1\frac{1}{4}$	$1\frac{3}{16}$	$2\frac{13}{16}$	$1\frac{41}{64}$	$1\frac{39}{64}$	$1\frac{1}{16}$	$1\frac{1}{32}$
2	3	$1\frac{11}{32}$	$1\frac{7}{32}$	3	$1\frac{3}{4}$	$1\frac{23}{32}$	$1\frac{1}{8}$	$1\frac{3}{32}$
$2\frac{1}{4}$	$3\frac{3}{8}$	$1\frac{1}{2}$	$1\frac{3}{8}$	$3\frac{3}{8}$	$1\frac{31}{32}$	$1\frac{59}{64}$	$1\frac{1}{4}$	$1\frac{13}{64}$
$2\frac{1}{2}$	$3\frac{3}{4}$	$1\frac{21}{32}$	$1\frac{17}{32}$	$3\frac{3}{4}$	$2\frac{3}{16}$	$2\frac{9}{64}$	$1\frac{1}{2}$	$1\frac{29}{64}$
$2\frac{3}{4}$	$4\frac{1}{8}$	$1\frac{13}{16}$	$1\frac{11}{16}$	$4\frac{1}{8}$	$2\frac{13}{32}$	$2\frac{23}{64}$	$1\frac{5}{8}$	$1\frac{37}{64}$
3	$4\frac{1}{2}$	2	$1\frac{7}{8}$	$4\frac{1}{2}$	$2\frac{5}{8}$	$2\frac{37}{64}$	$1\frac{3}{4}$	$1\frac{45}{64}$

* ASA B18.2-1941.
All dimensions in inches.

TABLE VIII

Across-Corners Dimensions (Minimum)—Bolt Heads and Nuts, Regular Series

Diameter		$\frac{1}{4}$	$\frac{5}{16}$	$\frac{3}{8}$	$\frac{7}{16}$	$\frac{1}{2}$	$\frac{9}{16}$	$\frac{5}{8}$	$\frac{3}{4}$	$\frac{7}{8}$
Bolt Heads	Square	$\frac{1}{2}$	$\frac{43}{64}$	$\frac{3}{4}$	$\frac{53}{64}$	1	$1\frac{5}{32}$	$1\frac{1}{4}$	$1\frac{1}{2}$	$1\frac{47}{64}$
	Hex.	$\frac{13}{32}$	$\frac{35}{64}$	$\frac{5}{8}$	$\frac{11}{16}$	$\frac{53}{64}$	$\frac{31}{32}$	$1\frac{1}{32}$	$1\frac{15}{64}$	$1\frac{29}{64}$
Nuts	Square	$\frac{37}{64}$	$\frac{3}{4}$	$\frac{53}{64}$	1	$1\frac{5}{64}$	$1\frac{5}{32}$	$1\frac{21}{64}$	$1\frac{1}{2}$	$1\frac{47}{64}$
	Hex.	$\frac{31}{64}$	$\frac{5}{8}$	$\frac{11}{16}$	$\frac{53}{64}$	$\frac{57}{64}$	$\frac{31}{32}$	$1\frac{7}{64}$	$1\frac{1}{4}$	$1\frac{29}{64}$
Diameter		1	$1\frac{1}{8}$	$1\frac{1}{4}$	$1\frac{3}{8}$	$1\frac{1}{2}$	$1\frac{5}{8}$	$1\frac{3}{4}$	$\frac{7}{8}$	2
Bolt Heads	Square	$1\frac{63}{64}$	$2\frac{15}{64}$	$2\frac{31}{64}$	$2\frac{47}{64}$	$2\frac{63}{64}$	$3\frac{15}{64}$	$3\frac{31}{64}$	$3\frac{47}{64}$	$3\frac{63}{64}$
	Hex.	$1\frac{21}{32}$	$1\frac{55}{64}$	$2\frac{1}{16}$	$2\frac{17}{64}$	$2\frac{31}{64}$	$2\frac{11}{16}$	$2\frac{57}{64}$	$2\frac{3}{32}$	$3\frac{5}{16}$
Nuts	Square	$1\frac{63}{64}$	$2\frac{15}{64}$	$2\frac{31}{64}$	$2\frac{47}{64}$	$2\frac{63}{64}$	$3\frac{15}{64}$	$3\frac{31}{64}$	$3\frac{47}{64}$	$3\frac{63}{64}$
	Hex.	$1\frac{21}{32}$	$1\frac{55}{64}$	$2\frac{1}{16}$	$2\frac{17}{64}$	$2\frac{31}{64}$	$2\frac{11}{16}$	$2\frac{57}{64}$	$3\frac{3}{32}$	$3\frac{5}{16}$

Compiled from ASA B18.2-1941.

TABLE IX

Elastic Stop Nuts

Note: All dimensions in inches. Compiled from catalogue of Elastic Stop Nut Corp. of America.

Nominal Size	Threads per Inch		Across Flats *F*	Std. Height *H*	Thin Height *T*
	NC	*NF*			
No. 2	56	64	1/4	5/32	
No. 3	48	56	1/4	5/32	
No. 4	40	48	1/4	5/32	1/8
No. 5	40	44	1/4	5/32	
No. 6	32	40	5/16	3/16	9/64
No. 8	32	36	11/32	1/4	3/16
No. 10	24	32	3/8	1/4	3/16
No. 12	24	28	7/16	21/64	7/32
Heavy Weight					
1/4	20		1/2	3/8	3/32
5/16	18		9/16	7/16	5/16
3/8	16		11/16	35/64	13/32
7/16	14		3/4	19/32	7/16
1/2	13		7/8	45/64	17/32
9/16	12		15/16	13/16	3/16
5/8	11		1 1/16	55/64	39/64
3/4	10		1 1/4	1	45/64
7/8	9		1 7/16	1 1/8	25/32
1	8		1 5/8	1 9/32	57/64
1 1/8	7		1 13/16	1 7/16	31/32
1 1/4	7		2	1 41/64	1 7/64
1 3/8	6		2 3/16	1 51/64	1 3/16
1 1/2	6		2 3/8	1 59/64	1 5/16
1 3/4	5		2 3/4	2 5/16	1 15/32
2	4 1/2		3 1/8	2 13/32	1 11/16
2 1/4	4 1/2		3 1/2	2 13/16	1 15/16
Light Weight					
1/4		28	7/16	21/64	7/32
5/16		24	1/2	23/64	17/64
3/8		24	9/16	15/32	9/32
7/16		20	5/8	15/32	21/64
1/2		20	3/4	39/64	21/64
9/16		18	7/8	45/64	3/8
5/8		18	15/16	49/64	13/32
3/4		16	1 1/16	57/64	27/64
7/8		14	1 1/4	1 1/64	31/64
1		14	1 7/16	1 9/64	37/64
1 1/8		12	1 5/8	1 17/64	43/64
1 1/4		12	1 13/16	1 29/64	49/64
1 3/8		12	2	1 19/32	25/32
1 1/2		12	2 3/16	1 3/4	13/16

TABLE X

Castellated Nuts (SAE)

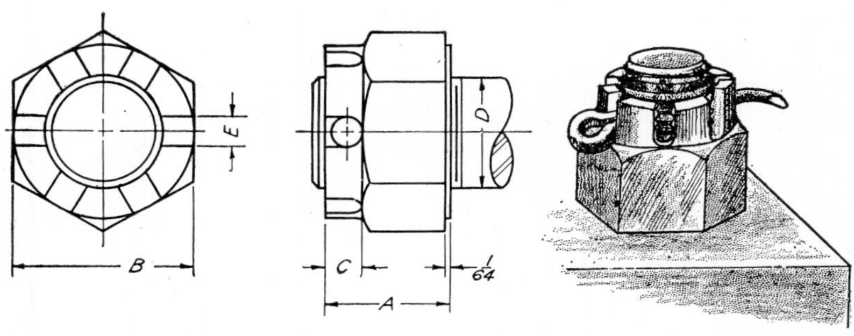

Dia. (*D*)	*Threads per Inch*	*A*	*B*	*C*	*E*	*Dia. of Cotter Pin* (*d*)
$\frac{1}{4}$	28	$\frac{9}{32}$	$\frac{7}{16}$	$\frac{3}{32}$	$\frac{5}{64}$	$\frac{1}{16}$
$\frac{5}{16}$	24	$\frac{21}{64}$	$\frac{1}{2}$	$\frac{3}{32}$	$\frac{5}{64}$	$\frac{1}{16}$
$\frac{3}{8}$	24	$\frac{13}{32}$	$\frac{9}{16}$	$\frac{1}{8}$	$\frac{1}{8}$	$\frac{3}{32}$
$\frac{7}{16}$	20	$\frac{29}{64}$	$\frac{5}{8}$	$\frac{1}{8}$	$\frac{1}{8}$	$\frac{3}{32}$
$\frac{1}{2}$	20	$\frac{9}{16}$	$\frac{3}{4}$	$\frac{3}{16}$	$\frac{1}{8}$	$\frac{3}{32}$
$\frac{9}{16}$	18	$\frac{39}{64}$	$\frac{7}{8}$	$\frac{3}{16}$	$\frac{5}{32}$	$\frac{1}{8}$
$\frac{5}{8}$	18	$\frac{23}{32}$	$\frac{15}{16}$	$\frac{1}{4}$	$\frac{5}{32}$	$\frac{1}{8}$
$\frac{11}{16}$	16	$\frac{49}{64}$	1	$\frac{1}{4}$	$\frac{5}{32}$	$\frac{1}{8}$
$\frac{3}{4}$	16	$\frac{13}{16}$	$1\frac{1}{16}$	$\frac{1}{4}$	$\frac{5}{32}$	$\frac{1}{8}$
$\frac{7}{8}$	14	$\frac{29}{32}$	$1\frac{1}{4}$	$\frac{1}{4}$	$\frac{5}{32}$	$\frac{1}{8}$
1	14	1	$1\frac{7}{16}$	$\frac{1}{4}$	$\frac{5}{32}$	$\frac{1}{8}$

TABLE XI

Slotted Head Machine Screws

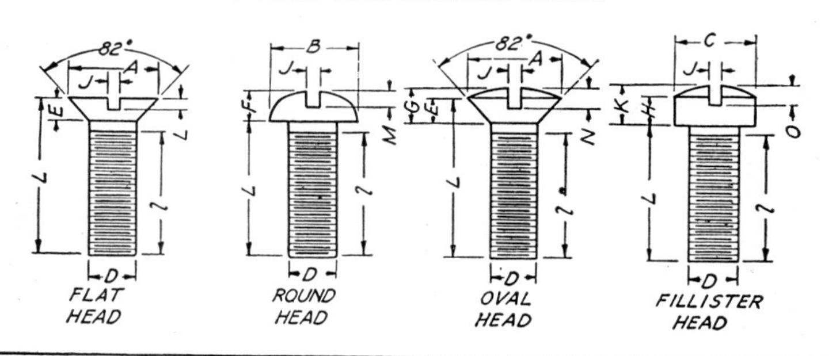

Size (Number) and Threads per Inch				American Standard Dimensions (Max.)												
Nominal Size	*Diameter D*	*Thread*		*Head Diameter*			*Height Dimensions*					*Slot Width*	*Slot Depth*			
		Coarse	*Fine*	*A*	*B*	*C*	*E*	*F*	*G*	*H*	*K*	*J*	*L*	*M*	*N*	*O*
0	.060	—	80	.119	.113	.096	.035	.053	.056	.045	.059	.023	.015	.039	.030	.025
1	.073	64	72	.146	.138	.118	.043	.061	.068	.053	.071	.026	.019	.044	.038	.031
2	.086	56	64	.172	.162	.140	.051	.069	.080	.062	.083	.031	.023	.048	.045	.037
3	.099	48	56	.199	.187	.161	.059	.078	.092	.070	.095	.035	.027	.053	.052	.043
4	.112	40	48	.225	.211	.183	.067	.086	.104	.079	.107	.039	.030	.058	.059	.048
5	.125	40	44	.252	.236	.205	.075	.095	.116	.088	.120	.043	.034	.063	.067	.054
6	.138	32	40	.279	.260	.226	.083	.103	.128	.096	.132	.048	.038	.068	.074	.060
8	.164	32	36	.332	.309	.270	.100	.120	.152	.113	.156	.054	.045	.077	.088	.071
10	.190	24	32	.385	.359	.313	.116	.137	.176	.130	.180	.060	.053	.087	.103	.083
12	.216	24	28	.438	.408	.357	.132	.153	.200	.148	.205	.067	.060	.096	.117	.094
$\frac{1}{4}$	.250	20	28	.507	.472	.414	.153	.175	.232	.170	.237	.075	.070	.109	.136	.109
$\frac{5}{16}$	.3125	18	24	.635	.590	.518	.191	.216	.290	.211	.295	.084	.088	.132	.171	.137
$\frac{3}{8}$	.375	16	24	.762	.708	.622	.230	.256	.347	.253	.355	.094	.106	.155	.206	.164
$\frac{7}{16}$	.4375	14	20	.812	.750	.625	.223	.328	.345	.265	.368	.094	.103	.196	.210	.170
$\frac{1}{2}$	.500	13	20	.875	.813	.750	.223	.355	.354	.297	.412	.106	.103	.211	.216	.190
$\frac{9}{16}$	.5625	12	18	1.000	.938	.812	.260	.410	.410	.336	.466	.118	.120	.242	.250	.214
$\frac{5}{8}$	.625	11	18	1.125	1.000	.875	.298	.438	.467	.375	.521	.133	.137	.258	.285	.240
$\frac{3}{4}$	.750	10	16	1.375	1.250	1.000	.372	.547	.578	.441	.612	.149	.171	.320	.353	.281

ASA B18.6-1947.

TABLE XII

Cap Screws

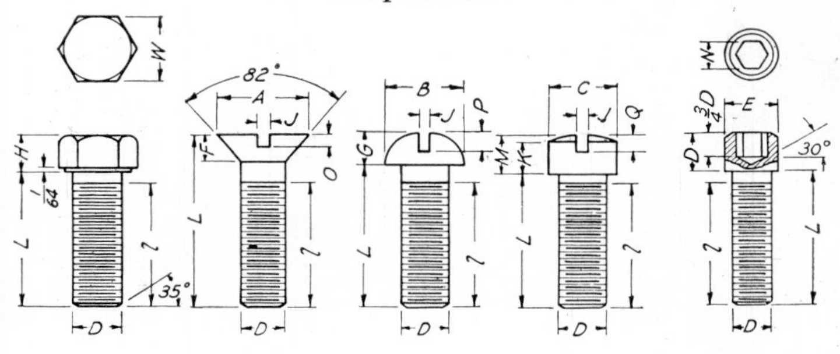

Nominal Size	American Standard Dimensions (Max.)														
	Head Diameter					*Height Dimensions*					*Slot Width*	*Slot Depth*			*Socket Width*
Dia.	*A*	*B*	*C*	*E*	*W*	*F* *Ave.*	*G*	*H*	*K*	*M*	*J*	*O*	*P*	*Q*	*N*
$\frac{1}{4}$	.500	.437	.375	$\frac{3}{8}$	$\frac{7}{16}$	.140	.191	$\frac{3}{16}$	.172	.216	.075	.069	.117	.097	$\frac{3}{16}$
$\frac{5}{16}$	.625	.562	.437	$\frac{7}{16}$	$\frac{1}{2}$	.176	.246	$\frac{15}{64}$	.203	.253	.084	.086	.151	.115	$\frac{7}{32}$
$\frac{3}{8}$	.750	.625	.562	$\frac{9}{16}$	$\frac{9}{16}$	.210	.273	$\frac{9}{32}$	.250	.314	.094	.103	.168	.143	$\frac{5}{16}$
$\frac{7}{16}$	.8125	.750	.625	$\frac{5}{8}$	$\frac{5}{8}$	.210	.328	$\frac{21}{64}$	.297	.368	.094	.103	.202	.168	$\frac{5}{16}$
$\frac{1}{2}$	.875	.812	.750	$\frac{3}{4}$	$\frac{3}{4}$	.210	.355	$\frac{3}{8}$	.328	.412	.106	.103	.219	.188	$\frac{3}{8}$
$\frac{9}{16}$	1.000	.937	.812	$\frac{13}{16}$	$\frac{13}{16}$	.245	.410	$\frac{27}{64}$	.375	.466	.118	.120	.253	.214	$\frac{3}{8}$
$\frac{5}{8}$	1.125	1.000	.875	$\frac{7}{8}$	$\frac{7}{8}$	.281	.438	$\frac{15}{32}$	.422	.521	.133	.137	.270	.240	$\frac{1}{2}$
$\frac{3}{4}$	1.375	1.250	1.000	1	1	.352	.547	$\frac{9}{16}$	.500	.612	.149	.171	.337	.283	$\frac{9}{16}$
$\frac{7}{8}$	1.625	—	1.125	$1\frac{1}{8}$	$1\frac{1}{8}$	.423	—	$\frac{21}{32}$	.594	.720	.167	.206	—	.334	$\frac{9}{16}$
1	1.875	—	1.321	$1\frac{5}{16}$	$1\frac{5}{16}$	.494	—	$\frac{3}{4}$	.656	.802	.188	.240	—	.372	$\frac{5}{8}$
$1\frac{1}{8}$	—	—	—	$1\frac{1}{2}$	$1\frac{1}{2}$	—	—	$\frac{27}{32}$	—	—	—	—	—	—	$\frac{3}{4}$
$1\frac{1}{4}$	—	—	—	$1\frac{3}{4}$	$1\frac{11}{16}$	—	—	$\frac{15}{16}$	—	—	—	—	—	—	$\frac{3}{4}$

ASA B18.3-1947.
ASA B18.6-1947.

TABLE XIII

Hexagonal-Head Self-Tapping Screws

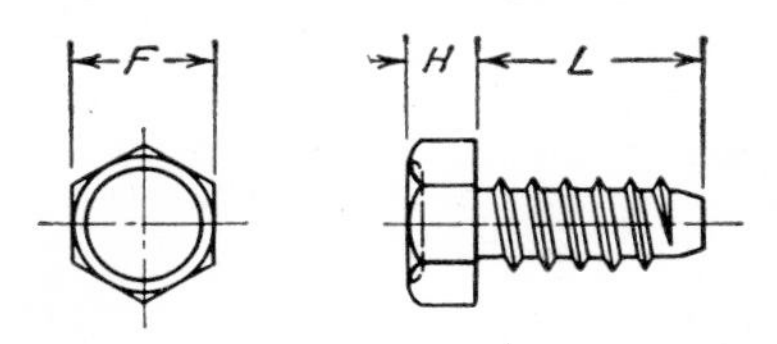

Nom. Size	*Across Flats F*	*Head Height H*	Lengths											
			3/16	1/4	3/8	1/2	5/8	3/4	7/8	1	1 1/4	1 1/2	1 3/4	2
No. 4	.187	.060	X	X										
No. 6	.250	.080	X	X	X									
No. 8	.250	.110		X	X	X	X	X	X	X				
No. 10	.312	.120			X	X	X	X	X	X				
No. 12	.312	.155				X	X	X	X	X	X	X		
1/4	.375	.190			X	X	X	X	X	X	X	X	X	X
5/16	.500	.230				X	X	X	X	X	X	X		
3/8	.562	.295					X	X	X	X	X	X	X	X
7/16	.625	.312						X	X	X	X	X	X	X
1/2	.750	.375						X	X	X	X	X	X	X

Note: All dimensions are in inches. Self-tapping screws are also available in the same head styles as machine screws. Dimensions of these head styles are the same as for machine screws.

Diameters of drilled holes for these screws vary with the thickness and type of material to be fastened. Consult manufacturers' catalogues for this data.

TABLE XIV

Wood Screws*

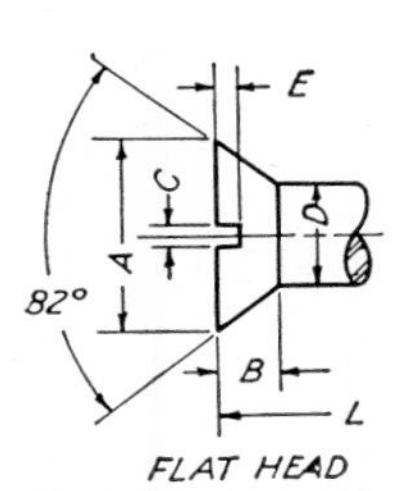

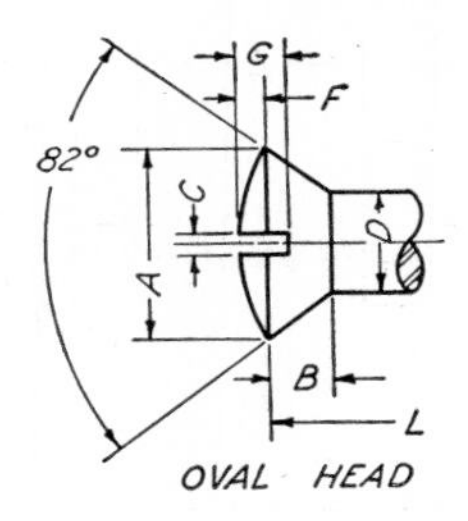

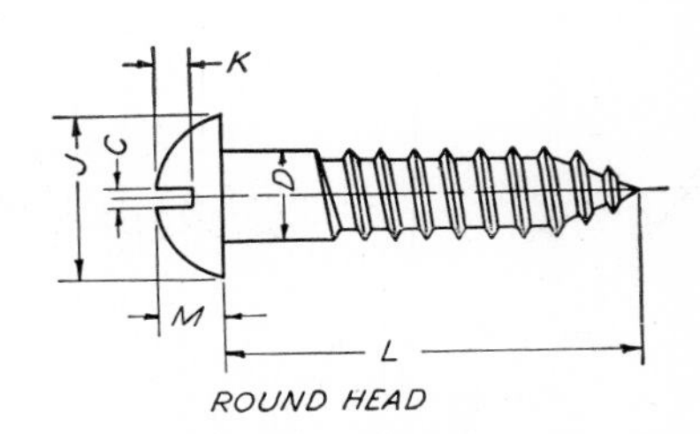

Screw No.	*Dia. (D)*	*A*	*B*	*C*	*E*	*F*	*G*	*J*	*K*	*M*	*Threads Per Inch*
0	.060	.112	.030	.025	.012	.018	.027	.106	.034	.047	32
1	.073	.138	.038	.027	.015	.022	.034	.130	.038	.056	28
2	.086	.164	.045	.030	.019	.025	.041	.154	.042	.064	26
3	.099	.190	.053	.032	.022	.029	.047	.178	.046	.072	24
4	.112	.216	.061	.034	.025	.033	.054	.202	.050	.080	22
5	.125	.242	.068	.037	.028	.037	.061	.228	.054	.089	20
6	.138	.268	.076	.039	.031	.040	.067	.250	.058	.097	18
7	.151	.294	.083	.041	.034	.044	.073	.274	.062	.105	16
8	.164	.320	.092	.043	.037	.048	.080	.298	.066	.113	15
9	.177	.346	.100	.045	.040	.051	.086	.322	.070	.121	14
10	.190	.371	.107	.048	.043	.055	.093	.346	.075	.130	13
12	.216	.424	.123	.052	.049	.063	.106	.395	.083	.146	11
14	.242	.476	.137	.057	.056	.070	.120	.443	.091	.162	10
16	.268	.528	.152	.061	.062	.077	.133	.491	.099	.178	9
18	.294	.580	.167	.066	.068	.085	.146	.539	.107	.195	8
20	.320	.632	.183	.070	.074	.092	.159	.587	.116	.212	8
24	.372	.736	.213	.079	.087	.107	.186	.683	.132	.244	7

* Compiled from ASA B18.6–1947.
Dimensions in inches.

TABLE XV

Washers (SAE Standard)

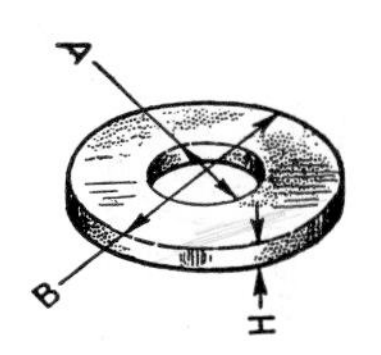

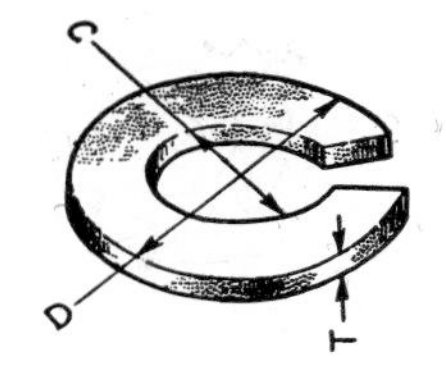

Plain				Lock Washers				
						Thickness (T)		
Nominal Size	*A*	*B*	*H*	*C*	*D*	*Regular*	*Light*	*Heavy*
$\frac{1}{4}$	$\frac{9}{32}$	$\frac{5}{8}$	$\frac{1}{16}$	0.265	0.453	$\frac{1}{16}$	$\frac{3}{64}$	$\frac{5}{64}$
$\frac{5}{16}$	$\frac{11}{32}$	$\frac{11}{16}$	$\frac{1}{16}$	0.328	0.578	$\frac{1}{16}$	$\frac{3}{64}$	$\frac{3}{32}$
$\frac{3}{8}$	$\frac{13}{32}$	$\frac{13}{16}$	$\frac{1}{16}$	0.390	0.640	$\frac{3}{32}$	$\frac{1}{16}$	$\frac{1}{8}$
$\frac{7}{16}$	$\frac{15}{32}$	$\frac{15}{16}$	$\frac{1}{16}$	0.453	0.767	$\frac{1}{8}$	$\frac{1}{16}$	$\frac{5}{32}$
$\frac{1}{2}$	$\frac{17}{32}$	$1\frac{1}{16}$	$\frac{3}{32}$	0.515	0.859	$\frac{1}{8}$	$\frac{1}{16}$	$\frac{11}{64}$
$\frac{9}{16}$	$\frac{19}{32}$	$1\frac{3}{16}$	$\frac{3}{32}$	0.593	0.968	$\frac{1}{8}$	$\frac{3}{32}$	$\frac{3}{16}$
$\frac{5}{8}$	$\frac{21}{32}$	$1\frac{5}{16}$	$\frac{3}{32}$	0.655	1.062	$\frac{5}{32}$	$\frac{3}{32}$	$\frac{13}{64}$
$\frac{11}{16}$	$\frac{23}{32}$	$1\frac{3}{8}$	$\frac{3}{32}$	0.718	1.155	$\frac{3}{16}$	$\frac{1}{8}$	$\frac{7}{32}$
$\frac{3}{4}$	$\frac{13}{16}$	$1\frac{1}{2}$	$\frac{1}{8}$	0.780	1.280	$\frac{3}{16}$	$\frac{1}{8}$	$\frac{1}{4}$
$\frac{7}{8}$	$\frac{15}{16}$	$1\frac{3}{4}$	$\frac{1}{8}$	0.905	1.437	$\frac{3}{16}$	$\frac{5}{32}$	$\frac{17}{64}$
1	$1\frac{1}{16}$	2	$\frac{1}{8}$	1.030	1.655	$\frac{1}{4}$	$\frac{3}{16}$	$\frac{5}{16}$
$1\frac{1}{8}$	$1\frac{3}{16}$	$2\frac{1}{4}$	$\frac{1}{8}$	1.155	1.905	$\frac{1}{4}$	$\frac{3}{16}$	$\frac{5}{16}$
$1\frac{1}{4}$	$1\frac{5}{16}$	$2\frac{1}{2}$	$\frac{5}{32}$	1.280	2.155	$\frac{1}{4}$	$\frac{3}{16}$	$\frac{5}{16}$
$1\frac{3}{8}$	$1\frac{7}{16}$	$2\frac{3}{4}$	$\frac{5}{32}$	1.405	2.280	$\frac{5}{16}$	$\frac{1}{4}$	$\frac{3}{8}$
$1\frac{1}{2}$	$1\frac{9}{16}$	3	$\frac{5}{32}$	1.530	2.530	$\frac{5}{16}$	$\frac{1}{4}$	$\frac{3}{8}$

TABLE XVI

Lock Washers

EXTERNAL

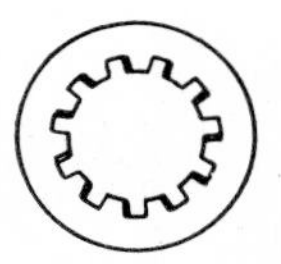

INTERNAL

Screw Size	External Tooth		Internal Tooth	
	O.D.	*Thickness*	*O.D.*	*Thickness*
No. 2			3/16	.012
No. 3			7/32	.016
No. 4	9/32	.016	17/64	.016
No. 5	1/4	.018	1/4	.018
No. 6	5/16	.018	9/32	.018
No. 8	3/8	.020	21/64	.020
No. 10	13/32	.022	3/8	.022
No. 12	15/32	.022	13/32	.022
1/4	1/2	.025	15/32	.025
5/16	19/32	.030	19/32	.030
3/8	11/16	.035	11/16	.035
7/16	3/4	.035	25/32	.035
1/2	57/64	.040	7/8	.040
9/16	31/32	.040	31/32	.040
5/8	1 1/16	.045	1 1/16	.045
11/16			1 5/32	.045
3/4	1 1/4	.050	1 1/4	.050
13/16			1 3/8	.050
7/8	1 13/32	.055	1 3/8	.055
1	1 5/8	.062	1 5/8	.062
1 1/8			1 13/16	.062
1 5/16			1 15/16	.062
1 1/2			2 1/2	.078
1 3/4			2 5/8	.078
1 7/8			2 1/2	.078

Note: All dimensions are in inches.

TABLE XVII

Cotter Pins

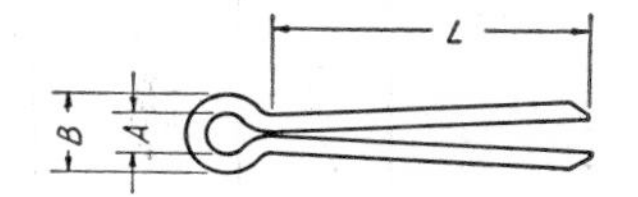

Bolt and Rod Dia. (NC)	Cotter Pins					
	Cotter Dia.	*A*	*B*	*Drill No.*	*Length*	
					Short	*Long*
$\frac{1}{4}$	$\frac{1}{16}$	$\frac{3}{32}$	$\frac{5}{32}$	48	$\frac{1}{2}$	$\frac{5}{8}$
$\frac{5}{16}$	$\frac{1}{16}$	$\frac{3}{32}$	$\frac{5}{32}$	48	$\frac{5}{8}$	$\frac{3}{4}$
$\frac{3}{8}$	$\frac{3}{32}$	$\frac{1}{8}$	$\frac{7}{32}$	36	$\frac{3}{4}$	$\frac{7}{8}$
$\frac{7}{16}$	$\frac{3}{32}$	$\frac{1}{8}$	$\frac{7}{32}$	36	$\frac{3}{4}$	1
$\frac{1}{2}$	$\frac{3}{32}$	$\frac{1}{8}$	$\frac{7}{32}$	36	$\frac{7}{8}$	$1\frac{1}{8}$
$\frac{9}{16}$	$\frac{1}{8}$	$\frac{5}{32}$	$\frac{9}{32}$	28	1	$1\frac{1}{4}$
$\frac{5}{8}$	$\frac{1}{8}$	$\frac{5}{32}$	$\frac{9}{32}$	28	$1\frac{1}{8}$	$1\frac{3}{8}$
$\frac{3}{4}$	$\frac{1}{8}$	$\frac{5}{32}$	$\frac{9}{32}$	28	$1\frac{1}{4}$	$1\frac{1}{2}$
$\frac{7}{8}$	$\frac{1}{8}$	$\frac{5}{32}$	$\frac{9}{32}$	28	$1\frac{3}{8}$	$1\frac{3}{4}$
1	$\frac{1}{8}$	$\frac{5}{32}$	$\frac{9}{32}$	28	$1\frac{5}{8}$	2

TABLE XVIII

Hexagonal and Square Machine Screw and Stove Bolt Nuts*

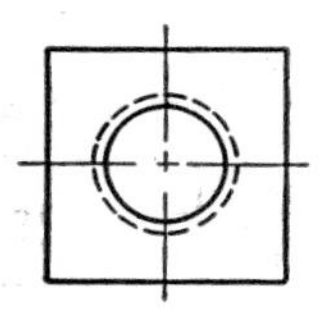

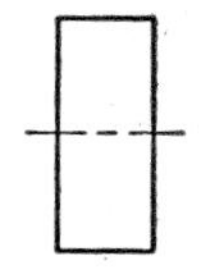

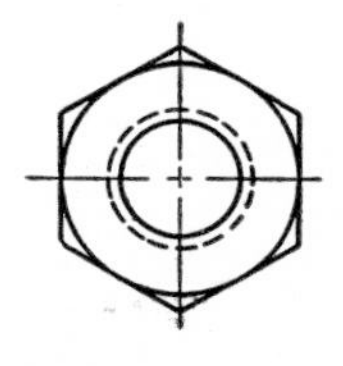

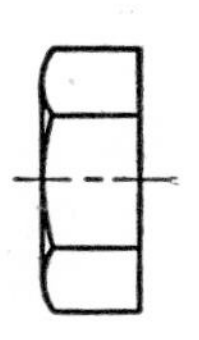

Diameter		*Number Size*										$\frac{1}{4}$	$\frac{5}{16}$	$\frac{3}{8}$
		0	1	2	3	4	5	6	8	10	12			
Across Flats (Nom.)		$\frac{5}{32}$	$\frac{5}{32}$	$\frac{3}{16}$	$\frac{3}{16}$	$\frac{1}{4}$	$\frac{5}{16}$	$\frac{5}{16}$	$\frac{11}{32}$	$\frac{3}{8}$	$\frac{7}{16}$	$\frac{7}{16}$	$\frac{9}{16}$	$\frac{5}{8}$
Across Corners (Min.)	Hex.	.171	.171	.205	.205	.275	.344	.344	.378	.413	.482	.482	.621	.692
	Square	.206	.206	.247	.247	.331	.415	.415	.456	.497	.581	.581	.748	.833
Thickness (Nom.)		$\frac{3}{64}$	$\frac{3}{64}$	$\frac{1}{16}$	$\frac{1}{16}$	$\frac{3}{32}$	$\frac{7}{64}$	$\frac{7}{64}$	$\frac{1}{8}$	$\frac{1}{8}$	$\frac{5}{32}$	$\frac{3}{16}$	$\frac{7}{32}$	$\frac{1}{4}$

* ASA B18.2-1941.
Dimensions in inches.

TABLE XIX

Small Rivets

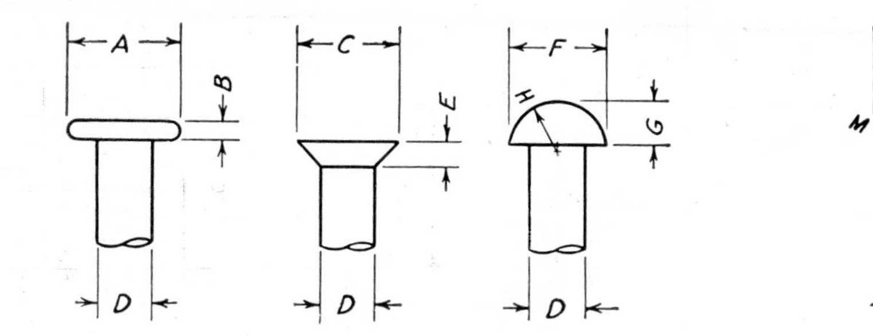

Rivet Dia. D	Flat		Csk.		Button			Pan					Truss		
	Dia. A	*Height* B	*Dia.* C	*Height* E	*Dia.* F	*Height* G	*Rad.* H	*Dia.* J	*Height* K	*Rad.* L	*Rad.* M	*Rad.* N	*Dia.* O	*Height* P	*Rad.* Q
$\frac{3}{32}$	.190	.032	.176	.040	.166	.071	.084	.163	.054	.030	.080	.326	.238	.032	.239
$\frac{1}{8}$	.250	.042	.231	.053	.219	.094	.111	.215	.072	.039	.106	.429	.313	.042	.314
$\frac{5}{32}$	.312	.052	.289	.066	.273	.117	.138	.268	.089	.049	.133	.535	.390	.052	.392
$\frac{3}{16}$	.374	.062	.346	.079	.327	.140	.166	.321	.107	.059	.159	.641	.468	.062	.470
$\frac{7}{32}$	.440	.073	.407	.094	.385	.165	.195	.378	.126	.069	.186	.754	.550	.073	.555
$\frac{1}{4}$	.500	.083	.463	.106	.435	.188	.221	.429	.143	.079	.213	.858	.625	.083	.628
$\frac{9}{32}$	.562	.094	.520	.119	.492	.211	.249	.482	.161	.088	.239	.963	.703	.094	.706
$\frac{5}{16}$	.624	.104	.577	.133	.546	.234	.276	.535	.178	.098	.266	1.070	.780	.104	.784
$\frac{11}{32}$	.686	.114	.635	.146	.600	.257	.304	.589	.196	.108	.292	1.176	.858	.114	.862
$\frac{3}{8}$	.750	.125	.694	.159	.656	.281	.332	.644	.215	.118	.319	1.286	.936	.125	.942
$\frac{7}{16}$	.874	.146	.808	.186	.765	.328	.387	.750	.250	.137	.372	1.500	1.093	.146	1.098

TABLE XX

American Standard Square and Flat Keys*

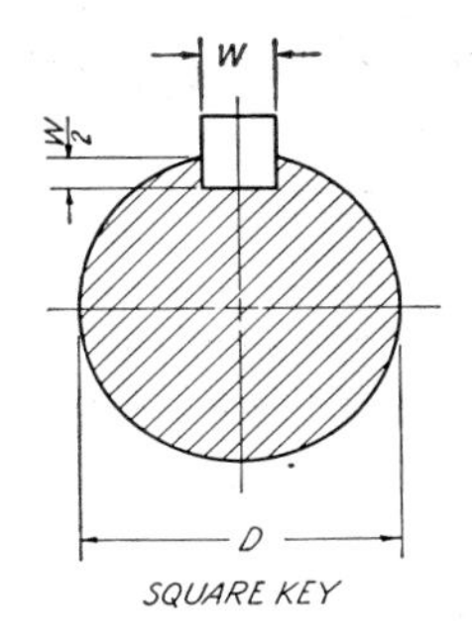

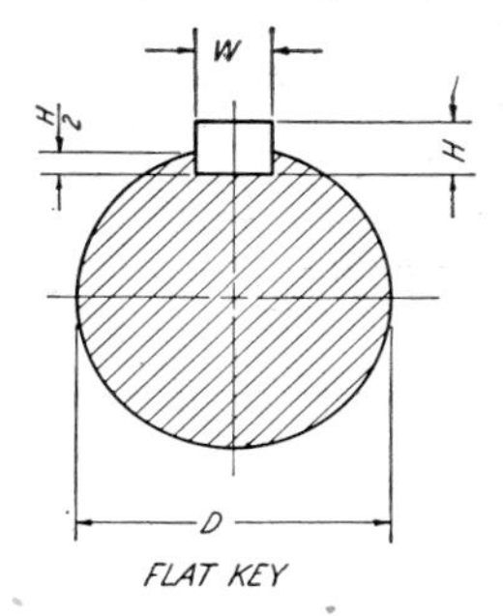

Shaft Diameter	*Square Stock Key* W	*Flat Stock Key* W × H	*Shaft Diameter*	*Square Stock Key* W	*Flat Stock Key* W × H
$\frac{1}{2}$–$\frac{9}{16}$	$\frac{1}{8}$	$\frac{1}{8} \times \frac{3}{32}$	$2\frac{5}{16}$–$2\frac{3}{4}$	$\frac{5}{8}$	$\frac{5}{8} \times \frac{7}{16}$
$\frac{5}{8}$–$\frac{7}{8}$	$\frac{3}{16}$	$\frac{3}{16} \times \frac{1}{8}$	$2\frac{7}{8}$–$3\frac{1}{4}$	$\frac{3}{4}$	$\frac{3}{4} \times \frac{1}{2}$
$\frac{15}{16}$–$1\frac{1}{4}$	$\frac{1}{4}$	$\frac{1}{4} \times \frac{3}{16}$	$3\frac{3}{8}$–$3\frac{3}{4}$	$\frac{7}{8}$	$\frac{7}{8} \times \frac{5}{8}$
$1\frac{5}{16}$–$1\frac{3}{8}$	$\frac{5}{16}$	$\frac{5}{16} \times \frac{1}{4}$	$3\frac{7}{8}$–$4\frac{1}{2}$	1	$1 \times \frac{3}{4}$
$1\frac{7}{16}$–$1\frac{3}{4}$	$\frac{3}{8}$	$\frac{3}{8} \times \frac{1}{4}$	$4\frac{3}{4}$–$5\frac{1}{2}$	$1\frac{1}{4}$	$1\frac{1}{4} \times \frac{7}{8}$
$1\frac{13}{16}$–$2\frac{1}{4}$	$\frac{1}{2}$	$\frac{1}{2} \times \frac{3}{8}$	$5\frac{3}{4}$–6	$1\frac{1}{2}$	$1\frac{1}{2} \times 1$

* ASA B17.1-1943.
All dimensions in inches.

TABLE XXI

American Standard Plain Taper and Gib Head Keys*

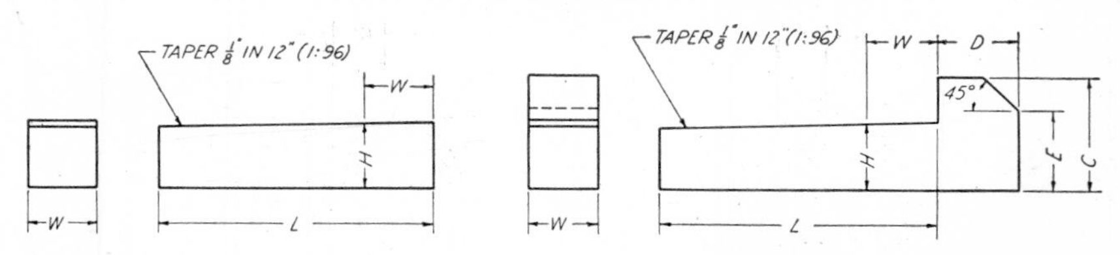

Plain Taper and Gib Head Keys (Square and Flat)			Gib Head					
			Square			*Flat*		
Diameter of Shaft	*Square Type*	*Flat Type*	*Height of Head*	*Length*	*Height to Cham-fer*	*Height of Head*	*Length*	*Height to Cham-fer*
D	$W = H$	$W \times H$	C	D	E	C	D	E
$\frac{1}{2}$–$\frac{9}{16}$	$\frac{1}{8}$	$\frac{1}{8} \times \frac{3}{32}$	$\frac{1}{4}$	$\frac{7}{32}$	$\frac{5}{32}$	$\frac{3}{16}$	$\frac{1}{8}$	$\frac{1}{8}$
$\frac{5}{8}$–$\frac{7}{8}$	$\frac{3}{16}$	$\frac{3}{16} \times \frac{1}{8}$	$\frac{5}{16}$	$\frac{9}{32}$	$\frac{7}{32}$	$\frac{1}{4}$	$\frac{3}{16}$	$\frac{5}{32}$
$\frac{15}{16}$–$1\frac{1}{4}$	$\frac{1}{4}$	$\frac{1}{4} \times \frac{3}{16}$	$\frac{7}{16}$	$\frac{11}{32}$	$\frac{11}{32}$	$\frac{5}{16}$	$\frac{1}{4}$	$\frac{3}{16}$
$1\frac{5}{16}$–$1\frac{3}{8}$	$\frac{5}{16}$	$\frac{5}{16} \times \frac{1}{4}$	$\frac{9}{16}$	$\frac{13}{32}$	$\frac{13}{32}$	$\frac{3}{8}$	$\frac{5}{16}$	$\frac{1}{4}$
$1\frac{7}{16}$–$1\frac{3}{4}$	$\frac{3}{8}$	$\frac{3}{8} \times \frac{1}{4}$	$\frac{11}{16}$	$\frac{15}{32}$	$\frac{15}{32}$	$\frac{7}{16}$	$\frac{3}{8}$	$\frac{5}{16}$
$1\frac{13}{16}$–$2\frac{1}{4}$	$\frac{1}{2}$	$\frac{1}{2} \times \frac{3}{8}$	$\frac{7}{8}$	$\frac{19}{32}$	$\frac{5}{8}$	$\frac{5}{8}$	$\frac{1}{2}$	$\frac{7}{16}$
$2\frac{5}{16}$–$2\frac{3}{4}$	$\frac{5}{8}$	$\frac{5}{8} \times \frac{7}{16}$	$1\frac{1}{16}$	$\frac{23}{32}$	$\frac{3}{4}$	$\frac{3}{4}$	$\frac{5}{8}$	$\frac{1}{2}$
$2\frac{7}{8}$–$3\frac{1}{4}$	$\frac{3}{4}$	$\frac{3}{4} \times \frac{1}{2}$	$1\frac{1}{4}$	$\frac{7}{8}$	$\frac{7}{8}$	$\frac{7}{8}$	$\frac{3}{4}$	$\frac{5}{8}$
$3\frac{3}{8}$–$3\frac{3}{4}$	$\frac{7}{8}$	$\frac{7}{8} \times \frac{5}{8}$	$1\frac{1}{2}$	1	1	$1\frac{1}{16}$	$\frac{7}{8}$	$\frac{3}{4}$
$3\frac{7}{8}$–$4\frac{1}{2}$	1	$1 \times \frac{3}{4}$	$1\frac{3}{4}$	$1\frac{3}{16}$	$1\frac{3}{16}$	$1\frac{1}{4}$	1	$\frac{13}{16}$
$4\frac{3}{4}$–$5\frac{1}{2}$	$1\frac{1}{4}$	$1\frac{1}{4} \times \frac{7}{8}$	2	$1\frac{7}{16}$	$1\frac{7}{16}$	$1\frac{1}{2}$	$1\frac{1}{4}$	1
$5\frac{3}{4}$–6	$1\frac{1}{2}$	$1\frac{1}{2} \times 1$	$2\frac{1}{2}$	$1\frac{3}{4}$	$1\frac{3}{4}$	$1\frac{3}{4}$	$1\frac{1}{2}$	$1\frac{1}{4}$

* ASA B17.1–1943.
All dimensions in inches. Minimum length = $4W$. Maximum length = $16W$.

TABLE XXII

Woodruff Key Dimensions*

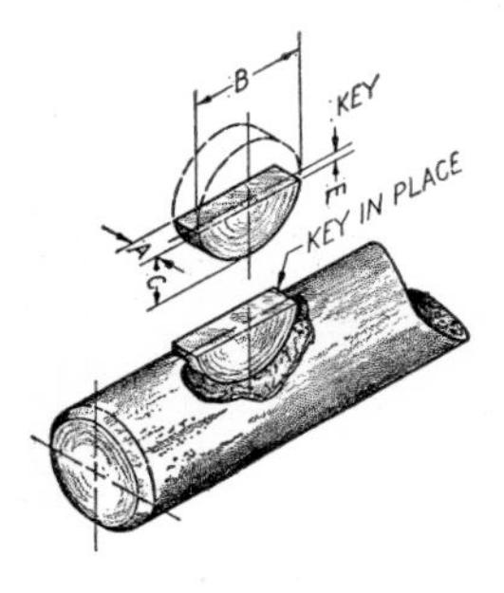

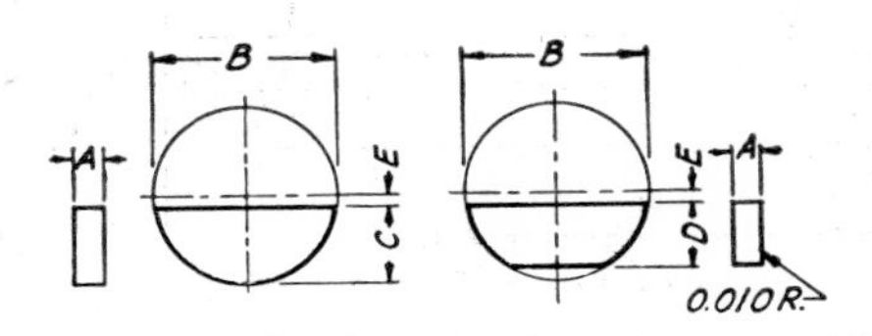

Key Number	*Nominal Size*	HEIGHT OF KEY		*Distance above Center E*	*Depth of Key Slot in Shaft*
		$C_{max.}$	$D_{max.}$		
204	$\frac{1}{16} \times \frac{1}{2}$	0.203	.194	$\frac{3}{64}$	.1718
304	$\frac{3}{32} \times \frac{1}{2}$	.203	.194	$\frac{3}{64}$	.1561
305	$\frac{3}{32} \times \frac{5}{8}$	.250	.240	$\frac{1}{16}$	.2031
404	$\frac{1}{8} \times \frac{1}{2}$	.203	.194	$\frac{3}{64}$	.1405
405	$\frac{1}{8} \times \frac{5}{8}$	.250	.240	$\frac{1}{16}$	.1875
406	$\frac{1}{8} \times \frac{3}{4}$	.313	.303	$\frac{1}{16}$	.2505
505	$\frac{5}{32} \times \frac{5}{8}$	.250	.240	$\frac{1}{16}$	.1719
506	$\frac{5}{32} \times \frac{3}{4}$	.313	.303	$\frac{1}{16}$	.2349
507	$\frac{5}{32} \times \frac{7}{8}$	.375	.365	$\frac{1}{16}$	.2969
606	$\frac{3}{16} \times \frac{3}{4}$	.313	.303	$\frac{1}{16}$	.2193
607	$\frac{3}{16} \times \frac{7}{8}$	.375	.365	$\frac{1}{16}$	.2813
608	$\frac{3}{16} \times 1$	.438	.428	$\frac{1}{16}$	.3443
609	$\frac{3}{16} \times 1\frac{1}{8}$	.484	.475	$\frac{5}{64}$	.3903
807	$\frac{1}{4} \times \frac{7}{8}$	.375	.365	$\frac{1}{16}$	.2500
808	$\frac{1}{4} \times 1$	.438	.428	$\frac{1}{16}$	.3130
809	$\frac{1}{4} \times 1\frac{1}{8}$	.484	.475	$\frac{5}{64}$	.3590
810	$\frac{1}{4} \times 1\frac{1}{4}$	.547	.537	$\frac{5}{64}$	.4220
811	$\frac{1}{4} \times 1\frac{3}{8}$	.594	.584	$\frac{3}{32}$	.4690
812	$\frac{1}{4} \times 1\frac{1}{2}$	.641	.631	$\frac{7}{64}$	.5160
1008	$\frac{5}{16} \times 1$	.438	.428	$\frac{1}{16}$	.2818
1009	$\frac{5}{16} \times 1\frac{1}{8}$	.484	.475	$\frac{5}{64}$	.3278
1010	$\frac{5}{16} \times 1\frac{1}{4}$	.547	.537	$\frac{5}{64}$	.3908
1011	$\frac{5}{16} \times 1\frac{3}{8}$	.594	.584	$\frac{3}{32}$	.4378
1012	$\frac{5}{16} \times 1\frac{1}{2}$	.641	.631	$\frac{7}{64}$	.4848
1210	$\frac{3}{8} \times 1\frac{1}{4}$	.547	.537	$\frac{5}{64}$	.3595
1211	$\frac{3}{8} \times 1\frac{3}{8}$	.594	.584	$\frac{3}{32}$	.4065
1212	$\frac{3}{8} \times 1\frac{1}{2}$	.641	.631	$\frac{7}{64}$	.4535

* ASA B17f-1930.

All dimensions in inches. Key numbers indicate the nominal key dimensions. The last two digits give the nominal diameter in eighths of an inch and the digits preceding the last two give the nominal width in thirty-seconds of an inch.

TABLE XXIII

Pratt and Whitney Keys

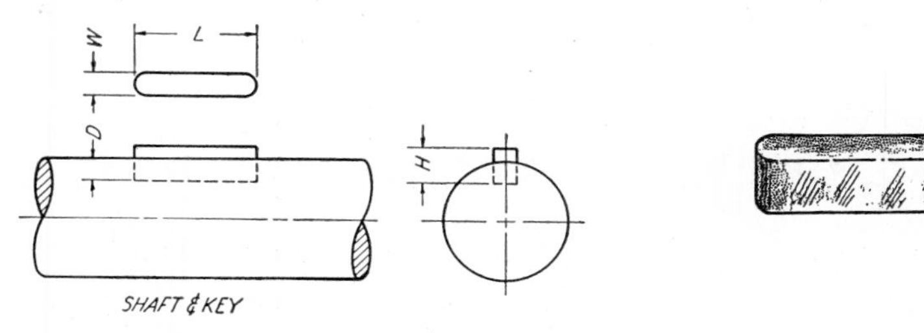

Key No.	*L*	*W*	*H*	*D*	*Key No.*	*L*	*W*	*H*	*D*
1	$\frac{1}{2}$	$\frac{1}{16}$	$\frac{3}{32}$	$\frac{1}{16}$	22	$1\frac{3}{8}$	$\frac{1}{4}$	$\frac{3}{8}$	$\frac{1}{4}$
2	$\frac{1}{2}$	$\frac{3}{32}$	$\frac{9}{64}$	$\frac{3}{32}$	23	$1\frac{3}{8}$	$\frac{5}{16}$	$\frac{15}{32}$	$\frac{5}{16}$
3	$\frac{1}{2}$	$\frac{1}{8}$	$\frac{3}{16}$	$\frac{1}{8}$	*F*	$1\frac{3}{8}$	$\frac{3}{8}$	$\frac{9}{16}$	$\frac{3}{8}$
4	$\frac{5}{8}$	$\frac{3}{32}$	$\frac{9}{64}$	$\frac{3}{32}$	24	$1\frac{1}{2}$	$\frac{1}{4}$	$\frac{3}{8}$	$\frac{1}{4}$
5	$\frac{5}{8}$	$\frac{1}{8}$	$\frac{3}{16}$	$\frac{1}{8}$	25	$1\frac{1}{2}$	$\frac{5}{16}$	$\frac{15}{32}$	$\frac{5}{16}$
6	$\frac{5}{8}$	$\frac{5}{32}$	$\frac{15}{64}$	$\frac{5}{32}$	*G*	$1\frac{1}{2}$	$\frac{3}{8}$	$\frac{9}{16}$	$\frac{3}{8}$
7	$\frac{3}{4}$	$\frac{1}{8}$	$\frac{3}{16}$	$\frac{1}{8}$	51	$1\frac{3}{4}$	$\frac{1}{4}$	$\frac{3}{8}$	$\frac{1}{4}$
8	$\frac{3}{4}$	$\frac{5}{32}$	$\frac{15}{64}$	$\frac{5}{32}$	52	$1\frac{3}{4}$	$\frac{5}{16}$	$\frac{15}{32}$	$\frac{5}{16}$
9	$\frac{3}{4}$	$\frac{3}{16}$	$\frac{9}{32}$	$\frac{3}{16}$	53	$1\frac{3}{4}$	$\frac{3}{8}$	$\frac{9}{16}$	$\frac{3}{8}$
10	$\frac{7}{8}$	$\frac{5}{32}$	$\frac{15}{64}$	$\frac{5}{32}$	26	2	$\frac{3}{16}$	$\frac{9}{32}$	$\frac{3}{16}$
11	$\frac{7}{8}$	$\frac{3}{16}$	$\frac{9}{32}$	$\frac{3}{16}$	27	2	$\frac{1}{4}$	$\frac{3}{8}$	$\frac{1}{4}$
12	$\frac{7}{8}$	$\frac{7}{32}$	$\frac{21}{64}$	$\frac{7}{32}$	28	2	$\frac{5}{16}$	$\frac{15}{32}$	$\frac{5}{16}$
A	$\frac{7}{8}$	$\frac{1}{4}$	$\frac{3}{8}$	$\frac{1}{4}$	29	2	$\frac{3}{8}$	$\frac{9}{16}$	$\frac{3}{8}$
13	1	$\frac{3}{16}$	$\frac{9}{32}$	$\frac{3}{16}$	54	$2\frac{1}{4}$	$\frac{1}{4}$	$\frac{3}{8}$	$\frac{1}{4}$
14	1	$\frac{7}{32}$	$\frac{21}{64}$	$\frac{7}{32}$	55	$2\frac{1}{4}$	$\frac{5}{16}$	$\frac{15}{32}$	$\frac{5}{16}$
15	1	$\frac{1}{4}$	$\frac{3}{8}$	$\frac{1}{4}$	56	$2\frac{1}{4}$	$\frac{3}{8}$	$\frac{9}{16}$	$\frac{3}{8}$
B	1	$\frac{5}{16}$	$\frac{15}{32}$	$\frac{5}{16}$	57	$2\frac{1}{4}$	$\frac{7}{16}$	$\frac{21}{32}$	$\frac{7}{16}$
16	$1\frac{1}{8}$	$\frac{3}{16}$	$\frac{9}{32}$	$\frac{3}{16}$	58	$2\frac{1}{2}$	$\frac{5}{16}$	$\frac{15}{32}$	$\frac{5}{16}$
17	$1\frac{1}{8}$	$\frac{7}{32}$	$\frac{21}{64}$	$\frac{7}{32}$	59	$2\frac{1}{2}$	$\frac{3}{8}$	$\frac{9}{16}$	$\frac{3}{8}$
18	$1\frac{1}{8}$	$\frac{1}{4}$	$\frac{3}{8}$	$\frac{1}{4}$	60	$2\frac{1}{2}$	$\frac{7}{16}$	$\frac{21}{32}$	$\frac{7}{16}$
C	$1\frac{1}{8}$	$\frac{5}{16}$	$\frac{15}{32}$	$\frac{5}{16}$	61	$2\frac{1}{2}$	$\frac{1}{2}$	$\frac{3}{4}$	$\frac{1}{2}$
19	$1\frac{1}{4}$	$\frac{3}{16}$	$\frac{9}{32}$	$\frac{3}{16}$	30	3	$\frac{3}{8}$	$\frac{9}{16}$	$\frac{3}{8}$
20	$1\frac{1}{4}$	$\frac{7}{32}$	$\frac{21}{64}$	$\frac{7}{32}$	31	3	$\frac{7}{16}$	$\frac{21}{32}$	$\frac{7}{16}$
21	$1\frac{1}{4}$	$\frac{1}{4}$	$\frac{3}{8}$	$\frac{1}{4}$	32	3	$\frac{1}{2}$	$\frac{3}{4}$	$\frac{1}{2}$
D	$1\frac{1}{4}$	$\frac{5}{16}$	$\frac{15}{32}$	$\frac{5}{16}$	33	3	$\frac{9}{16}$	$\frac{27}{32}$	$\frac{9}{16}$
E	$1\frac{1}{4}$	$\frac{3}{8}$	$\frac{9}{16}$	$\frac{3}{8}$	34	3	$\frac{5}{8}$	$\frac{15}{16}$	$\frac{5}{8}$

The length L may vary but should always be at least $2W$.

TABLE XXIV

Standard Taper Pins

No. of Pin	Diameter at Large End		Max. Length
	D	*D*	*L*
00000	.094	$\frac{3}{32}$	$\frac{3}{4}$
0000	.109	$\frac{7}{64}$	$\frac{7}{8}$
000	.125	$\frac{1}{8}$	1
00	.141	$\frac{9}{64}$	$1\frac{1}{8}$
0	.156	$\frac{5}{32}$	$1\frac{1}{4}$
1	.172	$\frac{11}{64}$	$1\frac{1}{4}$
2	.193	$\frac{3}{16}$	$1\frac{1}{2}$
3	.219	$\frac{7}{32}$	$1\frac{3}{4}$
4	.250	$\frac{1}{4}$	2
5	.289	$\frac{19}{64}$	$2\frac{1}{4}$
6	.341	$\frac{11}{32}$	3
7	.409	$\frac{13}{32}$	$3\frac{3}{4}$
8	.492	$\frac{1}{2}$	$4\frac{1}{2}$
9	.591	$\frac{19}{32}$	$5\frac{1}{4}$
10	.706	$\frac{23}{32}$	6
11	.860	$\frac{55}{64}$	$7\frac{1}{4}$
12	1.032	$1\frac{1}{32}$	9
13	1.241	$1\frac{15}{64}$	11
14	1.523	$1\frac{33}{64}$	13

TABLE XXIV(*a*)

Standard Taper Pins—Diameters at Small End

Length	Number of Pin										
	0	1	2	3	4	5	6	7	8	9	10
$\frac{3}{4}$	.140	.156	.177	.203	.235	.273	.325				
1	.135	.151	.172	.198	.230	.268	.320	.388			
$1\frac{1}{4}$		.146	.167	.193	.224	.263	.315	.383	.466		
$1\frac{1}{2}$			.162	.188	.219	.258	.310	.378	.461	.560	.675
$1\frac{3}{4}$				.182	.214	.252	.304	.372	.455	.554	.669
2					.209	.247	.299	.367	.450	.549	.664
$2\frac{1}{4}$						.242	.294	.362	.445	.544	.659
$2\frac{1}{2}$							.289	.357	.440	.539	.654
$2\frac{3}{4}$							.284	.352	.435	.534	.649
3							.279	.346	.429	.528	.643

TABLE XXV

Dowel Pins

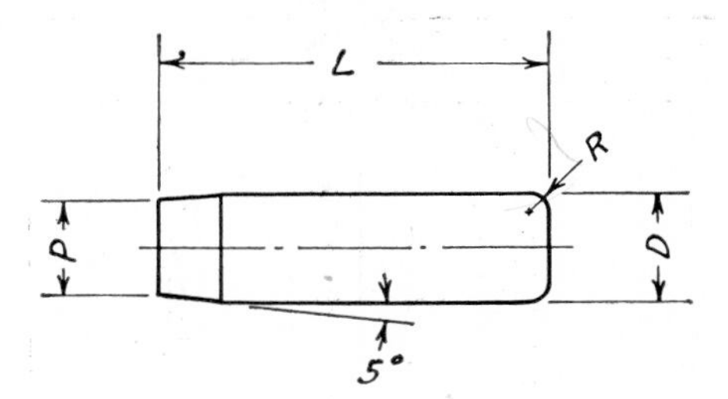

NOMINAL DIA.	*Max Dia. D*	*Min Dia. D*	*Point Dia. P*	*Radius R*	*Lengths L*
$\frac{1}{8}$	.1253	.1251	.119	$\frac{3}{64}$	Every $\frac{1}{8}$ from $\frac{3}{8}$ to 1
$\frac{1}{8}$	.1261	.1259	.119	$\frac{3}{64}$	Every $\frac{1}{4}$ from 1 to 2
$\frac{3}{16}$	.1878	.1876	.176	$\frac{3}{64}$	Every $\frac{1}{8}$ from $\frac{1}{2}$ to 1
$\frac{3}{16}$	.1886	.1884	.176	$\frac{3}{64}$	Every $\frac{1}{4}$ from 1 to 2
$\frac{1}{4}$	.2503	.2501	.239	$\frac{1}{16}$	Every $\frac{1}{8}$ from $\frac{1}{2}$ to 1
$\frac{1}{4}$	.2511	.2509	.239	$\frac{1}{16}$	Every $\frac{1}{4}$ from $\frac{1}{2}$ to $2\frac{1}{2}$
$\frac{5}{16}$	.3128	.3126	.301	$\frac{1}{16}$	Every $\frac{1}{8}$ from $\frac{1}{2}$ to 1
$\frac{5}{16}$	.3136	.3134	.301	$\frac{1}{16}$	Every $\frac{1}{4}$ from 1 to $3\frac{1}{2}$
$\frac{3}{8}$	.3753	.3751	.364	$\frac{5}{64}$	Every $\frac{1}{8}$ from $\frac{1}{2}$ to 1
$\frac{3}{8}$	.3761	.3759	.364	$\frac{5}{64}$	Every $\frac{1}{4}$ from 1 to $3\frac{3}{4}$
$\frac{7}{16}$	.4378	.4376	.4205	$\frac{3}{32}$	Every $\frac{1}{8}$ from $\frac{1}{2}$ to 1
$\frac{7}{16}$	.4386	.4384	.4205	$\frac{3}{32}$	Every $\frac{1}{4}$ from 1 to 4
$\frac{1}{2}$	.5003	.5001	.483	$\frac{7}{64}$	Every $\frac{1}{8}$ from $\frac{5}{8}$ to 1
$\frac{1}{2}$	.5011	.5009	.483	$\frac{7}{64}$	Every $\frac{1}{4}$ from 1 to 4
$\frac{5}{8}$	.6253	.6251	.608	$\frac{1}{8}$	Every $\frac{1}{4}$ from 1 to 5
$\frac{5}{8}$	.6261	.6259	.608	$\frac{1}{8}$	
$\frac{3}{4}$	.7503	.7501	.728	$\frac{1}{8}$	Every $\frac{1}{4}$ from 2 to 6
$\frac{3}{4}$	.7511	.7509	.728	$\frac{1}{8}$	
$\frac{7}{8}$	.8753	.8751	.853	$\frac{1}{8}$	Every $\frac{1}{4}$ from 2 to 6
$\frac{7}{8}$	.8761	.8759	.853	$\frac{1}{8}$	
1	1.0003	1.0001	.978	$\frac{1}{8}$	Every $\frac{1}{4}$ from 2 to 6
1	1.011	1.0009	.978	$\frac{1}{8}$	

Notes: All dimensions are in inches. Two sizes of pin are available in each nominal diameter.

Compiled from catalogue of The Allen Mfg. Co., Hartford, Conn.

TABLE XXVI

Wrought Iron and Steel Pipe

Standard Weight							Heavy			
					Nominal Wall Thickness		*Nominal Wall Thickness*			
							Extra Heavy		*Double Extra Heavy*[2]	
Nominal Size	*Outside Diameter (All Weights)*	*Threads per Inch*	*Tap Drill Sizes*[1]	*Distance Pipe Enters Fitting*	*Wrought Iron*	*Steel*	*Wrought Iron*	*Steel*	*Wrought Iron*	*Steel*
$\frac{1}{8}$	.405	27	$\frac{11}{32}$	$\frac{5}{16}$	.070	.068	.098	.095	—	—
$\frac{1}{4}$	.540	18	$\frac{7}{16}$	$\frac{7}{16}$	.090	.088	.122	.119	—	—
$\frac{3}{8}$	.675	18	$\frac{19}{32}$	$\frac{7}{16}$	.093	.091	.129	.126	—	—
$\frac{1}{2}$	.840	14	$\frac{23}{32}$	$\frac{9}{16}$	.111	.109	.151	.147	.307	.294
$\frac{3}{4}$	1.050	14	$\frac{15}{16}$	$\frac{9}{16}$	.115	.113	.157	.154	.318	.308
1	1.315	$11\frac{1}{2}$	$1\frac{5}{32}$	$\frac{11}{16}$	.136	.133	.183	.179	.369	.358
$1\frac{1}{4}$	1.660	$11\frac{1}{2}$	$1\frac{1}{2}$	$\frac{11}{16}$	.143	.140	.195	.191	.393	.382
$1\frac{1}{2}$	1.900	$11\frac{1}{2}$	$1\frac{23}{32}$	$\frac{11}{16}$	.148	.145	.204	.200	.411	.400
2	2.375	$11\frac{1}{2}$	$2\frac{3}{16}$	$\frac{3}{4}$	.158	.154	.223	.218	.447	.436
$2\frac{1}{2}$	2.875	8	$2\frac{5}{8}$	$1\frac{1}{16}$	.208	.203	.282	.276	.565	552
3	3.500	8	$3\frac{1}{4}$	$1\frac{1}{8}$	.221	.216	.306	.300	.615	.600
$3\frac{1}{2}$	4.000	8	$3\frac{3}{4}$	$1\frac{3}{16}$	.231	.226	.325	.318	—	—
4	4.500	8	$4\frac{1}{4}$	$1\frac{3}{16}$	.242	.237	.344	.337	.690	.674
5	5.563	8	$5\frac{5}{16}$	$1\frac{5}{16}$	.263	.258	.383	.375	.768	.750
6	6.625	8	$6\frac{3}{8}$	$1\frac{3}{8}$	.286	.280	.441	.432	.884	.864
8	8.625	8	—	—	.329	.322	.510	.500	.895	.875

ASA B36.10-1939.
ASA B2.1-1945.
All dimensions in inches.
1. Not American Standard.
2. Not American Standard but is commercially available. See ASA B36.10-1939 for sizes larger than 8″.

TABLE XXVII

Malleable-iron Screwed Fittings*

For use under maximum working steam pressures of 150 lbs. per sq. in.

ELBOW — TEE — CROSS — 45° ELBOW — 45° Y-BRANCH — STREET ELBOW — 45° STREET ELBOW — STREET TEE — STRAIGHT / REDUCING COUPLINGS

Nominal Pipe Size	*Center to End, Elbows, Tees and Crosses*	*Length of Thread*	*Center to End 45-Deg. Elbows*	*Width of Band*	*Inside Diameter of Fitting*		*Metal Thickness*	*Outside Diameter of Band*	*Center to Male End Elbows, Tees*	*Center to Male End 45° Elbows*	*Length of External Thread*	*Length of Reducing Couplings*	*Port Diameter Male End*	*Center to End Inlet*	*Center to End Outlet*	*End to End*	*Length of Straight Couplings*	*Thickness of Ribs of Couplings*
	A	$B_{Min.}$	C	$E_{Min.}$	$F_{Min.}$	$F_{Max.}$	G	H	J	K	$L_{Min.}$	M	$N_{Max.}$	T	U	V	W	
$\frac{1}{8}$	0.69	0.25		0.200	0.405	0.435	0.090	0.693	1.00		0.2638		0.20				0.96	0.090
$\frac{1}{4}$	0.81	0.32	0.73	0.215	0.540	0.584	0.095	0.844	1.19	0.94	0.4018	1.00	0.26				1.06	0.095
$\frac{3}{8}$	0.95	0.36	0.80	0.230	0.675	0.719	0.100	1.015	1.44	1.03	0.4078	1.13	0.37	0.50	1.43	1.93	1.16	0.100
$\frac{1}{2}$	1.12	0.43	0.88	0.249	0.840	0.897	0.105	1.197	1.63	1.15	0.5337	1.25	0.51	0.61	1.71	2.32	1.34	0.105
$\frac{3}{4}$	1.31	0.50	0.98	0.273	1.050	1.107	0.120	1.458	1.89	1.29	0.5457	1.44	0.69	0.72	2.05	2.77	1.52	0.120
1	1.50	0.58	1.12	0.302	1.315	1.385	0.134	1.771	2.14	1.47	0.6828	1.69	0.91	0.85	2.43	3.28	1.67	0.134
$1\frac{1}{4}$	1.75	0.67	1.29	0.341	1.660	1.730	0.145	2.153	2.45	1.71	0.7068	2.06	1.19	1.02	2.92	3.94	1.93	0.145
$1\frac{1}{2}$	1.94	0.70	1.43	0.368	1.900	1.970	0.155	2.427	2.69	1.88	0.7235	2.31	1.39	1.10	3.28	4.38	2.15	0.155
2	2.25	0.75	1.68	0.422	2.375	2.445	0.173	2.963	3.26	2.22	0.7565	2.81	1.79	1.24	3.93	5.17	2.53	0.173
$2\frac{1}{2}$	2.70	0.92	1.95	0.478	2.875	2.975	0.210	3.589	3.86	2.57	1.1375	3.25	2.20	1.52	4.73	6.25	2.88	0.210
3	3.08	0.98	2.17	0.548	3.500	3.600	0.231	4.285	4.51	3.00	1.2000	3.69	2.78	1.71	5.55	7.26	3.18	0.231
$3\frac{1}{2}$	3.42	1.03	2.39	0.604	4.000	4.100	0.248	4.843	5.09		1.2500	4.00	3.24				3.43	0.248
4	3.79	1.08	2.61	0.661	4.500	4.600	0.265	5.401	5.69	3.70	1.3000	4.38	3.70	2.01	6.97	8.98	3.69	0.265
5	4.50	1.18	3.05	0.780	5.563	5.663	0.300	6.583	6.86		1.4063		4.69					
6	5.13	1.28	3.46	0.900	6.625	6.725	0.336	7.767	8.03		1.5125		5.67					

* ASA B16c-1939.

TABLE XXVIII

125 Lb. American Standard Cast-iron Screwed Fittings

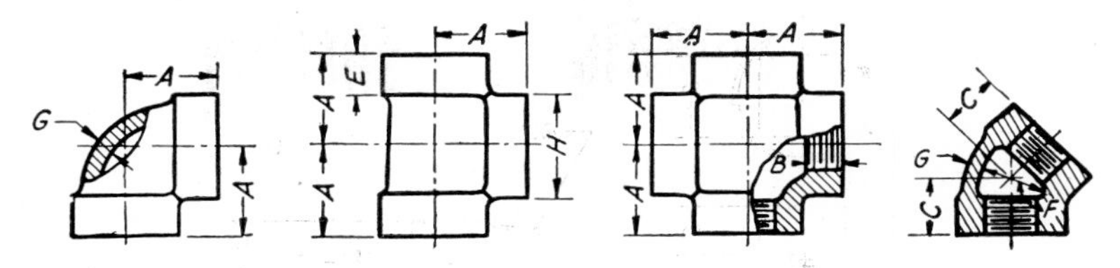

Nominal Pipe Size	Center to End, Elbows, Tees, and Crosses	Length of Thread	Center to End, 45-deg. Elbows	Width of Band	Inside Diameter of Fitting		Metal Thickness	Outside Diameter of Band
	A	$B_{Min.}$	C	$E_{Min.}$	$F_{Min.}$	$F_{Max.}$	$G_{Min.}$	$H_{Min.}$
$\frac{1}{4}$	0.81	0.32	0.73	0.38	0.540	0.584	0.110	0.93
$\frac{3}{8}$	0.95	0.36	0.80	0.44	0.675	0.719	0.120	1.12
$\frac{1}{2}$	1.12	0.43	0.88	0.50	0.840	0.897	0.130	1.34
$\frac{3}{4}$	1.31	0.50	0.98	0.56	1.050	1.107	0.155	1.63
1	1.50	0.58	1.12	0.62	1.315	1.385	0.170	1.95
$1\frac{1}{4}$	1.75	0.67	1.29	0.69	1.660	1.730	0.185	2.39
$1\frac{1}{2}$	1.94	0.70	1.43	0.75	1.900	1.970	0.200	2.68
2	2.25	0.75	1.68	0.84	2.375	2.445	0.220	3.28
$2\frac{1}{2}$	2.70	0.92	1.95	0.94	2.875	2.975	0.240	3.86
3	3.08	0.98	2.17	1.00	3.500	3.600	0.260	4.62
$3\frac{1}{2}$	3.42	1.03	2.39	1.06	4.000	4.100	0.280	5.20
4	3.79	1.08	2.61	1.12	4.500	4.600	0.310	5.79
5	4.50	1.18	3.05	1.18	5.563	5.663	0.380	7.05
6	5.13	1.28	3.46	1.28	6.625	6.725	0.430	8.28
8	6.56	1.47	4.28	1.47	8.625	8.725	0.550	10.63
10	8.08	1.68	5.16	1.68	10.750	10.850	0.690	13.12
12	9.50	1.88	5.97	1.88	12.750	12.850	0.800	15.47

ASA B16d-1941.

All dimensions in inches.

TABLE XXIX

American Standard Pipe Plugs and Caps

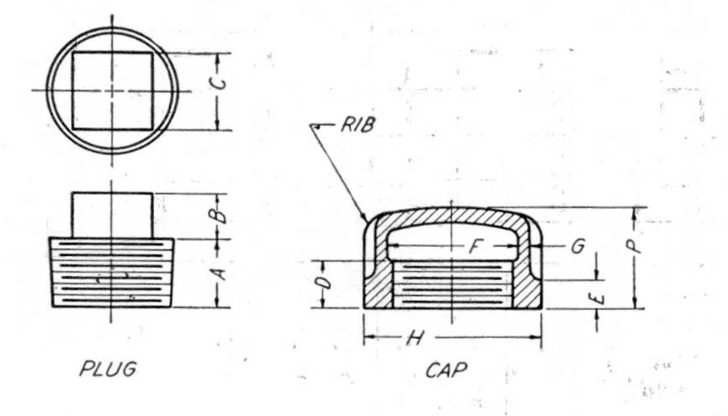

Nominal Pipe Size	PLUG*			CAP†						
	Length of Thread	*Height of Square*	*Width Across Flats*	*Length of Thread*	*Width of Band*	*Inside Diameter of Fitting*	*Metal Thickness*	*Outside Diameter of Band*	*Height*	*Thickness of Ribs*
	$A_{\text{Min.}}$	$B_{\text{Min.}}$	$C_{\text{Nom.}}$	$D_{\text{Min.}}$	$E_{\text{Min.}}$	$F_{\text{Max.}}$	G	$H_{\text{Min.}}$	$P_{\text{Min.}}$	
$\frac{1}{8}$	.37	.24	$\frac{9}{32}$	—	—	—	—	—	—	—
$\frac{1}{4}$	.44	.28	$\frac{3}{8}$	—	—	—	—	—	—	—
$\frac{3}{8}$	.48	.31	$\frac{7}{16}$	—	—	—	—	—	—	—
$\frac{1}{2}$	.56	.38	$\frac{9}{16}$	.43	.249	.897	.105	1.197	.87	.105
$\frac{3}{4}$	.63	.44	$\frac{5}{8}$	.50	.273	1.107	.120	1.458	.97	.120
1	.75	.50	$\frac{13}{16}$	.58	.302	1.385	.134	1.771	1.16	.134
$1\frac{1}{4}$	.80	.56	$\frac{15}{16}$	.67	.341	1.730	.145	2.153	1.28	.145
$1\frac{1}{2}$	.83	.62	$1\frac{1}{8}$	.70	.368	1.970	.155	2.427	1.33	.155
2	.88	.68	$1\frac{5}{16}$	.75	.422	2.445	.173	2.963	1.45	.173
$2\frac{1}{2}$	1.07	.74	$1\frac{1}{2}$	.92	.478	2.975	.210	3.589	1.70	.210
3	1.13	.80	$1\frac{11}{16}$	.98	.548	3.600	.231	4.285	1.80	.231
$3\frac{1}{2}$	1.18	.86	$1\frac{7}{8}$	1.03	.604	4.100	.248	4.843	1.90	.248
4	—	—	—	1.08	.661	4.600	.265	5.401	2.08	.265
5	—	—	—	1.18	.780	5.663	.300	6.583	2.32	.300
6	—	—	—	1.28	.900	6.725	.336	7.767	2.55	.336

* For other types of plugs see ASA B16c-1939.
† The outside radius of top of cap is equal to $3 \times F$.

TABLE XXX

Cast-iron Pipe Flanges and Flanged Fittings*

For use under maximum working pressures of 125 lbs. per sq. in.

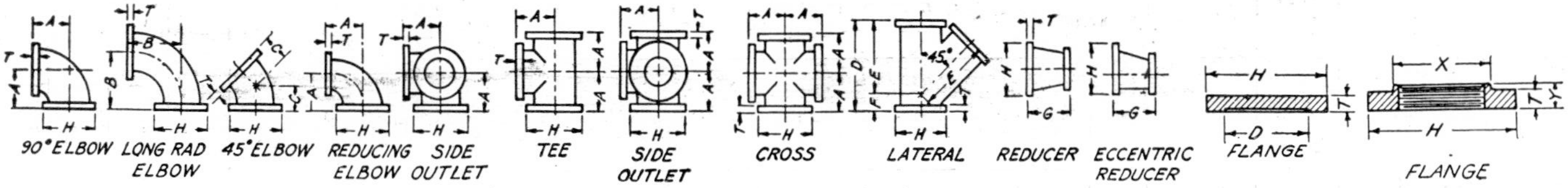

90° ELBOW — LONG RAD ELBOW — 45° ELBOW — REDUCING ELBOW — SIDE OUTLET — TEE — SIDE OUTLET — CROSS — LATERAL — REDUCER — ECCENTRIC REDUCER — FLANGE — FLANGE

Nominal Pipe Size	Center to Face, Elbow Tees, Etc.	Center to Face, Long Radius Elbow	Center to Face, 45-deg. Elbow	Face to Face, Lateral	Center to Face, Lateral	Center to Face, "Y" and Lateral	Face to Face Reducer	Diameter of Flange	Thickness of Flange	Diameter of Hub	Length of Hub	Diameter of Holes in Flanges	Number of Bolts for Flanges	Diameter of Bolts for Flanges	Length of Bolts for Flanges	Diameter of Bolt Circle
D	A	B	C	D	E	F	G	H	T	X	Y					
1	3½	5	1¾	7½	5¾	1¾	...	4¼	7/16	1 15/16	11/16	5/8	4	1/2	1¾	3⅛
1¼	3¾	5½	2	8	6¼	1¾	...	4⅝	1/2	2 5/16	13/16	5/8	4	1/2	2	3½
1½	4	6	2¼	9	7	2	...	5	9/16	2 9/16	7/8	5/8	4	1/2	2	3⅞
2	4½	6½	2½	10½	8	2½	5	6	5/8	3 1/16	1	3/4	4	5/8	2¼	4¾
2½	5	7	3	12	9½	2½	5½	7	11/16	3 9/16	1⅛	3/4	4	5/8	2½	5½
3	5½	7¾	3	13	10	3	6	7½	3/4	4¼	1 3/16	3/4	4	5/8	2½	6
3½	6	8½	3½	14½	11½	3	6½	8½	13/16	4 13/16	1¼	3/4	8	5/8	2¾	7
4	6½	9	4	15	12	3	7	9	15/16	5 5/16	1 5/16	3/4	8	5/8	3	7½
5	7½	10¼	4½	17	13½	3½	8	10	15/16	6 7/16	1 7/16	7/8	8	3/4	3	8½
6	8	11½	5	18	14½	3½	9	11	1	7 9/16	1 9/16	7/8	8	3/4	3¼	9½
8	9	14	5½	22	17½	4½	11	13½	1⅛	9 11/16	1¾	7/8	8	3/4	3½	11¾
10	11	16½	6½	25½	20½	5	12	16	1 3/16	11 15/16	1 15/16	1	12	7/8	3¾	14¼
12	12	19	7½	30	24½	5½	14	19	1¼	14 1/16	2 3/16	1	12	7/8	3¾	17

*ASA B16.1–1948.

TABLE XXXI

Loose Fit (Class 1)—Large Allowance, Interchangeable

This fit provides for considerable freedom and embraces certain fits where accuracy is not essential.

Size			Limits				Tightest Fit	Loosest Fit
From	*Up to and Incl.*	*Mean*	*Hole or External Member*		*Shaft or Internal Member*		*Allowance*	*Allowance + Tolerances*
			+		−	−	+*	+*
0	$\frac{3}{16}$	$\frac{1}{8}$	0.001	0.000	0.001	0.002	0.001	0.003
$\frac{3}{16}$	$\frac{5}{16}$	$\frac{1}{4}$	0.002	0.000	0.001	0.003	0.001	0.005
$\frac{5}{16}$	$\frac{7}{16}$	$\frac{3}{8}$	0.002	0.000	0.001	0.003	0.001	0.005
$\frac{7}{16}$	$\frac{9}{16}$	$\frac{1}{2}$	0.002	0.000	0.002	0.004	0.002	0.006
$\frac{9}{16}$	$\frac{11}{16}$	$\frac{5}{8}$	0.002	0.000	0.002	0.004	0.002	0.006
$\frac{11}{16}$	$\frac{13}{16}$	$\frac{3}{4}$	0.002	0.000	0.002	0.004	0.002	0.006
$\frac{13}{16}$	$\frac{15}{16}$	$\frac{7}{8}$	0.002	0.000	0.002	0.004	0.002	0.006
$\frac{15}{16}$	$1\frac{1}{16}$	1	0.003	0.000	0.003	0.006	0.003	0.009
$1\frac{1}{16}$	$1\frac{3}{16}$	$1\frac{1}{8}$	0.003	0.000	0.003	0.006	0.003	0.009
$1\frac{3}{16}$	$1\frac{3}{8}$	$1\frac{1}{4}$	0.003	0.000	0.003	0.006	0.003	0.009
$1\frac{3}{8}$	$1\frac{5}{8}$	$1\frac{1}{2}$	0.003	0.000	0.003	0.006	0.003	0.009
$1\frac{5}{8}$	$1\frac{7}{8}$	$1\frac{3}{4}$	0.003	0.000	0.004	0.007	0.004	0.010
$1\frac{7}{8}$	$2\frac{1}{8}$	2	0.003	0.000	0.004	0.007	0.004	0.010
$2\frac{1}{8}$	$2\frac{3}{8}$	$2\frac{1}{4}$	0.003	0.000	0.004	0.007	0.004	0.010
$2\frac{3}{8}$	$2\frac{3}{4}$	$2\frac{1}{2}$	0.003	0.000	0.005	0.008	0.005	0.011
$2\frac{3}{4}$	$3\frac{1}{4}$	3	0.004	0.000	0.005	0.009	0.005	0.013
$3\frac{1}{4}$	$3\frac{3}{4}$	$3\frac{1}{2}$	0.004	0.000	0.006	0.010	0.006	0.014
$3\frac{3}{4}$	$4\frac{1}{4}$	4	0.004	0.000	0.006	0.010	0.006	0.014
$4\frac{1}{4}$	$4\frac{3}{4}$	$4\frac{1}{2}$	0.004	0.000	0.007	0.011	0.007	0.015
$4\frac{3}{4}$	$5\frac{1}{2}$	5	0.004	0.000	0.007	0.011	0.007	0.015
$5\frac{1}{2}$	$6\frac{1}{2}$	6	0.005	0.000	0.008	0.013	0.008	0.018
$6\frac{1}{2}$	$7\frac{1}{2}$	7	0.005	0.000	0.009	0.014	0.009	0.019
$7\frac{1}{2}$	$8\frac{1}{2}$	8	0.005	0.000	0.010	0.015	0.010	0.020

ASA B4a-1925.
* Note: (+) denotes clearance or amount of looseness
All dimensions in inches.

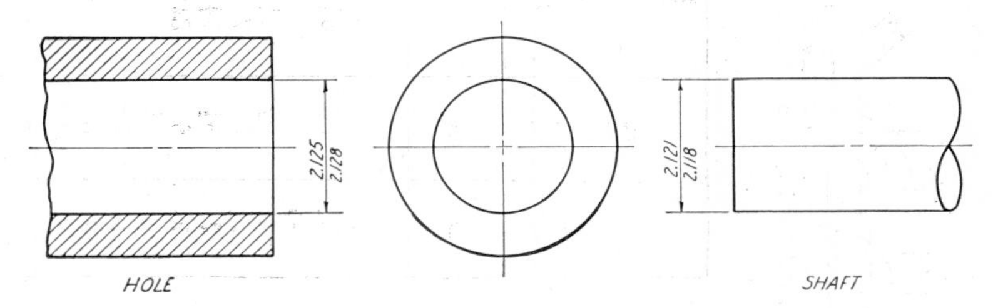

Example of loose fit.

TABLE XXXI (Continued)

Free Fit (Class 2)—Liberal Allowance, Interchangeable

For running fits with speeds of 600 r.p.m. or over, and journal pressures of 600 lb. per sq. in. or over.

Size			Limits				Tightest Fit	Loosest Fit
From	Up to and Incl.	Mean	Hole or External Member		Shaft or Internal Member		Allowance	Allowance + Tolerances
			+		−	−	+*	+*
0	$\frac{3}{16}$	$\frac{1}{8}$	0.0007	0.0000	0.0004	0.0011	0.0004	0.0018
$\frac{3}{16}$	$\frac{5}{16}$	$\frac{1}{4}$	0.0008	0.0000	0.0006	0.0014	0.0006	0.0022
$\frac{5}{16}$	$\frac{7}{16}$	$\frac{3}{8}$	0.0009	0.0000	0.0007	0.0016	0.0007	0.0025
$\frac{7}{16}$	$\frac{9}{16}$	$\frac{1}{2}$	0.0010	0.0000	0.0009	0.0019	0.0009	0.0029
$\frac{9}{16}$	$\frac{11}{16}$	$\frac{5}{8}$	0.0011	0.0000	0.0010	0.0021	0.0010	0.0032
$\frac{11}{16}$	$\frac{13}{16}$	$\frac{3}{4}$	0.0012	0.0000	0.0012	0.0024	0.0012	0.0036
$\frac{13}{16}$	$\frac{15}{16}$	$\frac{7}{8}$	0.0012	0.0000	0.0013	0.0025	0.0013	0.0037
$\frac{15}{16}$	$1\frac{1}{16}$	1	0.0013	0.0000	0.0014	0.0027	0.0014	0.0040
$1\frac{1}{16}$	$1\frac{3}{16}$	$1\frac{1}{8}$	0.0014	0.0000	0.0015	0.0029	0.0015	0.0043
$1\frac{3}{16}$	$1\frac{3}{8}$	$1\frac{1}{4}$	0.0014	0.0000	0.0016	0.0030	0.0016	0.0044
$1\frac{3}{8}$	$1\frac{5}{8}$	$1\frac{1}{2}$	0.0015	0.0000	0.0018	0.0033	0.0018	0.0048
$1\frac{5}{8}$	$1\frac{7}{8}$	$1\frac{3}{4}$	0.0016	0.0000	0.0020	0.0036	0.0020	0.0052
$1\frac{7}{8}$	$2\frac{1}{8}$	2	0.0016	0.0000	0.0022	0.0038	0.0022	0.0054
$2\frac{1}{8}$	$2\frac{3}{8}$	$2\frac{1}{4}$	0.0017	0.0000	0.0024	0.0041	0.0024	0.0058
$2\frac{3}{8}$	$2\frac{3}{4}$	$2\frac{1}{2}$	0.0018	0.0000	0.0026	0.0044	0.0026	0.0062
$2\frac{3}{4}$	$3\frac{1}{4}$	3	0.0019	0.0000	0.0029	0.0048	0.0029	0.0067
$3\frac{1}{4}$	$3\frac{3}{4}$	$3\frac{1}{2}$	0.0020	0.0000	0.0032	0.0052	0.0032	0.0072
$3\frac{3}{4}$	$4\frac{1}{4}$	4	0.0021	0.0000	0.0035	0.0056	0.0035	0.0077
$4\frac{1}{4}$	$4\frac{3}{4}$	$4\frac{1}{2}$	0.0021	0.0000	0.0038	0.0059	0.0038	0.0080
$4\frac{3}{4}$	$5\frac{1}{2}$	5	0.0022	0.0000	0.0041	0.0063	0.0041	0.0085
$5\frac{1}{2}$	$6\frac{1}{2}$	6	0.0024	0.0000	0.0046	0.0070	0.0046	0.0094
$6\frac{1}{2}$	$7\frac{1}{2}$	7	0.0025	0.0000	0.0051	0.0076	0.0051	0.0101
$7\frac{1}{2}$	$8\frac{1}{2}$	8	0.0026	0.0000	0.0056	0.0082	0.0056	0.0108

ASA B4a-1925.
* Note: (+) denotes clearance or amount of looseness.
All dimensions in inches.

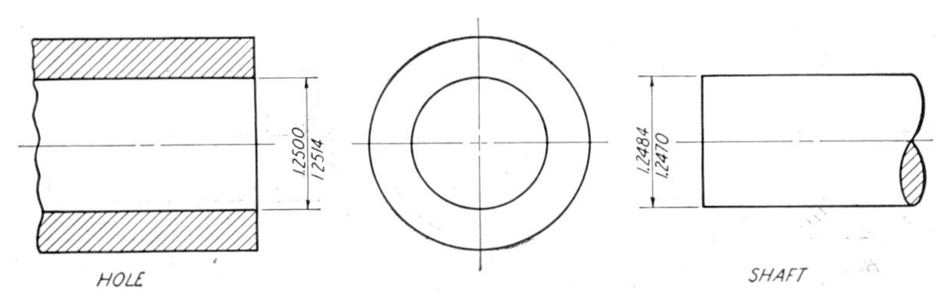

Example of free fit.

TABLE XXXI (Continued)

Medium Fit (Class 3)—Medium Allowance, Interchangeable

For running fits under 600 r.p.m. and with journal pressures less than 600 lb. per sq. in.; also for sliding fits, and the more accurate machine-tool and automotive parts.

Size			Limits				Tightest Fit	Loosest Fit
From	Up to and Incl.	Mean	Hole or External Member		Shaft or Internal Member		Allowance	Allowance + Tolerances
			+		−	−	+*	+*
0	$\frac{3}{16}$	$\frac{1}{8}$	0.0004	0.0000	0.0002	0.0006	0.0002	0.0010
$\frac{3}{16}$	$\frac{5}{16}$	$\frac{1}{4}$	0.0005	0.0000	0.0004	0.0009	0.0004	0.0014
$\frac{5}{16}$	$\frac{7}{16}$	$\frac{3}{8}$	0.0006	0.0000	0.0005	0.0011	0.0005	0.0017
$\frac{7}{16}$	$\frac{9}{16}$	$\frac{1}{2}$	0.0006	0.0000	0.0006	0.0012	0.0006	0.0018
$\frac{9}{16}$	$\frac{11}{16}$	$\frac{5}{8}$	0.0007	0.0000	0.0007	0.0014	0.0007	0.0021
$\frac{11}{16}$	$\frac{13}{16}$	$\frac{3}{4}$	0.0007	0.0000	0.0007	0.0014	0.0007	0.0021
$\frac{13}{16}$	$\frac{15}{16}$	$\frac{7}{8}$	0.0008	0.0000	0.0008	0.0016	0.0008	0.0024
$\frac{15}{16}$	$1\frac{1}{16}$	1	0.0008	0.0000	0.0009	0.0017	0.0009	0.0025
$1\frac{1}{16}$	$1\frac{3}{16}$	$1\frac{1}{8}$	0.0008	0.0000	0.0010	0.0018	0.0010	0.0026
$1\frac{3}{16}$	$1\frac{3}{8}$	$1\frac{1}{4}$	0.0009	0.0000	0.0010	0.0019	0.0010	0.0028
$1\frac{3}{8}$	$1\frac{5}{8}$	$1\frac{1}{2}$	0.0009	0.0000	0.0012	0.0021	0.0012	0.0030
$1\frac{5}{8}$	$1\frac{7}{8}$	$1\frac{3}{4}$	0.0010	0.0000	0.0013	0.0023	0.0013	0.0033
$1\frac{7}{8}$	$2\frac{1}{8}$	2	0.0010	0.0000	0.0014	0.0024	0.0014	0.0034
$2\frac{1}{8}$	$2\frac{3}{8}$	$2\frac{1}{4}$	0.0010	0.0000	0.0015	0.0025	0.0015	0.0035
$2\frac{3}{8}$	$2\frac{3}{4}$	$2\frac{1}{2}$	0.0011	0.0000	0.0017	0.0028	0.0017	0.0039
$2\frac{3}{4}$	$3\frac{1}{4}$	3	0.0012	0.0000	0.0019	0.0031	0.0019	0.0043
$3\frac{1}{4}$	$3\frac{3}{4}$	$3\frac{1}{2}$	0.0012	0.0000	0.0021	0.0033	0.0021	0.0045
$3\frac{3}{4}$	$4\frac{1}{4}$	4	0.0013	0.0000	0.0023	0.0036	0.0023	0.0049
$4\frac{1}{4}$	$4\frac{3}{4}$	$4\frac{1}{2}$	0.0013	0.0000	0.0025	0.0038	0.0025	0.0051
$4\frac{3}{4}$	$5\frac{1}{2}$	5	0.0014	0.0000	0.0026	0.0040	0.0026	0.0054
$5\frac{1}{2}$	$6\frac{1}{2}$	6	0.0015	0.0000	0.0030	0.0045	0.0030	0.0060
$6\frac{1}{2}$	$7\frac{1}{2}$	7	0.0015	0.0000	0.0033	0.0048	0.0033	0.0063
$7\frac{1}{2}$	$8\frac{1}{2}$	8	0.0016	0.0000	0.0036	0.0052	0.0036	0.0068

ASA B4a-1925.
* Note: (+) denotes clearance or amount of looseness.
All dimensions in inches.

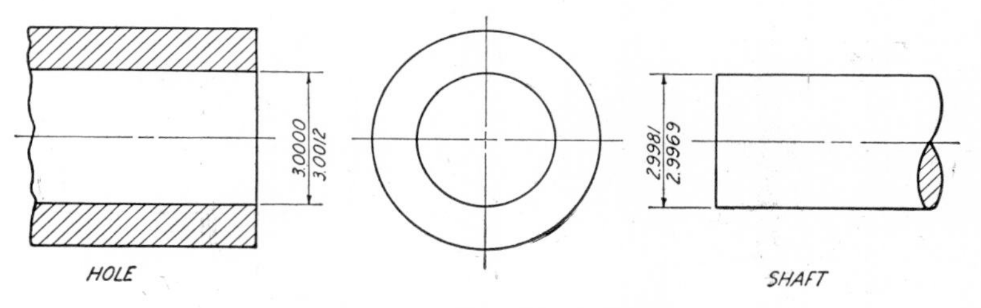

Example of medium fit.

TABLE XXXI (Continued)

Snug Fit (Class 4)—Zero Allowance, Interchangeable

This is the closest fit which can be assembled by hand and necessitates work of considerable precision. It should be used where no perceptible shake is permissible and where moving parts are not intended to move freely under load.

Size			Limits				Tightest Fit	Loosest Fit
From	*Up to and Incl.*	*Mean*	*Hole or External Member*		*Shaft or Internal Member*		*Allowance*	*Allowance + Tolerances*
			+			−		+*
0	$\frac{3}{16}$	$\frac{1}{8}$	0.0003	0.0000	0.0000	0.0002	0.0000	0.0005
$\frac{3}{16}$	$\frac{5}{16}$	$\frac{1}{4}$	0.0004	0.0000	0.0000	0.0003	0.0000	0.0007
$\frac{5}{16}$	$\frac{7}{16}$	$\frac{3}{8}$	0.0004	0.0000	0.0000	0.0003	0.0000	0.0007
$\frac{7}{16}$	$\frac{9}{16}$	$\frac{1}{2}$	0.0005	0.0000	0.0000	0.0003	0.0000	0.0008
$\frac{9}{16}$	$\frac{11}{16}$	$\frac{5}{8}$	0.0005	0.0000	0.0000	0.0003	0.0000	0.0008
$\frac{11}{16}$	$\frac{13}{16}$	$\frac{3}{4}$	0.0005	0.0000	0.0000	0.0004	0.0000	0.0009
$\frac{13}{16}$	$\frac{15}{16}$	$\frac{7}{8}$	0.0006	0.0000	0.0000	0.0004	0.0000	0.0010
$\frac{15}{16}$	$1\frac{1}{16}$	1	0.0006	0.0000	0.0000	0.0004	0.0000	0.0010
$1\frac{1}{16}$	$1\frac{3}{16}$	$1\frac{1}{8}$	0.0006	0.0000	0.0000	0.0004	0.0000	0.0010
$1\frac{3}{16}$	$1\frac{3}{8}$	$1\frac{1}{4}$	0.0006	0.0000	0.0000	0.0004	0.0000	0.0010
$1\frac{3}{8}$	$1\frac{5}{8}$	$1\frac{1}{2}$	0.0007	0.0000	0.0000	0.0005	0.0000	0.0012
$1\frac{5}{8}$	$1\frac{7}{8}$	$1\frac{3}{4}$	0.0007	0.0000	0.0000	0.0005	0.0000	0.0012
$1\frac{7}{8}$	$2\frac{1}{8}$	2	0.0008	0.0000	0.0000	0.0005	0.0000	0.0013
$2\frac{1}{8}$	$2\frac{3}{8}$	$2\frac{1}{4}$	0.0008	0.0000	0.0000	0.0005	0.0000	0.0013
$2\frac{3}{8}$	$2\frac{3}{4}$	$2\frac{1}{2}$	0.0008	0.0000	0.0000	0.0005	0.0000	0.0013
$2\frac{3}{4}$	$3\frac{1}{4}$	3	0.0009	0.0000	0.0000	0.0006	0.0000	0.0015
$3\frac{1}{4}$	$3\frac{3}{4}$	$3\frac{1}{2}$	0.0009	0.0000	0.0000	0.0006	0.0000	0.0015
$3\frac{3}{4}$	$4\frac{1}{4}$	4	0.0010	0.0000	0.0000	0.0006	0.0000	0.0016
$4\frac{1}{4}$	$4\frac{3}{4}$	$4\frac{1}{2}$	0.0010	0.0000	0.0000	0.0007	0.0000	0.0017
$4\frac{3}{4}$	$5\frac{1}{2}$	5	0.0010	0.0000	0.0000	0.0007	0.0000	0.0017
$5\frac{1}{2}$	$6\frac{1}{2}$	6	0.0011	0.0000	0.0000	0.0007	0.0000	0.0018
$6\frac{1}{2}$	$7\frac{1}{2}$	7	0.0011	0.0000	0.0000	0.0008	0.0000	0.0019
$7\frac{1}{2}$	$8\frac{1}{2}$	8	0.0012	0.0000	0.0000	0.0008	0.0000	0.0020

ASA B4a-1925.
* Note: (+) denotes clearance or amount of looseness.
All dimensions in inches.

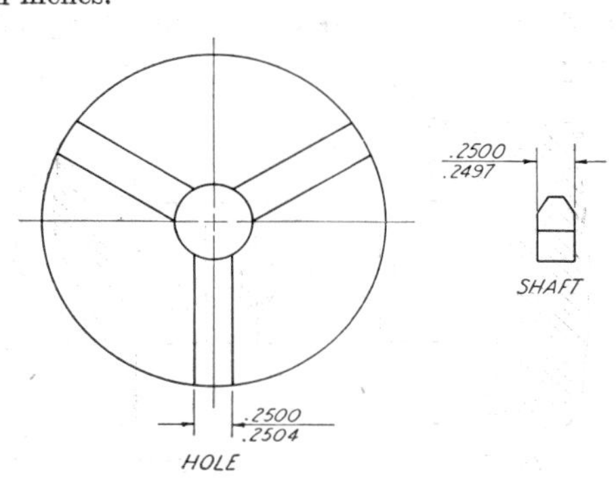

Drill chuck body and jaws. Example of snug fit.

TABLE XXXI (Continued)

Wringing Fit (Class 5)—Zero to Negative Allowance
Selective Assembly

This is also known as a "tunking fit" and it is practically metal-to-metal. Assembly is usually selective and not interchangeable.

Size			Limits				Tightest Fit	Loosest Fit
From	*Up to and Incl.*	*Mean*	*Hole or External Member*		*Shaft or Internal Member*		*Allowance*	*Allowance + Tolerances*
			+	−	+	−	−*	+*
0	3/16	1/8	0.0003	0.0000	0.0002	0.0000	0.0002	0.0003
3/16	5/16	1/4	0.0004	0.0000	0.0003	0.0000	0.0003	0.0004
5/16	7/16	3/8	0.0004	0.0000	0.0003	0.0000	0.0003	0.0004
7/16	9/16	1/2	0.0005	0.0000	0.0003	0.0000	0.0003	0.0005
9/16	11/16	5/8	0.0005	0.0000	0.0003	0.0000	0.0003	0.0005
11/16	13/16	3/4	0.0005	0.0000	0.0004	0.0000	0.0004	0.0005
13/16	15/16	7/8	0.0006	0.0000	0.0004	0.0000	0.0004	0.0006
15/16	1 1/16	1	0.0006	0.0000	0.0004	0.0000	0.0004	0.0006
1 1/16	1 3/16	1 1/8	0.0006	0.0000	0.0004	0.0000	0.0004	0.0006
1 3/16	1 3/8	1 1/4	0.0006	0.0000	0.0004	0.0000	0.0004	0.0006
1 3/8	1 5/8	1 1/2	0.0007	0.0000	0.0005	0.0000	0.0005	0.0007
1 5/8	1 7/8	1 3/4	0.0007	0.0000	0.0005	0.0000	0.0005	0.0007
1 7/8	2 1/8	2	0.0008	0.0000	0.0005	0.0000	0.0005	0.0008
2 1/8	2 3/8	2 1/4	0.0008	0.0000	0.0005	0.0000	0.0005	0.0008
2 3/8	2 3/4	2 1/2	0.0008	0.0000	0.0005	0.0000	0.0005	0.0008
2 3/4	3 1/4	3	0.0009	0.0000	0.0006	0.0000	0.0006	0.0009
3 1/4	3 3/4	3 1/2	0.0009	0.0000	0.0006	0.0000	0.0006	0.0009
3 3/4	4 1/4	4	0.0010	0.0000	0.0006	0.0000	0.0006	0.0010
4 1/4	4 3/4	4 1/2	0.0010	0.0000	0.0007	0.0000	0.0007	0.0010
4 3/4	5 1/2	5	0.0010	0.0000	0.0007	0.0000	0.0007	0.0010
5 1/2	6 1/2	6	0.0011	0.0000	0.0007	0.0000	0.0007	0.0011
6 1/2	7 1/2	7	0.0011	0.0000	0.0008	0.0000	0.0008	0.0011
7 1/2	8 1/2	8	0.0012	0.0000	0.0008	0.0000	0.0008	0.0012

ASA B4a-1925.

* Note: (−) denotes interference of metal or negative allowance. (+) denotes clearance or amount of looseness.

All dimensions in inches.

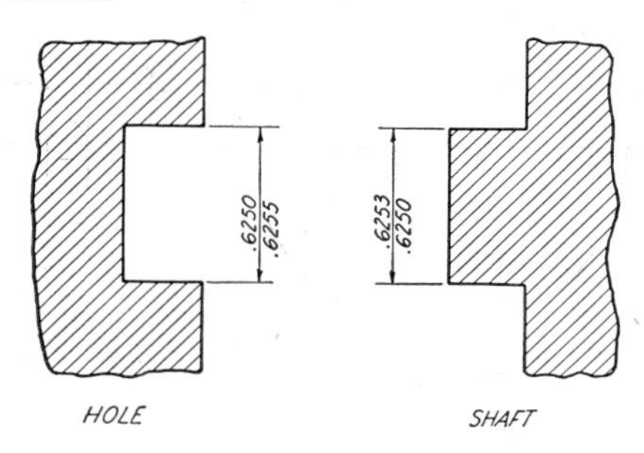

Locating keys, tongues, or dowels. Example of wringing fit.

TABLE XXXI (Continued)

Tight Fit (Class 6)—Slight Negative Allowance
Selective Assembly

Light pressure is required to assemble these fits and the parts are more or less permanently assembled, such as the fixed ends of studs for gears, pulleys, rocker arms, etc. These fits are used for drive fits in thin sections or extremely long fits in other sections, and also for shrink fits on very light sections. Used in automotive, ordnance, and general machine manufacturing.

Size			Limits				Tightest Fit	Loosest Fit
From	*Up to and Incl.*	*Mean*	*Hole or External Member*		*Shaft or Internal Member*		*Allowance*	*Allowance + Tolerances*
			+		+	+	−*	*
0	3/16	1/8	0.0003	0.0000	0.0003	0.0000	0.0003	+0.0003
3/16	5/16	1/4	0.0004	0.0000	0.0005	0.0001	0.0005	+0.0003
5/16	7/16	3/8	0.0004	0.0000	0.0005	0.0001	0.0005	+0.0003
7/16	9/16	1/2	0.0005	0.0000	0.0006	0.0001	0.0006	+0.0004
9/16	11/16	5/8	0.0005	0.0000	0.0007	0.0002	0.0007	+0.0003
11/16	13/16	3/4	0.0005	0.0000	0.0007	0.0002	0.0007	+0.0003
13/16	15/16	7/8	0.0006	0.0000	0.0008	0.0002	0.0008	+0.0004
15/16	1 1/16	1	0.0006	0.0000	0.0009	0.0003	0.0009	+0.0003
1 1/16	1 3/16	1 1/8	0.0006	0.0000	0.0009	0.0003	0.0009	+0.0003
1 3/16	1 3/8	1 1/4	0.0006	0.0000	0.0009	0.0003	0.0009	+0.0003
1 3/8	1 5/8	1 1/2	0.0007	0.0000	0.0011	0.0004	0.0011	+0.0003
1 5/8	1 7/8	1 3/4	0.0007	0.0000	0.0011	0.0004	0.0011	+0.0003
1 7/8	2 1/8	2	0.0008	0.0000	0.0013	0.0005	0.0013	+0.0003
2 1/8	2 3/8	2 1/4	0.0008	0.0000	0.0014	0.0006	0.0014	+0.0002
2 3/8	2 3/4	2 1/2	0.0008	0.0000	0.0014	0.0006	0.0014	+0.0002
2 3/4	3 1/4	3	0.0009	0.0000	0.0017	0.0008	0.0017	+0.0001
3 1/4	3 3/4	3 1/2	0.0009	0.0000	0.0018	0.0009	0.0018	−0.0000
3 3/4	4 1/4	4	0.0010	0.0000	0.0020	0.0010	0.0020	−0.0000
4 1/4	4 3/4	4 1/2	0.0010	0.0000	0.0021	0.0011	0.0021	−0.0001
4 3/4	5 1/2	5	0.0010	0.0000	0.0023	0.0013	0.0023	−0.0003
5 1/2	6 1/2	6	0.0011	0.0000	0.0026	0.0015	0.0026	−0.0004
6 1/2	7 1/2	7	0.0011	0.0000	0.0029	0.0018	0.0029	−0.0007
7 1/2	8 1/2	8	0.0012	0.0000	0.0032	0.0020	0.0032	−0.0008

ASA B4a-1925.

* Note: (−) denotes interference of metal or negative allowance. (+) denotes clearance or amount of looseness.

All dimensions in inches.

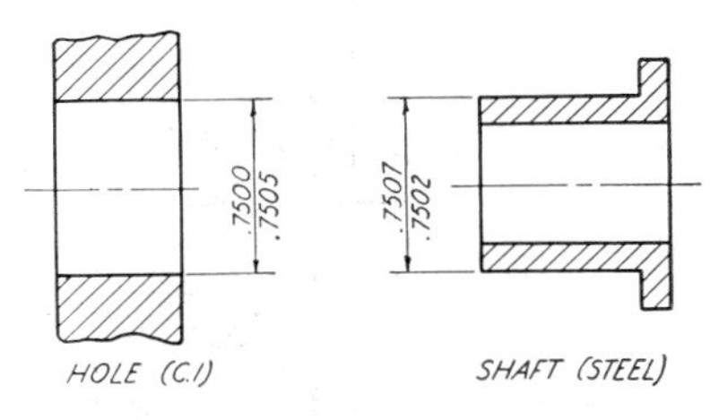

Jig bushing. Example of tight fit.

TABLE XXXI (Continued)

Medium Force Fit (Class 7)—Negative Allowance
Selective Assembly

Considerable pressure is required to assemble these fits and the parts are considered permanently assembled. These fits are used in fastening locomotive wheels, car wheels, armatures of dynamos and motors, and crank disks to their axles or shafts. They are also used for shrink fits on medium sections or long fits. These fits are the tightest which are recommended for cast-iron holes or external members as they stress cast iron to its elastic limit.

Size			Limits				Tightest Fit	Loosest Fit
From	*Up to and Incl.*	*Mean*	*Hole or External Member*		*Shaft or Internal Member*		*Allowance*	*Allowance + Tolerances*
			+		+	+	−*	*
0	$\frac{3}{16}$	$\frac{1}{8}$	0.0003	0.0000	0.0004	0.0001	0.0004	+0.0002
$\frac{3}{16}$	$\frac{5}{16}$	$\frac{1}{4}$	0.0004	0.0000	0.0005	0.0001	0.0005	+0.0003
$\frac{5}{16}$	$\frac{7}{16}$	$\frac{3}{8}$	0.0004	0.0000	0.0006	0.0002	0.0006	+0.0002
$\frac{7}{16}$	$\frac{9}{16}$	$\frac{1}{2}$	0.0005	0.0000	0.0008	0.0003	0.0008	+0.0002
$\frac{9}{16}$	$\frac{11}{16}$	$\frac{5}{8}$	0.0005	0.0000	0.0008	0.0003	0.0008	+0.0002
$\frac{11}{16}$	$\frac{13}{16}$	$\frac{3}{4}$	0.0005	0.0000	0.0009	0.0004	0.0009	+0.0001
$\frac{13}{16}$	$\frac{15}{16}$	$\frac{7}{8}$	0.0006	0.0000	0.0010	0.0004	0.0010	+0.0002
$\frac{15}{16}$	$1\frac{1}{16}$	1	0.0006	0.0000	0.0011	0.0005	0.0011	+0.0001
$1\frac{1}{16}$	$1\frac{3}{16}$	$1\frac{1}{8}$	0.0006	0.0000	0.0012	0.0006	0.0012	0.0000
$1\frac{3}{16}$	$1\frac{3}{8}$	$1\frac{1}{4}$	0.0006	0.0000	0.0012	0.0006	0.0012	0.0000
$1\frac{3}{8}$	$1\frac{5}{8}$	$1\frac{1}{2}$	0.0007	0.0000	0.0015	0.0008	0.0015	−0.0001
$1\frac{5}{8}$	$1\frac{7}{8}$	$1\frac{3}{4}$	0.0007	0.0000	0.0016	0.0009	0.0016	−0.0002
$1\frac{7}{8}$	$2\frac{1}{8}$	2	0.0008	0.0000	0.0018	0.0010	0.0018	−0.0002
$2\frac{1}{8}$	$2\frac{3}{8}$	$2\frac{1}{4}$	0.0008	0.0000	0.0019	0.0011	0.0019	−0.0003
$2\frac{3}{8}$	$2\frac{3}{4}$	$2\frac{1}{2}$	0.0008	0.0000	0.0021	0.0013	0.0021	−0.0005
$2\frac{3}{4}$	$3\frac{1}{4}$	3	0.0009	0.0000	0.0024	0.0015	0.0024	−0.0006
$3\frac{1}{4}$	$3\frac{3}{4}$	$3\frac{1}{2}$	0.0009	0.0000	0.0027	0.0018	0.0027	−0.0009
$3\frac{3}{4}$	$4\frac{1}{4}$	4	0.0010	0.0000	0.0030	0.0020	0.0030	−0.0010
$4\frac{1}{4}$	$4\frac{3}{4}$	$4\frac{1}{2}$	0.0010	0.0000	0.0033	0.0023	0.0033	−0.0013
$4\frac{3}{4}$	$5\frac{1}{2}$	5	0.0010	0.0000	0.0035	0.0025	0.0035	−0.0015
$5\frac{1}{2}$	$6\frac{1}{2}$	6	0.0011	0.0000	0.0041	0.0030	0.0041	−0.0019
$6\frac{1}{2}$	$7\frac{1}{2}$	7	0.0011	0.0000	0.0046	0.0035	0.0046	−0.0024
$7\frac{1}{2}$	$8\frac{1}{2}$	8	0.0012	0.0000	0.0052	0.0040	0.0052	−0.0028

ASA B4a-1925.

* Note: (−) denotes interference of metal or negative allowance. (+) denotes clearance or amount of looseness.

All dimensions in inches.

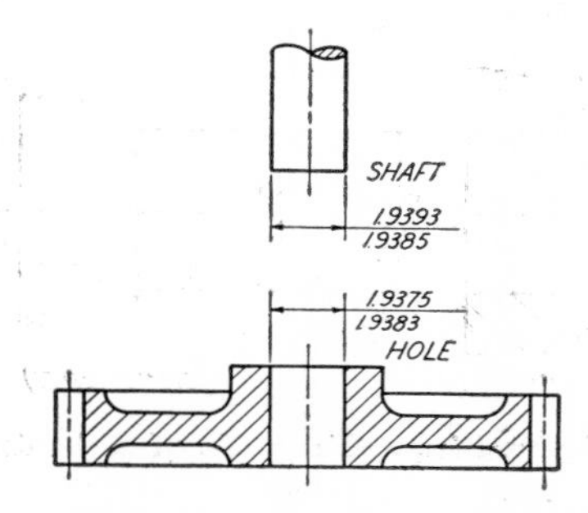

Cast-iron gear and steel shaft. Example of medium force fit.

TABLE XXXI (Concluded)

Heavy Force and Shrink Fit (Class 8)
Considerable Negative Allowance—Selective Assembly

These fits are used for steel holes where the metal can be stressed to its elastic limit. These fits cause excessive stress for cast-iron holes. Shrink fits are used where heavy force fits are impractical, as on locomotive wheel tires, heavy crank disks of large engines, etc.

Size			Limits				Tightest Fit	Loosest Fit
From	*Up to and Incl.*	*Mean*	*Hole or External Member*		*Shaft or Internal Member*		*Allowance*	*Allowance + Tolerances*
			+	−	+	+	−*	*
0	$\frac{3}{16}$	$\frac{1}{8}$	0.0003	0.0000	0.0004	0.0001	0.0004	+0.0002
$\frac{3}{16}$	$\frac{5}{16}$	$\frac{1}{4}$	0.0004	0.0000	0.0007	0.0003	0.0007	+0.0001
$\frac{5}{16}$	$\frac{7}{16}$	$\frac{3}{8}$	0.0004	0.0000	0.0008	0.0004	0.0008	−0.0000
$\frac{7}{16}$	$\frac{9}{16}$	$\frac{1}{2}$	0.0005	0.0000	0.0010	0.0005	0.0010	0.0000
$\frac{9}{16}$	$\frac{11}{16}$	$\frac{5}{8}$	0.0005	0.0000	0.0011	0.0006	0.0011	−0.0001
$\frac{11}{16}$	$\frac{13}{16}$	$\frac{3}{4}$	0.0005	0.0000	0.0013	0.0008	0.0013	−0.0003
$\frac{13}{16}$	$\frac{15}{16}$	$\frac{7}{8}$	0.0006	0.0000	0.0015	0.0009	0.0015	−0.0003
$\frac{15}{16}$	$1\frac{1}{16}$	1	0.0006	0.0000	0.0016	0.0010	0.0016	−0.0004
$1\frac{1}{16}$	$1\frac{3}{16}$	$1\frac{1}{8}$	0.0006	0.0000	0.0017	0.0011	0.0017	−0.0005
$1\frac{3}{16}$	$1\frac{3}{8}$	$1\frac{1}{4}$	0.0006	0.0000	0.0019	0.0013	0.0019	−0.0007
$1\frac{3}{8}$	$1\frac{5}{8}$	$1\frac{1}{2}$	0.0007	0.0000	0.0022	0.0015	0.0022	−0.0008
$1\frac{5}{8}$	$1\frac{7}{8}$	$1\frac{3}{4}$	0.0007	0.0000	0.0025	0.0018	0.0025	−0.0011
$1\frac{7}{8}$	$2\frac{1}{8}$	2	0.0008	0.0000	0.0028	0.0020	0.0028	−0.0012
$2\frac{1}{8}$	$2\frac{3}{8}$	$2\frac{1}{4}$	0.0008	0.0000	0.0031	0.0023	0.0031	−0.0015
$2\frac{3}{8}$	$2\frac{3}{4}$	$2\frac{1}{2}$	0.0008	0.0000	0.0033	0.0025	0.0033	−0.0017
$2\frac{3}{4}$	$3\frac{1}{4}$	3	0.0009	0.0000	0.0039	0.0030	0.0039	−0.0021
$3\frac{1}{4}$	$3\frac{3}{4}$	$3\frac{1}{2}$	0.0009	0.0000	0.0044	0.0035	0.0044	−0.0026
$3\frac{3}{4}$	$4\frac{1}{4}$	4	0.0010	0.0000	0.0050	0.0040	0.0050	−0.0030
$4\frac{1}{4}$	$4\frac{3}{4}$	$4\frac{1}{2}$	0.0010	0.0000	0.0055	0.0045	0.0055	−0.0035
$4\frac{3}{4}$	$5\frac{1}{2}$	5	0.0010	0.0000	0.0060	0.0050	0.0060	−0.0040
$5\frac{1}{2}$	$6\frac{1}{2}$	6	0.0011	0.0000	0.0071	0.0060	0.0071	−0.0049
$6\frac{1}{2}$	$7\frac{1}{2}$	7	0.0011	0.0000	0.0081	0.0070	0.0081	−0.0059
$7\frac{1}{2}$	$8\frac{1}{2}$	8	0.0012	0.0000	0.0092	0.0080	0.0092	−0.0068

ASA B4a-1925.

* Note: (−) denotes interference of metal or negative allowance. (+) denotes clearance or amount of looseness.

All dimensions in inches.

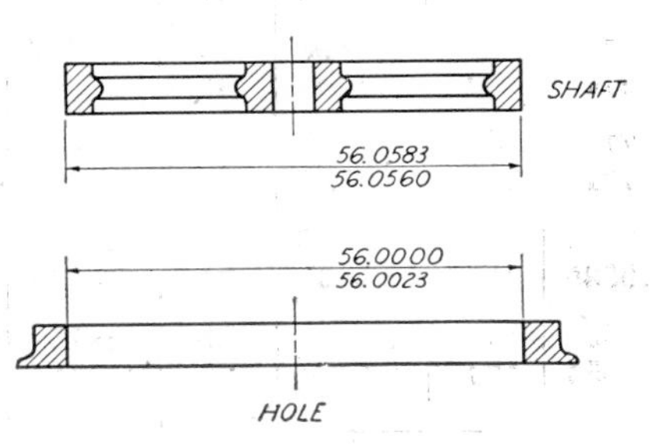

Shrinking a locomotive tire on wheel. Example of shrink fit.

TABLE XXXII
Single Row Radial Bearings—Type 3000

Principal Dimensions

For radial or combined loads from either direction where thrust is to be resisted by a single bearing and is not great enough to require use of angular contact type. For capacities under thrust or combined loads, use factors "*F*" given under "Bearing Selection."

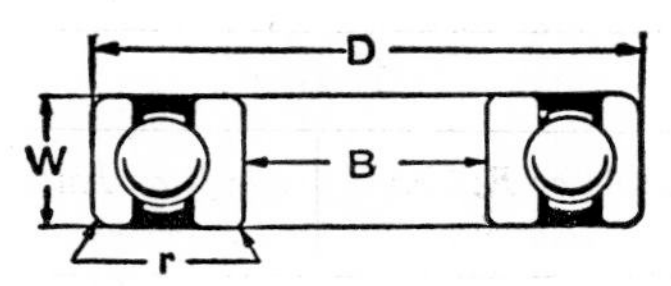

Brg. No.	Bore *B*		Diameter *D*		Width *W*		Balls		Radius r*
	Mm	*Inch*	*Mm*	*Inch*	*Mm*	*Inch*	*Diam.*	*No.*	
3200	10	.3937	30	1.1811	9	.3543	$\frac{7}{32}$	7	.025
3300	10	.3937	35	1.3780	11	.4331	$\frac{1}{4}$	7	.025
3201	12	.4724	32	1.2598	10	.3937	.210	8	.025
3301	12	.4724	37	1.4567	12	.4724	$\frac{9}{32}$	7	.04
3202	15	.5906	35	1.3780	11	.4331	.210	9	.025
3302	15	.5906	42	1.6535	13	.5118	$\frac{5}{16}$	7	.04
3203	17	.6693	40	1.5748	12	.4724	$\frac{9}{32}$	8	.04
3303	17	.6693	47	1.8504	14	.5512	$\frac{11}{32}$	7	.04
3204	20	.7874	47	1.8504	14	.5512	$\frac{5}{16}$	8	.04
3304	20	.7874	52	2.0472	15	.5906	$\frac{13}{32}$	7	.04
3205	25	.9843	52	2.0472	15	.5906	$\frac{5}{16}$	9	.04
3305	25	.9843	62	2.4409	17	.6693	$\frac{13}{32}$	8	.04
3206	30	1.1811	62	2.4409	16	.6299	$\frac{11}{32}$	9	.04
3306	30	1.1811	72	2.8346	19	.7480	$\frac{15}{32}$	8	.04
3207	35	1.3780	72	2.8346	17	.6693	$\frac{7}{16}$	9	.04
3307	35	1.3780	80	3.1496	21	.8268	$\frac{17}{32}$	8	.06
3208	40	1.5748	80	3.1496	18	.7087	$\frac{15}{32}$	9	.04
3308	40	1.5748	90	3.5433	23	.9055	$\frac{19}{32}$	8	.06
3209	45	1.7717	85	3.3465	19	.7480	$\frac{15}{32}$	10	.04
3309	45	1.7717	100	3.9370	25	.9843	$\frac{21}{32}$	8	.06
3210	50	1.9685	90	3.5433	20	.7874	$\frac{15}{32}$	11	.04
3310	50	1.9685	110	4.3307	27	1.0630	$\frac{23}{32}$	8	.08
3211	55	2.1654	100	3.9370	21	.8268	$\frac{1}{2}$	11	.06
3311	55	2.1654	120	4.7244	29	1.1417	$\frac{25}{32}$	8	.08

* Radius r indicates maximum fillet radius in housing or on shaft which bearing radius will clear.
Pages 140–143 from Vol. I, *New Departure Hand Book*.

TABLE XXXII (Continued)
Radax Bearings—Type 30,000

Principal Dimensions

Single row angular contact; provide maximum capacity for one-direction thrust loads. Mounted two bearings opposed for combined loads or thrust from either direction. For capacities under these loads, use factors "*F*" given under "Bearing Selection."

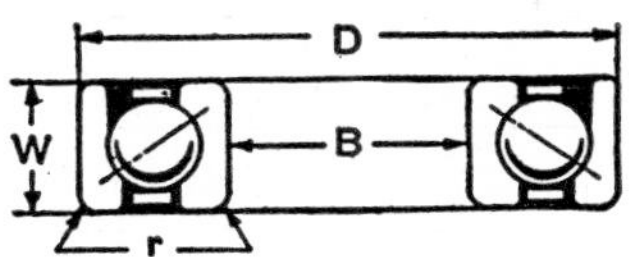

Brg. No.	Bore *B*		Diameter *D*		Width *W*		Balls		Radius *r**
	Mm	*Inch*	*Mm*	*Inch*	*Mm*	*Inch*	*Diam.*	*No.*	
30204			47	1.8504	14	.5512	$\frac{11}{32}$	10	
30304	20	.7874	52	2.0472	15	.5906	$\frac{3}{8}$	10	.04
30404			72	2.8346	19	.7480	$\frac{9}{16}$	8	
30205			52	2.0472	15	.5906	$\frac{11}{32}$	11	.04
30305	25	.9843	62	2.4409	17	.6693	$\frac{7}{16}$	10	.04
30405			80	3.1496	21	.8268	$\frac{5}{8}$	9	.06
30206			62	2.4409	16	.6299	$\frac{3}{8}$	12	.04
30306	30	1.1811	72	2.8346	19	.7480	$\frac{1}{2}$	10	.04
30406			90	3.5433	23	.9055	$\frac{11}{16}$	9	.06
30207			72	2.8346	17	.6693	$\frac{7}{16}$	12	.04
30307	35	1.3780	80	3.1496	21	.8268	$\frac{9}{16}$	11	.06
30407			100	3.9370	25	.9843	$\frac{3}{4}$	9	.06
30208			80	3.1496	18	.7087	$\frac{1}{2}$	12	.04
30308	40	1.5748	90	3.5433	23	.9055	$\frac{5}{8}$	11	.06
30408			110	4.3307	27	1.0630	$\frac{13}{16}$	10	.08
30209			85	3.3465	19	.7480	$\frac{1}{2}$	13	.04
30309	45	1.7717	100	3.9370	25	.9843	$\frac{11}{16}$	11	.06
30409			120	4.7244	29	1.1417	$\frac{7}{8}$	10	.08
30210			90	3.5433	20	.7874	$\frac{1}{2}$	14	.04
30310	50	1.9685	110	4.3307	27	1.0630	$\frac{3}{4}$	11	.08
30410			130	5.1181	31	1.2205	$\frac{15}{16}$	10	.08
30211			100	3.9370	21	.8268	$\frac{9}{16}$	14	.06
30311	55	2.1654	120	4.7244	29	1.1417	$\frac{13}{16}$	12	.08
30411			140	5.5118	33	1.2992	1	10	.08
30212			110	4.3307	22	.8661	$\frac{5}{8}$	14	.06
30312	60	2.3622	130	5.1181	31	1.2205	$\frac{7}{8}$	12	.08
30412			150	5.9055	35	1.3780	$1\frac{1}{16}$	10	.08

* Radius *r* indicates maximum fillet radius in housing or on shaft which bearing radius will clear. Page 143 from Vol. I, *New Departure Hand Book*.

TABLE XXXIII*

Shaft Mounting Fits for SAE or A.B.E.C.-1 Standard Bearings

The *"theoretical fits"* given in this table are those which could result if the shaft diameters and bearing bores were to vary the full limits of their respective tolerances. Actually, bearing bores are ground uniformly close to the minimum limit and investigation by the Annular Bearing Engineers Committee has proved that well over 95% of actual installations result in the *"expected fits"* given below.

Bearing and Bore Numbers	Bearing Bore		Shaft Revolving						Shaft Stationary					
	Diameters		Diameters		Expected Fit		Theoret. Fit		Diameters		Expected Fit		Theoret. Fit	
	Max.	Min.	Max.	Min.	Loose or Tight	Tight	Loose	Tight	Max.	Min.	Max. Loose	Min. Loose	Loose	Tight
34	.1575	.1572	.1576	.1573					.1573	.1570				
35	.1969	.1966	.1970	.1967	.0001L	.0003	.0002	.0004	.1967	.1964	.0004	.0000	.0005	.0001
36	.2362	.2359	.2363	.2360					.2360	.2357				
37	.2756	.2753	.2757	.2754					.2754	.2751				
38	.3150	.3147	.3151	.3148	.0001L	.0003	.0002	.0004	.3148	.3145	.0004	.0000	.0005	.0001
39	.3543	.3540	.3544	.3541					.3541	.3538				
8006	.2362	.2359	.2363	.2360					.2360	.2357				
8007, 8102	.2756	.2753	.2757	.2754	.0001L	.0003	.0002	.0004	.2754	.2751	.0004	.0000	.0005	.0001
8008, 8103	.3150	.3147	.3151	.3148					.3148	.3145				
8009	.3543	.3540	.3544	.3541	.0001L	.0003	.0002	.0004	.3541	.3538				
8011	.4331	.4328	.4333	.4330	.0000L	.0004	.0001	.0005	.4329	.4326	.0004	.0000	.0005	.0001
8013	.5118	.5115	.5120	.5117	.0000L	.0004	.0001	.0005	.5116	.5113				
8014	.5512	.5509	.5514	.5511	.0000L	.0004	.0001	.0005	.5510	.5507	.0004	.0000	.0005	.0001
8016	.6299	.6296	.6301	.6298	.0000L	.0004	.0001	.0005	.6297	.6294	.0004	.0000	.0005	.0001
8026	1.0236	1.0232	1.0239	1.0235	.0000L	.0006	.0001	.0007	1.0233	1.0229	.0006	.0000	.0007	.0001
N.D. 8-6	.2362	.2359	.2363	.2360					.2360	.2357				
N.D. 8-7	.2756	.2753	.2757	.2754	.0001L	.0003	.0002	.0004	.2754	.2751	.0004	.0000	.0005	.0001
N.D. 8	.3150	.3147	.3151	.3148					.3148	.3145				
N.D. 10-9	.3543	.3540	.3544	.3541	.0001L	.0003	.0002	.0004	.3541	.3538				
N.D. 10	.3937	.3934	.3939	.3936	.0000L	.0004	.0001	.0005	.3935	.3932	.0004	.0000	.0005	.0001
N.D. 12-11	.4331	.4328	.4333	.4330	.0000L	.0004	.0001	.0005	.4329	.4326				
N.D. 12	.4724	.4721	.4726	.4723	.0000L	.0004	.0001	.0005	.4722	.4719				
N.D. 13	.5118	.5115	.5120	.5117					.5116	.5113				
N.D. 15	.5906	.5903	.5908	.5905	.0000L	.0004	.0001	.0005	.5904	.5901	.0004	.0000	.0005	.0001
N.D. 16	.6299	.6296	.6301	.6298					.6297	.6294				
N.D. 17	.6693	.6690	.6695	.6692	.0000L	.0004	.0001	.0005	.6691	.6688	.0004	.0000	.0005	.0001
N.D. 20	.7874	.7870	.7877	.7873	.0000L	.0006	.0001	.0007	.7871	.7867	.0006	.0000	.0007	.0001
N.D. 25	.9843	.9839	.9846	.9842	.0000L	.0006	.0001	.0007	.9840	.9836	.0006	.0000	.0007	.0001
0	.3937	.3934	.3939	.3936					.3935	.3932				
1	.4724	.4721	.4726	.4723	.0000L	.0004	.0001	.0005	.4722	.4719	.0004	.0000	.0005	.0001
2	.5906	.5903	.5908	.5905					.5904	.5901				
3	.6693	.6690	.6695	.6692	.0000L	.0004	.0001	.0005	.6691	.6688	.0004	.0000	.0005	.0001
4	.7874	.7870	.7877	.7873	.0000L	.0006	.0001	.0007	.7871	.7867	.0006	.0000	.0007	.0001
5	.9843	.9839	.9846	.9842	.0000L	.0006	.0001	.0007	.9840	.9836	.0006	.0000	.0007	.0001
6	1.1811	1.1807	1.1814	1.1810	.0000L	.0006	.0001	.0007	1.1808	1.1804	.0006	.0000	.0007	.0001
7	1.3780	1.3775	1.3784	1.3779	.0001T	.0007	.0001	.0009	1.3776	1.3771	.0007	.0001	.0009	.0001
8	1.5748	1.5743	1.5752	1.5747	.0001T	.0007	.0001	.0009	1.5744	1.5739	.0007	.0001	.0009	.0001
9	1.7717	1.7712	1.7721	1.7716	.0001T	.0007	.0001	.0009	1.7713	1.7708	.0007	.0001	.0009	.0001
10	1.9685	1.9680	1.9689	1.9684	.0001T	.0007	.0001	.0009	1.9681	1.9676	.0007	.0001	.0009	.0001
11	2.1654	2.1648	2.1659	2.1653	.0001T	.0009	.0001	.0011	2.1649	2.1643	.0009	.0001	.0011	.0001
12	2.3622	2.3616	2.3627	2.3621					2.3617	2.3611				
13	2.5591	2.5585	2.5596	2.5590	.0001T	.0009	.0001	.0011	2.5586	2.5580	.0009	.0001	.0011	.0001
14	2.7559	2.7553	2.7564	2.7558					2.7554	2.7548				
15	2.9528	2.9522	2.9533	2.9527	.0001T	.0009	.0001	.0011	2.9523	2.9517	.0009	.0001	.0011	.0001
16	3.1496	3.1490	3.1501	3.1495	.0001T	.0009	.0001	.0011	3.1491	3.1485	.0009	.0001	.0011	.0001
17	3.3465	3.3457	3.3471	3.3464	.0002T	.0012	.0001	.0014	3.3458	3.3451	.0012	.0002	.0014	.0001
18	3.5433	3.5425	3.5439	3.5432					3.5426	3.5419				
19	3.7402	3.7394	3.7408	3.7401	.0002T	.0012	.0001	.0014	3.7395	3.7388	.0012	.0002	.0014	.0001
20	3.9370	3.9362	3.9376	3.9369					3.9363	3.9356				
21	4.1339	4.1331	4.1345	4.1338	.0002T	.0012	.0001	.0014	4.1332	4.1325	.0012	.0002	.0014	.0001
22	4.3307	4.3299	4.3313	4.3306					4.3300	4.3293				

* Reproduced with permission from Vol. I, *New Departure Hand Book.*

TABLE XXXIII (Continued)
Housing Mounting Fits for A.B.E.C.-1 and A.B.E.C.-2 Bearings

The housing fits given in this table are those which would result if the bearing diameters and housing bores were to vary the full allowable limits. Actually, bearing diameters are ground uniformly close to the maximum and with housings properly bored, fits well within the limits given will be obtained in practice.

Bearing and Bore Numbers			Bearing Outer Diam.		Housing Stationary						Housing Revolving					
Series			*Diameters*		*Diameters*		*Expect. Fit*		*Theoret. Fit*		*Diameters*		*Expect. Fit*		*Theoret. Fit*	
Lgt.	*Med.*	*Hvy.*	*Max.*	*Min.*	*Max.*	*Min.*	*Min. Loose*	*Max. Loose*	*Tight*	*Loose*	*Max.*	*Min.*	*Tight*	*Loose*	*Tight*	*Loose*
34			.6299	.6295	.6303	.6298					.6298	.6293				
35, 36			.7480	.7476	.7484	.7479					.7479	.7474				
37, 38			.8661	.8657	.8665	.8660	.0000	.0005	.0001	.0008	.8660	.8655	.0002	.0002	.0006	.0003
39			1.0236	1.0232	1.0240	1.0235					1.0235	1.0230				
8102, 8103			.8661	.8657	.8665	.8660					.8660	.8655				
8006, 7 & 8			.9449	.9445	.9453	.9448	.0000	.0005	.0001	.0008	.9448	.9443	.0002	.0002	.0006	.0003
8009			1.1811	1.1807	1.1815	1.1810					1.1810	1.1805				
8011, 8013			1.2598	1.2593	1.2603	1.2597	.0000	.0007	.0001	.0010	1.2597	1.2591	.0003	.0003	.0007	.0004
8014, 8016			1.3780	1.3775	1.3785	1.3779	.0000	.0007	.0001	.0010	1.3779	1.3773	.0003	.0003	.0007	.0004
8026			2.0472	2.0466	2.0479	2.0479	.0000	.0010	.0001	.0013	2.0472	2.0464	.0004	.0004	.0008	.0006
N.D. 8-6, 8-7, 8			.9453	.9449	.9457	.9452	.0000	.0005	.0001	.0008	.9452	.9447	.0002	.0002	.0006	.0003
N.D. 10-9, 10			1.1028	1.1024	1.1032	1.1027	.0000	.0005	.0001	.0008	1.1027	1.1022	.0002	.0002	.0006	.0003
N.D. 12-11, 12			1.2603	1.2598	1.2608	1.2602	.0000	.0007	.0001	.0010	1.2602	1.2596	.0003	.0003	.0007	.0004
N.D. 13			1.1816	1.1811	1.1821	1.1815					1.1815	1.1809				
N.D. 15			1.3785	1.3780	1.3790	1.3784	.0000	.0007	.0001	.0010	1.3784	1.3778	.0003	.0003	.0007	.0004
N.D. 16			1.4966	1.4961	1.4971	1.4965					1.4965	1.4959				
N.D. 17			1.7328	1.7323	1.7333	1.7327					1.7327	1.7321				
N.D. 20			1.8509	1.8504	1.8514	1.8508	.0000	.0007	.0001	.0010	1.8508	1.8502	.0003	.0003	.0007	.0004
N.D. 25			2.0477	2.0472	2.0482	2.0476					2.0476	2.0470				
0			1.1811	1.1807	1.1815	1.1810	.0000	.0005	.0001	.0008	1.1810	1.1805	.0002	.0002	.0006	.0003
1			1.2598	1.2593	1.2603	1.2597	.0000	.0007	.0001	.0010	1.2597	1.2591	.0003	.0003	.0007	.0004
2	**0**		1.3780	1.3775	1.3785	1.3779	.0000	.0007	.0001	.0010	1.3779	1.3773	.0003	.0003	.0007	.0004
	1		1.4567	1.4562	1.4572	1.4566					1.4566	1.4560				
3			1.5748	1.5743	1.5753	1.5747	.0000	.0007	.0001	.0010	1.5747	1.5741	.0003	.0003	.0007	.0004
	2		1.6535	1.6530	1.6540	1.6534					1.6534	1.6528				
4	**3**		1.8504	1.8499	1.8509	1.8503	.0000	.0007	.0001	.0010	1.8503	1.8497	.0003	.0003	.0007	.0004
5	**4**		2.0472	2.0466	2.0479	2.0471	.0000	.0010	.0001	.0013	2.0472	2.0464	.0004	.0004	.0008	.0006
6	**5**		2.4409	2.4403	2.4416	2.4408	.0000	.0010	.0001	.0013	2.4409	2.4401	.0004	.0004	.0008	.0006
7	**6**	**4**	2.8346	2.8340	2.8353	2.8345	.0000	.0010	.0001	.0013	2.8346	2.8338	.0004	.0004	.0008	.0006
8	**7**	**5**	3.1496	3.1490	3.1503	3.1495	.0000	.0010	.0001	.0013	3.1496	3.1488	.0004	.0004	.0008	.0006
9			3.3465	3.3457	3.3473	3.3463	.0000	.0012	.0002	.0016	3.3466	3.3456	.0005	.0004	.0009	.0009
10	**8**	**6**	3.5433	3.5425	3.5441	3.5431					3.5434	3.5424				
11	**9**	**7**	3.9370	3.9362	3.9378	3.9368	.0000	.0012	.0002	.0016	3.9371	3.9361	.0005	.0004	.0009	.0009
12	**10**	**8**	4.3307	4.3299	4.3315	4.3305					4.3308	4.3298				
13	**11**	**9**	4.7244	4.7236	4.7252	4.7242	.0000	.0012	.0002	.0016	4.7245	4.7235	.0005	.0004	.0009	.0009
14			4.9213	4.9203	4.9223	4.9211	.0001	.0015	.0002	.0020	4.9214	4.9202	.0006	.0005	.0011	.0011
15	**12**	**10**	5.1181	5.1171	5.1191	5.1179	.0001	.0015	.0002	.0020	5.1182	5.1170	.0006	.0005	.0011	.0011
16	**13**	**11**	5.5118	5.5108	5.5128	5.5116					5.5119	5.5107				
17	**14**	**12**	5.9055	5.9045	5.9065	5.9053	.0001	.0015	.0002	.0020	5.9056	5.9044	.0006	.0005	.0011	.0011
18	**15**	**13**	6.2992	6.2982	6.3002	6.2990					6.2993	6.2981				
19	**16**		6.6929	6.6919	6.6939	6.6927	.0001	.0015	.0002	.0020	6.6930	6.6918	.0006	.0005	.0011	.0011
20	**17**	**14**	7.0866	7.0856	7.0876	7.0864	.0001	.0015	.0002	.0020	7.0867	7.0855	.0006	.0005	.0011	.0011
21	**18**	**15**	7.4803	7.4791	7.4815	7.4801	.0001	.0018	.0002	.0024	7.4804	7.4790	.0007	.0007	.0013	.0013
22	**19**	**16**	7.8740	7.8728	7.8752	7.8738					7.8741	7.8727				
		17	8.2677	8.2665	8.2689	8.2675	.0001	.0018	.0002	.0024	8.2678	8.2664	.0007	.0007	.0013	.0013
	20		8.4646	8.4634	8.4658	8.4644					8.4647	8.4633				
	21	**18**	8.8583	8.8571	8.8595	8.8581	.0001	.0018	.0002	.0024	8.8584	8.8570	.0007	.0007	.0013	.0013
	22		9.4488	9.4476	9.4500	9.4486					9.4489	9.4475				

TABLE XXXIV

Twist Drill Sizes*					
Number Sizes				*Letter Sizes*	
No. Size	*Decimal Equivalents*	*No. Size*	*Decimal Equivalents*	*Size Letter*	*Decimal Equivalents*
1	.2280	41	.0960	*A*	.234
2	.2210	42	.0935	*B*	.238
3	.2130	43	.0890	*C*	.242
4	.2090	44	.0860	*D*	.246
5	.2055	45	.0820	*E*	.250
6	.2040	46	.0810	*F*	.257
7	.2010	47	.0785	*G*	.261
8	.1990	48	.0760	*H*	.266
9	.1960	49	.0730	*I*	.272
10	.1935	50	.0700	*J*	.277
11	.1910	51	.0670	*K*	.281
12	.1890	52	.0635	*L*	.290
13	.1850	53	.0595	*M*	.295
14	.1820	54	.0550	*N*	.302
15	.1800	55	.0520	*O*	.316
16	.1770	56	.0465	*P*	.323
17	.1730	57	.0430	*Q*	.332
18	.1695	58	.0420	*R*	.339
19	.1660	59	.0410	*S*	.348
20	.1610	60	.0400	*T*	.358
21	.1590	61	.0390	*U*	.368
22	.1570	62	.0380	*V*	.377
23	.1540	63	.0370	*W*	.386
24	.1520	64	.0360	*X*	.397
25	.1495	65	.0350	*Y*	.404
26	.1470	66	.0330	*Z*	.413
27	.1440	67	.0320		
28	.1405	68	.0310		
29	.1360	69	.0292		
30	.1285	70	.0280		
31	.1200	71	.0260		
32	.1160	72	.0250		
33	.1130	73	.0240		
34	.1110	74	.0225		
35	.1100	75	.0210		
36	.1065	76	.0200		
37	.1040	77	.0180		
38	.1015	78	.0160		
39	.0995	79	.0145		
40	.0980	80	.0135		

* Fraction size drills range in size from $\frac{1}{16}$–4″ and over in diameter—by 64ths.

TABLE XXXV

STANDARD WIRE AND SHEET-METAL GAGES
(Dimensions in decimal parts of an inch)

Gage Number	*(A) Brown & Sharpe or American*	*(B) American Steel & Wire Co.*	*(C) Piano Wire*	*(E) U.S. St'd.*	*Gage Number*
0000000	.6513	.4900	....	.5000	0000000
000000	.5800	.4615	.004	.4688	000000
00000	.5165	.4305	.005	.4375	00000
0000	.4600	.3938	.006	.4063	0000
000	.4096	.3625	.007	.3750	000
00	.3648	.3310	.008	.3438	00
0	.3249	.3065	.009	.3125	0
1	.2893	.2830	.010	.2813	1
2	.2576	.2625	.011	.2656	2
3	.2294	.2437	.012	.2500	3
4	.2043	.2253	.013	.2344	4
5	.1819	.2070	.014	.2188	5
6	.1620	.1920	.016	.2031	6
7	.1443	.1770	.018	.1875	7
8	.1285	.1620	.020	.1719	8
9	.1144	.1483	.022	.1563	9
10	.1019	.1350	.024	.1406	10
11	.0907	.1205	.026	.1250	11
12	.0808	.1055	.029	.1094	12
13	.0720	.0915	.031	.0938	13
14	.0641	.0800	.033	.0781	14
15	.0571	.0720	.035	.0703	15
16	.0508	.0625	.037	.0625	16
17	.0453	.0540	.039	.0563	17
18	.0403	.0475	.041	.0500	18
19	.0359	.0410	.043	.0438	19
20	.0320	.0348	.045	.0375	20
21	.0285	.0317	.047	.0344	21
22	.0253	.0286	.049	.0313	22
23	.0226	.0258	.051	.0281	23
24	.0201	.0230	.055	.0250	24
25	.0179	.0204	.059	.0219	25
26	.0159	.0181	.063	.0188	26
27	.0142	.0173	.067	.0172	27
28	.0126	.0162	.071	.0156	28
29	.0113	.0150	.075	.0141	29
30	.0100	.0140	.080	.0125	30
31	.0089	.0132	.085	.0109	31
32	.0080	.0128	.090	.0102	32
33	.0071	.0118	.095	.0094	33
34	.0063	.0104	.100	.0086	34
35	.0056	.0095	.106	.0078	35
36	.0050	.0090	.112	.0070	36
37	.0045	.0085	.118	.0066	37
38	.0040	.0080	.124	.0063	38
39	.0035	.0075	.130	.....	39
40	.0031	.0070	.138	.....	40

(*A*) Standard in U.S. for sheet metal and wire (except steel & iron).
(*B*) Standard for iron and steel wire (U.S. Steel Wire Gage).
(*C*) American Steel and Wire Company's music (or piano) wire gage sizes. Recognized by U.S. Bureau of Standards.
(*E*) U.S. Standard for iron and steel plate. However, plate is now generally specified by its thickness in decimals of an inch.

TABLE XXXVI

Trigonometric Functions

Angle	Sine	Cosine	Tan	Co-Tan	Angle
0°	0.0000	1.0000	0.0000	*Infin.*	90°
1°	0.0175	0.9998	0.0175	57.290	89°
2°	.0349	.9994	.0349	28.636	88°
3°	.0523	.9986	.0524	19.081	87°
4°	.0698	.9976	.0699	14.301	86°
5°	.0872	.9962	.0875	11.430	85°
6°	.1045	.9945	.1051	9.5144	84°
7°	.1219	.9925	.1228	8.1443	83°
8°	.1392	.9903	.1405	7.1154	82°
9°	.1564	.9877	.1584	6.3138	81°
10°	.1736	.9848	.1763	5.6713	80°
11°	.1908	.9816	.1944	5.1446	79°
12°	.2079	.9781	.2126	4.7046	78°
13°	.2250	.9744	.2309	4.3315	77°
14°	.2419	.9703	.2493	4.0108	76°
15°	.2588	.9659	.2679	3.7321	75°
16°	.2756	.9613	.2867	3.4874	74°
17°	.2924	.9563	.3057	3.2709	73°
18°	.3090	.9511	.3249	3.0777	72°
19°	.3256	.9455	.3443	2.9042	71°
20°	.3420	.9397	.3640	2.7475	70°
21°	.3584	.9336	.3839	2.6051	69°
22°	.3746	.9272	.4040	2.4751	68°
23°	.3907	.9205	.4245	2.3559	67°
24°	.4067	.9135	.4452	2.2460	66
25°	.4226	.9063	.4663	2.1445	65°
26°	.4384	.8988	.4877	2.0503	64°
27°	.4540	.8910	.5095	1.9626	63°
28°	.4695	.8829	.5317	1.8807	62°
29°	.4848	.8746	.5543	1.8040	61°
30°	.5000	.8660	.5774	1.7321	60°
31°	.5150	.8572	.6009	1.6643	59°
32°	.5299	.8480	.6249	1.6003	58°
33°	.5446	.8387	.6494	1.5399	57°
34°	.5592	.8290	.6745	1.4826	56°
35°	.5736	.8192	.7002	1.4281	55°
36°	.5878	.8090	.7265	1.3764	54°
37°	.6018	.7986	.7536	1.3270	53°
38°	.6157	.7880	.7813	1.2799	52°
39°	.6293	.7771	.8098	1.2349	51°
40°	.6428	.7660	.8391	1.1918	50°
41°	.6561	.7547	.8693	1.1504	49°
42°	.6691	.7431	.9004	1.1106	48°
43°	.6820	.7314	.9325	1.0724	47°
44°	.6947	.7193	.9657	1.0355	46°
45°	.7071	.7071	1.0000	1.0000	45°
Angle	Cosine	Sine	Co-Tan	Tan	**Angle**

TABLE XXXVII
Table of Chords

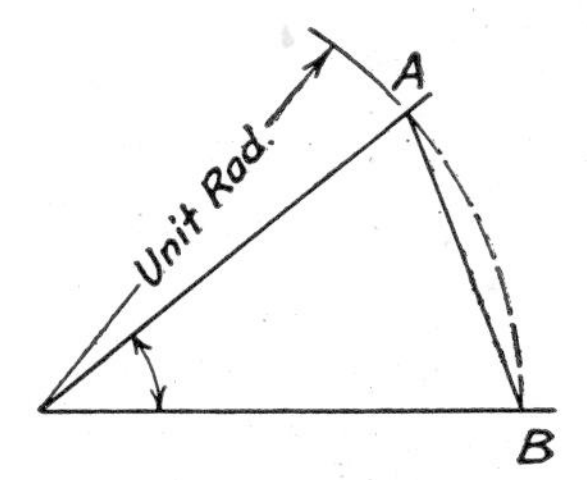

Chord AB is tabulated

TABLE OF CHORDS
TABULATED VALUES ARE CHORD LENGTHS OF ARCS OF UNIT RADIUS SUBTENDING THE SPECIFIED ANGLES. USE MULTIPLES FOR ACCURACY.

DEGREES	0′	10′	20′	30′	40′	50′
0	.0000	.0029	.0058	.0087	.0116	.0145
1	.0174	.0204	.0233	.0202	.0291	.0320
2	.0349	.0378	.0407	.0436	.0465	.0494
3	.0523	.0553	.0582	.0611	.0640	.0669
4	.0698	.0727	.0756	.0785	.0814	.0843
5	.0872	.0901	.0930	.0959	.0988	.1017
6	.1047	.1076	.1105	.1134	.1163	.1192
7	.1221	.1250	.1279	.1308	.1337	.1366
8	.1395	.1424	.1453	.1482	.1511	.1540
9	.1569	.1598	.1627	.1656	.1685	.1714
10	.1743	.1772	.1801	.1830	.1859	.1888
11	.1917	.1946	.1975	.2004	.2033	.2062
12	.2090	.2119	.2148	.2177	.2206	.2235
13	.2264	.2293	.2322	.2351	.2380	.2409
14	.2437	.2466	.2495	.2524	.2553	.2582
15	.2610	.2639	.2668	.2697	.2726	.2755
16	.2783	.2812	.2841	.2870	.2899	.2927
17	.2956	.2985	.3014	.3042	.3071	.3100
18	.3129	.3157	.3186	.3215	.3243	.3272
19	.3301	.3330	.3358	.3387	.3416	.3444
20	.3473	.3502	.3530	.3559	.3587	.3616
21	.3645	.3673	.3702	.3730	.3759	.3788
22	.3816	.3845	.3873	.3902	.3930	.3959
23	.3987	.4016	.4044	.4073	.4101	.4130
24	.4158	.4187	.4215	.4243	.4272	.4300
25	.4329	.4357	.4385	.4414	.4442	.4471
26	.4499	.4527	.4556	.4584	.4612	.4641
27	.4669	.4697	.4725	.4754	.4782	.4810
28	.4838	.4867	.4895	.4923	.4951	.4979
29	.5008	.5036	.5064	.5092	.5120	.5148
30	.5176	.5204	.5232	.5261	.5289	.5317
31	.5345	.5373	.5401	.5429	.5457	.5485
32	.5513	.5541	.5569	.5596	.5624	.5652
33	.5680	.5708	.5736	.5764	.5792	.5820
34	.5847	.5875	.5903	.5931	.5959	.5986
35	.6014	.6042	.6069	.6097	.6125	.6153
36	.6180	.6208	.6236	.6263	.6291	.6318
37	.6346	.6374	.6401	.6429	.6456	.6484
38	.6511	.6539	.6566	.6594	.6621	.6649
39	6676	.6703	.6731	.6758	.6786	.6813
40	.6840	.6868	.6895	.6922	.6950	.6977
41	.7004	.7031	.7059	.7086	.7113	.7140
42	.7167	.7194	.7222	.7249	.7276	.7303
43	.7330	.7357	.7384	.7411	.7438	.7465
44	.7492	.7519	.7546	.7573	.7600	.7627
45	.7654	.7680	.7680	.7734	.7761	.7788

TABLE XXXVIII

Abbreviations and Symbols

Alternating current	a-c
Aluminum	Al.
American Standard	Am. Std.
Approved	App.
Average	avg.
Ball bearing	bb
Brown & Sharpe	B & S
Babbitt	Bab.
Brass	Br.
Bronze	Bro.
Brinell hardness number	Bhn.
Cast iron	C.I.
Center line	CL or ℄
Center to center	c to c.
Centimeter	cm.
Chemical	chem.
Circular	cir.
Circular pitch	CP
Copper	Cop.
Cold rolled steel	C.R.S.
Counterbore	c'bore
Countersink	c's'k
Cubic	cu.
Cubic inch	cu.in.
Cubic foot	cu.ft.
Cubic yard	cu.yd.
Cylinder	cyl.
Degree	deg. or °
Diameter	D., Dia., or Diam.
Direct current	d-c
Diagonal	diag.
Diametral pitch	DP
Drawing	Dwg.
Drawn	Dr.
Detail drawing	Dtl.dwg.
Efficiency	eff.
Electric	elec.
Engineer	engr.
External	ext.
Fabricate	fab.
Fillister	fil.
Finish	fin.
Foot	ft. or ′
Gallon	gal.
Galvanized iron	G.I.
Grind	G or gr.
Harden	hdn.
Hexagonal	hex.
Horsepower	hp.
Hour	hr.
Impregnate	impreg.
Inch	in. or ″
Inside Diameter	I. D.
Internal	int.
Left hand	L.H.
Lateral	lat.
Long	lg.
Longitudinal	long.
Linear foot	lin. ft.
Machine	mach.
Malleable iron	Mal. I.
Material	mat.
Maximum	max.
Meter	m.
Mile	mile
Millimeter	mm.
Miles per hour	mph
Minimum	min.
Minute (angular measure)	′
Minute (time)	min.
Outside diameter	O.D.
Pattern	patt.
Phosphor bronze	Phos. Bro.
Piece	pc.
Pitch	P
Pitch diameter	P.D.
Plate	pl.
Pound	# or lb.
Pounds per square foot	lb.per.sq.ft.
Pounds per square inch	lb.per.sq.in.
Pratt & Whitney	P & W.
Quantity	quan.
Radius	R or Rad.
Required	req. or req'd.
Revolution per minute	rpm
Right hand	R.H.
Round	rd.
Round bar	φ
Screw	sc.
Second (time)	sec.
Second (angular measure)	″
Section	sec.
Society of Automotive Engineers	SAE
Square	sq.
Square inch	sq.in.
Square foot	sq.ft.
Standard	std.
Steel	Stl.
Steel casting	Stl.C.
Thousand	M
Ton	ton
Thread	thd.
Traced	Tr.
Volt	v
Watt	w
Weight	wt.
Woodruff key	Wdrf. key
Wrought iron	W. I.
Yard	yd.
Year	yr.

TABLE XXXIX

Code for Indicating Criticisms

A code consisting of letters and numerals that can be used in combination to indicate errors on a drawing is given below. A student should note each error and then if he feels that he does not understand the true nature of a mistake he should consult his instructor.

Item Letter	*Item*	*Defect Number*	*Defects*
E	Entire Drawing	1	Not Neat
V	View	2	Balance or Spacing Poor
L	Line	3	Off Scale
D	Dimension	4	Out of Projection
S	Scale	5	Wrong
F	Figure, Fraction or Letter	6	Omitted
T	Thread	7	Unnecessary
N	Notation	8	Poorly Made
		9	Location Poor

Examples: Dimension off scale.......... D-3 Thread omitted.......... T-6

ASA STANDARDS

A few of the more than 500 standards approved by the American Standards Association are listed below. Copies may be obtained from the Association's offices at 29 West 39th Street, New York, N. Y.

A13-1928 Identification of Piping Systems, Scheme for
B1.1-1949 Unified and American Screw Threads for Screws, Bolts, Nuts, and Other Threaded Parts
B1.2-1951 Screw Thread Gages and Gaging
B1.3-1941 Acme and Other Translating Threads
B2.1-1945 Pipe Threads
B4.1-1947 Limits and Fits for Engineering and Manufacturing (Part I)
B5c1-1947 Milling Cutter Teeth
B5.1-1949 T-Slots—Their Bolts, Nuts, Tongues and Cutters
B5.4-1948 Taps, Cut and Ground Threads
B5.6-1941 Jig Bushings
B5.10-1943 Machine Tapers
B5.12-1950 Twist Drills, Straight Shank
B5.14-1949 Reamers
B5.15-1950 Involute Splines, Side Bearing
B5.20-1947 Machine Pins
B6.1-1932 Spur Gear Tooth Form
B16.1-1948 Cast Iron Pipe Flanges and Flanged Fittings, Class 125
B16b-1944 Cast Iron Pipe Flanges and Flanged Fittings for Maximum WSP of 250 lb
B16b1-1931 Cast Iron Pipe Flanges and Flanged Fittings for 800 lb Hydraulic Pressure

B16b2-1931	Cast-Iron Pipe Flanges and Flanged Fittings for Maximum WSP of 25 lb
B16c-1939	Malleable-Iron Screwed Fittings, 150 lb
B16.4-1949	Cast-Iron Screwed Fittings for Maximum WSP of 125 and 250 lb
B16e-1939	Steel Pipe Flanges and Flanged Fittings
B16.9-1951	Steel Butt-Welding Fittings
B16.10-1939	Face-to-Face Dimensions of Ferrous Flanged and Welding End Valves
B17c-1927	Transmission Shafting, Code for Design of
B17f-1930	Woodruff Keys, Keyslots, and Cutters
B17.1-1943	Shafting and Stock Keys
B18a-1927	Small Rivets
B18.2-1952	Wrench-Head Bolts and Nuts and Wrench Openings
B18.3-1947	Socket Set Screws and Socket Head Cap Screws
B18.4-1950	Large Rivets
B18.5-1952	Round Unslotted Head Bolts
B18.6-1947	Slotted and Recessed Head Screws, Machine, Cap, Wood, Tapping, and Slotted Headless Type
B18.9-1950	Plow Bolts, Dimensions of
B36.1-1950	Welded and Seamless Steel Pipe (ASTM A53-44)
B36.2-1950	Welded Wrought-Iron Pipe
B36.3-1950	Lap-Welded and Seamless Steel Pipe for High Temperature Service, Specifications for
B36.10-1950	Wrought-Iron and Wrought-Steel Pipe
B45.1-1932	Foundry Patterns of Wood (CS 19-32)
B48.1-1933	Inch-Millimeter Conversion for Industrial Use
Z10.1-1941	Abbreviations for Scientific and Engineering Terms
Z10.5-1949	Electrical Quantities, Letter Symbols for
Z10.7-1950	Letter Symbols for Aeronautical Sciences
Z14.1-1946	Drawings and Drafting Room Practice
Z15.1-1932	Engineering and Scientific Charts for Lantern Slides
Z15.2-1938	Time-Series Charts, Manual of Design and Construction
Z15.3-1943	Engineering and Scientific Graphs for Publications
Z32.2.1-1949	Welding Symbols and Instructions for Their Use
Z32.2-1941	Graphical Symbols for Use on Drawings in Mechanical Engineering
Z32.3-1946	Graphical Symbols for Power Control and Measurement
Z32.5-1944	Symbols for Telephone, Telegraph, and Radio Use
Z32.9-1943	Graphical Electrical Symbols for Architectural Plans

GLOSSARY OF COMMON SHOP TERMS

(For structural terms see Chapter 24)

Anneal (*v*). To heat a piece of metal to a particular temperature and then allow it to cool slowly for the purpose of removing internal stresses.

Bore (*v*). To enlarge a hole using a boring bar in order to make it smooth, round, and co-axial. Boring is usually done on a lathe or boring mill.

Boss (*n*). A circular projection which is raised above a principal surface of a casting or forging.

Braze (*v*). To join two pieces of metal by the use of hard solder. The solder is usually a copper-zinc alloy.

Broach (*v*). To machine a hole to a desired shape, usually other than round. The cutting tool, known as a broach, is pushed or pulled through the rough finished hole. It has transverse cutting edges.

Burnish (*v*). To smooth or apply a brilliant finish.

Bushing (*n*). A removable cylindrical sleeve which is used to provide a bearing surface.

Carburize (*v*). To harden the surface of a piece of low grade steel by heating in a carbonizing material to increase the carbon content and then quenching.

Caseharden (*v*). To harden a surface as described above or through the use of potassium cyanide.

Chamfer (*v*). To bevel an external edge or corner.

Chase (*v*). To cut screw threads on a lathe using a chaser, a tool shaped to the profile of a thread.

Chill (*v*). To cool the surface of a casting suddenly so that the surface will be white and hard.

Chip (*v*). To cut away or remove surface defects with a chisel.

Color-harden (*v*). See caseharden. A piece is color-hardened mainly for the sake of appearance.

Core (*v*). To form a hole or hollow cavity in a casting through the use of a core.

Counterbore (*v*). To enlarge the end of a cylindrical hole to a certain depth, as is often done to accommodate the head of a fillister head screw. (*n*) The name of the tool used to produce the enlargement.

Countersink (*v*). To form a conical enlargement at the end of a cylindrical hole to accommodate the head of a screw or rivel. (*n*) The name of the tool used to form a conical shaped enlargement.

Crown (*n*). The angular or curved contour of the outer surface of a part such as on a pulley.

Die (*n*). A metal block used for forming or stamping operations. A thread-cutting tool for producing external threads.

Die Casting (*n*). A casting which has been produced by forcing a molten alloy having an aluminum, copper, zinc, tin, or lead base into a metal mold composed of two halves.

Die Stamping (*n*). A piece which has been cut or formed from sheet metal through the use of a die.

Draw (*v*). To form metal, which may be either cold or hot, by a distorting or stretching process. To temper steel by gradual or intermittent quenching.

Drill (*v*). To form a cylindrical hole in metal. (*n*) A revolving cutting tool designed for cutting at the point.

Drop Forging (*n*). A piece formed while hot between two dies under a drop hammer.

Face (*v*). To machine on a lathe a flat face which is perpendicular to the axis of rotation of the piece.

Feather (*n*). A rectangular sliding key which permits a pulley to move along the shaft parallel to its axis.

File (*v*). To shape, finish, or trim with a fine-toothed metal cutting tool which is used with the hands.

Fillet (*n*). A rounded filling which increases the strength at the junction of two surfaces which form an internal angle.

Fit (*n*). The tightness of adjustment between the contacting surfaces of mating parts.

Flange (*n*). The top and bottom member of a beam. A projecting rim added on the end of a pipe or fitting for making a connection.

Forge (*v*). To shape hot metals by hammering, using a hand-hammer or machine.

Galvanize (*v*). To coat steel or iron by immersion in a bath of zinc.

Graduate (*v*). To mark off or divide a scale into intervals.

Grind (*v*). To finish a surface through the action of a revolving abrasive wheel.

Key (*n*). A piece used between a shaft and a hub to prevent the movement of one relative to the other.

Keyway or Keyseat (*n*). A longitudinal groove cut in a shaft or a hub to receive a key. A key rests in a keyseat and slides in a keyway.

Knurl (*v*). To roughen a cylindrical surface to produce a better grip for the fingers.

Lap (*v*). To finish or polish with a piece of soft metal, wood, or leather impregnated with an abrasive.

Lug (*n*). A projection or ear which has been cast or forged as a portion of a piece to provide a support or to allow the attachment of another part.

Malleable Casting (*n*). A casting which has been annealed to toughen it.

Mill (*v*). To machine a piece on a milling machine by means of a rotating toothed cutter.

Neck (*v*). To cut a circumferential groove around a shaft.

Pack-harden (*v*). To case-carburize and harden.

Peen (*v*). To stretch or bend over metal using the peen end (ball end) of a hammer.

Pickle (*v*). To remove scale and rust from a casting or forging by immersing it in an acid bath.

Plane (*v*). To machine a flat surface on a planer, a machine having a fixed tool and a reciprocating bed.

Polish (*v*). To make a surface smooth and lustrous through the use of a fine abrasive.

Punch (*v*). To perforate a thin piece of metal by shearing out a circular wad with a non-rotating tool under pressure.

Ream (*v*). To finish a hole to an exact size using a rotating fluted cutting tool known as a reamer.

Rivet (*n*). A headed shank which more or less permanently unites two pieces. (*v*) To fasten steel plates with rivets.

Round (*n*). A rounded external corner on a casting.

Sandblast (*v*). To clean the surface of castings or forgings by means of sand forced from a nozzle at a high velocity.

Shear (*v*). To cut off sheet or bar metal through the shearing action of two blades.

Shim (*n*). A thin metal plate which is inserted between two surfaces for the purpose of adjustment.

Spline (*n*). A keyway, usually for a feather key. See feather.

Spotface (*v*). To finish a round spot on the rough surface of a casting at a drilled hole for the purpose of providing a smooth seat for a bolt or screw head.

Spot Weld (*v*). To weld two overlapping metal sheets in spots by means of the heat of resistance to an electric current between a pair of electrodes.

Steel Casting (*n*). A casting made of castiron to which scrap steel has been added.

Swage (*v*). To form metal with a "swage block," a tool so constructed that through hammering or pressure the work may be made to take a desired shape.

Sweat (*v*). To solder together by clamping the pieces in contact with soft solder between and then heating.

Tack weld (*n*). A weld of short intermittent sections.

Tap (*v*). To cut an internal thread, by hand or with power, by screwing into the hole a fluted tapered tool having thread-cutting edges.

Temper (*v*). To reduce the hardness of a piece of hardened steel through reheating and sudden quenching.

Template (*n*). A pattern cut to a desired shape which is used in layout work to establish shearing lines, to locate holes, etc.

Tumble (*v*). To clean and smooth castings and forgings through contact in a revolving barrel. To further the results, small pieces of scrap are added.

Turn (*v*). To turn-down or machine a cylindrical surface on a lathe.

Upset (*v*). To increase the diameter or form a shoulder on a piece during forging.

Weld (*v*). To join two pieces of metal by pressure or hammering after heating to the fusion point.

BIBLIOGRAPHY OF ENGINEERING DRAWING AND ALLIED SUBJECTS

ARCHITECTURAL DRAWING

Field, W. B., *An Introduction to Architectural Drawing.* McGraw-Hill, 1943, 245 pp.
Morgan, S. W., *Architectural Drawing.* McGraw-Hill, 1950, 227 pp.
Turner, W. W., *Fundamentals of Architectural Design.* McGraw-Hill, 1930, 175 pp.

AERONAUTICAL DRAFTING AND ENGINEERING

Anderson, N. H., *Aircraft Layout and Detail Design.* McGraw-Hill, 1941, 306 pp.
Apalategui, J. J., *Aircraft Analytic Geometry with Applications to Aircraft.* Macmillan, 1944, 277 pp.
Faulconer, T. P., *Introduction to Aircraft Design.* McGraw-Hill, 1942, 273 pp.
Leavell, S. and Bungay, S., *Aircraft Production Standards.* McGraw-Hill, 1943, 267 pp.
LeMaster, C. A., *Aircraft Sheet Metal Work.* American Technical Society, 1944, 388 pp.
Meadowcroft, N., *Aircraft Detail Drafting.* McGraw-Hill, 1942, 215 pp.
Nelson, W., *Airplane Lofting.* McGraw-Hill, 1941, 147 pp.
Svensen, C. L., *A Manual of Aircraft Drafting.* Van Nostrand, 1941, 272 pp.
Tharratt, G., *Aircraft Production Illustration.* McGraw-Hill, 1944, 201 pp.

BLUEPRINT READING

Bush, G. F., *Reading Engineering Drawings.* Wiley, 1942, 60 pp.
DeVette, W. A. and Kellogg, D. E., *Blueprint Reading for the Metal Trades.* Bruce, 1942, 132 pp.
Dick, A. A., *Blueprint Reading:* Ronald, 1942, 157 pp.
Dwight, C., *Blueprint Reading in the Machine Industries.* McGraw-Hill, 1943, 144 pp.
Heine, G. M. and Dunlap, C. H., *How to Read Electrical Blueprints.* American Technical Society, 1942, 318 pp.
Hobart, D. E., *Notes and Problems in Blueprint Reading of Machine Drawings.* Harper, 1942, 105 pp.
Lincoln Electric Co., *Simple Blueprint Reading.* Cleveland, 1941, 146 pp.
Norcross, C., *Aircraft Blueprints and How to Read Them.* McGraw-Hill, 1942, 106 pp.
Owens, A. A. and Slingluff, B. F., *How to Read Blueprints.* Winston, 1942, 64 pp.
Spencer, H. C. and Grant, H. E., *Blueprint Language of the Machine Industries.* Macmillan, 1947, 255 pp.
Thayer, H. R., *Blueprint Reading and Sketching.* McGraw-Hill, 1941, 250 pp.
Weir, J. J., *Blueprint Reading.* McGraw-Hill, 1941, 82 pp.

CASTINGS

Campbell, H. I., *Metal Castings.* Wiley, 1936, 318 pp.

CATALOGS
(Instruments)

Alteneder, Theo., and Sons, Philadelphia, Pa.
Boston Gear Works, Inc., Chicago, Ill. (Gears, etc.)
Crane Co., Chicago, Ill. (Pipe Fittings.)
Elliott, B. K., Co., Pittsburgh, Pa.
Eugene Dietzgen Co., Chicago, Ill.
Frederic Post Co., Chicago, Ill.
Keuffel & Esser Co., Hoboken, N. J.
New Departure, Bristol, Conn. (Ball-Bearing Handbook.)
Timken Roller Bearing Co., Canton, Ohio. (Roller Bearings.)
U. S. Blue Co., Chicago, Ill.

CHARTS AND DIAGRAMS

Levens, A. S., *Nomography.* Wiley, 1948, 176 pp.
Mavis, F. T., *The Construction of Nomographic Charts.* International, 1950, 132 pp.

DESCRIPTIVE GEOMETRY

Bradley, H. C. and Uhler, E. H., *Descriptive Geometry for Engineers.* International, 1950, 266 pp.
Hood, G. J., *Geometry of Engineering Drawing.* McGraw-Hill, 1946, 362 pp.
Larkins, J. T., Jr., *Descriptive Geometry.* Prentice-Hall, 1939, 317 pp.
Levens, A. S. and Eggers, H., *Descriptive Geometry.* Harper, 1941, 240 pp.
Miller, H. W., *Descriptive Geometry.* Wiley, 1941, 254 pp.
Roever, W. H., *The Mongean Method of Descriptive Geometry.* Macmillan, 1934, 151 pp.
Street, W. E., *Technical Descriptive Geometry.* Van Nostrand, 1948, 179 pp.
Warner, F. M., *Applied Descriptive Geometry.* McGraw-Hill, 1946, 238 pp.
Watts, E. F. and Rule, J. T., *Descriptive Geometry.* Prentice-Hall, 1946, 301 pp.
Wellman, B. L., *Technical Descriptive Geometry.* McGraw-Hill, 1948, 508 pp.

DESCRIPTIVE GEOMETRY PROBLEMS

Paré, E. G. and others, *Descriptive Geometry Worksheets.* Macmillan, 1950, 72 plates.
Turner, W. W., *Basic Problems in Descriptive Geometry.* Ronald, 1944, 60 sheets.
Uhler, E. H., *Problems in Descriptive Geometry.* International, 1943, 157 plates.
Watts, E. F. and Goodrich, A. L., *Problems in Descriptive Geometry.* Prentice-Hall, 1946, 64 plates.

DIE CASTING

Chase, H., *Die Castings.* Wiley, 1934, 264 pp.

ENGINEERING DRAWING

Brodie, H. J., *Engineering Drawing and Mechanism.* Harper, 1942, 241 pp.
Carter, I. N. and Thompson, H. L., *Engineering Drawing.* International, 1943, 462 pp.

French, T. E., *Engineering Drawing.* McGraw-Hill, 1947, 694 pp.
Giesecke, F. E. and others, *Technical Drawing.* Macmillan, 1949, 730 pp.
Hesse, H. C., *A Manual in Engineering Drawing.* Macmillan, 1942, 118 pp.
Hobart, D. E., *Engineering Drawing.* Heath, 1941, 437 pp.
Hoelscher, R. P. and others, *Industrial Production Illustration.* McGraw-Hill, 1947, 243 pp.
Jordan, H. H. and Hoelscher, R. P., *Engineering Drawing.* Wiley, 1935, 528 pp.
Orth, H. D., Worsencroft, R. R., and Doke, H. B., *Basic Engineering Drawing.* Ronald, 1946, 346 pp.
Radzinsky, H., *Making Patent Drawings.* Macmillan, 1945, 96 pp.
Sahag, L. M., *Engineering Drawing.* Ronald, 1942, 394 pp.
Schumann, C. H., *Technical Drafting.* Harper, 1940, 796 pp.
Svensen, C. L., *Drafting for Engineers.* Van Nostrand, 1935, 554 pp.
———, *Essentials of Drafting,* 3rd ed. Van Nostrand, 1943, 295 pp.
Thayer, H. R., *Industrial Drawing.* McGraw-Hill, 1942, 195 pp.

ENGINEERING DRAWING PROBLEMS

Carter, I. N. and Thompson, H. L., *Engineering Drawing Problems.* International, 1943, 160 plates.
Cooper, C. D. and others, *Engineering Drawing Problems.* McGraw-Hill, 1948, 97 plates.
French, T. E. and McCully, H. M., *Engineering Drawing Sheets.* McGraw-Hill, 1941, 103 plates.
Giesecke, F. E. and others, *Technical Drawing Problems.* Macmillan, 1947, 105 sheets.
Higbee, F. G. and Russ, I. M., *Engineering Drawing Problems.* Wiley, 1940, 90 plates.
Levens, A. S. and Edstrom, A. E., *Problems in Engineering Drawing.* McGraw-Hill, 1947, 72 plates.
Luzadder, W. J., Bolds, M. H., Arnold, J. N., and Thompson, F. H., *Problems in Engineering Drawing.* Prentice-Hall, 1950, 70 plates.
———, *Problems in Engineering Drawing,* Abridged. Prentice-Hall, 1950, 40 plates.
Orth, H. D., Worsencroft, R. R., and Doke, H. B., *Problems in Basic Engineering Drawing.* Irwin-Farnham.
Quier, K. E., *Engineering Drafting Problems.* Harper, 1943, 80 plates.
Russ, J. M., *Quiz Questions.* McGraw-Hill, 1948, 54 pp.
Spencer, H. C. and Grant, H. E., *Technical Drawing Problems.* Macmillan, 1948, 138 plates.
Turner, W. W., *Basic Problems in Engineering Drawing.* Ronald, 1947, 102 sheets.

HANDBOOKS

Colvin, F. H., *Aircraft Handbook.* McGraw-Hill.
———, and Stanley, F. A., *American Machinists Handbook and Dictionary of Shop Terms.* McGraw-Hill.
Kent, W., *Mechanical Engineers Handbook.* Wiley.
Kidder, F. E., *Architects and Builders Handbook.* Wiley.
Lawle, F. F., *Standard Handbook for Electrical Engineers.* McGraw-Hill.
Machinery Handbook. Industrial Press.
Marks, L. S., *Mechanical Engineers Handbook.* McGraw-Hill.

Merriman, T., *American Civil Engineers Handbook*. Wiley.
O'Rourke, C. E., *General Engineering Handbook*. McGraw-Hill.
Steel Construction. American Institute of Steel Construction.
Walker, J. H., Crocker, S., and Allen, J. R., *Piping Handbook*. McGraw-Hill.

JIG AND FIXTURE DESIGN

Bryant, L. A. and Dickinson, T. A., *Jigs and Fixtures*. Pitman, 1947, 222 pp.
Colvin, F. H. and Haas, L. L., *Jigs and Fixtures*. McGraw-Hill, 1943, 373 pp.
Hinman, C. W., *Die Engineering Layouts and Formulas*. McGraw-Hill, 1943, 497 pp.
Jones, F. D., *Jig and Fixture Design*. Industrial Press, 1937, 350 pp.

LETTERING

De Garmo, E. P. and Jonassen, F., *Technical Lettering*. Macmillan, 1941, 18 pp.
Dodman, F. E., *Lettering*. Macmillan, 1942, 20 pp.
French, T. E. and Turnbill, W. D., *Lessons in Lettering*, Vols. 1 and 2. McGraw-Hill, 1924.

MACHINE DESIGN

Maleev, V. L., *Machine Design*. International, 1946, 579 pp.
Norman, C. A., Ault, E. S., and Zarobsky, I. F., *Fundamentals of Machine Design*. Macmillan, 1938, 486 pp.
Spotts, M. F., *Design of Machine Elements*. Prentice-Hall, 1948, 402 pp.

MACHINE DRAWING

Lent, D., *Design of Machine Elements*. Prentice-Hall, 1951, 560 pp.
Svensen, C. L., *Machine Drawing*. Van Nostrand, 1933, 248 pp.
Tozer, E. F. and Rising, H. A., *Machine Drawing*. McGraw-Hill, 1934, 317 pp.

MAP AND TOPOGRAPHIC DRAWING

Greitzer, S. L., *Elementary Topography and Map Reading*. McGraw-Hill, 1944, 160 pp.
Hinks, A. R., *Maps and Surveys*. Cambridge, 1933 (Macmillan), 284 pp.
Sloane, R. C. and Montz, I. M., *Elements of Topographic Drawing*. McGraw-Hill, 1943, 251 pp.

PATTERN DESIGN

Hall, B. R. and Kiley, H. E., *Pattern Design*. International, 1939, 193 pp.

PERSPECTIVE

Everett, H. E. and Lawrence, W. H., *Freehand and Perspective Drawing*. American Technical Society, 1917, 142 pp.

Lawson, P. J., *Practical Perspective Drawing.* McGraw-Hill, 1943, 215 pp.
Lubschez, B. J., *Perspective.* Van Nostrand, 1927, 129 pp.
Turner, W. W., *Simplified Perspective.* Ronald, 1947, 236 pp.

PIPE

Day, L. J., *Standard Plumbing Details.* Wiley, 1938, 119 plates.
Svensen, C. L., *A Handbook on Piping.* Van Nostrand, 1918, 359 pp.

SHEET-METAL WORK

Frazer, R. H. and Berthiaume, O., *Practical Aircraft Sheet-metal Work.* McGraw-Hill, 1942, 193 pp.
Norcross, C. and Quinn, J. D., *How to Do Aircraft Sheetmetal Work.* McGraw-Hill, 1942, 285 pp.
O'Rourke, F. J., *Sheet-metal Pattern Drafting.* McGraw-Hill, 1942, 189 pp.

SHOP PRACTICE

Begeman, M. L., *Manufacturing Processes.* Wiley, 1942, 579 pp.
Boston, O. W., *Engineering Shop Practice,* Vol. 1. Wiley, 1933, 589 pp.
———, *Metal Processing.* Wiley, 1941, 630 pp.
Campbell, H. L., *The Working, Heating, Treating, and Welding of Steel.* Wiley, 1940, 230 pp.
Marek, C. T., *The Production and Design of Castings.* Wiley, 1950, 372 pp.
Wendt, R. E., *Foundry Work.* McGraw-Hill, 1942, 261 pp.
Young, J. F., *Materials and Processes.* Wiley, 1944, 628 pp.

SKETCHING

Katz, H., *Technical Sketching.* Macmillan, 1949, 176 pp.
Turner, W. W., *Freehand Sketching for Engineers.* Ronald, 1946, 97 pp.
Zipprich, A. E., *Freehand Drafting.* Van Nostrand, 1924, 131 pp.

STRUCTURAL DRAFTING

Bishop, C. T., *Structural Drafting.* Wiley, 1941, 287 pp.

TECHNICAL DICTIONARY

Tweney, C. F. and Hughes, L. E. C., *Chambers Technical Dictionary.* Macmillan, 1940, 957 pp.

TOOL DESIGN

Cole, C. B., *Tool Design.* American Technical Society, 1941, 498 pp.
Donaldson, C. and LeCain, G. H., *Tool Design.* Harper, 1943, 443 pp.

WELDING

Churchill, H. D. and Austin, J. B., *Weld Design.* Prentice-Hall, 1949, 216 pp.
Elzea, L. S., *Aircraft Welding.* McGraw-Hill, 1942, 121 pp.
Lincoln Electric Co., *Simple Blueprint Reading.* Cleveland, 1941, 146 pp.
Lincoln Electric Co., *Procedure Handbook of Arc Welding Design and Practice.* Cleveland, 1940, 1117 pp.

TEXT FILMS

"Engineering Drawing." 7 films, 6 strips. McGraw-Hill, 1947.
"Engineering Drawing." 16 films. Purdue University.

MOTION PICTURES FOR TEACHING ENGINEERING DRAWING

The motion-picture lessons* described by Professor Justus Rising on the following pages have been prepared at Purdue University by Professor Rising and your author in collaboration with the staff in the preparation of the script. The motion picture on Capital Letters was prepared by Professor Rising and Mr. M. H. Bolds. These pictures are available on a rental basis from the Purdue Research Foundation. Address Professor Justus Rising, Purdue University, Lafayette, Indiana. The initials in parentheses have the following significance: Q = silent picture; S = sound on film; T = printed titles; V = commentary read by teacher; C = continuous projection; I = intermittent projection; W = work sheet.

Freehand Drafting (*QTWI*) shows sketching as antecedent to drawing.

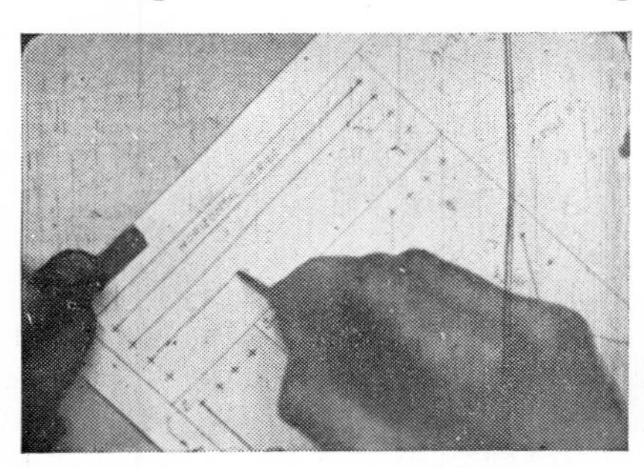

Demonstrates sharpening of pencil and proper strokes for sketching the various lines. Illustrates short and long horizontal, vertical, and inclined lines, large and small circles and ellipses. Demonstration is divided into several parts at end of each of which student completes suitable exercise on work sheet.

Orthographic Projection (*QTWI*) demonstrates with models the proper way to represent an object by means of three orthographic views. Shows the use of the scale for making measurements and the use of T-square and triangle for constructing the views, as well as the method of transferring a measurement from one view to another or of constructing the third view by projecting from the other two views. The lesson is divided into four parts, at the end of which the student works a suitable problem on a work sheet. Lantern slides for chalk-board projection permit the instructor to show the

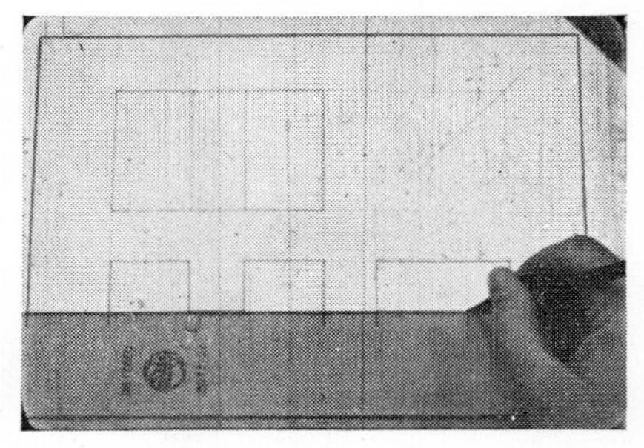

student the correct solution of the problem.

Structural Drawing (*QTW*) shows the preparation and use of the chisel-

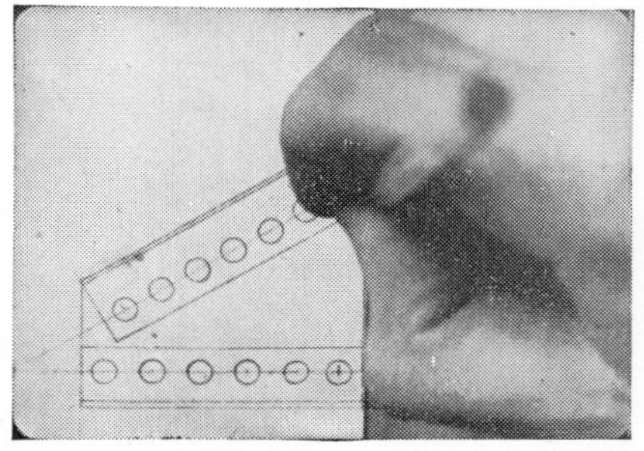

pointed pencil for making pencil drawings on tracing paper for blueprinting. The various steps of making a structural drawing are completed in the following order so that an efficient performance results:

* Reproduced by permission of Professor Justus Rising.

1. Location of gauge lines.

2. Size of members and minimum clearance determine location of members.

3. Size of plates determined by number of rivets in group, edge distance, and spacing of rivets.

Testing T-square and Triangles (*QT*) shows how to check smoothness and

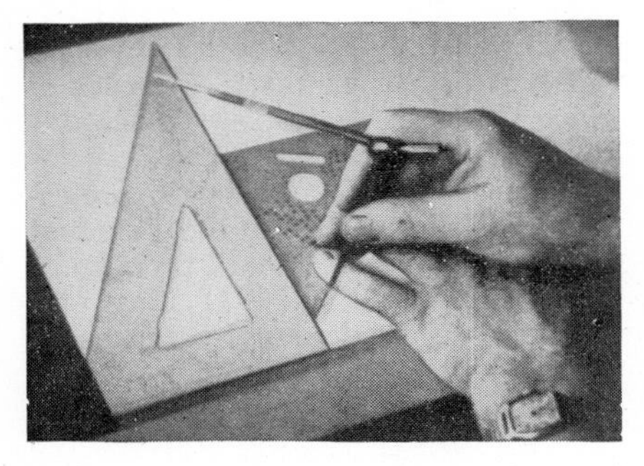

straightness of T-square blade and T-square head, straightness of edge of drawing board, smoothness and straightness of edges of triangles, and angles of triangles accurately without the use of auxiliary apparatus.

Capital Letters (*SWC*) describes and demonstrates, one at a time, the construction on ruled grids of single-stroke, inclined commercial gothic capital let-

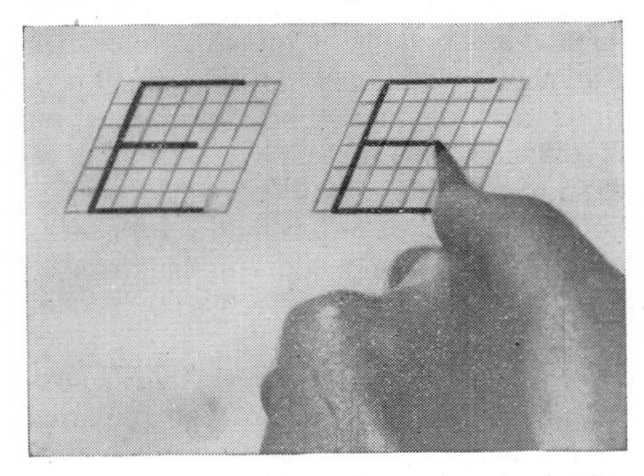

ters, ampersand, and numerals. The student is provided with a work sheet containing grids similar to those shown on the screen. As soon as the demonstration of a new character is completed, the student immediately makes it on his work sheet, after which the motion picture demonstrates the next letter and the student again makes it on his work sheet.

By using pieces of blank film of proper length between the various demonstration periods, time is provided for constructing the letters without stopping the projector. Classroom lights are turned out by the teacher at the beginning of each demonstration on the screen and are turned on again at the end to enable the student to work.

Lower-case Letters (*SWC*) explains and demonstrates the construction of each of the 26 lower-case letters. After the demonstration of each letter the

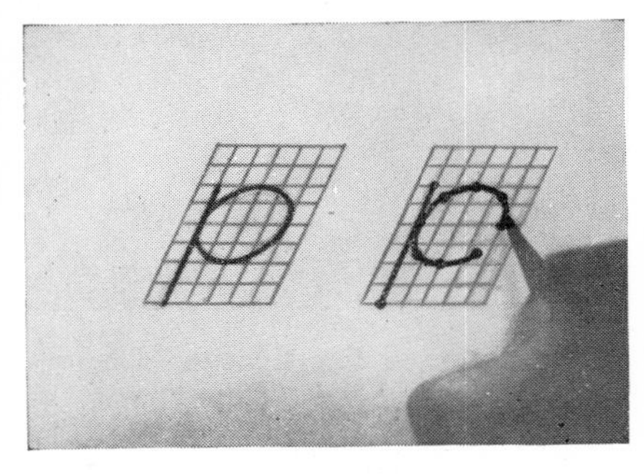

room lights are turned on to permit the student to make the letter. Blank film inserted between scenes permits projector to be run continuously and insures a snappy lesson completed in the time allowed.

Use of T-square and Triangles (*SWI*) illustrates the sharpening of the pencil

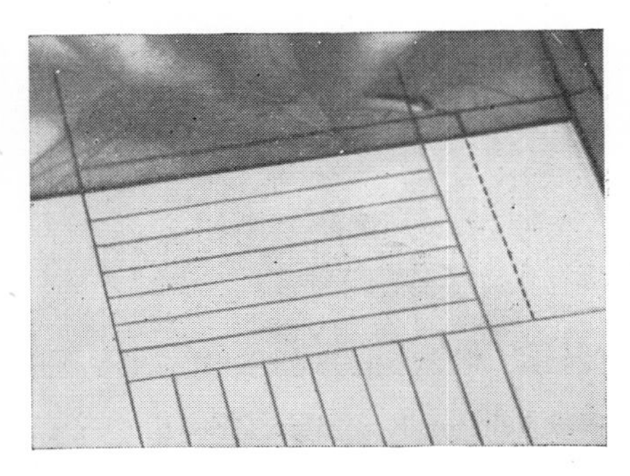

and the use of T-square and triangles, with a step-by-step explanation of the making of a drawing exercise. Six exercises show the proper technique for drawing horizontal, vertical, and inclined lines, both solid and dotted, with provision for stopping the film at the end of each scene so that the student may repeat the action of the film on his own work sheet.

Auxiliary Views (*QVWI*) illustrates principles of auxiliary views by means of models. Shows method for constructing auxiliary views for straight

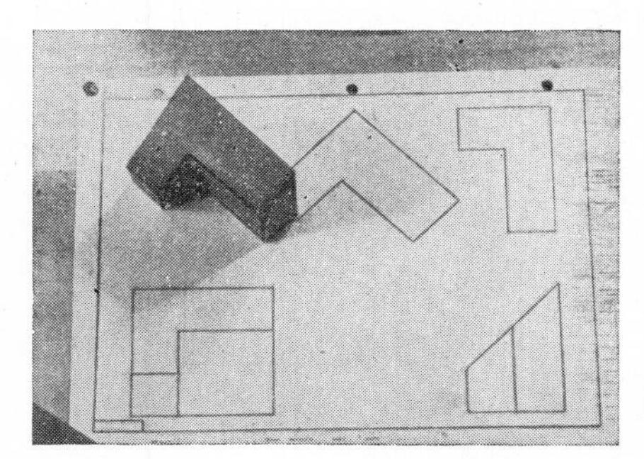

line and curved line figures. Demonstration divided into three parts, at end of each of which student works a suitable problem. Lantern slides for chalk-board projection permit instructor to show students correct solutions.

Pictorial Drawing (*QVWI*) demonstrates principles of isometric and oblique drawing by means of models and shows the construction of objects with

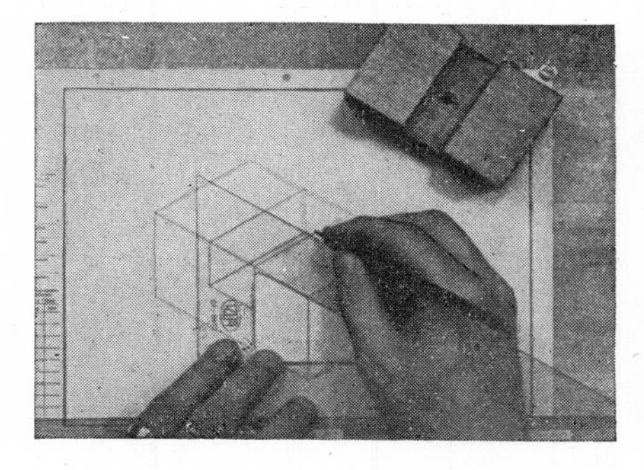

isometric and nonisometric lines and circles. Gives similar demonstration for oblique drawing. Lesson divided into four parts, at the end of each of which student works a suitable exercise on the exercise sheet. Lantern slides for chalk-board projection permit instructor to show correct solutions.

Screw Threads (*QVWI*) defines by means of models and drawings the important terms associated with screw threads. Complete step-by-step construction of national threads and square threads is shown. The meaning of each line of the drawing is explained by reference to a model. The lesson is divided into parts, at the end of each of which the student completes a suitable exercise on a work sheet.

Lantern slides for chalk-board projection permit instructor to show student the correct solution of each problem.

Sectional Views (*QVWI*) illustrates principles of sectioning by means of models and celluloid cutting planes.

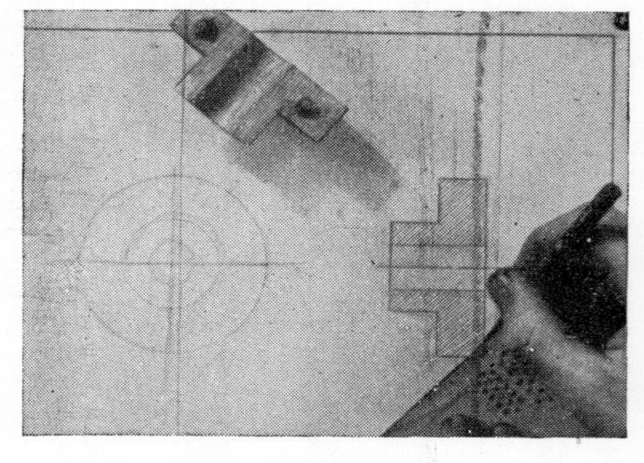

Full section, half section, and offset sections are shown. The demonstration is divided into four parts, at end of each of which the student works a suitable problem. Lantern slides for chalk-board projection permit instructors to show the students correct solutions of problems.

Development of Surfaces (*QVWI*) explains the construction of the patterns of surfaces by means of models and drawings. Describes the methods for right prism and oblique prism, for right cylinders, for right pyramids, for right cone, and oblique cone. The demonstration is divided into four parts, at the end of each of which the student works a suitable problem. Lantern slides for chalk-board projection permit the instructor to show the students the correct solution.

Intersection of Surfaces (*QVWI*) explains by means of models and drawings the principles for finding the lines of intersection between intersecting surfaces. It discusses the problem of finding the intersection of two prisms, of two cylinders, of cylinder, and cone. The demonstration is divided into four parts, at the end of each of which the student works a suitable problem. Lantern slides for chalk-board projection permit the instructor to show the student the correct solution.

Applied Geometry (*QVWI*) explains the following geometric construction:

(1) By means of T-square and 30°–60° triangle, to construct a hexagon when the distance across corners is known.

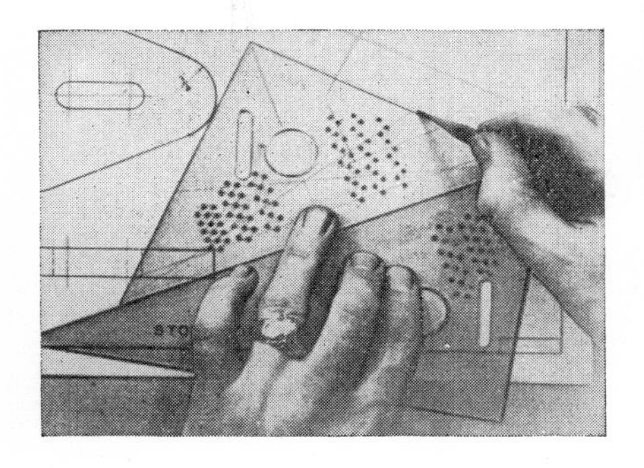

(2) To bisect a line.

(3) To construct a hexagon by means of the compass, T-square, and 30°–60° triangle when the distance across flats is known.

(4) To draw a straight line tangent to a circle at a point on the circle.

(5) To draw a tangent to a circle from a point outside.

(6) To draw an arc tangent to two lines, which make 90° with each other.

(7) To draw an arc tangent to two straight lines, which do not make 90° with each other.

(8) To draw an arc tangent to a circle and to a straight line.

(9) To draw an arc tangent to two circles.

The demonstration is divided into nine parts, at the end of each of which the student, on a previously prepared work sheet, solves a suitable problem.

Ink Work and Tracing (*QVWC*) demonstrates the various steps involved in making ink tracings on tracing cloth. Compares working qualities of "dull" and "slick" sides of the cloth, shows use of Scotch tape to attach cloth to drawing board, and application of tracing cloth powder to insure uniform surface conditions. Attention is directed to methods and precautions to be ob-

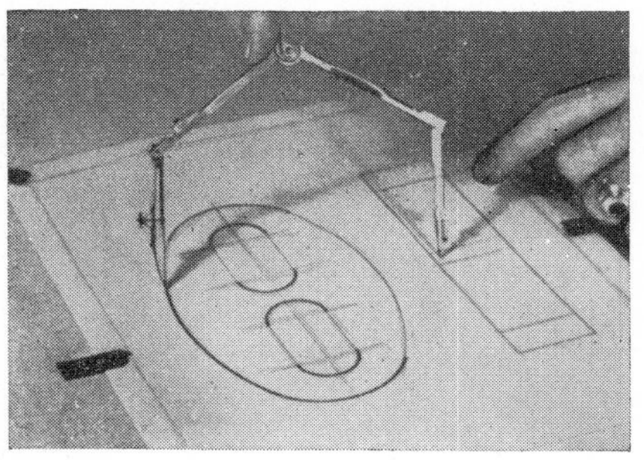

served in opening the ink bottle and in filling and cleaning the drawing-pens. The width of line for various purposes and the measurement and control therof is explained in detail. The importance of the "order of inking" to the efficient production of good tracings is emphasized. The proper handling and adjustment of the tracing tools is a fundamental part of the film. The picture concludes with demonstrations of faulty lines produced by improper manipulation of the pen, and the use of the eraser and soapstone for the correction of errors. Work sheet is objective quiz based on film.

Use of T-square and Triangles (*QVWI*) discusses and demonstrates the basic principles for the correct use of the T-square and triangles. In addition, it makes the following demonstration on the screen exactly as they would appear to the student on his own drawing board.

The following manipulations are exemplified:

(1) Horizontal lines with the T-square.
(2) Vertical lines with T-square and triangles.

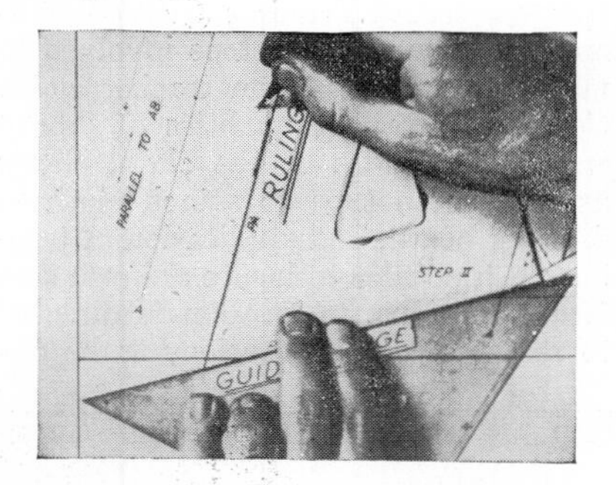

(3) Lines making 60° with the horizontal.
(4) Lines making 45° with the horizontal.
(5) Lines making 30° with the horizontal.
(6) Lines making 15° with the horizontal.
(7) Lines making 75° with the horizontal.
(8) Parallel lines.
(9) Perpendicular lines.
(10) Lines making 30° with an inclined line.
(11) Lines making 45° with an inclined line.
(12) Lines making 60° with an inclined line.
(13) Lines making 15° with an inclined line.

The picture is divided into ten sections, at the end of each of which the student, on a previously prepared work sheet, solves a suitable problem.

INDEX

INDEX

D

E

F

G

W